APPENDIX 4   AREAS FOR t DISTRIBUTIONS

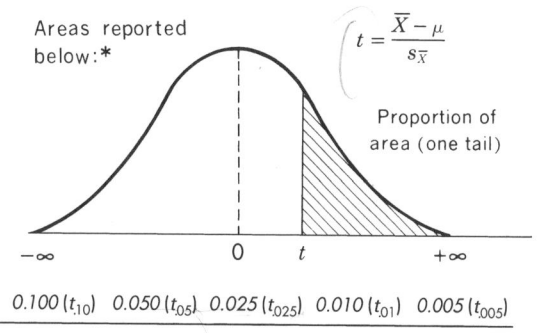

Areas reported below:*

$$t = \frac{\overline{X} - \mu}{s_{\overline{X}}}$$

Proportion of area (one tail)

df	0.100 $(t_{.10})$	0.050 $(t_{.05})$	0.025 $(t_{.025})$	0.010 $(t_{.01})$	0.005 $(t_{.005})$
1	3.078	6.314	12.706	31.821	63.657
2	1.886	2.920	4.303	6.965	9.925
3	1.638	2.353	3.182	4.541	5.841
4	1.533	2.132	2.776	3.747	4.604
5	1.476	2.015	2.571	3.365	4.032
6	1.440	1.943	2.447	3.143	3.707
7	1.415	1.895	2.365	2.998	3.499
8	1.397	1.860	2.306	2.896	3.355
9	1.383	1.833	2.262	2.821	3.250
10	1.372	1.812	2.228	2.764	3.169
11	1.363	1.796	2.201	2.718	3.106
12	1.356	1.782	2.179	2.681	3.055
13	1.350	1.771	2.160	2.650	3.012
14	1.345	1.761	2.145	2.624	2.977
15	1.341	1.753	2.131	2.602	2.947
16	1.337	1.746	2.120	2.583	2.921
17	1.333	1.740	2.110	2.567	2.898
18	1.330	1.734	2.101	2.552	2.878
19	1.328	1.729	2.093	2.539	2.861
20	1.325	1.725	2.086	2.528	2.845
21	1.323	1.721	2.080	2.518	2.831
22	1.321	1.717	2.074	2.508	2.819
23	1.319	1.714	2.069	2.500	2.807
24	1.318	1.711	2.064	2.492	2.797
25	1.316	1.708	2.060	2.485	2.787
26	1.315	1.706	2.056	2.479	2.779
27	1.314	1.703	2.052	2.473	2.771
28	1.313	1.701	2.048	2.467	2.763
29	1.311	1.699	2.045	2.462	2.756
30	1.310	1.697	2.042	2.457	2.750
40	1.303	1.684	2.021	2.423	2.704
60	1.296	1.671	2.000	2.390	2.660
120	1.289	1.658	1.980	2.358	2.617
∞	1.282	1.645	1.960	2.326	2.576

*Example: For the shaded area to represent .025 of the total area of 1.0, the value of t with 19 degrees of freedom is 2.093.
This table was computed by the authors using MINITAB.

SECOND CANADIAN EDITION

Statistics
A First Course

Donald H. Sanders
Educational Consultant
Fort Worth, Texas

Robert K. Smidt
California Polytechnic State University
San Luis Obispo, California

Aminmohamed Adatia
University of Regina
Regina, Saskatchewan

Glenn A. Larson
University of Regina
Regina, Saskatchewan

Toronto   Montréal   Boston   Burr Ridge, IL   Dubuque, IA   Madison, WI   New York   San Francisco
St. Louis   Bangkok   Bogotá   Caracas   Kuala Lumpur   Lisbon   London   Madrid
Mexico City   Milan   New Delhi   Santiago   Seoul   Singapore   Sydney   Taipei

The **McGraw·Hill** Companies

McGraw-Hill Ryerson

Statistics: A First Course
Second Canadian Edition

ISBN: 0-07-095438-0

1 2 3 4 5 6 7 8 9 10 TCP 0 9 8 7 6 5

Printed and bound in Canada

Statistics Canada information is used with the permission of the Minister of Industry, as Minister responsible for Statistics Canada. Information on the availability of the wide range of data from Statistics Canada can be obtained from Statistics Canada's Regional Offices, its World Wide Web site at http://www.statcan.ca, and its toll-free access number 1-800-263-1136.

Care has been taken to trace ownership of copyright material contained in this text; however, the publisher will welcome any information that enables them to rectify any reference or credit for subsequent editions.

Vice President, Editorial and Media Technology: *Patrick Ferrier*
Sponsoring Editor: *Leanna MacLean*
Signing Editor: *Cathy Koop*
Developmental Editor: *Kamilah Reid Burrell*
Marketing Manager: *David Groth*
Supervising Editor: *Jaime Duffy*
Copy Editor: *Karen Rolfe*
Production Coordinator: *Mary Pepe*
Composition: *Shepherd Inc.*
Cover Design: *Dianna Little*
Cover Image Credit: Cover Image: © *George Lepp/Stone*
Printer: *Transcontinental Printing Group*

National Library of Canada Cataloguing in Publication Data

      Statistics : a first course / Donald H. Sanders ... [et al.]. — 2nd Canadian ed.

Includes index.
ISBN 0-07-091177-0

     1. Statistics—Textbooks. I. Sanders, Donald H.

QA276.12.S72 2004   519.5   C2004-900191-4

To My Loving Family: Naaz, Alia, and Adil.

A. A.

Dedicated to Allan, Christina, Melanie, Valerie, Christopher, Blake, and Carson.

G. L.

About the Authors

DONALD H. SANDERS is the author of eight books about computers and statistics. Over 20 editions of these texts have been published in English, and several have been released in French, German, Spanish, Chinese, and other languages. Well over a million copies of these books have been used in college courses and in industry and government training programs.

Dr. Sanders has 20 years of teaching experience. After receiving degrees from Texas A&M University and the University of Arkansas, he was a professor at the University of Texas at Arlington and at Memphis State University. He was a tenured full professor at Texas Christian University for 14 years.

In addition to his books, Dr. Sanders has contributed articles to journals such as *Data Management, Automation, Banking, Journal of Small Business Management, Journal of Retailing,* and *Advanced Management Journal*. He has also encouraged his graduate students to contribute articles to national periodicals, and over 70 of these articles have been published. Dr. Sanders has chaired the "Computers and Data Processing" Subject Examination Committee, CLEP Program, College Entrance Examination Board, Princeton, New Jersey.

ROBERT K. SMIDT earned a B.S. in mathematics from Manhattan College, an M.S. in statistics from Rutgers University, and a Ph.D. in statistics from the University of Wyoming. Dr. Smidt has taught at the University of Florida, University of Wyoming, Rutgers University, Oregon State University, Cuesta College, Fashion Institute of Technology, for LaVerne College at Vandenberg AFB, for Chapman College at the California Men's Colony, and for the Continuing Education Institute. He is currently professor and former chair of the Statistics Department at Cal Poly, San Luis Obispo, California.

Dr. Smidt has broad statistical consulting experience. He has worked for or with the Department of Defense at the Pentagon, Lawrence Livermore National Laboratory, Tenera, Diablo Canyon Nuclear Power Plant, Bechtel Power Corporation, Cogimet, Lindamood-Bell Learning Processes, Fred Streit Associates, Division of Business and Economic Research of the University of Wyoming, County of San Luis Obispo, and the California State Water Resources Control Board. He helped establish the university-wide statistical consulting service at Cal Poly and has extensive consulting experience within the university.

Dr. Smidt has contributed to journals such as *Biometrics, Journal of Clinical Neuropsychology, Medical Anthropology, Journal of the Lepidopterists' Society,* and *American Journal of Orthodontics and Dentofacial Orthopedics,* and to collections such as *Statistical Case Studies, A Collaboration between Academe and Industry* and *Familias y relaciones de genero en transformacion.*

AMINMOHAMED ADATIA earned a B.S. (Honours) in mathematics and an M.S. in applied mathematics from the University of Liverpool, U.K., an M.S. in statistics from the University of Saskatchewan, and a Ph.D. in statistics from the University of Western Ontario. Dr. Adatia has published research articles in the areas of reliability studies, statistical computing, statistical estimation and sampling. He is currently an Associate Professor in the Department of Mathematics and Statistics at the University of Regina.

GLENN A. LARSON earned a B.A. (Honours) from the University of Saskatchewan and an M.Math from the University of Waterloo. He has 32 years of experience teaching statistics and mathematics. In addition, Mr. Larson has statistical consulting experience, in areas ranging from wildlife populations to groundwater measurements and medical research. He is currently an Assistant Professor in the Department of Mathematics and Statistics at the University of Regina.

Contents

	Looking Ahead	1
1.1	What to Expect	2
1.2	Statistics: What Is It?	2
1.3	Uses of Statistics	5
1.4	Performing Statistical Studies	6
1.5	Role of the Computer in Statistics	11
	Looking Back	15
	Exercises	15
	Topics for Review and Discussion	16
	Projects/Issues to Consider	16
	Computer/Calculator Exercises	17

CHAPTER 1

Let's Get Started

	Looking Ahead	18
2.1	Unfavourable Opinions and the Bias Obstacle	19
2.2	Aggravating Averages	20
2.3	Disregarded Dispersions	21
2.4	The Persuasive Artist	22
2.5	The *Post Hoc Ergo Propter Hoc* Trap	28
2.6	Antics with Semantics and Trends	29
2.7	Follow the Bouncing Base (If You Can)	30
2.8	Avoiding Spurious Accuracy and Other Pitfalls	31
	Looking Back	32
	Exercises	33
	Topics for Review and Discussion	36
	Projects/Issues to Consider	36
	Computer/Calculator Exercises	36

CHAPTER 2

Thinking Critically about Data: Liars, #$%& Liars, and a Few Statisticians

CHAPTER 3
Descriptive Statistics

	Looking Ahead	37
3.1	Introduction to Data Collection	38
3.2	Data Organization and Frequency Distributions	39
3.3	Graphic Presentations of Frequency Distributions	49
3.4	Measures of Central Tendency	61
3.5	Computing Measures of Dispersion and Relative Position	73
3.6	Summarizing Qualitative Data	94
	Looking Back	96
	Exercises	98
	Topics for Review and Discussion	102
	Projects/Issues to Consider	102
	Computer/Calculator Exercises	103

CHAPTER 4
Probability Concepts

	Looking Ahead	104
4.1	Some Basic Considerations	105
4.2	Probabilities for Compound Events	111
4.3	Random Variables, Probability Distributions, and Expected Values	125
	Looking Back	136
	Exercises	137
	Topics for Review and Discussion	140
	Projects/Issues to Consider	141
	Computer/Calculator Exercises	141

CHAPTER 5
Probability Distributions

	Looking Ahead	142
5.1	Binomial Experiments	143
5.2	Determining Binomial Probabilities	144
5.3	The Poisson Distribution	152
5.4	The Normal Distribution	157
5.5	Normal Approximation of the Binomial	173
	Looking Back	177
	Exercises	177
	Topics for Review and Discussion	181
	Projects/Issues to Consider	181
	Computer/Calculator Exercises	182

CHAPTER 6

Sampling Concepts

	Looking Ahead	183
6.1	Sampling: The Need and the Advantages	184
6.2	Sampling Distribution of Means—A Pattern of Behaviour	186
6.3	Sampling Distribution of Proportions	201
	Looking Back	207
	Exercises	207
	Topics for Review and Discussion	209
	Projects/Issues to Consider	210
	Computer/Calculator Exercises	210

CHAPTER 7

Estimating Parameters

	Looking Ahead	211
7.1	Estimate, Estimation, Estimator, Et Cetera	212
7.2	Interval Estimation of the Population Mean: Some Basic Concepts	215
7.3	Estimating the Population Mean	220
7.4	Estimating the Population Proportion	238
7.5	Estimating the Population Variance	246
7.6	Determining Sample Size to Estimate μ or p	252
	Looking Back	257
	Exercises	258
	Topics for Review and Discussion	261
	Projects/Issues to Consider	262
	Computer/Calculator Exercises	262

CHAPTER 8

Testing Hypotheses: One-Sample Procedures

	Looking Ahead	265
8.1	The Hypothesis-Testing Procedure in General	266
8.2	One-Sample Hypothesis Tests of Means	275
8.3	One-Sample Hypothesis Tests of Proportions	304
8.4	One-Sample Hypothesis Tests of Variances and Standard Deviations	310
	Looking Back	316
	Exercises	317
	Topics for Review and Discussion	321
	Projects/Issues to Consider	322
	Computer/Calculator Exercises	322

CHAPTER 9

Inference: Two-Sample Procedures

	Looking Ahead	324
9.1	Hypothesis Tests of Two Variances	325
9.2	Inferences about Two Means	335
9.3	Inferences about Two Proportions	375
	Looking Back	383
	Exercises	384
	Topics for Review and Discussion	391
	Projects/Issues to Consider	392
	Computer/Calculator Exercises	392

CHAPTER 10

Analysis of Variance

	Looking Ahead	398
10.1	Analysis of Variance: Purpose and Procedure	399
10.2	An ANOVA Example	405
10.3	The One-Way ANOVA Table and Computers to the Rescue	412
10.4	Two-Way Analysis of Variance	426
	Looking Back	435
	Exercises	436
	Topics for Review and Discussion	441
	Projects/Issues to Consider	441
	Computer/Calculator Exercises	441

CHAPTER 11

Chi-Square Tests: Goodness-of-Fit and Contingency Table Methods

	Looking Ahead	445
11.1	Chi-Square Testing: Purpose and Procedure	446
11.2	The Goodness-of-Fit Test	448
11.3	The Contingency Table Tests	459
	Looking Back	475
	Exercises	475
	Topics for Review and Discussion	479
	Projects/Issues to Consider	480
	Computer/Calculator Exercises	480

	Looking Ahead	482
12.1	Introductory Concepts	483
12.2	Simple Linear Regression Analysis	490
12.3	Statistical Inference in Simple Linear Regression Analysis	500
12.4	Simple Linear Correlation Analysis	514
12.5	Multiple Linear Regression and Correlation	528
	Looking Back	556
	Exercises	557
	Topics for Review and Discussion	564
	Projects/Issues to Consider	564
	Computer/Calculator Exercises	565

CHAPTER 12

Linear Regression and Correlation

	Looking Ahead	568
13.1	Non-parametric Methods: Uses, Benefits, and Limitations	569
13.2	Sign Tests	570
13.3	The Wilcoxon Signed Rank Test	583
13.4	The Mann-Whitney Test	592
13.5	The Kruskal-Wallis Test	600
13.6	Runs Test for Randomness	609
13.7	Spearman Rank Correlation Coefficient	615
	Looking Back	625
	Exercises	625
	Topics for Review and Discussion	633
	Projects/Issues to Consider	633
	Computer/Calculator Exercises	634

CHAPTER 13

Non-parametric Statistical Methods

1	Selected Values of the Binomial Probability Distribution	A-2
2	Areas under the Standard Normal Probability Distribution	A-9
3	A Brief Table of Random Numbers	A-10

APPENDICES

4   Areas for t Distributions   A-11

5   F Distribution Tables   A-12

6   Chi-Square Distribution   A-15

7   Critical Values of T for $\alpha = 0.05$ and $\alpha = 0.01$
     in the Wilcoxon Signed Rank Test   A-16

8   Distribution of U in the Mann-Whitney Test   A-17

9   Critical Values for r in the Runs Test for Randomness   A-19

10   Selected Values of the Poisson Probability Distribution   A-20

11   Entering and Editing Data in MINITAB   A-24

12   Answers to Odd-Numbered Self-Testing Review Questions
     and Exercises   A-26

CREDITS   A-73
SUBJECT INDEX   I-1
INDEX OF APPLICATIONS   I-12

Preface

If I had only one day left to live, I would live it in my statistics class ... it would seem so much longer.

— Quotation in a university student calendar

Welcome to the Second Canadian Edition of *Statistics: A First Course*! This textbook continues the efforts of the first edition to present the subject of statistics to Canadian students in a way that time spent on the subject doesn't seem like the eternity suggested by the quotation above. As the name implies, this book is designed for Canadian students at an early stage in college or university programs. Our objective is to introduce students to many of the important concepts and procedures they will need to (1) evaluate the data we are all presented with every day through newspapers, television, and organizational reports; (2) improve their ability to make better decisions over a wide range of topics; and (3) improve their ability to measure and cope with changing conditions both at home and in the work environment. This textbook makes every effort to support student learning and provide motivation. We present the concepts clearly, and we support these concepts with examples and exercises to make the textbook as useful and user-friendly as possible.

Using carefully selected examples, the book attempts to

1. Present material in a relaxed and informal way that won't intimidate students, while covering all of the important concepts.

2. Demonstrate the wide range of relevant issues and questions that can be addressed with the help of statistical analysis techniques by presenting over *1,750* realistic problems in the areas of health care, business and economics, the social and physical sciences, engineering, education, and leisure activities.

3. Convince students that they can do statistics by including relevant examples and minicases that use real data.

4. Incorporate widely available, inexpensive technologies in order to reduce the drudgery of hand calculations and allow for some exploration of concepts.

We have also incorporated Canadian examples throughout the text and have drawn heavily from the most recent Canadian Census data. We have done this because we truly believe that providing students with a context that is relevant and familiar will help them become more fully engaged in the study of statistics. This is the primary aim of this book: to actively engage the students of today to become the responsible decision makers of tomorrow.

Changes to the Second Edition

Throughout this edition we have made every effort to update data sets, add motivational topics of interest to Canadian students through examples and exercises, and change the focus of our discussions of "percentage" to "proportions." Key highlights of new and updated material in the second edition include

Chapter 1, Let's Get Started

■ Sections 1.1 and 1.2 have been improved to facilitate a smoother, more immediate introduction to statistics.

■ Section 1.4 now introduces statistical problem solving in three steps, as opposed to six.

Chapter 3, Descriptive Statistics

■ The discussion of percentiles has been clarified.

Chapter 4, Probability Concepts

■ Section 4.2 has been improved by the addition of coverage of Bayes' Theorem.

Chapter 5, Probability Distributions

■ Addition of coverage on various distributions, including Exponential, Geometric, Hypergeometric, and Multinomial.

■ Addition of a list of examples where the Poisson Distribution would be appropriate.

■ *New* Section 5.5 covering Normal Approximation of the Binomial including examples and a Self-Testing Review.

Chapter 10, Analysis of Variance

■ *New* Section 10.4 covering Two-Way ANOVA, including a discussion of Randomized Block Design.

Chapter 11, Chi-Square Tests: Goodness-of-Fit and Contingency Table Methods

■ Coverage of the tests for goodness-of-fit and for homogeneity of proportions, as well as the Contingency Table, have been clarified.

Chapter 12, Linear Regression and Correlation

■ Addition of summary boxes describing
   —Straight-Line Regression Model.
   —Confidence Interval and *t* Test for Slope.
   —Sum of Squares, Degrees of Freedom, and Mean Squares.
   —ANOVA Table for Simple Linear Regression.
   —Analysis of Variance *F*-test for Regression Slope.
   —Multiple Linear Regression Model.

■ Addition of coverage on
   —Measuring the strength of linear relationships.
   —A *t* test for ρ, the population correlation coefficient.
   —Correlation and causation.
   —Another formula for computing the correlation.
   —Using dummy variables to model qualitative independent variables.
   —Partial *F*-test: Testing the significance of a portion of a regression model.
   —Checking regression assumptions.

Chapter 13, Non-parametric Statistical Methods
- Addition of coverage on Wilcoxon Signed Rank test for the median or mean of a single population.

Features of this Edition

Looking Ahead
Each chapter begins with a preview of the contents in that chapter and lists the learning objectives. This lets students know what they can expect to learn in each chapter.

L O O K I N G   A H E A D

Y ou'll learn procedures in this chapter to help you decide if sample results *support* a hypothesis about a parameter value or if the results show that the hypothesis should be *rejected*. That is, from our examination of sampling concepts, we can figure out what type of sample results should happen if the hypothesized population value is correct. If the sample results differ substantially from what we expect, the difference is called a statistically significant difference, and this difference is the basis for rejecting the hypothesis being tested.

But we're getting ahead of ourselves. Before the chapter asks you to test hypotheses and make decisions, it outlines a general hypothesis-testing procedure for you to use to conduct one-sample hypothesis tests of means, proportions, and variances. (In later chapters, we'll look at hypothesis-testing procedures that involve two or more samples.)

Thus, after studying this chapter, you should be able to

- Explain the necessary steps in the general hypothesis-testing procedure.

- Perform one-sample hypothesis tests of means (both one- and two-tailed versions) when the population standard deviation is known, as well as when it's not available.

- Perform one-sample hypothesis tests of proportions for both one- and two-tailed testing situations.

- Perform one-sample hypothesis tests of variances for both one- and two-tailed testing situations.

Statistics in Action
In the body of the chapters are minicases keyed with icons that identify them as belonging to one of the following categories: (1) Business/Economics, (2) Physical Science/Engineering, (3) Health, (4) Social Science, (5) Education, and (6) Leisure Activities.

STATISTICS IN ACTION

Did You Know ... ?

If the soft drink bottles recycled in Canada in one year were placed end to end, they would stretch from Vancouver Island to St. John's, NF, over 26 times. Recycling aluminum soft drink cans in Canada for one year saves enough electricity to supply 15,000 Canadian households for an entire year.

Key Formulas

Formulas used for the first time are boxed and numbered for easy reference. In addition, these key formulas are listed at the back of the text, and on the text's Online Learning Centre.

When a *sample* data set is used, the standard deviation is found with

$$s = \sqrt{\frac{\Sigma(x - \bar{x})^2}{n - 1}} \qquad (3.5)$$

where s = sample standard deviation
      x = values of the observations
      $\bar{x}$ = mean of the sample
      n = number of observations in the sample

Key Concepts

Important concepts unique to the study of statistics are set apart from the text and highlighted for easy reference and review.

Percentile

The kth percentile, P_k, is a value such that at most k percent of the data are smaller in value than P_k, and at most $(100 - k)$ percent are larger.

Self-Testing Reviews

Problems that support the learning objectives punctuate each section, and allow students to practise the skills they have just learned. The answers are provided at the end of the text to provide immediate feedback on students' understanding of the units.

Self-Testing Review 5.2

6. In 2001 at the University of Ottawa, the male to female student ratio was 41 to 59. (For ease of computation, assume the ratio is 40 to 60, or 2 to 3.) Suppose 12 students are randomly selected. Find the probability that

    a) Exactly eight are female.

    b) At least eight are male.

    c) Fewer than five are female.

    d) Between six and nine (including six and nine) are male.

7. According to Statistics Canada, 85 percent of Canadian households own a VCR. Ten households are randomly selected across the country and are asked if they own a VCR. Find the probability that

    a) Exactly eight own a VCR.

    b) Fewer than seven own a VCR.

    c) At least six own a VCR.

Logic Flowcharts

Procedural steps are outlined in coloured flow charts that are often easier for students to follow than narrative summaries alone.

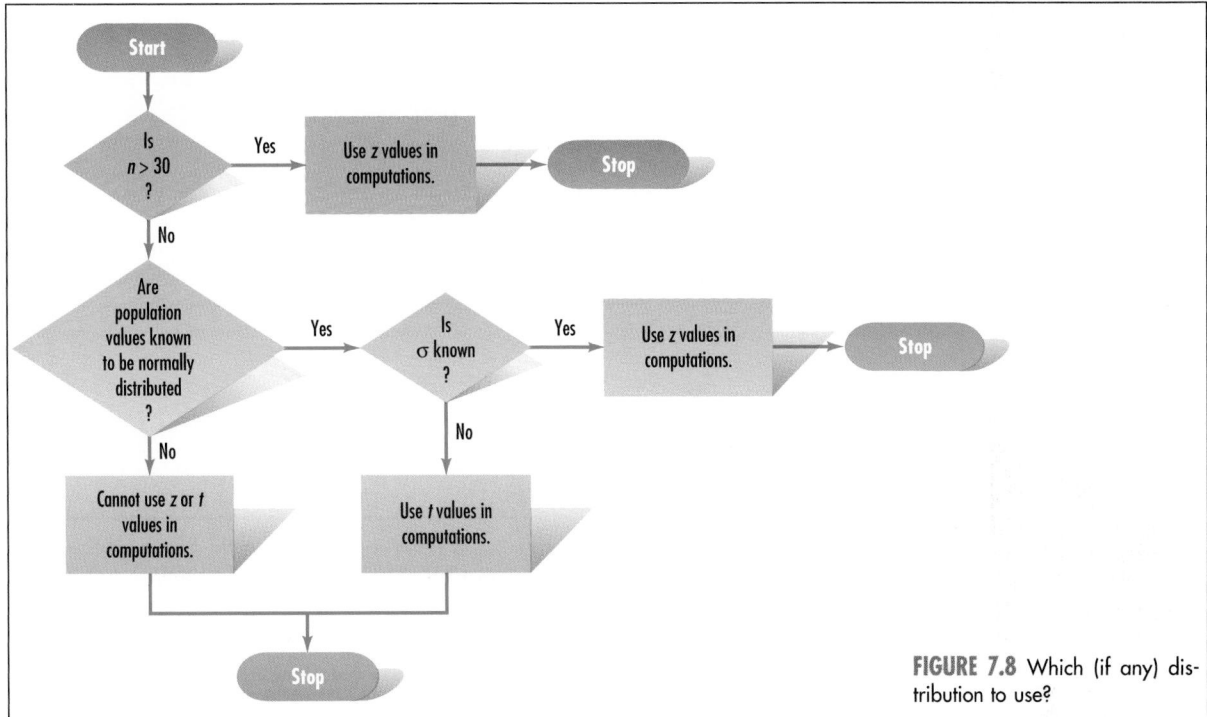

FIGURE 7.8 Which (if any) distribution to use?

Looking Back

This short section provides students with a summary of the main points presented in each chapter. This tool is useful as a reference for students as well as for review before exams.

L O O K I N G   B A C K

1. A number of basic terms were defined early in this chapter, and you saw that the probability of a specified event was the relative likelihood of that event occurring. Simple probabilities are assigned using *a priori*, relative frequency, and intuitive approaches. Regardless of how probability values are assigned, though, a probability of 0 means that an event can never occur, and a probability of 1 means it will always occur. Probabilities of interest, of course, lie between these two extremes.

2. In the language of probability, a simple event is one that can't be broken down any further. But we're often interested in the relative chance that some combination of events—that is, a compound event—may occur. We first considered a conditional probability—the probability that event B occurs, given that event A has already happened [or $P(B|A)$]. Often, we can use contingency tables to present the facts for a conditional probability situation. To compute the probability of both A and B happening, we multiply the probability of the first event times the conditional probability of the second event, given that the first has happened.

End-of-Chapter Problems

At the end of each chapter is a comprehensive set of new and real-world problems similar to those problems found throughout the chapter.

Projects/Issues to Consider

This section recommends topics for student research that are based on chapter material. Many of the projects require the student to collect, analyze, and interpret data. Over 60 projects are presented.

Computer/Calculator Exercises

This section presents problems that are keyed to chapter topics. With appropriate hardware/software resources, students can see that tedious procedures can be carried out with a few keystrokes. There are over *250* such exercises.

This icon indicates that an exercise in the section asks students to use one of the many data sources on the Internet that they can link to through the book's Web site at www.mcgraw hill.ca/college/sanders. The underlined "address" is actually the name of the link at that site. We refer to links rather than actual URLs for the data sources in case one of the sources changes its address or closes down.

Exercises

54. A binomial experiment is conducted with $n = 13$ and $p = .35$. Find the probability that the number of successes is

   a) Exactly five.

   b) At least five.

55. A binomial experiment is conducted with $n = 6$ and $p = .40$. Find the probability that

   a) There are no successes.

   b) There is at least one success.

Topics for Review and Discussion

1. What is binomial probability distribution? Discuss the conditions and requirements for a binomial experiment.

2. Why is the formula for combinations incorporated into the formula for computing binomial probabilities?

3. How may a Poisson distribution be used? What are the conditions and requirements for the use of such a distribution?

4. The binomial and Poisson distributions are examples of discrete probability distributions. Discuss.

5. Probabilities for continuous probability distributions are represented by areas under the curve. Discuss.

6. Discuss the procedure for computing normal curve probabilities.

7. Discuss the procedure far determining a z score (standard score) when a specified area under the standard normal curve is given. Use several examples in your explanation.

Projects/Issues to Consider

1. Conduct a library search to find examples of binomial, Poisson, and normally distributed variables. Write a brief report outlining your findings.

2. Collect a data set from your classmates and other students by asking each of them the following questions:

   a) Would you rather take a class in statistics than a class in physics?

   b) How many siblings do you have?

   c) In a typical week, how many hours do you study?

Does it appear that the number of people who would rather take a class in statistics than a class in physics is a binomial random variable? Does it appear that the number of siblings students have is a Poisson variable? Does it look like the number of hours in a week students study is a normal variable? How did you make your determinations? Write a brief report on your findings.

Computer/Calculator Exercises

1. Use your computer software package to simulate the results of 100 students taking the QuickQuiz presented in this chapter. (If your software permits, you may use a **RANDOM** command and a **BINOMIAL** subcommand with $n = 5$ and $p = .25$.) Discuss your results.

2. The average number of customers who go to a teller's station at the credit union in an hour is 12. Assuming a Poisson distribution, use your software package to simulate the number of customers who go to a teller's station each hour during a 40-hour period. Discuss your results.

3. The mid-arm muscle circumference (MAMC) for males is normally distributed with a mean of 273 mm and a standard deviation of 29.18 mm. Simulate the MAMC measure for 500

males. What percent of the measures in your simulation were greater than 341 mm? Compare your results with those found in Example 5.18 in this chapter.

4. In The Data & Story Library at DASLDist, you can find a series of data sets under the category of "Distributions." For each of the data sets, plot the data and see which of the sets you think could have a normal distribution.

5. In The Data & Story Library at DASLMult, you can find at least one data set under the category of "Multivariate Normality." For each of the variables in the data set, plot the variable and see if you think it has a normal distribution.

MINITAB and TI-83 Graphing Calculator

The use of technology to support computing, analysis, and decision-making efforts is demonstrated in many example problems. Icons indicate such material:

 for MINITAB

and for the TI-83.

Screens and printouts from MINITAB, and screens from the TI-83, are reproduced in the book. Instructions for using the software and the calculator are provided in the accompanying captions.

FIGURE 5.2 (*a*) **To obtain this MINITAB output, click on Calc, Probability Distributions, Binomial,** click in the circle next to **Probability,** enter 5 **as Number of Trials and** .25 as **Probability of Success,** click in the circle to the left of **Input Column** and enter the column containing the values of *r*, denoted *X* by MINITAB, and click **OK.** (*b*) To calculate binomial probabilities on the TI-83, we can use the binompdf command, which is option 0 under the **DISTR** menu. The **DISTR** menu is the 2nd function of the VARS key. **The syntax is binompdf(n,p,x).** From the home screen access the binompdf function, enter binompdf(5,0.25,3) and **ENTER** to get 0.0879, which is P(3) in the **Quick Quiz example.** To see the entire distribution we can store the *X* values in L1 and then store binompdl(5,0.25,L1) into **L2.** (See screen 1.) Note that the set brackets, { }, are the 2nd functions of the (keys and the **STO** key used to store the list. Then to see the distribution, go to **STAT>Edit** as shown in screen 2.

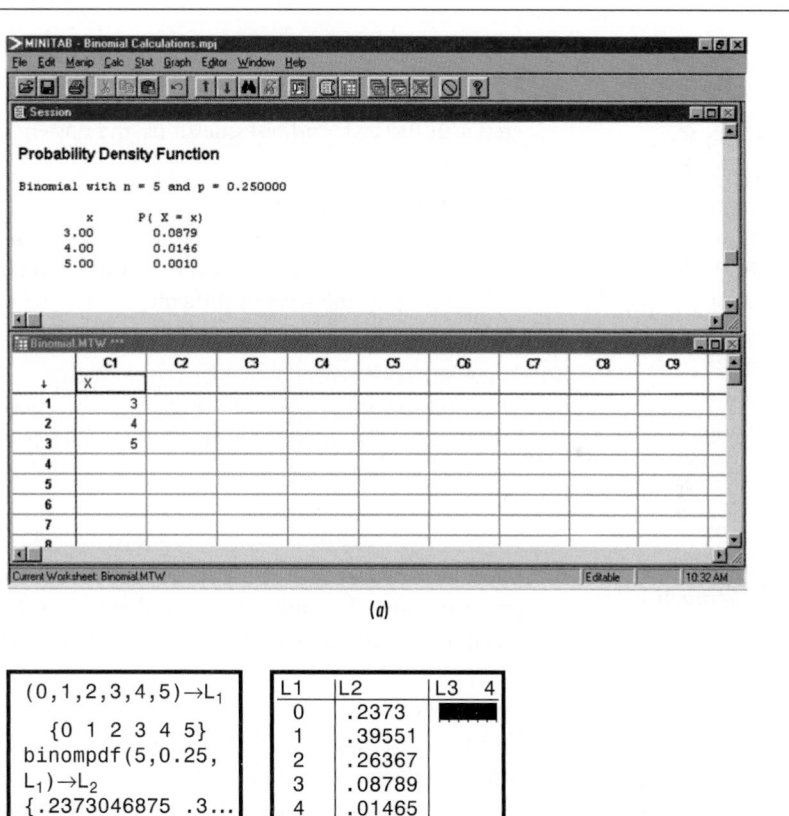

(*a*)

Screen 1   Screen 2

(*b*)

Entering and Editing Data in MINITAB

Appendix 11 is a brief, illustrated introduction to the program that will get students up and running quickly.

Index of Applications

This index guides instructors and students to examples and exercises discussing topics from specific fields, such as health or business.

Instructor's Supplements

Integrated Learning

Your *Integrated*-Learning Sales Specialist is a McGraw-Hill Ryerson representative who has the experience, product knowledge, training, and support to help you assess and integrate any of the below-noted products, technology, and services into your course for optimum teaching and learning performance. Whether it's how to use our Computerized Test Bank, help your students improve their grades, or put your entire course online, your *i*-Learning Sales Specialist can help you do it. Contact your local *i*-Learning Sales Specialist today to learn how to maximize all of McGraw-Hill Ryerson's resources!

Instructor's Resource Guide

This comprehensive manual contains the complete solutions to all even-numbered exercises in the text, and test questions and answers for every chapter.

Computerized Test Bank

This resource contains individual chapter tests; a sample final exam; and true/false, multiple choice, and short-answer questions. The answers to all questions are given, along with a rating of the level of difficulty.

Microsoft® PowerPoint® Lecture Slides

These full-colour slides include chapter objectives, definitions of key terms, graphics, and additional examples. By accessing the slides through the Online Learning Centre, you can use them to enhance your lectures and add your own material.

Instructor's Online Learning Centre (OLC)

The OLC at www.mcgrawhill.ca/college/sanders includes a password-protected Web site for instructors. The site offers downloadable supplements and access to PageOut, the McGraw-Hill Ryerson Web site development centre.

PageOut

This unique point-and-click course Web site tool enables you to create a high quality course Web site without knowing HTML coding. With PageOut, you can post your syllabus on-line, assign McGraw-Hill Online Learning Centre content, add links to important off-site resources, and maintain student results in the on-line gradebook. In addition, content cartridges are also available for course management systems such as WebCT and Blackboard, to expand the reach of your course and open up distance-learning options. Contact your local *i*-Learning Sales Specialist for details.

Superior Service

Service takes on a whole new meaning with McGraw-Hill Ryerson and *Statistics: A First Course*, Second Canadian Edition. More than just bringing you the textbook, we have consistently raised the bar of innovation and educational research—both in statistics and in education in general. These investments in learning and the education community have helped us to understand the needs of students and educators across the country, and allowed us to foster the growth of truly innovative, integrated learning.

i-Learning Services Program

McGraw-Hill Ryerson offers a unique iServices package designed for Canadian faculty. Our mission is to equip providers of higher education with superior tools and resources required for excellence in teaching. For additional information, visit *www.mcgrawhill.ca/highereducation/eservices/*.

Teaching, Technology, & Learning Conference Series

The educational environment has changed tremendously in recent years, and McGraw-Hill Ryerson continues to be committed to helping you acquire the skills you need to succeed in this new milieu. Our innovative Teaching, Technology, & Learning Conference Series brings together faculty from across Canada with 3M Teaching Excellence award winners to share teaching and learning best practices in a collaborative and stimulating environment. Preconference workshops on general topics, such as teaching large classes and technology integration, will also be offered. We will also work with you at your own institution to customize workshops that best suit the needs of your faculty.

Research Reports into Mobile Learning and Student Success

These landmark reports, undertaken in conjunction with academic and private-sector advisory boards, are the result of research into the challenge professors face in helping students succeed and the opportunities that new technology presents to impact teaching and learning.

Student Supplements

Data CD-ROM

Every copy of *Statistics: A First Course,* Second Canadian Edition, is accompanied by a data CD that includes data from tables, examples, and exercises throughout the text. The data files are named descriptively. Beside each example or exercise in the text for which data are provided, appears the name of the corresponding data file (in parentheses).

Student Solutions Manual *007-091188-6*

The Student Study Guide and Solutions Manual contains Study Objectives, Section Overviews, Key Terms & Formulas, Worked Examples, Practice Exercises and Solutions, and Hints & Cautions. In addition, students receive solutions to odd-numbered exercises.

Student Online Learning Centre (OLC)

This electronic learning aid, located at www.mcgrawhill.ca/college/sanders, offers a wealth of materials, including quizzes, Web links, word problems, and much more!

Σ-STAT is an educational resource designed by Statistics Canada and made available to Canadian educational institutions through our Online Learning Centre. Using 450,000 current CANSIM (Canadian Socio-economic Information Management System) Time Series and the most recent (as well as historical) census data, Σ-STAT lets you bring data to life in colourful graphs and maps. You can access data such as federal debt, imports and exports, population, income, language, and more. Easy-to-use, thorough, and dynamic, Σ-STAT is a stimulating teaching and learning resource that spurs students on to discover Canada, past and present.

Acknowledgements

Comments and suggestions that have been invaluable to the development of the Second Canadian Edition were provided by a variety of reviewers, and a debt of gratitude is owed to the following educators:

Paul Cabilio	*Acadia University*
Louise Routledge	*British Columbia Institute of Technology*
Dorothy Levay	*Brock University*
John H. Walker	*Brock University*
Patrick Farrell	*Carleton University*
Shirley Mills	*Carleton University*
Ray Sproule	*Malaspina University College*
Peter D.M. Macdonald	*McMaster University*
John G. Reid	*Mount Saint Vincent University*
Paramjit Gill	*Okanagan University College*
Rohana J. Karunamuni	*University of Alberta*
Alan W. Donald	*University of British Columbia*
Peter Lui	*University of British Columbia*
David P.M. Scollnick	*University of Calgary*
Gemai Chen	*University of Calgary*
Lida Shadabi	*University of Calgary*
Nancy Morrison	*University of Calgary*
Gary Umphrey	*University of Guelph*
Augustin Vukov	*University of Toronto*
James R. Adcock	*University of Western Ontario*
David C. Vaughn	*Wilfred Laurier University*
J. Richard Elliott	*Wilfred Laurier University*
Augustine Wong	*York University*

Thanks also to those who participated in the development of the First Canadian Edition:

Ed Holland	*John Abbott College*
Deli Li	*Lakehead University*
Ed Fox	*Niagara College*
Sam Fefferman	*Northern Alberta Institute of Technology*
Charmaine Dean	*Simon Fraser University*
N.G.N. Prasad	*University of Alberta*
Smiley Cheng	*University of Manitoba*
Dennis O'Shaughnessy	*University of Saskatchewan*
Hatem A. Howlader	*University of Winnipeg*

Special thanks to all members of the Department of Mathematics and Statistics at the University of Regina for their support and many helpful suggestions. Special thanks also to Karen Howden and Nadine Griffiths for their interest and encouragement.

Finally, we wish to thank the staff at McGraw-Hill Ryerson. This includes Cathy Koop, Senior Sponsoring Editor; Leanna MacLean, Sponsoring Editor; Kamilah Reid Burrell, Developmental Editor; David Groth, Marketing Manager; Kelly Dickson, Editorial Services Manager; Jaime Duffy, Supervising Editor; Mary Pepe, Production Coordinator; Dianna Little, Interior Design; and others whom we do not know personally, but who made important contributions.

Amin Adatia
Glenn Larson

Statistics

A First Course
SECOND CANADIAN EDITION

FOR THE INSTRUCTOR

- **Want to access your supplements *without* having to bring them all to class?**

- **Want an *easy* way to get your course on-line?**

- **Want to *free up more time* in your day to get more done?**

Of course you do!

Then check out your
Online Learning Centre!

- Downloadable Supplements
- PageOut
- Online Resources

CHAPTER 1

Let's Get Started

LOOKING AHEAD

This chapter gives you an understanding of the purpose of this book (and this course). You'll see that the word *statistics* is used in several ways, and you'll also learn the meaning of other important terms. The need for statistics is outlined here, and a series of steps that are used to perform statistical studies is presented. Finally, the role of the computer in statistics is briefly discussed. Thus, after studying this chapter, you should be able to

- Define the meaning of the terms in boldface type such as **statistics, population, census, sample, parameter, statistic, descriptive statistics,** and **statistical inference.**

- Understand and explain why a knowledge of statistics is needed.

- Outline the basic steps in performing statistical studies.

- Obtain a simple random sample.

- Discuss the role of computers and data analysis software in statistical work.

1.1 What to Expect

You may have heard—and you may even agree—that you need to understand statistics to live in the modern world. That may alarm you, especially if you have never placed mathematics and statistics on your top ten list of favourite things to do. Moreover, you may have heard disturbing rumours about the difficulty of statistics courses. We would like to allay some of your worries.

First, we did not write this book for mathematicians or statisticians. We wrote it for beginning students. You will not need calculus or matrix algebra or any other exotic mathematical skills. A knowledge of high school algebra will be more than enough.

Second, we have tried to bring statistics to you, rather than dragging you to the statistics. The examples in this book are drawn from a wide variety of disciplines—life sciences, computer science, business, physics, and athletics. Understanding statistics really will help you understand your own studies better.

1.2 Statistics: What Is It?

To most people, statistics means "numerical descriptions"—batting averages, unemployment figures, failure rates, proportion of voters who favour a proposal, gasoline prices, etc. Such numbers describe collections of data, but often the purpose of calculating these numbers goes beyond the description of the data sets. Frequently, the data are a sample selected from some larger set of data whose characteristics we may wish to estimate. For example, a sample of Canadian voters would allow you to estimate the true proportion of all Canadian voters who favour a certain proposal.

So, the study of statistics can be divided into two broad areas: (1) describing collections of data and (2) making inferences (estimates, decisions, predictions, etc.) based on sampling.

> **Descriptive statistics** consists of collecting, summarizing, and presenting sample data using numerical and graphical methods.
> **Inferential statistics** consists of making estimates, decisions, predictions, or other generalizations about a larger set of data based on sampling.

Definitions

Like other areas of study, statistics has its own terminology. Several important terms used in statistics are defined below.

> A **population** is the complete collection of measurements, objects, or individuals under study.

You'll notice in this definition that *population* isn't limited to a group of people. Rather, the word refers to *all* of the measures, counts, or qualities that are of interest in a study. Thus, a population may be all batteries built in a day's production run, the weights of all packages in a shipment, the odometer readings on all the police cars in Toronto, or the outstanding balances on all credit accounts in a Sears department store. To gain information about this characteristic of interest, a researcher may occasionally try to survey all the elements in a population. Such a survey is called a **census.** But a census is expensive, time-consuming, and sometimes impossible to obtain, so it's more common to first select a sample from the population and then analyze the sample data.

Since a *sample* is only a subset of a population, the data of interest that it supplies are necessarily incomplete. But if sampling is done scientifically, it's usually possible to obtain sample results that are sufficiently accurate for the researcher's needs.

> A **sample** is a portion or subset taken from a population.

Two other statistical terms are closely related to the concepts we've just examined.

The average (arithmetic mean) weight of all packages in a population is a single number, and this number is a *parameter.* Other parameters are (1) the proportion of all hospital patients receiving a treatment who are responding favourably to the treatment and (2) the average lifetime (in hours) of all batteries. Thus, if a proportion figure or an average value describes a population, it is a parameter.

Often, however, a parameter is unknown and a *statistic* must be used.

> A **parameter** is a numerical characteristic of a population.
> A **statistic** is a numerical characteristic of a sample.

A statistic is to a sample what a parameter is to a population—it's a single value that summarizes some characteristic of interest. Thus, if we receive a shipment of 1,000 packages, select a sample of 25 of them, weigh each of the 25, and compute the average weight of the 25 packages, the result is a statistic. But if we compute the average weight of all 1,000 packages in the shipment, the result is a parameter.

The subject of statistics consists of two essential parts: (1) descriptive statistics and (2) inferential statistics. *Figure 1.1* presents an overview of these categories.

Descriptive statistics is the focus of the next two chapters. With a knowledge of descriptive procedures, you can evaluate information presented in reports, articles, and broadcasts and improve your ability to measure and thus cope with changing conditions. In Chapter 2, for example, you'll see how statistical methods have been improperly used to confuse or deliberately mislead people. Many of the invalid uses presented involve descriptive procedures. In Chapter 3 we'll consider data collection and classification, measures of central tendency, and measures of dispersion that are frequently used to describe data.

The second part of statistics is **inferential statistics,** which is the process of using the known sample data to make inferences concerning some unknown aspect (usually a parameter) of a population. Statistical inference concepts allow an analyst to use sample data to estimate an unknown population parameter of interest—for example, the average weight of all 1,000 packages in the shipment described earlier. If the average weight of the sample of 25 packages is 3.2 kilograms, the average weight of all 1,000 packages may be estimated with confidence to be between 3.0 and 3.4 kilograms. Or perhaps the analyst will use statistical inference to conduct a test to see if the average weight of all 1,000 packages is 3.5 kilograms. On the basis of the sample statistic of 3.2, the analyst can assess the strength of evidence that the population mean weight falls below the specified 3.5-kilogram parameter.

Figure 1.2 graphically presents the statistical inference process of using a sample statistic to make a judgment about an unknown population parameter. In chapters 4 and 5, you'll learn the conceptual foundations of probability that support sampling

FIGURE 1.1 An overview of descriptive statistics and statistical inference.

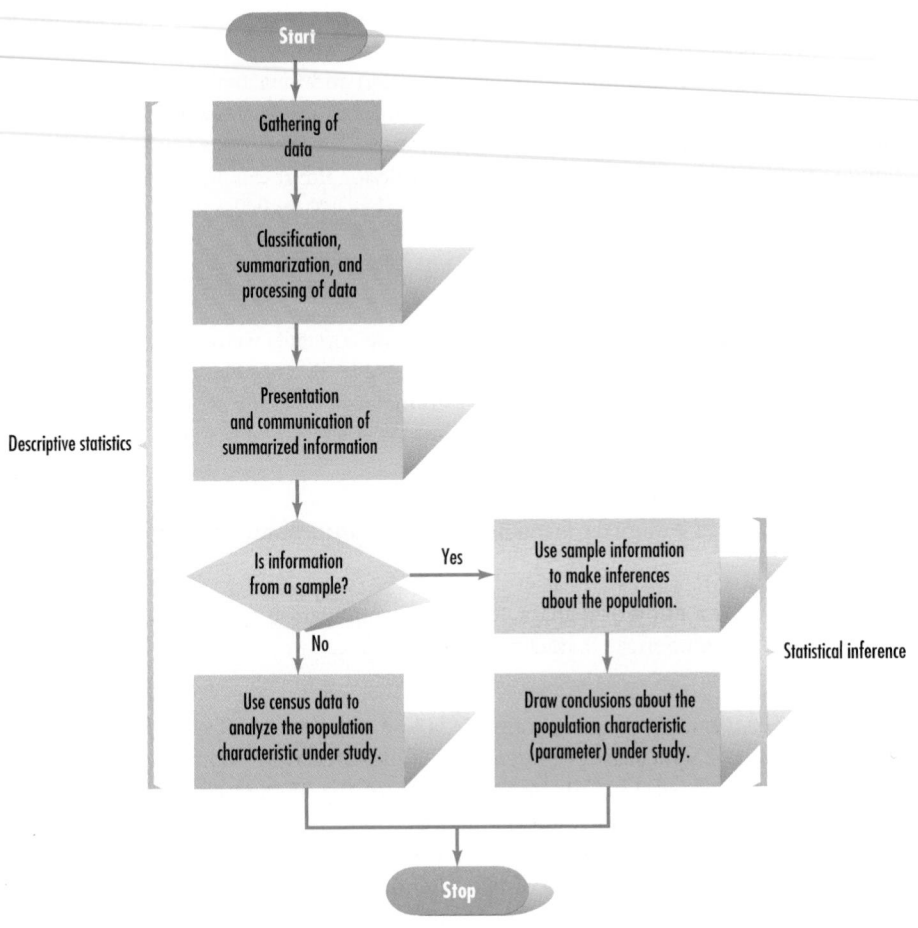

FIGURE 1.2 The statistical inference process involves the use of a known sample statistic to arrive at a judgment about an unknown population parameter.

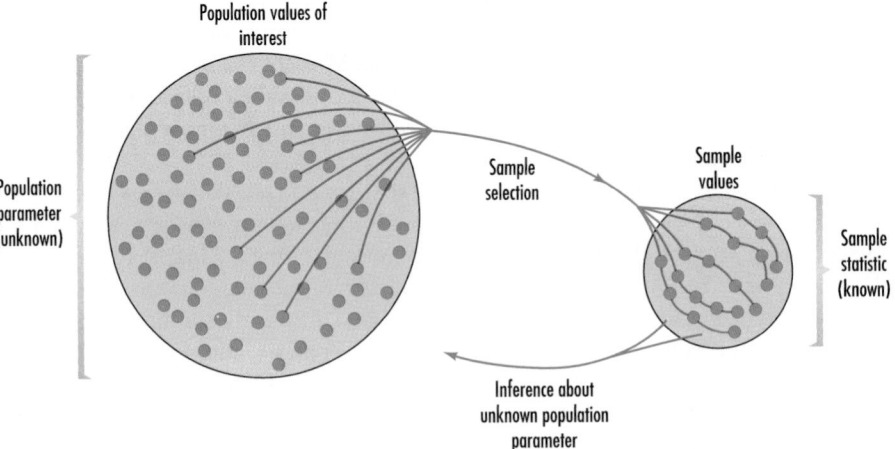

applications. Then, in the remaining chapters you'll see how statistical inference concepts are applied.

Most of the chapters in this book contain *self-testing review sections* following the presentation of important material. You're encouraged to test your understanding of the reviewed subjects presented in these sections before moving to the next topic. Answers to self-testing reviews are given at the end of the chapters. You'll also find at the end of a chapter (1) a *looking back* chapter summary, (2) *additional exercises* (with answers to selected exercises found at the back of the book), (3) *topics for review and discussion*, (4) *projects/issues to consider*, and (5) *computer/calculator* exercises.

1.3 Uses of Statistics

The following examples are presented as illustrations of how statistics can be used in order to (1) describe and understand numerical relationships and (2) make better decisions.

Describing Relationships between Variables

The amount of data that's gathered, processed, and presented to people is overwhelming. Thus, it's necessary that you be able to sift through this huge mass to identify and describe those sometimes obscure relationships between variables that are often so important in decision making. Consider these examples:

Example 1.1 A management consultant wants to compare a client's investment return for this year with related figures from last year. He summarizes masses of revenue and cost data from both periods and, based on his findings, presents his recommendations to his client. ◆

Example 1.2 A public health official decides to see if there is any connection between inhaling the smoke produced by cigarette smokers (second-hand smoking) and the incidence of asthma in young children. She applies statistical techniques to large amounts of data and reaches conclusions that will affect the health of large numbers of people. ◆

Example 1.3 A marketing manager wants to analyze the relationships that may exist between the demand for her product and such demographic factors as income, age, and ethnic background. On the basis of the relationships that may exist, she can advise her staff to design an appropriate advertising campaign. ◆

Aiding in Decision Making

Statistical methods allow people to make better decisions in the face of uncertainty. Consider these examples:

Example 1.4 The purchasing manager for a processing plant that supplies fresh poultry to three provinces is responsible for buying chickens in shipments of 10,000 birds. Standards specify that the chickens should weigh 2.7 kilograms on average. (Birds over that weight tend to be too tough; lighter birds are too scrawny.) The truck of a new supplier rolls up to the unloading dock with a shipment. The supplier's salesperson assures the manager that the shipment meets standards. Should the shipment be accepted on the basis of this claim? Probably not. Rather, statistical inference techniques are used to select a sample of, say, 50 birds from the population of 10,000. Each bird in the sample is weighed, the average weight of the 50 birds is computed, some other statistical calculations are made, and a conclusion about the average weight of the population of 10,000 birds is then reached. Given this information, the manager can now make a more informed decision about accepting the shipment. ◆

Example 1.5   A quality-control engineer at a plant that produces bicycle parts knows that certain variations will exist in the parts produced. These variations can be tolerated if they don't exceed specified limits more than 1 percent of the time. By using a carefully designed sampling plan, the engineer arrives at reliable conclusions or inferences about the quality of a production run. These conclusions are based on examining a relatively small number of parts randomly selected from those produced during the run. ◆

Example 1.6   Suppose that the manager of a hair stylist shop has advertised that 90 percent of the firm's customers are satisfied with the company's services. If a consumer activist believes that this is an exaggerated statement that might require legal action, she can use statistical inference techniques to decide whether or not to sue the shop. ◆

Example 1.7   A personnel manager has noted that job applicants who score high on a manual dexterity test later tend to perform well in product assembly, while those with lower test scores tend to be less productive. By applying a statistical technique known as regression analysis (the subject of Chapter 12), the manager can forecast how productive a new applicant will be on the job on the basis of how well he or she performs on the test. ◆

1.4 Performing Statistical Studies

Results of researchers' interesting studies are widely reported by TV, newspapers, and magazines. We read about the lack of safety of SUVs, the beneficial effects of taking vitamin supplements, and the popularity of political candidates.

Sometimes we also hear of studies where the design of the study itself is questionable (as in the "Statistics in Action" box on page 7) or studies where the results are apparently contradictory.

For example, the DrWeil.com Web site reported that recent studies have concluded that taking vitamin C may help to

- Prevent colds.

- Boost mental ability in later life.

- Protect against some forms of dementia.

- Prevent gallbladder disease.

- Prevent a type of nerve pain (reflex sympathetic dystrophy).

- Reduce the risk of cardiovascular disease, cancer, cataracts, and other chronic conditions.

- Offer protection by destroying certain DNA–damaging free radicals believed to underlie cancer and other diseases.

On the other hand, other studies have concluded that taking vitamin C may

- Promote the formation of free radicals (perhaps causing cancer).

- Harden or clog arteries.

- Cause or promote mutation.

Which of these conclusions are valid? Can vitamin C be both beneficial and harmful? How do we perform a statistical study that produces valid results?

There are a few basic steps to follow to obtain valid and useful results from a study.

1. *Identify your objective:* Identify the specific question to be answered, and clearly identify the relevant population.

2. *Collect sample data:* Decide on a sampling method. The sample data should be representative of the population, so the way in which sample data are collected is crucial to the usefulness of the study.

3. *Analyze the data and form conclusions.*

Step 1: Identify Your Objective
The researcher must clearly understand and correctly define exactly what the study is to accomplish. For example, is the goal to study a population and then estimate an unknown average or proportion, or is it to impose a treatment on the group and then gauge the response? If samples are needed (and they usually are), how large should they be, and how should they be taken? Time and effort are wasted if the answers to such questions are unclear.

Step 2: Collect Sample Data
We typically get our data from three common sources:

1. Data available from others.

2. Data resulting from an experiment.

3. Data collected in an observational study.

We will look at each of these in turn.

Data from Others Data may be obtained from either internal or external sources. Internal data are obtained from within an organization. External data are supplied by outside sources such as the Angus Reid Group, *Canadian Business, Canadian Journal of Economics, Canadian Medical Association Journal, National Post,* Statistics Canada, and *The Globe and Mail.* Many of these and similar publications are available on the Internet. For example, Statistics Canada's Web site is www.statcan.ca, and *The Globe and Mail's* Web site is www.theglobeandmail.com. Good sources of financial data can be found at www.globeinvestor.com and www.nationalpost.com.

STATISTICS IN ACTION

Eggs Prevent Cancer?
Dr. Andrew Weil, a renowned author, was asked "What do you think of the new research from Harvard showing that eating eggs while you're a teenager protects against breast cancer? Should I encourage my daughter to eat more eggs?" In his reply, Dr. Weil said the results were from a Nurses' Health Study, which reported that women who ate an egg daily when they were teenagers were 18 percent less likely to develop breast cancer later in life. Dr. Weil noted that the nature of the study itself called the results into question, since the participating nurses were 40 to 65 years old when they answered questions about their teenage diets. He said, "I'm not sure that anyone can remember with accuracy what he or she ate on a daily basis 22 to 53 years earlier. Based on results of this study, I wouldn't urge teenage girls to eat more eggs. It's fine to eat some eggs, especially those fortified with omega-3 fatty acids, but the best way for girls to protect themselves against breast cancer later in life is with a healthy, varied diet."

It's generally preferable to gather available data from **primary sources**—those that initially gather the data and first publish them—rather than from **secondary sources**—those that republish the data. This is true because secondary sources may introduce reproduction errors and may not explain how the facts were gathered or what limitations exist to their use. Secondary sources may also fail to show how the primary source defined the variables.

In many cases the data needed by decision makers simply aren't available elsewhere, and so there's no alternative but to gather them. There are advantages to gathering new data, for someone who's aware of the problem can define the variables so that the resulting facts possess the properties needed to solve the problem. The two most common ways of collecting data are through experiments and observational studies.

Data from an Experiment In order to understand an experiment, it is helpful to first introduce several terms. First, the experiment involves a sample from a population of interest. The members of the sample are called **experimental units,** though when dealing with people they are more often referred to as **subjects.** The experimenter manipulates these experimental units by subjecting them to one of several **treatments.** These treatments are created by changing the values, or **levels,** of one or more **factors.** The **response** of each experimental unit to its treatment is observed, and comparisons are made across the various treatments. We'll give a few examples before we formally define an experiment.

Example 1.8   Nancy King, a municipal engineer, is concerned with high amounts of nitrates found in local water wells. These amounts, though fluctuating from day to day and between wells, seem to be close to unhealthy levels. Two purification methods that might lower these amounts are available: a filtering system and a chemical treatment. How should Nancy decide whether either of these purification methods should be used, and, if so, which one?

◆ **Solution:**
Obviously, Nancy will design an experiment to help make her decision. Her experimental units will be a sample taken from all the water wells found in the municipality. She decides to take 12 wells and subject each to one of three treatments: (1) the filtering system, (2) the chemical treatment, or (3) no purification. (The third treatment is called a **control** and is necessary to make comparisons to see if either of the other two treatments have any effect.) The single factor in her experiment is purification method, and its levels are (1) filtering system, (2) chemical treatment, and (3) control. Notice in an experiment that has only one factor, the treatments and levels of the factor are the same. Nancy would apply her treatments to her wells, allow sufficient time for any effect to occur, and then measure her response, which is the amount of nitrates then found in the wells. ◆

Example 1.9   Dwayne Head, the director of a physical fitness and nutrition centre, is interested in investigating the effects of different diets and aerobic exercise routines on body fat. He is primarily concerned with two types of diets: one high in protein and the other high in carbohydrates, and with three exercise routines: spinning, jazzercise, and step. How should Dwayne design an experiment to see if any combination of diet and exercise plan has a different effect on body fat than the others?

◆ **Solution:**
The basic difference between Dwayne's situation and that of Nancy's from the previous example is that Dwayne has two factors he is interested in—diet and exercise. Diet has

two levels: (1) high protein and (2) high carbohydrate, and exercise has three levels: (1) spinning, (2) jazzercise, and (3) step. As any one subject in the experiment will use only one type of diet and one type of exercise, there are six treatments: (1) high protein with spinning, (2) high protein with jazzercise, (3) high protein with step, (4) high carbohydrate with spinning, (5) high carbohydrate with jazzercise, and (6) high carbohydrate with step. Dwayne would take subjects from his club, say, 60 of them, and randomly assign ten to each of the treatments. After a sufficient amount of time, Dwayne would measure the change in their percentage of body fat and make comparisons across the six treatments. ◆

We are now ready to define an *experiment*:

> An **experiment** is the process of subjecting experimental units to treatments and observing their response.

The advantage of experiments over observational studies, our last method of collecting data, is that it is possible for properly designed experiments to give evidence of causation; that is, with an experiment, we have justification for saying that a treatment "caused" the response to change. That type of statement is not justifiable in observational studies.

Data from an Observational Study In an **observational study,** a researcher collects data without imposing any treatments on the subjects or experimental units. For example, the registrar at a university might observe the high school averages of admission applicants; a sociologist might examine the economic status of inner-city minorities; a biologist could observe the change in marine life near a seaside construction project. While such data certainly can be valuable, it is harder to justify any conclusion that involves causation. An example will clarify this idea.

Example 1.10 A reading specialist collected data on the reading skills of students in Grade 3 from three different elementary schools. She found (using methods we will explain in later chapters) that there were substantial differences in the reading abilities of the students between these schools. Should she conclude that attending these schools causes a difference in the reading abilities of the students?

◆ **Solution:**
Absolutely not! There are many factors other than the school attended that could cause differences in the reading skills of the students. For example, one could be an urban school with a high proportion of students for whom English is a second language. Another might have a strong special education program with a large number of students with dyslexia, and another might be in an affluent suburb where any child with reading difficulties immediately enters a remedial reading program. While she could determine that there are differences between the three schools, she would be ill-advised to claim that the schools themselves are causing the differences to occur. ◆

One type of observational study is a **survey.** In a survey, a researcher asks a sample of subjects from a population one or more questions and records the responses. For example, a pollster might solicit the opinion of potential voters on the construction of a new prison, a social scientist will elicit the beliefs of people concerning an afterlife, a market researcher will try to determine the preferences of consumers for different automobile features. When the data are supplied by people, personal interviews and mail questionnaires are commonly used data collection tools.

In a personal interview, an interviewer asks a respondent the prepared questions that appear on a form and then records the answers in the spaces provided. This data gathering approach allows the interviewer to clarify any terms that aren't understood by the respondent, and it results in a high percentage of usable returns. But it's an expensive approach and is subject to possible errors introduced by the interviewer's manner in asking questions. Interviews are often conducted over the telephone. This is less expensive, but, of course, some households have unlisted numbers, and this may bias the survey results.

When mail questionnaires are used, the questions are printed on forms, and these queries are designed so that they can be answered by the respondent with check marks or with a few words. The use of questionnaires is often less expensive than personal interviews, but the percentage of usable returns is generally lower. Also, those who do answer may not always be the ones to whom the questionnaire was addressed, and/or they may respond because of a non-representative interest or a passionate interest in the survey subject.

Collecting the Data

Data can be gathered from an entire population; that is, a **census** of the population is taken. Usually, though, data gathered in experiments and observational studies come from samples. A sample should be representative of the population, but there are many ways that samples can be selected. The various types of samples and the many ways they may be selected are topics that may be found in various textbooks on survey sampling. For our purposes in this textbook, we will be assuming we are dealing with a *simple random sample.*

> A **simple random sample** is a sample selected in such a way that every possible sample of a given size has the same chance of being picked, and every item in the population has an equal change of being selected.

Selecting a Simple Random Sample

In order to select a simple random sample, let's assume that every item in a population is numbered, and each number is written on a slip of paper. Now if each numbered slip of paper is placed in a bowl and mixed, and if a group of slips is then picked, the items represented by the selected slips constitute a simple random sample.

A more practical approach is often to use a computer programmed to carry out this random selection process. Or a random sample can be obtained by using a *table of random numbers.* Each digit in such a table is determined by chance and has an equal likelihood of appearing at any single-digit space in the table. Appendix 3 at the back of the book contains a random number table.

To show the use of random numbers in simple random sampling, suppose we have a list of 200 customer accounts eligible for a consumer survey and we want a sample of 20 of them. We could obtain a simple random sample in the following manner:

1. Assign each and every customer account a number from 000 to 199. Each account should have a unique number. The first account would be labelled 000, the second 001, and so on.

2. Next, consult a table of random numbers. Table 1.1 is a brief excerpt from such a table.

3. It's essential that we preplan how to select a sequence of digits from the table so that no bias enters into the selection process. In our case, we need a sequence of three digits. Let's say that our pattern of selection is the last three digits of each block of numbers and that we will work down a column.

4. Select a random number in the preplanned pattern and match the random number assigned to an account. For example, account number 124 is selected first, and then account number 109 is added to the sample. If we have a random number we cannot use, as in the case of 379, we proceed to the next random number, 194, and continue this process of selection until there's a sample of 20 accounts.

TABLE 1.1 AN EXAMPLE OF A TABLE OF RANDOM NUMBERS

5,124	0,746	6,296	9,279
5,109	1,971	5,971	1,264
4,379	6,296	8,746	5,899
8,194	3,721	4,621	3,634

Sampling Errors The goal in sampling is to select a portion of the population that displays all of the characteristics of the population. If we're to make a judgment about a population from sample results, we want those results to be as typical of the population as possible. Unfortunately, it's extremely difficult, if not impossible, to have a sample that's completely representative of the population. And it would be unreasonable to expect a sample result to have *exactly* the same value as some population attribute. Thus, **sampling error** is to be expected. You'll see in later chapters that researchers have learned how to objectively assess and cope with such error. Of course, errors may also be introduced by people as they code and record sample data. And, as we'll see in the next chapter, results obtained from a biased sample may be worthless.

Step 3: Analyze the Data and Form Conclusions After the sample data has been collected, it is usually summarized in the form of tables or charts, and key quantitative measures are computed. This information facilitates problem understanding, and allows an analyst to present important points to others. The analyst then uses the summaries and descriptive measures computed as a basis for making any relevant statistical inferences and for identifying desirable courses of action. The validity of the options selected is, of course, determined by the analyst's skill and the quality of his or her information. Future chapters focus on specific methods of analyzing data and forming conclusions.

Figure 1.3 expands *Figure 1.1* and summarizes the steps in performing a statistical study.

1.5 Role of the Computer in Statistics

Computers are efficiently used when data input isn't trivial, similar tasks are performed repeatedly, or processing complexities present no practical alternative to computer use. Since many statistical problems have a large volume of input data, are repetitive, and are relatively complex, the computer is a vital tool to those who solve these problems. Procedures that could take hours, days, or weeks with a calculator are accurately completed in seconds or minutes with a computer.

STATISTICS IN ACTION

Who Uses Stat Packages?
Statistical software packages are widely used now that desktop computers are everywhere. Let's look at just three examples. Bionetics Corporation biostatisticians rely on stat packages to study the effects that space flight has on the physical condition of astronauts. Scientists from developing countries rely on similar software to analyze their human populations. And MGM/United Artists analysts gather data from people who watch an advance screening of a new film. A stat package is then used to analyze the data and arrive at a prediction of the film's market success.

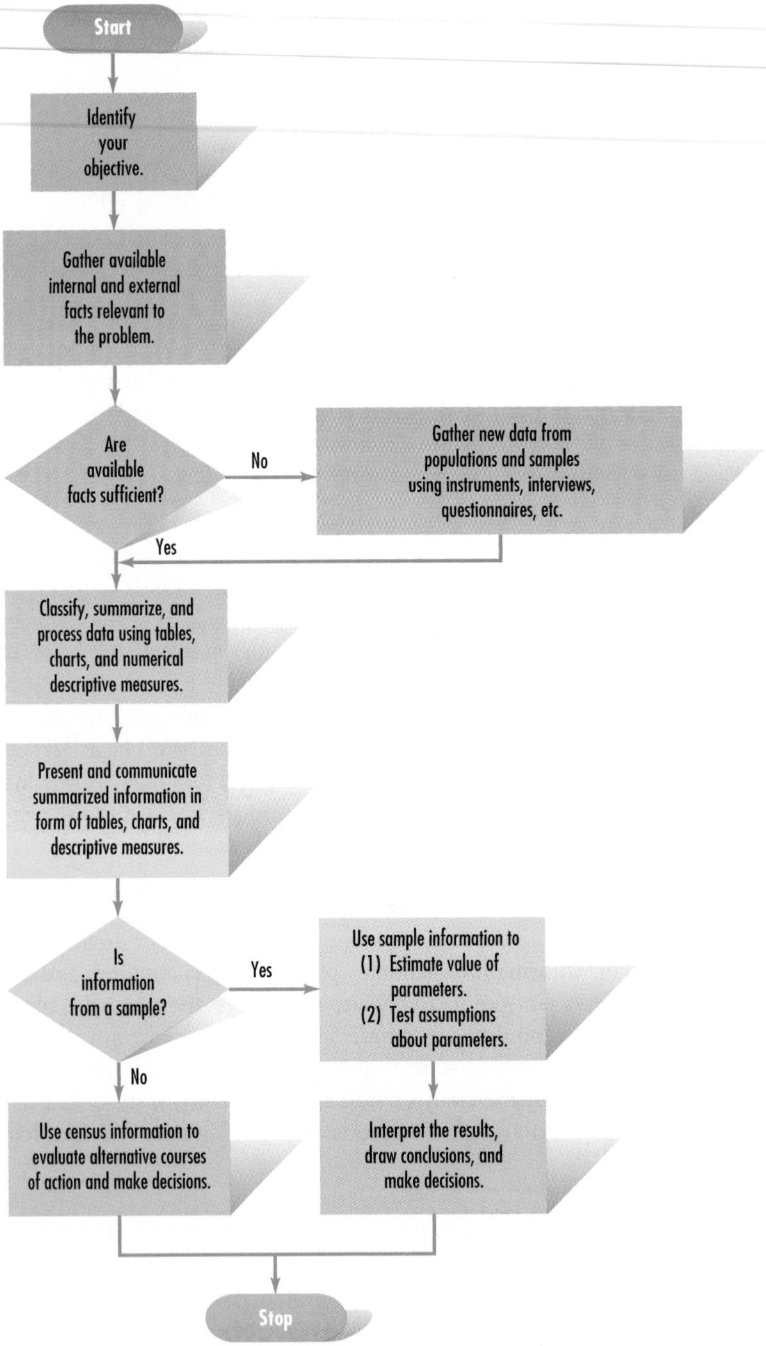

FIGURE 1.3 Steps in performing
statistical studies.

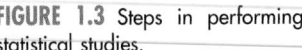

Start

Identify
your
objective.

Gather available
internal and external
facts relevant to
the problem.

Are
available
facts sufficient?   No →   Gather new data from
populations and samples
using instruments, interviews,
questionnaires, etc.

Yes

Classify, summarize, and
process data using tables,
charts, and numerical
descriptive measures.

Present and communicate
summarized information in
form of tables, charts, and
descriptive measures.

Is
information
from a sample?   Yes →   Use sample information to
(1) Estimate value of
    parameters.
(2) Test assumptions
    about parameters.

No

Use census information to
evaluate alternative courses
of action and make decisions.

Interpret the results,
draw conclusions, and
make decisions.

Stop

The problems you'll encounter in this book typically use relatively small sets of input data. Because of that, it will be easy for you to do many of the problems with a scientific calculator. But even so, you'll see in a few instances that our calculations can become tedious when done by hand. It's usually desirable, though, to follow the hand calculations discussed in the text and then use similar steps to solve a few additional problems. Once you've done that, you'll understand the uses and limitations of the procedures and be able to correctly interpret the results they produce. Then you can use a computer to carry out similar future work with the background necessary to understand the output.

Spreadsheets and Statistical Packages

Data analysis involves separating a mass of related facts into constituent parts and then studying and interpreting those parts to reach a conclusion. Two tools used for data analysis are electronic spreadsheets and statistical analysis packages. The spreadsheet is a program that accepts user-supplied data values and relationships in the columns and rows of its worksheet. The intersection of a spreadsheet column and row is called a *cell*. Values in the cells can be changed to answer "what-if" questions. For example, a city manager can quickly see what may happen to yearly tax receipts if a new mill rate is passed by the city council. A popular spreadsheet program is Microsoft's *Excel*. Statistical analysis packages are similar to spreadsheets, but statistical packages are preprogrammed with many more of the specialized formulas and built-in procedures a user may need to carry out a range of statistical studies. Like spreadsheets, statistical programs can

- Accept data from other sources.

- Copy and move data to duplicate the contents of one cell (or group of cells) into other locations or to erase the contents of one or more cells in one place and place them in another.

- Add or remove data items, columns, or rows.

- Format the way cells, rows, and columns are laid out and then save this format for future updates.

- Perform analyses on single and multiple sets of data and then print summary values and analysis results.

- Use numeric data to produce charts and graphs.

Many of the most able general-purpose statistical programs such as MINITAB, SAS, and SPSS were first written for large computer systems, and they've been around in various forms for many years. Each of these products is available in a version that runs on personal computers. Many other general-purpose packages can be found. *Statgraphics*, for example, performs many statistical procedures and offers users many types of graphic output.

 A recently released MINITAB program is used throughout this book to demonstrate statistical concepts, but earlier MINITAB versions and other software packages can easily handle the examples we'll discuss in later chapters. The latest releases are designed to be easier to learn and simpler to use. For example, the first thing a user of the MINITAB *for Windows* program sees on the computer screen after the program is initiated is a main MINITAB window (*Figure 1.4a*). This window features a *Menu* bar and *Data* and *Session* subwindows.

The Session window. This is
where MINITAB displays
non-graphical output such as
tables of statistics.

The Menu Bar.

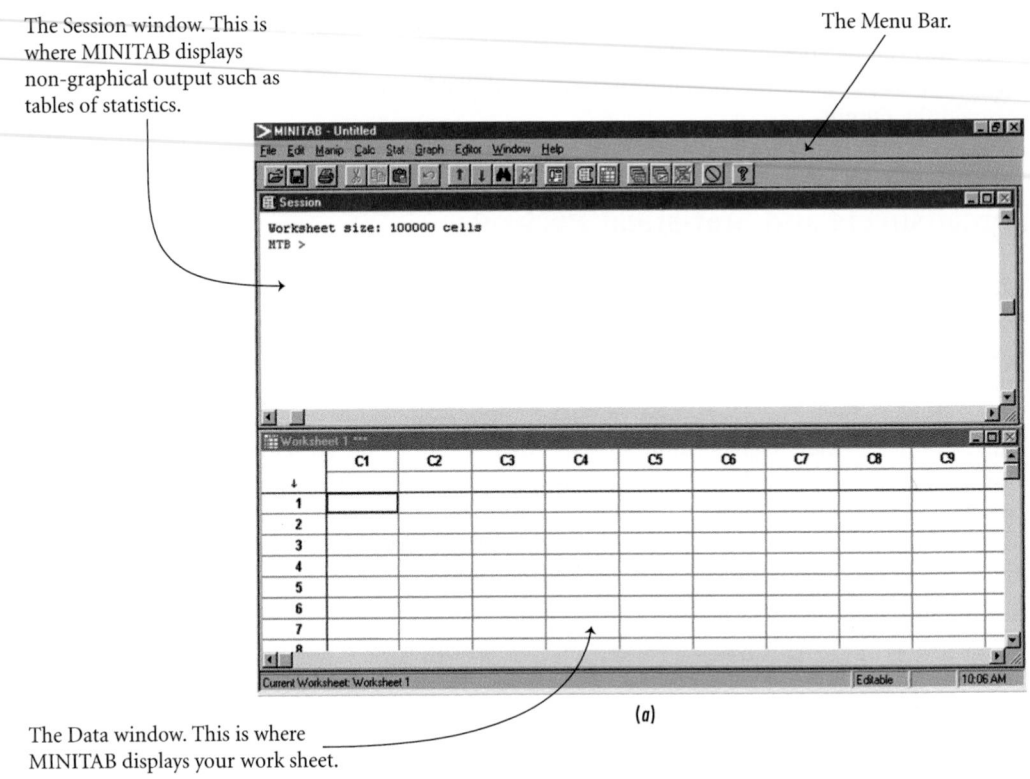

(a)

The Data window. This is where
MINITAB displays your work sheet.

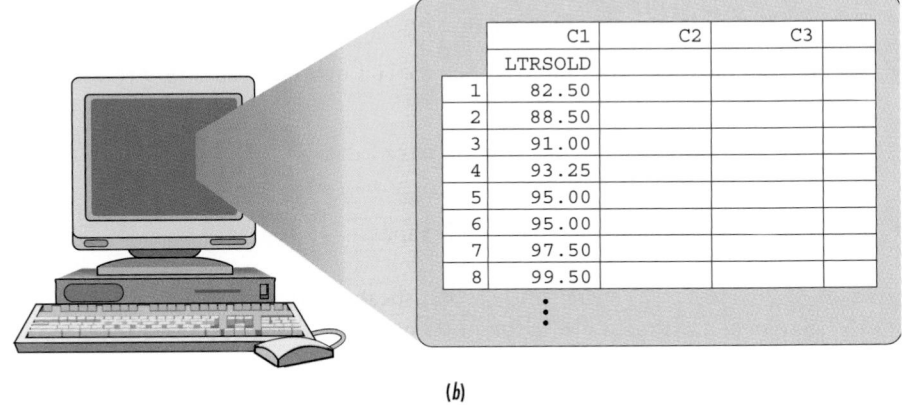

(b)

FIGURE 1.4 (a) The main window
of the *MINITAB for Windows* software package. (b) Data entry in the
MINITAB for Windows statistical
package.

The *Menu* bar gives a listing of the main selection options available to the user. When
one of these main options is selected, a pull-down submenu is displayed to offer further choices. The *Session* window displays non-graphical output such as tables and the
results of calculations. The *Data* window displays rows and columns, and new data are
entered into the cells of this window. Once entered, the data may be saved and then
called back into the Data window at a later time for use or for modification. The details of how to do such tasks are presented in Appendix 11. For the moment, you may
think of the MINITAB program as a gigantic calculator, ready to easily do our most tedious or horrific calculations.

Today, powerful hand-held graphing calculators, with built-in data analysis capabilities and communications ports for receiving data, offer many of the efficiencies of spreadsheets and statistical packages. One such calculator, the Texas Instruments TI-83™, is used frequently in this book as a problem-solving tool.

LOOKING BACK

1. The purpose of this book is to give you a grasp of statistical concepts and methods so that you can generate and then interpret statistical results. The word *statistics* refers to the body of knowledge developed to design studies, gather data, and then classify, summarize, interpret, and present these data to support needed decisions. Thus, statistics refers to a subject of study. The word *statistics* shouldn't be confused with the word *statistic,* which is a number that describes a sample characteristic. The word *parameter* refers to a number that describes a population characteristic. You need a knowledge of both descriptive statistics and statistical inference to describe and understand numerical relationships and make better decisions.

2. The steps in performing a statistical study are described in this chapter. The first step is to identify the objective, and the second step is to collect relevant data. In some cases data might be collected from the entire population, but in most cases the data collected will be from a sample taken from the population. A simple random sample is one type of sample selected in such a way that every item in the population has an equal chance of being selected and every possible sample of the same size has the same chance of being picked. Random samples are often picked with the help of computer programs and tables of random numbers. Although sample results are subject to sampling error, researchers have learned how to objectively assess and cope with such error. After the data are collected, the third step is to analyze the data and form conclusions.

3. Computers are efficiently used in statistical work. Generalized prewritten software packages are commonly used to carry out statistical studies. Two software tools commonly used for data analysis are the spreadsheet and the statistical package.

Exercises

Match each of the following terms to its correct definition:

TERMS	DEFINITIONS
1. Parameter	a. The complete collection of items under study
2. Statistical inference	b. A number that describes a sample characteristic
3. Census	c. Procedures for collecting, classifying, summarizing, and presenting data
4. Statistics	d. A number that describes a population characteristic

TERMS	DEFINITIONS
5. Population	e. The science of gathering and summarizing data and using results to make decisions
6. Descriptive statistics	f. A subset of the population
7. Sample	g. The process of arriving at a conclusion about a population parameter on the basis of a sample statistic
8. Statistic	h. A survey of all the elements in a population

9. A psychologist wants to study the behaviour patterns of the 8,430 students at the University of Regina. She decides to start by obtaining a random sample of 30 students and asking the average number of hours each member of the sample sleeps on a week-day night. For each of the following questions, identify whether the type of sample obtained is or is not a simple random sample.

a) Each student is assigned a number from 0001 to 8,430. A number from 1 to 281 is randomly selected, and every 281st student on the list from that point on is then included in the sample.

b) Students are separated into academic majors, and a proportional number of students are selected from each academic major.

c) Students are listed by number (0001 to 8,430) and a computer is used to randomly generate a list of 30 numbers representing the students to be used in the sample.

d) Suppose I am interested in knowing the average weight of all the students who are currently taking Statistics200. To do this, I randomly pick 12 students in class, record their weight, and calculate their average. Then I use this calculated average as an estimate for the true average weight of the whole class. Identify the population of interest, the sample, the parameter, and the statistic.

10. A manufacturer of DVD players is interested in knowing the proportion of all its DVD players that are defective. To do this, the manufacturer selects 36 of the DVD players, examines them for defects and calculates the proportion of the 36 players that are defective. Then the manufacturer uses this calculated proportion as an estimate for the true proportion of all players that are defective. Identify the population of interest, the sample, the parameter, and the statistic.

11. There are 560 students enrolled in a statistics course at the local university. How would you use the random number table from Appendix 3 to obtain a random sample of 20 of them?

12. There are 83 members of a population. How would you use the random number table in Appendix 3 to obtain a random sample of 10 of them?

Topics for Review and Discussion

1. List three reasons it might be more practical to obtain data values from a sample rather than from the entire population.

2. "A population parameter is a single fixed value while sample statistics from the same population can vary." Discuss why this statement is true.

3. What's the difference between a population parameter and a sample statistic?

4. How are sample statistics used to make decisions about population parameters?

5. Outline the steps used in performing a statistical study.

6. Discuss the relationship between descriptive statistics and inferential statistics.

7. What's the difference between a spreadsheet and a statistical software program?

8. How may a statistical software program be used?

9. Discuss the reasons for sampling errors.

Projects/Issues to Consider

1. Obtain an article from a recent newspaper or periodical that discusses the results of a statistical study. What is the implied population? If possible, determine how the sample was obtained. Decide if there seems to be a better way to take the sample.

2. Go to the library and investigate primary and secondary sources. Make a list of at least three of each type.

Computer/Calculator Exercises

1. In 2002, the *Maclean's Guide to Canadian Universities* published the total number of full-time students at Canadian universities. Enter and save the following information in a computer file named FULL_TIME_STUDENTS. Name your columns UNIVERSITY and FULL_TIME_STUDENTS. (We'll use this data set in Chapter 3.)

University	Full-Time Students
1 Acadia	3,679
2 Alberta	26,875
3 Bishop's	1,898
4 Brandon	1,788
5 UBC	24,906
6 Brock	7,213
7 Calgary	21,700
8 Cape Breton (UCCB)	2,651
9 Carleton	12,962
10 Concordia	11,795
11 Dalhousie	10,638
12 Guelph	13,931
13 Lakehead	4,952
14 Laurentian	3,711
15 Laval	22,819
16 Lethbridge	5,540
17 Manitoba	16,554
18 McGill	21,024
19 McMaster	13,529
20 Memorial	12,625
21 Moncton	4,529
22 Montreal	32,030
23 Mount Allison	2,274
24 Mount Saint Vincent	2,125
25 New Brunswick	9,522
26 Nipissing	1,830
27 UNBC	2,181
28 Ottawa	17,891
29 UPEI	2,751
30 Quebec/Chicoutimi	2,797
31 Quebec/Hull	2,073
32 Quebec/Montreal	18,077
33 Quebec/Rimouski	1,940
34 Quebec/Trois-Rivieres	5,387
35 Queen's	14,997
36 Regina	6,547
37 Ryerson	10,636
38 St. Francis Xavier	3,478
39 Saint Mary's	5,098

University	Full-Time Students
40 St. Thomas	2,409
41 Saskatchewan	14,676
42 Sherbrooke	11,008
43 Simon Fraser	10,547
44 Toronto	42,098
45 Trent	4,044
46 Victoria	11,350
47 Waterloo	19,089
48 Western	23,689
49 Wilfrid Laurier	7,377
50 Windsor	9,649
51 Winnipeg	4,368
52 York	29,235

2. Sort the data from the file named FULL_TIME_STUDENTS into two columns named UNIVERSITY1 and FULL_TIME_STUDENTS1 so that the data are listed in an ascending order (from lowest to highest) according to the number of full-time students enrolled at each university. Since you'll want the university name carried along with the appropriate number of students enrolled, be sure to select UNIVERSITY as well as FULL_TIME_STUDENTS for your columns to be sorted.

3. There are 548 students enrolled in a management program. Use a software program to generate a random sample of 25 of them.

4. There are 157 restaurants listed in a local phone book. As a public health official, your job is to inspect the kitchens of ten of them each week. Assuming you number the restaurants 1 to 157, use a software program to select a random sample of 10 restaurants to be inspected.

 5. World Wide Web "addresses" appearing underlined and in blue throughout the text refer to links that can be accessed via this book's Web site at www.mcgrawhill.ca/college/sanders. The links, which call up primary sources such as Statistics Canada and the Data and Story Library (DASL), are included under "Student Resources" at the site. The DASL site is one of a number of sites on the World Wide Web that contain data sets that can be downloaded. Access DASL and click on *Data Subjects*. On the new screen, click on a subject of your choice. From the choices, download at least one data file and save it for analysis in future chapters.

CHAPTER 2

Thinking Critically about Data: Liars, #$%& Liars, and a Few Statisticians

LOOKING AHEAD

In this chapter, you'll see several ways that statistics may be applied and misapplied. You'll also learn about tables and charts that legitimately help people understand and communicate numeric data, and you'll see how computer graphics software can help prepare these aids. The chapter then concludes with a series of questions you may ask yourself to reduce your chances of being misled.

Thus, after studying this chapter, you should be able to

- Appreciate and understand the purposes of different methods of describing data.

- Begin to think critically about the way data are presented and identify how people's biases, conscious or not, can affect how they present data.

- Distinguish between some valid and invalid uses of statistics.

- Point out at least six ways in which statistics may be misused.

- Give examples of how statistics have been misapplied.

- Discuss the types of tables and charts that are used to honestly analyze and present numeric facts and how measures of central tendency and dispersion help provide information about a set of data.

- Recall several questions you can ask yourself during your evaluation of quantitative information to reduce your chances of being misled.

2.1 Unfavourable Opinions and the Bias Obstacle

Some Unfavourable Views

Consider the following comments:

"There are three kinds of lies: lies, damned lies, and statistics."—*Benjamin Disraeli*

"Get the facts first and then you can distort them as much as you please."—*Mark Twain*

"In earlier times they had no statistics, and so they had to fall back on lies. Hence the huge exaggerations of primitive literature—giants or miracles or wonders! They did it with lies and we do it with statistics; but it is all the same."—*Stephen Leacock*

"He uses statistics as a drunken man uses lampposts—for support rather than illumination."—*Andrew Lang*

Given such opinions, it's evident that some people hold unfavourable views of statistics. But appearances and reality are often at odds. Statistics is a wonderful science that can help us learn and grow in the presence of chaos. Cancer studies, investigations of prejudice and discrimination, measurements of how children learn, modelling of demands on transit systems, experiments on effects of pollution—these are all examples of powerful uses of statistics. But some people, usually non-statisticians who do not understand (or ignore) the basic ideas you will learn in this book, have given statistics a black eye. For it's true that statistical tools have been misapplied by politicians, advertising agencies, lawyers, bureaucrats—the list is virtually endless—confusing people or misleading them. It's unnecessary to dwell on the motives of those who misuse statistical tools. Technical errors may be made innocently, or valid statistical facts may be deliberately twisted, but the results are the same—people become misinformed and misled.

In this chapter we'll point out a few ways that statistical procedures have been misused. As a consumer of numerical facts, you should be alert to the possibility of unwarranted statistical conclusions. It's no exaggeration to say that this course in statistics is worth your time if it succeeds in helping you do a better job of distinguishing between valid and improper uses of quantitative techniques.

The Bias Difficulty

You know that an early step in statistical problem solving is gathering relevant data. *Bias* is a systematic favouring of one outcome over another. The wording of questionnaires often fails to produce focused answers. Even worse, questions may be slanted to elicit answers that reinforce the questioner's own biases. For example, one American politician asked his constituents if they favoured "elimination of waste in the defense budget," and 95 percent naturally replied "yes." Another politician pointed out to the same constituents that any substantial cuts ... will mean the U.S.A. will no longer be number one in military strength. Then only 27 percent indicated that they didn't mind if the U.S.A. became number two behind Russia.

Some people collecting or analyzing data may be tempted to use the "finagle factor" to give more emphasis to those facts that support their preconceived opinions than to

STATISTICS IN ACTION

Innocent Error?

The Canadian Hockey Association ruled on May 19, 2003, in Regina that checking would be allowed only among players 11 years of age and older. The move reversed a decision of the previous year that allowed kids as young as nine to bodycheck. Association President Bob Nicholson said the earlier decision was based on flawed research. An investigation by CBC News found serious errors in a study commissioned out of Lakehead University in Thunder Bay, Ontario. Lakehead University professor Bill Montelpare initially concluded that, based on his study, there was no significant difference in injury rates between the comparison groups. He has since issued a supplemental report to the Canadian Hockey Association rescinding his earlier findings.

those that conflict with their opinions. As Thomas L. Martin, Jr., wrote in his *Malice in Blunderland*:

> The Finagle Factor allows one to bring actual results into immediate agreement with *desired* results easily and without the necessity of having to repeat messy experiments, calculations or designs. [When discovered, the Finagle Factor] was instantly and immensely popular with engineers and scientists, but found its greatest use in statistics and in the social sciences where actual results so often greatly differ from those desired by the investigator ...
> Thus:

$$(\text{Desired results on paper}) = (\text{Finagle factor}) \times (\text{actual results})$$

How can the finagle factor be employed? It can be (and often is) used by advertisers. Suppose that you see on television a professional-looking actor saying (with great sincerity) that "eight out of ten doctors recommend the ingredients found in Gastro-Dismal elixir." Does this message convince you to rush out and buy a bottle? Even assuming that the "eight out of ten" figure is correct, it's likely that the doctors were merely approving a number of common ingredients found in many non-prescription products. They probably weren't specifically recommending Gastro-Dismal as being any better than other similar brands. (In fact, it's possible that the separate recommended ingredients could be put together in some preposterous way by Gastro-Dismal employees so as to be injurious to health.)

Although bias in the form of the finagle factor is generally consciously applied, bias can also appear unintentionally. Sometimes, for example, a researcher is led to faulty conclusions because of unintentionally biased input data.

2.2 Aggravating Averages

Let's assume that Sandy Concord decides to buy a small vineyard in a remote region. Sandy finds a vineyard that suits her needs and is surprised when the realtor tells her that the 100 grape growers in the area have an average annual income of nearly $83,000. Six months later a rally is called to protest a proposed increase in property taxes. It's pointed out then that the average income in the area is only $13,000 and that no new taxes can be afforded. Sandy is naturally confused.

How could there be such a drop in average income in just six months? The answer is that nothing has really changed—it is just that the word *average* is being used to mean two different quantities. An *average* is a measure used to portray a typical value of a data set. Such a measure is described as a *measure of central tendency*. Both $83,000 and $13,000 are correct and legitimate measures of central tendency! The 100 growers in the area include 99 whose net income is about $13,000, and one who has invested millions of dollars in a showplace vineyard spread over hundreds of acres. This one grower nets approximately $7 million annually. Thus, one measure of central tendency—the *arithmetic mean, or average*—(99 people × $13,000 + 1 person × $7,000,000) ÷ 100 people = $82,870, or nearly $83,000. To summarize,

> The **arithmetic mean** (or **average**) of a group of values is a central tendency measure that is found by first adding all the values to get a total and by then dividing the total by the number of values.

The value of $13,000 is an alternative measure of typicalness or central tendency called the *median*.

> The **median** of a group of values occupies the middle position after all the values are arranged in an ascending or descending order.

Thus, the median of $13,000 represents the earnings of the middle grower in the group of 100.

Another measure of typicalness or central tendency is the *mode*.

> The **mode** of a group of values is the score that occurs most often. If no value occurs more than once, there's no mode. And when there's a tie between two values for the greatest count, the data set is said to be bimodal.

You can see from this example that the average (mean) of nearly $83,000 is misleading because it distorts the general situation. Yet it's not a lie; it has been correctly computed. The problem of the aggravating average is often traced to different peoples' perception of the word *average*—while properly used it is synonymous with mean, it is sometimes broadly interpreted to include other measures of central tendency such as the median or mode. It's common for one of these measures of central tendency to be used when it isn't appropriate and where it is selected to deliberately mislead the consumer of the information. We will take a more detailed look at measures of central tendency in Chapter 3. For the moment, we just want you to be aware that different types of measures are used to convey different types of information.

2.3 Disregarded Dispersions

Suppose that Karl is being pressured to coach the track team. Karl isn't enthused about this prospect. He does a little checking and finds that the four high jumpers can clear an average of only 120 centimetres and that the three pole vaulters can manage an average height of only 300 centimetres. Karl concludes that his first venture into athletic management is likely to result in considerable verbal abuse from supporters. Is Karl correct? Probably, but not because of the data he has gathered. Karl has been the victim of aggravating averages (arithmetic means in this example). Had he checked further, he would have found that one of his four high jumpers consistently clears 200 centimetres—good enough to win every time in the competition he will face—while the other three can each only manage to stumble over 100 centimetre heights. Likewise, in the pole vault there is one athlete who vaults 470 centimetres (with a bamboo pole) and two others who can each manage to explode for only 220 centimetres.

The moral here is that measures of central tendency alone often don't adequately describe the true picture. A measure of *dispersion* must also be considered.

> **Dispersion** is the amount of spread or scatter that occurs in the data.

We are simply making the further distinction here that disregarded dispersion exists when the scatter of the values about the central measure is large enough that ignoring it tends to mislead. Of course, disregarded dispersions and aggravating averages are usually found acting in concert to confuse and mislead. To summarize, the story is often told of the Chinese warlord who was leading his troops into battle with a rival when he came to a river. Since there were no boats and since the warlord remembered that he had read somewhere the average depth of the water in the river was only 70 centimetres at that time of year, he ordered his men to wade across. After the crossing, the warlord was surprised to learn that a number of his soldiers had drowned. Although the average depth was indeed just 70 centimetres, in some places it was only ankle deep, while in other places it was over the heads of many who became the unfortunate victims of disregarded dispersion. If the soldiers had spent their free moments between battles looking over the measures of dispersion in Chapter 3, perhaps they would not have found themselves out of their depth.

2.4 **The Persuasive Artist**

Statistical tables and charts are prepared to summarize data, uncover relationships, and interpret and communicate numerical facts to those who can use them.

Statistical Tables

Statistical tables efficiently organize classified data into columns and rows so users can quickly find the facts needed. In the right side of *Figure 2.1*, for example, the data in the table are classified by year and by total trips.

Line Charts

A **line chart** is one in which data points on a grid are connected by a continuous line to convey information. The vertical axis in a line chart is usually measured in quantities (dollars, litres) or percentages, while the horizontal axis is often measured in units

FIGURE 2.1 A statistical table and a single-line chart. (*Source:* Statistics Canada, The Daily, Friday, July 5, 2002, Domestic Travel, 1998 to 2001.)

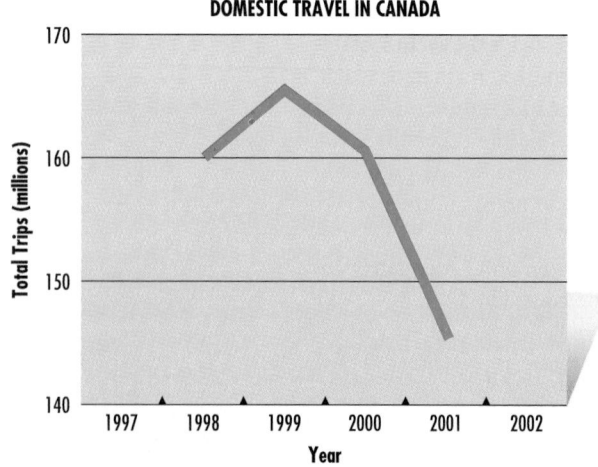

DOMESTIC TRAVEL IN CANADA

	1998	1999	2000	2001
Total trips (millions)	159.2	164.1	162.1	144.2
Same-day trips (millions)	75.3	78.2	78.7	70.3
Overnight trips (millions)	84	85.9	83.4	73.9
Number of nights (millions)	270.3	275.5	274.2	243.8

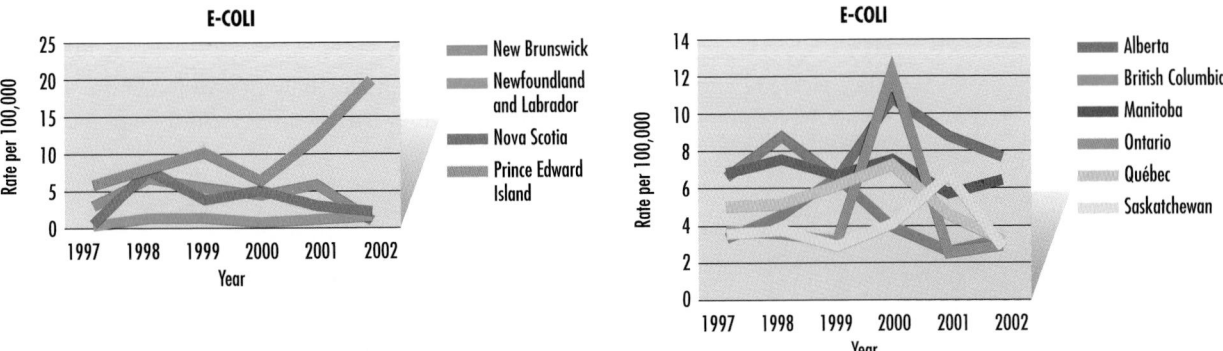

FIGURE 2.2 Multiple series shown on line charts. (*Source:* Laboratory Centre for Disease Control.)

of time (and thus a line chart becomes a time-series chart). Line charts don't present specific data as well as tables, but they're usually able to show relationships more clearly. As you can see in *Figure 2.1*, a table and a line chart are frequently used together in a presentation. The *single-line* chart in the left side of *Figure 2.1* shows the total number of domestic trips in Canada over a period of several years.

Of course, multiple series can also be depicted on line charts, as shown in *Figure 2.2*. The lines in both of these figures are plotted against the same baseline.

Bar Charts

A **bar** (or column) **chart** uses the length of horizontal bars or height of vertical columns to represent quantities or percentages. As in the case of line charts, one scale on the bar chart measures values while the other may show time or some other variable. The bars typically start from a zero point and are frequently used to show multiple comparisons. Bars may be clustered to show how identified categories of interest can differ (*Figure 2.3*).

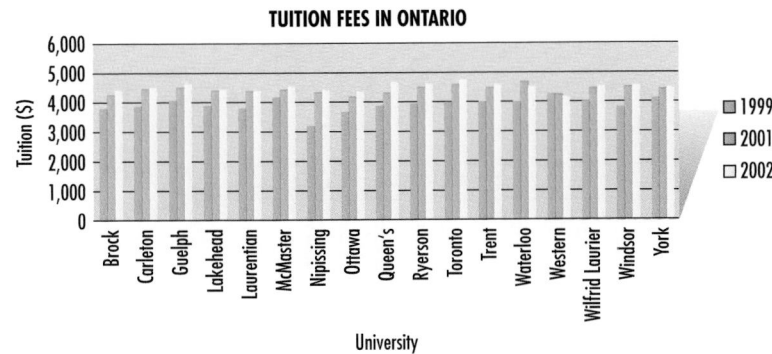

FIGURE 2.3 Clustered bar chart. (*Source:* Data obtained from the *Maclean's Guide to Canadian Universities* 1999, 2001, 2002.)

Pie Charts

Pie charts are circles divided into sectors, usually to show the component parts of a whole (see *Figure 2.4*). A technique sometimes used is to present a combination of charts.

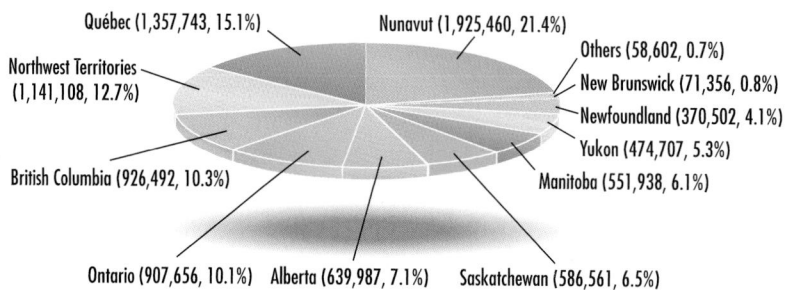

Source: Statistics Canada.

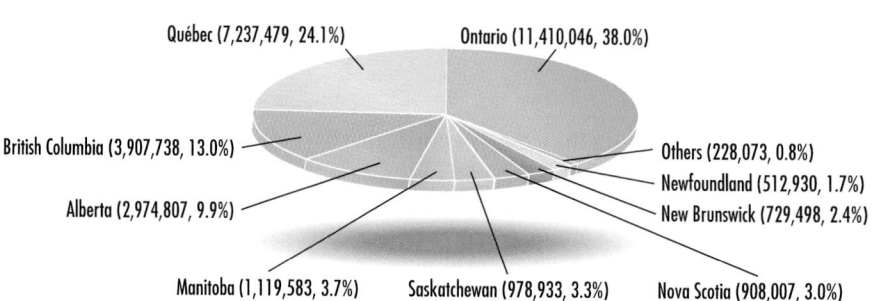

Source: Statistics Canada, http://www12.statcan.ca/english/census01/products/standard/popdwell/ Table–PR.cfm

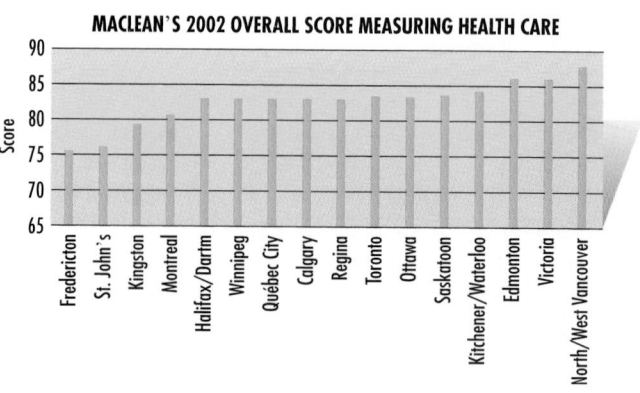

FIGURE 2.4 A combination of pie and bar charts.

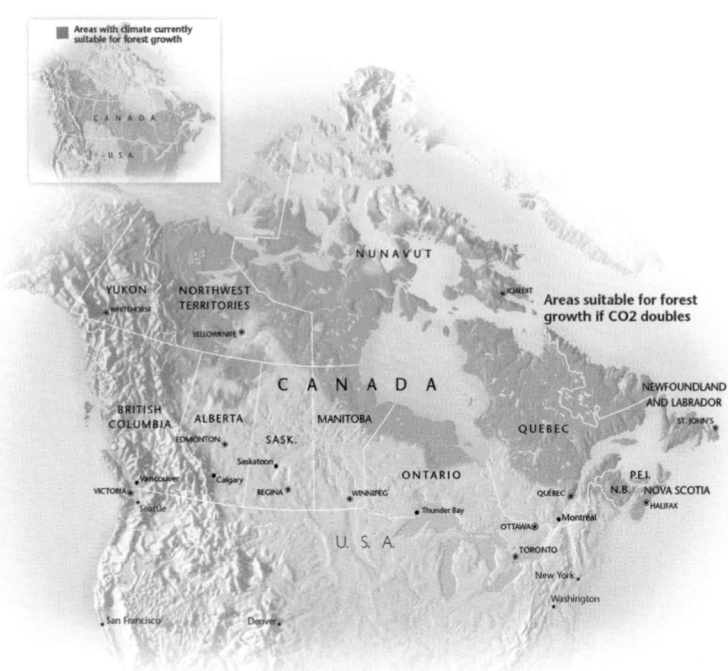

FIGURE 2.5 Predicting Canada's climate in 2050.

Combination and Other Charts

Other types of charts that are used to display quantitative facts are **statistical maps,** which present data on a geographical basis (see *Figure 2.5*), and **pictographs,** or pictorial charts, which use picture symbols to convey meaning. Pictographs must be used with caution as we'll see shortly.

Misusing Graphics

So much for the ways that data can be honestly presented. But the purpose of some persuasive artists is to take honest facts and create misleading impressions. How is this done? There are numerous tricks, but we'll limit our discussion here to just a few examples.

Suppose you're running for reelection to a legislative body and during your past two-year term, grants have increased in your district from $8 million to $9 million. Now, as your fellow politicians know, this isn't a particularly good record, but the voters don't need to know that. In fact, you can perhaps turn this possible liability into an asset with the help of a persuasive artist. *Figure 2.6a* shows one way to present the information honestly. But since your goal is to mislead without actually lying, you prefer instead to distribute *Figure 2.6b* during your campaign. The difference between *Figure 2.6a* and *Figure 2.6b*, of course, lies in the changing of the vertical scale in the latter figure. (The wavy line correctly indicates a break in the vertical scale, but this is often not considered by unwary consumers of this type of information.) By breaking the vertical scale and by then changing the proportion between the vertical and horizontal scales, you've given the impression that you've been doing a good job of getting grants. And to further impress (and mislead) your constituents, you can keep the vertical scale used in *Figure 2.6b* and then compress the horizontal (time) scale.

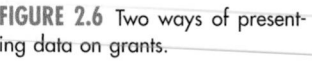

FIGURE 2.6 Two ways of presenting data on grants.

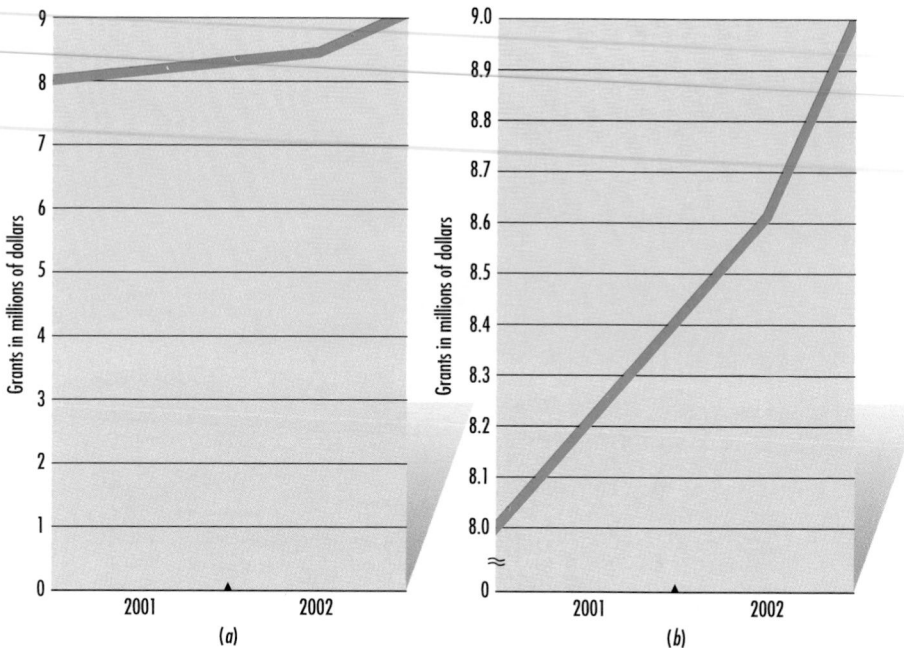

Having received favourable comments on your grants chart, you decide to employ another trick. New industry has come into your district during the past two years. There has been some increase in air and water pollution as a result, but there has also been an increase in average weekly wages of unskilled workers from $160 per week to $240 per week. Of course, you had little to do with bringing in the new industry, and there's also some disturbing evidence that the fact that wage increases have *followed* the new plants doesn't necessarily mean that they were *caused* by the new industry. But you see no reason to complicate matters.

How can you best communicate this wage increase information to your constituents? After trying several approaches, you decide to use the pictograph in *Figure 2.7a*. The height of the small money bag represents $160, and the height of the large bag is correctly proportioned to represent $240. What's wrong and misleading, though, is the *area* covered by each figure. The space occupied by the larger bag creates a misleading visual impression. But that was the intent, wasn't it? If you think this example is far-fetched, consider *Figures 2.7b* and *c*.

Let's now assume that in spite of your persuasive artwork the voters have seen fit to throw you out of office in favour of another candidate. However, you're able to find work in your father's manufacturing company. One of the first jobs you're given is to prepare reports for shareholders and the union explaining company progress over the past year. The company has done well, and profits have amounted to 25 cents of every sales dollar. This can be accurately presented in picture form, as shown in *Figure 2.8a*. But a stronger impact can be made on shareholders if the coin is shown from the perspective of *Figure 2.8b*. Since you don't want the union members to become restless, though, you can show them the profit situation from the perspective of *Figure 2.8c*.

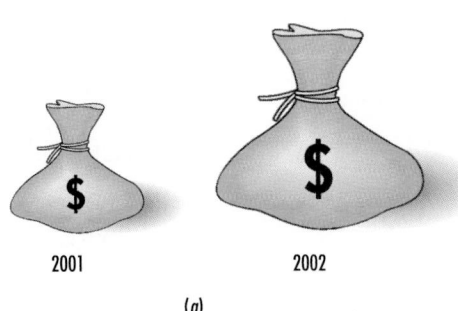

2001   2002

(a)

FIGURE 2.7 (a) The first of our perfidious pictographs. (b) Note the absence of any break in the vertical scale, which compounds the area misrepresentation, (*Source: Fort Worth Star Telegram,* February 4, 1984, p.9B. Reprinted with permission.) (c) And note the absence of any scale at all in this figure. (*Source: PC World,* April 1986, p. 272. Reprinted with permission.)

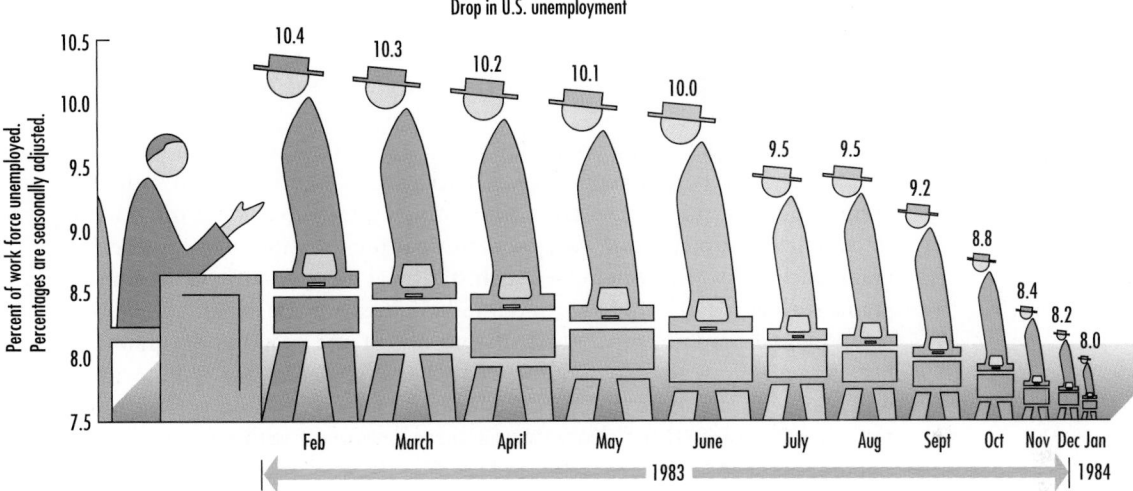

Drop in U.S. unemployment

Data: U.S. Department of Labor.

(b)

Net sales—Toys

(c)

FIGURE 2.8 Three visual perspectives of profits.

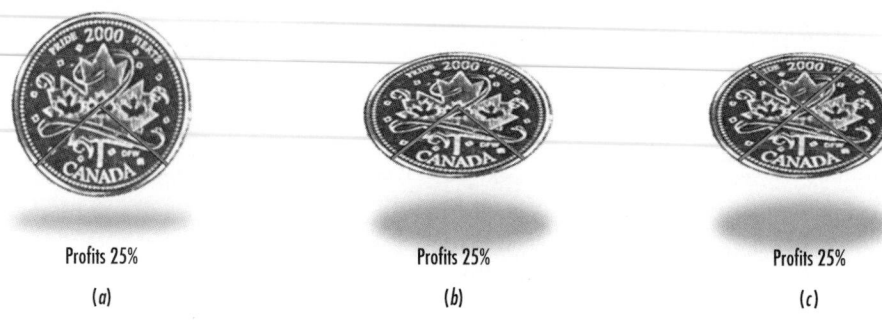

Profits 25%	Profits 25%	Profits 25%
(a)	(b)	(c)

Computer Spreadsheets and Statistics Packages

Much of the graphical and computational work we do in this and future chapters is now easily done by different software packages. It used to be that individual programs would perform a few tasks and multiple programs would often be required to complete a project from inception to final presentation. Now spreadsheet programs such as *Excel* have increased their statistical functionality, while statistical programs such as MINITAB, SPSS, and SAS have many of the data manipulation, presentation, and graphics capabilities of spreadsheet and graphics programs. This has been a tremendous advance. But there have been problems, usually not with the software, but with the users. Some of the misuses of statistics we mention in this chapter are the outgrowth of people using these programs without completely understanding what they are asking for and, as a result, what they are getting. Computers don't think, but sometimes computer output gives an aura of authority to otherwise spurious results. A person who doesn't know the first thing about statistics can still usually get these software packages to generate some type of graph or other output. So a good motto would be *caveat emptor,* "let the buyer beware"—at least when what you are buying is someone else's computer-generated "analysis."

2.5 The *Post Hoc Ergo Propter Hoc* Trap

The Latin phrase for the logical reasoning fallacy that states that because B *follows* A, B was *caused* by A is *post hoc ergo propter hoc,* which means "after this, therefore because of this." Erroneous cause-and-effect conclusions are often drawn because of the misuse of quantitative facts. Of course, as the following examples show, some errors are easy to spot:

Example 2.1   Increased imports of oranges into Canada have been followed by decreases in the national birthrate. Therefore, oranges were the cause of the decrease in births. ◆

Example 2.2   As the percentage of Canadian homes owning at least one smoke detector increased, the funding to the Canadian Broadcasting Corporation (CBC) decreased. Would the CBC do better by lobbying for the elimination of smoke detectors? ◆

2.6 Antics with Semantics and Trends

What Does That Mean?

Failing to define terms that are important to a clear understanding of the message, making improper comparisons between unlike or unidentified things, using an alleged statistical fact to jump to a conclusion that ignores other possibilities or that is quite illogical, using jargon to cloud the message when simple words and phrases are suitable—all these antics with semantics are used to confuse and mislead. The following examples should be adequate to illustrate this unfortunate fact:

Example 2.3 The U.S. Federal Trade Commission (FTC) took exception to the advertised claim made by the manufacturers of Hollywood Bread that their product had fewer calories per slice than other breads. According to the FTC, the claim was misleading since the Hollywood slice was thinner than normal. Actually, there was no significant difference in the number of calories when equal amounts of bread were compared. ◆

Example 2.4 "The Egress carburetor is up to 10 percent less polluting and up to 50 percent more efficient." Less polluting than what, a steel mill? And more efficient than what, a Boeing 747? ◆

Example 2.5 Figures on many controversial or sensitive issues, such as marijuana smoking, rape, etc., are not reliable because many cases remain unreported. ◆

The Trend Must Go On!

Another way that a person may misuse statistical facts is to assume that because a pattern has developed in the past in a category, that pattern will certainly continue into the future. Such uncritical extrapolation, of course, is foolish. Changes in technology, population, and lifestyles all produce economic and social changes that may quickly produce an upturn or a downtrend in an existing social pattern or economic category. The invention of the automobile, for example, brought about significant growth in the petroleum and steel industries and a rapid decline in the production of buggies and buggy whips. Yet, as British editor Norman MacRae has noted, an extrapolation of the trends of the 1880s would show today's cities buried under horse manure.

One more example of the advertiser's art should be sufficient here. A raisin advisory board ran this ad in a women's magazine a few years ago: "Your husband could dance with you for 11 minutes on the energy he'd get from 49 raisins. Think what would happen if he never stopped eating them." As Stephen Campbell observed in his *Flaws and Fallacies in Statistical Thinking*, "I can think of a lot of things that might happen to a man if he never stopped eating raisins—and they are all painful."

Of course, the judicious projection of past patterns or trends into the future can be a very useful tool for the planner and decision maker. But the failure to apply a generous measure of common sense to extrapolations of past quantitative patterns can lead to faulty conclusions that people are seriously asked to accept.

STATISTICS IN ACTION

Reservations about Reserves

In 1950 the world's "known" oil reserves were 75 billion barrels. Twenty years later people had sucked up 180 billion barrels, but the world's reserves were then ... 455 billion barrels. The numbers for iron, copper, and other minerals also move around. For example, reserves of iron ore were placed at 19,000 million metric tons in 1950. By 1970, however, over 9,000 million metric tons had been mined, and reserves were then 251,000 million metric tons—a snappy increase of over 1,000 percent! "Known reserves" calculations, like figures from public opinion polls, are subject to limitations. Reserve numbers can tell us where we have been, and approximately where we are, but they can't serve very well as the base for reliable projections.

2.7 Follow the Bouncing Base (If You Can)

In an editorial on minimum competency in English and math published on April 7, 1978, the editors of the *Pensacola Journal* actually stated that "After all, if you give the test to four students and four flunk, that's a 50 percent failure rate."[1]

People today are often confused because they fail to follow the bouncing base—that is, the base period used in computing percentages. A few examples will show how failure to clarify the base may lead to misunderstanding:

Example 2.6   A worker is asked to take a 20 percent pay cut from his weekly salary of $500 during a recessionary period. Later, a 20 percent increase is given to the worker. Is he happy? The answer may depend on what has happened to the base. If the *cut* is computed using the earlier period (and the salary of $500) as the base, the reduced pay amounts to $400 ($500 × 0.80). But if the pay *increase* of 20 percent is figured on a base that has been shifted from $500 to $400, the worker winds up with a restored pay of $480 (1.20 × $400). Thus, the bouncing base has cost him $20 each week, and this isn't likely to please him. ◆

Example 2.7   An **index number** is a measure that shows how much a composite group has changed with respect to a base period that's usually defined to have a value of 100. An important example is the Canadian *Consumer Price Index* (CPI). The CPI is a popular series that periodically measures the cost of a large basket of goods and services purchased by Canadians. The CPI uses 1992 as its base year and assigns to the prices that prevailed in that year an index number value of 100. By 1997 the index value had risen to 107.6, and in 1998 the index reached 108.6. These numbers mean that there was a 7.6 percent increase between 1992 and 1997, and a 8.6 percent increase between 1992 and 1998. Thus it would take $107.60 in 1997 to buy the same quantity of goods and services that could be obtained for $100 in 1992. So far, so good. But let's assume that a reporter now misuses these figures during an article and notes that there has been a $8.6 - 7.6 = 1.0$ *percent increase* in prices between 1997 and 1998. It's true that the numbers 108.6 and 107.6 represent percentages, and it's also true that there's a difference of 1.0 *percentage point* between 1997 and 1998. But the percentage increase was actually 0.93 percent $[((108.6 - 107.6)/107.6) \times 100 = 0.93]$. In this case the reporter failed to shift the base to 1997. ◆

Example 2.8   Percentage increases can easily exceed 100 percent. For example, a company whose sales have increased from $1 million in 1997 to $4 million in 1999 has had a percentage increase of 300 percent $[(\$4 \text{ million} - \$1 \text{ million})/\$1 \text{ million}]$. Of course, the sales in 1999 relative to the sales in 1997 were 400 percent—($4 million/$1 million) × 100—and this percentage relative figure is sometimes confused with the percentage increase value. Remember, though, that percentage decreases exceeding 100 percent aren't possible if the original data are positive values. For example, *Newsweek* magazine reported some years ago that the Chinese government had cut the salaries of certain officials by 300 percent. Of course, once 100 percent is gone, there isn't anything left. Embarrassed editors later admitted that the cut was 66.67 percent rather than

---

[1] Ron McCuiston in *The Matyc Journal*, Winter 1979, p. 59. From "Standard Deviations of the Square Root of Infinity." Reprinted with permission of *The Matyc Journal*, Inc.

300 percent. And a more recent article in *Datamation* began with these words: "We certainly understood the new industry economics. Oil prices had plunged more than 100% in the past two years. ..." ◆

The previous examples show only a few types of abuses that may be associated with the use of percentages. But they do give you an idea of the importance of following the bouncing base.

2.8 Avoiding Spurious Accuracy and Other Pitfalls

Spurious (and Curious) Accuracy

Statistical data based on sample results are often reported in precise numbers. It's not unusual for several decimal places to be used, and the apparent precision lends an air of infallibility to the information reported. Yet the accuracy image may be false. To illustrate, W.E. Urban, a statistician for the New Hampshire Agricultural Experiment Station, wrote a letter to the editor of *Infosystems* magazine taking issue with a previously published article. "Your magazine," wrote Urban, "has provided me with an excellent example of impeccable numerical accuracy and ludicrous interpretation which I will save for my statistics classes. With a total sample size of 55, reporting percentages with two decimal places is utter nonsense." The first sample percentage quoted in the article was 31.25, but, as Urban noted, the corresponding estimate of the population was likely to have been anywhere between 12 and 62 percent! As Urban concluded: "I realize that it is painful to throw away all the nice decimals the computer has given us ... but who are we kidding?" The reply of the editor: "No one. You're right."

Spurious accuracy isn't limited to sample results. The *Information Please Almanac* once listed the number of Hungarian-speaking people at 13,000,000, while in the same year the *World Almanac* placed the number at 8,001,112. Thus, there was a difference of about 5 million people in the estimates. This isn't particularly surprising. But isn't it curious that the *World Almanac* figure could be so precise? Does it stand to reason that the accuracy could be so great when the figures are well up into the millions?

Oscar Morgenstern summarizes the issue of spurious accuracy with these words:

> It is pointless to treat material in an "accurate" manner at a level exceeding that of the basic errors. The classical case is, of course, that of the story in which a man, asked about the age of a river, states that it is 3,000,021 years old. Asked how he could give such accurate information, the answer was that 21 years ago its age was given as 3 million years.

Avoiding Other Pitfalls

An important function of any statistics course is to help people distinguish between valid and invalid uses of quantitative tools. Thus, information found in the following chapters should help you avoid many of the pitfalls discussed in this chapter. But even after you finish this book, you'll find that it isn't always easy to recognize or cope with

statistical fallacies. You must remain on the defence to avoid serious statistical blunders. To avoid pitfalls, you might ask yourself questions such as the following:

- *Who is the source of the information you are asked to accept?* Some groups may use statistics to support preconceived positions. Using essentially the same raw data, labour unions might show that corporate profits are high and thus higher wage demands are reasonable, while the company might make a case to show that profit margins are low and labour productivity isn't keeping up with productivity in other industries. Also, politicians of opposing parties use the same government statistics relating to employment, taxation, national debt, welfare spending, budgets, and defence appropriations to draw surprisingly different conclusions to present to voters.

- *What evidence is offered by the source in support of the information?* Suspicious methods of data collection and/or presentation should put you on guard. And, of course, you should determine the relevancy of the supporting information to the issue being considered.

- *What information is missing?* What isn't made available by the source may be more important than what is supplied. If assumptions about trends, methods of computing percentages or making comparisons, definitions of terms, measures of central tendency and dispersion used, sizes of samples employed, and other important facts are missing, there may be ample cause for skepticism.

- *Is the conclusion reasonable?* Have valid statistical facts or statements been used to support the jump to a conclusion that ignores other plausible possibilities? Does the conclusion seem logical and sensible?

LOOKING BACK

1. Many have uncritically accepted statistical conclusions only to discover later that they've been misled. The aim of this chapter isn't to show you how to misapply statistics so that you can better con fellow humans. Rather, the purpose has been to alert you to the possibility of misleading statistical information so that you can better distinguish between valid and invalid uses of statistical techniques.

2. Poorly worded and/or slanted questions may be used to gather data, and a "finagle factor" may be used to support preconceived opinions. You should be aware of the bias that may exist in the information you're asked to accept.

3. One measure of central tendency is the arithmetic mean, or average. However, often the word *average* is used as a broad term that applies to several measures of central tendency including the arithmetic mean, but also the median or the mode. It's common for one of these measures of central tendency to be used where it isn't appropriate and where it's selected to deliberately mislead. But averages alone usually don't adequately describe a data set. Dispersion—the amount of spread or scatter that occurs in the data—must also be considered. Disregarded dispersions and aggravating averages are usually found acting in concert to confuse and mislead.

4. Statistical tables and charts are prepared to summarize data, uncover relationships, and interpret and communicate numerical facts to those who can use them. We've considered the legitimate uses of statistical tables and charts. But persuasive artists can easily take honest facts and create misleading impressions, as you've seen in this chapter.

5. Consumers of statistical information must be alert to the argument that be-cause B follows A, B was caused by A. Erroneous cause-and-effect conclu-sions are often drawn because of the misuse of quantitative facts. Failing to define terms, making improper or illogical comparisons, using an alleged sta-tistical fact to jump to a conclusion, using jargon and lengthy words to cloud a message—all these antics with semantics are used to confuse and mislead. Also, assuming that because a pattern has developed in the past, that pattern will certainly continue into the future is foolish, but such assumptions aren't un-usual.

6. People are often misled or confused because of a bouncing base—that is, the base period used in computing percentages. Statistical data are often re-ported in precise numbers, and several decimal places may be used. This ap-parent precision lends an air of infallibility to the information reported. But as we've seen, the accuracy may be spurious (and curious).

7. To avoid the pitfalls presented in this chapter, you might ask yourself these questions: (1) Who is the source of the information you're asked to accept? (2) What evidence is offered in support of the information? (3) What evi-dence is missing? (4) Is the conclusion reasonable?

Exercises

1. An advertisement for Guardian Fund appeared in *Money Forecast* as follows: "A $10,000 investment in Guardian Fund made in 1950 with income, dividends and capital gains rein-vested would be worth over one and one-half million dollars." Analyze this statement.

2. Professor Archer and Professor Albert are offering courses in Statistics 200 next semester. Your friend tells you that the Sta-tistics I class average last semester for each professor was a C. You investigate and find that Professor Archer's grades were as follows:

B C D C D B C C D B B C D C B D D C C B C B

And Professor Albert's grades were

A A F A F F A F F A A F A F A A F A F A F F

Looking at the two different grade distributions, which profes-sor would you rather have? Why?

3. Your financial planner informs you that the minimum in-vestment amounts for each of five different mutual funds are $500, $2,500, $25,000, $2,000, and $2,000 respectively, and that the typical minimum investment is $2,000. However, your friend calculates the average minimum investment to be $6,400. How can they both be correct?

4. In a survey mailed to 2,000 readers of *Macworld*, it was found that 97 percent use Macintosh computers. What is the fallacy behind the following statement: "Macintosh computers are enjoying huge popularity since 97 percent of the people sur-veyed use them?"

5. If 10,522 people filed sexual harassment complaints in a recent year, while 6,883 filed such suits in the preceding year, does this necessarily show that much more sexual harassment has occurred?

6. *USA Today* published a study that showed there was one centenarian (aged 100 or over) for every 3,961 people in Iowa. In Alaska, there was one centenarian for every 36,670 people. Is there anything fallacious about this statement: "Go to Iowa and you'll live longer"?

7. Recent studies have been made about the risk factors for heart disease. Among the findings: Walnuts may help prevent the dis-ease, but certain types of baldness are bad. Dr. James Muller, in an article in the *New York Times*, said he was skeptical of these risk factors. He noted that the California Walnut Commission sup-ported research demonstrating that walnuts are heart-healthy, and the Upjohn Corporation (makers of a hair cream) financed the baldness study. What do you think of Dr. Muller's observations?

8. "According to the alumni office, the average Prestige U. grad-uate, Class of '93, makes $86,123 a year." Comment on this fic-tional press release.

9. "An independent laboratory test showed that Krinkle Gum toothpaste users report 36 percent fewer cavities." Discuss this advertisement.

10. "Grogain cream has been used by a quarter of a million customers to cure baldness. We have a double-your-money-back guarantee, and only 2 percent of those who used Grogain were not helped and asked for a refund." Discuss this advertisement.

11. "There are as many people whose income is above average as there are people with below-average income." Discuss the type of "average" for which this statement is always true.

12. "Our firm's income has gone from $5 million to $10 million in just 1 year—an increase of 200 percent." Discuss this statement.

13. "Since 66 percent of all rape and murder victims were one-time friends or relatives of their assailants, you are safer at night in a public park with strangers than you are at home." Comment on this remark.

14. Lotto 6/49 results are available from Western Canada Lottery Corporation. The following graphs show the number of times each of the first ten numbers were drawn from June 12, 1982, to June 19, 2002. Which seems to present the information more honestly? Why?

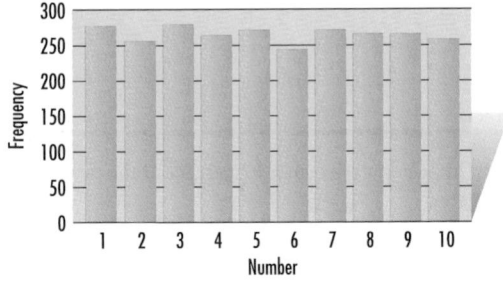

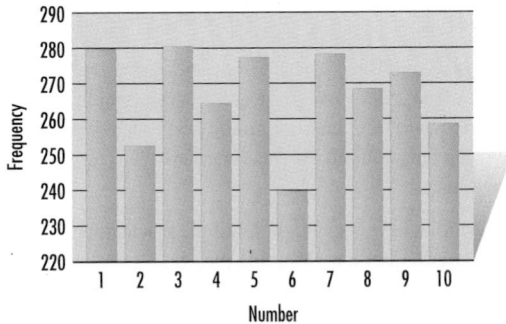

15. The pie charts that follow are similar to those found in a paper discussing a manufacturing problem (M. Gilmore and D. J. Smith, "Set-up Reduction in Pharmaceutical Manufacturing: An Action Research Study," *Inter. Jour. of Operations & Production Management*, 1996). They represent the activities of a high-speed compressing machine before and after a team effort to reduce the time spent in the set-up process and thereby increase the time the machine is spent running.

Activities before set-up reduction

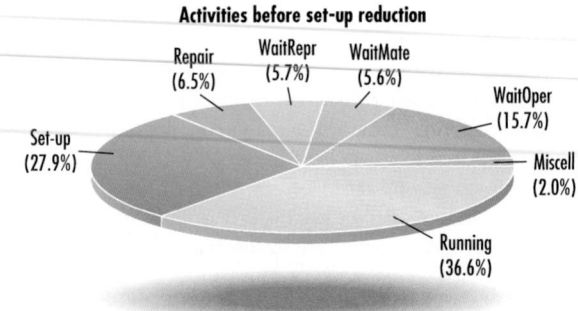

Activities after set-up reduction

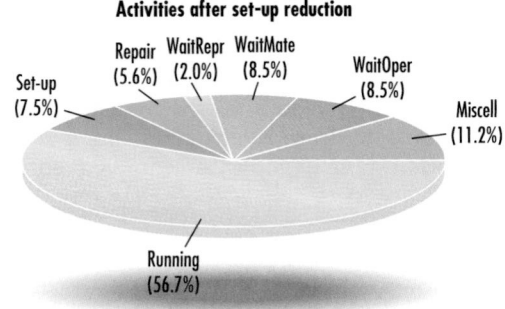

a) Does it appear that the team's efforts were successful?

b) Is there an alternative way of presenting the data that might make the comparison easier?

16. The data given below were obtained from Statistics Canada:

FEDERAL REVENUE FOR THE YEARS 1996–2001 ($Millions)					
	96–97	**97–98**	**98–99**	**99–2000**	**00–01**
Total revenue	152,541	165,179	168,827	179,513	190,409
Own source revenue	152,005	164,656	168,325	178,959	189,840
Income taxes	88,223	101,265	102,613	112,196	119,992
Consumption taxes	32,007	33,806	34,480	36,011	38,773
Other taxes	1,022	861	820	530	542
Contributions to Social Insurance Plans	19,846	19,242	19,798	18,933	19,086
Sales of goods and services	6,051	4,016	4,165	4,243	4,258
Investment income	4,536	4,710	5,545	6,264	6,533
Other revenue from own sources	321	754	900	778	655
General-purpose transfers	474	464	477	539	555
Specific-purpose transfers	62	58	24	14	13

FEDERAL EXPENDITURE FOR THE YEARS 1996–2001 ($Millions)

	96–97	97–98	98–99	99–2000	00–01
Total expenditures	166,041	160,672	166,216	172,770	181,340
General government services	5,785	5,940	6,173	5,793	8,429
Protection of persons and property	16,094	15,731	16,626	18,442	19,248
Transportation and communications	3,306	3,191	1,989	1,719	1,974
Health	1,177	1,327	1,666	1,723	2,902
Social services	48,459	48,453	49,295	50,384	51,574
Education	3,355	3,415	4,128	4,507	4,832
Resource conservation and industrial development	6,013	5,170	4,734	5,386	5,716
Environment	1,271	1,529	1,491	1,546	1,529
Recreation and culture	2,839	2,796	2,934	2,968	3,144
Labour, employment and immigration	1,514	2,209	2,551	2,777	2,299
Housing	1,964	1,862	1,865	1,927	1,881
Foreign affairs and international assistance	3,837	3,689	4,045	4,307	4,606
Regional planning and development	304	289	347	377	360
Research establishments	1,307	1,329	1,541	1,862	2,008
General purpose transfers	23,834	20,203	22,748	24,796	25,822
Debt charges	44,916	43,443	43,967	44,139	44,984
Other expenditures	67	87	107	108	23
Surplus or deficit	–13,499	4,507	2,610	6,742	9,068

Source: Statistics Canada, Table 385–0002.

The following charts illustrate some parts of the above data:

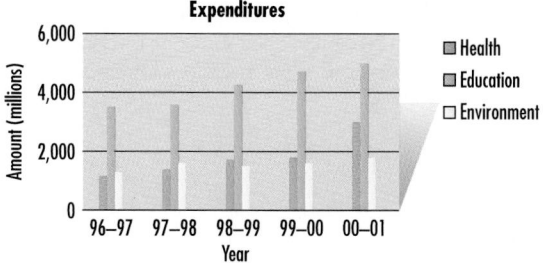

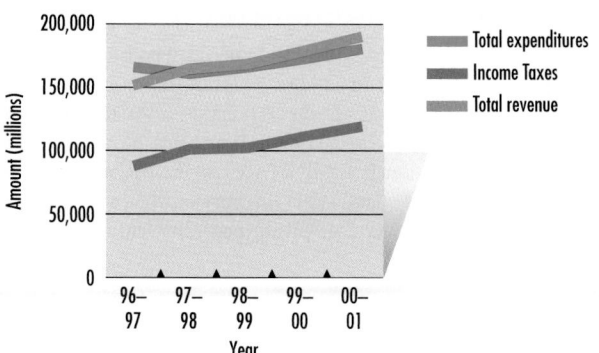

a) In November 1999, provincial and territorial finance ministers met in Toronto to discuss how Ottawa should spend its expected $5.5 billion budget surplus. Ontario, Quebec, and Alberta wanted to focus on tax cuts. Atlantic Canada was more concerned about social programs, and the Prairie provinces wanted more farm aid. Would you support the provinces that are asking for a reduction in taxes? Explain your answer by making reference to the trends observed from the graphs and by constructing one or more other graphs that illustrate the extent to which the increase in income tax helped reduce the deficit.

b) In the years 94–95 and 95–96, federal expenditures on Education were $6,242 million and $6,254 million respectively. The table shows that in 96–97 the amount spent on Education was cut to $3,355 million. What effect do you think the education cuts had on university students? Justify your answer with relevant statistical data.

c) Identify the major sources of the increase in the federal government revenue between the years 96–97 and 00–01.

d) Identify the major sources of the change from a deficit in 96–97 to a surplus in the following years.

e) In March 2002, the *Briarpatch* magazine reported that the average debt load of a Saskatchewan student was $25,000. What are some factors contributing to student debt? Obtain data on student debt for the years between 1992 and 2002. Use a graph to illustrate the trend. The chart presented below shows tuition fees at universities in Western Canada. Does this show that the increase in tuition fees contributes significantly towards students' debt?

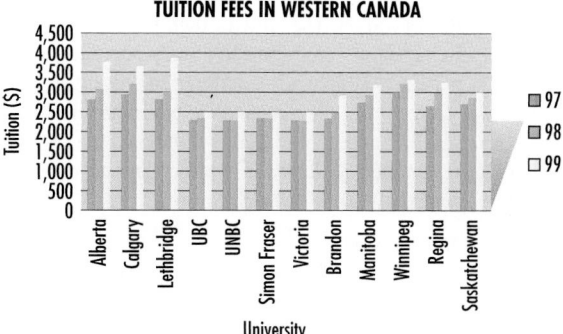

Source: Statistics Canada.

Topics for Review and Discussion

1. Prior to the 1999 provincial election in Saskatchewan, most of the polls predicted an NDP majority. Why were the polls wrong? You'll have to do outside research to answer this question.

2. Why were the polls wrong in 1948 when they predicted that Dewey would defeat Truman for U.S. president? You'll have to do outside research to answer this question.

3. The word *average* is a broad term that people sometimes apply to several measures of central tendency. Identify and define three such measures.

4. "Averages alone don't adequately describe the true picture of a set of data." Why is this statement true?

5. What is a

  a) Statistical table?

  b) Line graph or chart?

  c) Bar graph or chart?

  d) Circle (pie) graph?

6. Give two examples of how persuasive artists can take honest facts and create misleading impressions.

7. How can antics with semantics be used to confuse and mislead?

8. "Percentage decreases exceeding 100 percent aren't possible if the original data are positive values." Explain why this is true.

9. What questions might you ask during the evaluation of quantitative information to avoid being misled?

Projects/Issues to Consider

1. Find examples in newspapers and periodicals of misleading graphics or questionable statistical usage, and prepare a report of your findings.

2. Design an advertisement that uses misleading statistics.

3. Students in Professor Larry Schuetz's classes at Linn Benton Community College conduct "Prove that Claim" projects each term. A student first identifies an ad that contains a claim of superiority for a product. The student then writes a letter to a company official (names are found in library reference books) asking that person to supply information that will substantiate the claim. A copy of this letter goes to the instructor, and when a reply is received, the student discusses the ad and the response in a class presentation. Follow these same steps to carry out your own Prove that Claim research project.

4. Prepare a presentation describing the rise in revenues of an organization. Construct two line graphs for the same information, with one showing a large increase and the other appearing to show that revenues are levelling off. Use different scales for your axes, and describe the impression that is made when these different scales are used.

5. Search the Internet for an interesting data set. Use the methods of this chapter to describe the data. Which methods can most easily be manipulated to create a false impression of the data? How would you recognize when someone is trying to present such a false impression? Write a report summarizing your conclusions.

Computer/Calculator Exercises

1. Use the World Wide Web to access the Data & Story Library at DASL. Click on *List All Methods,* then on Histogram. You will find several story names. Click on any interesting-sounding title and read the story and view the corresponding graph. Evaluate the information presented in the graph. Does it seem to match or justify the statements made in the story?

2. Use the World Wide Web to perform an Internet search for "data set" or "data library." From the list of sites, find one that has a set of observations on a variable that you find interesting. Download or copy and paste this information into a statistical package such as MINITAB. Use the package to create visual displays of the data. Write a report on the interesting aspects of the data that these graphs helped you identify.

CHAPTER 3

Descriptive Statistics

LOOKING AHEAD

You saw in Chapter 1 that descriptive statistics is a term applied to the procedures of data collection, classification, summarization, and presentation. We'll now be concerned with all these aspects of statistical description. That is, in this chapter we'll (1) consider the collection and organization of raw data, (2) examine ways to classify and graphically present data in a frequency distribution format, and (3) show the procedures used to compute selected central tendency and dispersion measures.

Thus, after studying this chapter, you should be able to

- Explain how to organize raw data into an array and how to construct and interpret a frequency distribution.

- Graphically present data in the form of a histogram, frequency polygon, stem-and-leaf display, dotplot, and boxplot.

- Present an overview of the types of measures that summarize and describe the basic properties of data sets.

- Compute such central tendency measures as the arithmetic mean, median, and mode.

- Compute such dispersion measures as the range, mean absolute deviation, and standard deviation.

- Use a percentage to summarize qualitative data.

All Numbers Aren't Created Equal

Some numbers are nominal measures that can be used only for identification. At a higher level are ordinal measures that place data values in a preference order. Horses finishing a race can be numbered 1, 2, 3, ... , as they cross the finish line. But this ranking says nothing about the time separating the winner from the second (or third) horse. Similarly, we know that gold, silver, and bronze medal winners in Olympic competition finished 1, 2, and 3, but the ranking alone doesn't tell us the closeness of the competition. Calculations based on nominal or ordinal data values are meaningless. Interval and ration measures also allow data values to be ranked in order but on a standard scale. The scale at the ratio level includes a true zero starting point, but this point is absent on an interval scale. Concepts for considering nominal and ordinal data are included in these chapters, but much of the analysis in this book involves the use of interval and ration data.

3.1 Introduction to Data Collection

We've seen in Chapter 1 that data are gathered early in the process of performing a statistical study. Data may be classified into either attribute or numerical types (*Figure 3.1*). Examples of **attribute** (also called qualitative or categorical) data are gender (two categories, male and female), political affiliation (Liberal, Conservative, New Democrat, and other categories), and citizenship (Canadian, American, Mexican, Nigerian, etc.). Attribute data are often assigned code numbers before being entered into computer databases (perhaps 1 = female, 2 = male). These numbers thus become a **nominal measure,** but they should be used only for identification purposes. It's foolish, for example, to add the female/male code numbers and compute an average gender value!

Statisticians generally focus on numerical data that represent counts or measurements. Of course, these numerical facts aren't all identical, since there's little reason to study such a situation. Rather, *variables* are the focus of the analyst's attention.

> A **variable** is a characteristic of interest that's possessed by each item under study. The value of this characteristic is likely to change or vary from one item in the data set to the next.

A value for a variable of interest is typically obtained either by counting or by using some measuring device. The number of mailboxes in post offices, for example, is found by counting. Similarly, counting is used to find the number of automobiles in a student parking lot. Thus, a **discrete variable** is generally one that has a countable or finite number of distinct values. A **continuous variable** is one that can assume any one of the countless number of values along a line interval. The value of a continuous variable is typically found with an instrument that measures the variable to some predetermined degree of accuracy. Two such instruments are the automobile odometer, which measures distance travelled, and the bathroom scale, which shows weights of individuals. The measured quantities produced by such instruments are continuously variable, but they are only approximate values. The pointer on a bathroom scale, for example, might read 65 kilograms. But if the pointer is lengthened and sharpened, and if the scale is calibrated more precisely, the reading might be 64.5 kilograms. Further refinements or better instruments might give readings of 64.42 kilograms, 64.4234 kilograms,

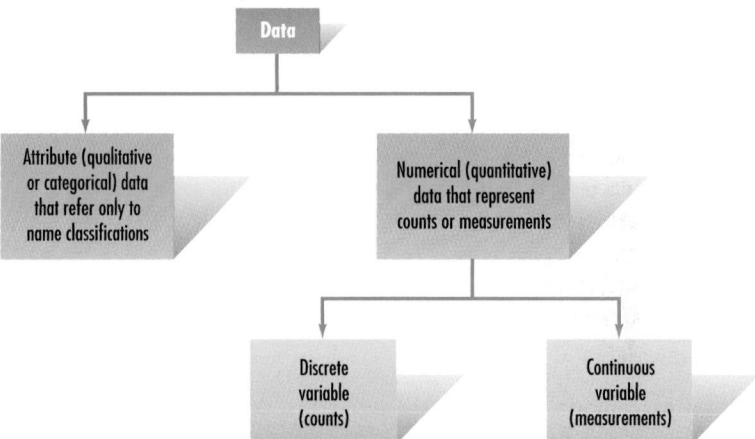

FIGURE 3.1 Basic types of data.

and so on. In addition to these "numerical" variables, there are also "categorical" variables, such as nationality, colour, gender, etc.

Self-Testing Review 3.1

The Lemon Marketing Corporation has asked you for information about the car you drive. For each question, identify each of the types of data requested as either attribute data or numeric data. When numeric data is requested, identify the variable as discrete or continuous.

1. What is the weight of your car?

2. In what city was your car made?

3. How many people can be seated in your car?

4. What's the distance travelled from your home to your school?

5. What's the colour of your car?

6. How many cars are in your household?

7. What's the length of your car?

8. What's the normal operating temperature (in degrees Celsius) of your car's engine?

9. What fuel economy (litres per 100 km) do you get in city driving?

10. Who made your car?

11. How many cylinders are there in your car's engine?

12. How many kilometres have you put on your car's current set of tires?

3.2 Data Organization and Frequency Distributions

Assuming that the data have been collected, let's now see how these facts may be organized.

The Raw Data

A listing of the units produced by each worker would likely be of little value to a production manager who's trying to determine overall worker productivity. To be meaningful, such unorganized raw data should be arranged in some systematic order.

An example of raw sales data is presented in Table 3.1. (Instructions of how to enter this data set into the MINITAB program are presented in Appendix 11.) Since we'll be computing various measures to summarize and describe these sales facts later in this chapter, let's make sure we understand this data set. The Slimline Beverage Company makes and sells a line of dietetic soft drink products. These products are sold in bottles and cans. In addition, soft drink syrups are sold to restaurants, theatres, and other outlets that mix small amounts of the syrup with carbonated water and sell the result in cups. The sales manager wants to see how a new Fizzy Cola syrup is selling, so the raw sales data on litres of syrup sold were gathered as shown in Table 3.1. (The continuous variable—litres sold—in this example has been measured to the nearest ¼ litre.) In its present form this unorganized mass of numbers probably isn't of much value to the manager. And what if there had been 500 values rather than just 50?

TABLE 3.1   RAW DATA (LITRES OF FIZZY COLA SYRUP SOLD BY 50 EMPLOYEES OF SLIMLINE BEVERAGE COMPANY IN 1 WEEK)

Employee	Litres Sold	Employee	Litres Sold
P.P.	95.00	R.N.	148.00
S.M.	100.75	S.G.	125.25
P.T.	126.00	A.D.	88.50
P.U.	114.00	R.O.	133.25
M.S.	134.25	E.Y.	95.00
F.K.	116.75	Y.O.	104.50
L.Z.	97.50	O.U.	135.00
F.E.	102.25	U.S.	108.25
A.N.	110.00	L.T.	122.50
R.J.	125.00	E.A.	107.25
O.O.	144.00	A.T.	137.00
U.Y.	112.00	R.I.	114.00
T.T.	82.50	N.S.	124.50
G.H.	135.50	I.T.	118.00
R.I.	115.25	N.I.	119.00
O.S.	128.75	G.C.	117.25
U.S.	113.25	A.S.	93.25
P.O.	132.00	N.C.	115.00
O.R.	105.00	Y.A.	116.50
F.T.	118.25	T.N.	99.50
W.O.	121.75	H.B.	106.00
O.F.	109.25	I.E.	103.75
R.T.	136.00	N.F.	115.25
K.H.	124.00	G.U.	128.50
E.I.	91.00	X.N.	105.00

The Data Array

Perhaps the simplest device for systematically organizing raw data is the **array**—an arrangement of data items in either an ascending (from lowest to highest value) or descending (from highest to lowest value) order. An array of the Fizzy Cola sales data given in Table 3.1 is presented in Table 3.2. This array, of course, is in an ascending order. Statistical packages such as MINITAB have built-in **Sort** commands and can easily sort an unordered raw data set into an array.

There are several advantages in arraying raw data:

- We see in Table 3.2 that the sales vary from 82.50 to 148.00 litres. The difference between the highest and lowest values—called the **range**—is 65.50 litres.

- The lower one-half of the values are distributed between 82.50 and 115.25 litres, and the upper 50 percent of the values vary between 115.25 and 148.00 litres.

- An array can show the presence of large concentrations of items at particular values. In Table 3.2, no single value appears more than twice, but in other arrays there may be a pronounced concentration.

In spite of these advantages, though, the array is still a rather awkward data organization tool, especially when the number of data items is large. Thus, there's often a need to arrange the data into a more compact form for analysis and communication purposes.

 Example 3.1   One indicator of the degree of acceptance of women in the workplace is a comparison of women's earnings to men's. The following table contains data on women's average wages in manufacturing as a percentage of men's (United Nations Women's Indicators and Statistics Database [Wistat], Version 3, CD-ROM) (Data = WomnWage).

Australia	82	Belgium	76	Czechoslovakia	68
Denmark	85	Finland	77	France	79
Germany	73	Greece	76	Hungary	72
Ireland	69	Japan	41	Luxemburg	65
Netherlands	77	New Zealand	75	Norway	86
Portugal	72	Spain	72	Sweden	89
Switzerland	68	United Kingdom	68	United States	68
Egypt	68	Kenya	74	Swaziland	54
Zambia	73	Costa Rica	74	El Salvador	94
Netherlands Antilles	65	Paraguay	66	Cyprus	58
Guam	51	Hong Kong	69	Korea	50
Myanmar	97	Singapore	55	Sri Lanka	88

Arrange the data in ascending order. Identify the range and the lower and upper halves of the data.

◆ **Solution:**

MINITAB was used to generate the data array in *Figure 3.2*. There we can see that the range is 97 − 41 = 56 percent. Since there are 36 countries, the lower half of the values would be the 18 smallest, 41 to 72 percent, while the upper half would be the 18 largest, 72 to 97 percent. ◆

TABLE 3.2 DATA ARRAY (LITRES OF FIZZY COLA SYRUP SOLD BY 50 EMPLOYEES OF SLIMLINE BEVERAGE COMPANY IN 1 WEEK)

Litres Sold	Litres Sold
82.50	115.25
88.50	116.50
91.00	116.75
93.25	117.25
95.00	118.00
95.00	118.25
97.50	119.00
99.50	121.75
100.75	122.50
102.25	124.00
103.75	124.50
104.50	125.00
105.00	125.25
105.00	126.00
106.00	128.50
107.25	128.75
108.25	132.00
109.25	133.25
110.00	134.25
112.00	135.00
113.25	135.50
114.00	136.00
114.00	137.00
115.00	144.00
115.25	148.00

Source: Table 3.1.

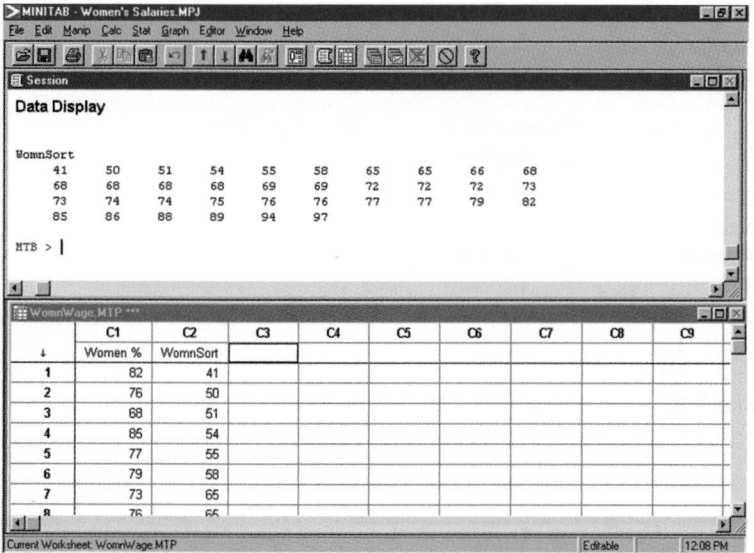

FIGURE 3.2 To obtain this MINITAB output, access the **Sort** Window by clicking on **Manip, Sort,** enter the column to be sorted in the box below **Sort column(s)** and also in the box to the right of **Sort by column,** name a new column to receive the data array in the box below **Store sorted columns(s) in,** click on **OK,** then type "Print c2" (or Print followed by the name of the column in quotes) in the Session Window.

Frequency Distributions

The purpose of a *frequency distribution* is to organize the data items into a compact form without obscuring essential facts. This purpose is achieved by grouping the arrayed data into a relatively small number of classes. Thus,

A **frequency distribution** (or **frequency table**) groups data items into classes and then records the number of items that appear in each class.

In Table 3.3, for example, we've grouped the litres sold into seven classes and then indicated the number of employees whose sales have turned up in each of the seven classes. (The term *frequency distribution* comes from this frequency of occurrence of values in the various classes.)

You'll notice in Table 3.3 that the data are now arranged in a compact form. A quick glance at the frequency distribution shows, for example, that the sales of about two-thirds of the employees ranged from 100 to 130 litres (the sales of 33 of the 50 employees are distributed in the middle three classes). In short, Table 3.3 gives us a reasonably good view of the overall sales pattern of Fizzy Cola syrup. But the compression of the data has resulted in some loss of detailed information. We no longer know, for example, exactly how many litres each employee sold. And we don't know from Table 3.3 that the values have a range or spread of exactly 65.50 litres. All we know about these matters is that there are two employees in the first class whose sales were somewhere between 80 and less than 90 litres and that the range of values is going to be somewhere between 50 and 70 litres. On balance, though, the advantage of gaining new insight into the data patterns that may exist through the use of a frequency distribution can often outweigh this inevitable loss of detail.

To construct a frequency distribution, it's necessary to determine (1) the number of classes that will be used to group the data, (2) the width of these classes, and (3) the

TABLE 3.3 FREQUENCY DISTRIBUTION (LITRES OF FIZZY COLA SYRUP SOLD BY 50 EMPLOYEES OF SLIMLINE BEVERAGE COMPANY IN 1 WEEK)

Litres Sold	Number of Employees (Frequencies)
80 and less than 90	2
90 and less than 100	6
100 and less than 110	10
110 and less than 120	14
120 and less than 130	9
130 and less than 140	7
140 and less than 150	2
	50

Source: Table 3.2.

number of observations—or the **frequency**—in each class. In the next section we'll look at the first two interrelated considerations. The last step is a routine transfer of information from an array to a distribution, so we'll not consider it here.

Classification Considerations

It's usually desirable to consider the following criteria when creating a frequency distribution:

1. In formal presentations, the number of classes used to group the data generally varies from a minimum of 5 to a maximum of 18. But there are few hard and fast rules. The actual number of classes used depends on such factors as the number of observations being grouped, the purpose of the distribution, and the arbitrary preferences of the analyst. You could group the data in Table 3.3 into many classes, with each class having a small width. Such a distribution can be useful for preliminary analysis, as we'll see in a few pages. But a distribution with many small classes may contain too much detail to be used in a formal data presentation. At the other extreme, a grouping of the data in Table 3.3 into only three classes with intervals of 22 litres each would result in the loss of important detail. The key is to use classes that give you a good view of the data pattern and enable you to gain insights into the information that is there.

2. Classes must be selected to conform to two rules: (*a*) all data items from the smallest to the largest must be included, and (*b*) each item must be assigned to one and only one class. Possible gaps and/or overlaps between successive classes that could cause this second rule to be violated must be avoided.

3. Except in rare cases, the *width* of each class—that is, the **class interval**—should be equal. (It's also often desirable to use class intervals that are multiples of numbers such as 5, 10, 100, 1,000, etc.) Although unequal class intervals may be needed in frequency distributions where large gaps exist in the data, such intervals may cause difficulties. For example, if frequencies in a distribution with unequal intervals are compared, the observed variations may merely be related to interval sizes rather than to some underlying pattern. Other difficulties of using unequal intervals can arise during the preparation of graphs. Table 3.3 has arbitrarily been prepared with seven classes of equal size. How was the interval width of 10 litres determined? The following simple formula first estimates a preliminary interval, and this interval is then rounded up to a convenient value:

$$\text{Width} = \frac{\text{range}}{\text{number of classes}} \quad \text{(and then round up)}$$

Of course, as we've seen in Table 3.2, the Fizzy Cola sales data range from a low of 82.50 litres to a high of 148.00 litres. Thus,

$$\text{Width} = \frac{148.00 - 82.50}{7} \quad \text{(and then round up)}$$

$$= 9.36, \text{ and this figure is then rounded up to the class interval size of 10 litres used in Table 3.3.}$$

TABLE 3.4   OPEN-ENDED DISTRIBUTION
                (TOTAL INCOME REPORTED
                BY SELECTED FAMILIES)

Total Income	Number of Families
Under $10,000	6
$10,000 and under $20,000	14
20,000 and under 30,000	18
30,000 and under 40,000	10
40,000 and under 50,000	5
50,000 and under 60,000	4
60,000 and over	3
	60

4. Whenever possible an open-ended class interval—one with an unspecified upper or lower class limit—should be avoided. Table 3.4 has such an interval, and so it's an example of an open-ended distribution. An open-ended class may be needed when a few values are extremely large or small compared with the remainder of the more concentrated observations or when confidential information might be revealed by stating an upper limit. For example, placing an upper limit on the data in Table 3.4 might tend to reveal the income of an easily identifiable family in a small community. But open-ended classes should be used sparingly because of graphing problems and because (as we'll soon see) it's impossible to compute estimates (guesses) of such important descriptive measures as the arithmetic mean and the standard deviation from an open-ended distribution.

5. When there's a concentration of raw data around certain values, it's desirable to construct the distribution so that these points of concentration fall at the **class midpoint,** or middle of a class interval. (The reason for this will become apparent later when we compute the arithmetic mean for data found in a frequency table.) In Table 3.3, the midpoint of the class "110 and less than 120" is 115 litres, the lower limit of that class is 110 litres, and the upper limit is 119.999 ... litres. Of course, another analyst could gather additional raw sales data for Fizzy Cola syrup and could then round the sales to the *nearest* litre. This analyst might then set up a distribution similar to the one in Table 3.3 with class intervals of 80 to 89, 90 to 99, 100 to 109, 110 to 119, and so on. In this case, the *stated* limits are only 9 litres apart, but the size of these class intervals is still 10 litres. Why? Because the class "110 to 119" has a real lower limit, or *lower boundary,* of 109.5 and a real upper limit, or *upper boundary,* of 119.5. A **class boundary** is thus a number that doesn't appear in the stated class limits but is rather a value that falls midway between the upper limit of one class and the lower limit of the next larger one. With the class "110 to 119," the class interval still has a width of 10 litres, but the class midpoint in this case is 114.5 litres.

☐ Example 3.2   In Example 3.1, we looked at women's average wages in manufacturing as a percentage of men's. We found that these 36 percentages went from 41 to 97 percent. Organize the data into a frequency distribution, and identify the class midpoints and boundaries.

◆ **Solution:**

With only 36 numbers to organize, a few classes, say, five or six, would be appropriate. We can see the widths both of these would give us before we select the number of classes to have.

$$\text{Width for five classes} = \frac{97 - 41}{5} = \frac{56}{5} = 11.2$$

$$\text{Width for six classes} = \frac{97 - 41}{6} = \frac{56}{6} = 9.3$$

As ten is a good width, we will use six classes with the first class "40 to 49." If the percentages were reported with one or more decimal places, the first class could be "40 to less than 50" (sometimes written "40 to < 50" or "40–< 50"). In any case, starting each class at a multiple of 10 (40, 50, . . .) allows us to talk about the 40s, the 50s, and so on.

Percentages	Number of Countries
40 to 49	1
50 to 59	5
60 to 69	10
70 to 79	13
80 to 89	5
90 to 99	2

The class midpoints are 44.5, 54.5, . . . , 94.5 and the class boundaries are 39.5, 49.5, 59.5, . . . , 99.5. ◆

Example 3.3   **Some Reel Data**   The data below represent the length in millimetres of 100 fish taken randomly from fishermen's catches. (Data = Dvrsole1).

331	339	339	340	341	346	347	358
364	366	370	371	371	371	373	374
381	381	384	386	387	387	388	389
390	392	393	394	395	397	398	398
398	403	404	405	408	409	410	410
411	412	413	414	415	417	419	419
420	420	421	423	425	427	436	439
439	451	363	345	361	337	442	351
341	357	292	373	360	380	375	357
388	384	349	350	386	394	334	379
355	376	382	327	393	366	316	389
390	405	356	342	400	366	385	362
369	412	364	457				

Both commercial fishermen and marine biologists are interested in the distribution of lengths of these fish, though for different reasons. What can be done to present the information that these groups need?

◆ **Solution:**

We decided to create a frequency distribution with eight classes. Eight was chosen because it gave a reasonable width to each class, 25, and included all the data. The resulting frequency distribution follows. Note that, while we cannot see the individual data points with this display, we probably have better insights about the lengths from examining this table than from looking at the raw data listed above.

Length (mm)	Number of Fish
275 and under 300	1
300 and under 325	1
325 and under 350	14
350 and under 375	24
375 and under 400	30
400 and under 425	22
425 and under 450	6
450 and under 475	2

Self-Testing Review 3.2

13. In its 2001 report on Canadian Colleges, *Maclean's* magazine reported the following tuition charges for international students at 43 Canadian colleges (Data = Intfees2001).

College	Fees	College	Fees
North Atlantic	6,600	St. Clair	12,007
NS Community	7,500	St. Lawrence	9,000
NB Community	5,000	Sault	8,981
Alfred	5,650	Seneca	10,000
Algonquin	9,995	Sir Sanford Fleming	10,250
Boreal	8,064	SIAST	8,928
Cambrian	8,949	Grande Prairie	4,880
Canadore	8,400	Grant MacEwan	10,000
Centennial	9,970	Medicine Hat	4,940
Confederation	9,775	NAIT	10,000
Fanshawe	9,826	BCIT	8,600
George Brown	9,375	Camosun	7,200
Georgian	10,000	Capilano	8,600
Humber	9,700	Douglas	8,239
Kemptville	4,048	Langara	8,250
Lambton	9,760	New Caledonia	6,400
Loyalist	8,350	North Island	6,000
Michener Institute	10,600	Northwest	5,770
Mohawk	9,850	Open University/College	4,590
Niagara	8,900	College of the Rockies	6,200
Northern	9,200	Selkirk	6,800
Ridgetown	4,528		

a) Organize the tuition fees into a frequency distribution with nine classes beginning with "3,500 to < 4,500," then "4,500 to < 5,500," ... and ending with "11,500 to < 12,500."

b) Is it possible to use five or seven classes rather than nine classes in the above frequency distribution?

c) What would have been reasonable class intervals if you had prepared frequency distributions using five or seven classes rather than nine?

14. The following listing (from the CAUT *Almanac of Post-Secondary Education in Canada, Second Edition, January 2003*) shows university presidents' compensation for 2001.

University	President	Total Compensation 2001 ($)
University of Toronto	Robert Birgeneau	378,823
University of Alberta	Roderick Fraser	278,000
University of Calgary	Harvey Weingarten	278,000
University of British Columbia	Martha C. Piper	270,000
McMaster University	Peter George	269,944
York University	Lorna Marsden	267,848
University of Guelph	Mordechai Rozanski	267,206
University of Waterloo	David Johnston	261,261
University of Victoria	David Turpin	258,700
University of Western Ontario	Paul Davenport	255,104
Queen's University at Kingston	William Leggett	251,917
Concordia University	Fredrick H. Lowy	244,139
Ryerson University	Claude Lajeunesse	241,217
Wilfrid Laurier University	Robert Rosehart	237,883
University of Lethbridge	William Cade	227,000
Dalhousie University	Thomas Traves	223,672
University of Manitoba	Emoke Szathmary	221,075
University of Windsor	Ross Paul	218,184
University of Saskatchewan	R. Peter MacKinnon	215,000
Simon Fraser University	Michael Stevenson	213,842
Trent University	Bonnie Patterson	202,197
Brock University	David Atkinson	200,671
Memorial University of Newfoundland	Axel Meisen	199,600
Carleton University	Richard Van Loon	196,630
Athabasca University	Dominique Abrioux	195,000
College universitaire de Saint-Boniface	M. Pul Ruest	189,130
Brandon University	Louis P. Visentin	189,130
Lakehead University	Frederick Gilbert	187,387
Saint Francis Xavier University	Sean E. Riley	182,662
University of Winnipeg	C. Rooke	178,841
University of Ottawa	Gilles Patry	174,389
Acadia University	Kelvin K. Ogilvie	173,628
University of Regina	David T. Barnard	173,000
University of Northern British Columbia	Charles Jago	172,500
Nipissing University	David Marshall	170,972
Mount Allison University	A. Wayne MacKay	170,000
Ontario College of Art and Design	Ronald Shuebrook	162,683
Nova Scotia College of Art and Design	Paul Greenhalgh	130,000
Laurentian University	Judith Woodsworth	111,905
Université Saint-Anne	André Roberge	92,163

a) Organize total compensation amounts into a frequency distribution with five classes beginning with "80,000 to < 140,000," then "140,000 to < 200,000," ... and ending with "320,000 to < 380,000."

b) What is the range of the values?

c) Organize total compensation amounts into a frequency distribution with seven classes.

15. Robert and Ginger Lee, owners of the Lee Health Foods Company, are studying the size of the orders placed by a sample of customers in an outlying county. In the past week, the following 30 orders have been received (Data = LeeHelth):

$42.50	$45.00	$47.75	$52.10	$29.00	$31.25
21.50	56.30	55.60	49.80	35.55	42.30
43.50	34.60	65.50	45.10	40.25	58.00
30.30	44.80	36.50	55.00	59.20	36.60
38.50	41.10	46.00	39.95	25.35	49.50

a) Arrange the data in an ascending array.

b) What is the range of values?

c) Organize the data items according to order size into a frequency distribution having the five classes "$20 to < $30," "$30 to < $40," ... , and "$60 to < $70."

d) Would it be possible to use six or seven classes rather than five classes in the above frequency distribution?

e) What would have been a reasonable class interval if you had prepared a frequency distribution using eight classes rather than five?

16. A few years ago *BusinessWeek* published the price of a share of common stock issued by 59 top U.S. firms. These firms (and their share prices to the nearest dollar) were as follows (Data = PriceShr):

Firm	Share Price	Firm	Share Price
IBM	131	Pac Tel	42
Exxon	55	Texaco	65
Philip Morris	67	Walt Disney	127
GE	67	Southwest Bell	54
Merck	106	Ford	34
Wal-Mart	36	Schlumberger	64
Bristol-Myers	77	NYNEX	76
A.T.&T.	33	US West	38
Coca-Cola	52	Eastman Kodak	46
P & G	87	Dow Chemical	53
Johnson & Johnson	90	Anheuser-Busch	47
Amoco	53	American Express	27
Chevron	75	McDonald's	34
Mobil	65	Hewlett-Packard	49
Pepsico	33	Microsoft	103
Du Pont	38	Schering-Plough	51
Bellsouth	52	Sears, Roebuck	32
GM	40	Fed. Natl. Mortge	46
Eli Lilly	83	Marion Merrell	39
GTE	32	Warner-Lambert	78
Atlantic Richfield	130	Pacific Gas & Elec	25
Waste Mgmt	43	Intel	52
Abbot Labs	47	Kellogg	83
3-M Corporation	91	Digital Equipment	82
American Inter	94	H. J. Heinz	37
Bell Atlantic	48	Emerson Electric	43
American Home	57	American Brands	46
Pfizer	108	Baxter Internatl	33
Ameritech	65	The Limited	25
Boeing	50		

a) Arrange the data in an ascending array.

b) What is the range of values?

c) Organize the data items according to share price into a frequency distribution table using eight classes. Use "$25 to < $40" for the first class.

17. The data that follow were found on the Antartica Streams Hydrology home page on the Internet as part of the Kodiak Island king crab survey data. The portion below represents the number of vessels registered for fishing over a 23-day period (Data = KodiakVI):

143	148	195	181	189	175	213	227	178	136	100	89	88
129	158	169	195	179	194	247	164	246	309			

a) Arrange the data in an ascending array.

b) What is the range of values?

c) Organize the data (number of vessels registered for fishing) into a frequency distribution table with six classes. Use "50 to < 100" for the first class.

3.3 Graphic Presentations of Frequency Distributions

Once data are grouped into a more compact form, the frequency distribution can be used for analysis, interpretation, and communication purposes. It's often possible to prepare a picture of a frequency distribution to achieve one or more of these aims. Such a picture of the data found in a frequency table is more likely to get the attention of the casual observer, and it may show trends or relationships that might be overlooked in a table.

The Histogram

One popular graphic tool is the *histogram*.

> A **histogram** is a bar graph that portrays the data found in a frequency distribution.

Figure 3.3 is a histogram of the Fizzy Cola syrup sales data found in Table 3.3. As you can see, this histogram simply consists of a set of vertical bars. Values of the variable being studied—in this case litres of syrup sold—are measured on an arithmetic scale on the horizontal axis. The bars in *Figure 3.3* are of equal width and correspond to the equal class intervals in Table 3.3; the height of each bar in *Figure 3.3* corresponds to the frequency of the class it represents. Thus, the area of a bar above each class interval is proportional to the frequencies represented in that class. If unequal class intervals were used in a frequency distribution, the areas of the bars above the various class intervals would still have to be proportional to the frequencies represented in the classes— e.g., if the third interval is twice as wide as each of the first two, the frequency of the third interval must be divided by two to get the appropriate height for the bar.

FIGURE 3.3 Histogram of frequency distribution of litres of Fizzy Cola syrup sold by 50 employees of Slimline Beverage Company in 1 week.

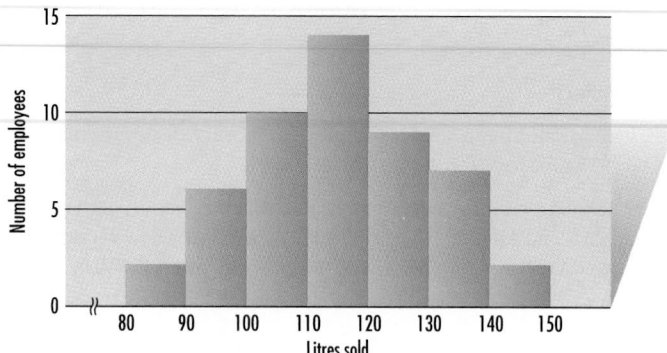

Example 3.4   Most statistical software packages and some calculators are programmed to produce histograms. A user merely enters a data set and then issues appropriate commands to tell the program what it should do. Use such a package or calculator to generate a histogram of the amount of Fizzy Cola sold by the 50 Slimline employees.

◆ **Solution:**

Figure 3.4a shows the MINITAB *default chart*—one that's automatically produced for a data set by the software without any formatting instructions from the user. You can see that the program has created 14 rather than 7 classes and has used class midpoints of 85, 90, 95, ... , rather than 85, 95, 105, ... To produce the same results as those shown in *Figure 3.3*—that is, to produce *Figure 3.4b*— the MINITAB user can modify the default graph with some simple instructions. Screen 2 of *Figure 3.4c* presents the histogram created by the T1-83 calculator. This can be obtained either from the raw, ungrouped data or from a frequency distribution such as is presented in Table 3.3. ◆

Example 3.5   Form a histogram for the data from Examples 3.1 and 3.2, women's average wages in manufacturing as a percentage of men's.

◆ **Solution:**

Using the same classes as in Example 3.2, we used MINITAB to obtain the histogram of *Figure 3.5*. ◆

Example 3.6   **Some Reel Data** In Example 3.3, we created a frequency distribution for the lengths in millimetres of 100 fish. This is reproduced below.

Length (mm)	Number of Fish
275 and under 300	1
300 and under 325	1
325 and under 350	14
350 and under 375	24
375 and under 400	30
400 and under 425	22
425 and under 450	6
450 and under 475	2

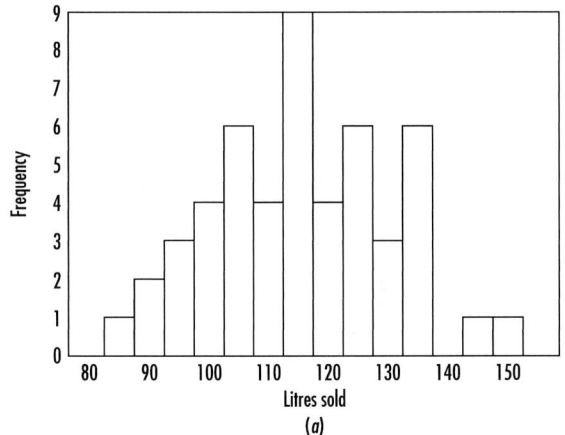

(a)

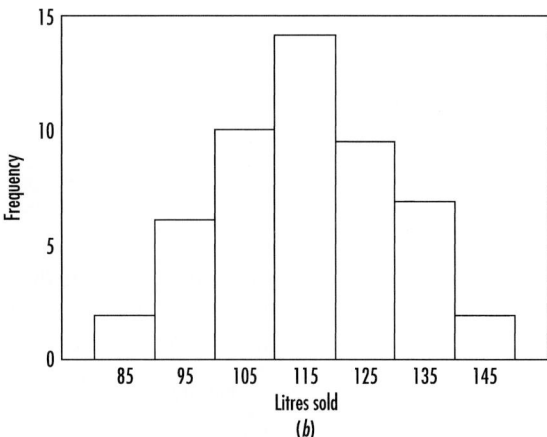

(b)

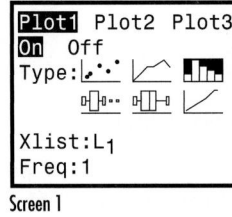

Screen 1

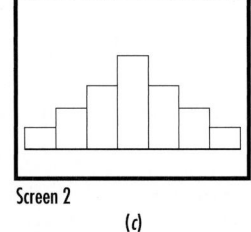

Screen 2

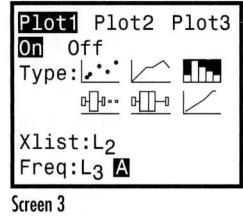

Screen 3

(c)

FIGURE 3.4 (a) To obtain this output, access the **Histogram** Window by clicking on **Graph, Histogram,** enter the column to be graphed in the box below **Graph variables,** and click **OK.** (b) To obtain this output, before clicking **OK,** click on **Options,** click in the circle to the left of **Number of intervals** and enter 7 in the box to the right, click in the circle to the left of **Midpoint/cutpoint positions** and enter 85 95 105 115 125 135 145 in the box to the right. (c) To obtain this output, first enter the data into a list **(L1).** Next set the parameters for the plot type by accessing the **STAT PLOT** menu, which is the 2nd function of the **Y** = key. Choose **Plot 1** and set the options as shown in screen 1. Next set the scale on the axes using the **WINDOW** key. Set the window as

Xmin = 80, Xmax = 150, Xscl = 10
Ymin = −4, Ymax = 18, Yscl = 5

Note that the x range should include the range of the data and Ymax should be at or above the maximum frequency. The Ymin is chosen to be −4 rather than 0 to allow space at the bottom of the screen to display the trace results. To make the histogram, press the **GRAPH** key. To see the frequencies for each interval, press **TRACE** and move from left to right with the cursor keys.

In screen 1, the **Freq** was set to 1 to make a histogram of the original, ungrouped data. To make a histogram from the grouped data in Table 3.3, first enter the midpoints 85, 95, ... , 145 into the list **L2** and the frequencies 2, 6, ... , 2 into **L3.** Then set **Plot 1** as shown in screen 3 above. Note that the midpoints are the **Xlist** and the frequencies are **Freq.** Graphing will produce the same histogram as in screen 2.

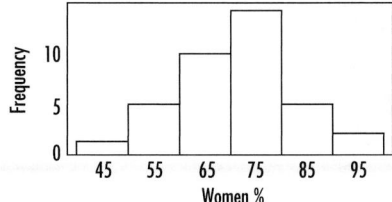

FIGURE 3.5 MINITAB output obtained with instructions similar to those of *Figure 3.4b.*

FIGURE 3.6 Histogram of fish lengths.

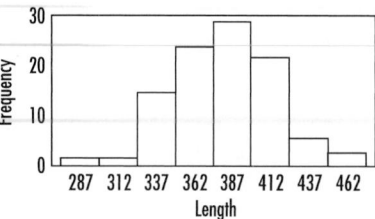

FIGURE 3.6 Histogram of fish lengths.

While this frequency distribution presents relevant information on the fish, often a picture of a frequency distribution has greater impact and can lead to more insights. With this in mind, create a histogram for this frequency distribution.

◆ **Solution:**

MINITAB was used to produce the histogram in *Figure 3.6*. This visual representation is usually easier to work with and understand than the corresponding frequency distribution, even though they portray the same information. ◆

The Frequency Polygon

Another popular graphic tool is the *frequency polygon.*

> A **frequency polygon** is a line chart that depicts the data found in a frequency distribution. It is thus a picture that may be used as an alternative to the histogram.

Figure 3.7 is a frequency polygon using the same data and plotted on the same scales as the histogram in *Figure 3.3*. (In fact, *Figure 3.3* has been reproduced as background in *Figure 3.7*.) As you can see, points are placed at the midpoints of each class interval. The height of each plotted point in *Figure 3.7*, of course, represents the frequency of the particular class. These points are then connected by a series of straight lines. It's customary to close the polygon at both ends by (1) placing points on the baseline half a class interval to the left of the first class and half a class interval to the right of the last class, then (2) drawing lines from the points representing the frequencies in the first and last classes to these baseline points (see *Figure 3.7*).

If the class intervals in a distribution are continuously reduced in size and if the number of items in the distribution is continually increased, the frequency polygon will re-

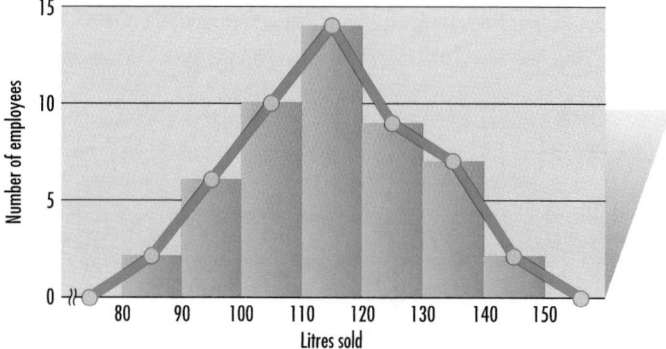

FIGURE 3.7 Frequency polygon of the distribution of litres of Fizzy Cola syrup sold by 50 employees of Slimline Beverage Company in 1 week.

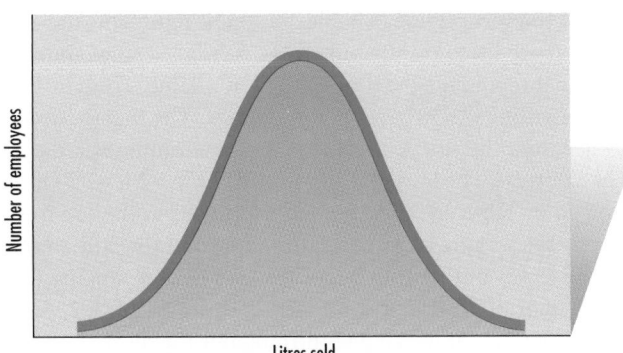

FIGURE 3.8 Generalized normal population distribution.

semble a smooth curve more and more closely. Thus, if the frequency polygon in *Figure 3.7* represented only a small sample of all the available data on Fizzy Cola syrup sales made by hundreds of employees, and if the frequency distribution—that is, the population frequency distribution—that could be prepared to account for all these data were made up of very narrow class intervals, the resulting population distribution curve might resemble the one shown in *Figure 3.8*. This bell-shaped, or **normal curve,** which describes the distribution of many kinds of variables in the physical sciences, social sciences, medicine, agriculture, business, and engineering, is very important in statistics and will be reintroduced in several later chapters.

Some Exploratory Data Analysis Presentations

Exploratory data analysis (EDA) is a term that refers to several techniques that analysts can use to get a feel for the data being studied. These EDA techniques can be used before (or in place of) more traditional analysis approaches. Stem-and-leaf displays, dotplots, and boxplots are examples of EDA tools in common use. We'll look at the first two tools here and discuss boxplots later in the chapter.

Stem-and-Leaf Display The **stem-and-leaf display** uses the actual data items in a data set to create a plot that looks like a histogram. The data array of the Fizzy Cola sales figures found in Table 3.2 is used in Table 3.5 to produce a stem-and-leaf display.

TABLE 3.5 A STEM-AND-LEAF DISPLAY OF THE SLIMLINE BEVERAGE COMPANY SALES FIGURES FOUND IN TABLE 3.2

Stem	Leaf Values	Number of Data Items
8	28	2
9	135579	6
10	0234556789	10
11	02344555667889	14
12	124455688	9
13	2345567	7
14	48	2

A *stem* is a number to the left of the vertical line in Table 3.5, and it represents the leading digit(s) of all data items that are listed on the same row. A *leaf* is a single number to the right of the vertical line that represents the trailing digit of a value. Thus, in Table 3.5 there are 50 leaf values representing the 50 items in our data set. The first stem value in the top row of Table 3.5 is 8, and the first leaf value is 2. These numbers are combined to give a sales figure of 82 litres. (The lowest sales value in Table 3.2 is 82.50 litres, but fractional units are dropped in Table 3.5.) The second leaf figure in the top row is used with its stem to produce a sales figure of 88 litres. In the second row, the stem of 9 is combined with each of the leaves in that row to get six sales figures ranging from 91 to 99 litres. The third-row stem of 10, when combined with leaves of 0, 2, 3, ... , produces data items of 100, 102, 103, ... , and so it goes throughout the display. The appearance of our stem-and-leaf plot would have looked just the same if we had used the raw sales data from Table 3.1 rather than the arrayed values from Table 3.2. But our leaf values wouldn't have been in sequence.

 Stem-and-leaf plots are simple to prepare, but it's even easier to turn the task over to a computer. Table 3.6a shows MINITAB's default output when it executes its **Stem-and-Leaf** command. You'll notice that MINITAB lists each stem on two lines. Leaf values of 0 through 4 are printed on the first of the two lines, and leaves 5 through 9 appear on the second. The first column (to the left of the stems) in the MINITAB output supplies additional information. This column begins at the top by accumulating the number of data values that have been accounted for in each line. There's one item in row 1, a total of two items in rows 1 and 2, four values through row 3, and 23 items are accounted for in the top seven rows. The parentheses in the next row show that we've arrived at the line that holds the middle or median value, and the number in the parentheses gives a count of the leaves on the line. Since there are 50

TABLE 3.6 STEM-AND-LEAF DISPLAYS PRODUCED BY MINITAB

```
MTB  >  STEM-AND-LEAF'LTRSOLD'

Stem-and-leaf of  LTRSOLD    N = 50
Leaf  Unit  =  1.0

      1      8  2
      2      8  8
      4      9  13
      8      9  5579
     12     10  0234
     18     10  556789
     23     11  02344
     (9)    11  555667889
     18     12  1244
     14     12  55688
      9     13  234
      6     13  5567
      2     14  4
      1     14  8

                (a)
```

```
MTB   >  STEM-AND-LEAF  'LTRSOLD';
SUBC >  INCREMENT 10.

Stem-and-leaf of  LTRSOLD     N = 50
Leaf  UNIT  =  1.0

      2     8   28
      8     9   135579
     18    10   0234556789
    (14)   11   02344555667889
     18    12   124455688
      9    13   2345567
      2    14   48

                (b)
```

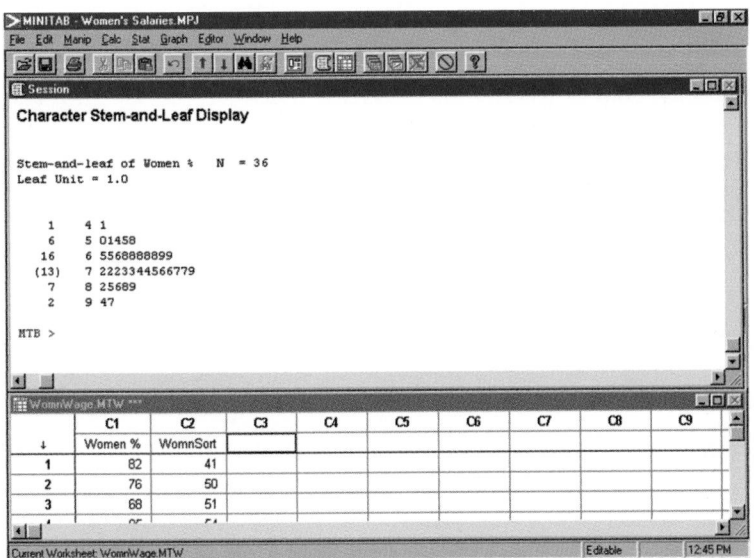

FIGURE 3.9 To obtain this MINITAB output, click on **Graph, Stem-and-Leaf,** enter the column to be graphed in the box below **Variables,** enter 10 in the box to the right of **Increment,** and click **OK.**

items in the data set and since we've accounted for 23 of them in the first seven rows, then the median is one of the early values in row 8 (about 115 in this case). After the median is reached, the figures in column 1 then show how many items remain on that line and on the lines below it in the data set. A simple subcommand in Table 3.6b allows MINITAB to duplicate Table 3.5.

Example 3.7
Produce a stem-and-leaf plot for the data from examples 3.1 and 3.2, women's average wages as a percentage of men's. List each stem on only one line.

◆ **Solution:**

Using MINITAB, we obtained the stem-and-leaf display of *Figure 3.9*. Compare this to *Figure 3.5* and notice the similarity of the shape of the histogram (vertically) to the way the lines of the stem-and-leaf plot extend horizontally.

Dotplot   A **dotplot** is a preliminary data analysis tool that groups the study data into many small classes or intervals and then shows each data item as a dot on a chart. Dotplots are usually generated by statistical software programs, and they often help analysts compare two or more data sets. You're certainly aware by now of the sales of Fizzy Cola syrup made by 50 Slimline Beverage employees (the data arrayed in Table 3.2). Let's assume, though, that the Slimline sales manager wants to compare the cola syrup sales with the syrup sales of Plum Natural—a carbonated diet drink with a fruit juice component. The sales of Plum Natural syrup by 50 Slimline employees are arrayed in Table 3.7. After entering the sales data for the two soft drink products into a MINITAB program (Data = SlimBoth), the sales manager can use a **DOTPLOT** command to initiate a built-in charting operation. Dotplots for the Fizzy Cola data and the Plum Natural data are shown in *Figure 3.10*. The manager can now see at a glance that cola sales are concentrated just below the 120-litre mark, while the heaviest sales of Plum Natural syrup fall below 80 litres. It's also obvious that the "average" sale of the cola syrup (as measured by both the arithmetic mean and the median) exceeds the "average" sales result obtained with the Plum Natural product. ◆

TABLE 3.7   ARRAY OF LITRES OF PLUM NATURAL SYRUP (SOLD BY 50 EMPLOYEES OF SLIMLINE BEVERAGE COMPANY IN 1 WEEK)

Litres Sold			
58.25	75.00	94.50	111.25
63.50	77.75	96.00	114.00
69.75	78.75	97.00	114.75
69.75	80.00	99.50	116.25
70.00	82.50	100.25	119.50
71.25	84.00	102.50	121.00
71.25	84.50	102.50	125.75
72.50	85.75	102.50	128.00
72.50	87.85	104.00	130.75
72.50	90.75	104.50	130.75
73.75	91.50	106.75	135.00
73.75	91.50	108.00	
74.00	91.50	110.50	

FIGURE 3.10 Dotplot of Slimline Sales.

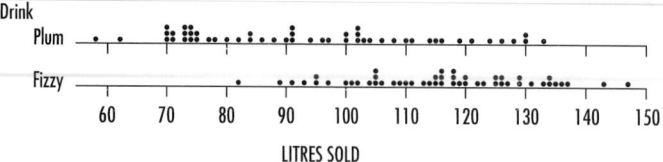

Dotplot for LITRES SOLD

Example 3.8 Obtain a dotplot for the women's average wages as a percentage of men's.

◆ **Solution:**

 Again using MINITAB, we obtained the **dotplot** display of *Figure 3.11*. ◆

FIGURE 3.11 To obtain this MINITAB output, click on **Graph, Dotplot,** enter the column to be graphed in the box below **Variables,** and click **OK.**

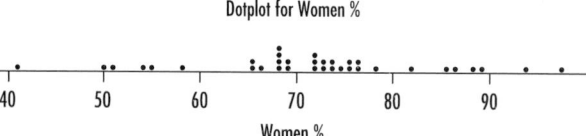

Dotplot for Women %

Example 3.9 **Some Reel Data** There was a suspicion that the lengths of fish differ by gender. Does this appear to be true (Data = DvrSole2)?

◆ **Solution:**

To begin the investigation of this claim, the gender of each fish was identified and the results summarized in the tables that follow.

Male							
331	339	339	340	341	346	347	358
364	366	370	371	371	371	373	374
381	381	384	386	387	387	388	389
390	392	393	394	395	397	398	398
398	403	404	405	408	409	410	410
411	412	413	414	415	417	419	419
420	420	421	423	425	427	436	439
439	451						

Female							
292	316	327	334	337	341	342	345
349	350	351	355	356	357	357	360
361	362	363	364	366	366	369	373
375	376	379	380	382	384	385	386
388	389	390	393	394	400	405	412
442	457						

```
MTB > Stem-and-leaf 'Length';
SUBC> By 'Sex Code'.
Character Stem-and-Leaf Display
Stem-and-leaf of Length   Sex Code = 1   N = 58     Stem-and-leaf of Length   Sex Code = 2   N = 42
Leaf Unit = 1.0                                      Leaf Unit = 1.0

                                                        1    29 2
                                                        1    30
                                                        2    31 6
                                                        3    32 7
        3    33 199                                     5    33 47
        7    34 0167                                    9    34 1259
        8    35 8                                      15    35 015677
       10    36 46                                     (8)   36 01234669
       16    37 011134                                 19    37 3569
       24    38 11467789                               15    38 0245689
       (9)   39 023457888                               8    39 034
       25    40 34589                                   5    40 05
       20    41 0012345799                              3    41 2
       10    42 001357                                  2    42
        4    43 699                                     2    43
        1    44                                         2    44 2
        1    45 1                                        1    45 7
                                            (a)
```

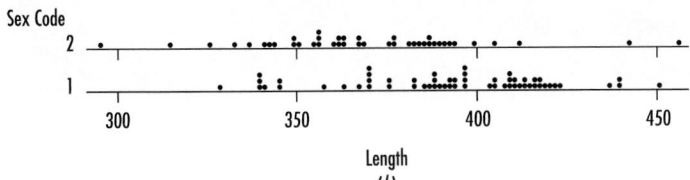

Dotplot for Length

(b)

Several different types of graphs could be used to compare the lengths of the males and females. In *Figure 3.12* there are MINITAB-generated stem-and-leaf displays (3.12*a*) and dotplots (3.12*b*) for the males (coded 1) and females (coded 2). From either, we can see that, in general, the males are indeed longer. ◆

FIGURE 3.12 (*a*) To obtain this MINITAB output, access the **Stem-and-Leaf** Window by clicking on **Graph, Stem-and-Leaf,** click in the square to the left of **By variable,** and in the box to the right enter a column of 1s and 2s, representing the males and females, respectively, then click **OK.** (They have been placed side by side for ease of comparison.) (*b*) Other than clicking **Dotplot** rather than **Stem-and-Leaf,** the sequence of actions is the same as (*a*).

Example 3.10 **Distant Data** Sometimes, graphical displays can produce some surprising and interesting results. The frequency polygon in *Figure 3.13* was created using 6,000 data points from the Voyager Photopolarimeter occulation data provided by

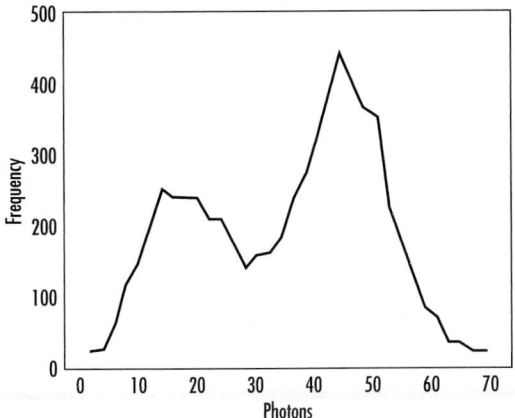

FIGURE 3.13 Frequency polygon of Voyager data.

Graphical methods can be used to unearth (in a manner of speaking) interesting results.

Mark Showalter of NASA's Planetary Data System. These data try to measure the opacity of Saturn's rings by counting the number of photons per 10 milliseconds that passed through the rings from a star. This section of data shows an interesting wave pattern in the rings, followed by a nearly empty gap called the Encke Gap. It's interesting to astronomers as both the wave pattern and the gap itself are caused by a tiny moon called Pan that orbits in the middle of the gap. ◆

Self-Testing Review 3.3

18. *Saskatchewan Traffic Accident Facts 2001* reported the following number of collisions involving a drinking driver for the years 1982 to 2001.

Year	Number of Collisions	Year	Number of Collisions
1982	3,790	1992	1,911
1983	3,596	1993	1,645
1984	3,138	1994	1,648
1985	2,733	1995	1,573
1986	2,823	1996	1,291
1987	3,036	1997	1,419
1988	2,625	1998	1,486
1989	2,288	1999	1,434
1990	1,924	2000	1,344
1991	2,100	2001	1,292

a) Arrange the data in an ascending array.

b) Organize the number of accidents into a frequency distribution table using six classes. Use 1,050 to < 1,550 (collisions) for the first class.

c) Draw a histogram for the frequency distribution.

d) Draw a frequency polygon.

e) Construct a stem-and-leaf display.

19. Cerebral vascular accident (CVA)—otherwise known as stroke—is an interruption of the flow of blood to the brain that's caused either by blockage or by rupture of an artery. CVA may be accompanied by partial or complete paralysis of the arms and legs. Many who suffer from CVA must undergo occupational therapy to rehabilitate paralyzed limbs. An occupational therapist working at a nursing home recorded the number of weeks each of 30 patients, selected from a random sample of CVA patients, underwent occupational therapy. The data are as follows (Data = CVA):

```
8  21  6  9  4  15  10  9  7  9  6  17  8  9  9
2  8  8  3  10  16  13  5  3  2  1  9  4  13  7
```

a) Construct a dotplot of the number of weeks of therapy for victims of CVA.

b) Organize the data items (number of weeks of therapy) into a frequency distribution table using six classes. Use "1 to < 5" weeks for the first class.

c) Draw a histogram for the frequency distribution.

d) Draw a frequency polygon.

e) Construct a stem-and-leaf display using two lines per stem.

20. In 2002, the *Maclean's Guide to Canadian Universities* published the following total number of full-time students at Canadian universities.

University	Full-Time Students	University	Full-Time Students
Acadia	3,679	Moncton	4,529
Alberta	26,875	Montréal	32,030
Bishop's	1,898	Mount Allison	2,274
Brandon	1,788	Mount Saint Vincent	2,125
UBC	24,906	New Brunswick	9,522
Brock	7,213	Nipissing	1,830
Calgary	21,700	UNBC	2,181
Cape Breton (UCCB)	2,651	Ottawa	17,891
Carleton	12,962	UPEI	2,751
Concordia	11,795	Québec/Chicoutimi	2,797
Dalhousie	10,638	Québec/Hull	2,073
Guelph	13,931	Québec/Montréal	18,077
Lakehead	4,952	Québec/Rimouski	1,940
Laurentian	3,711	Québec/Trois-Rivières	5,387
Laval	22,819	Queen's	14,997
Lethbridge	5,540	Regina	6,547
Manitoba	16,554	Ryerson	10,636
McGill	21,024	St. Francis Xavier	3,478
McMaster	13,529	Saint Mary's	5,098
Memorial	12,625	St. Thomas	2,409

University	Full-Time Students	University	Full-Time Students
Saskatchewan	14,676	Western	23,689
Sherbrooke	11,008	Wilfrid Laurier	7,377
Simon Fraser	10,547	Western	23,689
Toronto	42,098	Windsor	9,649
Trent	4,044	Winnipeg	4,368
Victoria	11,350	York	29,235
Waterloo	19,089		

a) Construct a stem-and-leaf display using a leaf unit of 1,000 (ignore the hundreds, tens, and ones places).

b) The University of Toronto and University of Montreal have the most students. Organize the other 50 data items (full-time students) into a frequency distribution table with seven classes. Use "1,500 to < 5,500" for the first class. (Data = Full_Time_Students)

c) Draw a histogram for the frequency distribution.

d) Draw a frequency polygon.

21. Universities are interested in seeing what percentage of undergraduate students finish their degrees in the expected number of years. The 2002 *Maclean's Guide to Canadian Universities* tabulated for each university the percentage of full-time second-year undergraduates who completed their degree within one year of the expected graduation date.

University	Percentage	University	Percentage
Acadia	79.2	New Brunswick	72.4
Alberta	79.4	Ottawa	89.2
Bishop's	74.4	Queen's	92.8
Brandon	54.0	Regina	65.7
Brock	76.6	Ryerson	77.3
Calgary	75.0	Saint Mary's	69.3
Cape Breton (UCCB)	76.9	Saskatchewan	83.0
Carleton	72.1	Sherbrooke	78.0
Concordia	78.6	Simon Fraser	82.3
Dalhousie	88.6	St. Francis Xavier	92.3
Guelph	87.7	St. Thomas	62.7
Lakehead	83.3	Toronto	90.2
Laurentian	69.3	Trent	82.1
Laval	83.2	UBC	90.5
Lethbridge	76.9	UPEI	71.7
Manitoba	76.2	Victoria	80.1
McGill	92.8	Waterloo	81.7
McMaster	87.1	Western	87.7
Memorial	70.7	Wilfrid Laurier	84.9
Moncton	94.6	Winnipeg	72.5
Montréal	88.7	Windsor	81.7
Mount Allison	72.6	York	83.8
Mount Saint Vincent	71.3		

a) Organize the data items (percentages) into a frequency distribution table with nine classes. Use "50 to < 55" for the first class.

b) Prepare a histogram of the frequency distribution.

c) Construct a stem-and-leaf display using two lines per stem.

22. As part of a student project, James Pollard took a sample of 24 nutrition bars and found the caloric content of each. The arrayed data follows (Data = Nutrbars):

130 170 170 180 200 219 220 220 220 225 230 230
230 234 240 250 252 280 296 310 368 440 465 490

a) Prepare a frequency distribution for the caloric content of the nutrition bars using eight intervals. Use "100 to < 150" for the first class.

b) Draw a frequency polygon of the frequency distribution.

c) Prepare a dotplot.

3.4   **Measures of Central Tendency**

A Preview

As seen in Chapter 2, there are several measures of central tendency. The purpose of these measures is to summarize in a single value the typical size, middle property, or central location of a set of values. The most familiar measure of central tendency is, of course, the arithmetic mean, which is simply the sum of the values of a group of items divided by the number of such items. But we also saw in Chapter 2 that the median and mode are other measures of central tendency that are commonly used. *Figure 3.14* shows some possibilities that could exist in different data sets. Suppose in *Figure 3.14a* that we have the monthly sales distributions of two Slimline products—Outrageous Orange (OO) and Rowdy Root Beer (RR). Although the spread of the sales data in each distribution looks the same, it's obvious that the average sales of root beer are greater than the average sales of the orange beverage; that is, the root beer sales are concentrated around a higher value than the orange sales.

The data sets in *Figure 3.14a* have **symmetrical distributions:** If you draw a perpendicular line from the peaks of these curves to the baseline, you'll divide the area of

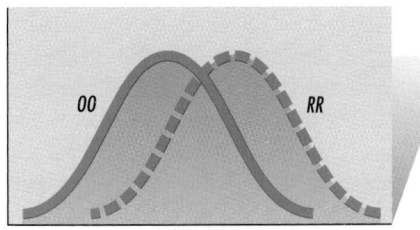

Average of *RR* > average of *OO*;
dispersion the same

(a)

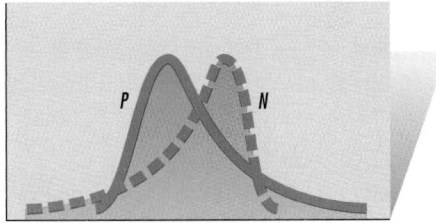

Asymmetrical distributions
(*P* is positively skewed to the right;
N is negatively skewed to the left.)

(b)

FIGURE 3.14 (*a*) Average of *RR* > average of *OO*; dispersion the same. (*b*) Asymmetrical distributions (*P* is positively skewed; *N* is negatively skewed).

the curves into two *mirror image* parts. As you can see in Figure 3.14b, however, curves may be skewed rather than symmetrical. A **skewed distribution** occurs when a few values are much larger or smaller than the typical values found in the data set. For example, distribution *P* in Figure 3.14b might be the curve resulting from Professor Phillips's first statistics test. Most of the test scores are concentrated around the lower values, but a few curve breakers made extremely high grades. When the extreme values tail off to the right (as in distribution *P*), the curve represents a positively skewed distribution (or, skewed to the right). Distribution *N* in Figure 3.14b, on the other hand, might be a curve of the test scores obtained by Professor Neilsen's statistics students. As you can see, most of the students made high scores (although a few unfortunates had extremely low grades). When extreme values tail off to the left (as in distribution *N*), the curve shows a negatively skewed distribution (or, skewed to the left).

Data often have a tendency to congregate about some central value, and this central value may then be used as a summary measure to describe the general data pattern. If the collected facts are to be processed by non-computer methods and are limited in number, an analyst may prefer to work directly with the ungrouped data—facts that haven't been put in a distribution format—rather than group them together in a frequency table. Likewise, if a computer is used, very large lists of ungrouped data can be easily processed in a few seconds without any need for a frequency distribution. But if we're using secondary data that have been compressed into a frequency table to make them more easily understood, we should be able to approximate or estimate the desired measures from the data in that format.

Table 3.8 shows some common symbols. As you can see, a population mean or proportion is designated by μ (mu) or p, while a sample mean or proportion is denoted by $\bar{x}$ or p. Similarly, a commonly used measure of dispersion—the standard deviation—is identified by σ (lowercase sigma) if it's computed from a population and by s if sample data are used.

Measuring Central Tendency

The Arithmetic Mean When people use the word *average,* they're usually referring to the arithmetic mean. And when you have totalled the test grades you've made in a

TABLE 3.8   DISTINCTIONS BETWEEN A POPULATION AND A SAMPLE

Area of Distinction	Population	Sample
Definition	Defined as a total of the items under consideration by the researcher.	Defined as a portion of the population selected for study.
Characteristics	Characteristics of a population are parameters.	Characteristics of a sample are statistics.
Symbols	Greek letters or capitals: μ = population mean σ = population standard deviation N = population size p = population proportion	Lowercase italic letters: $\bar{x}$ = sample mean s = sample standard deviation n = sample size $\hat{p}$ = sample proportion

subject during a school term and divided by the number of tests taken, you've computed the arithmetic mean. The arithmetic mean is the most commonly used measure of central tendency.

Let's review the computation of the mean by considering the statistics grades made by Peter Parker[1] during one agonizing semester. (The grades have been arrayed in a descending order.)

```
75
75
61
50
40
25
10
 5
 1
```
342 Total of all grades

It's customary to let the letter *x* represent the values of a variable (such as Peter's grades). Thus, the formulas to compute the mean are

$$\mu = \frac{\Sigma x}{N} \quad \text{(for a population)} \tag{3.1}$$

$$\bar{x} = \frac{\Sigma x}{n} \quad \text{(for a sample)} \tag{3.2}$$

where μ = arithmetic mean of a population
$\bar{x}$ = arithmetic mean of a sample
Σ (capital sigma) = "the sum of"
N = number of *x* items in the population
n = number of *x* items in the sample

Since, in the case of Peter's grades, Σx is 342, Peter's mean semester grade is 38 (342/N or 342/9 = 38). (These scores represent the population of all grades made by Peter in the course, but if a sample of test scores made by all students in a class had yielded the same data, the sample mean would be exactly the same.)

The Median You've seen that the median is a measure of central tendency that occupies the middle position in an array of values. That is, half the data items fall below the median, and half are above that value. Note that the word *array* has been emphasized; it's necessary to put the data into an ascending or descending order before selecting the

---

[1]A name selected in memory of another loser, Sir Peter Parker, the British naval commander during the Revolutionary Battle of Sullivan's Island outside Charleston, South Carolina. During the battle, while giving orders aboard *HMS Bristol*, Sir Peter had the "unspeakable mortification" to have a cannon ball carry away the seat of his pants. (According to an old ballad, it "propelled him along on his bumpus.")

median value. In the example of Peter's grades, the middle value in the array, and thus the median grade, is 40.

75
75
61
50

40 median

25
10
5
1

The median position—not the median value—is found by using the formula $(n + 1)/2$, where n in this example is 9. Thus, $(9 + 1)/2$ is 5, which is the median position in Peter's grade array. Although the median in this example differs by a small amount from the mean, the ultimate result of using either the mean or the median as the semester average grade is the same—Peter has failed the course. As we saw in the example of the grape-growers' income in the last chapter, however, one or a few extremely high (or extremely low) values in a data set can cause a substantial difference between the mean and the median.

What if Peter's instructor had dropped Peter's lowest grade before computing the median? In that event, the median position is $(8 + 1)/2$ or 4.5. When we have a non-integer position such as 4.5, we take the average of the two nearest numbers, in this case the fourth and fifth numbers. In Peter's grade array the median would be the mean of the two middle scores 40 and 50—that is, the median value would then be 45.

75
75
61

$$50 \quad \frac{50 + 40}{2} = 45$$
$$40$$

25
10
5

The Mode The mode, by definition, is the most commonly occurring value in a series. Thus, in the example of Peter's grades, the mode is 75—a measure that appeals to Peter but not to his professor. Although not of much use in our grade example, the mode may be an important measure to a clothing manufacturer who must decide how many dresses of each size to make. Obviously, the manufacturer wants to produce more dresses in the most commonly purchased size than in the other sizes.

Other Measures In addition to the mean, median, and mode, there are other specialized measures of central tendency that are occasionally used. One measure gaining acceptance is the **trimmed mean,** a compromise between the mean and the median. It is calculated by "trimming," or dropping, the smallest and largest numbers (or the two smallest and the two largest or the three smallest, etc.) from the data set and calculating the mean of the remaining numbers. For example, a 5 percent trimmed mean would be calculated by dropping the smallest 5 percent and the largest 5 percent of a data set and computing the mean of the remaining 90 percent of the original data. A trimmed mean is a compromise in that if you drop none of your data, you get an ordinary mean, while if you drop all but one value, you get the median. For example, trimming the two lowest and the two highest scores from Peter's grades, his trimmed mean would be found as follows:

$$\text{Trimmed mean} = \frac{61 + 50 + 40 + 25 + 10}{5} = \frac{186}{5} = 37.2$$

Example 3.11 What are the mean, median, and mode of the data on women's average wages as a percentage of men's? (See data on pages 41, 44, 45, and 56.)

◆ **Solution:**
The total of all 36 observations is 2,574; therefore,

$$\bar{x} = \frac{2,574}{36} = 71.50$$

The median will be the average of the 18th and 19th values. These are found easily in the stem-and-leaf display of *Figure 3.9* (page 55). The first three lines contain the first 16 values. So the 18th and 19th values are the second and third numbers on the fourth line and both are 72; therefore, the median is 72. This stem-and-leaf display can also be used to find the mode. A quick examination reveals that the value that occurs the most often, five times, is 68; so 68 is the mode. ◆

Example 3.12 **AIDS in the Americas** The table that follows gives the rate of incidence of AIDS per 100,000 in 1995 for the Americas as reported to the World Health Organization (WHO) (Data = AIDSAmer):

Antigua Barbuda	7.3	Anguilla	0.0	Argentina	5.6
Bahamas	131.4	Barbados	44.1	Bermuda	77.2
Belize	4.5	Bolivia	0.2	Brazil	7.3
Canada	4.6	Cayman Islands	17.6	Chile	1.5
Colombia	3.3	Costa Rica	4.7	Cuba	0.8
Dominica	5.7	Dominican Republic	4.0	Ecuador	1.0
El Salvador	6.7	French Guiana	62.5	Grenada	6.7
Guadeloupe	31.9	Guatemala	1.1	Guyana	9.5
Haiti	0.0	Honduras	13.7	Jamaica	13.5
Martinique	14.3	Mexico	4.2	Montserrat	0.0
Netherlands Antilles	0.0	Nicaragua	0.8	Panama	7.2
Paraguay	0.5	Peru	1.7	Saint Lucia	9.1
Saint Vincent	7.1	Saint Kitts & Nevis	10.9	Suriname	4.7
Turks and Caicos Is.	0.0	Trinidad & Tobago	19.7	Uruguay	3.7
USA	22.7	Venezuela	2.4	Virgin Is. (British)	10.0

Describe the central tendency of this data set.

FIGURE 3.15 (*a*) To obtain this MINITAB output, click on **Stat, Basic Statistics, Display Descriptive Statistics,** enter the column to be summarized in the box below **Variables,** and click **OK.** (*b*) To use the TI-83 to calculate a mean and median, first enter the data into a list. Access **STAT** > **Edit** and enter the data into an available list. List **L1** is used in this example. Next access **STAT**>**Calc** and choose **1-Var Stats** from the menu. (See screen 1.) This will paste the command onto the home screen. The cursor will be after 1-Var Stats. Enter **L1** by pressing **2nd key** followed by the **1** key. This tells the calculator that the data is in list **L1.** Press enter and you will see the results in screen 2. The arrow at the bottom of screen 2 indicates that more output can be seen by scrolling down. Doing so results in the information of screen 3.

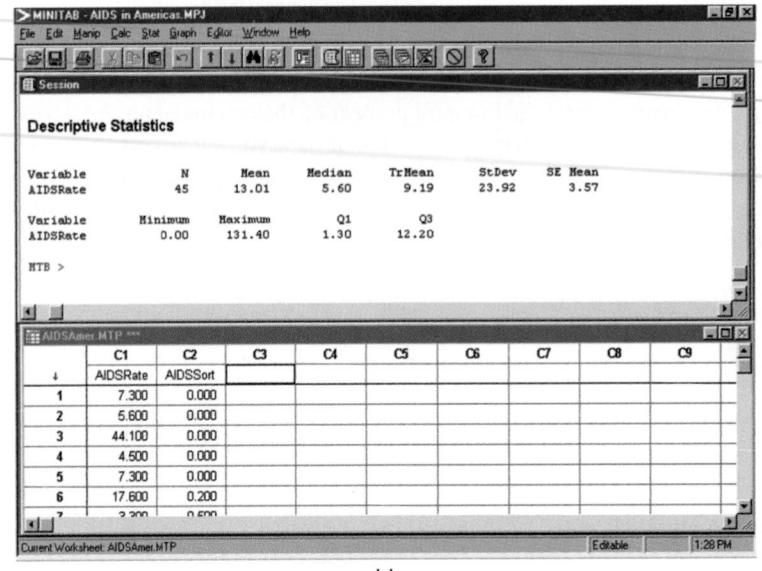

(*a*)

```
EDIT CALC TESTS
1:1-Var Stats
2:2-Var Stats
3:Med-Med
4:LinReg(ax+b)
5:QuadReg
6:CubicReg
7↓QuartReg
```
Screen 1

```
1-Var Stats
x̄=13.00888889
Σx=585.4
Σx²=32794.86
Sx=23.92196425
σx=23.65467135
↓n=45
■
```
Screen 2

```
1-Var Stats
↑n=45
minX=0
Q₁=1.3
Med=5.6
Q₃=12.2
maxX=131.4
```
Screen 3

(*b*)

◆ Solution:

Rather than calculating a single measure of central tendency, often people calculate several measures and compare them. We will examine the measures that MINITAB and the TI-83 calculator easily provide. MINITAB generated the information in *Figure 3.15a*. The mean is 13.01, the median equals 5.60, and the 5 percent trimmed mean is 9.19. A TI-83 calculator produced the screens found in *Figure 3.15b*. The mean, denoted by $\bar{x}$, is again 13.01 (rounded to two decimal places). The median, denoted Med, is equal to 5.6. (See screen 3.) The substantial differences between the mean and the median are the reason it makes sense to report more than one measure of central tendency. The causes of these differences will be discussed soon. ◆

Summary of Comparative Characteristics

There's no general rule that will always identify the proper measure of central tendency to use. In a perfectly symmetrical distribution with a single peak, the issue of which measure to use is simplified because the arithmetic mean, median, and mode have the

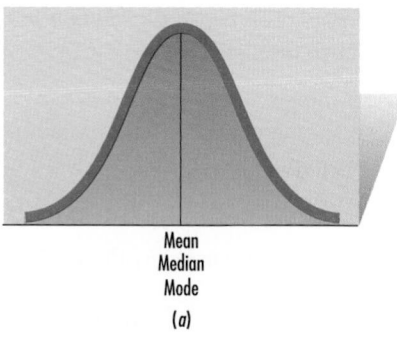

Mean
Median
Mode

(a)

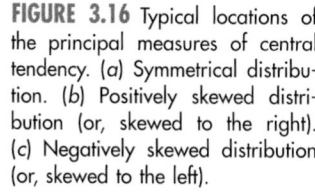

FIGURE 3.16 Typical locations of the principal measures of central tendency. (a) Symmetrical distribution. (b) Positively skewed distribution (or, skewed to the right). (c) Negatively skewed distribution (or, skewed to the left).

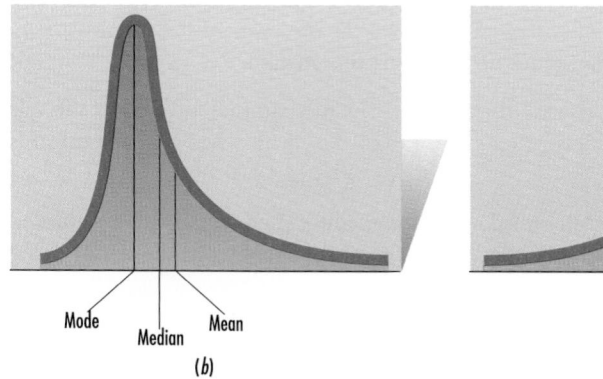

Mode Mean
   Median

(b)

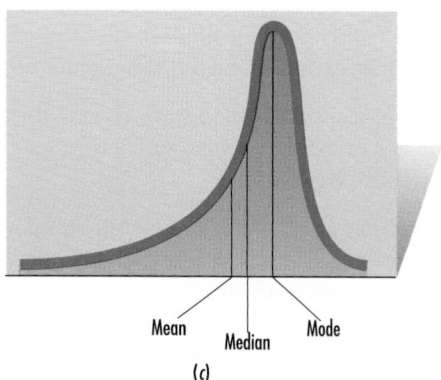

Mean   Mode
   Median

(c)

same value (see *Figure 3.16a*). But if the data produce a skewed distribution, the values of the three measures are different. In a positively skewed distribution, for example, the mode is defined to be under the peak of the curve and has the smallest value; the mean, influenced by the extremely large values, is pulled out from under the peak of the distribution in the direction of those extreme values and has the largest value; the median lies between the mode and the mean (see *Figure 3.16b*). In a negatively skewed distribution, the mode has the largest value and is still found under the peak of the curve; the mean has the smallest value because extremely small data items have been used in its computation; and, again, the median lies between the mode and the mean (see *Figure 3.16c*). In many situations, it is wise to give more than one of these measures to present a more complete picture of the data and its distribution.

A summary of comparative characteristics for each measure follows.

The Arithmetic Mean Some of the more important characteristics of the mean:

1. *It's the most familiar and most widely used measure.* Long explanations of its meaning are thus not usually required.

2. *It's a computed measure that uses the value of every observation.* A change in the value of any observation will change the mean value; however, the mean value may not be the same as any of the observation values.

3. *Its value may be distorted too much by a relatively few extreme values.* Because it is affected by all the values of the variable, the mean (as we saw in Chapter 2) can lose its representative quality in badly skewed data sets. To confirm this, look at the value of the mean and median computed in Example 3.13 (page 68), and then take a look at the original data.

4. *It cannot be computed from an open-ended distribution in the absence of the original raw data.* This point has been discussed earlier.

5. *It's a useful measure when using sample data to make inferences about a population.* As we'll see in Chapters 6 through 8, the mean of a sample of observations is used to estimate the value of the population mean or to test a hypothesis about the population mean.

The Median Some of the important characteristics of the median:

1. *It's easy to define and easy to understand.* The computation and interpretation of the median, as we have seen, isn't difficult.

2. *It's affected by the number of observations but not by the value of these observations.* Thus, extremely high or low values don't distort the median.

3. *It's frequently used in badly skewed distributions.* The median isn't affected by the values of extreme items, so it's a better choice than the mean when a distribution is badly skewed.

4. *It may be computed in an open-ended distribution.* Since the median value is located in the median class interval and since that interval is virtually certain of not being open-ended, the median may be found.

The Mode Some of the characteristics of the mode:

1. *It's generally a less widely used measure than the mean or median.*

2. *It may not exist in some sets of data, or there may be more than one mode in other data sets.*

3. *It's not affected by extreme values in a distribution.*

4. *It can be especially useful when the data is highly skewed or bimodal or multi-modal in nature.*

Example 3.13 **Some Reel Data** Our suspicion that the lengths of fish differed by gender was confirmed in the last section (pages 56–57), where we used graphical techniques to see that the males tended to be longer. See if the measures of central tendency would also support this conclusion.

◆ **Solution:**

Using MINITAB, we obtain the output in *Figure 3.17* in which the mean, median, and trimmed mean are all greater for the males than for the females. We also note that the mean, median, and trimmed mean are very close to each other for the males and also for the females. This suggests a lack of extreme values or a sharp skew in either direction (in which case the mean would be tugged in that direction). ◆

Example 3.14 **How many of us are there?** The United Nations gave the 1996 total population (in thousands) of 225 countries. We used MINITAB to produce the histogram and descriptive statistics in *Figure 3.18*. What can you say based on this information (Data = Populatn)?

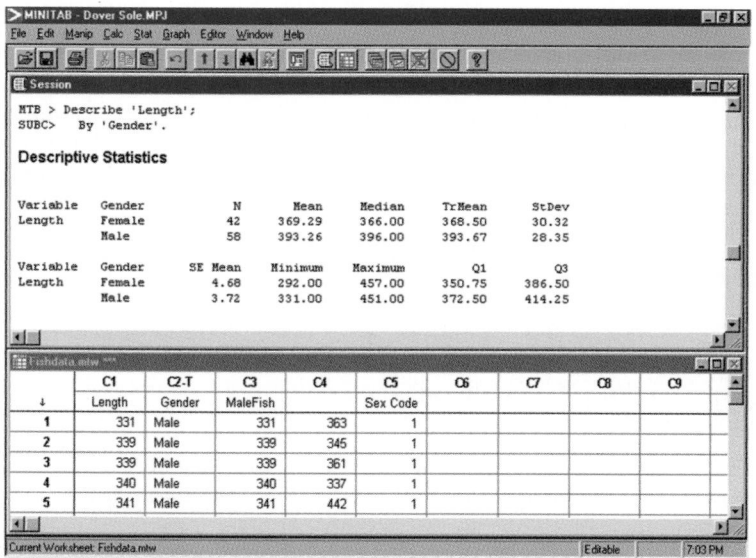

FIGURE 3.17 To obtain this MINITAB output, click on **Stat, Basic Statistics, Display Descriptive Statistics,** enter the column to be summarized in the box below **Variables,** click in the square to the left of **By variable** and to the right enter a column indicating the gender of each fish, and click **OK.**

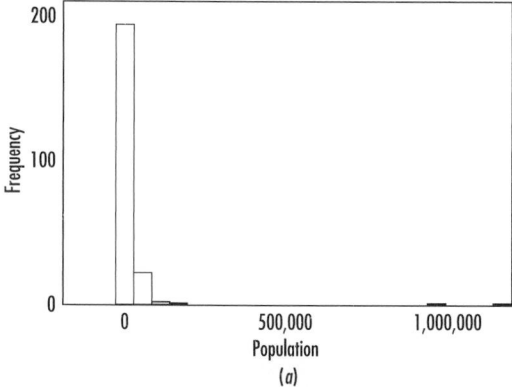

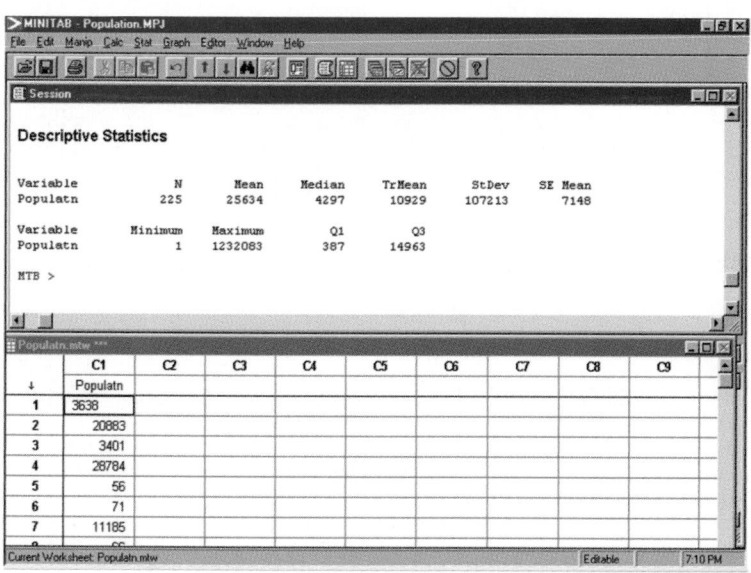

FIGURE 3.18 (a) Histogram and (b) descriptive statistics for population data.

◆ **Solution:**

Notice the differences between the mean, median, and trimmed mean and the two extremely large values around 900,000 and 120,000 (India and China, respectively). The mean is pulled in the direction of these two large values and could give a misleading view as to what value represents a "typical" population. Without the histogram, this difference between the mean and median could be caused by one or more outliers or by an extreme skew to the distribution. Here is a case where it would be best to present both a graph and more than one measure of location in order to present a "true" picture of the population distribution. ◆

Self-Testing Review 3.4

23. Peter Parker's instructor uses a computer to average student grades. One of Peter's classmates has a semester arithmetic mean grade of 84. The instructor has accidentally deleted one of the student's grades from the computer storage medium. The remaining test scores for this student are 92, 76, 66, 95, 80, 79, 89, and 85. What's the value of the missing test score?

24. The number of faulty assemblies per day detected by a quality control inspector during a 15-day period was 57, 34, 39, 32, 35, 40, 27, 34, 29, 18, 20, 32, 25, 60, and 38.

    a) What's the mean number of faulty assemblies for the period?

    b) What's the value of the median?

25. Each year *Money* magazine consultants compile a list of 50 blue-chip stocks. These stocks are analyzed and suggestions are made about which ones to buy, which to hold, and which to sell. In one issue, the consultants recommended 17 "buys" and published this buy list with the quoted prices of each stock (Data = Buys):

Stock	Price	Stock	Price
Syntex	26.25	H. J. Heinz	38.75
Marion Merrell Dow	26.00	Rite Aid	23.00
Eli Lilly	61.25	GM E Shares	28.25
Merck	42.00	Schering-Plough	61.25
Warner-Lambert	66.75	British Telecom	58.00
Borden	27.25	Stanhome	33.00
McGraw-Hill	61.50	Glaxo Holdings	24.75
Abbott Labs	27.75	Hubbell B Shares	51.00
Bristol-Myers	64.75		

    a) Compute the mean price of a share of stock.

    b) Compute the median price of a share of stock.

    c) Organize the data into a frequency distribution with the first class being "20.00 to < 30.00."

    d) Estimate the mean price of a share of stock from the frequency distribution and compare it to the true value.

26. *Saskatchewan Traffic Accident Facts 2001* reported for the years 1991 to 2001 the following number of collisions involving pedestrians or cyclists who had been drinking:

Year	Number of Collisions	Year	Number of Collisions
1991	39	1997	23
1992	29	1998	23
1993	35	1999	33
1994	32	2000	27
1995	23	2001	26
1996	18		

a) Compute the mean number of collisions.

b) Compute the median number of collisions.

c) Compute a trimmed mean by dropping the largest and smallest value and calculating the average of the remaining data.

d) Determine the mode, if there is one.

27. *WordPerfect The Magazine* published the amount of hard drive space (in megabytes) needed by seven popular electronic dictionaries. The data are

American Heritage	3.8	Funk & Wagnall's	5.9
Instant Definitions	2.3	Multilex	12.4
Random House Webster's	8.7	Reference Lib. CD-ROM	0.19
The Writer's Toolkit	7.2		

a) Calculate the mean number of megabytes.

b) Calculate the median number of megabytes.

28. The price (in cents) of one litre of regular gas on May 6, 2003, for several Canadian cities is listed below:

City	Price	City	Price
St. John's	81.3	Windsor	61.1
Charlottetown	73.2	London	66.8
Halifax	70.3	Winnipeg	65.2
Saint John	74.6	Saskatoon	69.9
Fredericton	70.9	Calgary	62.4
Ottawa	66.4	Vancouver	75.9
Toronto	66.9	Sudbury	67.8

a) Calculate the mean gas price.

b) Calculate the median gas price.

c) Determine the mode, if there is one.

29. As part of an experiment conducted in Biology II lab, the air volume exhaled after each student had inhaled fully was measured for the 13 students in the lab. The air volume figures (in litres) are

1.7   3.2   0.5   1.2   1.5   2.6   1.7   0.5   0.5   1.7   0.4   4.4   2.5

a) Calculate the mean air volume exhaled.

b) Calculate the median air volume exhaled.

c) Determine the mode, if there is one.

30. The following table lists seven Canadian Nobel Prize winners and their ages at the time they received the prize:

Name	Frederick Banting	J.J.R. Macleod	Gerhard Herzberg	John Polanyi	Sidney Altman	Michael Smith	Bertram Brockhouse
Year	1923	1923	1971	1986	1989	1993	1994
Age	32	47	67	57	60	61	76

a) Calculate the median age of these Nobel Prize winners at the time they received the prize.

b) Calculate the mean age of these Nobel Prize winners at the time they received the prize.

c) Compute a trimmed mean by ignoring the largest and smallest value and calculate the average of the remaining five values.

31. On July 17, 2002, Statistics Canada reported the crime rates (per 100,000 population) for the following sample of Canadian metropolitan areas in 2001:

City	Total Criminal Code Offences per 100,000 Population in 2001	City	Total Criminal Code Offences per 100,000 Population in 2001
Regina	16,387	Hamilton	7,102
Saskatoon	13,360	Montréal	6,830
Vancouver	11,314	St. Catharines-Niagara	6,826
Winnipeg	10,947	Saint John	6,612
Victoria	9,996	Sherbrooke	6,541
Halifax	9,354	Ottawa	5,946
Edmonton	9,032	Kitchener	5,709
Thunder Bay	8,602	Toronto	5,343
London	7,894	Trois-Rivières	5,094
Sudbury	7,535	Chicoutimi-Jonquière	4,986
Windsor	7,374	Québec	4,986
Calgary	7,137		

Source: Statistics Canada, The Daily, Friday, July 17, 2002, Crime Statistics 2001.

a) Calculate the mean number of criminal code offences per 100,000 population for this sample of metropolitan areas.

b) Calculate a trimmed mean by dropping the two largest and smallest values and computing the mean of the remaining values. In this example, which do you think gives a better measure of the typical crime rate, the mean or the trimmed mean? Explain.

c) Calculate the median number of criminal code offences per 100,000 population for this sample of metropolitan areas.

3.5 Computing Measures of Dispersion and Relative Position

A Preview

What if two data sets have the same average? Does this mean that there's no difference in these sets? Perhaps, but then again, perhaps not. In *Figure 3.19*, distributions X and Y would have the same average, but they're certainly not identical. The difference lies in the amount of spread, scatter, or dispersion of the values in each distribution as measured along the horizontal axis. Obviously, the dispersion in distribution X is greater than the spread of the values in distribution Y.

A **measure of dispersion** is one that measures the variability that exits in a data set. Such measures are usually expressed in the units of the original observations—such as litres sold, dollars earned, or kilometres driven. These measures may be computed for ungrouped data and approximated for data grouped into frequency distributions.

There are at least two reasons for measuring dispersion. The first reason is to form a judgment about how well the average value depicts the data. For example, if a large amount of scatter exists among the items in a data set, the average size used to summarize those values may not be representative of the data being studied. This isn't a new thought; we saw in Chapter 2 the dangers of disregarded dispersions.

A second reason for measuring dispersion is to learn the extent of the scatter so that steps may be taken to control the existing variation. For example, a tire maker tries to produce a product that has a long average life. But the manufacturer also wants to build tires of a uniform high quality so there isn't a wide spread in lifetimes. (You're pleased with the 80,000 km you got from a set of these tires, but I'm really steamed with the 30,000 km I got with my set of the same tires.) By measuring the existing variation, the manufacturer may see a need to improve the uniformity of the product through better inspection and other quality control procedures.

Measuring Dispersion

Three measures of dispersion are often computed from ungrouped data. These measures are the range, the mean absolute deviation, and the standard deviation.

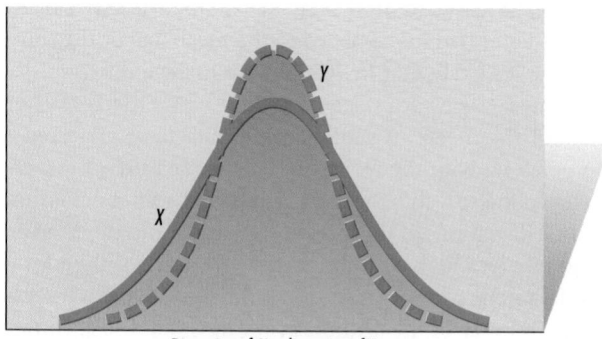

Dispersion of *X* > dispersion of *Y*;
average the same

FIGURE 3.19 Distributions with the same mean and different dispersions.

The Range   The range is the simplest measure of dispersion, and we've seen that it's merely the difference between the highest and lowest values in an array. The range is used to report the movement of stock prices over a time period, or high and low temperature readings for a 24-hour period.

The Mean Absolute Deviation   Let's assume that after his recent academic ordeal our friend Peter Parker decides to use his mechanical skills to rebuild and then sell a pickup truck. Unfortunately, Peter doesn't yet own a truck, and he can't afford newer models or older "collectible" vehicles. What his budget can manage is a clunker in the 15- to 20-year age bracket. A fellow student who works part-time at a vehicle auction house tells Peter that her company is planning sales at two locations. At Peter's urging, his friend reports that the mean age of all pickups to be auctioned at sale A is 19, while the mean age of trucks to be sold at sale B is 31. Peter quickly decides to attend sale A. The actual ages of the trucks to be sold at each auction areas as follows:

Ages of Trucks at Sale A		Ages of Trucks at Sale B	
2		18	
2		19	
2		19	
4		19	
5		19	
7		19	
10		20	
11		20	
11		45	
34		45	
35		46	
35		47	
50		48	
58		50	
266	Total age	434	Total age

$$\bar{x} = \frac{266}{14} = 19 \qquad\qquad \bar{x} = \frac{434}{14} = 34$$

When Peter arrives at the sale A site, he learns to his dismay that all the trucks are likely to be beyond his financial reach. If Peter had looked beyond the mean age of the sample of trucks to be sold at each sale, it's likely that he would have made a different decision. What Peter apparently wanted was a mean age of 19 and very little spread or scatter of the individual ages about the mean. In short, Peter would have preferred a small measure of dispersion to go along with the mean of 19. One measure of dispersion that would have alerted Peter to the spread of ages is the **mean absolute deviation (MAD)**—an average of the absolute deviations of the individual items about their mean. Before tackling this measure, though, let's look at an important property of the mean.

The difference between each data item and the mean of all the data items in a set is called a **deviation.** An important property of the arithmetic mean is that the algebraic sum of all the deviations is always zero. That is, $\sum(x - \bar{x}) = 0$ when we have sample data, and $\sum(x - \mu) = 0$ when we have population values. To illustrate this property, suppose we have the following observations: 2, 3, 4, 7, and 9. The mean of these items is 25/5 or 5. We have done some calculations in the following table.

x	$(x - \bar{x})$	$|x - \bar{x}|$	$(x - \bar{x})^2$
2	−3	3	9
3	−2	2	4
4	−1	1	1
7	+2	2	4
9	+4	4	16
25	0	12	34

As you can see from the total of the second column, $\Sigma(x - \bar{x})$ must equal zero. But since our interest lies in measuring variability, we don't really care whether individual values are above or below the mean—that is, whether the deviations are positive or negative—we are interested only in knowing how far away each value is from the mean. The two most popular methods used to eliminate negatives from any calculations are to take absolute values or to square. In the third column of the table, we take the absolute value of the deviations and add these non-negative values to obtain $\Sigma|x - \bar{x}| = 12$. In the fourth column, we square the deviations and add to produce $\Sigma(x - x)^2 = 34$. So both absolute values and squares eliminate negative values, and each total will be used in a measure of dispersion.

Now let's calculate the mean absolute deviation. To do this, it's necessary to (1) compute the mean of the items being studied; (2) determine the absolute deviation, which is the numeric difference of each item from the mean without regard to the algebraic sign; and (3) compute the mean of these absolute deviations. The appropriate formula is

$$\text{MAD} = \frac{\Sigma|x - \bar{x}|}{n} \quad \text{(for a sample)} \tag{3.3}$$

where MAD = mean absolute deviation
   x = values of the sample observations
   $\bar{x}$ = mean of the sample observations
   $|\ |$ = algebraic signs of the deviations are to be ignored (we consider only absolute values)
   n = total number of sample observations

Table 3.9 shows how to compute the MAD for the ages of pickup trucks to be auctioned at sale B. You can verify that if the signs of the deviations about the mean aren't ignored, the sum of these deviations is zero. Thus, it's impossible to compute the MAD unless absolute values are used. The MAD in our example is 13.57 years. (Would the mean absolute deviation have been larger or smaller if we had computed it for those trucks being sold at auction A?)

Unlike the range, the MAD takes every observation into account and shows the average scatter of the data items about the mean; however, it's still relatively simple to understand and compute.

Example 3.15 We had calculated the mean of the women's average wages as a percentage of men's and found that it was 71.5 (see page 65). With that information, calculate the mean absolute deviation.

TABLE 3.9 COMPUTATION OF THE MEAN ABSOLUTE DEVIATION (PETER PARKER'S PICK)

Ages of Trucks at Sale B (1)	Arithmetic Mean Age (2)	$(x) - (\bar{x})$ (1) – (2)	$|x - \bar{x}|$ |(1) – (2)|
18	31	–13	13
19	31	–12	12
19	31	–12	12
19	31	–12	12
19	31	–12	12
19	31	–12	12
20	31	–11	11
20	31	–11	11
45	31	14	14
45	31	14	14
46	31	15	15
47	31	16	16
48	31	17	17
50	31	19	19
434		0	19

$$\bar{x} = \frac{434}{14} = 31$$

$$MAD = \frac{\Sigma|x - \bar{x}|}{n} = \frac{190}{14} = 13.57 \text{ years}$$

TABLE 3.10 COMPUTATION OF MAD (WOMEN'S AVERAGE WAGES)

Women %	$(x - \bar{x})$	$|x - \bar{x}|$
82	10.5	10.5
76	4.5	4.5
68	–3.5	3.5
85	13.5	13.5
77	5.5	5.5
79	7.5	7.5
73	1.5	1.5
76	4.5	4.5
72	0.5	0.5
69	–2.5	2.5
41	–30.5	30.5
65	–6.5	6.5
77	5.5	5.5
75	3.5	3.5
86	14.5	14.5
72	0.5	0.5
72	0.5	0.5
89	17.5	17.5
68	–3.5	3.5
68	–3.5	3.5
68	–3.5	3.5
68	–3.5	3.5
74	2.5	2.5
54	–17.5	17.5
73	1.5	1.5
74	2.5	2.5
94	22.5	22.5
65	–6.5	6.5
66	–5.5	5.5
58	–13.5	13.5
51	–20.5	20.5
69	–2.5	2.5
50	–21.5	21.5
97	25.5	25.5
55	–16.5	16.5
88	16.5	16.5
		322.0

◆ **Solution:**

Table 3.10 contains the necessary calculations. The total of the third column is 322, so,

$$MAD = \frac{\Sigma|x - \bar{x}|}{n} = \frac{322}{36} = 8.9 \quad ◆$$

The Standard Deviation The standard deviation is also used with the mean, and it is generally the most important and useful measure of dispersion. In a precise sense, the population **standard deviation** is the square root of the average of the squared deviations of the individual data items about their mean. What a tongue twister! In easier-to-understand terms, though, the standard deviation is a measure of how far away items in a data set are from their mean. As we'll see later, usually a majority of the values in the data set will likely fall no more than one standard deviation away from their mean, and only a few will lie more than three standard deviations from the mean.

Like the calculation of the MAD, the computation of the standard deviation is based on, and is representative of, the deviations of the individual data items about the mean of those values. Another similarity with the mean absolute deviation is that, as the actual observations become more widely scattered about their mean, the standard deviation becomes larger and larger. Of course, if all the items in a series are identical in value—that is, if there is no spread or scatter of values about the mean—the standard deviation is zero. We disregarded algebraic signs to calculate the MAD, but to compute the standard deviation we square all deviations to eliminate negative values.

Before we can compute a standard deviation, though, we must determine if our data set represents a population or a sample. We must know this fact so that the correct formula can be used. To calculate the standard deviation for a population we use

$$\sigma = \sqrt{\frac{\Sigma(x - \mu)^2}{N}}$$

(3.4)

where σ = population standard deviation
   x = values of the observations
   μ = mean of the population
   N = number of observations in the population

When a *sample* data set is used, the standard deviation is found with

$$s = \sqrt{\frac{\Sigma(x - \bar{x})^2}{n - 1}}$$

(3.5)

where s = sample standard deviation
   x = values of the observations
   $\bar{x}$ = mean of the sample
   n = number of observations in the sample

As you can see, formulas 3.4 and 3.5 are similar, but a denominator of $n - 1$ (rather than N) is used to compute the sample measure. The sample standard deviation is often used to estimate the value of an unknown population standard deviation, and, as you'll see in Chapter 7, the use of $n - 1$ produces better estimates.

Table 3.11 shows the calculation of the standard deviation for the ages of trucks to be auctioned at sale *B*. These trucks represent a sample of those Peter could consider, so we'll use formula 3.5. The steps in the computation are

1. The arithmetic mean of the data is computed. (We've seen that it is 31.)

2. The mean is subtracted from each individual age in column 1. (See column 3.)

3. The deviations of the individual ages about the mean (column 3) are squared, thus eliminating negative values (see column 4). The squared deviations are then totalled. This total is $\Sigma(x - \bar{x})^2$.

4. Divide the total in column 4 (it's 2,654) by $(n - 1)$—in this case $(14 - 1)$ or 13. The value obtained here (204.15) is the square of the standard deviation and is called the **variance.** The symbols for sample and population variances are s^2 and σ^2, respectively. Take another look at these steps needed to compute the variance, for it's an important statistical measure in its own right. In chapters 7 and 8 we'll see how to estimate and test hypotheses about the population variance, and then in later pages we'll compute the variances of several samples as a part of an *analysis of variance* procedure that's used to see if the arithmetic means of several populations are likely to be equal. Note that although the variance measures the amount of variability that exists about the mean of a data set, it's not expressed in the units of the original data. That is, the variance in our example is 204.15, but this value represents the variability of *squared ages*. Thus, to obtain a measure of dispersion expressed in terms of the original values, the following final step is needed.

TABLE 3.11 COMPUTATION OF THE SAMPLE STANDARD DEVIATION: UNGROUPED DATA (PETER PARKER'S PICK)

Ages of Trucks at Sale B (x) (1)	Arithmetic Mean Age ($\bar{x}$) (2)	$(x - \bar{x})$ (1) – (2) (3)	$(x - \bar{x})^2$ [(1) – 2)]² (4)
18	31	–13	169
19	31	–12	144
19	31	–12	144
19	31	–12	144
19	31	–12	144
19	31	–12	144
20	31	–11	121
20	31	–11	121
45	31	14	196
45	31	14	196
46	31	15	225
47	31	16	256
48	31	17	289
50	31	19	361
434		0	2,654

$$\bar{x} = \frac{434}{14} = 31$$

$$s = \sqrt{\frac{\Sigma(x - \bar{x})^2}{n - 1}} = \sqrt{\frac{2,654}{14 - 1}} = \sqrt{204.15} = 14.29 \text{ years}$$

5. *The standard deviation is computed by taking the positive square root of the variance.* As you can see in Table 3.11, the standard deviation for our example is 14.29 years of age. Would the standard deviation figure have been larger or smaller if we had computed it for the trucks to be sold at auction *A*?

It's not too difficult to use formula 3.5 with a small sample data set. But when many more items are included, the procedure becomes tedious. In that case, you might prefer to use a shortcut variation of formula 3.5 (the symbols haven't changed). Although it can be shown algebraically that the following formula 3.6 is equivalent to formula 3.6, we'll spare you the proof.

$$s = \sqrt{\frac{n(\Sigma x^2) - (\Sigma x^2)}{n(n - 1)}} \tag{3.6}$$

Note: (Σx^2) means to square each of the values of *x* and then compute the sum, and $(\Sigma x)^2$ means to first add the values of *x* and then square the sum.

Table 3.12 shows that this alternative approach yields the same results achieved in Table 3.11. Of course, if you have a statistical software package, you can simply let the computer do the work. In *Figure 3.20*, we can see how MINITAB processed our data. The standard deviation is a built-in function on the TI-83 calculator as well as all other scientific calculators.

TABLE 3.12 AN ALTERNATIVE COMPUTATION
OF THE SAMPLE STANDARD DEVIATION

Ages of Trucks at Sale B (x) (1)	$(x)^2$ (2)
18	324
19	361
19	361
19	361
19	361
19	361
20	400
20	400
45	2,025
45	2,025
46	2,116
47	2,209
48	2,304
50	2,500
434	16,108

$$s = \sqrt{\frac{n(\Sigma x^2) - (\Sigma x^2)}{n(n-1)}} = \sqrt{\frac{14(16,108) - (434)^2}{14(14-1)}}$$

$$= \sqrt{\frac{225,512 - 188,356}{182}} = \sqrt{204.15} = 14.29 \text{ years}$$

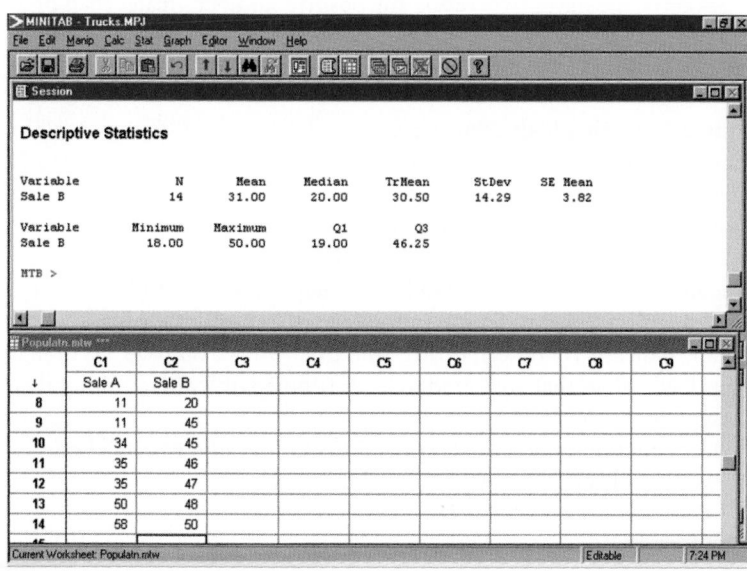

FIGURE 3.20 Output produced by the MINITAB statistical package when supplied with Peter Parker's sale B data set. There are several measures we have not yet seen. MINITAB is programmed to produce a "trimmed" or modified mean (TrMean) that averages the middle 90 percent of the values in a data set. The meanings of Q_1 and Q_3 are discussed later in this chapter. An explanation of SE Mean must wait until Chapter 6.

◼ **Example 3.16**   **AIDS in the Americas** In Example 3.12 (page 65), we found that the mean rate of incidence of AIDS per 100,000 in 1995 for the Americas was 13.01. Obtain the standard deviation of this data set.

◆ **Solution:**

Two possible ways of answering this question are to use either formula 3.5 or 3.6. But, examining *Figures 3.15a* and *3.15b*, we find that MINITAB and the TI-83 calculator, in addition to calculating the measures of central tendency that we have previously considered, also compute several other items, including the standard deviation, denoted as "StDev" by MINITAB and as "Sx" by the TI-83 calculator. Both agree that for this data, $s = 23.92$. ◆

Interpreting the Standard Deviation

We know that dispersion is the amount of spread or scatter that occurs in a data set. If, for example, the values in the set are clustered tightly about their mean, the measured dispersion—in this case the standard deviation—is small. But if we have other data sets where the values become more and more scattered about their means, the standard deviations for those sets become larger and larger. To summarize, then, if a standard deviation is small, the items in the data set are bunched about their mean, and if the standard deviation is large, the data items are widely dispersed about their mean. To drive home this generalization in a more tangible way, let's first consider *Chebyshev's theorem.*

Russian mathematician P. P. Chebyshev has been dead for a century now, but his theorem lives on.

Chebyshev's Theorem

Chebyshev's theorem states that the proportion of *any* data set that lies within k standard deviations of the mean (where k is any positive number greater than or equal to 1) is *at least* $1 - (1/k^2)$.

Thus, if we substitute 2 for k in the theorem, we get $1 - (1/k^2) = 1 - (1/2^2) = 1 - (1/4) = 3/4$, or, in percentage form, $3/4 \times 100 = 75$ percent. This result means that *at least* 75 percent of the items in *any* data set (no matter how skewed it is) must lie within two standard deviations of the mean. And at least 88.9 percent $[1 - (1/3^2)$ or $8/9]$ of the items in *any* data set must fall within three standard deviations of the mean.

Chebyshev's theorem shows us how the standard deviation is related to the scatter of data items. But it tells us only the minimum percentage of items that must fall within given intervals in any data set. We've seen earlier (and in *Figure 3.8* on page 53) though that many data sets have values that are found to be distributed or scattered about their means in reasonably symmetrical ways.

For bell-shaped distributions, known as normal distributions, the *empirical rule* applies and is of greater significance than Chebyshev's theorem.

Empirical Rule

The **empirical rule** for distributions that are generally bell-shaped or normal is that

- About 68 percent of all data items lie within one standard deviation of the mean ($\mu \pm 1\sigma$ or $\bar{x} \pm 1s$).

- About 95 percent of all data items lie within two standard deviations of the mean ($\mu \pm 2\sigma$ or $\bar{x} \pm 2s$).

- About 99.7 percent of all data items lie within three standard deviations of the mean ($\mu \pm 3\sigma$ or $\bar{x} \pm 3s$).

Let's look at an example of an application of this empirical rule. Suppose that many people are given a new type of IQ test, and the resulting raw scores are organized into a frequency distribution. A frequency polygon is prepared from the distribution and is found to be symmetrical in shape. The arithmetic mean of this mound-shaped distribution is 100 points, and the standard deviation is ten points. In this situation, the mean IQ score is directly under the peak of the curve, and the following relationships exist: (1) about 68 percent of the test scores fall within one standard deviation of the mean— that is, about 68 percent of the people have test scores between 90 and 110 points; (2) about 95 percent of the test scores fall within two standard deviations of the mean— that is, about 95 percent of those taking the test have scores between 80 and 120 points; and (3) virtually all (99.7 percent) of the test scores fall within three standard deviations of the mean (scores between 70 and 130). *Figure 3.21* shows these relationships.

The relationships that exist between the mean and the standard deviation in a bell-shaped distribution may also be used for analysis purposes with distributions that are only approximately symmetrical. Let's return to our Slimline Fizzy Cola example and interpret the meaning of the standard deviation of 14.78 litres, since that distribution is approximately normal. We can conclude that about the middle two-thirds of the 50 employees sold syrup quantities between $\bar{x} \pm 1s$, that is, between 115.20 litres $\pm$ 14.78

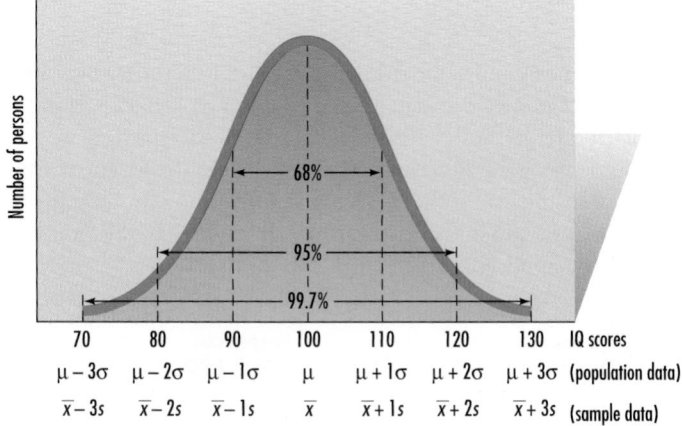

FIGURE 3.21 Illustration of the empirical rule.

litres (or from 100.42 to 129.98 litres). Furthermore, about 95 percent of the employees sold syrup quantities between $\bar{x} \pm 2s$, or between 85.64 and 114.76 litres. You can verify from the data array in Table 3.2 on page 41 that 66 percent of the employees sold between 100.42 and 129.98 litres and that 96 percent of them sold between 85.64 and 144.76 litres. All the 50 employees in our sample sold syrup quantities between $\bar{x} \pm 3s$.

Example 3.17   **AIDS in the Americas** In examples 3.12 (page 65) and 3.16 (page 80) we found that the mean and standard deviation for the rate of incidence of AIDS per 100,000 in 1995 for 45 countries in the Americas were 13.01 and 23.92, respectively. Calculate $\bar{x} \pm 1s$, $\bar{x} \pm 2s$, and $\bar{x} \pm 3s$, and see how well Chebyshev's theorem and the empirical rule describe this data set.

◆ Solution:

In the table that follows, we have the values of k, the intervals $\bar{x} \pm ks$, the fewest number of countries that should be in each interval as given by Chebyshev's theorem, the approximate number of countries as given by the empirical rule, and the actual number of countries in the data set that fell into each interval. Notice that Chebyshev's theorem is always correct. However, sometimes just knowing the fewest possible values that could fall in an interval might not be too informative or descriptive of a data set. Also notice that the empirical rule is far from being correct for $k = 1$ (30.6 vs 41). This is because the data are not normal and, in fact, have a right, or positive, skew. (You might guess there was a lack of normality from knowing that a bell-shaped curve should be able to go three standard deviations on either side of the mean, but $\bar{x} \pm 3s$ goes from −58.75 to 84.77, including negative percents, which are not possible.)

k	$\bar{x} - ks$	$\bar{x} + ks$	Chebyshev's Theorem $\times$ 45	Empirical Rule $\times$ 45	Actual
1	−10.91	36.93	At least $1 - 1/1^2 = 0$	Approx. 68 percent or 30.6	41
2	−34.83	60.85	At least $1 - 1/2^2 = 33.75$	Approx. 95 percent or 42.75	42
3	−58.75	84.77	At least $1 - 1/3^2 = 40$	Approx. 99.7 percent or 44.9	44 ◆

Example 3.18   **Some Reel Data** In several examples, we have looked at the lengths of 100 fish. Let's repeat the process we did in Example 3.17 and calculate $\bar{x} \pm 1s$, $\bar{x} \pm 2s$, and $\bar{x} \pm 3s$ for this sample and see how well Chebyshev's theorem and the empirical rule describe the lengths of these fish.

◆ Solution:

We first computed the sample mean and standard deviation and found that they were 383.19 and 31.38, respectively. Then we calculated $\bar{x} \pm ks$ for $k = 1$, 2, and 3, counted the number of lengths in each interval, and made the following table. This time we find that the empirical rule gives a very good description of the data set. To see the reason, look at *Figure 3.6* (page 52), a histogram of the fish lengths. Examining this graph, you will find that the distribution has a roughly normal or bell shape, the condition necessary for the empirical rule to be applicable.

k	$\bar{x} - ks$	$\bar{x} + ks$	Chebyshev's Theorem $\times$ 100	Empirical Rule $\times$ 100	Actual
1	351.81	414.57	At least $1 - 1/1^2 = 0$	Approx. 68 percent or 68	66
2	320.43	445.95	At least $1 - 1/2^2 = 75$	Approx. 95 percent or 95	96
3	289.05	477.33	At least $1 - 1/3^2 = 88.9$	Approx. 99.7 percent or 99.7	100 ◆

Measures of Position

STATISTICS IN ACTION

A Case of Confusing Comparisons

Suppose Mary Loewen has become so interested in the Slimline Beverage Company that she applies for a job as a salesperson. As part of the screening process for the position, Mary takes a sales aptitude test and scores 135. Does this indicate that Mary has a potential for sales? Even if Mary finds out the average score on this test is 100 so that she knows she is "above average," is she slightly, moderately, or dramatically so? To answer this question, Mary would like to find out how high her score is in relation to everyone else who applies for the job.

One way of identifying whether a value is high or low, good or bad is to convert the value from its original unit of measurement to a new unit called a **z score.** A z score takes a value from a data set and indicates how many standard deviations it is above or below the mean. This process is called standardization, and the resulting z score is sometimes called a **standard score.** The formula to convert a value, x, to its corresponding z score is

$$z = \frac{x - \mu}{\sigma} \quad \text{for a population} \tag{3.7}$$

or

$$z = \frac{x - \bar{x}}{s} \quad \text{for a sample} \tag{3.8}$$

Note that, while the symbols are different, both of these formulas call for subtraction of the mean and division by the standard deviation.

◻ Example 3.19 Mary finds out that the mean score on the aptitude test is 100, while the standard deviation is 25. Convert Mary's score of 135 to its associated z score.

◆ Solution:
Standardizing Mary's score, we calculate

$$z = \frac{x - \mu}{\sigma} = \frac{135 - 100}{25} = 1.40$$

So Mary scored 1.4 standard deviations above average. ◆

One useful property of z scores is that they provide us with a means of comparing values measured in different units.

◻ Example 3.20 While at Slimline, Mary notices that there is a position open in sensory analysis (taste testing). Taking a second aptitude test, this one in sensory analysis, she scores 85. If the mean and standard deviation of this test are 60 and 10, respectively, does Mary appear to have a greater propensity for sales or sensory analysis?

◆ Solution:
Converting Mary's aptitude score in sensory analysis, we obtain

$$z = \frac{x - \mu}{\sigma} = \frac{85 - 60}{10} = 2.50$$

The mean annual earnings of a sample of firefighters is $30,000, and the data show a standard deviation of $800. The mean annual income of a sample of master plumbers is $56,000, and their standard deviation is $1,400. A comparison of these two standard deviations seems to suggest that firefighters' earnings are more uniform while greater income variability exists in the plumbing ranks. Following a dispute among firefighters and plumbers at a local watering hole, a statistics student decided to use the coefficient of variation (CV) to measure the relative dispersion that actually exists among the groups. For the firefighters,

$$\begin{aligned} CV &= s/\bar{x}(100) \\ &= \$800/\$30,000 \ (100) \\ &= 2.67 \text{ percent} \end{aligned}$$

And for the plumbers

$$\begin{aligned} CV &= s/\bar{x}(100) \\ &= \$1,400/\$56,000 \ (100) \\ &= 2.50 \text{ percent} \end{aligned}$$

Thus, the plumbers' annual earnings are actually slightly *more* uniform (there's less relative dispersion) than are the earnings of the firefighters.

So Mary scored 2.5 standard deviations above the mean in sensory analysis, while she scored only 1.4 standard deviations above the mean in sales. It looks like Mary's inclination is more towards tasting than sales. ◆

Another way of describing the position of a value is to see where it stands in relation to all the other values in a set of data. Quartiles and percentiles are two of the most popular measures of position. Unfortunately, there are no universally agreed upon definitions of these terms, so different authors and computer programs often use different procedures and obtain different results.

Informally and intuitively, the kth percentile, P_k, is a value such that k percent of the data are less than or equal to P_k. The following is a more formal definition.

Percentile

The kth percentile, P_k, is a value such that at most k percent of the data are smaller in value than P_k, and at most $(100 - k)$ percent are larger.

The procedure for determining the value of any percentile is as follows:

Calculating P_k, the kth percentile

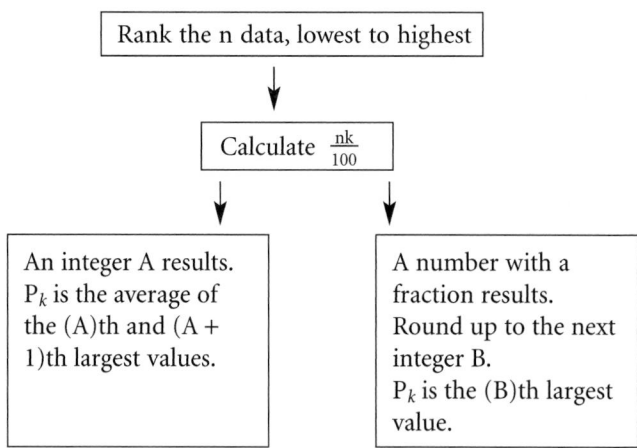

Example 3.21   What is the 40th percentile of the sales of Fizzy Cola Syrup?

◆ **Solution:**

Because there are 50 values in the sales figures, n = 50, and because we want to find the 40th percentile, k = 40. Therefore $\frac{nk}{100} = \frac{50(40)}{100} = 20$. Since this is an integer, the median is halfway between the numbers in the 20th and 21st positions. Examining the data array of Table 3.2 (page 41), we see that the 20th value is 112.00 and the 21st is 113.25. The midway point is found by averaging the two numbers, so

$$P_{40} = \frac{112.00 + 113.25}{2} = 112.63$$ ◆

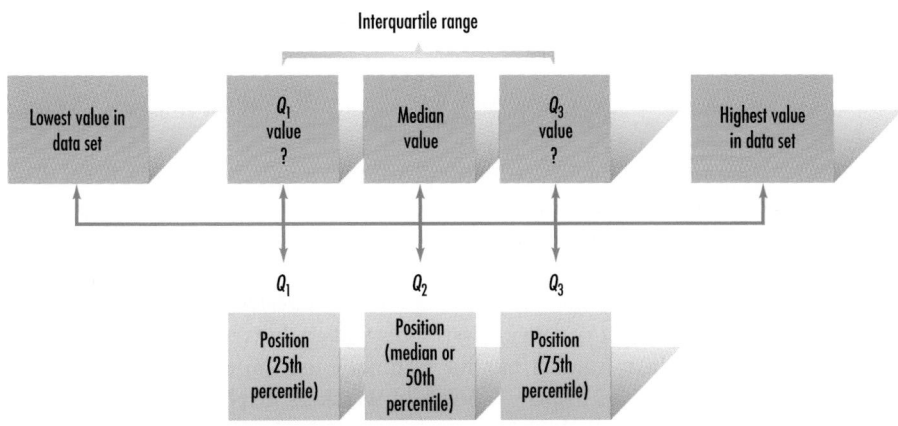

FIGURE 3.22 Illustration of interquartile range.

Using Measures of Position to Describe Dispersion

Recall that the range, defined as the distance between the smallest and largest values, is one measure used to describe dispersion. Another commonly used measure of dispersion is the **interquartile range (IQR),** which is the width of the interval containing the middle 50 percent of the values. The *first quartile,* Q_1, is another name for the 25th percentile, the *second quartile,* Q_2, is another name for the median or 50th percentile, and the *third quartile,* Q_3, is another name for the 75th percentile. The interquartile range is simply the distance or difference between Q_3 and Q_1. *Figure 3.22* illustrates the interquartile range.

The ages of Peter Parker's trucks at Sale B are once again displayed in Table 3.13. To find Q_1, or P25, note that $14(25)/100 = 3.5$, so Q_1 is the number in position 4, which is 19. To find Q_3, or P75, note that $14(75)/100 = 10.5$, so Q_3 is the number in position 11, which is 46. Thus the interquartile range is IQR = $46 - 19 = 27$.

TABLE 3.13   DETERMINING THE INTERQUARTILE RANGE

Ages of Trucks at Sale B

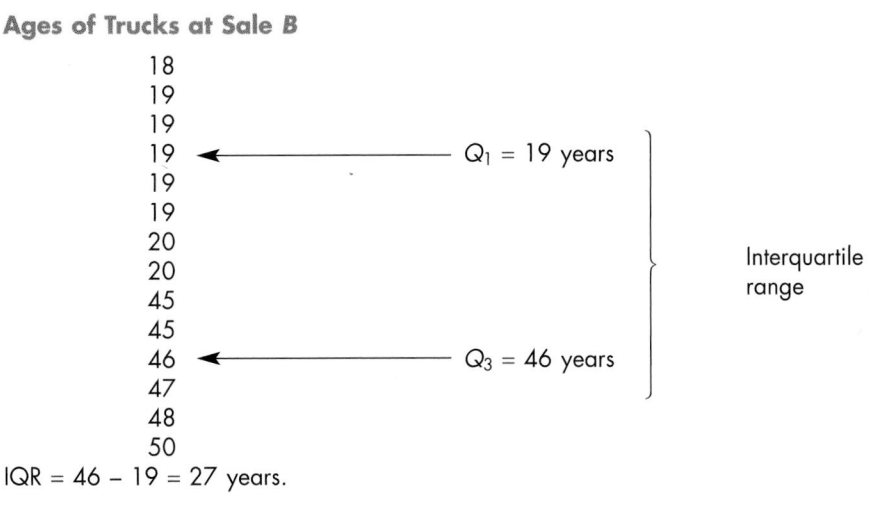

IQR = $46 - 19 = 27$ years.

As mentioned earlier, different books may follow slightly different appproaches, and the results may be slightly different. In *Figure 3.20* (page 79) we saw that MINITAB calculated Q_1 to be 19 and Q_3 to be 46.25. Using these values we would calculate IQR = 46.25 − 19 = 27.25, rather than 27. Slight differences can be expected.

We now know that the middle 50 percent of the trucks range in age from 19 to 46 years, and the interquartile range of 27 years shows that the middle 50 percent of the trucks varied with an age spread of 27 years.

Box-and-Whiskers Display You saw earlier that stem-and-leaf displays and dotplots are exploratory data analysis tools that analysts use to get a feel for the data being studied. Another graphic technique used in exploratory analysis is the box-and-whiskers display. A **box-and-whiskers display** (also called a **boxplot**) shows the middle half of the values in a data set—the values that lie in the interquartile range—as a box and then draws lines, or whiskers, extending to the left and right from the box to indicate the remaining 50 percent of the data items. *Figure 3.23a* shows the boxplot generated by the MINITAB software package when supplied with our Slimline Company data set, and *Figure 3.23b* shows the boxplot generated by the TI-83 graphing calculator for the same data. While MINITAB's boxplot has a vertical orientation and the TI-83's orientation is horizontal, they convey the same information.

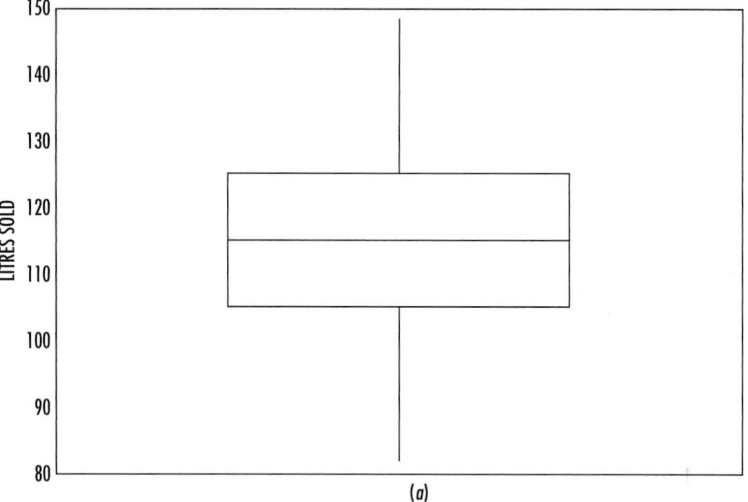

(a)

FIGURE 3.23 (*a*) To obtain this MINITAB output, click on **Graph, Boxplot,** enter the column to be graphed as **Y** in the box below **Graph variables,** and click **OK.** (*b*) To make this TI-83 boxplot, set the **STAT PLOT** window as shown in screen 1. Note we are assuming the data is in L1. Set the window as

Xmin = 80, Xmax = 150, Xscl = 10
Ymin = 0, Ymax = 1, Yscl = 1

(The *y* range is not relevant in making boxplots.)

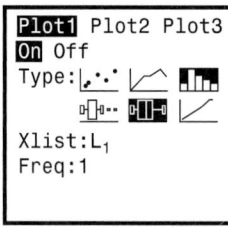

Screen 1

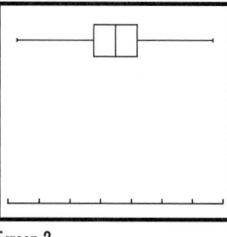

Screen 2

(*b*)

As you can see in either *Figure 3.23a* or *Figure 3.23b*, the box is a rectangle. The line inside the box shows the median location. Each end at the box is called a **hinge.** For our purposes, the left or **lower hinge** of a box is basically the same as Q_1, and the right or **upper hinge** is essentially the same as Q_3. (Different approaches are used in texts and software packages to define and calculate hinges and quartiles. The results are only slightly different, so we'll not go into these details.) To understand hinge terminology a little better, try this experiment: (1) Put a column of evenly spaced and arrayed numbers on a sheet of paper, with the lowest value placed at the top edge and the largest value placed at the bottom edge of the sheet. (2) Fold the paper in the middle so it's half as long. (3) Now fold the paper in the middle again, crease it, and then unfold it to its original shape. You'll find that the two outer creases—or hinges—should be about where the Q_1 and Q_3 data values are located, and the middle crease should locate the median. In other words, in this experiment the median divides the entire data set into a lower and upper half; the lower hinge is the median of the lower half, and the upper hinge is the median of the upper half.

The boxplot thus gives analysts a quick pictorial representation of what's sometimes called a **five-number summary** of the data set. As we've seen, these numbers are the median, the two hinges, and the smallest and largest values. Boxplots can also tell at a glance if a data set is reasonably symmetrical, or if it's skewed. How? A median mark that's about in the centre of the box, as it is in the plot in *Figure 3.23*, tells the analyst that the data set is reasonably symmetrical. But a median mark that's closer to the upper hinge indicates negative skewness, while a mark that's closer to the lower hinge suggests positive skewness. Also, skewness is indicated if one whisker line is appreciably longer than the other. For example, a longer upper whisker suggests positive skewness. Data items that are extremely large or extremely small compared to the rest of the data set are called outliers, and these outliers are often identified by special symbols (for example, an asterisk) on the boxplot.

Example 3.22   **AIDS in the Americas** What information can be ascertained about the AIDS data by looking at its five-number summary and box-and-whiskers display?

◆ **Solution:**

The five-number summary is part of MINITAB's descriptive statistics output and is given for the AIDS data in *Figure 3.15* on page 66. Combining these with the box-and-whiskers display of *Figure 3.24*, we can see a positive skew combined with outliers, indicating that the AIDS epidemic has struck several countries more severely than others. ◆

Example 3.23   **Some Reel Data** We have looked at stem-and-leaf displays and dotplots for the lengths of fish broken down by gender. Now compare the male and female fish by creating side-by-side box-and-whisker displays of the lengths for the two genders.

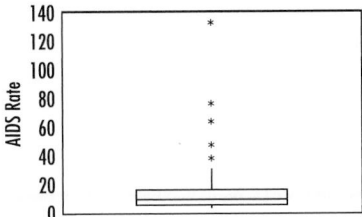

FIGURE 3.24 MINITAB boxplot of AIDS data.

FIGURE 3.25 (*a*) To obtain this graph, access the **Boxplot** Window by clicking on **Graph, Boxplot,** enter the length column as the *Y* (*measurement*) variable and the gender column as the *X* (*category*) variable, then click **OK.** (*b*) We put the female lengths in list **L1** and the males in **L2.** Set up two STAT plots, one for each gender. Access **STAT PLOT** by pressing **2nd** followed by Y=. Then choose **Plot 1** and set it as shown in screen 1. Next access **STAT PLOT** again, choose **Plot 2** and set it as in screen 2. Next we need to set the scale on the axes using the **WINDOW** key. Set the window as

Xmin = 275, Xmax = 475,
Xscl = 25
Ymin = 0, Ymax = 3, Yscl = 1

Xmin and Xmax are chosen to cover the range of the data. The values of Ymin and Ymax do not affect the graph. Press **GRAPH** to plot. Then **TRACE** will allow you to see the key values in the boxplot. Note that in the upper left corner of the screen you can see which plot is currently being traced.

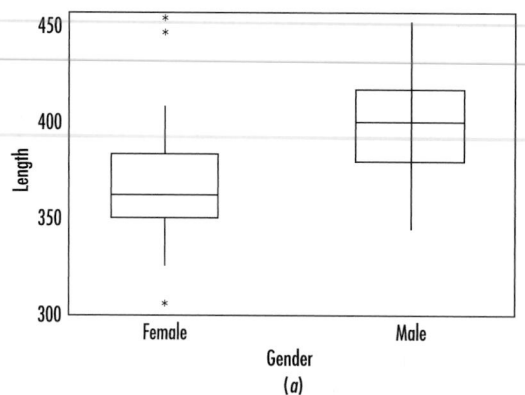

(*a*)

Screen 1

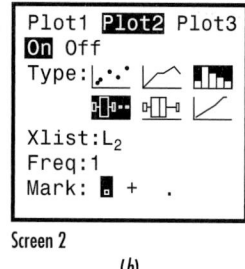

Screen 2

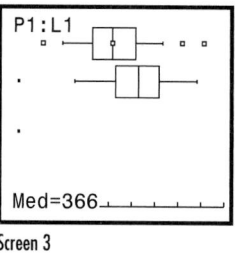

Screen 3

(*b*)

◆ **Solution:**

Figure 3.25a contains a MINITAB-generated side-by-side box-and-whisker display for the female and male fish, while screen 3 of *Figure 3.25b* contains a similar display created by a TI-83 calculator. From either display, it is easy to see the tendency of the males to be longer, as well as how much the lengths overlap. ◆

Summary of Comparative Characteristics

There's no rule that will always identify the proper dispersion measure to use. In picking a measure, the characteristics of each must be considered, and the type of data available must be evaluated. A summary of comparative characteristics for each measure of dispersion discussed in the preceding pages is given below.

The Range Some of the characteristics of the range include the following:

1. *It's the easiest measure to compute.* Since its calculation involves only one subtraction, it is also the easiest measure to understand.

2. *It emphasizes only the extreme values.* Because the more typical items are completely ignored, the range may give a very distorted picture of the true dispersion pattern.

The Mean Absolute Deviation Some of the characteristics of the MAD include the following:

1. *It gives equal weight to the deviation of every observation.* Thus, it's more sensitive than measures such as the range or quartile deviation that are based on only two values.

2. *It's an easy measure to compute.* It is also not difficult to understand.

3. *It's not influenced as much by extreme values as the standard deviation.* The squaring of deviations in the calculation of the standard deviation places more emphasis on the extreme values.

4. *Its use is limited in further calculations.* Because absolute values are used, the average deviation is not as well suited as the standard deviation for further computations.

5. *It can't be approximated from an open-ended distribution.*

The Standard Deviation Included among the characteristics of the standard deviation are the following:

1. *It's the most frequently encountered measure of dispersion.* Because of the mathematical properties it possesses, it's more suitable than any other measure of dispersion for further analysis involving statistical inference procedures. We shall use the standard deviation extensively in later chapters.

2. *It's a computed measure whose value is affected by the value of every observation in a series.* A change in the value of any observation will change the standard deviation value.

3. *Its value may be distorted too much by a relatively few extreme values.* Like the mean, the standard deviation can lose its representative quality in badly skewed data sets.

4. *It can't be approximated from an open-ended distribution.* As formulas 3.4 and 3.5 show, if the mean cannot be computed, neither can the standard deviation.

The Interquartile Range Some of the characteristics of the interquartile range include the following:

1. *It's similar to the range in that it's based on only two values.* As we've seen, these two values identify the range of the middle 50 percent of the values.

2. *It's frequently used in badly skewed data sets.* The interquartile range will not be affected by the size of the values of extreme items, and so it may be preferable to the average or standard deviation when a data set is badly skewed.

3. *It may be computed in an open-ended distribution.* Since the upper and lower 25 percent of the values are not considered in the computation of the interquartile range, an open-ended distribution presents no problem.

4. *It's not affected by extreme values in a distribution.*

Example 3.24 **Some Reel Data** Previously, we compared the lengths of male and female fish using various graphs and numerical measures. Box-and-whiskers displays for the lengths of each gender are given in *Figure 3.25*. See if these give any additional information about the lengths. Then use these graphs and the descriptive statistics of *Figure 3.17* (page 69) to compare the variability of the lengths.

◆ **Solution:**

Figure 3.25 makes the tendency of the males to be longer clear. We can see that the two largest females are outliers, and, other than these two outliers, about 25 percent of the males (those in the top whisker) are longer than all the other females.

From *Figures 3.17* and *3.25*, we can see that there is little difference in the variability of the lengths for the males and females. The standard deviations, 28.35 and 30.32, are close, with the females being slightly more variable. The interquartile ranges,

$$414.25 - 372.50 = 41.75 \text{ and } 386.50 - 350.75 = 35.75$$

are also close, with slightly greater variability indicated for the males. So there is little indication of a difference in the variability of the genders, as also is indicated by the box-and-whiskers displays. While the males' box-and-whiskers display is higher because of the greater average length, the size or spread of the boxes is very close, indicating similar amounts of variability. ◆

Self-Testing Review 3.5

32. Let's suppose that Peter Parker repeats the statistics course, and this time his grades are:

50   85   45   60   1   85   50   85   55

   a) What is the population mean of this set of grades?

   b) What is the range of Peter's grades?

   c) What is the value of the mean absolute deviation?

   d) What is the value of the population variance?

   e) What is the value of the population standard deviation?

33. There are nine branches of The Gap in a local area. Each day the manager takes a "midday read" of store sales in the area. One day the midday read for the nine stores is

$1,256   2,726   1,224   2,588   3,294   1,893   2,537   3,177   2,460

   a) Calculate the mean midday read.

   b) Find the range.

   c) Compute the sample variance.

   d) Compute the sample standard deviation.

   e) Compute the z score for a midday read of $1,256.

34. *Consumer Reports* has described the fuel economy of various sports cars. These cars and their fuel ratings (litres per 100 km) are

Mazda MX-6	9.4	Hyundai Scoupe	7.4
Dodge Stealth	11.8	VW Corrado	9.4
Toyota Celica	8.7	Isuzu Impulse	8.1
Mazda Miata	7.8	Geo Storm	8.1
Toyota MR2	8.4	Mercury Capri	8.4
Mitsubishi Eclipse	8.1		

a) Calculate the sample variance.

b) Obtain the sample standard deviation.

c) Compute the z score for a Dodge Stealth.

d) Compute the z score for a Geo Storm.

35. *Fortune* magazine has identified a list of ten top–rated publishing and printing companies. A numerical rating was given to each company based on such characteristics as quality of management, quality of products or services, innovativeness, and so on. The companies and their ratings are

Company	Score	Company	Score
Berkshire Hathaway	7.92	R. R. Donnelley	6.94
Reader's Digest	7.14	New York Times	6.67
Gannett	7.12	Tribune	6.67
Dow Jones	7.04	Times Mirror	6.66
Knight-Ridder	6.95	McGraw-Hill	5.95

a) Find the range.

b) Compute the sample mean.

c) Obtain the sample standard deviation.

d) Compute the standard score of McGraw-Hill.

e) Compute the standard score of Gannett.

f) What is the first quartile?

g) What is the 80th percentile?

36. The March 18, 2002, issue of *Forbes* magazine listed 497 billionaires from around the world. The table below is a list of ten Canadian billionaires by net worth:

Name	Net Worth ($billions)	Name	Net Worth ($billions)
K. Thompson and family	14.9	Jeffrey Skoll	2.2
G. Weston and family	4.2	Jim Pattison	2.0
J., A. and J. Irving	4.1	Eugene Melnyk	1.8
Charles Bronfman	2.5	Wallace McCain	1.7
Bernard Sherman	2.5	Paul Desmarais	1.6

a) Calculate the range.

b) Calculate the standard deviation (assuming this data set is a population).

c) Calculate the standard deviation (assuming this data set is a sample).

d) Assuming the data set is a population, compute the standard score of G. Weston and family.

e) What is the third quartile?

f) What is the 20th percentile? Interpret your result in the context of the question.

37. A psychologist administered a verbal aptitude test and calculated the mean and standard deviation as 64.4 and 5.78, respectively.

   a) At least 75 percent of the scores will fall between what two values (use Chebyshev's theorem)?

   b) At least 89 percent of the scores will fall between what two values?

   c) If it is known that the distribution of these scores is symmetrical and bell shaped, use the empirical rule to determine the range of scores of the middle 68 percent of those who took the test.

   d) Use the empirical rule to determine the range of scores that would include the middle 95 percent of those who took the test.

   e) Use the empirical rule to determine the range of scores that would include the middle 99.7 percent (almost all) of those who took the test.

38. The lifetimes of batteries of a certain type have an average of 55 months and a standard deviation of 3 months.

   a) The lifetimes of at least 75 percent of the batteries would fall between what two values (use Chebyshev's theorem)?

   b) The lifetimes of at least 89 percent of the batteries would fall between what two values?

   c) If it is known that the distribution of these lifetimes is symmetrical and bell-shaped, use the empirical rule to determine the range of months that would include about 68 percent of the lifetimes.

   d) Use the empirical rule to determine the range of months that would include about 95 percent of the lifetimes.

   e) Use the empirical rule to determine the range of months that would include about 99.7 percent of the lifetimes.

39. As part of a class project, Bob Cantu examined a questionnaire sent to 50 universities' head basketball coaches. Twenty-five responded. The data that follow are the number of years each had been coaching at their university (Data = Coachyrs):

7 6 8 5 9 4 7 7 6 6 13 2 1 20 1 1 7 6 7 5 8 4 8 3 6

   a) Calculate the sample mean years of coaching.

   b) What is the range of values?

   c) Compute the mean absolute deviation.

   d) Calculate the sample variance and standard deviation.

   e) Obtain the standard score for ten years of coaching.

   f) What is the 90th percentile??

   g) What are the values of Q_1 and Q_3?

   h) Obtain the interquartile range.

40. The following listing (from the CAUT *Almanac of Post-Secondary Education in Canada, Second Edition, January 2003*) shows University Research Income (in millions of dollars) for a sample of Canadian universities in 2000 and 2001.

University	Research Income in 2001 ($millions)	Research Income in 2000 ($millions)
Toronto	469.632	371.705
Montreal	349.542	213.104
McGill	280.267	234.340
Alberta	240.548	206.667
UBC	193.432	165.992
Laval	187.383	168.382
McMaster	184.845	106.892
Calgary	172.101	134.507
Ottawa	150.813	114.567
Western	131.585	108.887
Guelph	106.338	96.697
Manitoba	101.570	76.016
Saskatchewan	101.442	71.813
Queen's	101.365	83.217
Waterloo	72.902	70.323
Dalhousie	70.260	77.130
Carleton	46.214	28.481
Victoria	41.573	30.647
Sherbrooke	41.481	44.153
Memorial	34.278	33.986
York	27.859	28.976
Simon Fraser	25.414	25.479
New Brunswick	21.949	24.202
Concordia	20.675	14.965
Windsor	13.279	10.866
Regina	13.034	9.932
Laurentian	11.762	7.127

a) Calculate the mean and standard deviation for the sample of university research incomes in 2000.

b) Calculate the mean and standard deviation for the sample of university research incomes in 2001.

c) Obtain the z scores for university research incomes of $120 million in 2000 and $150 million in 2001.

d) The z score for $120 million in 2000 is greater than the z score for $150 million in 2001. Why?

e) Use Chebyshev's theorem and the values of the mean and standard deviation to analyze the distribution of university research incomes in 2001.

41. The following are the figures for absences in Dr. Flower's environmental science class:

Days Absent	No. of Students
1 to <4	9
4 to <7	6
7 to <10	13
10 to <13	9
13 to <16	1

What is the median class for the number of days absent?

42. The following are the daily sales figures for September at The Children's Place at the Willow Grove Mall (Data = Kidplace):

Date	Sales (In $)	Date	Sales (In $)
1	2,300	16	1,480
2	2,677	17	1,412
3	3,312	18	1,888
4	3,876	19	3,972
5	9,194	20	2,401
6	4,909	21	3,101
7	5,358	22	2,080
8	2,843	23	2,446
9	3,107	24	2,892
10	3,290	25	3,811
11	3,753	26	8,244
12	5,113	27	3,348
13	3,603	28	3,034
14	2,594	29	2,926
15	2,482	30	2,753

a) Prepare a frequency distribution of these sales figures with six classes. Use "$750 to < $2,250" for the first class.

b) Find the median sales figure and the values of Q_1 and Q_3.

c) What is the value of the 80th percentile?

3.6 Summarizing Qualitative Data

You'll remember from *Figure 3.1* (page 38) that data are found in attribute and numerical forms. Attribute data deal with some non-numeric quality or category (the colour of cars in a parking lot, the makes of those cars, the province or territory of birth of a person born in Canada). Numeric code numbers can be given to car colours, car makes, and birthplaces, but using these numbers to compute averages would be meaningless. Thus, we've been concentrating in this chapter on the second data category—numerical data—which does allow us to compute summary measures of central tendency and dispersion.

There is, however, a way that attribute data may be summarized so that meaningful arithmetic operations are possible. The key is to measure the relative frequency with which a particular characteristic occurs. This measure, used to summarize attribute or qualitative data, is the *proportion,* and it is used extensively in later chapters.

If, for example, a machine produces 250 parts and a quality control check shows that 21 of the parts are defective, the proportion of defective parts is (21/250) or .084. This proportion can be used in an analytical approach to give a production manager help in deciding if corrective action is needed. And if a candidate receives 540 votes in a poll of 1,200 voters before an election—that is, the candidate gets (540/1,200) or .45 of the poll votes—the candidate's campaign manager can use this qualitative summary measure for analysis and planning purposes. Similarly, a television executive whose program is watched in 252 of the 900 homes surveyed (that is, in .28, or 28 percent of the homes) at the time the program is aired can also use this proportion to make future programming decisions. We'll summarize qualitative data as proportions in this book. A percentage, of course, is obtained simply by moving the percentage decimal point two places to the right. Thus, .28 is 28 percent in percentage terms.

Example 3.25 **Top Ten Movies Ever—Worldwide** The *Movie Times* has compiled a list of the top gross-earning movies worldwide (until April 8, 2003). The following are the top ten movies:

Movie	Year	Gross ($ millions)
Titanic	1997	1835
Harry Potter and the Sorcerer's Stone	2001	968.7
Star Wars: Episode I—The Phantom Menace	1999	925.5
Jurassic Park	1993	920
The Lord of the Rings: The Two Towers	2002	872.5
The Lord of the Rings: The Fellowship of the Ring	2001	860
Harry Potter and the Chamber of Secrets	2002	858.5
Independence Day	1996	813.1
Spider-Man	2002	806.7
Star Wars	1997	797.9

Calculate the total gross earnings of these ten movies and calculate the percentage of this total earned by each movie.

◆ **Solution:**

As we often do, we let the computer do the work. In *Figure 3.26*, not only did MINITAB calculate the percentages, it drew a graph of the percentages called a pie chart in which each "slice" of the pie is proportional in size to the percentage earned by each movie. ◆

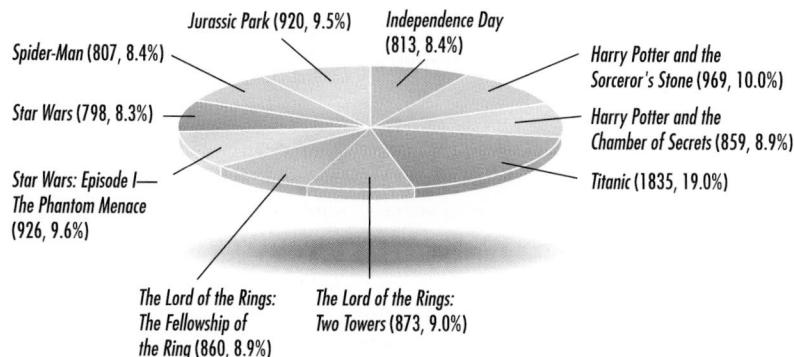

FIGURE 3.26 To obtain this MINITAB output, click on **Graph, Pie Chart,** click in the circle to the left of **Chart table,** enter a column containing the names of the movies in the box to the right of **Categories in** and a column containing the earnings of each movie in the box to the right of **Frequencies in,** and click **OK.**

Self-Testing Review 3.6

43. A quality control officer keeps records on each batch of microchips. The records for one day are as follows:

	Batch 1	Batch 2	Batch 3	Batch 4	Batch 5
Number defective	23	17	8	35	26
Number not defective	152	162	97	258	174

Determine the percentage of defective microchips in each batch.

44. It was reported that of 310 colleges and universities, 31 are public 4-year institutions, 107 are public 4-year schools, 142 are private 4-year schools, and 30 are private 2-year institutions. What proportion of the total is represented by each type of institution?

45. In "Dexamethasone as Adjunctive Therapy in Bacterial Meningitis" (*Journal of the American Medical Assoc.*, 1997), McIntyre et al. reported that, of 260 cases of *Haemophilus* influenza type *b* treated with dexamethasone, eight people suffered severe hearing loss. In 233 cases not treated with dexamethasone, 27 people suffered severe hearing loss. What percentage suffered severe hearing loss in each group?

46. A survey was conducted concerning a complete ban of smoking in public and commercial buildings. In the survey, 20 of 147 smokers reported that they supported the smoking ban in bars, while 349 of 553 non-smokers said that they supported the smoking ban in bars. What is the percentage that support the smoking ban in bars in each group?

47. A survey of 50 city employees was conducted. One question asked employees to indicate the type of exercise they enjoyed, where they were allowed to check as many types as they wanted. The results are as follows:

Exercise	Walking	Jogging	Running	Cycling	Swimming	Dancing	Other
Number	35	8	5	23	20	7	22

Determine the percentage each type of exercise is selected in the survey.

LOOKING BACK

1. Data may be classified in either attribute or numerical categories. Attribute or qualitative data are names that reveal nothing about size or rank. Numerical data consist of variables that are counted or measured. A discrete variable has a countable or limited number of values, while a continuous variable is one that may assume any one of the countless number of values along a line interval. The value of a continuous variable is typically found with an instrument that can measure the variable to some predetermined degree of accuracy. Categorical variables are qualities such as brand or colour that vary from item to item.

2. Statistical description begins with the collection of raw data. These unorganized facts may then be arranged in some systematic order. One simple device for organizing raw data is the data array—an arrangement of data items in either an ascending or descending order. A frequency distribution is a tool for grouping data items into classes and then recording the number of

items that appear in each class. The compression of data into a frequency table results in some loss of information, but an analyst may gain new insight into the data patterns that exist. It's usually desirable to consider several rules when creating a frequency distribution. For example, the number of classes used to group the data generally varies between 5 and 18. Classes must be selected so that all data items are included, and each item must be assigned to only one class. Whenever possible, class intervals should have equal widths, and open-ended classes should be avoided. If possible, the distribution should be designed so that any data concentration points fall at the class midpoints.

3. A graphic presentation of the data found in a frequency distribution can show trends or relationships that might be overlooked in a table, and such graphs are more likely to get the attention of casual observers. A histogram is a bar graph of a frequency distribution. Statistical software packages are programmed to produce histograms of user-supplied data sets. A frequency polygon is a line chart of a frequency distribution and is thus an alternative to the histogram. The stem-and-leaf display, an exploratory data analysis tool, looks like a histogram, but the plot includes the actual data. Another exploratory data analysis tool—the dotplot—shows each data item as a dot on a chart. Dotplots are often used to compare two or more data sets.

4. The properties of frequency distribution data may be summarized and described by measures of central tendency and dispersion. Skewness may also be present. In this chapter we've looked first at the computation of measures of central tendency such as the mean, median, and mode. In selecting the proper average to use, the characteristics of each measure must be considered, and the type of data available must be evaluated. The mean, for example, is the most familiar measure, is affected by the value of every observation, can be distorted by extreme values, and cannot be found from an open-ended distribution. The median is easy to understand, isn't affected by extreme values, and can be used in badly skewed or open-ended distributions. The mode is not affected by extreme values, but it's not used as much as the mean or median, and it may not exist in some data sets.

5. A measure of dispersion gauges the variability that exists in a data set, and it's usually expressed in the units of the original observations. Such a measure is needed to form a judgment about the reliability of the average value and to learn the extent of the scatter of the observations so that steps may be taken to control the existing variation. Three measures of dispersion for ungrouped data are the range, mean absolute deviation, and standard deviation. The standard deviation is a measure of how far items in a data set are from their mean. Before a standard deviation can be computed, it must be known if the data set represents a population or a sample so that the correct formula can be used. The primary measure of dispersion for grouped (or ungrouped) data is the standard deviation. If a frequency distribution is bell-shaped (normal) or approximately so, about two-thirds of the items in the distribution lie within one standard deviation of the mean, about 95 percent of the items fall within two standard deviations of the mean, and virtually all of the observations are within three standard deviations of the mean. Measures of relative position can also be useful to help understand a data set. A z or standard score gives distance from the mean expressed in units of number of standard deviations. A percentile indicates the percentage of a data set that is less than the percentile's value. The interquartile range measures the existing dispersion in terms of the distance between selected observation points,

and these points are the first and third quartile values. Subtracting Q_1 from Q_3 produces the interquartile range. A box-and-whiskers display shows the values that lie in the interquartile range as a box, and it then draws lines, or whiskers, usually extending to the minimum and maximum values from the ends (or hinges) of the box to show the remaining 50 percent of the data items. An analysis of the measures of dispersion discussed in this chapter shows that the range is the easiest to compute, but it emphasizes only extreme values. The mean absolute deviation gives equal weight to the deviation of every data item and is easy to compute, but its use is limited. The standard deviation is the most frequently used measure because it's the most suitable for further analysis. Its value is affected by the size of every data item, but its value may be distorted by extreme data items, and it cannot be computed from an open-ended distribution. The interquartile range is based on two quartile values that identify the range of the middle 50 percent of the values, it may be used in badly skewed data sets, and it may be computed in an open-ended distribution, but it ignores 50 percent of the data set.

6. Attribute or qualitative data may be summarized by measuring the relative frequency with which a particular characteristic occurs. This process produces a percentage *or a proportion*—a measure that's used extensively in later chapters.

Exercises

48. People are weight conscious, so *Consumer Reports* did a study of 39 models of bathroom scales. The models studied and their prices (in dollars) are given below (Data = Scales):

Scale Model	Price	Scale Model	Price
Health O Meter 840	50	Medixact Hydraulic	65
Thinner MS-7	50	Metro Fashion	20
Metro Thin Scale	50	Counselor 410	14
Borg Hot Dota	28	Sunbeam 12280	25
Sunbeam 12657	65	Polder 6200	24
Counselor 2121	40	Medixact Proshape	48
Salter Electronic	50	Sunbeam 12509	15
Counselor 850	22	Counselor 197	10
Counselor 1100	32	Salter Hampshire	17
Health O Meter 811	30	Health O Meter 150	50
Health O Meter 190	79	Sunbeam 12200	25
Metro Big Dial	50	Counselor 550	22
Borg Digital	23	Krups 881	60
Health O Meter 1706	20	Krups 830	30
Sunbeam 12573	35	Terraillon Eyedrop	30
Sunbeam 12756	24	Health O Meter 50	10
Metro Digital	25	Metro Fashion 2000	12
Seca Doctor's	120	Health O Meter 180	20
Polder	35	Borg 3300	12
Health O Meter 1715	35		

a) Form an array of the scale price data in an ascending order.

b) Prepare a frequency distribution of scale prices with eight classes. Use "$10 and < $25" for the first class.

c) Prepare a histogram of the scale price data with eight classes.

d) Find the median scale price.

e) Find the values of Q_1 and Q_3.

f) Construct a stem-and-leaf display of the scale price data.

g) Construct a boxplot of the scale price data.

h) Find the interquartile range.

i) Compute the sample mean price of the scales.

j) Compute the sample variance and standard deviation.

49. The following list (compiled from Statistics Canada data in 2002) gives the population sizes of a sample of 27 Canadian cities (Data = City populations):

City	Population (thousands)
Brandon	41,037
Calgary	951,395
Charlottetown	58,358
Edmonton	937,845
Fredericton	81,346
Guelph	117,344
Halifax	359,183
Hamilton	662,401
Kingston	146,838
Kitchener	414,284
Lethbridge	67,374
London	432,451
Medicine Hat	61,735
Montréal	3,426,350
Ottawa-Hull	1,063,664
Regina	192,800
Saint John	122,678
Saskatoon	225,927
Sault Ste. Marie	78,908
St. Catharines-Niagara	377,009
St. John's	172,918
Thunder Bay	121,986
Toronto	4,682,897
Vancouver	1,986,965
Victoria	311,902
Windsor	307,877
Winnipeg	671,274

a) Form an array of these population sizes in ascending order.

b) Compute the 7.5 percent trimmed mean for the population size data.

c) Find the median population size and the values of Q_1 and Q_3.

d) What is the value of the 40th percentile?

e) Construct a boxplot of the population size data.

f) Find the interquartile range for the population size data.

Note: In questions g and h, use only the 21 cities whose population sizes are less than 700,000.

g) Construct a frequency distribution of the population sizes using seven classes. Use "0 but < 100,000" for the first class.

h) Construct a histogram of the population sizes using seven classes.

50. The *American Journal of Psychiatry* published the results of a study to see if there was a possible type of brain dysfunction associated with infantile autism. Each child in the study was given a behavioural test and graded on a scale from 0 to 116 (where 0 = absence of symptoms, and 116 = maximum severity of symptoms). The scores of the 21 children in the study were (Data = Behavior):

27 35 65 67 47 46 63 44 34 51 17 40 41
60 24 48 29 73 60 41 47

a) Construct a stem-and-leaf display of the score data.

b) Compute the sample mean score.

c) Compute the median score.

d) Compute the Q_1 and Q_3 scores.

e) Compute the range.

f) Calculate the *z* score for a grade of 50.

g) Find the 40th percentile.

51. A grandparent recently bought a grandchild one share of common stock in each of nine corporations. The prices paid (in dollars) were 31.25, 33.50, 104.75, 25.50, 53.25, 57.25, 30.75, 35.00, 58.50.

a) Calculate the mean price per share (assume that the data set is a population).

b) Calculate the median price per share.

c) Calculate the range.

d) Calculate the mean absolute deviation.

e) Calculate the population standard deviation.

52. The *Lancet* published an article describing a study of 12 heart patients. The study dealt with the effects of increased inspired oxygen concentrations on exercise performance. The oxygen consumption (ml/min per kg) of each of the 12 patients during an exercise test was

9.7 21.0 14.3 15.2 12.8 8.6 10.9 8.3 19.1 7.0
19.5 12.5

a) Obtain the median, Q_1, and Q_3.

b) Construct a boxplot of oxygen consumption.

53. The following list gives the profits (in millions of dollars) of nine Canadian banks for the appropriate fiscal year ending in 2001.

Company	Profit
Royal Bank of Canada	2,411
Cdn. Imp. Bank of Commerce	1,686
Bank of Nova Scotia	2,169
Toronto-Dominion Bank	1,383
Bank of Montreal	1,471
National Bank of Canada	563
HSBC Bank Canada	214
Laurentian Bank of Canada	90.7
Canadian Western Bank	30.1

a) Compute the mean profit (assume this is a population of interest).

b) What is the 70th percentile?

c) Compute the population standard deviation.

d) Calculate the standard score for the Bank of Montreal.

54. Olympic Games gold medallists' times for the 100 metre sprint are listed below:

Year	Name	Country	Time
1956	Bobby Morrow	USA	10.5
1960	Armin Hary	GER	10.2
1964	Bob Hayes	USA	10.0
1968	Jim Hines	USA	9.95
1972	Valery Borzov	USSR	10.14
1976	Hasely Crawford	TRI	10.06
1980	Allan Wells	GBR	10.25
1984	Carl Lewis	USA	9.99
1988	Carl Lewis	USA	9.92
1992	Linford Christie	GBR	9.96
1996	Donovan Bailey	CAN	9.84
2000	Maurice Greene	USA	9.87

a) Compute the interquartile range.

b) Determine the range.

c) Compute the sample standard deviation.

55. In July 2002, a sample of Canadian companies revealed the following numbers of employees.

Company	Employees
Air Canada	38,440
Canadian Pacific Railway	15,840
Canadian Tire Corp.	41,000
Hudson's Bay Co.	71,000
Loblaw Companies	114,000
Royal Bank of Canada	57,568
Sears Canada	56,000
Shoppers Drug Mart	29,000
Telus Corp.	27,765
Toronto-Dominion Bank	45,565

a) Compute the sample mean number of employees.

b) Compute the median number of employees.

c) What is the value of the 30th percentile?

d) Compute the sample standard deviation.

e) Calculate the z score of Air Canada.

f) Calculate the z score of Hudson's Bay Co.

56. Fast food is a fact of life, but such food is often saturated with fat. Healthy selections were made from the breakfast menus at four popular fast-food restaurants, and the number of calories in each selection was determined. The data are

Restaurant	Calories
Burger King	615
Jack-in-the-Box	387
McDonald's	567
Wendy's	440

a) Compute the sample mean number of calories.

b) Compute the median number of calories.

c) Compute the mean absolute deviation.

d) Determine the range.

e) Compute the sample standard deviation.

57. The minimum temperatures for the provincial capitals on Canada Day, 2002, are listed below:

Capital	Temperature	Capital	Temperature
Victoria	12	Quebec City	20
Edmonton	5	Fredericton	13
Regina	10	Halifax	11
Winnipeg	15	St. John's	15
Toronto	20	Charlottetown	14

a) Compute the interquartile range.

b) What is the value of the 20th percentile?

c) What is the value of the 90th percentile?

d) What is the median?

58. A study in *The Journal of Abnormal Psychology* reported on the results obtained with a family assessment device that was given to functional and dysfunctional families. On the Family Environment Scale for cohesion, the functional families had a mean score of 7.17 scale points and a standard deviation of 1.49.

a) According to Chebyshev's theorem, at least 75 percent of all functional families should score between what two values?

b) According to Chebyshev's theorem, at least 89 percent of all functional families should score between what two values?

c) When the Family Environment Scale for cohesion was measured for a sample of dysfunctional families, there was a mean of 5.57 scale points and a standard deviation of 2.49. According to Chebyshev's theorem, at least 75 percent of all dysfunctional families should score between what two values?

d) According to Chebyshev's theorem, at least 89 percent of all dysfunctional families should score between what two values?

59. To prepare adequate facilities for students, a university must determine the percentages of male and female students enrolled. The following data are obtained for 2002:

University	Male	Female
Mount Saint Vincent	340	1,785
Guelph	5,154	8,777
UPEI	1,045	1,706
Moncton	1,721	2,808
Mount Allison	923	1,223
Waterloo	10,308	8,781
Brandon	644	1,144
Regina	2,619	3,928

What is the percentage of female students of each university?

60. The number of traffic tickets issued for a sample period by five Morristown police officers is given below:

Officer Name	No. of Tickets
C. Morris	16
A. Trapper	9
L. Perez	10
J. Ketchum	8
F. Wheeler	5

a) What is the sample mean number of tickets written?

b) What is the median number of tickets written?

61. After 6 holes, a sample of 25 golfers at the Duffers International Tournament had the following scores (Data = Duffers):

71 68 85 96 12 92 37 41 54 25 66 15 73
23 14 55 65 43 88 92 19 22 51 62 84

Construct a stem-and-leaf display for these scores.

62. A study is conducted to find the mean income of a population of salespersons. The study concludes that for the population of 100 salespersons, the mean income is $33,000. It's discovered later that the income of the last person in the group was incorrectly reported to be $20,000 when it should have been

$50,000. What's the true mean income of the population?

63. Entrance exam scores for a sample of applicants to Jeopardy University are tabulated below:

990 1,403 1,059 1,213 763 1,352 898 999 1,181
1,264 269 428 582 381 1,141 760 455 345

a) Compute the range of these scores.

b) Compute the sample mean score.

c) Compute the mean absolute deviation.

d) Compute the standard deviation.

64. True or false? If the sample average and the sample median of a given sample are both equal to zero, then the sample standard deviation will also be equal to zero. Explain.

65. Can the median and the standard deviation of a data set both be equal to 0? If so, give an example. If not, explain why it is not possible.

66. A student scored 82 on a statistics mid-term where the class average was 70 and the class standard deviation was σ. Suppose on the statistics final exam, he received a 90, where the average was 80 and the standard deviation was 6. If the standardized scores were the same on both exams, find σ, the standard deviation of the mid-term marks.

67. The home page of the Long-Term Ecological Research (LTER) Network contains links to many data sets. One such data set references a paper by Gonzalez G., X. Zou, and S. Borges, 1996, "Earthworm Abundance and Species Composition in Abandoned Tropical Croplands: Comparison of Tree Plantations and Secondary Forests." *Pedobiologia* 40:385–391. It describes a study conducted within the subtropical wet forest life zone of the Luquillo Experimental Forest (LEF) of Puerto Rico. Part of the data included samples taken from mahogany trees of earthworm fresh weight (gm/m^2) and earthworm density (gm/m^2):

Weight	Density
7.98	43
9.74	31
8.98	25
11.26	40
4.41	10
1.87	11

a) Compute the mean and the standard deviation of the fresh weight of the earthworms.

b) Compute the z score for a fresh weight of 8.00.

c) Compute the mean and the standard deviation of the density of the earthworms.

d) Compute the z score for a density of 30.

Topics for Review and Discussion

1. Discuss the differences between discrete data and continuous data. Give three examples of each type of data.

2. What are the advantages of putting raw data into an array? What information can be readily found from an array?

3. Give an advantage of organizing data into a frequency distribution. What is a disadvantage?

4. Discuss some basic criteria to use when organizing a frequency distribution.

5. What difficulty may be encountered when using open-ended classes in distributions?

6. What is a histogram? How does it differ from a bar graph?

7. What is a frequency polygon? What are the advantages of using a frequency polygon?

8. Discuss the differences and similarities of a stem-and-leaf display and a histogram.

9. Discuss several situations where a stem-and-leaf display should not be used.

10. Discuss three measures of central tendency described in this chapter. What are the characteristics of each?

11. What basic assumption is needed to approximate the arithmetic mean from grouped data?

12. Discuss the relationship between the mean, median, and mode in a symmetric, mound-shaped distribution. Discuss the relationship among the three measures of central tendency when the distribution is positively skewed. What about the relationship when it is negatively skewed?

13. Discuss the differences in qualitative and quantitative data. What types of statistics can be found only with quantitative data? How can we describe quantitative data?

14. Why is it necessary to measure dispersion to describe a data set?

15. Why is it necessary to eliminate the algebraic signs of the deviations when computing measures of dispersion? Discuss the different ways of doing this when computing the mean absolute deviation and the standard deviation.

16. Discuss the relationship between the variance and the standard deviation. Why is the standard deviation a more commonly used measure?

17. Identify the main characteristics of the range, mean absolute deviation, and the standard deviation.

18. Discuss the key elements of a box-and-whisker plot. Where is the interquartile range in such a plot?

Projects/Issues to Consider

1. Go to your school library and obtain a set of raw data (not statistics) you find interesting. You might want to use a current periodical or a journal from your field of study. Write a report describing the data, and include the following in your report:

  a) Identify your source. Include the date of publication.

  b) What is the population for your data? How was the sample obtained?

  c) Arrange the data in array form.

  d) Find the range, Q_1, the median, and Q_3.

  e) Find the interquartile range.

  f) Does your data have a mode?

  g) Construct a box-and-whisker plot.

  h) Construct a stem-and-leaf display of your data. You may find it easier to round off your data for a better display.

  i) Construct a frequency distribution using a convenient number of classes.

  j) Construct a histogram and a frequency polygon.

  k) From your histogram and your box-and-whisker plot, discuss the shape of your distribution. Is it symmetric, skewed left, or skewed right?

2. Collect a data set from your classmates, friends, neighbours, and so on, by asking each of them how much weight they have gained since their high school graduation. Prepare a report about these weight gains, using as many of the techniques in this chapter as necessary to describe the distribution of the data.

Computer/Calculator Exercises

1. After you've retrieved the computer file named FULL_TIME_STUDENTS that you created for the Chapter 1 Computer/Calculator exercise, use your software package or graphics calculator to produce

a) A default histogram (one the package produces automatically), and then construct a histogram.

b) A stem-and-leaf display for this data set.

c) A dotplot for this data set.

d) A boxplot for this data set.

e) The basic statistical measures (mean, media, standard deviation, minimum value, maximum value, Q_1, Q_3, ...) for this data set.

2. Locate the fees for international students at the 43 colleges used in Self-Testing Review 3.2, problem 13. Now, enter these 43 data items into your software package or graphics calculator to produce (Data = Intfees 2001)

a) An array of the data.

b) A histogram for this data set.

c) A stem-and-leaf display for this data set.

d) A boxplot for this data set.

e) The basic statistical measures (mean, median, standard deviation, minimum value, maximum value, Q_1, Q_3, ...) for this data set. (You may want to save this data set since it will be used in computer exercises sections in later chapters.)

3. Enter the *Consumer Reports* bathroom-scale price data used for end-of-chapter exercise problem 48 into your software package or graphics calculator and then produce (Data = Scales)

a) An array of the data.

b) A histogram for this data set.

c) A stem-and-leaf display for this data set.

d) A boxplot for this data set.

e) The basic statistical measures (mean, median, standard deviation, minimum value, maximum value, Q_1, Q_3, ...) for this data set.

4. A listing of the population sizes of 27 Canadian cities is given for end of chapter exercise problem 49. Use these population figures and your software package or graphics calculator to produce (Data = Populations)

a) An array of the data.

b) A histogram for this data set.

c) A stem-and-leaf display for this data set.

d) A boxplot for this data set.

e) The basic statistical measures (mean, median, standard deviation, minimum value, maximum value, Q_1, Q_3, ...) for this data set.

5. In computer/calculator exercise 5 of Chapter 1, you downloaded a data set from DASL (The Data & Story Library) to your computer. For that data set, obtain the following:

a) An array of the data.

b) A histogram for this data set.

c) A stem-and-leaf display for this data set.

d) A boxplot for this data set.

e) The basic statistical measures (mean, median, standard deviation, minimum value, maximum value, Q_1, Q_3, ...) for this data set.

6. In computer/calculator exercise 2 of Chapter 2, you used the World Wide Web to perform an Internet search for "data set" and downloaded the data set into a statistical package such as MINITAB. Use the package or graphics calculator to obtain the following:

a) A histogram for this data set.

b) A stem-and-leaf display for this data set.

c) A boxplot for this data set.

d) The basic statistical measures (mean, median, standard deviation, minimum value, maximum value, Q_1, Q_3, ...) for this data set.

CHAPTER 4

Probability Concepts

In this chapter you'll learn the basic probability concepts that form the foundation for statistical inference. There are many statistical applications for which it is necessary to use probability concepts to make decisions under conditions of uncertainty. For example, probability studies have been made in the health fields that link second-hand smoking to asthma in young children. In the business world, other such studies have sought to find marketing strategies to use to attract those in the 18 to 25 age group. And psychologists have used probability studies to try to learn if attention deficit disorder is due to heredity or to environmental factors. In this chapter we'll look at (1) basic probability definitions and the methods used to assign probabilities for simple events, (2) methods of computing probabilities for compound events, and (3) the concepts of random variables, probability distributions, and expected values.

Thus, after studying this chapter, you should be able to

- Define probability terms and explain how simple probabilities may be assigned.

- Explain the concepts of conditional, independent, and mutually exclusive events.

- Correctly use multiplication and addition rules to perform probability computations.

- Differentiate between discrete and continuous random variables.

- Discuss the concept of a probability distribution.

- Compute the expected value and standard deviation of a discrete random variable.

4.1 Some Basic Considerations

Deep thinkers have often been fascinated by probability concepts. Consider the following quotes:

But to us, probability is the very guide of life.—*Bishop Joseph Butler (1736)*

The principal means for ascertaining truth—induction and analogy—are based on probabilities; so that the entire system of human knowledge is connected with the theory of probability.—*Pierre Simon, Marquis de Laplace (1819)*

These thinkers have certainly elevated the importance of probability to a high level. Perhaps when you finish this and the later chapters in the book, you'll agree with them. Before we can discuss the subject, though, we should define a few basic terms.

Let's suppose you toss a coin and note the side that lands face up. Then, you roll a die and count the number of dots on the top. Finally, you choose a lottery winner at random and determine which type of major purchase the person makes first. In each of these instances, you have performed a *probability experiment.*

> A **probability experiment** is any action for which an outcome, response, or measurement is obtained that can't be predicted with certainty.

That wasn't so bad, so let's look at another term.

For example, if you toss a coin, the possible outcomes are heads or tails (we don't consider that the coin might land on edge). When you roll a die, all the possible outcomes are 1, 2, 3, 4, 5, and 6. And when you choose a lottery winner to determine the type of first major purchase after winning the lottery, you may find a luxury vehicle (L), a cruise (C), or an "other" purchase (R). The sample space is L, C, R.

Now, let's consider two other related terms.

If you roll a die, you could be interested in the *event* that you get a 3. Specific events are symbolized with capital letters in this chapter. Thus, we might let T represent the *simple event* of having the die land on a 3. Or we could simply note that $T = \{3\}$. Later in this chapter we'll investigate events that consist of more than one simple outcome. If we roll a die, for example, we might want to analyze the event A that the outcome is *less than* a 5. In this case we could say $A = \{1, 2, 3, 4\}$. The *sample space* and event A in this example can be presented with a graphic aid called a *Venn diagram* in this way:

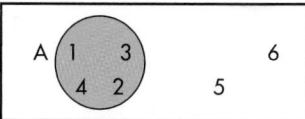

> An **event** is a subset or collection of outcomes from the sample space.

> A **simple event** is one that can't be broken down any further; that is, it is an individual outcome from the sample space.

> A **sample space** is the set of all possible simple outcomes, responses, or measurements of an experiment.

As you can see, the sample space = {1, 2, 3, 4, 5, 6}, and event A = {1, 2, 3, 4}.

Assigning Simple Probabilities

The **probability** of a specified event, say, E, may be defined as the relative likelihood of that event occurring. We denote this as $P(E)$, which is read as "P of E." Let's look now at three methods—*a priori*, relative frequency, and intuition—that can be used to assign probabilities.

A priori (**Classical**) **Probability**   In some experiments, such as the tossing of a coin or the rolling of a die, it is reasonable to believe that each of the possible outcomes has the same chance of happening. If so, the probability of various events can be determined before the fact, or ***a priori*** (prior to any statistical experiments). For example, intuitively we believe that when a coin is tossed, the two outcomes are equally likely, so it makes sense to assign a probability of 1/2 or .5 to each of the two outcomes. This doesn't mean that if you flipped a coin twice, you would get one head and one tail. It does mean, though, that if you flipped the coin a large number of times, the proportion of heads would approach .5.

You might try to flip a quarter ten times and record the number of heads. The MINITAB program was used to simulate this experiment, and it produced the sample results shown in *Figure 4.1* (0 = head, and 1 = tail). For this experiment, we got six heads

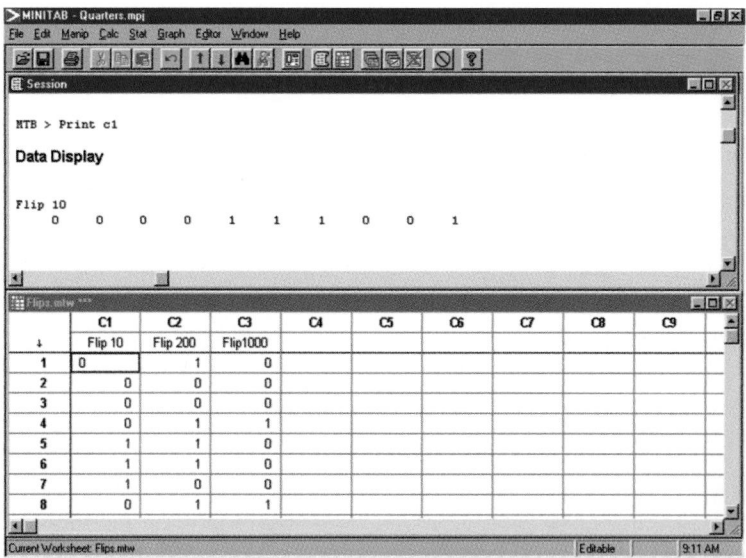

FIGURE 4.1 MINITAB simulation of coin-toss experiment.

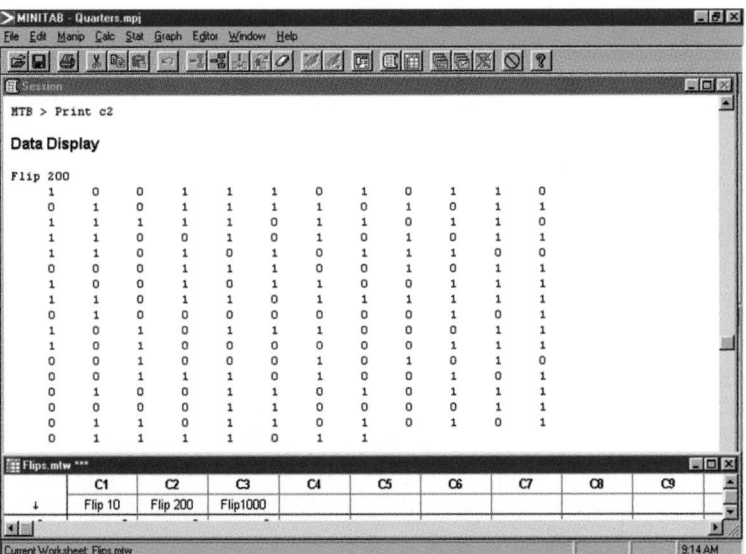

FIGURE 4.2 MINITAB display for 200 tosses of a coin.

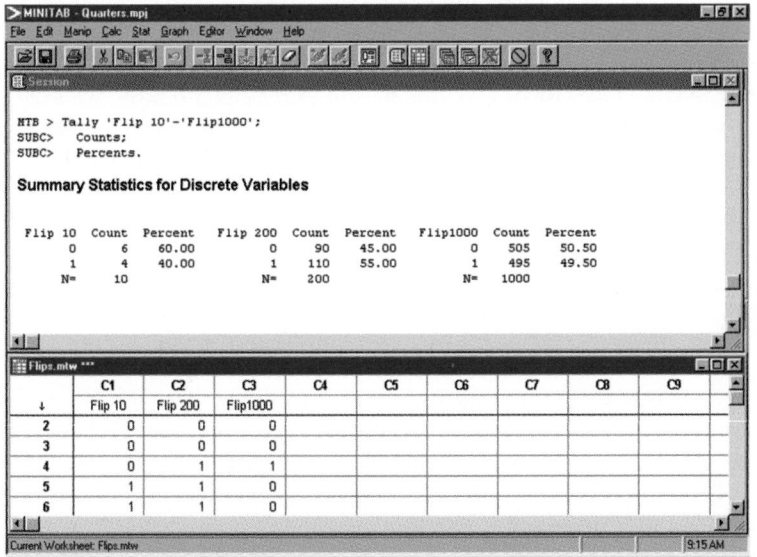

FIGURE 4.3 MINITAB simulation of coin-toss experiment—summary.

STATISTICS IN ACTION

What Are the Chances?

For centuries schizophrenics were believed to be possessed by devils or even angels. Research now indicates that the tendency to develop schizophrenia is hereditary. While the average child has a 1 percent chance of being stricken, the child of a schizophrenic parent faces 10 times those odds. If both parents are affected, the likelihood of a child being stricken jumps to 40 percent. But children of parents with schizophrenia raised by adoptive parents who do not have the disorder have a somewhat reduced factor. If one identical twin has the condition, there is a 50 percent chance the other will. Although genetics play a major role, environmental factors may help trigger the disorder.

in ten "tosses" for a proportion of .6. Note that the first four tosses were heads. But as the number of trials increased, the proportion of heads got closer to .50. We then had MINITAB simulate tossing the quarter 200 times. The results are given in *Figure 4.2*. This time we got 90 heads in 200 trials for a relative proportion of .45. Continuing along, we simulated the tossing of the quarter 1,000 times. For this experiment, we got 505 heads for a relative proportion of .5050. *Figure 4.3* tallies the results of our three experiments. To summarize, then, when we say $P(H) = .5$, we mean that if we performed the experiment a very large number of times, the proportion of heads would be very close to .50.

Similarly, it makes sense to assign a probability of 1/6 to each of the 6 equally likely simple outcomes from the roll of a fair (not loaded) die. Let's denote the probability of a certain event E as $P(E)$. If we know in advance that the sample space consists of equally probable outcomes, we can assign the value to $P(E)$ as follows:

$$P(E) = \frac{\text{number of simple outcomes favourable to the event}}{\text{total number of simple outcomes}} = \frac{f}{n} \qquad (4.1)$$

Thus, if $A =$ {the die lands on a number less than 5}, then $P(A) = 4/6$ since there are four ways of being successful (1 or 2 or 3 or 4) out of the six possible outcomes.

Relative Frequency (Empirical) Probability Suppose we randomly choose a lottery winner from a list of lottery winners to find the probability that this person's first major purchase was a luxury vehicle (L). In this instance, we must have some empirical data to determine the answer. We do some research and find that our list has 386 lottery winners. Of these, 184 first purchased a luxury vehicle, 127 first purchased a cruise, and 75 made "other" purchases. We can now use the following method to assign probabilities to each simple event:

$$P(E) = \frac{\text{number of favourable outcomes}}{\text{total number of trials}} = \frac{f}{n} \qquad (4.2)$$

For the event $L =$ {the person purchases a luxury vehicle}, we assign $P(L) = 184/386$ or a probability of .4767. Likewise, if $C =$ {the person purchases a cruise}, we assign $P(C) = 127/386$, which is a probability value of .3290. And if $R =$ {the person makes an "other" purchase}, then $P(R) = 75/386$ or .1943. Each of the three values just computed is an example of a **relative frequency** (or **empirical**) **probability**—one that's determined by observation and/or experimentation.

In many calculations rounding takes place. Normally, four decimals of accuracy will be used in calculations.

Intuition A third method used to assign probabilities is intuition. A salesperson might make an educated guess and say "there's a 40 percent probability that I'll make a sale to my next customer." This last method isn't scientifically based but rather is based on a subjective hunch. Or a plant manager may believe that there's a .60 probability that the union will call a strike next week. This probability is the manager's subjective estimate of the likelihood of a strike and is not an *a priori* or empirical value. The accuracy of the strike estimate, of course, depends on the manager's experience and skill.

Regardless of how probability values are assigned, though, the following two properties must apply:

1. Probability is measured on a scale from 0 to 1. That is, a probability of interest—say, $P(E)$—is always $0 \leq P(E) \leq 1$. If an event is *impossible,* we assign 0 as its probability. An event that is *certain to occur* has a probability of 1. All other probabilities—those of interest to us—are found between these extremes.

2. The probabilities of all the simple events, say, E, within a sample space must add up to 1. That is, $\sum P(E) = 1$.

Let's look at some examples of these conditions:

Example 4.1 When we roll a fair die, we assign $P(1) = P(2) = P(3) = P(4) = P(5) = P(6) = 1/6$. Thus, the sum of the probabilities of all possible simple events is $1/6 + 1/6 + 1/6 + 1/6 + 1/6 + 1/6 = 6/6$ or 1. ◆

Example 4.2 If we had reason to believe the die was not fair, we could assign the following probabilities: $P(1) = .2$, $P(2) = .1$, $P(3) = .3$, $P(4) = .2$, $P(5) = .1$, $P(6) = .1$. Each of the assigned probabilities is between 0 and 1, and the sum of the probabilities of all possible simple events is still 1. ◆

Example 4.3 The probabilities of $P(1) = .3$, $P(2) = .1$, $P(3) = .1$, $P(4) = .2$, $P(5) = .1$, and $P(6) = .3$ could *not* be assigned to the outcomes for the roll of a loaded die since the sum of the probabilities is not 1. ◆

Example 4.4 The probabilities of $P(1) = .4$, $P(2) = .1$, $P(3) = .3$, $P(4) = -.2$, $P(5) = .1$, and $P(6) = .3$ could *not* be assigned to the outcomes for the roll of a loaded die since each probability must be between 0 and 1, and $P(4) = -.2$ isn't valid. ◆

Example 4.5 A few paragraphs earlier we assigned probabilities of 184/386, 127/386, and 75/386 to the events that a lottery winner's first major purchase was a luxury vehicle, a cruise, or an "other" purchase. Note that each probability is between 0 and 1 and the sum of the probabilities is 386/386 or 1. ◆

Self-Testing Review 4.1

1. A card is drawn at random from a standard deck of 52 cards. What is the probability it is a club? (*Figure 4.4* is included here for you non-card players. There are four suits—clubs, diamonds, hearts, and spades—in the deck, and there are 13 cards in each suit.)

2. If a card is drawn at random from a standard deck of 52 cards, what is the probability it is a face card? (There are three face cards—jack, queen, and king—in each of the four suits.)

3. In the general population there are four types of blood: A, B, AB, and O. The relative proportions of people having each type are .42, .10, .03, and .45, respectively. What is the probability that a person selected at random will have type O blood? (For the purpose of blood donation, type O is called the *universal donor* since it can safely be transfused to people with any blood type.)

A Standard Deck of Cards

A♥ — Ace of hearts	A♦ — Ace of diamonds	A♣ — Ace of clubs	A♠ — Ace of spades
2♥ — Two of hearts	2♦ — Two of diamonds	2♣ — Two of clubs	2♠ — Two of spades
3♥ — Three of hearts	3♦ — Three of diamonds	3♣ — Three of clubs	3♠ — Three of spades
4♥ — Four of hearts	4♦ — Four of diamonds	4♣ — Four of clubs	4♠ — Four of spades
5♥ — Five of hearts	5♦ — Five of diamonds	5♣ — Five of clubs	5♠ — Five of spades
6♥ — Six of hearts	6♦ — Six of diamonds	6♣ — Six of clubs	6♠ — Six of spades
7♥ — Seven of hearts	7♦ — Seven of diamonds	7♣ — Seven of clubs	7♠ — Seven of spades
8♥ — Eight of hearts	8♦ — Eight of diamonds	8♣ — Eight of clubs	8♠ — Eight of spades
9♥ — Nine of hearts	9♦ — Nine of diamonds	9♣ — Nine of clubs	9♠ — Nine of spades
10♥ — Ten of hearts	10♦ — Ten of diamonds	10♣ — Ten of clubs	10♠ — Ten of spades
J♥ — Jack of hearts	J♦ — Jack of diamonds	J♣ — Jack of clubs	J♠ — Jack of spades
Q♥ — Queen of hearts	Q♦ — Queen of diamonds	Q♣ — Queen of clubs	Q♠ — Queen of spades
K♥ — King of hearts	K♦ — King of diamonds	K♣ — King of clubs	K♠ — King of spades

52 cards

4 suits (♥, ♦, ♣, ♠)

13 cards in each suit

(A, 2, 3, 4, 5, 6, 7, 8, 9, 10, J, Q, K)

FIGURE 4.4 Standard deck of playing cards.

4. It has been predicted that in 2007 there will be a demand for 7,500 new teachers. Out of this total there will be a need for 3,900 elementary teachers and 3,600 secondary teachers. What's the probability that a new teaching job in 2007 will be for a secondary teacher?

5. The Regina Police Service reported that in 2001 there were 22,069 property crimes in Regina. Of these, there were 3,848 motor vehicle thefts. What is the probability that any one of these randomly selected property crimes is a motor vehicle theft?

6. In the annual reader survey of *Home-Office Computing,* it was found that 68 percent of the respondents run a home-based business, 6 percent run a business that is not home based, 9 percent plan to start a business, and 17 percent work at home part of the week. A reader is selected at random. What is the probability that he or she runs a business that is home based?

7. On the television game show *The Price is Right,* there is a segment called "Showcase Showdown." The contestant is asked to spin a wheel that has 20 equally spaced sectors marked in amounts 5, 10, 15, ... , 100. If a pointer on the wheel lands on the sector marked 100, the contestant wins $1,000. What's the probability that the contestant spins the wheel and wins $1,000?

8. The Calgary Police Service reported that in 2001 there were a total of 9,025 attacks against persons. Of these, there were 17 homicides, 808 sex offences, 1,187 robberies, 6,599 assaults, and 414 miscellaneous. If one of these attacks is selected at random, what is the probability that it is a robbery?

9. A loaded die is tossed. Determine which of the following assignments could be made for the probabilities of each simple outcome. If an assignment cannot be made, tell why.

a) $P(1) = .3$ $P(2) = .2$ $P(3) = .3$ $P(4) = .1$ $P(5) = .2$ $P(6) = .1$

b) $P(1) = .1$ $P(2) = 1.2$ $P(3) = .2$ $P(4) = .1$ $P(5) = .2$ $P(6) = .1$

c) $P(1) = .1$ $P(2) = .1$ $P(3) = .1$ $P(4) = .1$ $P(5) = .3$ $P(6) = .3$

d) $P(1) = .2$ $P(2) = .3$ $P(3) = .2$ $P(4) = -.1$ $P(5) = .2$ $P(6) = .2$

e) $P(1) = .3$ $P(2) = .3$ $P(3) = .3$ $P(4) = .1$ $P(5) = 0$ $P(6) = 0$

10. Statistics Canada reported that in 2001 there were 30,007,095 people living in Canada. In this population there were 3,888,550 who were 65 years of age or older and 26,118,545 who were under 65. If a Canadian of that year is selected at random, what is the probability that, at that time, he or she was 65 years of age or older?

11. Statistics Canada has estimated that in 2006 the Canadian population will be 32,228,700, and that of these people, 4,302,200 will be 65 or over and 27,926,500 will be under 65. If a Canadian of that year is selected at random, what is the probability that, at that time, he or she will be 65 years of age or older?

12. It has been reported that of 4,000 principals in public elementary schools, 800 are female. If a principal from a public elementary school is selected at random, what's the probability that the principal is female?

13. Statistics Canada reported that in 2000, there were 56,020 police officers in Canada and that 7,658 were female. If a police officer is selected at random from this work force, what is the probability that this officer is female?

4.2 Probabilities for Compound Events

We've just looked at ways to determine the probabilities of simple events. But we're often interested in the relative chance that some combination of events may occur. Such a combination is called a *compound event.*

> A **compound event** is one that combines two or more events.

There are three categories of compound events of interest to us. In the following pages, we'll determine the probability that in a single experimental trial

1. Event A occurs, given that (or on the condition that) event B has happened. The notation for this conditional outcome is P(A, given B) or $P(A \mid 0B)$.

2. Both events A and B happen. The notation here is P(A and B).

3. Either event A occurs, or event B occurs, or they both occur. The notation for this outcome is P(A or B).

Conditional Probability Concepts

When additional facts are available for an experiment, probability values for an event can be reassessed in the light of new information. For example, suppose you are playing a game (such as *Trivial Pursuit*) involving the use of a die. Your opponent rolls the die but does not let you see the outcome. You will win the game if your opponent rolls a 3, so you are interested in the probability of this occurrence. In the previous section we saw that it's reasonable to assign P(die lands on a 3) = P(T) = 1/6. However, suppose you are given additional information about the outcome of that roll, namely, that the roll has landed on an odd number. If we designate the event that the die lands on an odd number as D, then D = {1, 3, 5}. We can now assess the relative chance that the roll will be a 3 in light of this new information.

Since our sample space has been reduced to three equally probable outcomes (1, 3, or 5), we can now say that the relative chance that the roll was a 3, given that the roll was an odd number, is 1/3. This is thus an example of a *conditional probability.*

> A **conditional probability** is the probability that one event will occur given that another has happened.

In our example, we have the conditional probability of T given D, which we can denote as P(T, given D) or $P(T \mid D)$. Note that for this example, the conditional probability is not the same as the simple probability. That is, $P(T \mid D) \neq P(T)$.

Let's look at another situation involving conditional probability. In problem 3 in Self-Testing Review 4.1, it's shown that the probability of randomly selecting a person with type O blood from the general population is .45. Now suppose when selecting an individual that you have additional information that the person selected is a female. What is the probability the person has type O blood, given that the person is a female? That is, what is $P(\text{type O}|\text{female})$? Intuitively, we can see that $P(\text{type O}|\text{female}) = .45$. The proportion of females with type O blood is .45. In other words, the additional information (that the person is female) didn't change the value of the probability of selecting a person who has type O blood. For this situation the conditional probability is the same as the simple probability—$P(\text{type O}|\text{female}) = P(\text{type O})$.

Now let's reconsider the list of 386 lottery winners. This time we're interested in the type of the first major purchase as well as whether the purchaser was male or female. The information gathered can be placed in the following table. This table is called a **contingency table** because it shows all the classifications of the variables being studied—that is, it accounts for all contingencies in a particular situation.

	Luxury Vehicle (L)	Cruise (C)	Other (R)	Total
Male (M)	145	85	23	253
Female (F)	39	42	52	133
Totals	184	127	75	386

We've seen that the probability that a lottery winner first purchases a luxury vehicle $[P(L)]$ is 184/386 or .4767. Now we'll investigate the conditional probability that the purchase is a luxury vehicle $[P(L)]$ given that the purchaser is male. To do this, we consider only the 253 purchasers who are male.

	Luxury Vehicle (L)	Cruise (C)	Other (R)	Total
Male (M)	145	85	23	253

Within this revised sample space consisting only of males, 145 purchased a luxury vehicle, so we can say $P(L|M) = 145/253 = .5731$.

Joint Probability—Multiplication Rule for Computing $P(A \text{ and } B)$

When a probability experiment is performed, it's sometimes necessary to find the probability that *both* events *A and B* occur. To do so, we use the following formula:

$$P(A \text{ and } B) = P(A) \times P(B|A) \qquad (4.3)$$

Thus, we must multiply the probability of the first event by the conditional probability of the second event, given that the first has occurred. Note that formula 4.3 can be restated by saying that $P(B|A) = \dfrac{P(A \text{ and } B)}{P(A)}.$

Some examples should help clarify the use of this **multiplication rule:**

Example 4.6   We have ten pieces of candy in a dish. We know that five pieces are red, three are green, and two are yellow. If we choose two pieces at random without looking (since we are busy concentrating on learning about probabilities), what's the probability that both are green?

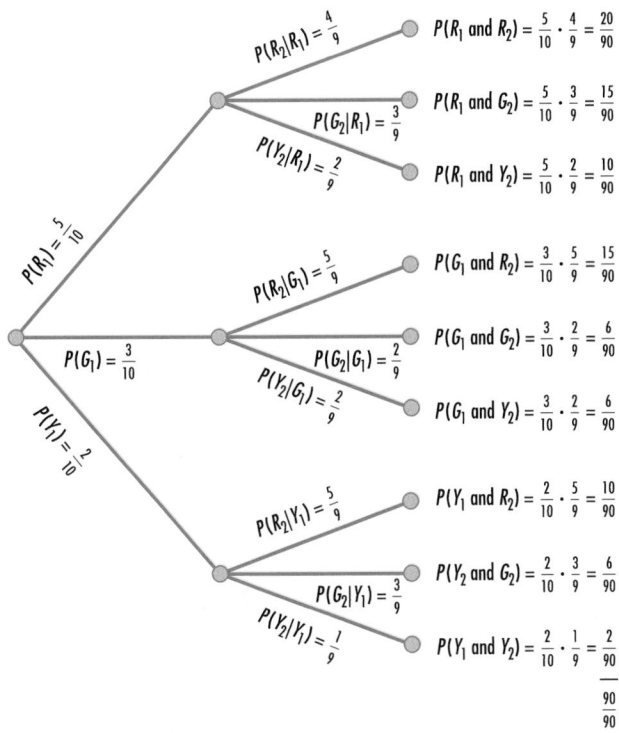

$P(R_2|R_1) = \frac{4}{9}$ ⟶ $P(R_1 \text{ and } R_2) = \frac{5}{10} \cdot \frac{4}{9} = \frac{20}{90}$

$P(G_2|R_1) = \frac{3}{9}$ ⟶ $P(R_1 \text{ and } G_2) = \frac{5}{10} \cdot \frac{3}{9} = \frac{15}{90}$

$P(Y_2|R_1) = \frac{2}{9}$ ⟶ $P(R_1 \text{ and } Y_2) = \frac{5}{10} \cdot \frac{2}{9} = \frac{10}{90}$

$P(R_1) = \frac{5}{10}$

$P(R_2|G_1) = \frac{5}{9}$ ⟶ $P(G_1 \text{ and } R_2) = \frac{3}{10} \cdot \frac{5}{9} = \frac{15}{90}$

$P(G_2|G_1) = \frac{2}{9}$ ⟶ $P(G_1 \text{ and } G_2) = \frac{3}{10} \cdot \frac{2}{9} = \frac{6}{90}$

$P(Y_2|G_1) = \frac{2}{9}$ ⟶ $P(G_1 \text{ and } Y_2) = \frac{3}{10} \cdot \frac{2}{9} = \frac{6}{90}$

$P(G_1) = \frac{3}{10}$

$P(Y_1) = \frac{2}{10}$

$P(R_2|Y_1) = \frac{5}{9}$ ⟶ $P(Y_1 \text{ and } R_2) = \frac{2}{10} \cdot \frac{5}{9} = \frac{10}{90}$

$P(G_2|Y_1) = \frac{3}{9}$ ⟶ $P(Y_2 \text{ and } G_2) = \frac{2}{10} \cdot \frac{3}{9} = \frac{6}{90}$

$P(Y_2|Y_1) = \frac{1}{9}$ ⟶ $P(Y_1 \text{ and } Y_2) = \frac{2}{10} \cdot \frac{1}{9} = \frac{2}{90}$

$\frac{90}{90}$

FIGURE 4.5 A tree diagram showing all the possible outcomes of drawing 2 pieces from 5 red, 3 green, and 2 yellow candies. Note that the total probability is 90/90 or 1.

◆ **Solution:**

Think of this as two actions—(1) choosing the first piece of candy and then (2) choosing the second without replacing the first. We let $A = $ {the first piece of candy is green}, and $B = $ {the second piece is green}. We next determine $P(A)$ and $P(B$, given $A)$. Since we began with ten pieces and five are red, three are green, and two are yellow, we can easily see that $P(A) = 3/10$. To compute $P(B|A)$—that is, that the second piece is green, given the first is green—we must reassess our new sample space. When event A occurs, a green piece is removed, and the new sample space consists of 9 pieces (5 red, 2 green, and 2 yellow). We can now see that $P(B|A) = 2/9$. To find $P(A$ and $B)$, we multiply $P(A) \times P(B|A) = 3/10 \times 2/9 = 6/90 = 1/15$. We have one chance in 15 to randomly choose two green pieces of candy. The tree diagram in *Figure 4.5* shows all the possible outcomes for this example. ◆

☐ **Example 4.7**   Two cards are selected from a deck of 52 cards. The first is not replaced after it is drawn. What's the probability that both cards are kings?

◆ **Solution:**

Let events $A = $ {the first card is a king} and $B = $ {the second card is a king}. Since there are four kings in the deck, we know $P(A) = 4/52$. Now we must evaluate $P(B|A)$. With one king removed, the altered sample space has 51 cards, 3 of which are kings. So $P(B|A) = 3/51$. We now use the multiplication rule for computing a joint probability to get $4/52 \times 3/51 = 1/221$ or .0045. ◆

☐ **Example 4.8**   Determine the probability a lottery winner selected at random from the list of 386 winners first purchased a luxury vehicle and is male.

◆ **Solution:**

Let's look at the contingency table again:

	Luxury Vehicle (L)	Cruise (C)	Other (R)	Total
Male (M)	145	85	23	253
Female (F)	39	42	52	133
Total	184	127	75	386

From the table we can see that there are 145 purchases in the cell in which the column of luxury vehicle purchases intersects the row for males. Thus, the probability of both is 145/386 or .3756. The formula to produce the same result:

$$P(L \text{ and } M) = P(L) \times P(M|L)$$

$$= \frac{184}{386} \times \frac{145}{184} = .4767 \times .7880 = .3760 \quad ◆$$

Independence of Events

We may often want to know if the occurrence of one event affects the chances that a second event will happen. Does the time you arrive at school affect the chances that your car will overheat? Does the colour of your socks (or lack thereof) affect the chances that you'll get a good grade on a statistics test? Well, note that if A is independent of B, then B is independent of A, so we say that A and B are independent.

Symbolically, we say events A and B are *independent* when $P(B) = P(B|A)$. In other words, the events A and B are independent when the probability of one of the events occurring is not affected by the additional knowledge that the other event has occurred.

> Two events A and B are **independent** when the occurrence (or the non-occurrence) of A does *not* affect the probability of the occurrence of B.

In our discussion of conditional probability we saw in the die example that $P(\text{die is } 3) = 1/6$. But we also saw that $P(\text{die is } 3$, given the die lands on an odd number$) = 1/3$. Since $1/6 \neq 1/3$, the events $T = \{$the die lands on a 3$\}$ and $D = \{$the die lands on an odd number$\}$ are *not* independent events. In contrast, we saw in an earlier example that $P(\text{person having type O blood}) = .45$, and $P(\text{person having type O blood, given the person is female } [F]) = .45$. Since the probability of event O is the same as the conditional probability of O, given F, we say the events O and F are independent events. In our lottery winner example, $P(\text{luxury vehicle}) = 184/386 = .4767$, and $P(\text{luxury vehicle, given the purchaser is male}) = 145/253 = .5731$. Since $.4767 \neq .5731$, we conclude the events are not independent. The type of purchase depends on whether or not the purchaser is male.

In many situations, the question of independence can be answered intuitively. We know the roll of one die is independent of the roll of another. An important concern in statistics is to assess if two variables are independent. For instance, studies have shown that the variables of gender and type of impulse control disorders are not independent variables. Pathological gambling tends to afflict mostly men, while kleptomania predominately affects women.

Let's look now at some other examples:

Example 4.9 Roll a die and toss a coin. The events A = {the die lands on a 4} and B = {the coin lands on tails} are independent. That is, $P(B) = 1/2$ and $P(B$, given $A) = 1/2$. Note that even when we know the die lands on a 4, the information does *not* change the relative likelihood that the coin will land on tails. ◆

Example 4.10 When we roll a pair of dice, the events A = {the first die lands on a 2} and B = {the second die lands on a 3} are independent. So $P(A) = 1/6$, and $P(A$ given $B) = 1/6$. ◆

Multiplication Rule for Computing $P(A$ and $B)$ for Independent Events

When we can determine that two events, A and B, are independent, we compute the probability that both of these events will occur as follows:

$$P(A \text{ and } B) = P(A) \times P(B) \tag{4.4}$$

Thus, we multiply the individual probabilities to determine the relative likelihood that both of two independent events occur. Note that when the events are independent, $P(B) = P(B \mid A)$ so that this formula is a special version of formula 4.3. Now let's illustrate this **multiplication rule for independent events** with some examples:

Example 4.11 If we roll a die and flip a coin, what's the probability that the die lands on a 4 and the coin on tails? ◆

◆ **Solution:**
From the previous discussion, we know that these events are independent, so we can compute P(die lands on a 4 *and* coin lands on tails) by multiplying P(die lands on a 4) times P(coin lands on tails). That is,

$$P(\text{die is 4 and coin is tails}) = \left(\frac{1}{6}\right)\left(\frac{1}{2}\right) = \frac{1}{12} \quad ◆$$

Example 4.12 If we choose a person at random from the general population, what's the probability that the person is a female with type O blood?

◆ **Solution:**
We saw earlier that the events of being a female and having type O blood are independent. So to compute P(person is female and has type O blood), we multiply P(person is female) times P(person has type O blood). The result (assuming half the population is female) is

$$P(\text{person is female and has type O blood}) = (.5)(.45) = .225 \quad ◆$$

Determining $P(A$ or $B)$ Using Addition Rules

For many experiments we may need to determine the probability that either of two events occurs. We've seen that the notation for this outcome is $P(A$ or $B)$. This notation thus determines the relative likelihood that A will occur without B, or B will

happen without *A*, or even possibly that both *A* and *B* will occur. Before we develop formulas to compute *P(A or B)*, though, we must define the concept of *mutually exclusive* events.

Events *A* and *B* are **mutually exclusive** if the occurrence of one during a single trial of an experiment prevents the occurrence of the other during that same trial. If events *A* and *B* are mutually exclusive, then these two events have no common outcome.

The Venn diagram for this case is

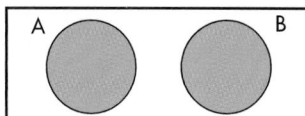

If we draw one card from a deck of 52 cards and let *A* = {the card is a 7} and let *B* = {the card is a king}, then events *A* and *B* are mutually exclusive because the drawing of a 7 in a single trial prevents the drawing of a king in that same trial. But if we draw one card from a deck of 52 cards and let *A* = {the card is a 7} and let *C* = {the card is red}, then events *A* and *C* are not mutually exclusive since the drawing of a 7 on a single trial doesn't prevent the drawing of a red card on that same trial. And if we select a person at random from the general population, then the events *O*(the person has type O blood) and *F*(the person is a female) are not mutually exclusive since the selection of a person with type O blood doesn't prevent that same person from being female. The Venn diagram for such situations is

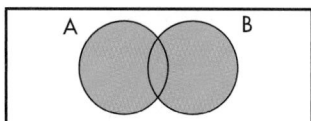

P(**A or B**) **for Mutually Exclusive Events**   When we know events *A* and *B* are mutually exclusive, we compute *P(A or B)* as follows:

$$P(A \text{ or } B) = P(A) + P(B) \tag{4.5}$$

That is, we *add* the individual probabilities to determine the relative likelihood that at least one or the other of two mutually exclusive events will occur. Some examples will illustrate the use of this **addition rule** when events are mutually exclusive:

Example 4.13   A card is chosen from a standard deck of 52 cards. What's the probability that it is a 7 or a king?

◆ **Solution:**
The events are mutually exclusive. Since there are four 7s in the deck, we can see that *P*(card is a 7) is 4/52. And since there are four kings in the deck, *P*(card is a king) is also 4/52. Thus, 4/52 + 4/52 = 8/52, and that's the answer. ◆

Example 4.14 Let's revisit the lottery winners where 184 winners first purchased a luxury vehicle, 127 purchased a cruise and 75 made "other" purchases. Now let's find the probability that a winner selected at random first purchased a cruise or an "other" purchase.

◆ **Solution:**
The events C (the purchase was a cruise) and R (the purchase was an "other" purchase) are mutually exclusive. So we compute the probability of C or R as follows:

$$P(C \text{ or } R) = P(C) + P(R) = \frac{127}{386} + \frac{75}{386} = \frac{202}{386} \quad ◆$$

$P(A \text{ or } B)$ for Events That Are Not Mutually Exclusive
When events A and B are *not* mutually exclusive, we must adjust the addition formula to compute the probability that at least one of them occurs in this way:

$$P(A \text{ or } B) = P(A) + P(B) - P(A \text{ and } B) \tag{4.6}$$

The following examples show the use of the addition rule when events aren't mutually exclusive:

Example 4.15 If we draw a card from a standard 52-card deck, what's the probability that the card is a 7 or it is red?

◆ **Solution:**
We know that $P(\text{card is a 7})$ is 4/52. And because half the cards in the deck are red (the others are black), $P(\text{card is red})$ is 26/52. Since the events are *not* mutually exclusive, we must also determine $P(\text{the card is both a 7 and it is red})$. A few non-card players may not know that there are two red 7s (the 7 of hearts and the 7 of diamonds), so $P(\text{the card is a 7 and it is red})$ is 2/52. We then use the addition formula for non-mutually exclusive events to find the probability that at least one of the specified events occurs. That is, $P(7 \text{ or red}) = P(7) + P(\text{red}) - P(7 \text{ and red}) = 4/52 + 26/52 - 2/52 = 28/52$. Note that the two red 7s have been counted twice—once as a 7 and once as a red card. The subtraction of 2/52 occurs so that the same cards are not double-counted. ◆

Example 4.16 What's the probability that a lottery winner chosen at random from our list either first purchased a luxury vehicle or is male?

◆ **Solution:**
The following contingency table will help give us the answer:

	Luxury Vehicle (L)	Cruise (C)	Other (R)	Total
Male (M)	145	85	23	253
Female (F)	39	42	52	133
Total	184	127	75	386

As you can see, $P(L) = 184/386$, $P(M) = 253/386$, and $P(L \text{ and } M) = 145/386$.

$$P(L \text{ or } M) = P(L) + P(M) - P(L \text{ and } M)$$

$$= \frac{184}{386} + \frac{253}{386} - \frac{145}{386} = \frac{292}{386} \text{ or } .7565 \quad ◆$$

The Complement of an Event

We've seen earlier that the sum of the probabilities of all the simple events in a sample space must equal 1. That is, $\sum P(E) = 1$. So when we toss a fair coin one time, there's a 1/2 chance we'll get a head, a 1/2 chance we'll get a tail, and the probabilities of the mutually exclusive outcome resulting from a single coin flip (112 + 1/2) must sum to 1. Let's assume now that we toss the coin four times and want to find the probability that we get *at least* one head. A direct and somewhat tedious way to solve this problem is discussed in the next chapter, but with a little logic we can tackle it here by first computing the probability that we get *all tails* and no heads in the four tosses. Since the tosses are independent events, $P(T) = (1/2)(1/2)(1/2)(1/2) = 1/16$. Thus, if the probability that we get four tails in four flips is 1/16, then the probability that we can expect at least one head at some time in the four tosses must be $1 - 1/16$ or 15/16.

We've just used the *complement* of an event to solve a problem.

> The **complement** of event E—denoted $\bar{E}$—consists of all possible outcomes from the sample space that are *not* in event E.

Thus, the complement of event E is the event that E *doesn't* happen. If we roll a die and let $E = \{$the roll of the die is less than 5$\}$, then $\bar{E} = \{$the roll of the die is 5 or more$\}$. And if we choose a lottery winner at random from our lottery winners and let $L = \{$the first purchase is for a luxury vehicle$\}$, then $\bar{L} = \{$the first purchase is not for a luxury vehicle$\}$.

Events E and $\bar{E}$ must be mutually exclusive, so $P(E$ or $\bar{E}) = P(E) + P(\bar{E})$. Since it's certain that event E will either occur or it will not occur, $P(E$ or $\bar{E}) = 1$. Thus, $P(E) + P(\bar{E}) = 1$, and solving this equation for $P(\bar{E})$ gives us a formula for computing the probability of the complement of an event:

$$P(\bar{E}) = 1 - P(E) \tag{4.7}$$

Perhaps some examples will help:

Example 4.17   We know the probability that A (the roll of a die is less than 5) is 4/6. So the probability that the roll is *not* less than a 5 is $1 - 4/6$ or 2/6. So the event $\bar{A}$ (the roll is a 5 or a 6) has a probability of 2/6. ◆

Example 4.18   Let's let $P(L)$ represent the probability that we randomly select a lottery winner who first purchased a luxury vehicle. Thus $P(L)$ is 184/386. And if we let $\bar{L}$ represent the complement in this example—that is, the winner does not purchase a luxury vehicle—then $P(\bar{L}) = 1 - P(L) = 1 - 184/386 = 202/386$. This is the same result we obtained earlier when we computed the probability that the lottery winner first purchased a cruise or an "other" purchase. As you can see, it's often easier to use the formula for complementary events to compute various probabilities. ◆

Example 4.19   A study published in *Physical Therapy* reported on the relationship that existed between a subject's age and the normal active range of motion of hip and knee joints. The sample consisted of 1,683 persons. Of the subjects in the group, 821 were male and 862 were female, 433 were 25 to 39 years of age, 727 were 40 to 59 years of age, and 523 were 60 to 74 years of age. A person is picked from this study at random (we'll assume that gender and age are independent variables). Find the probability that the subject is

a) Age 25 to 39.
b) A female.
c) A female aged 25 to 39.
d) Not a female aged 25 to 39.
e) Age 25 to 39 or is a female.

◆ **Solution:**
a) There were 433 people aged 25 to 39 out of the sample of 1,683. Thus, 433/1,683 = .2573.
b) There were 862 females, so 862/1,683 = .5122.
c) To compute this joint probability (no pun intended), we'll use the multiplication rule for independent events. Thus, the probability is (.2573) (.5122) = .1318.
d) Using the rule for complements, the probability is 1 − .1318 = .8682.
e) We use the addition rule for non-mutually exclusive events in this example. Thus, *P*(age 25 to 39 or female) = .2573 + .5122 − .1318 = .6377. (We have to remember to subtract here so that the females in the given age category are not counted twice.) ◆

An Application of Probability—Bayes' Theorem

One form of Bayes' Theorem is the following:

$$P(A|B) = \frac{P(A)P(B|A)}{P(A)P(B|A) + P(\overline{A})P(B|\overline{A})}$$

Consider the process of "screening" for a disease such as cancer. Let A denote the event the person being tested has the disease, and B, the event of a positive biopsy—that is, B occurs when the diagnostic procedure indicates the person *does* have the disease. We will assume that $P(A) = 0.0001$, $P(B|A) = 0.99$ (the test correctly identifies 99 percent of all people who have the disease), and $P(B|\overline{A}) = 0.001$ (the test gives one false positive, on the average, out of every 1,000 people). Find $P(B|A)$, the probability a person actually does have cancer, given that the biopsy says he or she does. The answer is not at all what we would expect.

$$P(A|B) = \frac{P(A)P(B|A)}{P(A)P(B|A) + P(\overline{A})P(B|\overline{A})} = \frac{(0.0001)(0.99)}{(0.0001)(0.99) + (0.9999)(0.001)} = 0.09$$

That is, only 9 percent of the people identified as having the disease actually do.
   The table below shows that $P(B|A)$ strongly depends on $P(A)$ and on $P(B|A)$, Note that as the disease becomes more prevalent, the result becomes closer to what we would expect.

P(A)	P(B | A)	P(A | B)
0.0001	0.001	0.09
	0.0001	0.49
0.001	0.001	0.49
	0.0001	0.90
0.01	0.001	0.91
	0.0001	0.99

This example calls into question the practicality of large-scale screening programs, especially if the testing itself may be a hazard, such as annual chest X-rays for tuberculosis.

Self-Testing Review 4.2

14. Three jars are used in the Pennsylvania Lottery Lucky Number drawing. Each jar contains ten ping-pong balls, and each ball is marked with a different digit 0, 1, 2, ... , 9. The balls are mixed, and one is randomly selected from each jar.

a) What is the probability that the ball selected from the first jar is a 7?

b) What is the probability that the ball selected from the second jar is a 7, given the ball from the first was a 7?

c) What's the probability the ball selected from the third jar is a 7, given that each of the balls in the first two jars was a 7?

d) On January 27, 1993, the lucky number for the Pennsylvania lottery was 777. What is the probability that this three-digit number will be drawn on any given day?

e) On the same day, the number in the New York Lottery was also 777. What's the probability that the number 777 will be selected in both states on the same day?

15. A single die is thrown. What is the probability it is

a) At least a 4?

b) An odd number?

c) A 4 or an odd number?

16. A box of parts contains eight good items and two defective items. If two are selected at random *with replacement*—that is, the first item *is* replaced before the second is drawn—find the probability that

a) Both items are good.

b) Both items are defective.

c) The first is good and the second is defective.

d) The first is defective and the second is good.

e) One is defective and the other isn't.

f) At least one is defective.

17. A box of parts contains eight good items and two defective ones. If two are selected at random *without replacement*—that is, the first item *isn't* replaced before the second is drawn—find the probability that

a) Both items are good.

b) Both items are defective.

c) The first is good and the second is defective.

d) The first is defective and the second is good.

e) One is defective and the other isn't.

f) At least one is defective.

18. A music collector owns the following CDs:

Artist	Number of Albums
Celine Dion	22
Shania Twain	4
Ricky Martin	8
Santana	30
Diana Krall	4
Sarah McLachlan	7
Other	150

What is the probability that a randomly selected CD from this collection is by

a) Shania Twain?

b) Ricky Martin?

c) Either Celine Dion or Santana?

d) One of the named artists?

19. A survey was given to three groups: 50 city residents, 50 college students, and 30 bicyclists. One question each person was asked was his or her opinion on municipal support of bicycling and alternative transportation. The results are as follows:

Rating	City	College	Cyclists
Excellent	3	0	0
Very good	8	3	0
Good	13	23	8
Not so good	15	15	8
Poor	9	7	11
Very poor	2	2	3

What's the probability that a randomly selected

a) City resident has an excellent opinion of municipal support of bicycling and alternative transportation?

b) City resident has at least a good opinion of municipal support of bicycling and alternative transportation?

c) College student has a not-so-good opinion of municipal support of bicycling and alternative transportation?

d) Person from the three groups combined has a good opinion of municipal support of bicycling and alternative transportation?

e) Person from the three groups combined has a poor or very poor opinion of municipal support of bicycling and alternative transportation?

20. A survey was taken in which demographics were recorded on the users of a university's recreation centre. The first table that follows describes the background of 199 rec centre users, while the second table gives the class level of the 178 students in the survey.

Type of User	Frequency	Class Levels	Frequency
Students	178	First year	30
Faculty/Staff	17	Second year	28
Alumni	2	Third year	37
Spouse	2	Fourth year	75
		Grad	8

What's the probability that a randomly selected person in the survey is

a) A student?

b) Not faculty/staff?

What's the probability that a randomly selected student in the survey is

c) A fourth-year student?

d) A first-year or fourth-year student?

e) Not a grad student?

21. MarineLand in Niagara Falls is interested in the entertainment value of its shows. Suppose 60 people who had viewed the shows were asked to rate their entertainment value. The following are the results:

Entertainment Value	Frequency
Outstanding	28
Good	14
Fair	5
Poor	13

What is the probability that a randomly selected person from this group

a) Thought the entertainment value was outstanding?

b) Thought the entertainment value was good or outstanding?

c) Thought the entertainment value was at least fair?

22. A survey was taken concerning the attitudes of students towards a university's no-alcohol policy. The table that follows represents a breakdown by gender of the responses to the question, Do you think the university should remain a dry campus?

	Response	
Gender	Yes	No
Male	20	30
Female	25	25

What is the probability that a randomly selected student in this survey

a) Responded "no"?

b) Is a female who responded "no"?

c) Responded "no" or is a female?

d) Responded "no," given that she is a female?

Now, show that the events of saying "no" and being female are not

e) Mutually exclusive.

f) Independent.

23. In a Canadian Motor Vehicle Traffic Collision Statistics (2000) report, the following information is given regarding licensed drivers:

NUMBER OF LICENSED DRIVERS BY GENDER AND BY AGE

Age Group	Males	Females	Total
< 16	25,484	17,701	43,185
16–19	558,444	486,789	1,045,233
20–24	886,050	807,296	1,693,346
25–34	2,000,747	1,873,982	3,874,729
35–44	2,530,510	2,365,842	4,896,352
45–54	2,124,205	1,942,558	4,066,763
55–64	1,337,787	1,131,753	2,469,540
65+	1,424,207	1,072,642	2,496,849
Total	10,887,434	9,698,563	20,585,997

A licensed Canadian driver is selected at random. Find the probability that this person

a) Is in the 25- to 34-year age category.

b) Is a male.

c) Is a male who is under 16 years of age.

d) Is either a female or is in the 65+ age category.

e) Is not in the 35- to 44-year age category.

f) Is not under 16 nor is female.

g) Is in the 20- to 24-year age category, given that the person is a male.

h) Is under 16, given that the person is female.

i) Is a male, given that the person is in the 20- to 24-year age category.

Now, are the events of being female and being in the 65+ age category

j) Mutually exclusive? Show why or why not.

k) Independent? Show why or why not.

24. The numbers of full-time students enrolled at universities in Nova Scotia in 2002 are given below:

University	Male	Female	Total
Acadia	1,582	2,097	3,679
UCCB	1,193	1,458	2,651
Dalhousie	4,574	6,064	10,638
Mount Saint Vincent	340	1,785	2,125
Saint Mary's	2,396	2,702	5,098
St. Francis Xavier	1,496	1,982	3,478
Total	11,581	16,088	27,669

A university student is chosen at random from the province. Find the probability that the student is

  a) From Acadia or Mount Saint Vincent University.

  b) Not from St. Francis Xavier University.

  c) A male from Saint Mary's University.

  d) Either from Dalhousie University or is a male.

  e) A female, given that the student is from UCCB.

Now, are the events of being female and being from St. Francis Xavier

  f) Mutually exclusive? Show why or why not.

  g) Independent? Show why or why not.

25. Statistics Canada reported that 2001 census counts for both sexes, for Canada, provinces, and territories are as follows:

Name	Under 20	20–64	65 and over	Total
Canada	7,778,865	18,339,680	3,888,550	30,007,095
Newfoundland and Labrador	128,220	321,650	63,055	512,930
Prince Edward Island	36,875	79,850	18,575	135,295
Nova Scotia	226,775	554,665	126,565	908,005
New Brunswick	180,770	449,795	98,935	729,500
Québec	1,753,650	4,524,015	959,815	7,237,480
Ontario	3,002,165	6,935,710	1,472,170	11,410,045
Manitoba	314,140	649,030	156,420	1,119,585
Saskatchewan	285,540	545,820	147,570	978,930
Alberta	840,550	1,825,855	308,405	2,974,810
British Columbia	976,350	2,398,305	533,090	3,907,735
Yukon	8,325	18,620	1,725	28,670
Northwest Territories	13,060	22,665	1,630	37,360
Nunavut	12,445	13,705	600	26,745

Source: Statistics Canada, 2001 Census of Population.

If a person residing in Canada in that year was selected at random, what is the probability that, at that time, he or she

  a) Was under 20?

  b) Was at most 64?

  c) Lived in Ontario?

  d) Lived in Alberta or British Columbia?

  e) Was from 20 to 64 and lived in Ontario?

  f) Was at least 20 and lived in Ontario?

  g) Was from 20 to 64 or lived in Saskatchewan?

  h) Was from 20 to 64, given that he or she lived in Saskatchewan?

  i) Was at least 65, given that he or she lived in British Columbia?

  j) Lived in British Columbia, given that he or she was from 20 to 64?

  k) Lived in Québec or Ontario, given that he or she was under 20?

4.3 Random Variables, Probability Distributions, and Expected Values

You saw in Chapter 3 that a variable is a characteristic of interest that's possessed by each item under study. Of course, the value of this characteristic will likely vary from one item in the data set to the next. You also saw in Chapter 3 that we can group observed data items into a frequency distribution and then graphically portray the results using a histogram or frequency polygon. And in this chapter you've learned some basic probability concepts. We can now build on what you've learned to introduce you to random variables and probability distributions.

Random Variables

Many probability experiments have outcomes that are *numerical* observations, counts, or measurements.

> A **random variable** (identified by a symbol such as x) has a single numerical value for each outcome of a probability experiment.

Thus, x can assume any of the numbers associated with the possible outcomes of the experiment, and the particular value that x assumes in any single trial of an experiment is a chance or random outcome.

You saw in Chapter 3 that a discrete variable has a countable or finite number of values. Similarly, a **discrete random variable** is one in which all possible values can be counted or listed. And like a continuous variable that can assume any one of the countless number of values along a line interval, a **continuous random variable** has an infinite number of values that can fall, without interruption, along an unbroken interval. Continuous random variables are typically created when measurements are involved. But since measurements can be produced to give any desired number of decimal points, it's impossible to list all the possible values.

Let's look at some probability experiment examples now to help clarify the terms we've just considered.

Example 4.20   We count the number of kernels on an ear of corn. The variable is discrete since the values of 1, 2, 3, ..., can be listed. ◆

Example 4.21   We measure the length of an ear of corn. The variable is continuous since possible values include 15.325 cm, 14.9873 cm, and so on. All such values couldn't possibly be listed. ◆

Example 4.22   We time the period needed to harvest the corn. We are measuring time, so the variable is continuous. ◆

Example 4.23   We determine the number of trucks needed to ship the corn. The variable is discrete. We can count the number of trucks, and we certainly can't send a fractional part of a truck to the grain buyer. ◆

Probability Distributions

If we list all the possible values of a discrete random variable from a probability experiment and further list all of the probabilities associated with these values, then we have created a *probability distribution for a discrete random variable.*

> A **probability distribution for a discrete random variable** gives the probability for each of the values of the random variable.

Let's create a probability distribution for a discrete random variable by considering all the possible outcomes that you could get in a single roll of your favourite pair of dice. Your little cousin has just used fingernail polish to paint one die red (!), but that won't ruin our example. The spots facing up in a single roll of the dice must total 2, 3, 4, ... , 11, or 12. What's the probability that in a single roll your result is 2? Since there's a 1/6 chance that the white die will produce a 1, and a 1/6 chance that the red die will show a 1, and since these are independent results, the probability that both yield a 1 to produce a total of 2 is (1/6) (1/6) or 1/36. Now what's the probability that in your next roll the result is 3? You can get this result either by rolling a 1 on the white die and a 2 on the red die or by getting a 2 on the white die and a 1 on the red die. The probability of a 1 on the white die and a 2 on the red die is computed as follows:

$$P(1 \text{ on white and 2 on red}) = P(1 \text{ on white}) \times P(2 \text{ on red}) = \left(\frac{1}{6}\right)\left(\frac{1}{6}\right) = \frac{1}{36}$$

The probability of 2 on white and 1 on red is

$$P(2 \text{ on white and 1 on red}) = P(2 \text{ on white}) \times P(1 \text{ on red}) = \left(\frac{1}{6}\right)\left(\frac{1}{6}\right) = \frac{1}{36}$$

Since we want to know the probability that one or the other of these mutually exclusive events will occur, we now use the *addition rule* to determine the probability of throwing a 3 with the pair of dice:

$$P(3) = P(1 \text{ on white and 2 on red}) + P(2 \text{ on white and 1 on red}) = \frac{1}{36} + \frac{1}{36} = \frac{2}{36}$$

The probabilities of throwing a 4, 5, 6, 7, 8, 9, 10, 11, or 12 may be computed in the same way. The complete probability distribution is shown in *Figure 4.6*.

There are two rules that apply to this or any other probability distribution:

1. The probabilities in a probability distribution are numbers that are on the interval from 0 to 1. That is, the probabilities—let's label them $P(x)$—are always $0 \leq P(x) \leq 1$. In our example, the values range from 1/36 (.0278) to 6/36 (.167).

2. All of the probabilities in a probability distribution must add up to 1. That is, $\Sigma P(x) = 1$. Since the distribution in our example is a complete listing of *all* the possible values of the random variable, the probability that one or the other of these values will occur is a certainty.

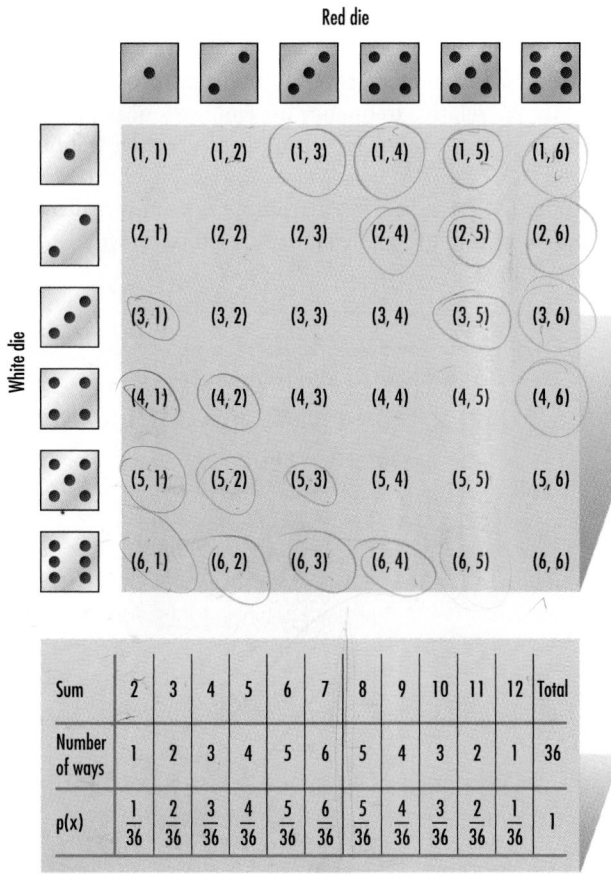

Sum	2	3	4	5	6	7	8	9	10	11	12	Total
Number of ways	1	2	3	4	5	6	5	4	3	2	1	36
p(x)	$\frac{1}{36}$	$\frac{2}{36}$	$\frac{3}{36}$	$\frac{4}{36}$	$\frac{5}{36}$	$\frac{6}{36}$	$\frac{5}{36}$	$\frac{4}{36}$	$\frac{3}{36}$	$\frac{2}{36}$	$\frac{1}{36}$	1

These rules should seem familiar to you since they are quite similar to the probability properties discussed earlier in the chapter.

Relative Frequency Distributions You saw earlier in this chapter that probabilities could be assigned based on the number of times each event of interest occurred in a total number of trials. If we didn't intuitively know that 1/6 was the probability of rolling a given face on a die, we could roll the die 6,000 times and observe the results. If the die is fair or true, the resulting frequency distribution would show that each face appeared *about* (not exactly) 1,000 times, as in column 2 in the following table:

Die Face	Face Appearances	Proportion of Times Face Appears
1	985	.1642
2	1,005	.1675
3	1,020	.1700
4	979	.1632
5	992	.1653
6	1,019	.1698
Total	6,000	1.0000

If we then divided each of these face totals by 6,000, we would get the proportion of times the surface faces up (column 3 in the table), and we would have a **relative frequency distribution.** As we'll see in later chapters, several important probability distributions are used to approximate the relative frequency distributions of the populations being studied. For now, let's look at the following example of a relative frequency distribution.

When first-year university students were asked for the number of universities they applied to other than the one they were attending, the student responses, together with their relative frequencies, were as follows:

Number of Other Universities Applied to (x)	Proportion of Times Response Was Given [$P(x)$]
0	.377
1	.147
2	.158
3	.137
4	.078
5	.047
6	.056
Total	1.000

Let's consider these questions relating to this relative frequency distribution:

Example 4.24   What's the probability that a randomly chosen first-year student applied to four universities other than the one he or she was attending?

◆ **Solution:**
From the table, we see that $P(x = 4)$ is .078. ◆

Example 4.25   What is the probability a first-year student applied to *at least* four universities other than the one she or he was attending?

◆ **Solution:**
In this context, "at least 4" means 4 *or* 5 *or* 6. Applying to four other universities is mutually exclusive to applying to five other schools, which, in turn, is mutually exclusive to applying to six others. So, $P(\text{at least } 4) = P(4) + P(5) + P(6) = .078 + .047 + .056 = .181$. ◆

Example 4.26   What's the probability that a first-year student applied to *at least* one other college?

◆ **Solution:**
We could add the probabilities of $x = 1, 2, 3, 4, 5$, and 6 to get the answer. A more efficient way, however, is to use the concept of complementary events. The complement to "applying to at least one other university" is "applying to no other university." From the table we see that $P(x = 0) = .377$, and $P(x \geq 1) = 1 - .377 = .623$. ◆

A Probability Distribution Graph   We've seen how probability distributions can be presented in tables. But discrete probability distributions are frequently shown graph-

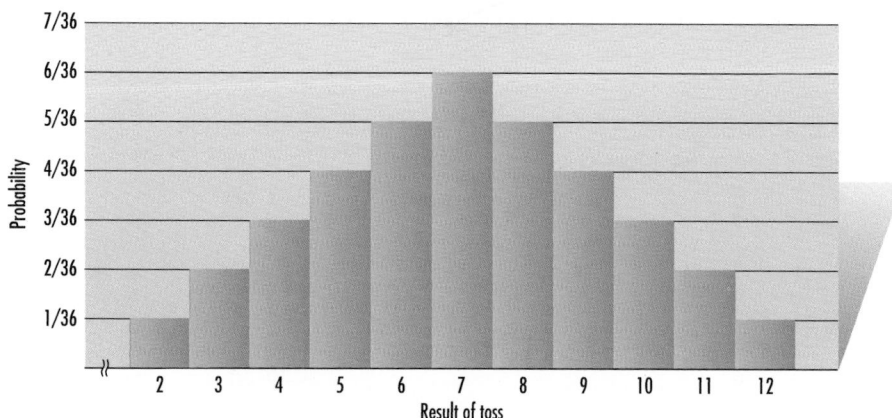

FIGURE 4.7 A histogram of the probability distribution of the results of throwing a pair of dice.

ically through the use of histograms (bar graphs) and frequency polygons (line graphs). We'll demonstrate the use of a histogram here, but other graphs depicting continuous probability distributions are also shown in the next chapter.

The probability distribution table giving the results of throwing a pair of dice was shown a few paragraphs earlier. The histogram for this same discrete probability distribution is shown in *Figure 4.7*. The possible numbers that could result when the pair of dice are rolled are centred in each bar on the horizontal axis. (These possible results are 2, 3, 4, ... , 11, 12.) And the probability values associated with each possible outcome are plotted on the vertical scale. Thus, the height of each bar corresponds to the probability of getting the associated numerical result when the dice are thrown.

Expected Values

Another way to describe a probability distribution is to determine the theoretical average (mean) value that we could expect if we conducted an infinite number of trials. This measure of central tendency for a random variable is called its **mean** or its **expected value.** And the formula used to compute the mean or expected value for a discrete random variable is

$$\mu = E(x) = \sum[x \cdot P(x)] \tag{4.8}$$

where μ = the mean of x
   $E(x)$ = the expected value of x
   x = the value of each possible outcome
   $P(x)$ = the probability of that possible outcome

That is,

$E(x)$ = [(value of possible outcome 1) (probability of outcome 1) + (value of possible outcome 2) (probability of outcome 2) + ⋯ + (value of possible outcome n)(probability of outcome n)].

A little earlier we were given the following information describing first-year university students:

Number of Other Universities Applied to (x)	Proportion of Times Response Was Given [P(x)]
0	.317
1	.147
2	.158
3	.137
4	.078
5	.047
6	.056

Now, let's calculate the expected value—that is, the mean number of university applications first-year students sent out to schools other than the ones they are attending:

$$\mu = E(x) = \sum[x \cdot P(x)]$$
$$= 0(.377) + 1(.147) + 2(.158) + 3(.137) + 4(.078) + 5(.047) + 6(.056) = 1.757$$

Of course, this doesn't mean that a particular student sent out 1.757 applications in addition to the one sent to the school being attended. (How would he or she submit three quarters of an application?) What it does mean is that if the responses of a large number of students are analyzed, the average would be about 1.757 applications submitted per student.

Let's now consider a few other examples that show how a knowledge of expected value can help you make better choices about how to risk your money.

Example 4.27   Suppose you're asked to buy a $25 raffle ticket for a car valued at $19,500 and you're told that "only" 1,000 tickets will be sold. Is this a good way to spend your money?

◆ **Solution:**
There are two possible outcomes. You'll either win the car and gain $19,475 (the $19,500 car less the $25 that you don't get back), or you'll lose the raffle and your $25. Thus, your expected value is

$$E(x) = [x \cdot P(x)]$$
$$= \left[(\$19,475)\left(\frac{1}{1,000}\right) + (-\$25)\left(\frac{999}{1,000}\right)\right] = [(\$19.475) + (-\$24.975)]$$
$$= -\$5.50$$

Since the expected value is negative, on the average you'll lose by buying the raffle ticket. You'll effectively contribute $5.50 for each ticket you buy. In fact, even if you buy all 1,000 tickets to assure a win, you'll still lose big time. ◆

Example 4.28   Now suppose Peter Parker of Chapter 3 fame offers to pay you a dollar for each spot that appears on the surface of a die in a single toss. The price charged by Peter for each roll of the die is $3.00. Would you want to play?

◆ **Solution:**

In Peter's game there are six possible outcomes and six different payout amounts, as shown in the following table:

Die Surface (and Dollar Value) (x)	Probability of Occurrence of Surface P(x)	Die Surface × Probability of Occurrence x · P(x)
1	1/6	.17
2	1/6	.33
3	1/6	.50
4	1/6	.67
5	1/6	.83
6	1/6	1.00
Totals	1.00	3.50

$\mu = E(x) = \Sigma[x \cdot P(x)]$
= \$3.50, the expected average win

If you played Peter's game long enough, you could expect an average win of \$3.50 on each roll of the die. It would be impossible, of course, to win \$3.50 on a single roll, but you ought to be able to eventually clean Peter out. If, for example, you play 1,000 games, your expected value will be (1,000) (\$3.50) or \$3,500, and your cost to play is (1,000) (\$3.00) or \$3,000. Peter again is victimized by statistical confusion. ◆

To further describe a probability distribution, we can calculate the standard deviation of the random variable. To obtain the standard deviation of a discrete random variable, we compute the following:

$$\sigma = \sqrt{\Sigma[(x - \mu)^2 P(x)]} \qquad (4.9)$$

where
σ = the standard deviation of a discrete random variable
$(x - \mu)^2$ = the square of the difference of each value from the mean
$P(x)$ = the probability of that possible outcome

The quantity under the square root is called the **variance** and is denoted by σ^2. That is,

$\sigma^2 = $ [(value of possible outcome 1 – the mean)^2(probability of outcome 1) + (value of possible outcome 2 – the mean)^2(probability of outcome 2) + ⋯ + (value of possible outcome n – the mean)^2(probability of outcome n)]

Example 4.29   Returning to the information on university applications, calculate the standard deviation of the number of university applications sent by first-year students to schools other than the one they are attending.

◆ **Solution:**

We begin by calculating the variance:

$\sigma^2 = (0 - 1.757)^2(.377) + (1 - 1.757)^2(.147) + (2 - 1.757)^2(.158) + (3 - 1.757)^2(.137)$
$+ (4 - 1.757)^2(.078) + (5 - 1.757)^2(.047) + (6 - 1.757)^2(.056)$
$= 3.361$

Then the standard deviation is computed by taking the square root of the variance:

$$\sigma = \sqrt{\Sigma[(x - \mu)^2 P(x)]} = \sqrt{\sigma^2} = \sqrt{3.364} = 1.83 \blacklozenge$$

This method of calculating the standard deviation of a discrete random variable can be tedious and cause rounding errors. A **shortcut** formula for the standard deviation that reduces these problems is

$$\sigma = \sqrt{\Sigma[x^2 P(x)] - \mu^2} \qquad (4.10)$$

While at first glance this may not look easier to calculate than the original formula for σ, the new formula requires only one subtraction, which decreases the labour and the amount of rounding error. ◆

□ **Example 4.30**   Returning to the example above, recalculate the standard deviation using the shortcut formula.

◆ **Solution:**
We first calculate

$$\begin{aligned}
\Sigma[x^2 P(x)] &= 0^2(.377) + 1^2(.147) + 2^2(.158) + 3^2(.137) + 4^2(.078) + 5^2(.047) + 6^2(.056) \\
&= 0(.377) + 1(.147) + 4(.158) + 9(.137) + 16(.078) + 25(.047) + 36(.056) \\
&= 6.451
\end{aligned}$$

Then,

$$\sigma = \sqrt{\Sigma[x^2 P(x)] - \mu^2} = \sqrt{6.451 - 1.757^2} = \sqrt{3.364} = 1.83 \blacklozenge$$

Self-Testing Review 4.3

26. During 20 consecutive concerts, Hootie and the Blowfish played 115 different songs. A probability distribution for the number of times each of the 115 songs was played follows:

Number of Times Song Was Played

(x)	P(x)
1	.174
2	.339
3	.235
4	.191
5	.017
6	.009
7	.009
8	.000
9	.017
10	.009
Total	1.000

a) Construct a probability histogram for x (the number of times a song was played).

b) Compute the expected value for x.

c) Calculate the standard deviation of x.

27. Autistic children are often evaluated and given a developmental score from 1 to 5, where 1 represents the absence of signs (normal development), and 5 represents the maximal severity of signs (severe retardation). One proposed probability distribution for the developmental scores of autistic children is as follows:

Developmental Score (x)	P(x)
1	.19
2	.05
3	.14
4	.48
5	.14
Total	1.00

Assuming that this probability distribution is correct:

a) What's the probability that an autistic child has a developmental score of 3?

b) What's the probability that an autistic child has a developmental score of at least 3?

c) Construct a probability histogram for x (the developmental score).

d) Find the expected value of x.

e) Calculate the standard deviation of x.

28. A committee was formed to study the problem of parking spaces (or lack thereof) at Studywell University. Research was done to study enrollment patterns. It was found that 8 percent of the students were enrolled in classes one day a week, 19 percent had classes two days a week, 35 percent attended classes on three days, 29 percent were in class four days a week, and 9 percent had classes on five days.

a) Construct a probability distribution table for x (the number of days a student is enrolled in classes at Studywell).

b) Construct a probability histogram for x.

c) What's the probability a student is enrolled at least three days a week?

d) Calculate the expected value for x.

e) Calculate the standard deviation of x.

29. An investor has a .60 probability of making a $20,000 profit and a .40 probability of suffering a $25,000 loss. What is the expected value? Should she make the investment based on the expected value?

30. A speculator is thinking about investing $1,000 in a company's stock. She believes there is .8 probability of a takeover. If there is a takeover, the stock she purchased would be worth $3,000. If there is no takeover, the stock becomes totally worthless, and she will lose her money. What is her expected profit for purchasing this stock? Should she make the investment based on the expected value?

31. An automobile dealership in Calgary has compiled the following sales data over the past year:

Numbers of Cars Sold per Day	Relative Frequency
0	.20
1	.30
2	.30
3	.15
4	.05
Total	1.00

a) What's the estimated probability (using past data) there will be more than two cars sold in a day?

b) What is the probability that at least one car will be sold in a day?

c) What is the expected value of the number of cars sold in a day?

d) Based on the expected value, how many cars would the dealer expect to sell in a 31-day month?

32. A business college generously provided information on 59 of the college's graduates. The probability distributions for the number of courses each student repeated, the number of quarters each student was on academic probation, and the number of quarters each student made the dean's list are as follows:

Repeats	Count	Qtrs Acad. Prob.	Count	Dean's List	Count
0	44	0	42	0	27
3	1	1	8	1	11
4	4	2	5	2	6
6	1	3	2	3	2
7	1	4	2	4	6
8	2	Total	59	6	2
9	1			9	2
11	1			10	2
12	1			12	1
14	1			Total	59
16	1				
19	1				
Total	59				

What's the probability that a randomly selected grad has

a) Not repeated any course?

b) Been on academic probation exactly one time?

c) Been on the dean's list multiple times?

Now,

d) Construct a probability histogram for x(the number of classes repeated).

e) Find the expected value of x.

f) Calculate the standard deviation of x.

g) Construct a probability histogram for y(the number of times on academic probation).

h) Find the expected value of y.

i) Calculate the standard deviation of y.

j) Construct a probability histogram for w(the number of times on the dean's list).

k) Find the expected value of w.

l) Calculate the standard deviation of w.

33. A college's basketball team played 30 games with a three-guard rotation. The probability distributions for $x =$ the number of rebounds and $y =$ the number of assists per game for the three guards are as follows:

Reb/Game	Count
4	2
5	3
6	4
7	4
8	5
9	3
10	2
11	3
12	1
13	1
14	2
Total	30

Ast/Game	Count
4	2
5	4
6	1
7	3
8	3
9	2
10	2
11	5
12	4
13	0
14	2
15	1
16	0
17	0
18	0
19	0
20	0
21	0
22	1
Total	30

What's the probability that in one game the guards

a) Get five rebounds?

b) Get no more than five rebounds?

c) Get more than ten assists?

Now,

d) Find the expected value of x.

e) Calculate the standard deviation of x.

f) Find the expected value of y.

g) Calculate the standard deviation of y.

L O O K I N G   B A C K

1. A number of basic terms were defined early in this chapter, and you saw that the probability of a specified event was the relative likelihood of that event occurring. Simple probabilities are assigned using *a priori*, relative frequency, and intuitive approaches. Regardless of how probability values are assigned, though, a probability of 0 means that an event can never occur, and a probability of 1 means it will always occur. Probabilities of interest, of course, lie between these two extremes.

2. In the language of probability, a simple event is one that can't be broken down any further. But we're often interested in the relative chance that some combination of events—that is, a compound event—may occur. We first considered a conditional probability—the probability that event B occurs, given that event A has already happened [or $P(B|A)$]. Often, we can use contingency tables to present the facts for a conditional probability situation. To compute the probability of both A and B happening, we multiply the probability of the first event times the conditional probability of the second event, given that the first has happened.

3. A second compound event category is the event that A *and* B both happen [or $P(A$ and $B)$]. To compute the joint probability A and B, we multiply the probability of the first event times the conditional probability of the second event, given that the first has happened $P(B|A)$. If we can see that the two events in question are independent—that is, that the simple probability of event B is the same as the conditional probability of B, given $A[P(B) = P(B|A)]$—then we can simply multiply the individual probabilities of events A and B to obtain our answer for $P(A$ and $B)$.

4. A third compound event is the event that either A or B or possibly both occur $[P(A$ or $B)]$. To compute the probability of A or B, we first add the individual probabilities of each event A and B, and then, to avoid double counting, we subtract the joint probability $[P(A$ and $B)]$. When it can be seen that A and B are mutually exclusive—that is, when the occurrence of one of these events within a single trial prevents the other from happening—we can compute the probability of A or B by simply adding the individual probabilities.

5. The complement of an event E, denoted $\bar{E}$, consists of all possible events in the sample space that are *not* in event E. Since events E and $\bar{E}$ are mutually exclusive and it's certain that either E will occur or $\bar{E}$ will happen, we can compute the probability of $\bar{E}$ by subtracting the probability of E from 1. Sometimes, to compute the probability of an event, it may be simpler to find the probability of its complementary event and then subtract that result from 1.

6. A random variable (identified by a symbol such as x) has a single numerical value for each outcome of a probability experiment. These outcomes occur at random. A discrete random variable is one in which all possible values can be listed, often as a result of a counting process. Continuous random variables can take on an infinite number of values that fall without interruption along an unbroken interval, and they are typically created when measurements are made.

7. If we list all of the possible values of a discrete random variable and further list all of the probabilities associated with these values, we have created a probability distribution. There are two rules that apply to any probability distribution. First, the probabilities in a probability distribution are between

0 and 1. That is, the possible probability distribution values are always $0 \leq P(x) \leq 1$. And second, all of the probabilities in a probability distribution must add up to 1. That is, $\sum P(x) = 1$. A relative frequency distribution is one that shows the proportion of cases falling within each class interval in a study. As we'll see later, several important probability distributions are used to approximate the relative frequency distributions of the populations being studied. Probability distributions are frequently shown in graphic form through the use of histograms and frequency polygons.

8. Another way to describe a probability distribution is to determine the theoretical average (mean) value that we could expect to get if we conducted an infinite number of trials. This measure of central tendency for a discrete random variable is called its mean or its expected value. We can also measure its dispersion by calculating the variance and standard deviation for a discrete random variable.

Exercises

34. A total of 7,581 Canadians were asked how they felt about walking alone in their neighbourhood after dark. Of this total, 5,417 said they felt "safe" or "fairly safe." What's the probability that a Canadian walking in his or her neighbourhood after dark feels "safe" or "fairly safe"?

35. According to Statistics Canada, there were 147,040 new housing starts in Canada in a recent year. Of these, 29,351 were in British Columbia. What is the probability that a new housing start in Canada during that year was in British Columbia?

36. Two cards are drawn from a deck, and the first is replaced before the second is drawn. What's the probability that

  a) Both cards are aces?

  b) The first card is an ace and the second a king?

  c) The first card is a king and the second an ace?

  d) One card is an ace and the other is a king?

37. Two cards are drawn from a deck, and the first is not replaced before the second is drawn. What is the probability that

  a) Both cards are aces?

  b) The first card is an ace and the second a king?

  c) The first card is a king and the second an ace?

  d) One card is an ace and the other is a king?

38. A bin contains 7 defective and 19 non-defective batteries.

  a) If one battery is selected at random, what is the probability it is defective?

  b) If two batteries are selected at random without replacing the first, what is the probability both batteries are defective?

  c) If two batteries are taken without replacement, what is the probability that both are not defective?

  d) If two batteries are taken without replacement, what's the probability that at least one is defective?

39. A die is loaded, and the following probabilities are assigned for the possible outcomes of a single roll:

$P(1) = .15$, $P(2) = .20$, $P(3) = .05$, $P(4) = .25$, $P(5) = .20$, and $P(6) = .15$

  a) Find the probability that when the die is rolled, it will land on a 1 or 5.

  b) What's the probability that when the die is rolled, it will land on at least a 4?

40. The Health of the Off-Reserve Aboriginal Population (Statistics Canada, Catalogue 82- 003) reported the Aboriginal population aged 15 or older living in Canada, 2000/01 as follows:

Age	Probability
15–24	.244
25–34	.245
35–44	.240
45–54	.158
55–64	.060
65+	.053

Find the probability that a randomly selected person from this population is

  a) Between 25 and 34 years old.

  b) More than 54 years old.

  c) Under 25 or over 64.

41. A study of 431 junior and senior undergraduate business students—they responded to a questionnaire—was recently reported in *Advanced Management Journal*. In this study, 99 students expressed an interest in international business. Of these 99, 46 were female and 53 were male. Find the probability that a person who completed the questionnaire

a) Expressed an interest in a career in international business.

b) Was female, given that the person expressed an interest in a career in international business.

c) Was female and expressed an interest in a career in international business.

42. The manufacturer of an electromechanical kitchen appliance investigated 50 consumer complaints. In 18 cases the reason for the complaint was electrical, in 27 cases the reason was mechanical, and in 5 cases the reason was due to appearance. Furthermore, it was found that nine of the complaints were made after the warranty had expired. Eight of the nine were electrical in nature and one was due to appearance. What's the probability that a complaint is

a) Due to electrical problems?

b) Made after the warranty has expired?

c) Made after the warranty has expired and is due to electrical problems?

d) Made after the warranty has expired or is due to electrical problems?

43. Campus Apartment Rentals advertised 1,706 available units for students. These units are in the West, South, and Centre City apartment complexes, and they have one, two, and three bedrooms. The following contingency table summarizes the available units:

	West	South	Centre City	Total
One bedroom	97	277	175	549
Two bedrooms	156	315	261	732
Three bedrooms	99	229	97	425
Total	352	821	533	1,706

An apartment advertised by Campus Apartment Rentals is selected at random. What is the probability it is

a) In Centre City?

b) A three-bedroom unit?

c) In Centre City and is a three-bedroom unit?

d) In Centre City or is a three-bedroom unit?

e) In Centre City, given it is a three-bedroom unit?

f) A three-bedroom unit, given it is in Centre City?

Now, consider these questions:

g) Are the events of being in Centre City and being a three-bedroom unit mutually exclusive? Why or why not?

h) Are the events of being in Centre City and being a three-bedroom unit independent? Why or why not?

44. Due to high gasoline prices, a study was done to investigate the relationship between size and manufacturer of newly purchased automobiles. The results are listed in the following contingency table.

Manu-facturer	Sub-compact	Com-pact	Mid-size	Large	Total
A	1,073	52	2,185	78	3,388
B	220	133	2,044	86	2,483
C	618	95	1,720	82	2,515
D	606	97	3,021	91	3,815
E	941	150	3,185	238	4,514
Total	3,458	527	12,155	575	16,715

A newly purchased automobile is chosen at random. What's the probability that it is

a) A subcompact?

b) Made by manufacturer A?

c) A mid-size automobile, given that it is made by manufacturer E?

d) A subcompact made by manufacturer A?

e) Made by manufacturer B or manufacturer D?

f) A subcompact or is made by manufacturer C?

g) Not a mid-size automobile?

h) Made by manufacturer D, given that it is a mid-size automobile?

45. The table below summarizes the community type and degree of pollution for 268 locations in Ontario.

Location/Pollution	Low	Moderate	High	Total
Rural	33	23	9	65
Suburban	8	23	20	51
Urban	7	10	73	90
Commercial	3	11	48	62
Total	51	67	150	268

Suppose that one of these locations is selected randomly. What's the probability that the location is

a) Suburban?

b) Not commercial?

c) Rural, given that pollution is low?

d) Highly polluted, given that the location is urban?

e) Urban or highly polluted?

f) Rural or not highly polluted?

g) Commercial and moderately polluted?

h) Rural and not highly polluted?

46. For each of the following, is the random variable discrete or continuous?

a) The number of courses you will pass this semester.

b) The length of time you will sleep tomorrow night.

c) The distance you drive tomorrow.

d) The number of students who attend your next statistics class.

e) The amount of gasoline you buy next week.

f) The number of pens you own.

g) The thickness of your statistics book.

47. For each of the following, is the random variable discrete or continuous?

a) The time required to complete a phone call to a prospective client.

b) The number of calls to the client.

c) The number of articles purchased by the client.

d) The shipping weight of the articles.

e) The distance the articles are shipped.

48. The following table contains the probability distribution for x = the number of retransmissions necessary to successfully transmit a 1024K data package through a double satellite media.

x	0	1	2	3
$P(x)$	.75	.10	.05	.10

a) What is the probability of a 1024K data package requiring at least one retransmission?

b) Construct a probability histogram for the random variable x.

c) Compute the expected value for x.

d) Compute the standard deviation of x.

49. The probability distribution for a random variable x follows:

x	0	1	2	3
$P(x)$	.3	.5	.1	.1

a) What is the probability that $x = 1$ or more?

b) Construct a probability histogram for the random variable x.

c) Obtain the mean of x.

d) Compute the standard deviation of x.

50. In the game "Plinko" on *The Price is Right*, a contestant drops a chip, which randomly falls into a slot that is marked with a dollar designation. There are nine slots, two of which are marked $0, two are marked $100, two are marked $500, two are marked $1,000, and one is labelled $5,000.

a) If a chip is dropped, what's the probability that it will land in a $1,000 slot?

b) What's the probability a chip will land in a slot valued at less than $1,000?

c) What is the expected value for this game?

51. The marketing department of Gogeturn, Inc., has determined that for the next fiscal year there is a probability of .40 that the company will lose $10,000, a probability of .50 that it will gain $20,000, and a probability of .10 that it will gain $30,000. What is the expected value in this situation?

52. Suppose that of all Regina *Leader Post* subscribers, 65 percent regularly read the comics, 25 percent regularly read the sports pages, and 15 percent don't regularly read either the comics or the sports pages. What is the probability that a subscriber selected at random regularly reads

a) Either the comics or the sports pages or both?

b) Both the comics and the sports pages?

c) The sports pages, given that he or she regularly reads the comics?

53. A charity organization is holding a lottery for the following prizes: one for $1,000, five for $500, and ten for $200. The charity plans to sell 1,000 tickets for the lottery. You are asked to set a ticket price that is three times as large as the fair price. What price do you recommend?

54. In a large Vancouver school, 70 percent of the students own a Sony PlayStation 2, 15 percent own a Microsoft Xbox, and 25 percent own neither a Sony PlayStation 2 nor a Microsoft Xbox. What is the probability that a student selected at random owns

a) Either a Sony PlayStation 2 or a Microsoft Xbox or both?

b) Both a Sony PlayStation 2 and a Microsoft Xbox?

c) A Microsoft Xbox, given that the student owns a Sony PlayStation 2?

55. Suppose that of all people attending an exhibition, 5 percent go on the bungee jump (event B), 40 percent (of all people attending) are teenagers (event T), and 10 percent of all teenagers attending go on the bungee jump.

a) Find P(T and B).

b) Find P(T|B).

c) Are events T and B independent? Explain.

d) Are events T and B mutually exclusive? Explain.

56. For two events, A and B, P(A) = .6 and P(B) = .2

a) If A and B are independent, find P(A and B) and P(A or B)

b) If A and B are dependent with P(A|B) = .7, find P(A and B) and P(B/A).

57. A thrift store sells both new and used items. Forty percent of the items in stock are used. Fifty percent are used or defective. If 25 percent of the store's items are defective, what percentage are both used and defective?

58. A shipment of sandwiches arrived containing the following percentages of types: 55 percent ham and cheese, 25 percent tuna and cheese, 15 percent ham with no cheese, 5 percent tuna with no cheese. A sandwich is selected at random from the shipment. Find the probability that it contains ham or cheese.

59. Of all customers at a confectionery store, 40 percent purchase a Lotto 6/49 ticket, sixty percent purchase a Lotto 6/49 ticket or a Super 7 ticket, and 30 percent purchase a Super 7 ticket.

a) What percentage purchase both a Lotto 6/49 ticket and a Super 7 ticket?

b) What percentage of people who purchase a Lotto 6/49 ticket also purchase a Super 7 ticket?

c) What percentage of people who purchase a Super 7 ticket also purchase a Lotto 6/49 ticket?

d) If L denotes the event that any one randomly selected customer purchases a Lotto 6/49 ticket, and S denotes the event that any one randomly selected customer purchases a Super 7 ticket, are L and S independent? Justify your answer.

60. An electronic scanner is successful in detecting flaws in a material in 80 percent of the cases. Three material specimens containing flaws will be tested with the scanner. Assume that the tests are independent. Find the probability that the scanner is successful in at least one of the three cases.

61. The following table shows the opinions of 2000 Canadians on the federal government gun registration program.

Person	Opinion			
	Opposed	Neutral	Favour	Total
Male	700	200	400	1,300
Female	300	100	300	700
Total	1,000	300	700	2,000

Let F, M, N, O denote the event that any one randomly selected person from this group is Female, Male, Neutral, Opposed, respectively.

a) Calculate the probability that a person selected at random from this group will be female or opposed.

b) Calculate the probability that a person selected at random from this group will be opposed, given that the person is male.

c) Are the events O and F independent? Explain.

d) Are the events O and F mutually exclusive? Explain.

Topics for Review and Discussion

1. (*a*) What is probability? (*b*) Discuss three applications of probability in everyday life.

2. (*a*) Discuss the three methods of assigning probability values. (*b*) Explain why a probability value can never be less than 0 or more than 1.

3. (*a*) When do you use a multiplication rule to determine probabilities? (*b*) When do you use an addition rule?

4. (*a*) Discuss the concept of independence of events. (*b*) Give an example of two events that are independent. (*c*) Give an example of two events that are not independent.

5. (*a*) Discuss the concept of mutually exclusive and non-mutually exclusive events. (*b*) Give two examples for each of these types of events.

6. Discuss the relationship between conditional probability and independent events.

7. Give an example of a probability distribution related to something you find interesting, for example, your major, sports, games, etc.

8. (*a*) Discuss the procedure used to find the expected value of a discrete probability distribution. (*b*) Interpret the probable outcome of a game that has a negative expected value.

Projects/Issues to Consider

1. Locate an article in a periodical that discusses a study involving the concepts of probability. Prepare a brief summary of the article for a class presentation.

2. Research the contributions of someone who pioneered in the development of probability concepts. Some possible names are Thomas Bayes, Jacques Bernoulli, Francis Galton, William Gossett, Karl Friedrich Gauss, Christian Huygens, Pierre-Simon de Laplace, Abraham De Moivre, Blaise Pascal, Karl Pearson, and Simeon Denis Poisson.

3. Roll a die 60 times and have a partner keep a record of which face lands up. Did you get what you expected? Do you think your die is fair? If you did not get ten rolls on each of the six numbers, explain why you still might think the die is fair. Now switch and have your partner roll the die 60 times while you keep the record of the outcomes. Combine the results. Write a paragraph discussing your findings.

 4. Use the World Wide Web to access "Chance News" at ChncNews. Click on one of the articles under "contents." Read the article and answer the "Discussion Questions."

 5. Use the World Wide Web to access Chance articles related to probability at ChncProb. Click on one of the articles. Read the article and answer the "Discussion Question."

Computer/Calculator Exercises

1. Review the simulation exercises shown in *Figures 4.1*, *4.2*, and *4.3*, and then use your software to simulate the tossing of the coin 50 times.

   a) How many heads did you get? How many tails?

   b) Use your software to simulate the tossing of the coin 200 times. How many heads did you get? How many tails?

   c) What conclusions can you draw from your experiments?

2. Use your software to simulate the rolling of a fair die 180 times.

   a) About how many times would you expect each of the six sides to appear face up in such an experiment?

   b) How may times did each of the six sides actually appear in your simulation?

   c) What conclusions can you draw from this experiment?

3. Use the World Wide Web to access the DASL probability page at DASLProb. Click on one of the stories and work through the indicated probability problem.

CHAPTER 5

Probability Distributions

LOOKING AHEAD

You learned basic concepts of probability and probability distributions in Chapter 4. Now we'll consider three probability distributions that are commonly used in statistics. These distributions are the *binomial, Poisson,* and *normal.* The binomial and Poissan are examples of discrete probability distributions, and the normal distribution is continuous. You'll see in the chapters that follow that an understanding of probability distributions—particularly the normal distribution—is essential to the study of sampling and statistical inference.

Thus, after studying this chapter, you should be able to

- Explain what a binomial distribution is, identify binomial experiments, and compute binomial probabilities.

- Compute the expected value and standard deviation of a binomial experiment.

- Explain what a Poisson distribution is, identify Poisson experiments, and compute Poisson probabilities.

- Explain the properties of a normal distribution, and use the mean and standard deviation of a normally distributed random variable to translate random variable values into standard scores.

- Compute probabilities for a normal distribution and explain their relationship to areas under the standard normal probability curve.

- Determine normal scores from specified probability requirements.

5.1 **Binomial Experiments**

You learned in Chapter 4 that a probability experiment is any action for which an outcome, response, or measurement is obtained. A binomial experiment is simply a particular type of probability experiment. In a **binomial experiment**

1. The same action (trial) is repeated a fixed number of times.

2. Each trial is independent of the others.

3. For each trial, there are just two outcomes of interest. One outcome may be designated "success," and the other "failure."

4. The probability of success remains constant for each trial.

The random variable r represents a count of the number of successes in n trials in the experiment. Since we can list the possible values of r, it is a discrete random variable.

Knowing how eager you are to participate in a binomial experiment, we've prepared an example that requires you to take the following QuickQuiz:

QuickQuiz

Answer each of the following. There are four choices for each question, one of which is correct.

1. What is the length of Alberta from north to south?
    a) 1,186 km   *b)* 1,217 km   *c)* 1,236 km   *d)* 1,251 km

2. How many different species of birds live in British Columbia?
    a) 321   *b)* 333   *c)* 362   *d)* 380

3. Prince Edward Island has how many kilometres of beaches?
    a) 650   *b)* 700   *c)* 750   *d)* 800

4. The Torngat mountains in Labrador rise up to how many metres above sea level?
    a) 1,676   *b)* 1,716   *c)* 1,806   *d)* 1,896

5. How long is the Mackenzie river?
    a) 3,978 km   *b)* 4,241 km   *c)* 4,322 km   *d)* 4,315 km

---

If you don't know the answers to these questions, you may decide that for each of the five questions, you will pick one of the four alternatives completely at random. You can think of each question as a trial where guessing the correct answer is a success and guessing a wrong answer is a failure. Thus, this nightmare of a test serves our purpose because it illustrates a binomial experiment.

For such a binomial experiment, we'll let n equal the number of trials. The probability of success is the same for each trial, and we'll designate p as the probability of success in a single trial. Next, we'll let q equal the probability of failure in a single trial Finally, since success and failure are complementary events, $p + q$ must equal 1.

For our QuickQuiz example, each question constitutes a trial, so n is 5. And since each question has four equally likely choices, one of which is correct, p is 1/4 and q is

3/4. The random variable r, which counts the number of correct answers (successes) can equal 0, 1, 2, 3, 4, or 5.

Now let's look at another binomial experiment example from a more useful (although still unpleasant) situation. Advertisements claim that 80 percent of the hypertension patients who respond to a drug have their condition controlled by taking 5 milligrams of the product per day. Ten such patients are given the drug to see if their hypertension has been controlled. This is a binomial experiment because each patient constitutes a trial, p is .80, q is .20, and $r = 0, 1, 2, 3, 4, 5, 6, 7, 8, 9$, or 10.

But not all experiments with repeated trials are binomial. Let's suppose that a bowl contains five green, three red, and seven blue chips. Two chips are picked at random, one at a time and without replacement, to see if they are both blue. This isn't a binomial problem because the trials (picking a chip) aren't independent. The probability of picking a blue chip for the second trial depends on whether or not the first chip is blue.

Self-Testing Review 5.1

Identify the binomial experiments in the following examples. If the experiment is binomial, describe a trial, find n, p, q, and list the values of r. If it isn't binomial, explain why.

1. An advertisement for Vantin claims a 77 percent end-of-treatment clinical success rate for flu sufferers. Vantin is given to 15 flu patients who are later checked to see if the treatment was a success.

2. Suppose that 32 percent of new health club members join in the winter, 24 percent join in the spring, 21 percent enrol in the summer, and 23 percent join in the fall. Seven people who joined health clubs last year are selected at random and asked for the season of the year they joined.

3. According to a study recently published in the *Journal of Abnormal Psychology*, 76 percent of students in Grade 7 have consumed alcoholic beverages in their lifetime. Five students in grade 7 are randomly selected across the country and asked if they have ever had an alcoholic drink.

4. A study showed that 83 percent of the patients receiving liver transplants survived at least three years. The files of six liver recipients were selected at random to see if each of the patients was still alive.

5. In a study of frequent fliers (those who made at least three domestic trips or one foreign trip per year), it was found that 67 percent had an annual income over $35,000. Twelve frequent fliers are selected at random and their income level is determined.

5.2 Determining Binomial Probabilities

Let's return to our terrible QuickQuiz. Suppose we're interested in finding the probability of correctly guessing exactly three questions on this test. This would give us a 60 percent correct score and would thus produce a barely passing grade at most schools. [Incidentally, the correct answers are (1) *b*, (2) *c*, (3) *d*, (4) *a*, and (5) *b*. How many did you guess correctly?] We'll designate the outcome of answering the first three questions correctly (*S*) and the last two incorrectly (*F*) as *SSSFF*. Since the trials (answering the questions) are independent, we can then compute $P(SSSFF)$ using the multiplication rule for independent events found in Chapter 4. Thus, $P(SSSFF) = P(S) \cdot P(S) \cdot P(S) \cdot P(F) \cdot P(F) = 1/4 \cdot 1/4 \cdot 1/4 \cdot 3/4 \cdot 3/4 = .00879$.

This .00879 value is the probability of getting the first three correct and the last two incorrect. Of course, there are other ways of getting exactly three correct out of the five questions (two such ways are *SFSFS* and *FFSSS*). Each of these ways is called a combination of five items taken three at a time (or choosing three out of five). We can list all the combinations of three successes out of five tries and see how many there are, but let's first discuss a formula that does just that.

Combinations

A **combination** is a selection of *r* items from a set of *n* distinct objects without regard to the order in which the *r* items are picked. The symbols $\binom{n}{r}$ and $_nC_r$ are both used to designate the number of ways to choose *r* items from a group of *n* objects. The formula to find $\binom{n}{r}$ is

$$\binom{n}{r} = \frac{n!}{r!\,(n-r)!} \tag{5.1}$$

where   *n!* (or *n factorial*) represents the product of all integers from *n* down to 1
   r! (or *r factorial*) represents the product of all integers from *r* down to 1

If *n* is 6, then $n! = 6 \cdot 5 \cdot 4 \cdot 3 \cdot 2 \cdot 1 = 720$. And if *r* is 4, then $r! = 4 \cdot 3 \cdot 2 \cdot 1 = 24$. For convenience, we define 0! to have a value of 1. Many calculators have a ! key and some have a $_nC_r$ key, where $_nC_r$ denotes $\binom{n}{r}$.

Let's use our combination formula now to solve some example problems.

Example 5.1   How many ways can we choose three items out of five—that is, what is the number of combinations of five things taken three at a time?

◆ **Solution:**

You'll recognize that this is the number of ways we could guess the correct answer to three of the five QuickQuiz questions.

The answer is

$$\binom{n}{r} = \frac{n!}{r!\,(n-r)!}$$

$$\binom{5}{3} = \frac{5!}{3!\,(5-3)!} = \frac{5!}{3!\,2!} = \frac{5 \cdot 4 \cdot 3 \cdot 2 \cdot 1}{(3 \cdot 2 \cdot 1)(2 \cdot 1)} = 10$$

The 10 combinations for the QuickQuiz example are *SSSFF, SSFSF, SFSFS, SFFSS, SF-SSF, FFSSS, FSFSS, FSSFS, SSFFS,* and *FSSSF.* As you can imagine, it's usually impractical to try to list all combinations. ◆

Example 5.2   How many ways can we choose two items out of seven? That is, what's the number of combinations of seven items taken two at a time?

◆ **Solution:**

$$\binom{n}{r} = \frac{n!}{r!\,(n-r)!}$$

$$\binom{7}{2} = \frac{7!}{2!\,(7-2)!} = \frac{7 \cdot 6 \cdot 5 \cdot 4 \cdot 3 \cdot 2 \cdot 1}{(2 \cdot 1)(5 \cdot 4 \cdot 3 \cdot 2 \cdot 1)} = 21 \quad ◆$$

Calculating Binomial Probabilities with a Formula

Let's return now to the problem of determining the probability of correctly guessing *exactly* three of the five questions on the QuickQuiz. We've seen that the probability of guessing the first three correctly and then missing the last two is .00879. We found this by multiplying three factors of 1/4 (the probability of success) times two factors of 3/4 (the probability of failure). Now, since each of the ten combinations of three successes and two failures has exactly the same probability of occurring, the probability of getting *any* three correct and two incorrect, no matter what the order, can be found by multiplying ten times .00879 to get the answer of .0879.

In general, for a binomial experiment with *n* trials, where *p* is the probability of success and *q* is the probability of failure in a *single* trial, the probability of *exactly r successes* in the *n* trials is given by this formula:

$$P(r) = \binom{n}{r} p^r q^{n-r} \text{ for any } r = 0, 1, 2, \dots, n. \tag{5.2}$$

To develop a probability distribution for *r*, the number of correctly guessed questions in the QuickQuiz, we can use formula 5.2 to compute $P(r)$ when *r* is 0, 1, 2, 3, 4, and 5 as follows:

$$P(r = 0) = \binom{5}{0}\left(\frac{1}{4}\right)^0\left(\frac{3}{4}\right)^5 = \frac{5!}{0!\,(5-0)!}\left(\frac{1}{4}\right)^0\left(\frac{3}{4}\right)^5 = 1 \cdot 1 \cdot (.2373) = .2373$$

$$P(r = 1) = \binom{5}{1}\left(\frac{1}{4}\right)^1\left(\frac{3}{4}\right)^4 = \frac{5!}{1!\,(5-1)!}\left(\frac{1}{4}\right)^1\left(\frac{3}{4}\right)^4 = 5 \cdot (.25)(.3164) = .3955$$

$$P(r = 2) = \binom{5}{2}\left(\frac{1}{4}\right)^2\left(\frac{3}{4}\right)^3 = \frac{5!}{2!\,(5-2)!}\left(\frac{1}{4}\right)^2\left(\frac{3}{4}\right)^3 = 10 \cdot (.0625)(.4219) = .2637$$

$$P(r = 3) = \binom{5}{3}\left(\frac{1}{4}\right)^3\left(\frac{3}{4}\right)^2 = \frac{5!}{3!\,(5-3)!}\left(\frac{1}{4}\right)^3\left(\frac{3}{4}\right)^2 = 10 \cdot (.0156)(.5625) = .0879$$

$$P(r = 4) = \binom{5}{4}\left(\frac{1}{4}\right)^2\left(\frac{3}{4}\right)^1 = \frac{5!}{4!\,(5-4)!}\left(\frac{1}{4}\right)^2\left(\frac{3}{4}\right)^1 = 5 \cdot (.0039)(.75) = .0146$$

$$P(r = 5) = \binom{5}{5}\left(\frac{1}{4}\right)^5\left(\frac{3}{4}\right)^0 = \frac{5!}{5!\,(5-5)!}\left(\frac{1}{4}\right)^5\left(\frac{3}{4}\right)^0 = 1 \cdot (.0010)(1) = .0010$$

Thus, the probability distribution for *r* is

r	*P(r)*
0	.2373
1	.3955
2	.2637
3	.0879
4	.0146
5	.0010
	1.0000

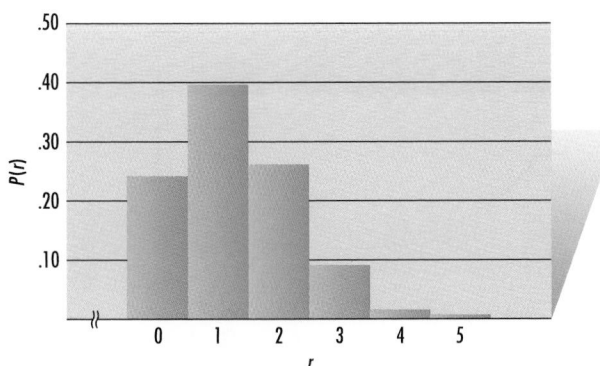

FIGURE 5.1 Our QuickQuiz probability distribution.

This probability distribution can be described in a histogram as shown in *Figure 5.1*.

Using a Table to Determine Binomial Probabilities

We've now laboriously calculated the probabilities [$P(r)$] of correctly guessing 0, 1, 2, 3, 4, and 5 of our QuickQuiz answers. Given the tedious nature of these calculations, it's not surprising that tables have been prepared to produce binomial values for a selected number of trials using predetermined probabilities of success. Such a table is presented in Appendix 1 in the back of this book. To get the same results from the table that we've just computed using formula 5.2, you first read down the left-hand column of the table to get to $n = 5$. Then scan across to the values under the $p = .25$ column. The entire probability distribution that we've just calculated is listed, and you can select any value you need. That's a lot easier than using the formula.

The probabilities for p listed in Appendix 1 go to only .50. But we can translate questions for greater values of p if we use the properties of a binomial experiment. Suppose you need to compute the probability of getting six successes in an experiment in which n is 9 and p is .70. To locate the correct entry, consider the equivalent probability of getting three failures in nine trials in which the probability of failure is .30. You can check the table and verify that this answer is .2668.

Now let's consider some other binomial probability examples.

Example 5.3 What's the probability of correctly guessing *at least* three of our QuickQuiz answers?

◆ Solution:
Since we are dealing with a binomial distribution with parameters $n = 5$ and $p = 0.25$, you can use formula 5.2 or the table in Appendix 1 to find the probability that $r \geq 3$—that is, $P(r = 3$ or 4 or 5). You find this probability by adding the corresponding probabilities. Thus, $P(r \geq 3) = .0879 + .0146 + .0010 = .1035$. The next time you think about taking a multiple-choice test without studying, remember that there is roughly a 10 percent chance of correctly guessing at least three questions out of five when four options are offered for each question. ◆

Example 5.4 What's the probability of correctly guessing from two to four questions in our QuickQuiz?

◆ Solution:
You can again use formula 5.2 or Appendix 1 to see that $P(2 \leq r \leq 4) = P(2) + P(3) + P(4) = .2637 + .0879 + .0146 = .3662$. ◆

FIGURE 5.2 (*a*) **To obtain this MINITAB output, click on Calc, Probability Distributions, Binomial,** click in the circle next to **Probability,** enter 5 **as Number of Trials and** .25 as **Probability of Success,** click in the circle to the left of **Input Column** and enter the column containing the values of *r,* denoted *X* by MINITAB, and click **OK.** (*b*) To calculate binomial probabilities on the T1-83, we can use the binompdf command, which is option 0 under the **DISTR** menu. The **DISTR** menu is the 2nd function of the VARS key. **The syntax is binompdf(n,p,x).** From the home screen access the binompdf function, enter binompdf(5,0.25,3) and **ENTER** to get 0.0879, which is P(3) in the **Quick Quiz example.** To see the entire distribution we can store the *X* values in L1 and then store binompdl(5,0.25,L1) into **L2.** (See screen 1.) Note that the set brackets, { }, are the 2nd functions of the (keys and the **STO** key used to store the list. Then to see the distribution, go to **STAT>Edit** as shown in screen 2.

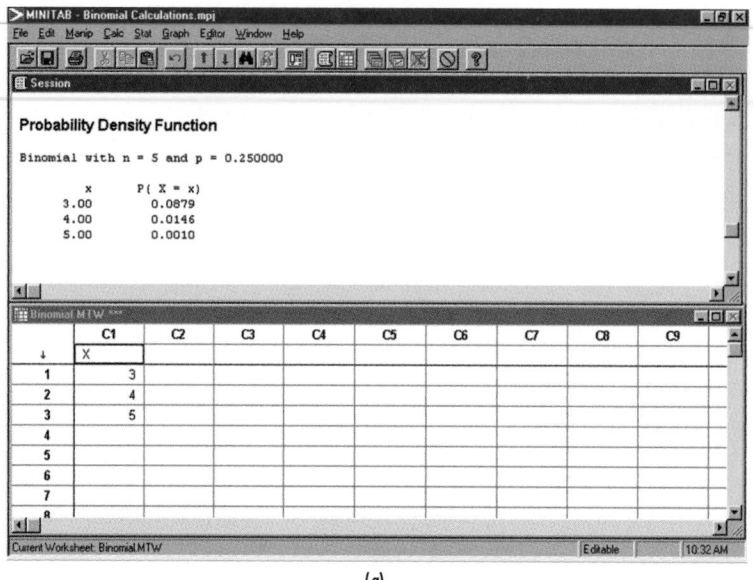

(*a*)

Screen 1   Screen 2

(*b*)

Using Statistical Software and Calculators to Determine Binomial Probabilities

Statistical programs such as MINITAB also can be used to circumvent the need to do tedious calculations by hand. It is as if MINITAB has tables similar to those we have in the back of this text. For example, in Example 5.3 we found the probability of guessing at least three of our QuickQuiz answers: $P(r \geq 3) = P(3) + P(4) + P(5) = .0879 + .0146 + .0010 = .1035$. MINITAB gives us the identical probabilities in *Figure 5.2a*. Calculators such as the TI-83 can also generate binomial probabilities. In screen 2 of *Figure 5.2b*, we can see the results of asking the TI-83 to produce $P(0)$ through $P(5)$ for the QuickQuiz example. While MINITAB and the TI-83 calculator could save us some time and effort here, imagine the savings that would be achieved if the QuickQuiz became the BigQuiz with 100 questions and we wanted to compute the probability of getting 30 or more answers correct!

Example 5.5   **Data down the Drain?** The paper by D. Butler and N. J. D. Graham, "Modeling Dry Weather Wastewater Flow in Sewer Networks," *Journal of Environmental Engineering,* 1995, describes a use of the binomial distribution. Domestic appliances (baths, showers, toilets, and the like) are connected to an outfall or sewage treatment works by a series of pipes. The authors propose a model under which each appliance has a probability p of discharging in a brief time interval. For example, if 30 appliances in an apartment building each have a probability of discharge of $p = .05$, and if discharges occur independently of each other, the probability of two or fewer discharging is (from the binomial tables) $P(0) + P(1) + P(2) = .2146 + .3389 + .2586 = .8121$. ◆

The Expected Value, Variance, and Standard Deviation of a Binomial Distribution

Recall from Chapter 4 that the expected value is the theoretical mean value for a random variable. And like any other probability distribution, each binomial random variable has an expected value. Since a binomial distribution is discrete, we can use the formula discussed in Chapter 4. Thus, to obtain the mean or expected value for the number of questions we could correctly guess on the QuickQuiz, we compute the value as follows:

$$\mu = E(x) = \Sigma x P(x)$$
$$= 0(.2373) + 1(.3955) + 2(.2637) + 3(.0879) + 4(.0146) + 5(.0010)$$
$$= 1.25$$

If many of your classmates take our QuickQuiz, the average number of questions answered correctly in the long run will be 1.25 per student. Thus, if 100 students take the test, we would expect about 125 correct answers, and if 1,000 take the test, we would expect to find about 1,250 correct responses.

Happily, though, there's a quicker way to find the mean or expected value when you're working with binomial probabilities. The formula that makes this possible is

$$\mu = E(x) = np \tag{5.3}$$

To find the expected value of a binomial distribution, simply multiply the number of trials by the probability of success in a single trial. Thus, in our QuickQuiz example, $\mu = E(x) = np = 5(.25) = 1.25$ questions.

You'll recall from Chapter 4 that we calculated two measures of dispersion, the variance and the standard deviation, for discrete random variables. But again for binomial random variables, we have a shortcut. The variance of a binomial distribution is found with this formula:

$$\sigma^2 = npq \tag{5.4}$$

So the variance in our QuickQuiz example is $\sigma^2 = npq = (5)(.25)(.75) = .9375$. The standard deviation of a binomial experiment is found by taking the square root of the variance, that is, with this formula:

$$\sigma = \sqrt{npq} \tag{5.5}$$

So the standard deviation in our QuickQuiz example is $\sigma = \sqrt{npq} = \sqrt{.9375} = .9682$ questions.

Now let's consider two more examples.

STATISTICS IN ACTION

A Puff a Day Keeps the Doctor in Pay

To gauge the association between passive smoking (breathing the smoke produced by others) and adult lung can-cer, the Environmental Protection Agency (EPA) compiled the results of 30 studies made in eight countries around the world. Each study compared lung cancer rates for two classes of non-smoking women—those living with smokers and those living with non-smokers. The EPA researchers now estimate that people who live or work among smokers experience a 20 to 30 percent increase in lung cancer risk. Other findings: Each year, environmental tobacco smoke causes 3,000 lung cancer deaths, helps to produce 150,000 to 300,000 respiratory infections in babies that result in 7,500 to 15,000 hospitalizations, triggers 8,000 to 26,000 new cases of asthma in previously unaffected children, and intensifies the symptoms in 400,000 to 1 million asthmatic children.

Example 5.6

Suppose that 67.5 percent of university students use a personal computer. If 20 students are selected at random, what's the expected number who use a computer? What's the variance and standard deviation for this distribution?

◆ Solution:

Define x to be the number of the 20 students who use a personal computer. If any one student's use or non-use of a personal computer is independent of any other student's use or non-use of a personal computer, then x is a binomial random variable with parameters $n = 20$ and $p = .675$.

The expected value is $E(x) = np = 20(.675) = 13.5$ students. The variance is $\sigma^2 = npq = (20)(.675)(.325) = 4.3875$. The standard deviation is $\sigma = \sqrt{npq} = \sqrt{4.3875} = 2.095$ students. ◆

Example 5.7

What to Expect down the Drain In the paper by D. Butler and N. J. D. Graham on wastewater flow, they justify using the formula for the binomial mean to calculate the expected number of discharges at any instant. For our example in which 30 appliances each have a probability of discharge of $p = .05$, the expected number of discharges is $E(x) = np = 30(.05) = 1.5$. ◆

Self-Testing Review 5.2

6. In 2001 at the University of Ottawa, the male to female student ratio was 41 to 59. (For ease of computation, assume the ratio is 40 to 60, or 2 to 3.) Suppose 12 students are randomly selected. Find the probability that

    a) Exactly eight are female.

    b) At least eight are male.

    c) Fewer than five are female.

    d) Between six and nine (including six and nine) are male.

7. According to Statistics Canada, 85 percent of Canadian households own a VCR. Ten households are randomly selected across the country and are asked if they own a VCR. Find the probability that

    a) Exactly eight own a VCR.

    b) Fewer than seven own a VCR.

    c) At least six own a VCR.

8. According to the Saskatchewan Government Insurance corporation, 35 percent of all collisions involving drinking drivers in Saskatchewan occur between midnight and 4:00 A.M. A random sample of 15 collisions involving drinking drivers in Saskatchewan is selected. Find the probability that

    a) Exactly five occurred between midnight and 4:00 A.M.

    b) At least nine occurred between midnight and 4:00 A.M.

    c) Seven or fewer occurred between midnight and 4:00 A.M.

9. Transport Canada reported that in a recent year 90 percent of drivers in New Brunswick wore shoulder belts. Assuming that percentage has not changed, find the probability that in a random sample of 20 drivers from New Brunswick there will be

a) At least 17 wearing shoulder belts.

b) Between 14 and 17 (inclusive) wearing shoulder belts.

c) At most 15 wearing shoulder belts.

10. According to Statistics Canada, 46 percent of women aged 45–64 years have an acceptable weight BMI (Body Mass Index). If 14 women from the 45–64 year category are randomly selected, find the probability that

a) Exactly ten will have an acceptable weight BMI.

b) At most four will have an acceptable weight BMI.

c) At least five would have an acceptable weight BMI.

11. A multiple-choice test has 20 questions, and each question has five choices, one of which is correct. You don't have a clue about the subject matter and guess your way through the test. What's the probability you guess

a) At least 12 questions correctly?

b) Fewer than five questions correctly?

c) At least ten questions correctly?

12. An advertisement for *Cold-Ex* claims an 80 percent end-of-treatment clinical success rate for the treatment of flu. Twelve patients are given *Cold-Ex* and then later checked to see if the treatment was successful. Let's assume the claim is correct.

a) What's the mean or expected number of patients who are successfully treated?

b) What is the standard deviation of this binomial random variable?

13. In a Statistics Canada survey of Grade 10 students, 57 percent of males and 80 percent of females brush their teeth two or more times a day. If 350 Grade 10 male students are selected, what is the

a) Mean or expected number who brush their teeth two or more times a day?

b) Standard deviation of the number who brush their teeth two or more times a day?

14. According to Statistics Canada, 85 percent of Canadian households own a VCR. Fifty households are randomly selected across the country and are asked if they own a VCR.

a) What is the mean or expected number of households that own a VCR?

b) What is the standard deviation of the number of households that own a VCR?

15. If 95 percent of the drivers in Quebec wear shoulder belts, and if 1,000 drivers from Quebec are selected at random, find the

a) Mean or expected number of drivers who wear shoulder belts.

b) Standard deviation of the number of drivers who wear shoulder belts.

16. A 2002 Statistics Canada report stated that people living in large metropolitan areas and urban centres have the longest life expectancies and disability-free life expectancies in Canada, while people living in Canada's northern remote communities are least healthy. Some of the factors that affect health are smoking rates, obesity rates, and heavy drinking rates. The following is a partial summary of the report.

	Life Expectancy (years)	Daily Smoking (age 12+) percent	Obese (age 20+) percent	Heavy Drinking (age 18+) percent
Canada	78.3	22	15	16
Richmond	81.2	9	6	10
Toronto	79.3	17	11	10
Montreal	77.9	21	12	15
Northern Sask.	73.3	33	22	24
Nunavut	69.8	48	28	18

Source: Statistics Canada, Cat. 82-003-SIE2002001.

a) If a random sample of ten people (age 12+) is selected from Canada, what is the probability that exactly five will be daily smokers?

b) If a random sample of ten people (age 12+) is selected from Nunavut, what is the probability that exactly five will be daily smokers?

c) If a random sample of 12 people (age 12+) is selected from Northern Saskatchewan, what is the probability that between three and five (inclusive) will be daily smokers?

d) If a random sample of 12 people (age 12+) is selected from Northern Saskatchewan, what is the probability that at most two will be daily smokers?

e) If a random sample of 100 people (age 12+) is selected from Toronto, what is the expected number of daily smokers selected?

f) If a random sample of 100 people (age 12+) is selected from Toronto, what is the standard deviation of the number of daily smokers selected?

g) If a random sample of 25 people (age 20+) is selected from Canada, what is the probability that exactly four will be obese?

h) If a random sample of 20 people (age 20+) is selected from Montreal, what is the probability that at least three will be heavy drinkers?

i) If a random sample of 20 people (age 18+) is selected from Richmond, what is the probability that no more than two will be heavy drinkers?

j) If a random sample of 100 people (age 18+) is selected from Canada, what is the expected number of heavy drinkers selected?

k) If a random sample of 100 people (age 18+) is selected from Canada, what is the standard deviation of the number of heavy drinkers selected?

5.3 The Poisson Distribution

We've just seen that if we know the probability of success in a single trial, the binomial probability distribution can tell us the probability of getting a specified number of successes for a given number of repeated independent trials. But other situations lend themselves to different probability distributions.

Suppose, for example, that we're interested in the number of specified occurrences that take place within a unit of time, distance, area, or volume rather than during a given number of trials. In that case, it's appropriate to use the **Poisson distribution** (named after Simeon Denis Poisson, the French mathematician who developed it). The

Poisson distribution can be used to calculate the probability that there will be a specified number of automobile accident claims coming to an insurance company during a period of time. Or, it may be used to calculate the probability that there will be a specific number of flaws found on the *surface space* of a sheet-metal panel used in the production of a space satellite.

Other examples where the Poisson distribution would be appropriate include

- Demand for a product within a given time interval.

- Number of accidents within a given time interval.

- Number of takeoffs and landings per hour at Vancouver International Airport.

- Counts per minute (CPM) from a radioactive source.

- Number of bacteria per petri dish.

- E-coli bacteria count per water sample taken in Walkerton.

- Number of white blood cells in a cubic centimetre of blood.

- Number of flat tires in 10,000 kilometres of driving.

In these and other situations, it's appropriate to use a Poisson distribution when the following conditions are met:

- An experiment consists of counting the number of times a certain event occurs during a given unit of time, distance, area, or volume.

- The probability that an event occurs is the same for each unit of time, distance, area, or volume.

- The number of events that occur in one unit is independent of the number that occur in other non-overlapping such units.

Like the binomial, the Poisson distribution is discrete since the values of the random variable can be listed.

When the Poisson distribution is appropriate, the probability of observing exactly x number of occurrences per unit of measure (hour, minute, cubic centimetre, kilometre, etc.) can be found using this formula:

$$P(x) = \frac{\mu^x e^{-\mu}}{x!} \qquad (5.6)$$

where $P(x)$ = the probability of exactly x number of occurrences
   μ = the mean number of occurrences per unit of time, distance, area, or volume
   e = a constant value of 2.71828 ...

Note that many calculators have a key for computing e^x.

To see how this formula is used, let's look at an example.

Example 5.8   An average of three cars arrive at a highway tollgate every minute. If this rate is approximated by a Poisson process, what's the probability that exactly five cars will arrive in a one-minute period?

◆ **Solution:**

The answer is found by using $P(x) = \dfrac{\mu^x e^{-\mu}}{x!}$, with $\mu = 3$ and $x = 5$:

$$P(x = 5) = \frac{(3^5)(e^{-3})}{5!} \quad \text{(If your calculator permits, find } e^{-3} \text{ by keying } -3 \text{ and then } e^x)$$

$$= \frac{(243)(.0498)}{120} = \frac{12.10}{120} = .1008$$

Thus, the probability that five cars arrive in one minute is .1008. Other results may be computed to show the probability of arrival of 0, 1, 2, 3, 4, 6, ... , cars at the tollgate. ◆

Appendix 10 at the back of the book has a table of Poisson probabilities for specified value of μ and x, and it gives us an easier way to solve this problem. The columns in this table represent selected values of μ, so our first step is to locate the column with a μ value of 3.0. Having located that column, we next identify the row with an x value of 5 that corresponds to the arrival of five cars in our example. The answer to our problem, then, is the value of .1008 that's found at the intersection of the identified column and row. The other entries in the μ column give the probability values for the arrival of 0, 1, 2, ... , cars at the tollgate. The total of all the entries under a specific μ column is approximately 1.00, and these entries collectively represent a probability distribution.

One other interesting feature of the Poisson distribution is that the variance is equal to the mean. This, of course, implies that for this distribution $\sigma = \sqrt{\mu}$.

Using Statistical Software and Calculators to Determine Poisson Probabilities

As with the binomial distribution, MINITAB and other software can be used to obtain Poisson probabilities. The solution in Example 5.8 was obtained by MINITAB and is presented in *Figure 5.3*.

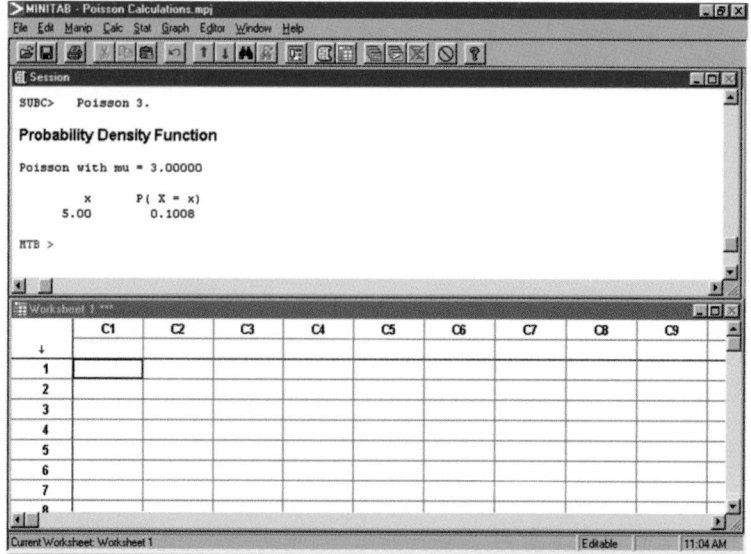

FIGURE 5.3 To obtain this **MINITAB** output, click in **Calc, Probability Distributions, Poisson,** click in the circle next to **Probability,** enter 3 as **Mean,** click in the circle to the left of **Input constant** and enter the value of $X = 5$, and click **OK.**

◻ **Example 5.9** **Real Data: It's the Pits?** T. Shibata ("Statistical and stochastic approaches to localized corrosion," *Corrosion Science,* 1996) reports the use of the Poisson distribution to describe the number of pits on the surface of a material. Suppose the mean rate of pitting on a surface is five per hour. What is the probability of two pits appearing in a one-hour period?

◆ **Solution:**

Using the Poisson formula,

$$P(x = 2) = \frac{(5^2)(e^{-5})}{2!} = \frac{(25)(.006738)}{2} = \frac{.1684}{2} = .0842$$

The identical result is found in the Poisson table of Appendix 10 in the $\mu - 5.0$ column and the $x = 2$ row. ◆

Self-Testing Review 5.3

17. A company reports that its computer is "down" an average of 1.2 times during an eight-hour shift. What's the probability that the computer will

    a) Be "down" three times during an eight-hour shift?

    b) Not be "down" during an eight-hour shift ($x = 0$)?

18. Getrich Bank records show that an average of 20 people arrive at a teller's counter during an hour. What's the probability that

    a) Exactly 30 will arrive during a one-hour period?

    b) Ten or fewer will arrive during a one-hour period?

    c) More than ten will arrive during a one-hour period?

19. The Colorall Paint factory uses "agent A" in the paint manufacturing process. There's an average of three particles of agent A in a cubic metre of the air emitted during the production process. What's the probability that there will be

    a) Five particles of agent A in a cubic metre of air emitted from the factory?

    b) No agent A in a cubic metre of air emission?

20. If a keyboard operator averages two errors per page of newsprint, and if these errors follow a Poisson process, what is the probability that

    a) Exactly four errors will be found on a given page?

    b) At least two errors will be found on a given page?

21. Police records show that there has been an average of four accidents per week on a new highway. If these accidents follow a Poisson process, what's the probability that there are

    a) Exactly six accidents in a week?

    b) Fewer than two accidents in a week?

22. Bigrig Trailer Corporation uses large panels of sheet metal in the manufacture of tandem trailers. If there is an average of three blemishes per panel and if the blemishes follow a Poisson process, what is the probability that there will be

    a) No blemishes on a given panel?

    b) Exactly two blemishes on a given panel?

23. A student health centre treats an average of ten cases of severe alcohol poisoning a semester. Assuming a Poisson distribution, find the probability that the health centre treats

   a) Twelve cases of severe alcohol poisoning a semester.

   b) Fewer than five cases of severe alcohol poisoning in a semester.

   c) More than 15 cases of severe alcohol poisoning a semester.

24. At a busy intersection, auto accidents occur in a manner satisfying the Poisson assumptions, at an average rate of 2.5 per month. Find the probability that in any one month, the number of auto accidents will be

   a) Zero.

   b) Two.

   c) At least one.

   d) No more than one.

25. Suppose garbage trucks arrive at a landfill site in a manner satisfying the Poisson assumptions, at an average rate of six per hour. Find the probability that in any one hour, the number of garbage trucks arriving will be

   a) Zero.

   b) Five.

   c) At least two.

   d) No more than three.

26. Many models of parasitic infections use the Poisson distribution. Suppose the number of parasites on a host has a Poisson distribution with a mean of ten. Find the probability that

   a) There are eight parasites on a host.

   b) There are eight or nine parasites on a host.

   c) There are no parasites on a host.

27. Industrial accidents commonly occur in a manner satisfying the Poisson assumptions, so that the Poisson distribution is of interest to insurance actuaries. Suppose that fatal accidents associated with a particularly hazardous occupation occur at a rate of .0059 per person-year on the average. If a company insures 1,000 such people for a given year, what is the probability that the number of fatality claims the company will have to meet will be

   a) Zero.

   b) At least seven.

   c) At most seven.

   d) Should the sum of the probabilities in (b) and (c) equal 1? Explain.

28. McNamara and Houston ("Risk-Sensitive Foraging: A Review of the Theory," *Bulletin of Mathematical Biology,* 1993) examine the effects of the energy gained by an animal during foraging on future reproductive success. One part includes a Poisson model for the number of food items of a type found during foraging. Suppose the number of certain food items found during foraging has a Poisson distribution with a mean of one. Find the probability that

   a) None of these food items is found.

   b) Two of these food items are found.

   c) At least one of these food items is found.

   d) No more than one of these food items is found.

5.4 **The Normal Distribution**

Both the binomial and Poisson distributions are **discrete probability distributions,** that is, they both have a countable or finite number of possible values and you can assign a positive probability to each possible value. But what if the outcomes of a probability experiment consist of an uncountably infinite number of values, such as a measurement of a person's weight? Theoretically, a person's weight could be any one of the infinitely many values corresponding to points on a line interval. If you try to assign a positive probability to each of these uncountable values, the probabilities will no longer sum to 1, as with discrete random variables. Instead we use a **continuous probability distribution,** which assigns a 0 probability to each individual value and a non-negative probability to an interval.

There are many different continuous probability distributions, but by far the most common and most important continuous probability distribution is the **normal** (or Gaussian) **distribution.** An expression of its importance—and its shape—was presented by W. J. Youden of the National Bureau of Standards as shown in *Figure 5.4a*. As indicated in *Figure 5.4a*, the normal curve is symmetrical (that is, the mean = median) and, because of its appearance, is sometimes called a bell-shaped curve. It's actually not a single curve but a family of curves, and each curve extends infinitely in either direction from the peak. *Figure 5.4b* shows three normal curves with the same mean but with different standard deviation values; *Figure 5.4c* shows three normal curves with the same standard deviation but with different mean values.

A normal distribution curve is defined by the following formula, which is based on its mean (μ) and its standard deviation (σ).

$$f(x) = \frac{1}{\sigma\sqrt{2\pi}}\, e^{-\frac{(x-\mu)^2}{2\sigma^2}}$$

But we don't need to concern ourselves with this formula. And we don't need to use the advanced mathematical techniques that would show that the total area under any normal distribution curve, as in all other probability distribution curves, is equal to 1.

Normal Distribution Probabilities

Recall from Chapter 4 (and from *Figure 4.7*, page 129) that a histogram could be used to graphically present a discrete probability distribution. And you may recall that the probability the variable takes on a specified value is equal to the area found in the corresponding bar of the probability histogram (assuming the width of the bar is one unit). But for continuous distributions, we don't find the probability that the variable assumes a specified value (since the probability that a continuous variable assumes a specified value is 0). Rather, we investigate the probability that the variable assumes any value within a given interval of values. We might, for instance, find the probability that the weight of a student in Grade 7 is between 45.2 and 47.8 kg.

Probabilities for continuous distributions are represented by areas under the curve. That is, the probability that the variable will have a value between *a* and *b* is the area under the curve between two vertical lines erected at points *a* and *b*. For example, if the breaking strength of a material is normally distributed with a mean of 110 kilograms and a standard deviation of 10 kilograms, the probability that a piece of this material has a breaking strength between 110 and 120 kilograms is the area under the curve covered by this interval, as shown in *Figure 5.5*.

FIGURE 5.4 Normal distributions.

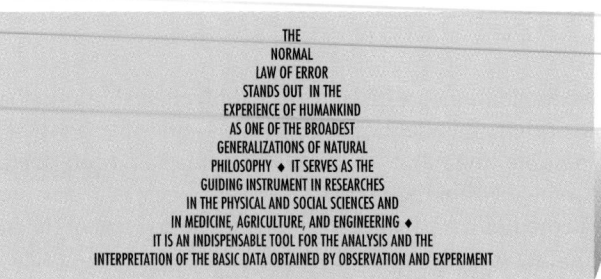

(a)

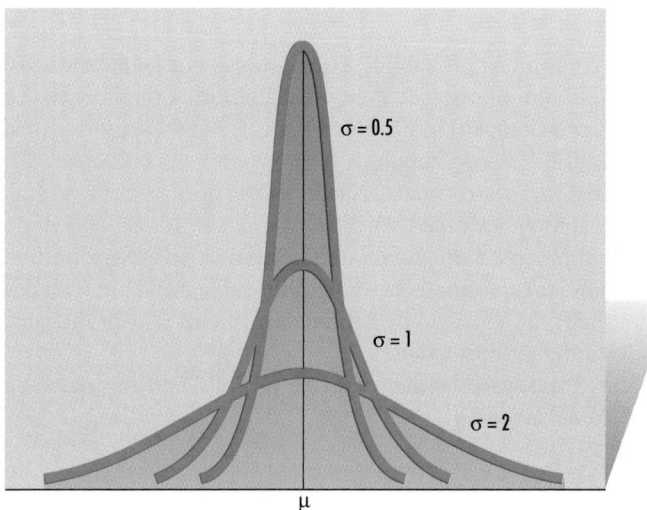

(b) Same mean; different standard deviation values

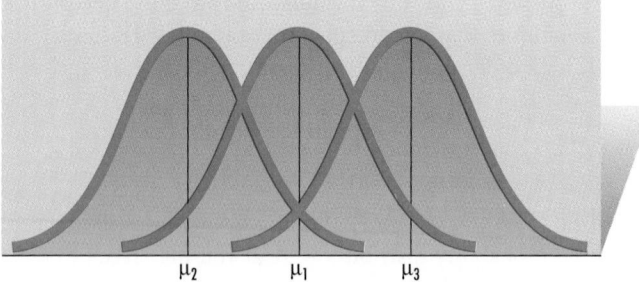

(c) Same standard deviation; different mean values

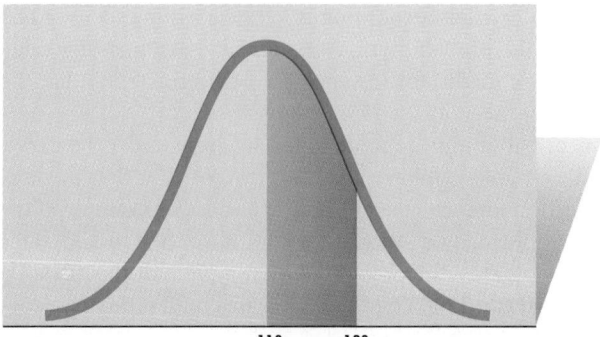

FIGURE 5.5 Probability of breaking strength between 110 and 120 kilograms.

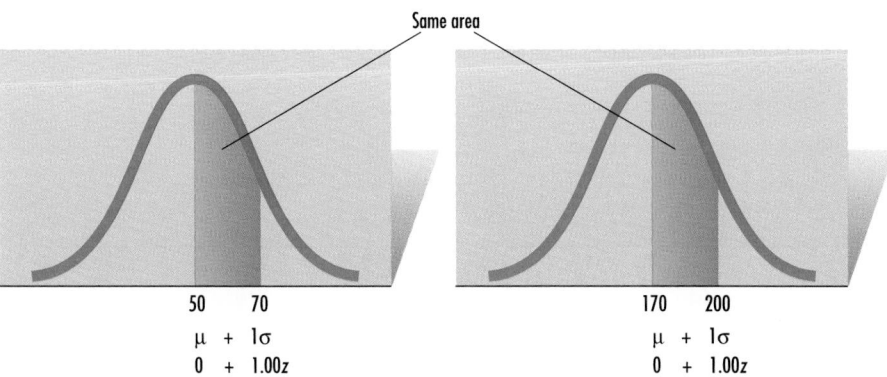

Although there are an infinite number of different normal distribution curves (one each for any given pair of values of its mean and standard deviation), mathematicians have simplified things for us by calculating areas under a special normal distribution curve that has a mean (μ) of 0 and a standard deviation (σ) of 1. This specific curve is known as the **standard normal distribution.** It's of particular use because its values represent standard deviation units. The random variable for the standard normal curve is represented by the symbol z. It is, in fact, identical to the **z value,** or **z score** used as a measure of relative position in Chapter 3. Thus, a z value of $+ 2.00$ indicates 2 standard deviation units above its mean, and a z value of -1.40 represents 1.40 standard deviation units below its mean. A z value of 0 corresponds to the mean.

These points are illustrated in *Figure 5.6*, where it is shown that an interval of a given number of standard deviations from the mean covers the same area in any normal curve. Thus, the interval from 50 to 70 for a normal curve with a mean of 50 and a standard deviation of 20 covers the same area as the interval from 170 to 200 in a normal curve with a mean of 170 and a standard deviation of 30. Both of these intervals cover a distance of one standard deviation from the mean—that is, both intervals extend from the mean (0) out to a z value of $+1.00$ on our standard normal distribution scale.

Remember that for any normal distribution

- The total area under the curve is 1.
- The probability that x lies in an interval, say between a and b, is equal to the area under the curve between the two points a and b.
- $P(x = a) = 0$
- This means that $P(x \geq a) = P(x > a)$ and $P(x \leq a) = P(x < a)$.

In fact, these rules also apply to any continuous probability distribution.

Calculating Probabilities for the Standard Normal Distribution

To compute the probability that a z value falls within a given interval of the standard normal curve, we determine the area under the curve within the specified interval. A table of area values for the standard normal curve is found in Appendix 2. The first column in the table gives value of z to the nearest tenth. The remaining columns give the second decimal place. The area values in the body of Appendix 2 represent the probability that a z value chosen at random will fall between the standardized mean of zero

FIGURE 5.7 The probability that a z value selected at random will fall between 0 and 2.27 or between −2.27 and 0 is .4884.

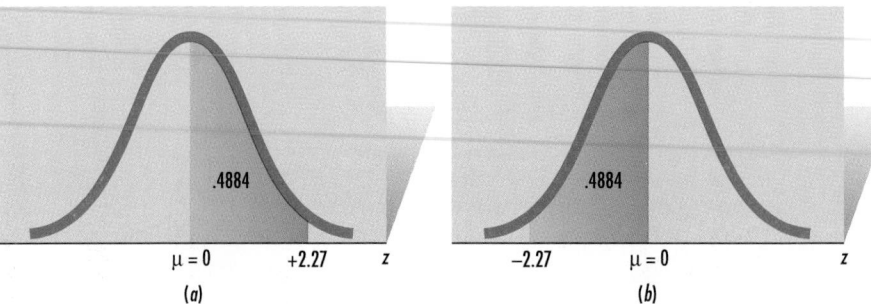

FIGURE 5.7 The probability that a z value selected at random will fall between 0 and 2.27 or between −2.27 and 0 is .4884.

and a specified z value, which we'll call z_0. This probability can be stated in symbol form as $P(0 < z < z_0)$.

Let's use the table in Appendix 2 to find the area under the normal curve between the mean and a z value of 2.27. Go down the first column in the table until you get to 2.2, and then move across to the column labelled .07. The area given by the table is .4884. Thus, the probability that a z value selected at random will fall between 0 and 2.27 is .4884. Or in abbreviated form, $P(0 < z < 2.27) = .4884$ (see *Figure 5.7a*). It's important to note here that since the normal curve is symmetric, area values for negative z scores are identical to their corresponding positive scores. Thus, the area under the curve between the mean of 0 and a z value of −2.27 is also .4884 (see *Figure 5.7b*).

Now let's consider some additional examples of the use of the table of area values.

Example 5.10   What is the area under the normal curve between vertical lines drawn at $z = -1.73$ and $z = +2.45$?

◆ **Solution:**
To answer this question, we must look up two separate areas. We first find the area between the mean of zero and a z value of −1.73 (remember that this area is the same as the area between the mean and a z value of +1.73). This area or probability is .4582. Next, we find that the area between the mean of zero and a z value of 2.45 is .4929. The required area obtained by adding .4582 and .4929 is .9511. Thus, $P(-1.73 < z < 2.45) = .9511$ (see *Figure 5.8*). ◆

Example 5.11   What's the area under the normal curve between a z value of −1.54 and a z value of −.76?

◆ **Solution:**
The area between the mean and a z value of −1.54 is .4382, and the area between the mean and a z value of −.76 is .2764. Since the given areas overlap, we subtract .2764 from .4382 to get .1618, which is the required area. Thus, $P(-1.54 < z < -.76) = .1618$ (see *Figure 5.9*). ◆

FIGURE 5.8 The area under the normal curve between vertical lines drawn at $z = -1.73$ and $z = +2.45$ is .9511.

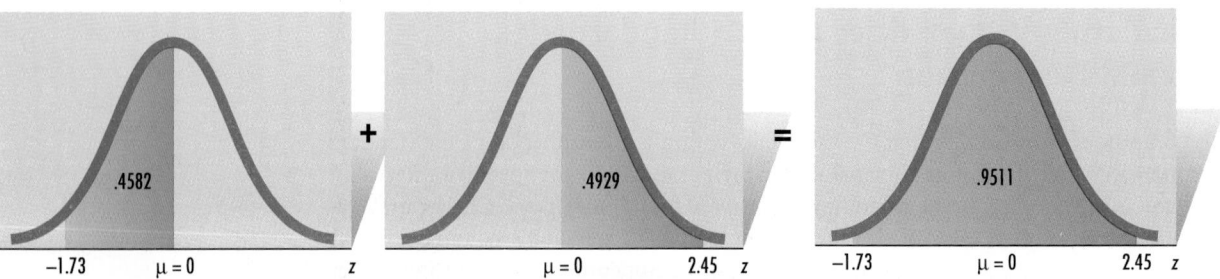

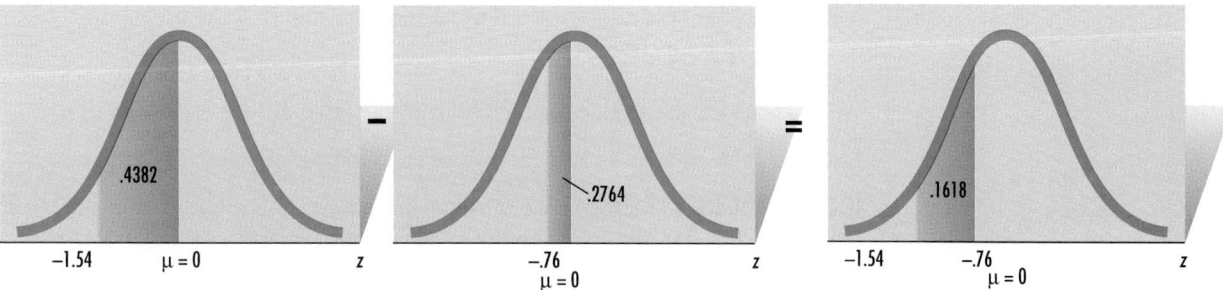

FIGURE 5.9 The area under the normal curve between a *z* value of − 1.54 and a *z* value of −.76 is .1618.

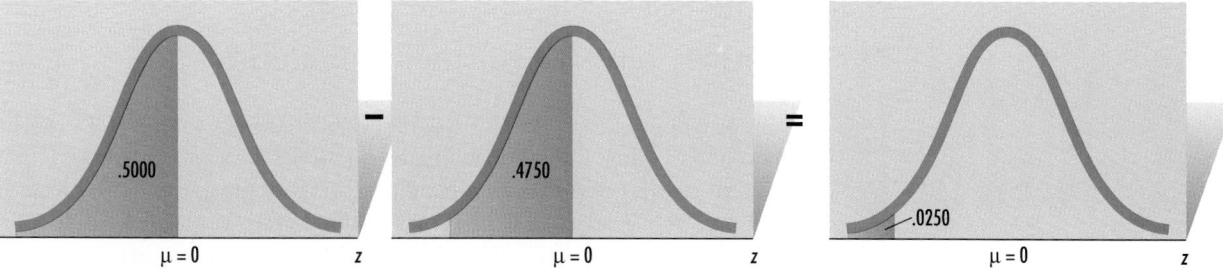

FIGURE 5.10 The area under the normal curve to the left of a *z* value of − 1.96 is .0250.

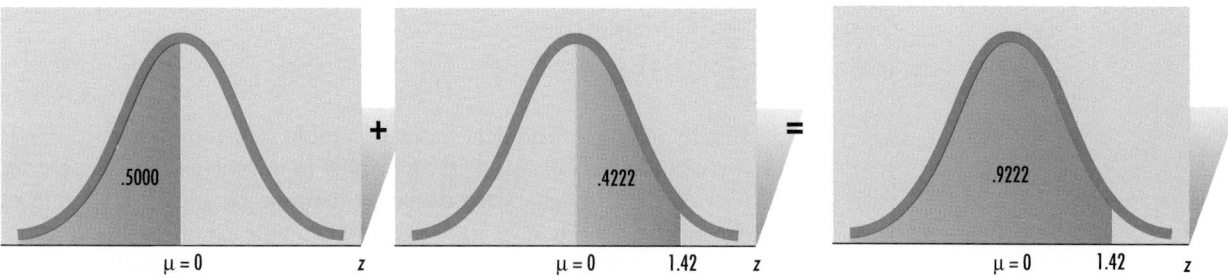

FIGURE 5.11 The area under the normal curve to the left of a *z* value of 1.42 is .9222.

Example 5.12   What's the area under the curve to the left of a *z* value of −1.96?

◆ Solution:
From the table in Appendix 2 you can see that the area between the mean and a *z* value of −1.96 is .4750. Since the curve is symmetric and the total area is 1, we know the total area to the left of the mean is .5. Thus, to find the required area we subtract .4750 from .5000 to get .0250. So $P(z < -1.96) = .0250$ (see *Figure 5.10*). ◆

Example 5.13   What's the area under the curve to the left of a *z* value of 1.42?

◆ Solution:
We know that the area to the left of the mean is .5. And from Appendix 2 we find that the area between the mean and a *z* value of 1.42 is .4222. So the required area = .5000 + .4222 = .9222—that is, $P(z < 1.42) = .9222$ (see *Figure 5.11*). ◆

You may have noticed that we've followed these steps to find the probability of getting a value within a particular interval:

1. We've identified the z value for each limit of the interval.

2. From the table of areas in Appendix 2 we've found the area for each z value.

3. If both limits of the interval are on opposite sides of the mean, we add the areas found in step 2; if the limits are on the same side of the mean, we subtract the smaller area from the larger one.

Sketching a picture of the needed area is helpful in such problems.

Using Statistical Software and Calculators to Determine Standard Normal Probabilities

Again, programs such as MINITAB and calculators such as the TI-83 can be used to obtain values for a probability distribution. One slight difference is that MINITAB gives us cumulative probabilities; that is, it gives us $P(z < z_0)$ instead of $P(0 < z < z_0)$. In some cases, that makes things even easier. In Example 5.13, we found $P(z < 1.42) = .9222$. Using MINITAB, we get the results in *Figure 5.12a*. A TI-83 calculator gives us the same cumulative probability in both screen 1 and screen 2 of *Figure 5.12b*.

Computing Probabilities for Any Normally Distributed Variable

Few normally distributed real-world data sets have a mean of 0 and a standard deviation of 1! As you can imagine, it would be impossible to include a separate table for each combination of mean and standard deviation that one might expect to find in such data sets. Fortunately, though, we have a way to compute areas (and thus probabilities) for normal curves that aren't standard. Since the z value (the random variable for the standard normal curve) corresponds to the number of standard deviations a score is from its mean, we can see how many standard deviations any normally distributed variable (x) is from its mean by using the formula for a population z score from Chapter 3:

$$z = \frac{x - \mu}{\sigma} \tag{5.7}$$

Thus, if we have a value of x for any normally distributed random variable and if we know the mean and standard deviation of its distribution, we can find the z score or standard score. Once we know the standard score, we can use Appendix 2 to find the required area(s) as we did in the previous section.

Now let's review how to compute z scores and learn how to use them to compute probabilities for any normally distributed random variable.

Example 5.14   If x is a normally distributed variable with a mean of 24 and a standard deviation of 3, what's the z score that corresponds to an x value of 19?

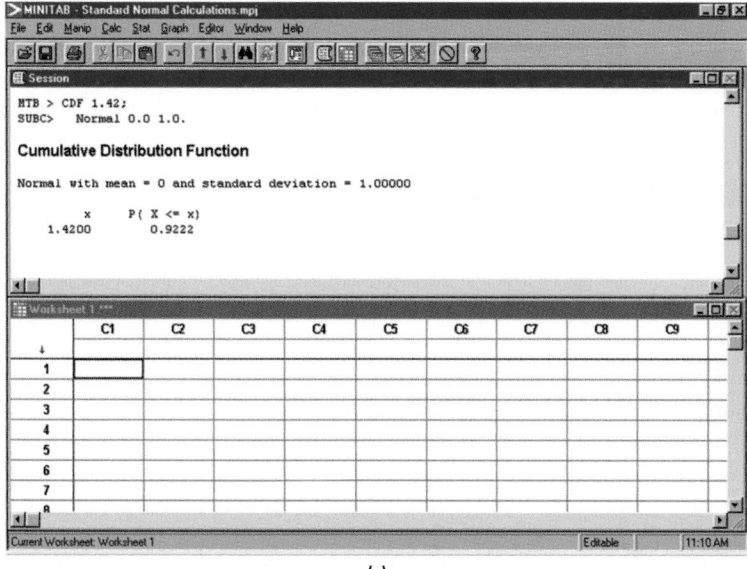

FIGURE 5.12 (*a*) To obtain this MINITAB output, click on **Calc, Probability Distributions, Normal,** click in the circle next to **Cumulative Probability,** click in the circle to the left of **Input constant** and enter the value of $X = 1.42$, and click **OK.** (*b*) To calculate normal probabilities on the TI-83, we use the **normalcdf** command from the **DISTR** menu. To calculate $P(L < X < R)$ the syntax is **normalcdf (L, R,** μ, σ). For example, in Example 5.13 we calculated $P(Z < 1.42.)$ From the home screen on the TI-83, enter **normalcdf** (–10, 1.42, 0, 1) and get .9222 as shown in screen 1. Note that even though there is no left boundary for $Z < 1.42$, the TI-83 syntax requires that we put one. In this example, –10 is chosen, but any value sufficiently far to the left could have been used. Since most of the standard normal distribution is contained in $-3 < Z < 3$, choosing –10 is fine to get four-decimal-place accuracy. In general, $\mu - 10\sigma$ is far enough to the left and $\mu + 10\sigma$ is far enough to the right to give adequate accuracy. The TI-83 can also sketch the distribution and shade the area. First set the window as

Xmin = –3.5, Xmax = 3.5, Xscl = 1
Ymin = –0.2, Ymax = 0.5, Yscl = 0

Note that –3.5 to 3.5 is chosen since almost all of a standard normal distribution is in that range. On the *y* axis, –0.2 is chosen to allow room at the bottom of the screen to see the calculated values. Access the **DISTR** > **DRAW** menu and choose the **ShadeNorm** command. As shown in the fourth line of screen 1, enter **ShadeNorm** (*–10, 1.42, 0, 1*) and press **ENTER.** The result is the shaded region and the probability shown in screen 2.

◆ **Solution:**

Using formula 5.7 we get

$$z = \frac{x - \mu}{\sigma} = \frac{19 - 24}{3} = -1.67$$

The score of 19 is 1.67 standard deviations below the mean of 24. ◆

☐ **Example 5.15**   If x is a normally distributed variable with a mean of 150 and a standard deviation of 24, what's the z score corresponding to an x value of 182?

◆ **Solution:**
Well,

$$z = \frac{x - \mu}{\sigma} = \frac{182 - 150}{24} = 1.33$$

The score of 182 is 1.33 standard deviations above the mean of 150. ◆

☐ **Example 5.16**   If x is a normally distributed variable with a mean of 100 and a standard deviation of 15, translate the following interval into an interval of z scores:

$$70 < x < 130$$

◆ **Solution:**
We find the z score that corresponds to each endpoint of the interval in this way:

$$z = \frac{70 - 100}{15} = -2.00 \quad \text{and} \quad z = \frac{130 - 100}{15} = 2.00$$

Thus, the z score interval corresponding to $70 < x < 130$ is $-2.00 < z < +2.00$ (see *Figure 5.13*). ◆

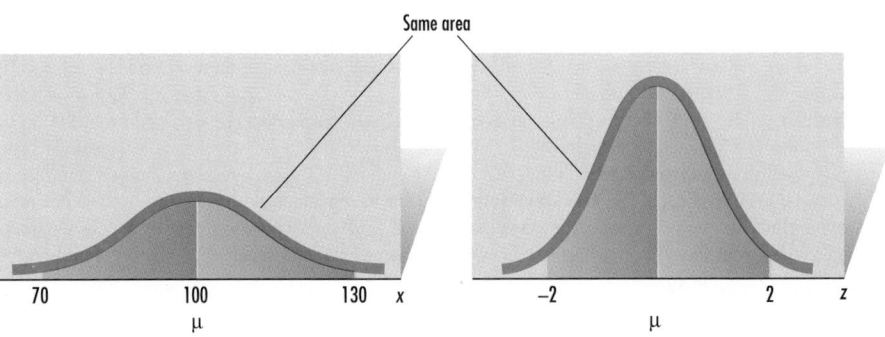

FIGURE 5.13 The z score interval corresponding to $70 < x < 130$.

☐ **Example 5.17**   For a certain IQ test, results are normally distributed with a mean of 100 points and a standard deviation of 15 points. What's the probability that a person chosen at random will have an IQ score between 70 and 130?

◆ **Solution:**
What we're looking for is $P(70 < x < 130)$. We don't have a table of areas for a normal distribution with a mean of 100 and a standard deviation of 15. But in Example 5.16 we found the z score interval that corresponded to this interval. So $P(70 < x < 130) = P(-2.00 < z < +2.00)$. We look up the required area in Appendix 2 for z values of ± 2.00 and find that it is .4772. Thus, the total area is .4772 + .4772 or .9544. About 95 percent of the population has an IQ score on this test between 70 and 130. It's important to realize that no matter what the normally distributed variable represents, about

95 percent of the population will fall within ±2.00 standard deviations from the mean (see *Figure 5.14*). ◆

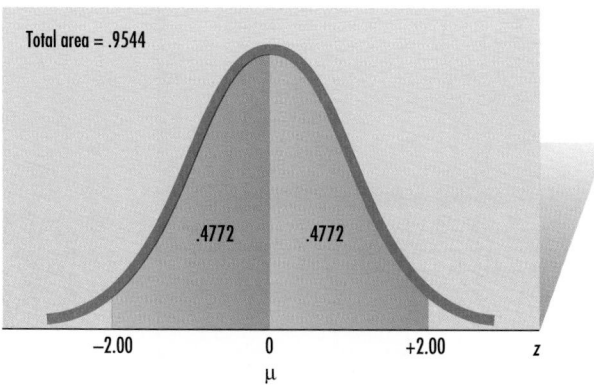

FIGURE 5.14 Area of the $z =$ distribution between −2.00 and 2.00.

Example 5.18 According to the *American Journal of Nutrition*, the mean midarm muscle circumference (MAMC) for males is a normally distributed random variable with a mean of 273 millimetres and a standard deviation of 29.18 millimetres. The MAMC for Clark Kent has been measured at 341 millimetres. What's the probability that a male in the population will have a MAMC measure greater than Clark's 341 millimetres?

◆ **Solution:**

We obviously don't have a table that lists areas under the normal curve with $\mu = 273$ and $\sigma = 29.18$. So to find the number of standard deviations Clark's measure is from the mean, we use the following z score formula:

$$z = \frac{x - \mu}{\sigma} = \frac{341 - 273}{29.18} = 2.33$$

Once we know that Clark's measure is 2.33 standard deviations above the mean, we can use Appendix 2 to find the area value that corresponds to 2.33. This value is .4901. And the area above (or greater than) .4901 is .0099 (.5000 − .4901). Thus, the probability of a male's MAMC being greater than Clark's is .0099. That is, less than 1 percent of adult males have a MAMC measure greater than Clark's. In symbols: $P(x > 341) = P(z > 2.33) = .0099$ (see *Figure 5.15*). ◆

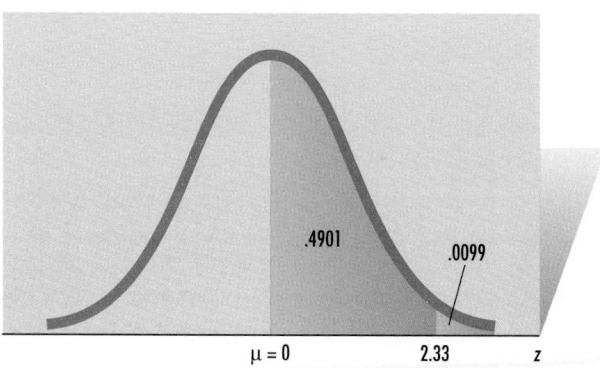

FIGURE 5.15 Area of the z distribution between 0 and 2.33.

FIGURE 5.16 To obtain this MINITAB output, click on **Calc, Probability Distributions, Normal,** click in the circle next to **Cumulative Probability,** enter 273 as **Mean** and 29.18 as **Standard deviation,** click in the circle to the left of **Input constant** and enter the value of X = 341, and click **OK.**

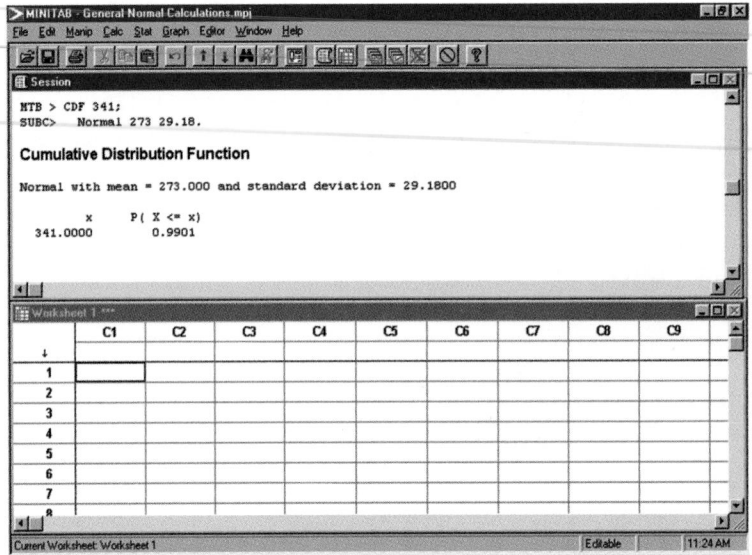

Using Statistical Software to Determine Normal Probabilities

We can use MINITAB to obtain the previous solution: $P(x > 341) = .0099$. However, because MINITAB gives us cumulative probabilities, we must use the complement rule of probabilities to find the final solution. So, using MINITAB, we find in *Figure 5.16* that $P(x \le 341) = .9901$. Then $P(x > 341) = 1 - P(x < 341) = 1 - .9901 = .0099$.

Finding *z* Scores from Given Probabilities

We've now seen how to find the area under the standard normal curve when we're given the *z* score boundaries. Now let's reverse the problem and find the *z* score boundaries when a specific area (probability) is given. You'll recall that the areas (which correspond to the probability that a standard normal score will fall between the mean and the specified *z* score) can be found in the body of the table in Appendix 2.

Example 5.19   An area of .4370 lies under the standard normal curve between the mean and a given positive *z* score (see *Figure 5.17*). What is the value of that *z* score?

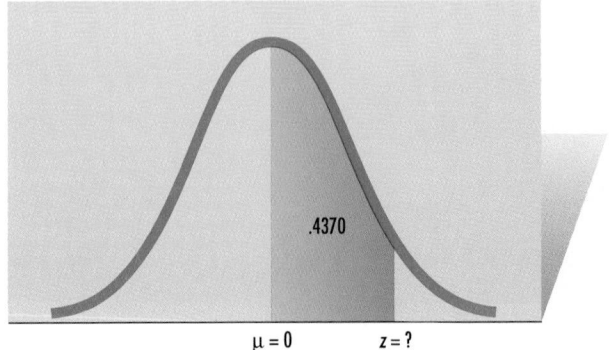

FIGURE 5.17 Area of .4370 between 0 and +z.

◆ **Solution:**

The area values are in the body of Appendix 2 and there we find .4370. The z score that corresponds to it is 1.53, which is the answer. ◆

Example 5.20 An area of .4808 lies under the normal curve between the mean and a given negative z score (see *Figure 5.18*). What's the value of that z score?

◆ **Solution:**

We look for .4808 in the body of Appendix 2 and see that the required z score is –2.07. ◆

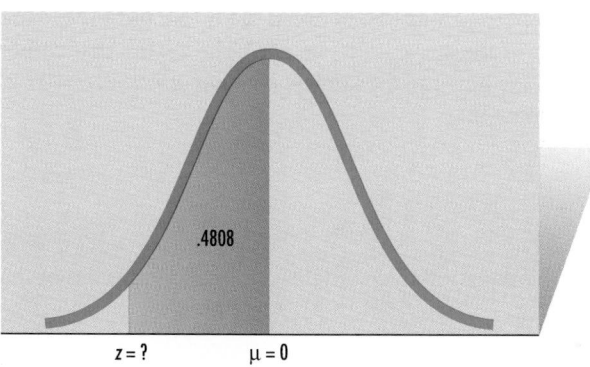

FIGURE 5.18 Area of .4808 between 0 and –z.

Example 5.21 Ninety percent of the normal curve lies to the left of a particular z score (see *Figure 5.19*). What's the value of that score?

◆ **Solution:**

The required z score must be to the right of the mean (since 50 percent is to the left of the mean). That leaves .4000 of the curve between the mean and the required z score. So now we must find the z value that corresponds to an area of .4000 in the table (.9000 – .5000). There's no entry in Appendix 2 for exactly .4000, but the closest entry to it, an area of .3997, corresponds to a z value of 1.28. ◆

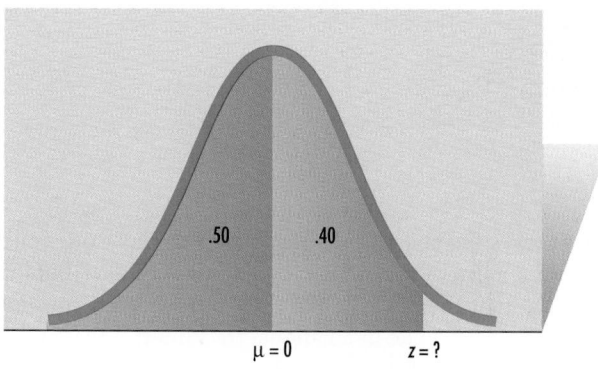

FIGURE 5.19 Area of .90 to the left of a particular value of z.

Finding Cutoff Scores for Normally Distributed Variables

In many practical situations involving a normally distributed variable, it's necessary to find a cutoff value. That is, it's necessary to locate a value that separates one group of the population from the others. Let's look at two examples involving cutoff values.

☐ **Example 5.22**   Scores for a particular civil service exam are normally distributed with a mean of 137 points and a standard deviation of 17.2 points. Applicants for civil service jobs must take this test, and the top 10 percent can be offered jobs. What is the cutoff score that separates the highest 10 percent of the test scores from the others, that is, what is the 90th percentile on this exam?

◆ **Solution:**

We must first find the standard z score that separates the lower 90 percent of the curve from the upper 10 percent (see *Figure 5.20*). To locate that value in Appendix 2, it's necessary to look up an area of .4000 in the table. (If we want an area of 10 percent to be to the right of our z score, then 40 percent must be between the mean and the z score since the total area in the right half of the curve is 50 percent.) The z score that comes closest to our requirements is 1.28. We now use the known values of $\mu = 137$, $\sigma = 17.2$, and $z = 1.28$ to determine x. We know that

$$z = \frac{x - \mu}{\sigma}$$

so we can multiply both sides of this equation by σ and then add μ to both sides of the equation to get this result:

$$x = \mu + z \cdot \sigma \qquad (5.8)$$

Thus, $x = 137 + (1.28)(17.2) = 159$, and anyone who scores above 159 on this civil service test is in the top 10 percent of the job applicants. ◆

FIGURE 5.20 90th percentile of z scores.

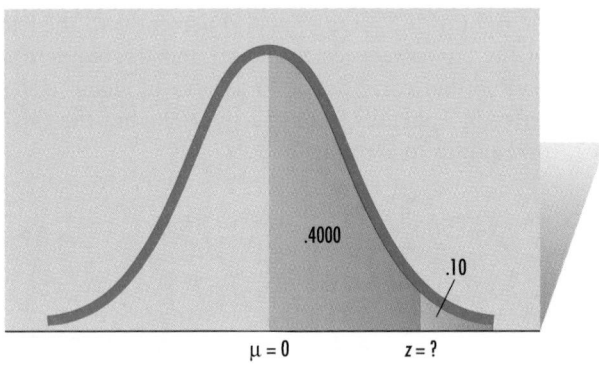

.4000

.10

$\mu = 0$ $z = ?$

☐ **Example 5.23**   The time it takes members of the track team to run a one-mile course is normally distributed with a mean of 5.6 minutes and a standard deviation of .76 minutes. The coach has decided that the 5 percent of the team who can run the course in the least time will be sent to participate in a national track meet. What is the cutoff score that will decide which members of the team will qualify (see *Figure 5.21*)?

◆ **Solution:**

If the area to the left of the required z score is .05, then the area between that z score and the mean is .4500. Looking up an area of .4500 in Appendix 2, we see it is halfway between the area entries of .4495 and .4505. The required z score is halfway between $z = -1.64$ and $z = -1.65$ so we'll use a z value of -1.645. Thus, $x = \mu + z \cdot \sigma = 5.6 + (-1.645)(.76) = 4.3498$. The qualifying time is 4.35 minutes. ◆

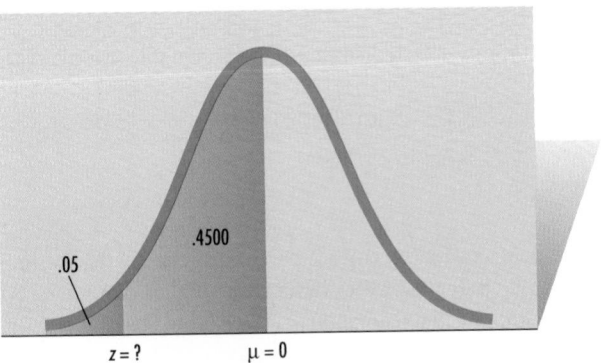

FIGURE 5.21 5th percentile of z scores.

Using Statistical Software to Find Cutoff Scores for Normally Distributed Variables

By now we should be accustomed to the ease with which a computer package can find probabilities. Using MINITAB on the previous example, we get the output in *Figure 5.22* with the correct qualifying time from the previous example.

Example 5.24 **Manufacturing Match Game** The paper by X. D. Fand and Y. Zhang "Assuring the Matchable Degree in Selective Assembly via a Predictive Model Based on Set Theory and Probability Method," *Transactions of the ASME*, 1996, discusses the manufacturing problem of accurately machining matching parts such as shafts that fit into a valve hole. They describe the sizes of both of these as having a normal distribution. Suppose a particular design requires a shaft with a diameter of 2.000 millimetres, but shafts with diameters between 21.990 and 22.010 are acceptable. Also suppose that the manufacturing process yields shafts with diameters normally distributed with a mean of 22.002 millimetres and a standard deviation of .005 millimetres. For this process, find (1) the probability of an acceptable shaft and also (2) the diameter that will be exceeded by only 2 percent of the shafts.

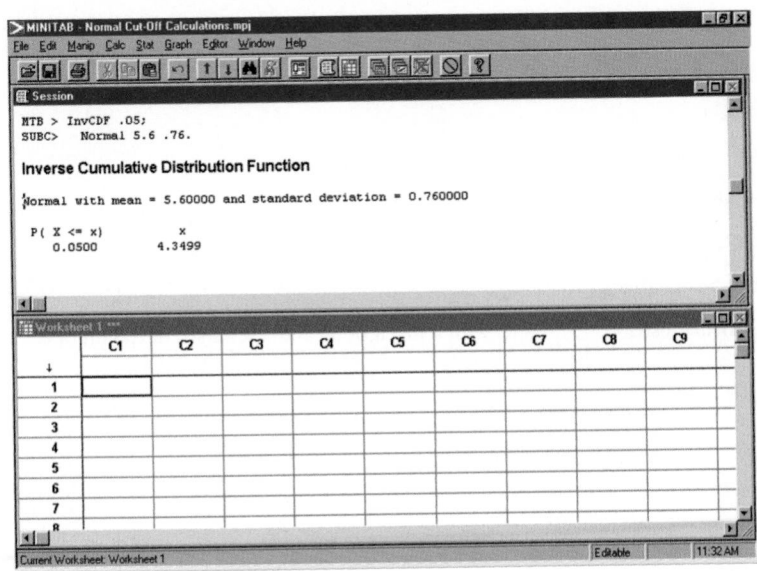

FIGURE 5.22 To obtain this **MINITAB** output, click on **Calc, Probability Distributions, Normal,** click in the circle next to **Inverse Cumulative Probability,** enter 5.6 as **Mean** and .76 as **Standard deviation,** click in the circle to the left of **Input constant** and enter the value of .05, and click **OK.**

◆ Solution

1. To find the probability that a randomly selected shaft will be acceptable, we calculate

$$z = \frac{21.990 - 22.002}{.005} = -2.40 \quad \text{and} \quad z = \frac{22.010 - 22.002}{.005} = 1.60$$

$$P(-2.40 < z < 1.60) = .4918 + .4452 = .9370$$

2. To find the diameter that will be exceeded by only 2 percent of the shafts, we recognize that this point must have 98 percent of the shafts with smaller diameters. So we look for the z value with an area of .9800 − .5000 = .4800. The closest z is 2.05. Then the diameter we want is

$$x = \mu + z \cdot \sigma = 22.002 + (2.05)(.005) = 22.0123 \quad \blacklozenge$$

Self-Testing Review 5.4

29. What's the area under the standard normal curve

  a) Between $z = -2.51$ and $z = 1.94$?

  b) Between $z = -2.83$ and $z = -.45$?

  c) To the right of $z = .97$?

  d) To the left of $z = 2.91$?

  e) Between $z = 2.53$ and $z = 3.09$?

  f) Between $z = -2.14$ and $z = -1.95$?

  g) To the left of $z = -2.84$?

  h) To the right of $z = -1.74$?

30. If z is the standard normal variable, find

  a) $P(0 < z < 1.71)$

  b) $P(z < 0.43)$

  c) $P(-2.19 < z < 2.14)$

  d) $P(z < -1.21)$

  e) $P(.75 < z < 1.86)$

  f) $P(z > -2.46)$

  g) $P(z > 2.92)$

  h) $P(-1.25 < z < 2.58)$

31. If x is a normally distributed variable with a mean of 50 and a standard deviation of 8, find

  a) $P(x > 50)$

  b) $P(48 < x < 72)$

  c) $P(54 < x < 60)$

32. If x is a normally distributed variable with a mean of 4 and a standard deviation of 1.2, find

a) $P(x < 3.5)$

b) $P(2 < x < 4.8)$

c) $P(1.5 < x < 5.2)$

33. A soft drink machine is regulated so that it discharges an average of 227 ml per cup. If the amount of drink dispensed per cup is normally distributed with a standard deviation of 14 ml, find the probability that the amount dispensed into any one cup is

a) More than 227 ml.

b) More than 250 ml.

c) Between 220 and 239 ml.

d) Less than 213 ml.

34. Knee flexion, a measure of the knee range of motion, is a normally distributed variable. *Physical Therapy* reported that the mean number of degrees of knee flexion found in the First National Health and Nutrition Exam Survey was 132°, with a standard deviation of 10 degrees. If a person is selected at random, find the probability that the knee flexion of that person is

a) Between 125 and 140°.

b) Between 145 and 155°.

c) Greater than 160°.

d) Less than 110°.

35. According to Statistics Canada criteria, the average body mass index (BMI) for women in the 20- to 24-year age group was found to be 25.7 with a standard deviation of 3. Assume the population of all values of the BMI for women in this age group is normally distributed. If a woman in this age group is selected at random, what is the probability that she has a BMI

a) Under 18.5 (underweight)?

b) Between 18.5 and 24.9 (acceptable)?

c) Between 25 and 30 (overweight)?

d) Over 30 (obese)?

36. According to Environment Canada, the average yearly rainfall in Vancouver is 1,055.4 mm. Assuming that the yearly rainfall amounts are normally distributed and the standard deviation is 172 mm, find the probability that the rainfall in Vancouver in any one randomly selected year is

a) Over 800.

b) Over 1,000.

c) Over 1,200.

37. In a consumer research study investigating how restaurant customers responded to being touched by those serving them, servers were divided into groups—those who touched customers, and those who did not. Tips were normally distributed, and servers who touched their customers received an average tip of 16.51 percent of the total bill, with a standard deviation of 4.47 percent. Find the probability that a server who touched his or her customer would receive a tip

a) Between 15 and 20 percent.

b) Greater than 18 percent.

c) Less than 10 percent.

38. Find the z score such that

a) Forty percent of the area under the standard normal curve lies to its left.

b) Ninety percent of the area under the standard normal curve lies to its right.

c) Ninety-five percent of the area under the standard normal curve lies between $-z$ and $+z$.

d) Twenty-five percent of the area under the standard normal curve lies to its left.

e) Five percent of the area under the standard normal curve lies to its right.

f) Ninety-nine percent of the area under the standard normal curve lies between $-z$ and $+z$.

39. For a certain population the Miller Analogy Test has normally distributed scores with a mean of 50 and a standard deviation of 5. What is the score on this test that is the cutoff value for the top 12 percent of the scores?

40. The life span of the Everrun Batteries used in an application is normally distributed with a mean of 3.5 years and a standard deviation of .4 year. The manufacturer decides to replace any battery that dies before the guarantee period is up and wants to set the length of that period so that no more than 5 percent of the batteries will have to be replaced. How long should the guarantee period be so that no more than 5 percent of the batteries will die (leaving 95 percent working)?

41. Kyser and Collins ("Reliability Enhancement of a New Computer by ESS," *Proceedings—Institute of Environmental Sciences,* 1995) describe a program to enhance the reliability of the CPU board in a massively parcel RISC processor system. A part of the paper concentrates on a parity problem labelled a Comm Logic failure. The errors seem to occur as a function of temperature and have a normal distribution with a mean of 80°C and a standard deviation of 20°C.

a) What is the probability that an error occurs at lower than 77°?

b) What is the probability that an error occurs at between 74 and 84°?

c) Above what temperature will 25 percent of the errors occur?

42. A 1996 paper from *Civil Engineering* ("An Examination of the Factor of Safe as it Relates to the Design of the Compressive Strength of Concrete," 1996, Daniel Gibbons) describes the compressive strength of concrete for freshwater exhibition tanks as having a mean of 6,000 psi and a standard deviation of 240 psi. Assuming the compressive strength is normally distributed,

a) What is the probability that the compressive strength of a sample of concrete is between 5,500 and 6,500 psi?

b) What is the probability that the compressive strength of a sample of concrete is between 5,000 and 5,900 psi?

c) What is the probability that the compressive strength of a sample of concrete is less than 6,840 psi?

d) What is the probability that the compressive strength of a sample of concrete is less than 5,800 psi?

e) Below what value will 20 percent of the compressive strengths of samples of concrete be?

f) Above what value will 70 percent of the compressive strengths of samples of concrete be?

g) Above what value will 15 percent of the compressive strengths of samples of concrete be?

43. Suppose that the heights of 16-month-old oak seedlings are normally distributed with a mean of 31.5 cm and a standard deviation of 10 cm.

a) What is the probability that the height of a randomly selected seedling will be between 24 and 38 cm?

b) What is the probability that the height of a randomly selected seedling will be less than 41 cm?

c) What is the probability that the height of a randomly selected seedling will be more than 24 cm?

d) What is the height above which 80 percent of the seedlings will grow?

e) What is the height above which 25 percent of the seedlings will grow?

5.5 Normal Approximation of the Binomial

Recall that a binomial random variable, x, is defined as the number of "successes" in n repeated independent trials of an experiment where p denotes the probability of "success" on any one trial, and $q = 1 - p$ denotes the probability of "failure" on any one trial. We have seen that the (exact) probability of observing r successes in n trials is $P(x = r) = \binom{n}{r} p^r q^{n-r}$. We have also seen the mean and standard deviation of a binomial distribution are $\mu_x = E(x) = np$ and $\sigma_x = \sqrt{npq}$.

You may have noticed that the amount of computation needed to compute binomial probabilities becomes onerous as n increases. Fortunately, it has been shown that, for large n, binomial probabilities may be approximated using normal probabilities. As a rule of thumb, if n is large enough so that both $np \geq 5$ and $n(1 - p) \geq 5$ (which means you are expecting at least five successes and at least five failures), then the binomial distribution may be approximated by a normal distribution with the same mean and standard deviation. For example, consider the binomial distribution with parameters $n = 10$ and $p = 0.5$. The exact binomial probabilities are shown below:

x	P(x)
0	0.0010
1	0.0098
2	0.0439
3	0.1172
4	0.2051
5	0.2461
6	0.2051
7	0.1172
8	0.0439
9	0.0098
10	0.0010

Note that the mean and standard deviation of x are

$$\mu_x = np = 10(.5) = 5, \quad \text{and} \quad \sigma_x = \sqrt{npq} = \sqrt{10(.5)(.5)} = 1.581$$

The graph below shows both the binomial probability histogram and the normal distribution with the same mean and standard deviation. As you can see, the approximation is close. We will use normal probabilities to approximate binomial probabilities.

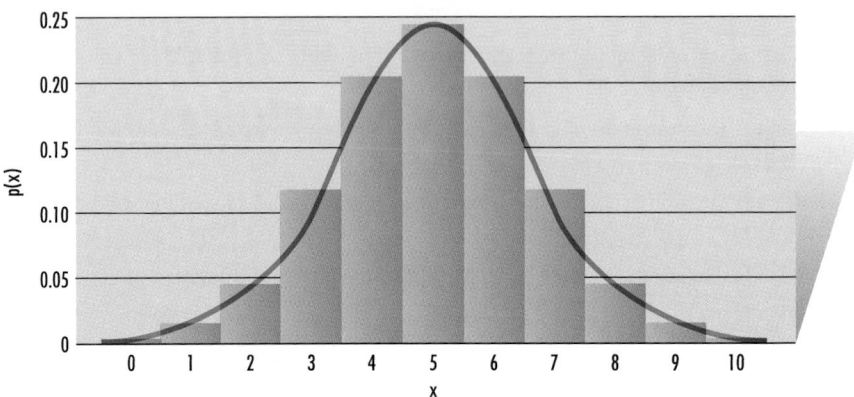

Continuity Correction

Since we will be using a continuous distribution to approximate a discrete distribution, we make a *continuity correction* to improve the accuracy of our approximation. Recall that a binomial probability may be represented by the area of the appropriate rectangle(s) in the probability histogram. When using the area under a normal curve to approximate the area of the rectangle(s), we find the area under the curve starting at the left-hand side of the first rectangle we want included up to the right-hand side of the last rectangle to be included. For example, $P(x = 5) \cong P(4.5 < x < 5.5)$, $P(5 \le x \le 8) \cong P(4.5 < x < 8.5)$, $P(5 < x < 10) = P(6 \le x \le 9) \cong P(5.5 < x < 9.5)$, etc. where on the left-hand side of these equations we are thinking of x as having a binomial distribution and on the right hand side we are thinking of x as having an approximately normal distribution. The area under the normal curve is used to approximate the area of the appropriate rectangle(s).

◻ **Example 5.25**   **Big Quiz** Suppose the QuickQuiz discussed in this chapter became a "BigQuiz" with 100 questions, and we want to compute the probability of getting more than 30 correct answers.

◆ **Solution:**

The random variable $x =$ the number of the 100 questions that are answered correctly has a binomial distribution with parameters $n = 100$ and $p = 1/4 = .25$. We note that $\mu_x = np = 100(.25) = 25$, and $\sigma_x = \sqrt{npq} = \sqrt{1,000(.25)(.75)} = 4.3301$. Since both $np \ge 5$ and $n(1 - p) \ge 5$ the normal approximation method is regarded as adequate.

Since we want to approximate the probability that x is greater than 30, the first rectangle whose area we wish to approximate is the one centred at 31, and the left-hand side of this rectangle is at 30.5. Therefore,

$$P(x > 30) = P\left(\frac{x - \mu_x}{\sigma_x} > \frac{30.5 - 25}{4.3301}\right) \cong P(z > 1.27) = .5 - .3980 = .1020$$

This approximation is certainly much shorter than calculating the exact probability. To find the exact probability we would have to use the binomial formula to find the probability that x is equal to any one of the 70 values 31, 32, 33, ... , 100. The exact probability is

$$P(x > 30) = \sum_{x=31}^{100} \binom{100}{x}(.25)^x(.75)^{100-x} = 0.1038. \; \blacklozenge$$

Example 5.26   **Canadians Need Big Vitamin D Supplements** A recent study from the University of Calgary reported that Canadians aren't getting enough bone-building vitamin D from sunshine, so people should be taking more vitamin D supplements to prevent brittle bones. Researchers found 97 percent of the study's participants had a vitamin D defciency at some point during the year but their levels of the vitamin rose during the spring and summer. Suppose the results of the study apply to all Canadians. If a random sample of 1,000 Canadians is tested, what is the approximate probability that the number of people in the sample who are deficient in vitamin D will be
(a) At least 960?
(b) At most 965?
(c) Between 965 and 980, inclusive?

◆ **Solution:**
The random variable x = the number of the 1,000 Canadians selected who are deficient in vitamin D, has a binomial distribution with parameters n = 1,000 and p = .97. We note that $\mu_x = np = 1{,}000(.97) = 970$, and $\sigma_x = \sqrt{npq} = \sqrt{1{,}000(.97)(.03)} = 5.3944$. Since both $np \geq 5$ and $n(1 - p) \geq 5$ the normal approximation method is regarded as adequate.

(a) Since we want to approximate the probability that x is at least 960, the first rectangle whose area we wish to approximate is the one centred at 960, and the left-hand side of this rectangle is at 959.5. Therefore,

$$P(x \leq 965) = P\left(\frac{x - \mu_x}{\sigma_x} > \frac{959.5 - 970}{5.3944}\right) \cong P(z > -1.95) = .5 + .4744 = .9744$$

(b) Since we want to approximate the probability that x is at most 965, we want to approximate the areas of all the rectangles beginning with the one centred at 0, up to and including the one centred at 965. The right-hand side of this rectangle is at 965.5. Therefore,

$$P(x \leq 965) = P\left(\frac{x - \mu_x}{\sigma_x} < \frac{965.5 - 970}{5.3944}\right) \cong P(z < -0.83) = .5 - .2967 = .2033$$

(c) Since we want to approximate the probability that x is between 965 and 980, inclusive, we want to approximate the areas of all the rectangles beginning with the one centred at 965 (with the left-hand side at 964.5), up to and including the one centred at 980 (with the right-hand side at 980.5). Therefore,

$$P(965 \leq x \leq 980) = P\left(\frac{964.5 - 970}{5.3944} < \frac{x - \mu_x}{\sigma_x} < \frac{980.5 - 970}{5.3944}\right)$$

$$\cong P(-1.02 < z < 1.95) = .3461 + .4744 = .8205 \quad \blacklozenge$$

Self-Testing Review 5.5

In the following, use the corrected normal curve method to approximate the requested probabilities.

44. Of the customers visiting the television section of a large electronics store, only 20 percent make a purchase. If 120 customers visit the television section tomorrow, find the approximate probability that at least 30 will make a purchase.

45. Assume that blue-collar workers in good physical condition have only a 10 percent probability of developing a stress-related health problem. If a random sample of 400 blue-collar employees in good physical condition is selected, what is the approximate probability that the number that will develop stress-related illnesses is

    a) Exactly 45?

    b) Fewer than 35?

    c) More than 35 but fewer than 40?

46. If the probability that a newborn child will be female is .50, find the approximate probability that in 100 births, 45 or fewer will be females.

47. A loan officer in a large bank has been assigned to screen 60 loan applications during the next week. If her past record indicates that in the long run she turns down 20 percent of the applicants, what is the approximate probability that 45 or more of the 60 applications will be approved?

48. A drug manufacturer states that only 10 percent of the patients using a particular drug will experience side effects. Doctors at a large university hospital use the drug in treating 200 patients. What is the approximate probability that 15 or fewer of the 200 patients experience side effects?

49. Use a corrected normal distribution to approximate the probability of getting exactly six heads and eight tails in 14 flips of a balanced coin, and compare the result with the corresponding exact value found in Appendix 1.

50. If 60 percent of the registered voters plan to vote for Blake Ackermann for mayor of a large city, what is the approximate probability that fewer than half of the voters, in a poll of 40 registered voters, plan to vote for Blake Ackermann?

51. The manager of a restaurant knows from experience that in the long run, only 80 percent of the people who make reservations for the evening show up for dinner. The manager decides one evening to overbook and accept 40 reservations when only 34 tables are available. What is the approximate probability that more than 34 parties will show up?

52. If 40 percent of the purchases at a store are for amounts over $100, what is the approximate probability that fewer than 20 of the purchases, in a sample of 60, are for amounts over $100?

53. The Canada Safety Council reported (in 2002) that 52 percent of Canadian adults who ride bicycles never or rarely wear a helmet. Assuming this is still true today, find the approximate probability that in a random sample of 200 Canadian adults who ride bicycles, the number who never or rarely wear a helmet will be

    a) At least 100.

    b) At most 100.

    c) 101 or 102.

LOOKING BACK

1. A binomial experiment is one in which there are a fixed number (n) of independent trials, and for each trial there are only two outcomes—success or failure. The probability of success in a single trial is p, and the probability of failure in a single trial is q. Thus, $p + q = 1$. The discrete random variable r counts the number of successes during the n trials. The binomial probability of getting exactly r successes in n trials can be computed using $P(r) = \binom{n}{r}p^r q^{n-r}$ or it may be found in the table of binomial probabilities in Appendix 1. The expected value [$E(x)$] of a binomial distribution can be computed using $E(x) = np$, and the standard deviation of such a distribution can be found using the formula $\sigma = \sqrt{npq}$.

2. The Poisson distribution is another useful discrete probability distribution. It's used to find the probability of a specific number of occurrences that take place per unit of time, distance, area, or volume rather than during a given number of trials. The formula

$$P(x) = \frac{\mu^x e^{-\mu}}{x!}$$

or the table in Appendix 10 can be used to calculate the probability of x occurrences within a given time or space unit.

3. The most important continuous probability distribution is the normal distribution. A normal distribution curve is symmetrical and bell shaped. The total area under the curve is 1. The probability that a normally distributed random variable will take on a value between a and b is the area under the normal curve between two vertical lines erected at points a and b. The area covered by an interval under the normal curve can be found by using a table of areas such as the one found in Appendix 2. This table shows the area between the mean of a normal curve and a given number of standard deviations from that mean. The z score (standard score) of a variable is used to represent the number of standard deviations. A z score is calculated by the formula

$$z = \frac{x - \mu}{\sigma}$$

4. Binomial probabilities may be approximated using the normal distribution. If n is large enough so that both np $\geq$ 5 and n(1 – p)$\geq$ 5 then the binomial distribution may be approximated by a normal distribution with the same mean and standard deviation. When using the normal approximation of the binomial, we use a continuity correction to improve the approximation.

Exercises

54. A binomial experiment is conducted with $n = 13$ and $p = .35$. Find the probability that the number of successes is

   a) Exactly five.

   b) At least five.

55. A binomial experiment is conducted with $n = 6$ and $p = .40$. Find the probability that

   a) There are no successes.

   b) There is at least one success.

56. It's found in an experiment that there's an average of 3.9 occurrences during a specified time interval. Assume a Poisson distribution applies and find the probability that there are

  a) Exactly four occurrences during the interval.

  b) Exactly three occurrences during the interval.

  c) Three or four occurrences during the interval.

57. It's found in an experiment that there's an average of 6.7 occurrences within a given space. Assume a Poisson distribution applies and find the probability that there

  a) Are no occurrences within the space.

  b) Is at least one occurrence within the space.

  c) Are more than 16 occurrences within the space.

58. If z is the standard normal variable, find the following probabilities:

  a) $P(0 \leq z \leq 1.53)$

  b) $P(-2.45 \leq z \leq 1.91)$

  c) $P(z \leq 1.96)$

  d) $P(-3.05 \leq z \leq -2.73)$

  e) $P(z \geq 2.58)$

  f) $P(z \leq -1.64)$

59. According to the 2001 Statistics Canada census, about 80 percent of all centenarians (people of aged 100 years and over) in Canada were women. If 15 centenarians were randomly selected from the 2001 Canadian population, what is the probability that

  a) Exactly ten were women?

  b) More than eight were women?

  c) Fewer than six were women?

60. *Marketplace,* a CBC consumer program, reported in 2002 that in an investigation they found about 40 percent of Grade 6 and 7 students carry backpacks that are heavier than those recommended by doctors. If 20 such students are randomly selected, find the probability that

  a) Between 12 and 15 (inclusive) carry backpacks that are within the doctors' recommendation.

  b) All are within the doctors' recommendation.

61. The I.C.T Telemarketing Group reports that the average employee makes five sales in an hour. Assuming a Poisson distribution applies, find the probability that an employee makes

  a) Three sales in an hour.

  b) Four sales in an hour,

  c) Three or four sales in an hour.

62. *The Health of Canada's Communities* (*2002*), a Statistics Canada report, considered factors affecting life expectancy of Canadians living in large metropolitan areas and urban centres. Some of the data is presented below.

	Life Expectancy (years)	Infrequent Exercise (age 12+)	High Stress (age 18+)	Depression (age 12+)
		%	%	%
Canada	78.3	22	26	7
Fraser Valley	78.6	15	30	12
Halifax	77.9	20	22	8
London	78.4	19	30	6
Saskatoon	78.9	22	27	10
Winnipeg	77.9	25	27	8

  a) If seven people (age 18 and over) are randomly selected from London, find the probability that more than four of the people selected have a high stress level.

  b) If 17 people (age 12 and over) are randomly selected from Saskatoon, find the probability that between four and seven (inclusive) of the people selected suffer from depression.

  c) If ten people (age 12 and over) are randomly selected from Winnipeg, find the probability that fewer than three of the people selected exercise infrequently.

  d) If 15 people (age 12 and over) are randomly selected from the Fraser Valley, find the probability that more than ten of the people selected exercise frequently.

63. In a *Gallup* poll, 60 percent of the eligible men questioned said they would date a coworker. If ten employed men are questioned, find the probability that

  a) More than seven would say they would date a coworker.

  b) Fewer than four would say they would date a coworker.

  c) At least nine would say they would date a coworker.

64. In 2000, a Saskatchewan Government Insurance report stated that about 15 percent of all licensed drivers in Saskatchewan were seniors (age 65+). If 28 drivers are randomly selected from the population of all licensed drivers in Saskatchewan in that year, find

  a) The expected number who are seniors.

  b) The standard deviation for this distribution.

65. A study of teenagers and their drug use was published in the *Journal of Abnormal Psychology.* Forty percent of the teenagers in the study were not living with both biological parents. If a sample of nine of these teenagers is selected, find the probability that

a) More than five are not living with both biological parents.

b) At least one is living with both biological parents.

c) Fewer than three are not living with both biological parents.

66. The fire department receives an average of 2.4 alarms per hour. Assuming a Poisson distribution applies, find the probability that

a) At least one alarm is received in one hour.

b) Two alarms are received in one hour.

67. Suppose that 55 percent of all three- to five-year-old children in Ontario attend preschool programs for at least a portion of the day. If 18 children aged three to five are chosen at random, what's the probability that

a) Fewer than six attend such a program?

b) Between 9 and 14 (inclusive) attend such a program?

68. A survey was designed to assess the extent to which soft plastic bread wrappers could be reused. Lead was detected in the printing on these wrappers. The mean amount of lead for these bags was 26 mg with a standard deviation of 6 mg. A soft plastic bread wrapper is selected at random. Find the probability (assuming a normal distribution) that the wrapper has

a) More than 30 mg of lead.

b) Less than 15 mg of lead.

c) Between 15 and 30 mg of lead.

69. In a Statistics Canada survey of Grade 10 students, 18 percent of males and 45 percent of females were on a diet or felt they had to lose weight. Suppose ten male and ten female Grade 10 students are selected at random. What is the probability that

a) All female students were on a diet or believed that they had to lose weight?

b) At least five male students were on a diet or believed that they had to lose weight?

70. A study of the effect of predator introduction to artificial ponds was published in *Ecology.* Experimenters found that the average density of zooplankton in the pond was 4.60 individuals/cl. Assuming a Poisson distribution applies, what is the probability that a centilitre of fluid from the artificial pond in the study had

a) No individuals?

b) Four individuals?

71. A nationwide study of academic dishonesty among junior and senior college students was published in *Psychology Today.* The survey found that 70 percent of men and women confessed to cheating during high school. If a sample of 20 college students is surveyed, what's the probability that

a) More than 12 confess to high school cheating?

b) Fewer than ten confess to high school cheating?

c) Between 10 and 15 (inclusive) confess to high school cheating?

72. The *New England Journal of Medicine* published a study about patients who were treated by angioplasty after a heart attack. The number of days between the heart attack and successful angioplasty was normally distributed with a mean of 12 days and a standard deviation of 2 days. Find the probability that a patient's time between a heart attack and successful angioplasty treatment is

a) More than seven days.

b) Less than 14 days.

c) Between 7 and 14 days.

73. According to Environment Canada, the average yearly precipitation in Regina is 384 mm. Assuming that the yearly precipitation amounts are normally distributed and the standard deviation is 93.9 mm, find the probability that the precipitation in Regina in any one randomly selected year is

a) Between 300 and 400 mm.

b) Over 400 mm.

74. According to Statistics Canada, 34 percent of households in Saskatchewan have air conditioning. If ten households from Saskatchewan are selected at random, find the probability that

a) More than five have air conditioning.

b) Between five and eight (inclusive) have air conditioning.

75. In a study of depressed patients, it was found that the age at onset of depression for those in dysfunctional families was normally distributed with a mean and standard deviation of 30.6 years and 9.1 years, respectively. A depressed person from a dysfunctional family is selected at random. Find the probability that the patient was

a) More than 21 years of age at the onset of depression.

b) Less than 45 years of age at the onset of depression.

76. In the study described in problem 75, it was found that the length of stay of depressed patients in a hospital was normally distributed with a mean of 23.3 days and a standard deviation of 7.7 days. A patient from a dysfunctional family, suffering from depression, is selected at random. What's the probability that his or her hospital stay was

a) Less than ten days?

b) Between 10 and 30 days?

77. The length of time students in Grade 6 watch TV each day was found to be normally distributed with a mean and standard deviation of 118.3 minutes and 43.1 minutes, respectively. If a student in Grade 6 is selected at random, find the probability that he or she watches

a) More than four hours of TV.

b) Between three and four hours of TV.

78. A Statistics Canada report on youth estimated that about 35 percent of Grade 10 students played four or more hours of computer games per week. If 250 Grade 10 students were randomly selected, find the

a) Expected number of Grade 10 students who played four or more hours of computer games per week.

b) Standard deviation of this distribution.

79. A Statistics Canada article, *The Health of Canada's Communities* (*2002*), reported that in Canada, 22 percent of people aged 12 years and over smoke daily. What is the approximate probability that in a random sample of 50 Canadians aged 12 and over, there will be fewer than ten daily smokers?

80. A Statistics Canada article, *The Health of Canada's Communities* (*2002*), reported that in Canada, 12 percent of people aged 12 and over are in poor health. What is the approximate probability that in a random sample of 50 Canadians aged 12 years and over, there will be at most five who are in poor health?

81. Find the *z* score such that

a) 30 percent of the curve lies to the left of *z*.

b) 10 percent of the curve lies to the right of *z*.

c) 90 percent of the curve lies between −*z* and +*z*.

d) 20 percent of the curve lies to the right of *z*.

82. The scores of an entrance exam are normally distributed with a mean and standard deviation of 550 and 95, respectively. Find the entrance score that separates the top 10 percent from the lower 90 percent.

83. If IQ scores on a particular test are normally distributed with a mean and standard deviation of 100 and 15, respectively, find the IQ score above which the top 5 percent of the population falls.

84. Suppose an experiment meets all the conditions of a binomial experiment, except that the number of trials is not fixed. If x denotes the number of the trial on which the first success occurs, then x has a geometric distribution. The probability of getting the first success on trial number x is given by $P(x) = p(1 - p)^{x-1}$ for $x = 1, 2, 3, \ldots$, where p is the probability of success on any one trial. This probability distribution is called the geometric distribution since the successive terms constitute a geometric progression. As an example, suppose the probability that any one box of Cracker Jack contains a

prize is 0.20. A boy purchases and opens boxes until he obtains one containing a prize. What is the probability that the number of boxes purchased will be (a) exactly five, and (b) at least five?

85. In the game of billiards, a players turn continues until he or she misses a shot. If the probability that Mr. Smith misses any one shot is 0.30 and the outcomes for successive shots are independent, what is the probability that (a) his turn consists of exactly four shots, and (b) his turn consists of at least four shots?

86. If we select a sample from a small finite population of successes and failures, without replacement, then the trials are not independent, and therefore the binomial distribution should not be used.

Suppose the population consists of $a + b$ elements where a are successes and b are failures. If a sample of size n is selected without replacement, the probability of obtaining x successes and $n - x$ failures is given by

$$P(x) = \frac{\binom{a}{x}\binom{b}{n-x}}{\binom{a+b}{n}},$$

and this probability distribution is called the hypergeometric distribution. In Lotto 6/49, a bettor selects six numbers, without replacement, from 1 to 49, and later a winning six-number combination is selected. Find the probability of getting (a) all six winning numbers, (b) exactly four of the winning numbers, (c) no winning numbers.

87. A shipment of 20 computer monitors is rejected and returned if 4 are checked for defects and at least one is found to be defective. Find the probability the shipment will be rejected and returned if the shipment actually contains five defective monitors.

88. The binomial distribution applies only to experiments involving two types of outcomes. The multinomial distribution involves more than two types of outcomes. Suppose we have k types of mutually exclusive outcomes, where p_k denotes the probability that the outcome of any one trial is of type k. Then, in n repeated independent trials, the probability of x_1 outcomes of type 1, x_2 outcomes of type 2, ... , and x_k outcomes of type k, is given by

$$P(x_1, x_2, \ldots, x_k) = \frac{n!}{x_1!\, x_2! \ldots x_k!}\, p_1^{x_1} p_2^{x_2} \cdots p_k^{x_k}.$$

Suppose the probability that a car driven from Winnipeg to Halifax meets with a serious accident is 0.01, the probability that it meets with a minor accident is 0.04, and the probability it does not meet with an accident is 0.95. What is the probability that among nine cars driven from Winnipeg to Halifax eight arrive without an accident while one has a minor accident?

89. The manager of a lottery kiosk found that in the long run, 30 percent of all customers purchase only one ticket, 60 percent purchase two tickets, and 10 percent purchase three or more tickets. Find the probability that of the next ten customers, two will purchase only one ticket, five will purchase two tickets, and three will purchase three or more tickets.

90. Suppose an experiment meets all the conditions of a Poisson experiment, except that the period of time is not fixed. If t denotes the time required to generate one Poisson occurrence, (or alternatively, the time between successive Poisson occurrences) then t has an exponential distribution. An exponential distribution curve is defined by the following formula:

$$f(t) = \begin{cases} \lambda e^{-\lambda t} & \text{if } t \geq 0 \\ 0 & \text{if } t < 0 \end{cases}$$

where λ denotes the mean number of occurrences per unit of time (this is a change from Section 5.3 where we used μ to denote the mean number of occurrences per unit of time). It has been shown that the mean of t is $1/\lambda$, which means that the mean time between occurrences is $1/\lambda$. It has also been shown that if t is exponential and v is any positive number, then

$$P(0 < t < v) = 1 - e^{-\lambda v}.$$

Police records show that there has been an average of four accidents per week on a new highway. If these accidents follow a Poisson process, and an accident has just happened, what's the probability that the next accident will happen within 48 hours?

91. The time in days during which an electrical generator is operational is a random variable that follows the exponential distribution with a mean of seven. What's the probability that a generator of this type will be operational for

    a) Less than five days?

    b) More than ten days?

Topics for Review and Discussion

1. What is binomial probability distribution? Discuss the conditions and requirements for a binomial experiment.

2. Why is the formula for combinations incorporated into the formula for computing binomial probabilities?

3. How may a Poisson distribution be used? What are the conditions and requirements for the use of such a distribution?

4. The binomial and Poisson distributions are examples of discrete probability distributions. Discuss.

5. Probabilities for continuous probability distributions are represented by areas under the curve. Discuss.

6. Discuss the procedure for computing normal curve probabilities.

7. Discuss the procedure far determining a z score (standard score) when a specified area under the standard normal curve is given. Use several examples in your explanation.

Projects/Issues to Consider

1. Conduct a library search to find examples of binomial, Poisson, and normally distributed variables. Write a brief report outlining your findings.

2. Collect a data set from your classmates and other students by asking each of them the following questions:

    a) Would you rather take a class in statistics than a class in physics?

    b) How many siblings do you have?

    c) In a typical week, how many hours do you study?

Does it appear that the number of people who would rather take a class in statistics than a class in physics is a binomial random variable? Does it appear that the number of siblings students have is a Poisson variable? Does it look like the number of hours in a week students study is a normal variable? How did you make your determinations? Write a brief report on your findings.

Computer/Calculator Exercises

1. Use your computer software package to simulate the results of 100 students taking the QuickQuiz presented in this chapter. (If your software permits, you may use a **RANDOM** command and a **BINOMIAL** subcommand with $n = 5$ and $p = .25$.) Discuss your results.

2. The average number of customers who go to a teller's station at the credit union in an hour is 12. Assuming a Poisson distribution, use your software package to simulate the number of customers who go to a teller's station each hour during a 40-hour period. Discuss your results.

3. The mid-arm muscle circumference (MAMC) for males is normally distributed with a mean of 273 mm and a standard deviation of 29.18 mm. Simulate the MAMC measure for 500 males. What percent of the measures in your simulation were greater than 341 mm? Compare your results with those found in Example 5.18 in this chapter.

4. In The Data & Story Library at <u>DASLDist</u>, you can find a series of data sets under the category of "Distributions." For each of the data sets, plot the data and see which of the sets you think could have a normal distribution.

5. In The Data & Story Library at <u>DASLMult</u>, you can find at least one data set under the category of "Multivariate Normality." For each of the variables in the data set, plot the variable and see if you think it has a normal distribution.

CHAPTER 6

Sampling Concepts

LOOKING AHEAD

Probability samples—the simple random, systematic, stratified, and cluster variations—were introduced and defined in Chapter 1. And chapters 4 and 5 focused on probability concepts and probability distributions. Now it's time to see why it is valid to use probability sample results to make inferences about population characteristics. Therefore, this chapter presents the theoretical and intuitive bases for using probability samples to estimate population values and to test hypotheses about those values.

Thus, after studying this chapter, you should be able to

- Appreciate the need for sampling and the advantages that sampling may provide.

- Trace the steps that are required to (a) produce a sampling distribution of sample means, (b) compute the mean of this sampling distribution, and (c) compute the standard deviation of this sampling distribution.

- Define the Central Limit Theorem and explain the relationship that exists between the standard error of the mean and the size of the sample.

- Trace the steps necessary to (a) produce a sampling distribution of sample proportions, (b) compute the mean of this sampling distribution, and (c) compute the standard deviation of this sampling distribution.

6.1   Sampling: The Need and the Advantages

The Need

Sampling occurs frequently in the course of daily events and shouldn't be viewed as a concept employed solely by statisticians. Although the samplings in daily life may not have the sophistication of formal statistical studies, they do serve a fundamental purpose of providing information for judgments. Here are a few examples:

1. A cook tastes a spoonful of soup to see if it has an acceptable flavour.

2. A prospective car buyer test-drives an automobile to compare it to others.

3. Pieces of ore are analyzed to learn the potential of a new mine.

You can undoubtedly add other similar examples to this list, but let's look now at the rationale for sampling.

Sampling is needed to provide sufficient information so that inferences can be made about the characteristics of a population. The population of interest can be *finite* or *infinite*.

> A **finite population** is one where the total number of members (items, measurements, and so on) is fixed and could be listed.

> An **infinite population** has an unlimited number of members.

Examples of finite populations are the computers installed in labs on your campus or the net weights of the 5,000 jars of jam filled in a production run. And to illustrate an infinite population, a computer could be programmed to generate the results produced by the rolling of a simulated pair of dice. If never turned off, the machine could produce an indefinitely large number of rolls of the dice.

Most of the time it's just not feasible to study an entire finite population to learn its true character, and, of course, it's impossible to consider all the elements in an infinite population. In the examples mentioned above, the cook can't taste the whole pot of soup to see if it's really acceptable, and the test driver can't drive the car for three years to find out if it will eventually be a lemon. But the data produced by sampling can be used to support judgments about the population.

STATISTICS IN ACTION

Do You Still Want to Conduct a Census?

A Canadian census is taken every five years. The estimated cost of the 1996 census was $30.32 per household. The number of households in 1996 was 11,412,000. That gives a total cost of $346,011,840.

The Advantages

Complete information acquired through a census is generally desirable. If every item in a population data set is examined, we can be confident in describing the population. But, as in many situations, what you want is not necessarily what you can get. Census data are a luxury in most situations and are usually not available for studying a population. Data gathering by sampling, rather than census taking, is the rule rather than the exception because of the following sampling advantages:

Cost Any data gathering effort incurs costs for such things as mailings, interviews, and data tabulations. The more data to be handled, the higher the costs likely will be. Consider a consumer survey of Canada: If an attempt were made to poll every citizen, the cost would easily run into many millions of dollars. Any benefits derived from such census data would likely be negated by the cost. For example, a national food company might want to make a product change to improve sales. The company could survey every potential customer, but it's very likely that the costs of a census would wipe out any additional revenues generated from a changed product. Any time a sample can be taken with less expenditure than that required for a census, cost becomes an acceptable (although not sufficient) reason for sampling.

Time Speed in decisions is often crucial. Let's assume you're the owner of a company and you've got an innovative idea for a better automobile antitheft device. You know that rival firms are also racing to create a similar product. Being the first to have a better product on the market may lead to high sales revenues, but do you actually have a better device? Will the public beat a path to your company's door for your idea, or will the new item fail to appeal to the public? Obviously, a census to help answer these questions requires too much time. The answer lies in sampling, since it can produce adequate information about the public's response to your idea in a shorter period.

Accuracy of Sample Results Sometimes a small sample provides information that's almost as accurate and sometimes even more accurate as the results obtained from a complete census. How is this possible? Remember that the object in sampling is to achieve representation of the population characteristics. There are sampling methods that produce samples that are highly representative of the population. In such cases, larger samples will not produce results that are significantly more accurate. Consider that soup again. If the cook has stirred it well before sampling, one or two sips should be sufficient to make a judgment about the entire pot. Any additional sips will serve only to decrease the volume of soup available for supper.

Other Advantages Destructive tests are often used to judge product quality. For example, a production manager may want to know the tensile strength of a truckload of iron bars she has received. To test their tensile strength, the bars are subjected to pressure until they break. All the bars can be tested, but only if the manager wants a truckload of broken bars. Since that's certainly not the case, a sample of bars must be used.

Sometimes the resources may be available for a census, but the nature of the population requires a sample. Suppose we're interested in the number of humpback whales left in the world. Environmental organizations may be willing to sponsor our count, but migration movements, births, and deaths prevent a complete count. One approach to the problem is to sample a small area of the ocean and use the results to make a projection.

Self-Testing Review 6.1

1. Give three illustrations of how sampling is used in daily life.

2. What is the difference between a finite and an infinite population?

3. What is the purpose in sampling?

4. Describe some advantages in using sample data to study population parameters.

5. Describe an appropriate population for each of the following samples:

a) Ten students from your statistics class.

b) A group of 37 psychology majors at your school.

c) Forty students from your school.

d) A group of 200 Saturn Icons assembled this week.

e) Stock prices today for 54 stocks listed on the Toronto Stock Exchange.

f) Fifteen schizophrenic patients undergoing an experimental treatment.

g) Seventy-two patients undergoing a new reconstructive knee surgery technique.

6. An auditor wants to estimate the mean invoice amount for a large batch of invoices. She selected a sample of 27 of the invoices and found they had a mean of $517.20. A subsequent computer analysis of the entire batch showed the true mean to be $512.73.

a) What is the population?

b) What is the sample?

c) What number is a parameter?

d) What number is a statistic?

7. If sampling is done correctly, there are never any errors in using the sample information to describe the population from which the sample was drawn. True or false?

8. If the population remains the same, then all samples from that population will produce the same information. True or false?

6.2 Sampling Distribution of Means— A Pattern of Behaviour

The sample mean seldom has exactly the same value as the population mean. Suppose the average income of a probability sample of city residents is $31,251. We could venture to say that the estimate of the population mean for all city residents is $31,251. But we intuitively know the chances are slim that the sample mean *exactly* equals the population mean. A different sample of residents would most likely yield a different mean, such as $31,282, while another sample might produce a mean of $31,244.

In stating that a sample mean is an approximation of the population mean, we've made an assumption that the sample mean is related in some manner to the population mean. We intuitively assume that the value of the sample mean tends towards the value of the population mean. As we shall see later in this chapter, our intuition is correct; the population characteristics determine the range of values a sample mean is likely to take.

Let's assume that we have a *population* of 15 cards. You'll remember from Chapter 3 (and Table 3.8 on page 62) that the population size is identified by N, so $N = 15$ in this case. These cards (and population values) are numbered from 0 through 14. And let's further assume that we want to select random samples (without replacement) of size 6 from this population. You'll also remember from Chapter 3 that the sample size is identified by n. The number of possible samples that could be selected is a combinations problem of the type discussed in Chapter 5. We've been using $\binom{n}{r}$ to represent the combination of n things taken r at a time, but in this case it might be clearer to use $\binom{N}{n}$ to represent the combination of N items in a population taken n at a time in a sample. Anyway,

$$\binom{15}{6} = \frac{15!}{6!\,9!} = 5,005 \text{ possible samples}$$

One of these 5,005 possible samples consists of the cards numbered 2, 4, 6, 8, 10, and 12; a *second* possible sample selection is made up of the cards numbered 1, 4, 3, 7, 8, and 12; and a *third* possible sample comprises the cards numbered 14, 0, 7, 10, 9, and 8. (You can figure out the other 5,002 possible samples next summer at your leisure.) The arithmetic means of these three possible samples, in the order presented, are 7.0, 5.8, and 8.2. If there are 5,005 possible samples, there are, of course, 5,005 possible sample means. And if we were to select all the 5,005 possible samples, compute the mean of each of these samples, and arrange the 5,005 sample means in a frequency distribution, this distribution would be called a *sampling distribution of means.*

> A **sampling distribution of means** is the distribution of the arithmetic means of all the possible random samples of size n that could be selected from a given population.

If we're not careful at this point, we can run into some difficulties with definitions. Let's pause here to consider the three fundamental types of distributions in *Figure 6.1*. There's nothing new about *Figure 6.1a*; it's merely the frequency distribution of whatever population happens to be under study and could, of course, take many shapes. The mean and standard deviation of the population distribution—the symbols, you'll recall, are μ and σ—were discussed in Chapter 3 and are familiar to us. And there's really nothing very new about the distributions in *Figure 6.1b*; they are simply the frequency distributions of several possible samples that could be selected from the population that is shown in *Figure 6.1a*. Sample distributions can have any shape but with simple random samples the shape tends to resemble that of the population. Each will have its own mean (remember that the symbol for the sample mean is $\bar{x}$) and its own standard deviation (that symbol is s). Of course, there are as many sample distributions as there are possible samples. Thus, for each of the 5,005 samples consisting of six cards from the population of 15 cards, there are 5,005 possible sample distributions and 5,005 possible sample means.

Finally, in *Figure 6.1c*, we come to the sampling distribution of the means—a distribution that is new to us and one that should not be confused with a sample distribution (even though the terms are confusingly similar). Thus, while we have 5,005 possible sample distributions—each with its own mean—there is but one sampling distribution of these 5,005 means. In the sampling distribution in *Figure 6.1c*, the possible sample mean values are distributed about the mean of the sampling distribution (sometimes called the grand mean). The mean of the sampling distribution is identified by the symbol $\mu_{\bar{x}}$, and is computed by adding up all the possible sample mean values and dividing by the number of samples. The standard deviation of the sampling distribution of the means measures the dispersion of the distribution and is identified by the symbol $\sigma_{\bar{x}}$.

Mean of the Sampling Distribution of Means

Be alert and pay attention now because we are about to attack you with a very important fact: *The mean of the sampling distribution of means is equal to the population mean—* that is, $\mu_{\bar{x}} = \mu$. "What's that?" you said, "I have read some ridiculous statements in the

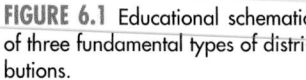

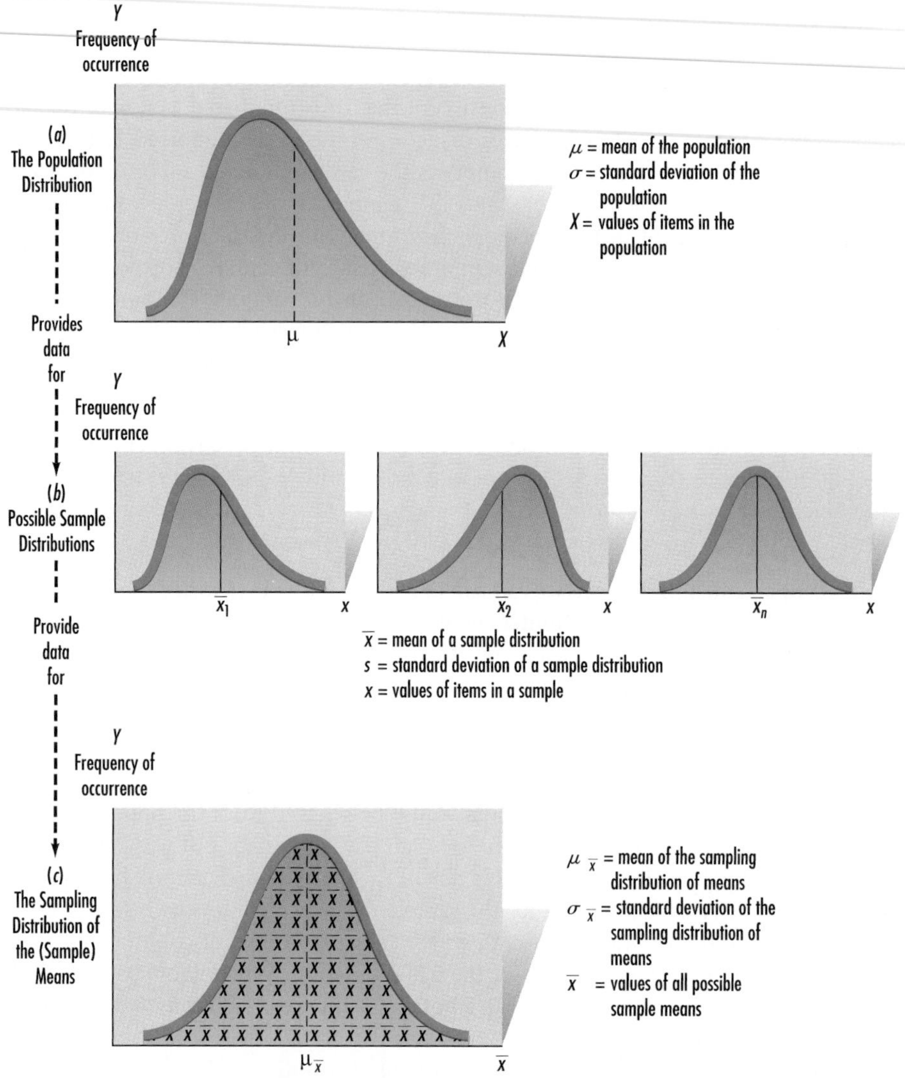

FIGURE 6.1 Educational schematic of three fundamental types of distributions.

y
Frequency of occurrence

(a)
The Population
Distribution

μ = mean of the population
σ = standard deviation of the population
X = values of items in the population

μ X

Provides data for

y
Frequency of occurrence

(b)
Possible Sample Distributions

$\overline{x}_1$ x $\overline{x}_2$ x $\overline{x}_n$ x

$\overline{x}$ = mean of a sample distribution
s = standard deviation of a sample distribution
x = values of items in a sample

Provide data for

y
Frequency of occurrence

(c)
The Sampling
Distribution of
the (Sample)
Means

$\mu_{\overline{x}}$ = mean of the sampling distribution of means
$\sigma_{\overline{x}}$ = standard deviation of the sampling distribution of means
$\overline{x}$ = values of all possible sample means

$\mu_{\overline{x}}$ $\overline{x}$

TABLE 6.1 THE PROBABILITY DISTRIBUTION FOR THE POPULATION OF DIE ROLLS OF A FOUR-SIDED DIE

x	$P(x)$
1	1/4
2	1/4
3	1/4
4	1/4

past, and more than a few of them have come from this book, but. ..." Anticipating just such a skeptical attitude, we've prepared an example.

The example will use an idea from Chapter 4, the idea of a discrete random variable, to help us understand the nature of the following population. Suppose we have a triangular, four-sided die with faces numbered 1, 2, 3, and 4. It's a balanced die, so when we roll it, we are equally likely to get any of these four faces. We can think about rolling this die over and over, an infinite number of times, and consider all the 1s, 2s, 3s and 4s we would get as a *population* of values. Alternatively, we can also think about this population as being generated by observing the values of the discrete random variable: $x =$ the number appearing on the top face of the die, whose probability distribution appears in Table 6.1. What is the mean of this population? Well, the mean of the population is identical to the mean or expected value of the discrete random variable x, so we can use the formula for the mean of a discrete random variable to compute the mean of this population. That is,

$$\mu = E(x) = \sum[x \cdot P(x)] = 1\left(\frac{1}{4}\right) + 2\left(\frac{1}{4}\right) + 3\left(\frac{1}{4}\right) + 4\left(\frac{1}{4}\right) = \frac{10}{4} = 2.5$$

So the population mean for the triangular die is 2.5.

Now suppose we take a sample of size $n = 2$ from this population by rolling the die twice. What samples would be possible? Well, we could get a 1 followed by a 1, a 1 followed by a 2, a 1 followed by a 3, and so on until a 4 followed by a 4. In all, there are 16 different samples, and these are listed in Table 6.2. Next to these samples, we have calculated and listed each sample mean. Since this column contains all the possible values of $\bar{x}$, we can compute the mean of the sampling distribution of $\bar{x}$ by calculating the mean of this column:

$$\mu_{\bar{x}} = \frac{1.0 + 1.5 + 2.0 + \cdots + 4.0}{16} = \frac{40}{16} = 2.5$$

Thus, as you can see, the mean for the population described in Table 6.1 equals the mean of the sample means given in Table 6.2. That is,

$$\mu_{\bar{x}} = \mu \tag{6.1}$$

 This isn't an isolated case. Let's go back to our earlier example of the population of 15 cards numbered 0 to 14. The sum of the integers on the 15 cards is 105, and the mean of this population of 15 numbers is 7 (105/15). We didn't take those 5,000+ different samples to prove that $\mu_{\bar{x}}$ equals this μ of 7. But we did take 150 samples of 6 cards from our population of 15, and we then computed the sample mean for each of these 150 samples. Well, actually we didn't do this tedious task at all. Rather, we turned it over to a computer running the MINITAB statistical package and promptly received the output shown in *Figure 6.2a*.

Basically, MINITAB simulated taking 150 samples of six data items randomly selected from the integers 0 to 14. Then the program (1) computed the mean of the 6 data items for each of the 150 samples and (2) stored these 150 sample means in a separate column (C7). Then the program computed the mean from the data set of 150 sample means. This value is 7.0167 (see *Figure 6.2a*), very close to the population mean of 7.00. A stem-and-leaf display (see *Figure 6.2b*) is then prepared to show the values of the 150 sample means. As you can see, the smallest of the 150 sample means has a value of 2.8, and the largest sample mean is 11.0. Finally, a box-and-whiskers display of our data set of 150 sample means is presented (see *Figure 6.2c*). You'll notice that the box representing the middle 50 percent of the sample means has a lower hinge of about 5.8 and an upper hinge of about 8.3.

 We repeated the simulation process using a TI-83 calculator. A histogram in screen 3 of *Figure 6.2d* pictorially represents the sample means. The properties of this graph are similar to the characteristics of the previous MINITAB sample. A dozen more simulations, each with 150 random samples, could be processed by the computer or calculator in short order. All of these simulations would undoubtedly produce different overall averages from their data sets of 150 sample means. But these dozen values, like our mean of 7.0167, would be close to the population mean of 7 because ultimately, as we've seen, $\mu_{\bar{x}} = \mu$.

As the devil's advocate, we may say "So what?" to the fact that $\mu_{\bar{x}} = \mu$. No one in a realistic situation really takes all possible sample combinations and calculates the

TABLE 6.2 THE POSSIBLE SAMPLES AND THEIR MEANS FROM TWO ROLLS OF A FOUR-SIDED DIE

Sample Data	Sample Means ($\bar{x}$)
1,1	1.0
1,2	1.5
1,3	2.0
1,4	2.5
2,1	1.5
2,2	2.0
2,3	2.5
2,4	3.0
3,1	2.0
3,2	2.5
3,3	3.0
3,4	3.5
4,1	2.5
4,2	3.0
4,3	3.5
4,4	4.0

STATISTICS IN ACTION

Drop-out Factors

Roger McIntire, a professor at the University of Maryland, has conducted a study to identify factors that will help predict if a student will drop out of college. Using a sample of 910 Maryland students, he found that those who worked more than 21 hours a week, paid more than 30 percent of their own expenses, commuted 8 minutes or more from home to campus, spent less than 2 hours a week socializing on campus, and had fewer than two friends on campus were the ones most likely to quit school. McIntire concluded that campus jobs and affordable housing might help more students stay in school.

FIGURE 6.2 (*a*) We generated 150 random samples of size 6 by clicking on **Calc, Random, Integer,** specifying 150 rows of data, *c1–c6* as the storage columns, 0 as the **Minimum value** and 14 as the **Maximum value,** and clicking on **OK.** Then we calculated the 150 means by clicking on **Calc, Row Statistics,** clicking in the circle next to **Mean,** specifying *c1–c6* as the **Input variables** and requesting that **MINITAB Store result in** *c7*, then clicking **OK.** Next we requested in the *Session Window* that **MINITAB** compute the mean of the 150 sample means. (*b*) A stem-and-leaf and (*c*) a box-and-whiskers plot of the 150 sample means. (*d*) We will use the TI-83 to take 150 samples of 6 each from the population {0,1,2, ... , 14} and calculate the sample means and store the results in a list. First, take a random sample using the **rand-Int** command on the **MATH**>**PRB** menu. Access the command from the home screen and enter rand-Int(0,14,6) to get a random sample of size 6. Screen 1 shows several samples. A sample is drawn each time you press **ENTER.** The mean of a sample can be calculated using the **mean** (function on the **LIST**>**MATH**) menu. The last line in screen 1 shows the mean of the last sample taken. (**Ans** is above the (−) key). Finally, to repeat this process 150 times, we can use the **seq** command found on the **LIST**>**OPS** menu. Screen 2 shows the command that must be executed to calculate 150 sample means and store them into L1. Screen 3 shows a histogram for the sample means in L1. (Recall how to make histograms from Chapter 3.) Also, we can calculate the mean and standard deviation of the sample means in L1 using 1-Var Stats L1 as in Chapter 3.

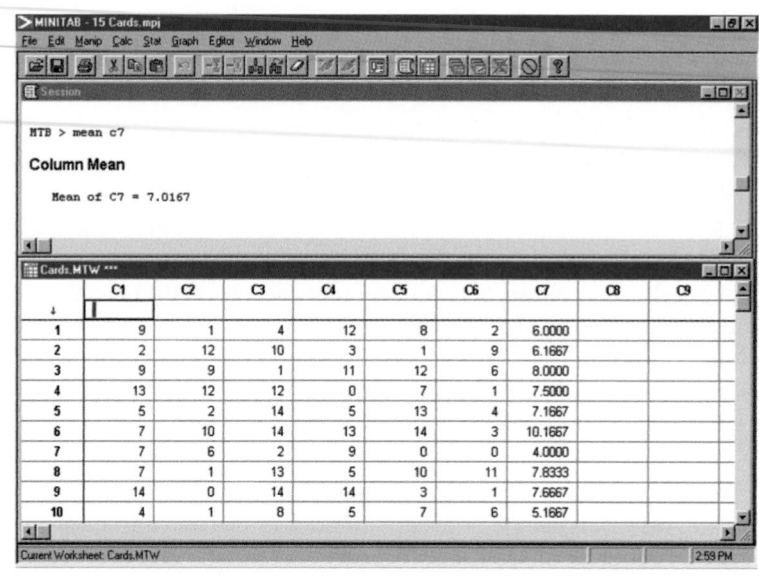

(*a*)

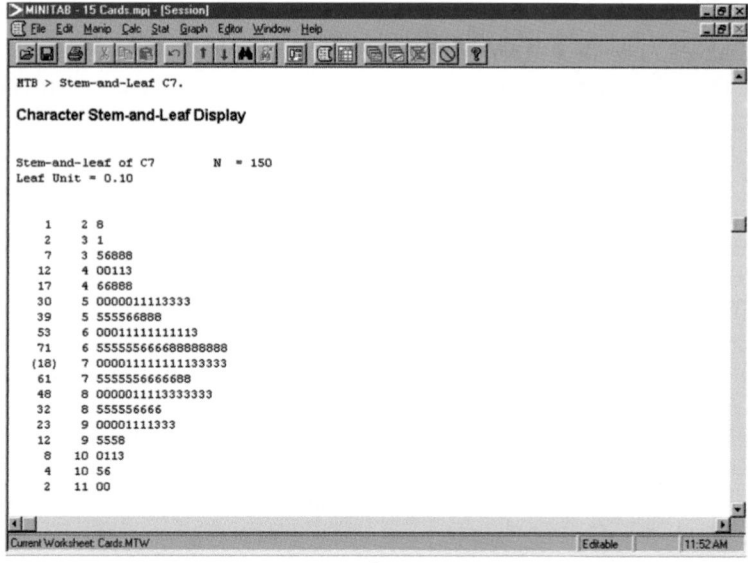

(*b*)

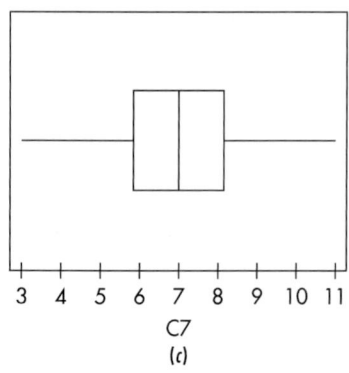

(*c*)

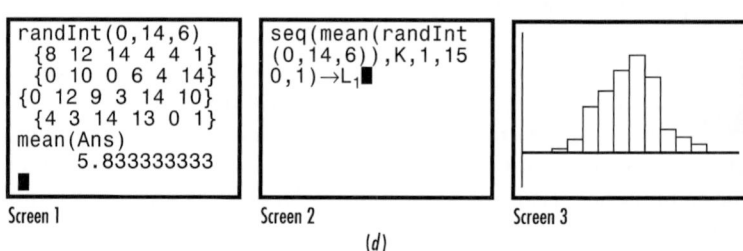

Screen 1   Screen 2   Screen 3

(*d*)

sample means. In practice, only one sample is taken. What benefit is there in discussing the sampling distribution? Shouldn't we really be concerned with the proximity of a single sample mean to the population mean? The answer is yes. In essence, the discussion of the sampling distribution *is* concerned with the proximity of a sample mean to the population mean.

You can see from Table 6.2 and *Figure 6.2* that the possible values of the sample means tend towards the value of μ. Since these values have frequencies of occurrence, the sampling distribution is essentially a probability distribution. If the sample size is sufficiently large ($n > 30$), the sampling distribution approximates the normal distribution whether or not the population is normally distributed. And the sampling distribution is normally distributed regardless of sample size if the population is normally distributed. *Figure 6.3* illustrates the sampling distribution as a normal distribution. Why is this important? Because this will help us learn how likely it is that $\bar{x}$ will be close to μ and exactly what we mean by "close."

You'll recall that in a normal probability distribution the likelihood of an outcome is determined by the number of standard deviations the outcome is from the mean of the distribution. Therefore, as you can see in *Figure 6.3*, there's a 68.3 percent chance that a sample selected at random will have a mean that lies within *1* standard deviation ($\sigma_{\bar{x}}$) of the population mean. Also, there's a 95.4 percent chance that the sample mean will lie within *2* standard deviations of the value of μ. Thus, a knowledge of the properties of the sampling distribution tells us the probable proximity of a sample mean outcome to the value of μ. With a knowledge of the sampling distribution, probability statements can be made about the range of possible values a sample mean may assume. This range of possible values can be calculated if a value for the standard deviation of the sampling distribution ($\sigma_{\bar{x}}$) is available. The computation of $\sigma_{\bar{x}}$ is shown in the next section.

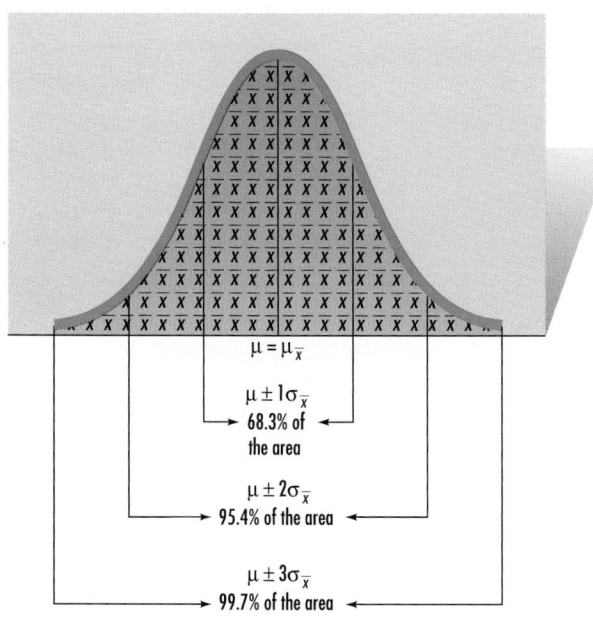

FIGURE 6.3 μ $\mu_{\bar{x}}$, and $\sigma_{\bar{x}}$ for the areas under the sampling distribution of means.

Standard Deviation of the Sampling Distribution of Means

To gauge the extent to which a sample mean can differ from the population mean, we need some measure of dispersion. In other words, we must be able to compute the likely deviation of a sample mean from the mean of the sampling distribution. That is, we must be able to compute the *standard error of the mean.*

> The **standard error of the mean** is the standard deviation of the sampling distribution of sample means and is represented by the symbol $\sigma_{\bar{x}}$.

Since we've seen the relationship that exists between $\mu_{\bar{x}}$ and μ, we might intuitively assume there is a relationship between $\sigma_{\bar{x}}$ and σ that will produce a shortcut method of computing $\sigma_{\bar{x}}$. As a matter of fact, we are right, and the value of $\sigma_{\bar{x}}$ may be computed with the following formula:

$$\sigma_{\bar{x}} = \frac{\sigma}{\sqrt{n}} \tag{6.2}$$

where σ = the population standard deviation
n = the sample size

From the random variable in Table 6.1, the value of σ is computed with the formula for the standard deviation of a discrete random variable:

$$\sigma = \sqrt{\Sigma(x - \mu)^2 \cdot P(x)}$$

For our die example, where $\mu = 2.5$, most of the work is done in the following table:

x	$P(x)$	$(x - \mu)$	$(x - \mu)^2$	$(x - \mu)^2 P(x)$
1	1/4	−1.5	2.25	0.5625
2	1/4	−0.5	0.25	0.0625
3	1/4	0.5	0.25	0.0625
4	1/4	1.5	2.25	0.5625
				1.2500

Using the sum of the last columns, we get

$$\sigma = \sqrt{1.25} = 1.12$$

Therefore, the standard error for the sampling distribution of the means given in Table 6.2 is computed as follows:

$$\sigma_{\bar{x}} = \frac{\sigma}{\sqrt{n}} = \frac{1.12}{\sqrt{2}} = 0.79$$

So we can see that the value of $\sigma_{\bar{x}}$ may be determined with a knowledge of the value of σ and the sample size.

The Relationship between n and $\sigma_{\bar{x}}$

The value of $\sigma_{\bar{x}}$ is, of course, a measure of the dispersion of sample means about μ. If the degree of dispersion decreases, the range of probable values a sample mean is likely to assume also decreases, meaning the value of any single sample mean will probably be closer to the value of the population mean as the standard error decreases. And with formula 6.2, the value of $\sigma_{\bar{x}}$ obviously must decrease as the size of n increases. That is,

$$\text{As } n \uparrow, \quad \sigma_{\bar{x}} = \frac{\sigma}{\sqrt{n}} \downarrow$$

To add meaning to this mathematical manipulation, let's again look at an example. Suppose we plan to take a sample of ten items from a population whose standard deviation is 20. Then the standard error of the mean of such a sample is

$$\sigma_{\bar{x}} = \frac{20}{\sqrt{10}} = 6.32$$

Ten items may provide adequate information for a particular purpose, but it's clear that more information could be obtained from a larger sample such as 20. To see this, we calculate the standard error based on $n = 20$:

$$\sigma_{\bar{x}} = \frac{20}{\sqrt{20}} = 4.47$$

More information provides a more precise estimate of the population parameter. As a matter of fact, a sample of 50 or 60 items would provide even more information and thus a more precise estimate. For example, with $n = 50$, the standard error becomes

$$\sigma_{\bar{x}} = \frac{20}{\sqrt{50}} = 2.83$$

The general principle is that as n increases, $\sigma_{\bar{x}}$ decreases. As the sample size increases, we have more information with which to estimate the value of μ, and thus the probable difference between the true value and any sample outcome decreases. *Figure 6.4* summarizes the points made in this section.

FIGURE 6.4 The relationship between n and $\sigma_{\bar{x}}$.

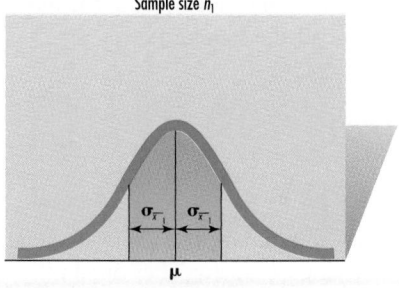
Sample size n_1

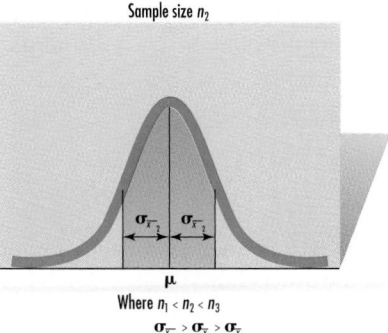
Sample size n_2

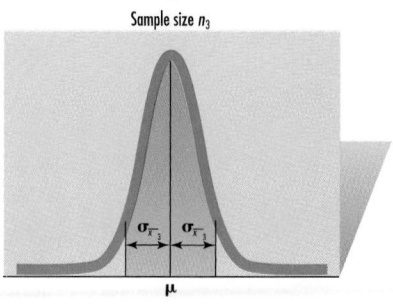
Sample size n_3

Where $n_1 < n_2 < n_3$
$\sigma_{\bar{x}_1} > \sigma_{\bar{x}_2} > \sigma_{\bar{x}_3}$

The Central Limit Theorem and the Sampling Distribution of the Sample Mean

Up to this point we've explained the concept of the sampling distribution of means in a rather intuitive way. Now, we're ready to formalize the concepts developed in previous sections including an important result called the *Central Limit Theorem*. A detailed and mathematical discussion of the Central Limit Theorem is beyond the scope of this book, but it basically indicates when a sample statistic has approximately a normal distribution.

The Sampling Distribution of $\bar{x}$

The sampling distribution of the means of all samples of size n has the following properties:

- The mean of the sampling distribution of means is equal to the population mean.

- The standard deviation of the sampling distribution of means ($\sigma_{\bar{x}}$) is equal to $\sigma/\sqrt{n}$.

- If the sample size (n) is sufficiently large—statisticians often use a value of more than (>) 30 here—the sampling distribution approximates the normal probability distribution. This is a result of the **Central Limit Theorem.**

- If the population is normally distributed, the sampling distribution is normal regardless of sample size.

A considerable amount of important theoretical material has been presented in the last few pages. Let's look now at some example problems to illustrate certain basic concepts.

Example 6.1   The director of a fitness centre has determined that the mean and standard deviation in the amount of time members spend at the centre per week are 5.2 and 2.2 hours, respectively. Suppose the director randomly takes a sample of three members. What are the mean and the standard error of the sampling distribution of $\bar{x}$ based on a sample of size $n = 3$?

◆ **Solution:**
The population mean (μ) is 5.2 hours. Since the population mean is equal to the mean of the sampling distribution, $\mu_{\bar{x}} = 5.2$ hours. The value of the standard error is

$$\sigma_{\bar{x}} = \frac{2.2}{\sqrt{3}} = 1.27 \; \blacklozenge$$

Example 6.2   Sam and Janet Evening want to estimate the average dollar amount of the orders filled by their South Pacific Catering Company. They obtain their estimate by selecting a simple random sample of 49 orders. Sam and Janet don't know it, but their orders are normally distributed with $\mu = \$120$ and $\sigma = \$21$. Now, what's the value of the standard error? What's the chance the sample mean will fall between $\mu - 1\sigma_{\bar{x}}$ and $\mu + 1\sigma_{\bar{x}}$? What's the probability the sample mean will lie between $116.50 and $124.00? Within what range of values does the $\bar{x}$ have a 95.4 percent chance of falling?

◆ **Solution:**

Well, $\sigma_{\bar{x}}$ is $\sigma/\sqrt{n} = \$21/7 = \$3.00$. The chance that $\bar{x}$ will lie between $\$120.00 \pm \$3.00$, or between $117.00 and $123.00, is $P(-1.00 < z < 1.00)$ or $2(.3413)$ or $.6826$. To find the probability that the sample mean will lie between $116.50 and $124.00, we follow the approach used in Chapter 5 to find the probability that a sample mean falls within a given range of values under a normal curve. In Chapter 5, a z value needed to solve a problem involving a single normally distributed variable was computed with this formula:

$$z = \frac{x - \mu}{\sigma}$$

But now we're dealing with a sampling situation, and the formula becomes

$$z = \frac{\bar{x} - \mu}{\sigma_{\bar{x}}}$$

So to find the chance that the $\bar{x}$ falls between $116.50 and $\mu - \$120$, we calculate

$$z_1 = \frac{\bar{x} - \mu}{\sigma_{\bar{x}}} = \frac{116.50 - 120.00}{3.00} = \frac{-3.50}{3.00} = -1.17$$

and then $P(\$116.50 < \bar{x} < \$120) = P(-1.17 < z < 0) = .3790$

And to find the chance that the $\bar{x}$ lies between $\mu = \$120$ and a value of $124.00, we calculate

$$z_2 = \frac{\bar{x} - \mu}{\sigma_{\bar{x}}} = \frac{124.00 - 120.00}{3.00} = \frac{4.00}{3.00} = 1.33$$

and $P(\$120 < \bar{x} < \$124) = P(0 < z < 1.33) = .4082$

So the chance that the $\bar{x}$ falls between $116.50 and $124.00 is $.3790 + .4082$ or $.7872$. And, finally, there's a 95.4 percent chance that any normal variable will fall within two standard deviations of its mean, so there's a 95.4 percent chance that $\bar{x}$ will fall between $\mu - 2\sigma_{\bar{x}}$ and $\mu + 2\sigma_{\bar{x}}$, or between $114.00 and $126.00. ◆

Let's carry out another computer simulation to test the reasonableness of some of these figures. *Figure 6.5* shows the results of using MINITAB to simulate 100 random samples of size 49 drawn from a normal population with a mean of $120.00 and a standard deviation of $21.00. The stem-and-leaf display shows the 100 sample means produced in this simulation, the histogram plots these 100 sample means, and the DESCRIBE command instructs the program to generate descriptive values. As you can see, the mean of the 100 sample means—$120.23 in this simulation—is close

FIGURE 6.5 A computer simulation of 100 samples of size 49 taken from a normal distribution with a μ of $120.00 and a σ of $21.00. The sample means of the 100 samples are shown in the stem-and-leaf display and are plotted in the histogram.

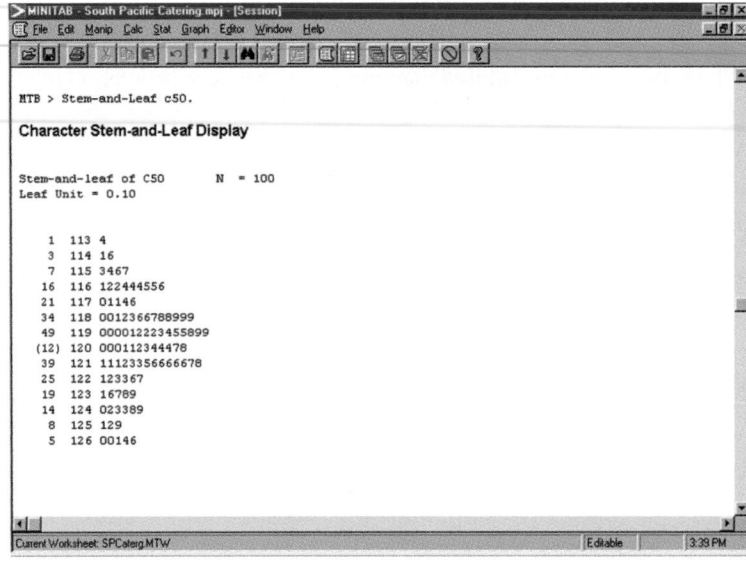

(a)

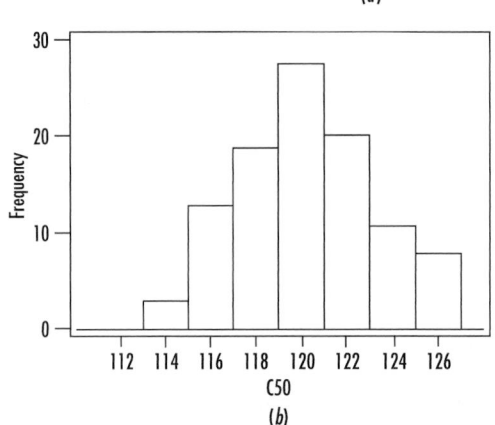

(b)

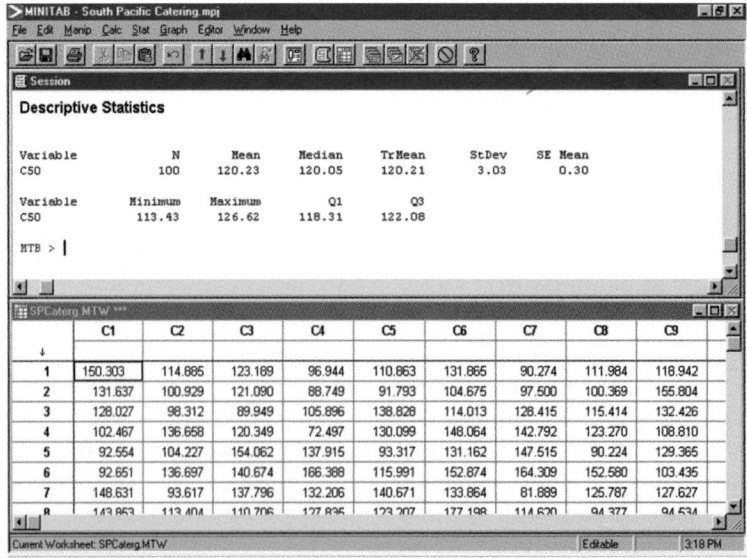

(c)

to the population mean of $120.00, as it must be. The smallest sample mean produced in this simulation is $113.43, and the largest sample mean is $126.62. The middle 50 percent of the sample means lie between $118.31 and $122.08 (the Q_1 and Q_3 values), but what sample mean values bound the middle 68 percent of the data set?

Our previous analysis showed that *about* the middle two-thirds of the sample means should fall within one standard deviation of μ or between $117.00 and $123.00. Do they in this simulation? Well, the middle 68 percent of the sample means fall between sample number 17 in the stem-and-leaf display and sample number 84 (inclusive) in that display. The value of sample mean number 17 is about $117.00, and the value of sample mean number 84 is about $123.70, so the simulation and the theory yield similar results. And 96 percent of the sample means in our simulation fall between $114.60 and $126.10—very close to our previously calculated 95.4 percent chance that a sample mean would lie within two standard deviations of μ or between $114.00 and $126.00.

Notice, too, in the descriptive measures computed for our data set of 100 sample means at the bottom of *Figure 6.5* that the standard deviation (STDEV) value is $3.03. This measure of dispersion for our group of 100 sample means is very close to the measure of dispersion we've computed for *all* possible sample means. That is, the $3.03 figure is close to the standard error value of $3.00, as it should be.

As noted in our earlier simulation example, if we were to conduct another simulation and instruct the statistical package to randomly select another 100 samples of size 49, we would get different sample items, different sample means, a different stem-and-leaf display, a different histogram, and different descriptive values. But the mean (and other values) of this next simulated data set will be close to the values we've just examined, and they'll be close to the population values of interest.

Example 6.3   A manager at the Write-On Pen Company wants to estimate the average number of pens sold per day on the basis of the mean of a sample of 100 days. If the true population mean is 5,650 pens per day and the population standard deviation is 700 pens, what is the chance that the mean of a random sample will have a value within 200 pens of the true mean?

◆ **Solution:**

The problem basically asks "What is the chance that the sample mean will lie between $\mu - 200$ and $\mu + 200$?" The manager is trying to find the chance that $\bar{x}$ will fall within $5,650 \pm 200$, or between 5,450 and 5,850. The Central Limit Theorem comes into play here. Even though we don't know that the population is normally distributed, because the sample size is large ($100 > 30$), the distribution of the sample means is approximately normal. So we can calculate the chance that $\bar{x}$ will fall between 5,450 and 5,850 by first finding the standard (z) scores for 5,450 and 5,850 and by then using the z table in Appendix 2 to find the probabilities. Knowing that the sampling distribution is normal, we can compute the z score for the value of a sample mean (as in Example 6.2) by

$$z = \frac{\bar{x} - \mu_{\bar{x}}}{\sigma_{\bar{x}}}$$

So to calculate the z scores of interest to the Write-On manager, we first find the value of $\sigma_{\bar{x}} = \sigma/\sqrt{n} = 700/\sqrt{100} = 70$. Then,

$$z = \frac{\bar{x} - \mu_{\bar{x}}}{\sigma_{\bar{x}}} = \frac{5,850 - 5,650}{70} = 2.86$$

We can substitute the value of $\bar{x}$ of 5,450 for 5,850 and see that the other z score is –2.86. So $P(5,450 < \bar{x} < 5,850) = P(-2.86 < z < 2.86)$. Consulting Appendix 2, we see the probability that a sample mean will fall within 2.86 standard errors to one side of a true mean is .4979. Since we're concerned with 2.86 standard errors to both sides of the mean, the total likelihood of a sample mean value between 5,650 ± 200 is .9958. So 99.58 percent of all possible samples will have a mean within 200 of the true population mean. ◆

Example 6.4   **Rings around Again** The frequency polygon that follows was introduced in Chapter 3. It represents 6,000 measurements of the number of photons per 10 milliseconds that passed through the rings of Saturn (from the Voyager Photopolarimeter occulation data provided by Mark Showalter of NASA's Planetary Data System). It clearly shows a non-normal pattern. What would the sampling distribution of the means of samples of size 100 look like?

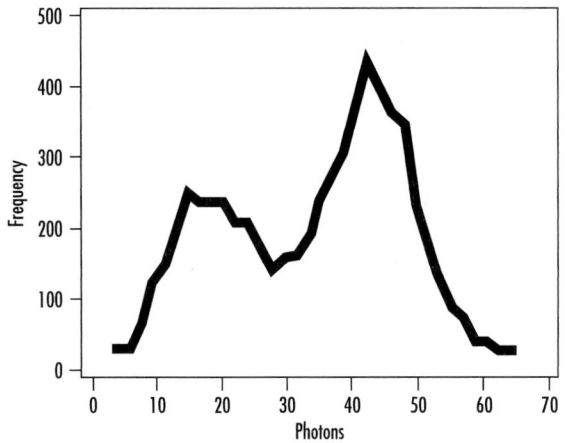

◆ **Solution:**

To demonstrate the Central Limit Theorem, we used MINITAB to take 500 samples of size $n = 100$ and created a histogram of the means of these 500 samples. You can see the difference in shape between the distribution of the original population and the normal pattern for the sampling distribution of these sample means.

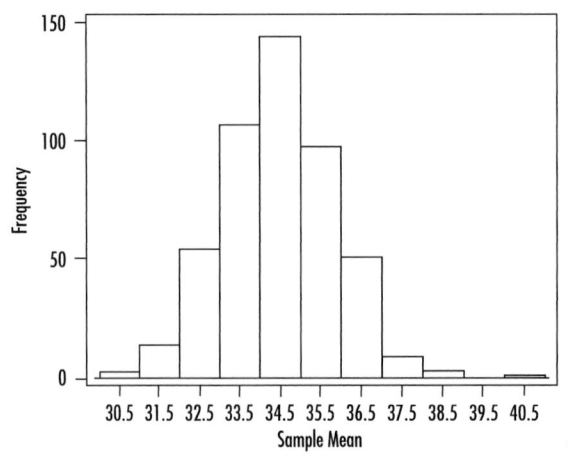

☐ **Example 6.5**   **One Time You Definitely Want to Be below Average** According to Saskatchewan Government Insurance (SGI), 60,396 speeding tickets were issued in Saskatchewan (cruise-control heaven) in 1999. The fines for these speed limit violations averaged $107.95 with a standard deviation of $30.31. What is the probability that a random sample of 60 of these fines yields a mean of more than $100? More than $110?

◆ **Solution:**

We know that the mean of the sampling distribution is

$$\mu_{\bar{x}} = \mu = \$107.95,$$

and can compute the standard error as

$$\sigma_{\bar{x}} = \frac{\sigma}{\sqrt{n}} = \frac{30.31}{\sqrt{60}} = \frac{30.31}{7.746} = \$3.913$$

Then to find the probability that the mean of the sample will be more than $100, we compute

$$z = \frac{\bar{x} - \mu_{\bar{x}}}{\sigma_{\bar{x}}} = \frac{100 - 107.95}{3.913} = \frac{-7.95}{3.913} = -2.03$$

$$P(\bar{x} > 100) = P(z > -2.03) = .5 + .4788 = .9788$$

For $110:

$$z = \frac{\bar{x} - \mu_{\bar{x}}}{\sigma_{\bar{x}}} = \frac{110 - 107.95}{3.913} = \frac{2.05}{3.913} = 0.52$$

$$P(\bar{x} > 110) = P(z > 0.52) = .5 - .1985 = .3015 ◆$$

Self-Testing Review 6.2

9. What is meant by the sampling distribution of means?

10. Discuss the difference between the mean of a sample distribution and the mean of the sampling distribution.

11. A large population of students took a math placement test. The population mean score was 37.1 and the population standard deviation was 5.2. If a random sample of 20 of these scores is selected, compute the mean and standard error of the sample mean.

12. A food packing company fills sacks of cereal using automated machinery. The fill amounts are normally distributed with a mean weight of 0.91 kg and a standard deviation of 0.05 kg.

    a) One of these sacks is selected at random. What is the probability that it weighs more than 0.95 kg?

    b) Twelve sacks are randomly selected and placed in a box for shipment. What's the probability that the mean weight of the sample of 12 sacks in the box exceeds 0.95 kg?

13. The Tite Wire Company makes wires for circus acts. The population mean thickness for the wires is 11.43 mm, and the population standard deviation is 0.762 mm. A sample of 100 pieces of wire is selected randomly, and the thickness of each sample member is measured.

a) What is the mean of the sampling distribution?

b) What is the standard deviation of the sampling distribution?

c) What may be said about the shape of the sampling distribution? Why?

d) Within what range of values does the sample mean have a 68.3 percent chance of falling?

e) Within what range of values does the sample mean have a 95.4 percent chance of falling?

14. The mean of all credit card balances for I.O.U. Credit Corporation is $200, and the standard deviation is $15. Within what range of values will the mean of a random sample have a 95.4 percent chance of falling if the sample consists of

a) 36 accounts?

b) 49 accounts?

c) 64 accounts?

d) What relationship do you observe between the sample size and the dispersion of the sampling distribution?

15. At the Keypon Trucking Company, the population average tonnage of freight handled per month is 225 tonnes, and the population standard deviation is 30 tonnes. What are the chances that in a random sample of 36 months the sample mean tonnage will have a value within 7 tonnes of the true mean?

16. The average test score of all students attending a university is 67 percent, and the population standard deviation is 14 percent. What's the probability that a random sample of 36 students will have a mean test score that is greater than 65 percent?

17. The values of the accounts receivable of the Rice Corporation are normally distributed with a mean of $10,000 and a standard deviation of $2,000. If a random sample of 400 accounts is selected, what's the probability that the sample mean will be between $10,100 and $10,200?

18. The average gasoline consumption of all families in Rocktown is 76.7 litres per week with a population standard deviation of 14.5 litres per week. What's the probability that the mean of a random sample of 50 families exceeds 80 litres per week?

19. A large population of children has a mean IQ score of 100 points and a standard deviation of 20 points. If a random sample of 30 children is selected, what's the probability that the mean IQ of the group exceeds 110?

20. Redo the previous exercise under the premise that the sample size is 50, rather than 30 children.

21. Suppose that the incomes of a population of 90 individuals in the same profession are approximately normally distributed with a mean of $64,500 and a standard deviation of $8,000. If a sample of 25 of these individuals is randomly taken,

a) What is the mean and standard error of the sampling distribution?

b) What is the probability that the mean of the sample will be less than $65,000?

6.3 **Sampling Distribution of Proportions**

When dealing with attribute (categorical) data, we're often interested in estimating population proportions. For example, a company might want to estimate the proportion of defective items produced by a machine, or it might be interested in the proportion of minority employees in its workforce. And we might be interested in the proportion of students who hope to become professional statisticians. As in the case of estimating a population mean, we estimate a population proportion on the basis of sample results. Let's look now at the relationship between a population proportion and the possible values a sample proportion may assume. That is, let's look at the *sampling distribution of proportions.*

> The **sampling distribution of proportions** is a distribution of the proportions of "successes" in all possible samples that could be taken in a given situation, where the samples are simple random samples of fixed size *n*.

STATISTICS IN ACTION

A Million-Dollar Tube?
A national random telephone survey of 1,007 adults commissioned by *TV Guide* magazine found that 46 percent of Americans would have to be paid at least $1 million to "give up watching absolutely all types of television" for the rest of their lives. While 63 percent of all adults surveyed often watch TV while eating, the percentage was 76 percent among 18- to 24-year-olds. Survey results had a margin of error of ±3.2 percent.

Mean of the Sampling Distribution of Proportions

The symbol p is used to denote the population proportion, while the $\hat{p}$ denotes the sample proportion. The symbol $\mu_{\hat{p}}$ refers to the mean of the sampling distribution of proportions. The sample proportion is defined as $\hat{p} = (x/n)$, where x is the number of items in a sample possessing the characteristic of interest, and n is the sample size.

Suppose we have a population of five students and we wish to take a simple random sample of three students to estimate the true proportion of students who have made the dean's list. Table 6.3 lists the population and each student's dean's-list status. What would the sampling distribution look like? Well, in Table 6.4 the possible proportions a sample might have are listed. And you can see that the mean of the sampling distribution in Table 6.4 is equal to the population proportion calculated in Table 6.3. Thus, the mean of a sampling distribution of proportions with simple random samples of size n is equal to the population proportion—that is, $\mu_{\hat{p}} = \text{p}$.

TABLE 6.3 POPULATION OF STUDENTS AND DEAN'S-LIST STATUS

Student	Dean's List?
A	Yes
B	No
C	Yes
D	No
E	No

$x = 2$ (the number of students on the dean's list)

$p = \dfrac{x}{N} = \dfrac{2}{5}$ or .40 (a proportion) $= 40\%$ (a proportion expressed as a percentage)

where   p = population proportion
N = population size
x = number of students on the dean's list

TABLE 6.4   SAMPLING DISTRIBUTION OF PROPORTIONS

Sample Combinations	Sample Date	Sample Proportion ($\hat{p}$)
1. A, B, C	Yes, no, yes	.667
2. A, B, D	Yes, no, no	.333
3. A, B, E	Yes, no, no	.333
4. A, C, D	Yes, yes, no	.667
5. A, C, E	Yes, yes, no	.667
6. A, D, E	Yes, no, no	.333
7. B, C, D	No, yes, no	.333
8. B, C, E	No, yes, no	.333
9. B, D, E	No, no, no	.000
10. C, D, E	Yes, no, no	.333

$$\mu_{\hat{p}} = \frac{\Sigma p}{\binom{N}{n}} = \frac{4.0}{10} \text{ or } .40$$

where $\mu_{\hat{p}}$ = mean of the sampling distribution of proportions

Standard Deviation of the Sampling Distribution of Proportions

The following definition shouldn't be too unexpected:

> The **standard error of proportion** is the standard deviation of the sampling distribution of sample proportions and is represented by the symbol $\sigma_{\hat{p}}$.

This measure may be computed with knowledge of the population proportion and sample size. The formula to compute $\sigma_{\hat{p}}$ is

$$\sigma_{\hat{p}} = \sqrt{\frac{p(1-p)}{n}} \tag{6.3}$$

where p = the population proportion possessing a particular characteristic
1 − p = the population proportion not possessing a particular characteristic
n = the sample size

Note: We will not consider the continuity correction, when dealing with proportions.

The Central Limit Theorem also has application for sample proportions. If the sample size is sufficiently large—that is, if the sample size (n) times the population proportion (p) is ≥ 5, and if n times (1 − p) is also ≥ 5—the sampling distribution will be approximately normally distributed. The implication of such a distribution is that probability statements can be made about the possible value of a sample proportion based on the knowledge of p and n. For example, when we have a large sample, there's a

95.4 percent chance that a sample proportion will fall within $\pm 2\ \sigma_{\hat{p}}$ of p. And there's approximately a 99.7 percent chance that a sample proportion will assume a value within $\pm 3\ \sigma_{\hat{p}}$ of p.

A few example problems illustrating some basic concepts of the sampling distribution of means were presented earlier. Let's now do the same thing with some problems related to the sampling distribution of proportions just presented.

Example 6.6 Statistics Canada reported that 58.5 percent of eligible Albertans voted in the 1997 general election. Assume that a simple random sample of size 20 is taken from these eligible voters. What would be the mean and the standard deviation of the sampling distribution of $\hat{p}$?

◆ **Solution:**
Since the percentage who voted is 58.5, the proportion of people who voted is $p = .585$. Since $\mu_{\hat{p}} = p$, the mean of the sampling distribution is also .585. The value of $\sigma_{\hat{p}}$ is computed as follows:

$$\sigma_{\hat{p}} = \sqrt{\frac{p(1-p)}{n}} = \sqrt{\frac{.585(1-.585)}{20}} = \sqrt{.0121387} = .110 \quad ◆$$

Example 6.7 A quality control manager at the Tack Nail Company has selected a random sample of 100 nails to estimate the proportion of nails in a production run that are acceptable. If we assume that the quality is terrible and only 90 percent of the nail population is acceptable, what are the chances that the sample proportion will be within .05 of the population proportion?

◆ **Solution:**
The basic question is, What are the chances that the value of $\hat{p}$ will be between p − .05 and p + .05—that is, .90 ± .05, or between .85 and .95. Because $n(p) = 100(.90) = 90 \geq 5$, and $n(1-p) = 100(.10) = 10 > 5$, the sampling distribution of $\hat{p}$ will be approximately a normal distribution. We'll therefore convert these values to z scores.

$$z = \frac{\hat{p} - p}{\sqrt{\frac{p(1-p)}{n}}} = \frac{.95 - .90}{\sqrt{\frac{.90(.10)}{100}}} = \frac{.05}{\sqrt{.0009}} = \frac{.05}{.03} = 1.67$$

With $z = 1.67$, we see in Appendix 2 that the area under the normal curve corresponding to a value of 1.67 is .4525. And, as the z value associated with .85 is easily seen to be −1.67, we have $P(.85 < \hat{p} < .95) \approx P(-1.67 < z < 1.67) = 2(.4525) = .9050.$ ◆

Example 6.8 Statistics Canada reported that 33.1 percent of all 1997 family incomes in New Brunswick were below $30,000. Suppose a random sample of 80 1997 family incomes from New Brunswick is selected. What is the probability that the proportion of incomes in this sample that are under $30,000 is over .30? .40?

◆ **Solution:**
The mean of the sampling distribution of proportions is $\mu_{\hat{p}} = p = .331$ while the standard error is

$$\sigma_{\hat{p}} = \sqrt{\frac{p(1-p)}{n}} = \sqrt{\frac{.331(1-.331)}{80}} = \sqrt{.0027679} = .0526$$

STATISTICS IN ACTION

Are You Superstitious?
A poll of 1,225 adults showed that women tend to be more superstitious than men. The poll also found that 38 percent of all respondents believe finding and picking up a penny is good luck, 24 percent say 7 is a lucky number, 16 percent think knocking on wood prevents bad luck, 14 percent say it's unlucky to walk under a ladder, and 13 percent believe Friday the 13th is an unlucky day.

To find the probability that the proportion of the sample will be over .30, we first compute

$$z = \frac{\hat{p} - p}{\sigma_{\hat{p}}} = \frac{.30 - .331}{.0526} = -.059$$

Then, using Appendix 2,

$$P(\hat{p} > .30) \approx P(z > - 0.59) = .5 + .7224 = .7224$$

Similarly for .40:

$$z = \frac{\hat{p} - p}{\sigma_{\hat{p}}} = \frac{.40 - .331}{.0526} = 1.31$$

and

$$P(\hat{p} > .40) \approx P(z > 1.31) = .5 - .4049 = .0951 \; \blacklozenge$$

Example 6.9   According to Statistics Canada, 60.3 percent of new residential units built are single detached homes. If a random sample of 35 new residential units is taken, what is the probability that less than half will be single detached homes?

◆ **Solution:**
The mean of the sampling distribution of proportions is

$$\mu_{\hat{p}} = p = .603$$

while the standard error is

$$\sigma_{\hat{p}} = \sqrt{\frac{p(1 - p)}{n}} = \sqrt{\frac{.603\,(1 - .603)}{35}} = \sqrt{.0068397} = .0827$$

To find the probability that the sample proportion is less than .50, we begin with

$$z = \frac{\hat{p} - p}{\sigma_{\hat{p}}} = \frac{.50 - .603}{.0827} = -1.25$$

And using Appendix 2,

$$P(\hat{p} < 50) \approx P(z < - 1.25) = .5 - .3944 = .1056 \; \blacklozenge$$

Example 6.10   **The Dominant Sex?** According to the United Nations (Statistics Division of the United Nations of Secretariat from Women's Indicators and Statistics Database [Wistat], Version 3, CD-ROM), in 1995, there were 105 women for every 100 men in the United States, Five hundred random samples of size 150 were taken from this type of population by MINITAB, and a histogram of the sample proportion of women in the samples follows. You can see that the shape of this histogram is approximately normal. Additionally, these sample proportions had a mean of .514 (vs $\mu_{\hat{p}} = p = .512$ and a standard error of .042 vs $\sigma_{\hat{p}} = \sqrt{p(1-p)/n} = \sqrt{.512(1-.512)/205} = .035$.

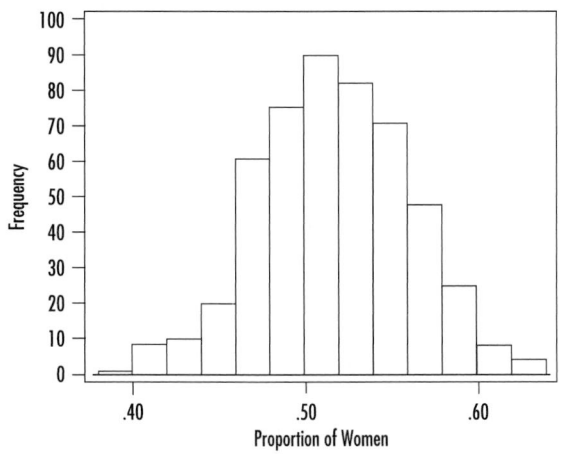

Self-Testing Review 6.3

22. What is the standard error of proportion?

23. Compute $\sigma_{\hat{p}}$ for each of the following size samples if $p = .57$.

a) $n = 10$.

b) $n = 100$.

c) $n = 1,000$.

d) Examine the responses to problems (a) to (c). What do you observe about the dispersion of the sampling distribution of proportions as the sample size increases?

24. Compute $\sigma_{\hat{p}}$ if $n = 100$ for each of the following values of p.

a) $p = .10$.

b) $p = .30$.

c) $p = .50$.

d) $p = .70$.

e) $p = .90$.

f) Examine the responses to problems (a) to (e). What pattern does the dispersion for the sampling distribution of proportions follow as the value of p changes? Why does this happen?

25. A guidance counsellor takes a random sample of 35 high school students to estimate the proportion who intend to enter university. Suppose the true proportion for this population is .60. What is the mean and standard deviation of the sampling distribution of proportions?

26. Vanity Press wants to estimate the proportion of books printed by an incompetent vendor that are defective and cannot be sold. If the true proportion of defective books is .085, what's the probability the sample proportion will be within .01 of the population proportion for a random sample of

a) 100 books?

b) 1,000 books?

c) 5,000 books?

27. It's known that 64 percent of the population of Jamesburg favour Arlene Groves for dogcatcher, What's the probability that a random sample of 100 voters will have a sample proportion favouring Ms. Groves that is between .60 and .68?

28. Fifty-five percent of a television viewing population watched a fantastically popular program called *Name That Variable* with host Bart Hart last Thursday evening. What's the probability that, in a random sample of 100 viewers, less than 50 percent watched the program?

29. Suppose that 53 percent of a voting population favours Phil A. Buster in an election. Let's assume, though, that only 50 people turn out to vote. If we can consider the voters to be a random sample of the electorate, what's the probability that Phil loses (gets less than 50 percent, or .50, of the vote)?

30. In 2001, CBC news reported the rollover resistance ratings for 2001 Sport Utility Vehicles (SUVs). Some of the ratings are

Vehicle		Rating	Risk of rollover
Chevrolet Blazer	4DR	*	greater than 40%
	4 × 2		
Ford Explorer	4 × 4	**	between 30% and 40%
GMC Jimmy	4DR	*	greater than 40%
	4 × 2		
Honda CR-V	4 × 4	***	between 20% and 30%
Jeep Grand Cherokee	4 × 4	**	between 30% and 40%
Mitsubishi Montero Sport	4 × 4	**	between 30% and 40%
Suzuki Vitara	4DR	***	between 20% and 30%
	4 × 4		

a) What is the approximate probability that in a random sample of 100 Honda CR = Vs involved in single-vehicle crashes, the proportion that will be categorized as rollover accidents will be at most 0.30? (Assume the probability of rollover for three-star vehicles is .25.)

b) What is the approximate probability that in a random sample of 250 Chevrolet Blazers involved in single-vehicle crashes, the proportion that will be categorized as rollover accidents will be more than 0.48? (Assume the probability of rollover for one-star vehicles is .5.)

c) What is the approximate probability that in a random sample of 300 SUVs with two-star ratings involved in a single-vehicle crashes, the proportion that will be categorized as rollover accidents will be between 0.32 and 0.38? (Assume the probability of rollover for two-star vehicles is .35.)

d) What are the expected number of rollover accidents for SUVs with one-star, two-star, and three-star rollover resistance ratings, when 1,000 single-vehicle crashes are considered from each category?

L O O K I N G   B A C K

1. A finite population is one where all members could be listed, while an infinite population is unlimited in size. A sample is a portion of the population selected for study. You've seen in this chapter that if a sample statistic is representative of a population parameter, it's possible to make an inference about the population measure from the sample figure. Although complete information, in the form of a census, may be desirable, sampling advantages such as reduced cost, faster response to questions, and acceptable accuracy often outweigh the disadvantage of sampling error.

2. Although sampling variation exists so that a statistic will not provide an exact value of a parameter, it's adequate for decision-making purposes to know that sample values are governed by population characteristics. When a simple random sample is used, the mean of a sampling distribution of either sample means or sample proportions is equal to the population parameter being sought—that is, μ or p. The standard deviation of the sampling distribution of sample means—the standard error at the mean ($\sigma_{\bar{x}}$)—is determined by σ and the sample size. And the standard deviation of the sampling distribution of proportions ($\sigma_{\hat{p}}$)—the standard error of proportion—may be computed with knowledge of the value of p and the sample size. Different samples that can be taken from a population will have different values, as we've seen in two computer simulations involving 150 and 100 samples. But the mean of these sample values tend towards the population parameter being sought.

3. The value of $\sigma_{\bar{x}}$ is a measure of the dispersion of sample means about the value of μ. If this value decreases, the range of probable values a sample mean may assume also decreases, meaning the value of any single sample mean will probably be closer to the value of the unknown μ as the standard error decreases. How can this desirable result be achieved? Unfortunately, reducing the standard error requires that we increase the sample size (and the sample cost, and the time required to take the sample ...).

4. The Central Limit Theorem states that if the sample size is sufficiently large, the sampling distribution of means and also of proportions are approximately normally distributed. Additionally, if the population is normally distributed, the sampling distribution of means is normal regardless of sample size. Given this normality property, it's possible to make probability statements concerning the possible values these statistics may assume. The value of a sample statistic will tend towards the parameter value, and a probability statement can be made about the proximity of the statistic to the parameter.

Exercises

31. The amount of fuel consumed by passenger cars on trips between Calgary and Edmonton is normally distributed with a mean of 20 litres and a standard deviation of 3 litres.

  a) What is the probability that a randomly selected passenger car making such a trip will consume more than 20.9 litres?

  b) A random sample of 36 passenger cars making such a trip is selected. What's the probability that the mean fuel consumption of these 36 cars is more than 20.9 litres?

  c) An automobile club selects a random sample of 100 passenger cars making such a trip. What's the probability that the mean fuel consumption of these 36 cars is more than 20.9 litres?

d) Examine your answers to questions a), b), and c). What happens to the probability of the fuel consumption being more than 20.9 litres as the sample size increases?

32. An educational research journal reported that a population of preservice teachers thought an average of 10.43 hours should be spent in testing each week. The population standard deviation was 3.72 hours, and the responses were normally distributed.

    a) One of these preservice teachers is questioned. What's the probability that he or she thinks that fewer than nine hours a week should be spent testing?

    b) A random sample of 20 preservice teachers is questioned. What's the probability that the mean time of the sample is fewer than nine hours a week?

    c) A random sample of 32 preservice teachers is questioned. What's the probability that the mean time of the sample is fewer than nine hours a week?

    d) Compare your answers for problems (a) to (c). What happens as the sample size is increased?

33. A survey found that the mean amount of lead found in the printed sections of a population of soft plastic bread wrappers was 26 mg with a standard deviation of 6 mg. A sample of 100 soft plastic bread wrappers is randomly selected.

    a) What is the mean and the standard deviation of the sampling distribution of sample means?

    b) Within what range of values does the sample mean have a 68.3 percent chance of falling?

    c) Within what range of values does the sample mean have a 95.4 percent chance of falling?

34. The *New England Journal of Medicine* published the results of a study of a population of patients who were treated by angioplasty after a heart attack. The number of days between the heart attack and a successful angioplasty procedure was normally distributed with a mean of 12 days and a standard deviation of 2 days. If a sample of 15 patients is selected from this population,

    a) What is the mean and the standard deviation of the sampling distribution of sample means?

    b) Within what range of values does the sample mean have a 68.3 percent chance of falling?

    c) Within what range of values does the sample mean have a 95.4 percent chance of falling?

35. Knee flexion, a measure of the knee range of motion, is a normally distributed variable. *Physical Therapy* recently reported that the population mean number of degrees of knee flexion found in the First National Health and Nutrition Exam Survey (NHANES I) was 132 degrees with a standard deviation of 10 degrees. Within what range of values will the mean of a random sample have a 95.4 percent chance of falling if we have a sample of

    a) 10 individuals?

    b) 100 individuals?

    c) 1,000 individuals?

    d) As the sample size increases, what happens to the dispersion of the sampling distribution?

36. According to Statistics Canada criteria, the average body mass index (BMI) for women in the 20- to 24-year age group was found to be 25.7 with a standard deviation of 3. Within what range of values will the mean of a random sample of women in this age group have a 99.7 percent chance of falling if we have a sample of

    a) 25 women?

    b) 49 women?

    c) 81 women?

    d) As the sample size increases, what happens to the dispersion of the sampling distribution?

37. The average length of all female babies born at Stork Memorial Hospital last year was 50 cm with a standard deviation of 0.5 cm. What are the chances that the mean of a random sample of 50 female babies born at Stork last year will be within 0.10 cm of the population mean?

38. The average weight of all male babies born at Stork Memorial Hospital last year was 3.16 kg with a standard deviation of 0.46 kg. What are the chances that the mean of a random sample of 64 male babies born at Stork last year will be within 0.14 kg of the population mean?

39. The breaking strength of a material is normally distributed with a population mean of 40 kg and a standard deviation of 8 kg. What is the probability that the mean breaking strength for a sample of 12 pieces of this material will be less than 43 kg?

40. The amount of fill (weight of contents) put into a glass jar of Saskatoon jelly is normally distributed with a mean of 830 g and standard deviation of 10 g. Find the probability that a random sample of 24 jars has a mean weight between 825 and 833 g.

41. Up Up and Away Airlines wants to estimate the proportion of frequent fliers (those who made at least three domestic flights or one foreign trip in the past year) who have an average income of more than $35,000 a year. If the true population proportion is .67, what are the chances that a simple random sample of 174 frequent fliers will be within .02 of the population proportion?

42. The manager of a car dealership wishes to estimate the proportion of new cars sold in the $13,500 to $17,400 price range. A *J. D. Power* report gives the true population proportion as .30. What are the chances that a simple random sample of 46 cars will be within .05 of the population proportion?

43. The mean change in total exercise time for all coronary patients taking NORVASC is 62 seconds with a standard deviation of 17 seconds. Find the probability that a sample of 37 coronary patients taking NORVASC would have a mean change in exercise time between 60 and 70 seconds.

44. Statistics Canada reported that 45 percent of all the households in Newfoundland that had access to paper recycling programs in 1994 participated in paper recycling. Assuming that this percentage remains the same today, find the probability that a random sample of 35 Newfoundland households that have access to paper recycling programs will have a sample proportion between .40 and .50.

45. A study shows that 46 percent of all employees of TGB Corporation are less willing to give up free time than they were five years ago. What's the probability that in a random sample of 25 employees, more than 50 percent will say they are less willing to give up free time than they were five years ago?

46. The *New England Journal of Medicine* reported that the population mean and standard deviation figures for the cost per case for psychiatric evaluation services for self-referred patients are $3,222 and $1,451, respectively. What's the probability that a random sample of 67 such patients will have a mean cost of more than $3,500?

47. The *New England Journal of Medicine* also reported that the population mean and standard deviation figures for the cost per case for patients with medical back problems are $406 and $98, respectively. What's the probability that the mean cost per case

for a random sample of 45 patients with medical back problems is between $375 and $450?

48. Another article in the *New England Journal of Medicine* reported that the number of days between a heart attack and successful angioplasty in a population of coronary patients is normally distributed with a mean of 12 days and a standard deviation of 2 days. What's the probability that the mean time between a heart attack and successful angioplasty treatment for a sample of 17 patients is between 11 and 13 days?

49. The *Journal of Abnormal Psychology* recently reported that the mean age at the onset of depression for a population of dysfunctional families is 30.6 years, and the standard deviation is 13.7 years. A sample of 42 depressed people from this population of dysfunctional families is selected at random. What's the probability that the mean age of this sample is between 25 and 35 years?

50. The population mean length of stay for patients at Keepum Memorial Hospital is 23.3 days, and the standard deviation is 11.0 days. What's the probability that the mean length of stay for a sample of 31 patients selected at random is between 25 and 27 days?

51. It was determined that the mean salary for a population of creative directors working for ad agencies in a recent year was $85,000, and the population standard deviation was $5,000. If random samples consisting of income records for 32 creative directors are examined, what's the salary range within which 95.4 percent of the sample means will fall?

52. The mean length of time a population of students in Grade 6 watch TV each day is found to be 118.3 minutes, and the standard deviation is 57.3 minutes. If samples of 46 students in Grade 6 are selected at random, determine the range of time that will include 99.7 percent of the sample means.

Topics for Review and Discussion

1. Discuss the importance of sampling. What are some reasons a decision maker would choose to take a sample rather than a census?

2. What is the difference between a parameter and a statistic? Identify three of each and give the symbols for each.

3. What is the difference between a sample distribution and a sampling distribution?

4. Discuss the consequences of the Central Limit Theorem. Under what conditions does it apply? Why is it important in statistical studies?

5. What is the standard error of the mean? Explain the relationship that exists between the standard error of the mean and the size of the sample.

6. Describe a situation where the students in your statistics class comprise a population and a situation where they are a sample.

7. What is the sampling distribution of proportions? How does the Central Limit Theorem apply to this distribution?

8. What information is needed to compute the standard error of proportions?

Projects/Issues to Consider

1. Locate a population data set that is of interest to you. You may use a periodical from the library or the Internet or distribute a questionnaire to your entire class with an appropriate question. After you've gathered your population data,

   a) Compute the population mean and standard deviation.

   b) Use the random number table in Appendix 3 at the back of this book and select a random sample from your data set.

   c) Compute the mean of your sample and the standard error of the mean.

   d) Analyze the relationship between your sample mean and the population mean.

2. Locate a population with a small number of values, say, five or six.

   a) Compute the population mean and standard deviation.

   b) Form all possible samples without replacement of $n = 3$.

   c) Compute the mean for each of your samples.

   d) Compute the mean of the set of means you've produced in (b), and compare your answer to the population mean found in (a).

   e) Compute the standard deviation for the set of values you've produced in (c). How does this value compare to the standard deviation of the population?

   f) Discuss the findings of this project.

3. Locate a population data set that will allow you to examine the proportion of a variable that interests you.

   a) Compute the population proportion.

   b) Form a random sample using the random number table in Appendix 3.

   c) Compute the sample proportion.

   d) Compute the standard deviation for the sampling distribution of proportions.

Computer/Calculator Exercises

1. Repeat the simulation experiment shown in *Figure 6.2* (page 190) and discussed in this chapter.

   a) What was the mean of your data set of 150 simulated sample means?

   b) Explain why your result differed from the value of 7.0167 shown in the chapter. (It would be very unusual if your value *did* equal 7.0167.)

2. Repeat the simulation experiment shown in *Figure 6.5* (page 196) and discussed in this chapter.

   a) What was the value of the smallest sample mean produced in your simulation?

   b) What was the value of the largest sample mean?

   c) What was the mean of your data set of 100 simulated sample means?

   d) Explain why your result differed (it quite probably did) from the value of $120.23 shown in the chapter.

 3. Use MINITAB to generate four artificial populations of 1,000 random integers each between 0 and 100 and place these in c96, c97, c98, and c99. You can do this by clicking on **Calc, Random Data, Integer.** In the *Integer Distribution* window, specify that you want to generate 1,000 rows of data to be stored in each of the columns c96, c97, c98, c99, where the minimum and maximum values are 0 and 100. Then take 500 samples of size $n = 4$ from each of the columns c96, c97, c98, c99.

This is done by placing, in c1 through c4, 500 randomly selected items from each of the columns c96, c97, c98, c99. You do this by clicking on **Calc, Random Data, Sample from columns.** In the *Sample from Columns* window, specify that you want to sample 500 rows, that the sampling is done from columns c96, c97, c98, and c99, and store the samples in c1 to c4. Each row of c1 through c4 could then represent a random sample of observations from this population. Calculate the mean of these 500 samples by taking the average of each of the rows in c1 through c4. This is done by clicking on **Calc, Row Statistics,** clicking in the circle to the right of **Mean,** specifying that the input variables are c1 to c4, and that the results should be stored in c5. Use the MINITAB **Display Descriptive Statistics** command to calculate the mean and standard deviation of the original population and of the sampling distribution of the sample mean. Comment on the mean and standard deviations. Then produce graphs of the original population and of the sampling distribution of the sample mean. Comment on the difference you see in their shapes.

 4. You are to obtain a data set from the Internet. One possible way to obtain a data set is to access the DASL library at DASLData; a second site with interesting data sets is the Chance data library at ChncData. Another way to find data is to go to sites that serve as directories to multiple sites with data sets. Two such sites are at NYUData and YorkData. Select one quantitative variable from that data set to represent a population. Enter that data into column 99 (c99) of MINITAB's data window. Then repeat the process described in the previous exercise.

CHAPTER 7

Estimating Parameters

Y ou'll recall from Chapter 1 that statistical inference is the process of arriving at a conclusion about an unknown population parameter on the basis of information obtained from a sample statistic. In the last three chapters we've been looking at the probability and sampling concepts that underlie this process. Now, in this chapter, we'll see how statistical inference concepts enable us to use sample data to estimate the value of an unknown population mean, proportion, or variance. (In the next chapters, we'll see how these same concepts permit us to make tests to see if assumptions about one or more unknown population parameters are likely to be true.)

Thus, after studying this chapter, you should be able to

- Explain the basic concepts underlying the estimation of population means, proportions, and variances.

- Compute estimates of the population mean at different levels of confidence when the population standard deviation is unknown as well as when it's available.

- Compute estimates of the population proportion at different levels of confidence.

- Compute estimates of the population variance at different levels of confidence.

- Understand when and how to use the appropriate probability distributions needed for estimation purposes.

- Determine the appropriate sample size to use to estimate the population mean or proportion at different levels of confidence.

7.1   Estimate, Estimation, Estimator, Et Cetera

To guess is cheap,
To guess wrongly is expensive.—***An old Chinese proverb***

As the proverb implies, a guess is easily made. Anyone can offer an opinion. The naive as well as the expert can produce a value if asked to do so. Joe Q. Public or the famous economist Marge Propensity can give a figure for next year's gross domestic product. But the task in estimation *isn't* just to produce a figure; the challenge is to produce one that has a reasonable degree of accuracy.

Need for Accuracy

Let's assume that a sales manager who must make a sales forecast for the next period asks you, her trusted assistant, to estimate the average dollar purchase made by a typical customer. Perhaps you base your estimate on a method such as rolling a pair of dice, drawing from a deck of cards, or reading a cup of soggy tea leaves. Now maybe your luck holds and your hunch doesn't cause later embarrassment. But consider the alternative: On the basis of your wild guess, your boss makes a grossly inaccurate sales forecast that leads to the loss of hundreds of thousands of dollars. This result brings the wrath of the company president down on your boss, and she, in turn ... Well, you get the picture.

In this chapter we'll see how to estimate the population mean, population proportion, and population variance with some degree of confidence that the resulting figures approximate the true values. Of course, our methods won't produce exact population values. Some error is inevitable in estimation (as the Roman poet Ovid once wrote, "The judgment of man is fallible"), but, as you'll see, the amount of error can be objectively assessed and controlled.

Some Terms to Consider

Although no formal definitions of the words *estimate* and *estimation* have yet appeared, you probably have a good grasp of their meanings. In case you don't, though, let's clarify some of the terms we'll be using.

Suppose the Adam and Eve Apple Orchards want to estimate the average dollar sales per day, and a sample of days has produced a sample mean of $800. In this case the statistic ($\bar{x}$, the sample mean) may be used to estimate the parameter (μ, the population mean). The sample value of $\bar{x} = \$800$ is an estimate of the population value, μ.

> An **estimate** is a specific value or quantity obtained for a statistic such as the sample mean, sample proportion, or sample variance.

Note, though, that an estimate isn't the same thing as an *estimator*.

> An **estimator** is any statistic (sample mean, sample proportion, sample variance) that is used to estimate a parameter.

Thus, the sample mean ($\bar{x}$) is an estimator of the population mean (μ), the sample proportion ($\hat{p}$) is an estimator of the population proportion (p), and the sample variance (s^2) is an estimator of the population variance (σ^2). A value we calculate from a sample for any of these is called an estimate.

There are several reasons for selecting a particular statistic to be an estimator. A complete discussion of all the reasons is beyond the scope of this book, but we'll mention one important criterion here. The sample mean is selected as an estimator of the population mean, the sample proportion is an estimator of the population proportion, and the sample variance is an estimator of the population variance because these statistics are unbiased.

The concept of expected value was introduced in Chapter 4, and in Chapter 6 we took a look at sampling distributions of statistics. If we study any statistic such as the sample mean, sample proportion, or sample variance, take every possible sample of the same size picked from the population in the same way, compute the value of the statistic under study for each sample selected, then the mean of all the values of the statistic is the mean or the *expected value* of the statistic. That is, the mean of the sampling distribution of a statistic is the expected value of that statistic. And if the expected value of the statistic equals the corresponding population parameter, we say that the statistic is an *unbiased estimator.*

> An **unbiased estimator** is one whose sampling distribution has a mean (expected value) that's equal to the population parameter to be estimated.

We've already seen in Chapter 6 that the mean of the sampling distribution of sample means equals the population mean, and the mean of the sampling distribution of sample proportions equals the population proportion. Similarly, the mean of the sampling distribution of sample variances equals the population variance when the sample variances are computed with this formula:

$$s^2 = \frac{\Sigma(x - \bar{x})^2}{n - 1}$$

Thus, sample means, proportions, and variances are unbiased estimators. This unbiased tendency of an estimator is highly desirable.

We're now ready to define *estimation.*

> **Estimation** is the entire process of using an estimator to produce an estimate of the parameter.

There are two estimation types—point and interval.

Point Estimation

The sample mean of $800 in our previous example is a *point estimate* because the value is only one point along a scale of possible values. But is it likely that a single numeric estimate will be correct? This question brings us to the concept of interval estimation.

STATISTICS IN ACTION

Canadian Economy Affected by SARS

A study commissioned by the Hotel Association of Canada says the SARS outbreak has cost Toronto's tourism industry up to $190 million in lost business. The study by the consulting firm KPMG looked at the period between March 2, the week of the first reported SARS death, and the end of May 2003.

The final numbers showed that, while the SARS-related losses were felt across the tourism sector, the hotel industry was hardest hit, with its revenue dropping by nearly 40 percent. The study also found the following decreases in tourism revenues:

Vancouver: $57 million (10 percent)
Montreal: $33 million (7 percent)
Calgary: $13 million (7 percent)
Ottawa: $700,000 (0.3 percent)

SARS (Severe Acute Respiratory Syndrome) is a recently discovered and sometimes fatal disease that attacks the respiratory system.

A **point estimate** is a single number used to estimate a population parameter, and the process of estimating with a single number is known as **point estimation**.

Interval Estimation A parameter is usually estimated to be within a spread of values—that is, within an interval bounded by two values—rather than as a single number. It's unlikely that any particular sample mean will be exactly equal to the population mean, so allowances must be made for sampling error. Thus,

An **interval estimate** is a spread of values used to estimate a population parameter, and the process of estimating with a spread of values is known as **interval estimation**.

With two methods of estimation, which one should be used? To answer this, let's look at the precision of a point estimate. You've seen in the computer simulations in Chapter 6 (and in *Figure 6.2* on page 190 and *Figure 6.5* on page 196) that the means of different random samples taken from a population have different values. Sample means are likely to be close to the population mean, but it's highly unlikely that the value of a sample mean will be exactly equal to the mean of the population from which the sample was taken. A point estimate is not only likely to be wrong, it also doesn't allow us to evaluate the precision of the estimate.

The precision of an estimate is set by the degree of sampling error. Although a point estimate will likely be off the mark, this doesn't prevent us from being confident that an interval estimate will contain the parameter within its given spread of values. For example, we may say that the daily average sales for the orchards is likely to be between $785 and $815 instead of simply saying that the true mean may be $800. Thus, the parameter is estimated to be within a certain spread or interval. And since allowance is made for sampling error, the precision of the estimate can be assessed. Of course, an interval estimate may be wrong. But in contrast to a point estimate, the probability of error for an interval estimator can be known.

Don't get the impression, though, that a point estimate is of little value in the estimation process. As you'll see in the following pages, the interval estimate is actually based on the point estimate. In fact, the *point estimate is adjusted for sampling error to produce an interval estimate.* The following pages deal with interval estimates of the population mean, population proportion, and population variance, and the accuracy of these estimates can be determined with some degree of confidence.

Self-Testing Review 7.1

Match the following numbered clues with the lettered responses given in the column on the right.

1. Estimators of population parameters.

2. Point-estimate for μ, the population mean.

3. Point estimate for p, the population proportion.

4. Point estimate for σ^2, the population variance.

    a. Point estimate

    b. Unbiased estimator

    c. The sample percent

    d. An interval estimate

5. If the expected value of the statistic equals the corresponding population parameter, we say the statistic is a(n) _____?

e. Sample statistics

6. A range of values used to estimate a population parameter.

f. The sample mean

7. A single value used as an estimator for a population parameter.

g. The sample variance

8. Why is an unbiased estimate desirable?

9. The difference between the population mean and the mean of a sample is most likely to be _____.

   a) zero

   b) a large value

   c) a small value

10. An interval estimate will _____ fall around the population mean.

   a) always

   b) probably

   c) occasionally

   d) never

7.2 Interval Estimation of the Population Mean: Some Basic Concepts

In practice, only one sample of a population is taken, the sample statistic (mean, proportion, variance) is calculated, and an estimate of the population parameter is made. Although this section focuses on basic concepts involved in estimating the population mean, many of the points raised also apply to estimating other parameters, including the population proportion or the population variance. To estimate the population mean, though, we must know something about its relationship to the sample means.

The Sampling Distribution—Again

A quick review of the concepts of the sampling distribution of means shows the theoretical basis for the interval estimation of the population mean. Suppose we have a sample size that is sufficiently large so that the sampling distribution is approximately normal. *Figure 7.1* shows that 95.4 percent of the possible outcomes of $\bar{x}$ are within $2\sigma_{\bar{x}}$ to each side of the mean of the sampling distribution. This means that if a mad statistician takes 1,000 samples of the same size from a population, about 954 of the sample means will fall within two standard errors to both sides of the population mean. (If this last sentence—and *Figure 7.1*—puzzles you, review Chapter 6.)

FIGURE 7.1 An educational schematic of the sampling distribution of the means when the sample size is large. There is a 95.4 percent chance that an $\bar{x}$ will have a value between $\mu \pm 2\sigma_{\bar{x}}$.

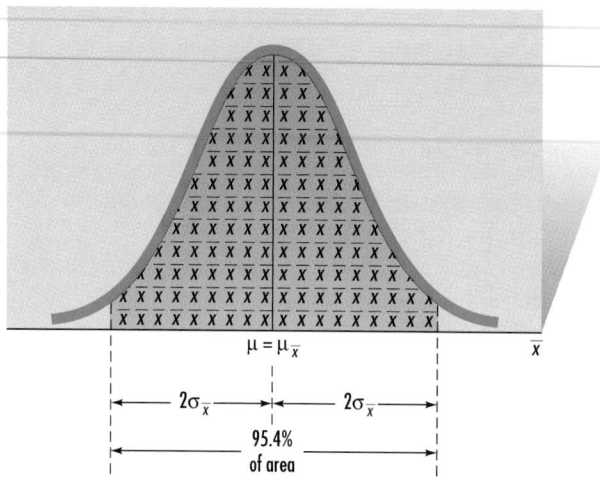

Interval Width Considerations

If 95.4 percent of the possible values of the sample mean fall within two standard errors of the population mean as shown in *Figure 7.1*, then obviously μ will not be farther than $2\sigma_{\bar{x}}$ from 95.4 percent of the possible values of $\bar{x}$. Now let's show in non-statistical terms the logic of the preceding sentence. Let's assume we have 1,000 towns located various distances from the city of Toronto and it happens that 95.4 percent of these towns are within a 150-kilometre radius of Toronto. If 954 towns are within a 150-kilometre radius of Toronto, then logically Toronto must fall within a 150-kilometre radius of each of these 954 towns. If Hamilton is within 150 kilometres of Toronto, then Toronto will certainly be no farther than 150 kilometres from Hamilton (see *Figure 7.2*). If we randomly select a large number of towns from the 1,000, Toronto will be within a radius of 150 kilometres of 95.4 percent of all the towns selected. If all this appears simple and trite, then we've accomplished something.

In returning to the statistical world, substitute the population mean for Toronto, let the possible sample means be the towns, and use $2\sigma_{\bar{x}}$ in place of the 150-kilometre radius. To repeat, then, if 95.4 percent of the sample means are within $2\sigma_{\bar{x}}$ of the value of μ, then certainly the value of μ must be within $2\sigma_{\bar{x}}$ of 95.4 percent of the sample

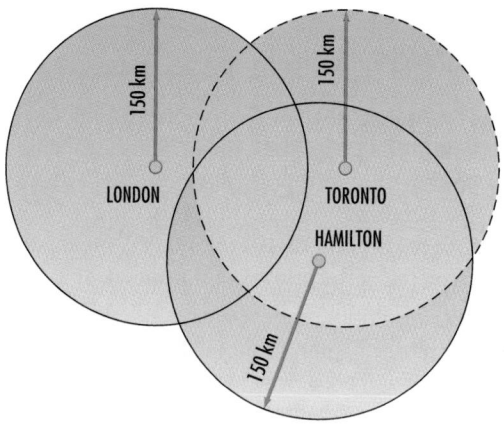

FIGURE 7.2 An illustration of distance relationships.

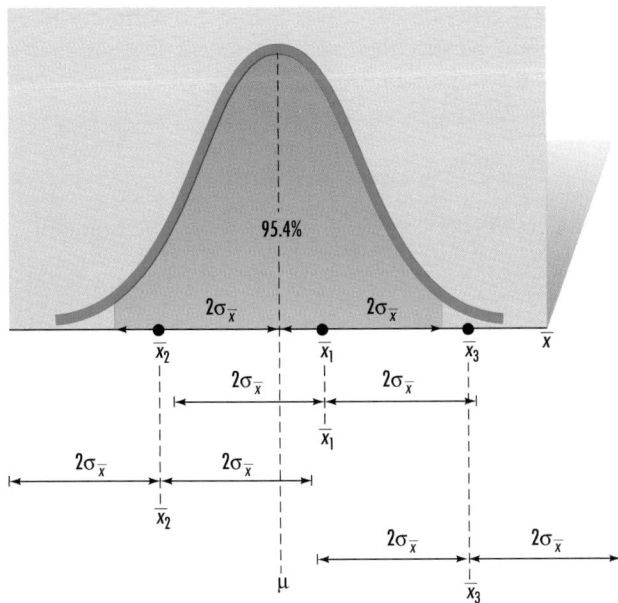

means. Thus, if we use the method of $\bar{x} \pm 2\sigma_{\bar{x}}$ to estimate the population mean, and if we construct a large number of intervals, 95.4 percent of the interval estimates will include μ.

Now let's assume that we have 1,000 possible samples and thus 1,000 sample means, three of which are shown in *Figure 7.3*. The population mean will be located within 95.4 percent of the 1,000 possible intervals that could be constructed using $\bar{x} \pm 2\sigma_{\bar{x}}$. Any specific single interval may or may not contain μ (note that in *Figure 7.3* the intervals produced using $\bar{x}_1$ and $\bar{x}_2$ do include μ, but the interval constructed using $\bar{x}_3$ fails to reach μ), but the method employed assures that if a large number of intervals are constructed, the value of μ will be included in 95.4 percent of them.

We'll not be limited to using a 95.4 percent probability of estimating the population mean for the rest of this book. Thus, we need to generalize what has been discussed so far so that we can apply different interval estimates to a variety of situations. To do so, we need one more idea, the level of confidence.

The Level of Confidence

Statisticians assign a level of confidence to the interval estimates they produce.

> The **confidence coefficient** refers to the probability of correctly including the population parameter being estimated in the interval that is produced. This probability is designated **1 − α** (1 − "alpha").

The word *confidence* is used because the probability value shows the likelihood that the computed spread of values will include the population mean. That is, the higher the level of probability associated with an interval estimator, the more confidence there is that the method of estimation will produce a result that contains the population mean.

In practice, the *confidence level* is generally identified before estimation. Thus, a 90 percent level of confidence might be specified, and this means that an analyst wants to be 90 percent sure that the population mean is included in the interval obtained.

> The **level of confidence** is the confidence coefficient expressed as a percent and equals $(1 - \alpha) \times 100$ percent.

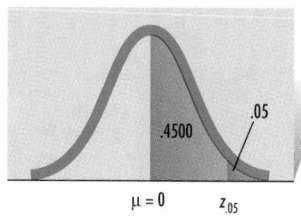

What's the appropriate z value to use to construct an interval estimate in which we can have 90 percent confidence that it will contain the population mean? The answer is the z value that separates the middle 90 percent of the area under the normal sampling distribution curve from the remaining 10 percent. Thus, to use the table for the standard normal distribution found in Appendix 2, we need to know the z value that divides 45 percent of the area in each half of the normal distribution from the remaining 5 percent. We will denote this z value with a subscript equal to the tail area of .05, so here the z value would be written as $z_{.05}$. Looking in the body of that table, we find the figure nearest to .4500 (or 45 percent). The z value corresponding to the table figure of .4495 is 1.64, and the z value for the table figure of .4505 is 1.65. The most accurate z value is thus 1.645. That is, the z value corresponding to an area of .45 (or 4.5 percent) is $z_{.05} = 1.645$. Thus, the interval estimate of μ using a 90 percent confidence level is

$$\bar{x} - 1.645\sigma_{\bar{x}} < \mu < \bar{x} + 1.645\sigma_{\bar{x}}$$

We are now ready to give a general form for an interval estimate of μ when the sampling distribution of the means is normal. The chance of error is labelled α and in decimal form equals 1.00 minus the confidence coefficient. For example, if the confidence coefficient is .95 (or the confidence level is 95 percent), then α is $1.00 - .95$ or .05. To have a confidence coefficient of $1 - \alpha$, the total error is divided evenly between the chance of overestimation and the chance of underestimation, and we would have an area of $\alpha/2$ in each tail of the normal distribution. Thus, an interval estimate for μ may be constructed in the following manner:

$$\underbrace{\bar{x} - z_{\alpha/2}\sigma_{\bar{x}}}_{\substack{\text{lower confi-}\\\text{dence limit}}} < \mu < \underbrace{\bar{x} + z_{\alpha/2}\sigma_{\bar{x}}}_{\substack{\text{upper confi-}\\\text{dence limit}}} \qquad (7.1)$$

where $\bar{x}$ = the sample mean (and point estimator of μ)
$\sigma_{\bar{x}}$ = the standard error of the mean
$z_{\alpha/2}$ = the z value such that $P(z > z_{\alpha/2}) = \alpha/2$
          [or, such that $P(-z_{\alpha/2} < z < z_{\alpha/2}) = 1 - \alpha$]

The confidence levels generally used in interval estimation are 90, 95, and 99 percent. The z values and the general forms of the interval estimates associated with these confidence levels are shown in Table 7.1. To summarize

TABLE 7.1 COMMONLY USED CONFIDENCE LEVELS AND CONFIDENCE INTERVALS FOR A LARGE SAMPLE

Confidence Level	z Value	General Form of the Interval Estimate
90	1.645	$\bar{x} - 1.645\sigma_{\bar{x}} < \mu < \bar{x} + 1.645\sigma_{\bar{x}}$
95	1.96	$\bar{x} - 1.96\sigma_{\bar{x}} < \mu < \bar{x} + 1.96\sigma_{\bar{x}}$
99	2.575	$\bar{x} - 2.575\sigma_{\bar{x}} < \mu < \bar{x} + 2.575\sigma_{\bar{x}}$

> **Confidence intervals** are those interval estimates based on specified confidence levels, and the upper and lower limits of the intervals are known as **confidence limits.**

The sampling error in estimating a population parameter is the distance between the true population parameter and the sample statistic. Thus, it we are estimating a population mean and if we have a sample size that is sufficiently large so that the sampling distribution is approximately normal, then this sampling error, or **error of estimate,** is likely to be less than $z_{\alpha/2}\sigma_{\bar{x}}$. The value of $z_{\alpha/2}\sigma_x$ is designated E and is called the **error bound,** or **maximum error of estimate.** You can see from this relationship that if the z value or confidence level is increased, then the size of $E =$ the error bound is also increased. And you can also see from formula 7.1 that the confidence interval width for a given level of confidence is equal to twice the value of the error bound. For example, if we have a normal sampling distribution and we are seeking to produce a 90 percent confidence interval, then the error bound is $E = 1.645(\sigma_x)$. And since this error bound is added to and subtracted from the sample mean point estimate, the confidence interval width is twice the value of the error bound or 2 times $1.645(\sigma_{\bar{x}})$.

At this point you may wonder why it's necessary to have various confidence levels when it seems logical that the highest level of confidence is desirable in estimating μ. You might be thinking, "If I'm required to give an accurate estimate of the true mean, why shouldn't I always use a 99 percent confidence level? It makes sense to have as much confidence as possible in my estimate!"

There's no question that it's highly desirable to have as much confidence as possible in the estimate. But it is also true that a small error bound is also desirable—we would prefer being confident that we are "off" by no more than 10 rather than being "off" by no more than 15. If higher confidence is desired, you must allow for more sampling error—that is, you must accept a larger error bound and a corresponding increase in the width of the interval. Table 7.1 shows this relationship between the confidence coefficient and the interval width. So the choice of high confidence (good) results in an interval whose width can be fairly wide (bad). Thus, the selection of the confidence coefficient should be based on a choice between wanting higher confidence versus wanting a smaller confidence interval.

One caution should be mentioned here. The confidence coefficient should be stated before the interval estimation. Sometimes a novice researcher calculates a number of interval estimates on the basis of a single sample while varying the confidence level. After obtaining these estimates, he or she then selects the one that seems most suitable. Such an approach is really manipulating data so that the results of a sample are the way a researcher would like to see them. This approach introduces the researcher's bias into the study, and it should be avoided.

STATISTICS IN ACTION

Two Polls—Two Stories: Both Correct?

Prior to the 1999 election in Ontario, a CBC-Environics survey suggested a dead heat (42 percent Tory, 41 percent Liberal, 16 percent NDP). But an Angus Reid survey released hours later suggested the Tories were poised to win another majority government (45 percent Tory, 37 percent Liberal, 16 percent NDP). On election night the Tories won 59 of the province's 103 seats, the Liberals 35, and the NDP 9. The popular vote was 45 percent Tory, 40 percent Liberal, and 12 percent NDP. Are both polls correct?

Self-Testing Review 7.2

11. What is the standard error of a sampling distribution?

12. If a mad statistician (or a sane one with a statistical software program) takes 10,000 samples of the same sufficiently large size from a population, how many of the corresponding sample means would be expected to fall within 1 standard error of the population mean? How many would fall within two standard errors of the population mean? How many would likely lie within three standard errors of the population mean?

13. For a sampling distribution with $n - 32$, within how many standard errors

   a) Will 80 percent of the sample means fall?

   b) Will 90 percent of the sample means fall?

   c) Will 95 percent of the sample means fall?

   d) As the level of confidence increases, what do you notice about the number of standard errors required for the confidence interval?

14. For a sampling distribution with $n = 40$, within how many standard errors

   a) Will 86 percent of the sample means fall?

   b) Will 92 percent of the sample means fall?

   c) Will 98 percent of the sample means fall?

15. What role does the level of confidence play in an interval estimate?

16. What happens to the width of an interval estimate as the level of confidence increases?

17. Why would someone use a 90 percent level of confidence instead of a 99 percent level if the 99 percent level has a greater chance of including the population mean?

18. If the confidence level is increased, what happens to the error bound?

19. Discuss the following statement: The width of a confidence interval is equal to twice the value of the error bound.

20. In your own words, discuss what a 95 percent confidence interval means.

21. We are 90 percent sure that the population mean is within the interval from $84.1 - 5.3$ to $84.1 + 5.3$. What is the level of confidence, the population parameter, the point estimate, and error bound for this situation?

22. We are 99 percent sure that the population mean is within the interval from $3.5 - .02$ to $3.5 + .02$. What is the level of confidence, the population parameter, the point estimate, and error bound for this situation?

7.3 Estimating the Population Mean

Now that we've considered the general form of (and the theoretical basis for) an interval estimate, let's look first at the approach used to estimate the population mean when the population standard deviation is known and the sampling distribution of the sample mean, $\bar{x}$, is normal. Remember that the sample mean is considered to be normally distributed whenever we sample from a normal population or when the sample size (n) exceeds 30. (Later, we'll consider situations where σ is unknown.)

Estimating the Population Mean When the Value of σ Is Known and the Distribution of $\bar{x}$ Is Normal

STATISTICS IN ACTION

Six Billion People Hard to Count

A United Nations report estimated that the world's population reached 6 billion on October 12, 1999, but according to the United States Census Bureau, the population of the world reached that number at 8:30 p.m. Eastern Time on July 18, 1999. The UN estimates that the world's population increases by about 78 million people per year, and the U.S. has a similar estimate of 200,000 people per day. When the population reached its first billion—in 1804, according to United Nations figures—it took 123 years to double to 2 billion.

When the population standard deviation (σ) is known, we may directly compute the standard error of the mean as follows (see page 194):

$$\sigma_{\bar{x}} = \frac{\sigma}{\sqrt{n}}$$

Then, if $\bar{x}$ is normally distributed, an interval estimate may be constructed in the following manner:

$$\underbrace{\bar{x} - z_{\alpha/2}\sigma_{\bar{x}}}_{\substack{\text{lower confidence} \\ \text{limit}}} < \mu < \underbrace{\bar{x} + z_{\alpha/2}\sigma_{\bar{x}}}_{\substack{\text{upper confidence} \\ \text{limit}}}$$

So let's now use this estimation procedure to solve some example problems.

Example 7.1 A manager at the Papyrus Paper Company wants to estimate the mean time required for a new machine to produce a ream of paper. A random sample of 36 reams required an average machine time of 1.5 minutes for each ream. Assuming $\sigma = 0.30$ minute, construct an interval estimate with a confidence level of 95 percent.

◆ **Solution:**

Because the sample size is large ($n = 36 > 30$), the sampling distribution of $\bar{x}$ is approximately normal. We have the following data: $\bar{x} = 1.5$ minutes, $\sigma = .30$, $n = 36$, and confidence level = 95 percent. The value of $\sigma_{\bar{x}}$ is computed as follows:

$$\sigma_{\bar{x}} = \frac{\sigma}{\sqrt{n}} = \frac{.30}{\sqrt{36}} = .05$$

With a 95 percent confidence level, the z value is $z_{.025} = 1.96$. Thus, the interval estimate of the true mean time (μ) is constructed as follows:

$$\bar{x} = z_{.025}\sigma_{\bar{x}} < \mu < \bar{x} + z_{.025}\sigma_{\bar{x}}$$
$$1.5 - 1.96(.05) < \mu < 1.5 + 1.96(.05)$$
$$1.402 \text{ minutes} < \mu < 1.598 \text{ minutes}$$

So we can be 95 percent confident that the population mean time required for the new machine to produce a ream of paper is between 1.4 and 1.6 minutes. ◆

We can use the data in this example, along with MINITAB computer simulations, to verify some of the concepts we've now considered. Let's assume in our Papyrus Paper Company example that the true population mean time for the machine to produce a ream is actually 1.48 minutes. The value of σ, we've seen, is .30 minute. If we were to take 15 random samples, with each sample containing the time data required to produce 36 reams, about how many of the 15 sample confidence intervals would include the value of $\mu = 1.48$ minutes if we use the 95 percent confidence level? We could answer this question without much hesitation if we were taking 1,000 random samples (the answer would be about 950 of them), but with just 15 samples we can't always be sure.

Figure 7.4a shows the results obtained when the statistical package simulates taking 15 random samples from a normally distributed population with a mean of 1.48 and a standard deviation of .30, with 36 sample items in each sample. The first sample data goes in column 1 (C1), the second in C2, and so on. Then MINITAB produces a 95 percent confidence interval for each of the 15 samples in C1 through C15. The means of each of the simulated samples are listed in the program output. The **SE Mean** gives the standard error figured earlier in this example, and the lower and upper confidence limits are given for each of the 15 intervals produced.

You'll see that 14 of the 15 samples have intervals that *include* the value of $\mu = 1.48$ minutes. Only the interval in C6 has failed to include this parameter. All intervals, of course, have the same width, but they have different lower and upper limits, as you would expect.

To graphically demonstrate how these lower and upper limits vary, *Figure 7.4b* shows another simulation, this time of 20 samples. The black vertical line shows the position of the value of $\mu = 1.48$ minutes. The 20 horizontal lines represent the confidence intervals calculated from the 20 samples; the 18 green lines are confidence intervals that correctly capture μ, the two red lines are confidence intervals that miss. Thus, in this second simulation, 18 of the 20 intervals include the population mean. Don't think that every simulation of 20 samples will always produce two samples that fail to include the value of μ in their intervals. The next simulation might easily have no "failures" or one or three failures. If we were to repeat this process over and over, because these are 95 percent confidence intervals, we would expect an average of 1 out of 20 (5 percent) to be incorrect.

To summarize the last few paragraphs, when we say that we have 95 percent (or 99 percent or …) confidence in an interval, it does not mean that the confidence interval will be correct 95 percent of the time. In fact, the interval is either right and it contains the population mean, or it is wrong and it does not contain the population mean. But, since we used a method that yields a correct interval 95 percent of the time, the odds are in our favour that any one particular interval we calculate is one of the many that yields a correct spread of values rather than one of the few that gives us an incorrect spread.

In Example 7.1, we were able to validly construct a confidence interval because we had a large sample size of $n = 36$, which is greater than 30. This ensures that the distribution of the sample means is approximately normal. In the next example, we'll consider the case in which we have a small sample. In order to use the normal distribution to compute a valid confidence interval with a small sample, we must both know the value of the population standard deviation and also believe that the population from which the sample is taken is normally distributed. ◆

Example 7.2
The Ledd Pipe Company has received a large shipment of pipes, and a quality control inspector wants to estimate the average diameter of the pipes to see if they meet minimum standards. She takes a random sample of 15 pipes, and the sample produces an average diameter of 2.55 millimetres. In the past, the diameters of the pipes have been normally distributed, and the population standard deviation has been 0.07 millimetres. Assuming that these still hold true, construct an interval estimate with a 99 percent level of confidence.

◆ **Solution:**

We have the following data from the problem: $\bar{x} = 2.55$, $\sigma = .07$, $n = 15$, and confidence level = 99 percent. The standard error of the mean is

$$\sigma_{\bar{x}} = \frac{\sigma}{\sqrt{n}} = \frac{.07}{\sqrt{15}} = .018$$

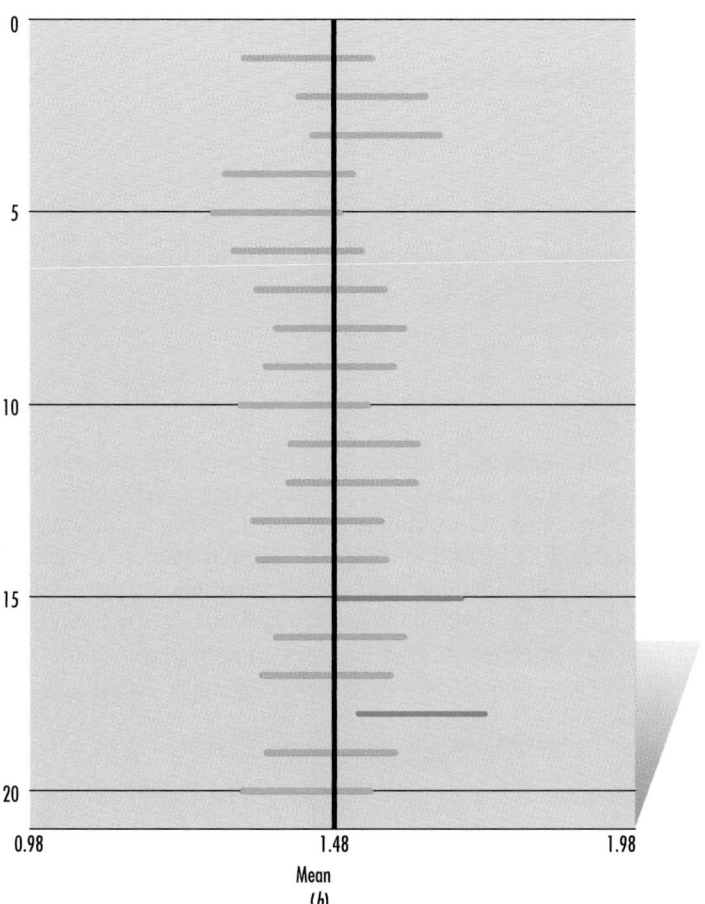

```
> MINITAB - Papyrus Paper Simulation .mpj - [Session]
File  Edit  Manip  Calc  Stat  Graph  Editor  Window  Help

MTB > ZInterval 95.0 .3 C1-C15.

Z Confidence Intervals

The assumed sigma = 0.300

Variable    N     Mean    StDev   SE Mean        95.0 % CI
C1          36   1.4723   0.2970   0.0500   ( 1.3742,   1.5703)
C2          36   1.5450   0.3353   0.0500   ( 1.4470,   1.6431)
C3          36   1.3962   0.3103   0.0500   ( 1.2982,   1.4942)
C4          36   1.4705   0.2691   0.0500   ( 1.3725,   1.5685)
C5          36   1.4541   0.2963   0.0500   ( 1.3561,   1.5521)
C6          36   1.3683   0.2576   0.0500   ( 1.2703,   1.4663)
C7          36   1.5532   0.2816   0.0500   ( 1.4551,   1.6512)
C8          36   1.4574   0.3030   0.0500   ( 1.3594,   1.5554)
C9          36   1.4426   0.3135   0.0500   ( 1.3446,   1.5406)
C10         36   1.5045   0.2708   0.0500   ( 1.4064,   1.6025)
C11         36   1.5206   0.2965   0.0500   ( 1.4226,   1.6186)
C12         36   1.5121   0.2946   0.0500   ( 1.4141,   1.6102)
C13         36   1.4793   0.2824   0.0500   ( 1.3813,   1.5773)
C14         36   1.4259   0.2345   0.0500   ( 1.3279,   1.5239)
C15         36   1.5292   0.3489   0.0500   ( 1.4312,   1.6272)

MTB >

Current Worksheet: Papyrus.MTW                    Editable      4:01 PM
```

(*a*)

FIGURE 7.4 (*a*) To obtain this MINITAB output, click on **Stat, Basic Statistics, 1-Sample Z,** enter the columns to be analyzed in the box below **Variables,** click in the circle to the left of **Confidence** interval, to the right of **Sigma** enter the value .30, and click **OK.** (*b*) A plot of twenty 95 percent confidence intervals.

Mean

(*b*)

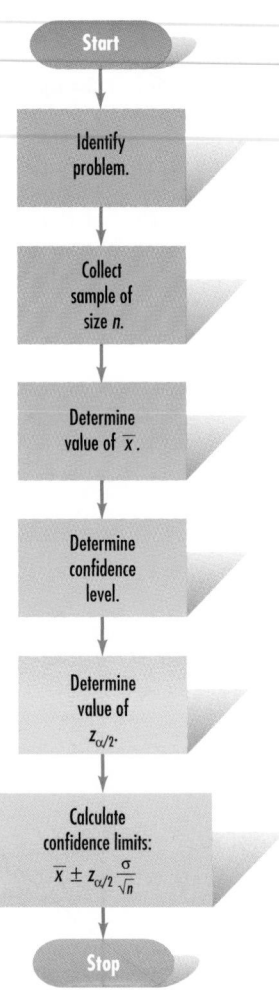

FIGURE 7.5 Procedure for the interval estimation of μ with σ known and $\bar{x}$ normal.

With a 99 percent confidence level, the z value is $z_{.005} = 2.575$. Therefore, the interval estimate of μ, the true average diameter of the shipment of pipes, is found as follows:

$$\bar{x} = z_{.005}\sigma_{\bar{x}} < \mu < \bar{x} + z_{.005}\sigma_{\bar{x}}$$
$$2.55 - 2.575(.018) < \mu < 2.55 + 2.575(.018)$$
$$2.504 \text{ mm} < \mu < 2,596 \text{ mm}$$

So the quality control inspector could be 99 percent confident that the true mean diameter of the pipes is between 2.5 and 2.6 millimetres. ◆

Note that the preceding examples are cases in which σ is known (or can be identified) and, either because the sample size exceeds 30 or because the sample is taken from a normal population, the sampling distribution of $\bar{x}$ is normal. The general procedure for interval estimation under such conditions is shown in *Figure 7.5*.

Estimating the Mean When σ Is Unknown and $n > 30$

In most situations, not only is the population mean unknown but the population standard deviation is also unknown. In fact, it's only in isolated cases that the value of σ is known, so it usually must be estimated along with the population mean.

The Estimator of σ You saw in Chapter 3 that the formula needed to compute the standard deviation for a set of population values is

$$\sigma = \sqrt{\frac{\Sigma(X - \mu)^2}{N}}$$

And you also saw in Chapter 3 that the formula needed to compute the standard deviation for a sample is

$$s = \sqrt{\frac{\Sigma(x - \bar{x})^2}{n - 1}}$$

(You might recall that, for both of these, the quantity under the square root is called the variance.) The only basic difference in these formulas is that a denominator of $n - 1$ (rather than n) is used to compute the sample measure. Let's briefly look at why we use a denominator of $n - 1$ rather than n to compute a sample standard deviation. The reason is based on the sampling distribution of sample variances.

Later in this chapter we'll also be estimating the population variance (σ^2). Our estimator of that parameter is the sample variance (s^2). As you might expect by now, we'll use this formula to arrive at a value for s^2:

$$s^2 = \frac{\Sigma(x - \bar{x})^2}{n - 1}$$

If we were computing the sample variance for its own sake, we *could* use a denominator of n in the formula. But we seldom are interested only in s^2. Rather, s^2 is almost always computed to provide an estimate for an unknown σ^2. And if we used a denominator of n, we would run into a bias problem. Why is that? Well, you've seen earlier that a sample mean is an unbiased estimator of μ because the mean of the sampling distribution of means from which $\bar{x}$ is taken equals the population mean—that is, because $\mu_{\bar{x}} = \mu$. But *if* we were to use a denominator of n to compute all the s^2 values needed to produce a sampling distribution of sample variances, the mean of that sampling distribution wouldn't equal σ^2. Instead, the mean of the sampling distribution of sample variances would be less than the population variance so there's a tendency for a sample variance computed with a denominator of n to also be less than σ^2. That is, the computed result would be biased towards understating σ^2, so this tendency must be removed. That's where a denominator of $n - 1$ comes in, because the use of $n - 1$ has the effect of slightly increasing the value of s^2, which eliminates the bias. (Using $n - 1$ wasn't someone's lucky hunch; its selection can be shown mathematically, but that's beyond the scope of this book.) Computed in this way, the sample variance is an unbiased estimator of the population variance. And so it is that a denominator of $n - 1$ is used also to compute the sample standard deviation and to thus arrive at a useful estimator of σ that needs no further manipulation.

Now that we've considered these details, let's look at how we obtain the estimated standard error needed to approximate the population mean when σ is unknown. The formula for this estimated standard error is

$$\hat{\sigma}_{\bar{x}} = \frac{s}{\sqrt{n}} \tag{7.2}$$

You'll notice that the mark ($\wedge$) over the standard error symbol (or any other symbol) means that we have an estimated value. And you'll also notice that the calculation of $\hat{\sigma}_{\bar{x}}$ is the same as the computation of $\sigma_{\bar{x}}$ except that the population standard deviation (σ) is replaced by the sample standard deviation (s).

If the population standard deviation is unknown, it is possible to compute a valid confidence interval using the normal distribution only when the sample size is relatively large (over 30). When using s as an estimate of σ, the general form of the interval estimate for large samples is altered slightly so that it appears as follows:

$$\underbrace{\bar{x} - z_{\alpha/2}\hat{\sigma}_{\bar{x}}}_{\substack{\text{lower confidence} \\ \text{limit}}} < \mu < \underbrace{\bar{x} + z_{\alpha/2}\hat{\sigma}_{\bar{x}}}_{\substack{\text{upper confidence} \\ \text{limit}}} \tag{7.3}$$

As you can see, we merely substituted the estimated value for the true value of the standard error of the mean. Again, let's look at some examples to illustrate the above points.

Example 7.3   On July 2, 2002, *The Globe and Mail* reported "City Chokes under Smog, Heat Alerts." The air-quality index in downtown Toronto that day was 54. (A reading of 32 or more is considered unacceptable.) Suppose an air-quality researcher wants to estimate the true mean air-quality index in downtown Toronto during the summer months. A random sample of 40 air-quality index measurements produces a mean of 37.8 with a standard deviation of 14.753. Estimate the true mean with a 90 percent confidence interval.

◆ **Solution:**
We have the following data: $\bar{x} = 37.8$, $s = 14.753$, $n = 40$, and the confidence level = 90 percent. Therefore the estimate of $\sigma_{\bar{x}}$ is computed as follows:

$$\hat{\sigma}_{\bar{x}} = \frac{s}{\sqrt{n}} = \frac{14.753}{\sqrt{40}} = 2.333$$

With a 90 percent confidence level, and with a sample size of over 30, we use the z value of $z_{.05} = 1.645$. The interval estimate is thus

$$\bar{x} - z_{.05}\hat{\sigma}_{\bar{x}} < \mu < \bar{x} + z_{.05}\hat{\sigma}_{\bar{x}}$$
$$37.8 - 1.645\,(2.333) < \mu < 37.8 + 1.645\,(2.333)$$
$$33.96 < \mu < 41.64$$

So the researcher can be 90 percent confident that the true mean air-quality index in downtown Toronto during the summer months is between 33.96 and 41.64. ◆

Example 7.4 The Rogers Poultry Company receives a large shipment of turkeys, and the manager wants to estimate the true mean weight of the turkeys to see if they meet Rogers's standards. A sample of 36 turkeys yields a mean weight of 3.60 kilograms with a sample standard deviation of .60 kilogram. Construct an interval estimate of the true mean weight with a 99 percent confidence level.

◆ **Solution:**
We have the following data: $\bar{x} = 3.60$, $s = .6$, $n = 36$, confidence level = 99 percent. The estimate of the standard error is computed as follows:

$$\hat{\sigma}_{\bar{x}} = \frac{s}{\sqrt{n}} = \frac{.6}{\sqrt{36}} = .10$$

With a 99 percent confidence level, the z value is $z_{.005} = 2.575$. Therefore, the interval estimate is

$$\bar{x} - z_{.005}\hat{\sigma}_{\bar{x}} < \mu < \bar{x} + z_{.005}\hat{\sigma}_{\bar{x}}$$
$$3.60 - 2.575(.10) < \mu < 3.60 + 2.575(.10)$$
$$3.34 \text{ kilograms} < \mu < 3.86 \text{ kilograms}$$

Thus, the manager can be 99 percent confident that the mean weight of the shipment of turkeys is between 3.34 and 3.86 kilograms. ◆

Example 7.5 Travis Greenley collected data from several students who took an Army Physical Fitness Test (APFT). One part of the test included the number of sit-ups each student was able to complete in two minutes. The data are below (Data = APFTSit):

				Sit-Ups				
38	95	86	63	68	73	26	43	90
30	71	100	92	57	71	67	47	56
68	61	61	92	64	83	50	66	51
87	64	80	58	60	103	14	39	88
75	60	87	70	66	95	26	75	61

 Use MINITAB or a TI-83 calculator to form a 90 percent and a 99 percent confidence interval for the mean number of sit-ups students can complete in two minutes.

◆ **Solution:**

Whether we use MINITAB or a TI-83, we first must calculate *s* and then use that value in the calculation of the 90 and 99 percent confidence intervals. *Figure 7.6a* and screens 3 and 4 of *Figure 7.6b* contain the confidence intervals. Both of these indicate a set of reasonable possibilities for μ = mean number of sit-ups students can do in two minutes. The 90 percent interval is narrower than the 99 percent interval, but has a greater risk of being incorrect. ◆

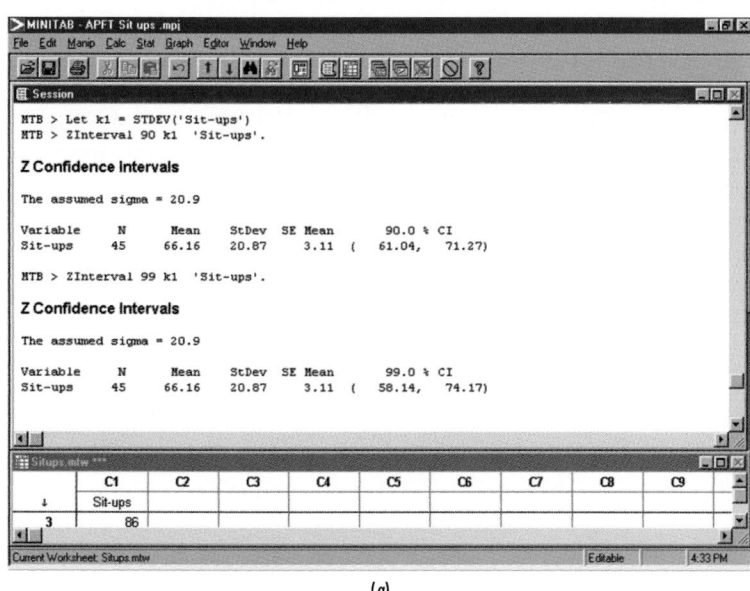

(a)

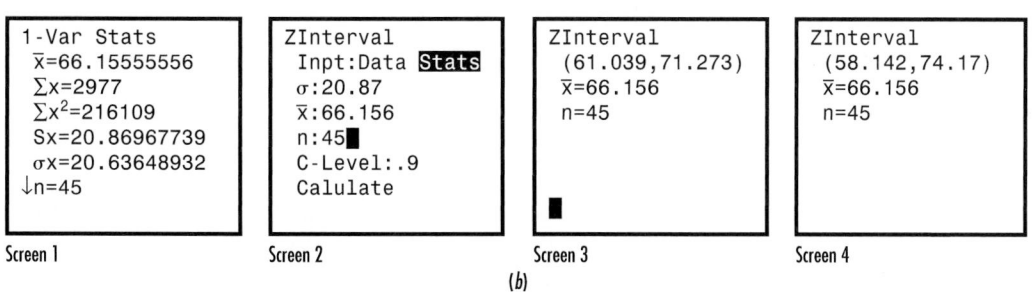

Screen 1   Screen 2   Screen 3   Screen 4

(b)

FIGURE 7.6 (a) To obtain the value of *s*, click on **Calc, Calculator,** to the right of **Store result in variable** enter *k1* (a MINITAB constant in which the answer for *s* will be stored), under **Functions** select **Std. dev.,** then select the column containing the data, and click **OK.** To then get a 90 percent confidence interval, click on **Stat, Basic Statistics, 1-Sample Z,** enter the column of data in the box below **Variables,** click in the circle to the left of **Confidence interval,** to the right of **Level** enter *90,* to the right of **Sigma** enter *k1,* and click **OK.** Repeat with a level of 99 to complete the process. (b) To obtain the confidence intervals, use the **ZInterval** command on the **STAT > TESTS** menu. Before using this command, first enter the data in a list and use the **1-Var Stats** command to calculate *s* as we learned in Chapter 3. (See screen 1.) We get *s* = 20.870 and $\bar{x}$ = 66.156. Access the **ZInterval** command and set the parameters as shown in screen 2. Note that we are using *s* from screen 1 in the σ field for screen 2 since we are using *s* to estimate σ. Move the cursor to **Calculate** and press **ENTER.** The result is shown in screen 3. If we repeat the **ZInterval** command using 99 percent confidence level, the results are shown in screen 4.

So far, all the confidence intervals we have looked at have been based on the normal distribution. This is valid as long as the sample size is large ($n > 30$) or we've taken a sample from a normal population with known σ. But what can we do if the sample size is small and σ is unknown? Under the right set of circumstances, we can still compute a confidence interval, but it will not be calculated with the use of the z distribution. What distribution should then be used? The following section provides us with the answer.

Estimating the Mean Using the t Distribution

The Central Limit Theorem in Chapter 6 told us that if the sample size is sufficiently large (>30), the sampling distribution of means approximates the normal (z) probability distribution regardless of the shape of the population distribution. It also told us that the sampling distribution is a normal distribution regardless of sample size if the population is normally distributed. But what if, in sampling from a normal population, the sample size is 30 or less and we have to use s as an estimator of an unknown σ? In that case, the appropriate sampling distribution of means follows a *t distribution* rather than a z distribution.

Student *t* Distribution

When sampling from a normal population, the statistic

$$t = \frac{\bar{x} - \mu}{s/\sqrt{n}}$$

follows a **t distribution** (often called the **student *t* distribution**) and has the following properties:

- It is similar to a z distribution with a zero mean and a symmetrical (bell) shape about that mean.

- But its shape depends on the sample size (the t distribution is really a family of distributions, and there's a different one for each sample size).

- With a small sample, the shape of the corresponding t distribution is less peaked than the z distribution, but as the sample size increases, the shapes of the t distributions lose their flatness and approximate the shape of the z distribution. (Thus, when $n > 30$, we often use z values as approximate t values—in fact, that is what we are doing when we use s as an estimate of σ to calculate confidence intervals in the large sample case.)

Figure 7.7 shows the effect of sample size on the shape of the t distributions, and *Figure 7.8* summarizes the conditions under which the t or z distributions are used for estimation purposes. You can see in *Figure 7.8* that it's possible to still use z values when the sample size is 30 or less if the value of σ is known and if it's also known that the items in the population are normally distributed (see Example 7.2 on page 222). But, as we mentioned in our discussion about large samples, the population standard

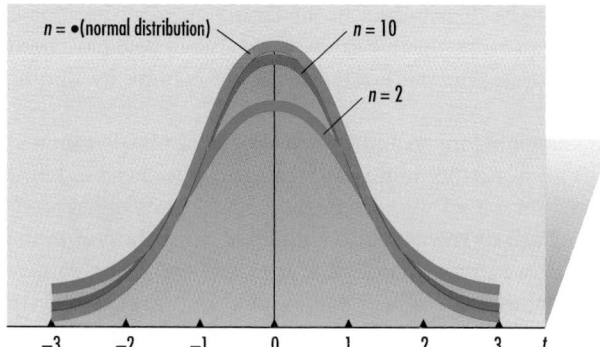

FIGURE 7.7 The effect of sample size on the shape of the t distributions.

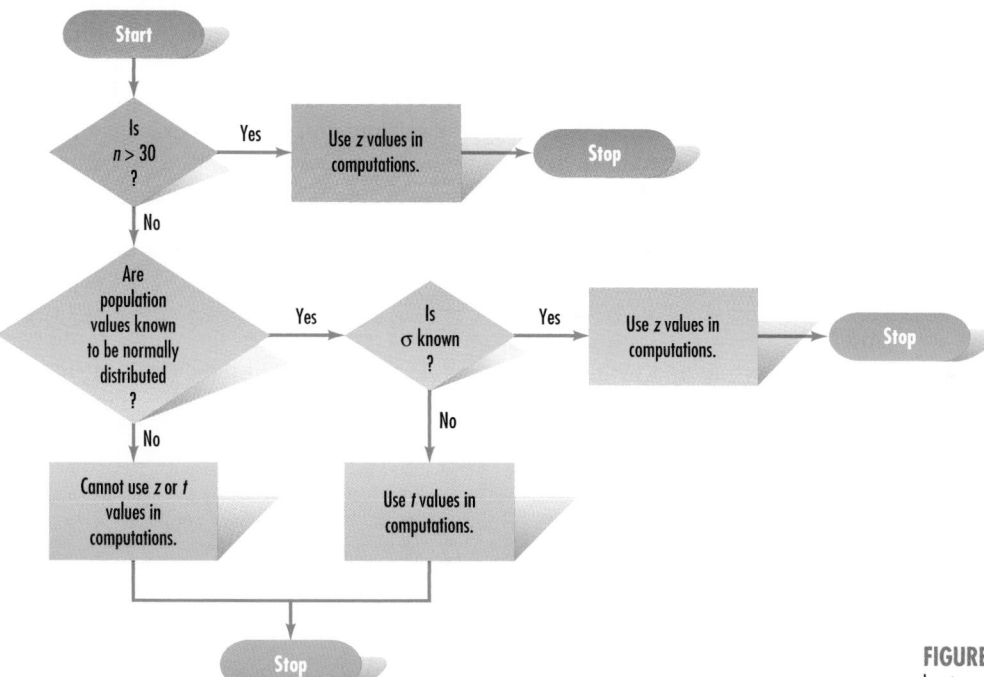

FIGURE 7.8 Which (if any) distribution to use?

deviation is usually unknown, so we'll consider more plausible situations in the next few pages.

If σ is unknown, the interval estimate of the mean of a normal population has the following form:

$$\underbrace{\bar{x} - t_{\alpha/2}\hat{\sigma}_{\bar{x}}}_{\substack{\text{lower confidence} \\ \text{limit}}} < \mu < \underbrace{\bar{x} + t_{\alpha/2}\hat{\sigma}_{\bar{x}}}_{\substack{\text{upper confidence} \\ \text{limit}}} \qquad (7.4)$$

Like the z value, the value of t depends on the confidence level.

Appendix 4 is a table of t distribution values.

The use of a t table is admittedly rather confusing at first. Some find it easier to locate the correct column by looking at the last row in the table (where df is ∞). This row presents familiar z values, since the last distribution in the family of t distributions is the normal distribution. So when you know that a z value of, say, 1.96 would have been used if the sample size had been large, you can locate the proper column by finding 1.96 in the last row.

Another factor that must be known before an appropriate t value can be determined is the degrees of freedom (df). This is a rather imposing term, but all we need to know at this time is that degrees of freedom = $n - 1$. For our purpose here, the df values identify the correct row in the table. (Each df row refers to a different t distribution in the family of curves.) Let's assume that we have a sample size of 17 and we want a 95 percent confidence level for an interval estimate. The α value is .05, and thus we refer to column $t_{.025}$ in Appendix 4. And since df = $17 - 1 = 16$, the necessary t value of 2.120 is found at the intersection of the 16 df row and the .025 column.

Let's look now at some examples of the use of the t distribution in estimating the population mean. In each of these examples, it's assumed that the population values are normally distributed. In Chapter 8 we will see a test that may be used to test the validity of this assumption of normality.

◼ Example 7.6
Hugh, the manager of a paint store, wants to estimate the mean amount of a product sold per day. Twenty business days are monitored, and an average of 32 litres is sold daily. The sample standard deviation is 12 litres. Calculate the confidence limits at the 95 percent confidence level.

◆ Solution:
We have the following information: The sample is from a normally distributed population, $\bar{x} = 32$, $s = 12$, $n = 20$, and the confidence level = 95 percent. With a confidence level of 95 percent and with a sample size of 20, α is .05 and the degrees of freedom are 19. Thus, from Appendix 4 under the $t_{.025}$ column, we see that the t value is 2.093. The estimate of $\sigma_{\bar{x}}$ is computed as follows:

$$\hat{\sigma}_{\bar{x}} = \frac{s}{\sqrt{n}} = \frac{12}{\sqrt{20}} = 2.683$$

The interval estimate is

$$\bar{x} - t_{.025}\hat{\sigma}_{\bar{x}} < \mu < \bar{x} + t_{.025}\hat{\sigma}_{\bar{x}}$$
$$32 - 2.093(2.683) < \mu < 32 + 2.093(2.683)$$
$$26.38 \text{ litres} < \mu < 37.62 \text{ litres}$$

So Hugh can be 95 percent confident that the mean amount of the product sold per day is between 26.38 and 37.62 litres. ◆

◼ Example 7.7
A purchasing agent at the Kelly Bread Company wants to estimate the mean daily usage of rye flour. She takes a sample of 14 days and finds that the sample mean is 173 kilograms, with a sample standard deviation of 45 kilograms. Construct a confidence interval with a 99 percent confidence level.

◆ Solution:
We are given that: The population is normally distributed, $\bar{x} = 173$, $s = 45$, $n = 14$, and the confidence level = 99 percent. The estimate of $\sigma_{\bar{x}}$ is computed as follows:

$$\hat{\sigma}_{\bar{x}} = \frac{s}{\sqrt{n}} = \frac{45}{\sqrt{14}} = 12.03 \text{ kilograms}$$

For a 99 percent confidence level, α is .01. With a sample size of 14, there are 13 degrees of freedom. Therefore, consulting Appendix 4 under $t_{.005}$, we see that the t value is 3.012. The interval estimate is

$$\bar{x}-t_{.005}\hat{\sigma}_{\bar{x}} < \mu < \bar{x} + t_{.005}\hat{\sigma}_{\bar{x}}$$
$$173 - 3.012(12.03) < \mu < 173 + 3.012(12.03)$$
$$136.77 \text{ kilograms} < \mu < 209.23 \text{ kilograms}$$

So the purchasing agent can be 99 percent confident that the mean daily usage of rye flour is between 136.8 and 209.2 kilograms. ◆

Example 7.8   Let's assume that you've looked at the table in your newspaper that shows the high temperatures recorded for cities in Canada on the fifth day of August. You select a random sample of 5 cities in Canada and record the following temperatures: 29, 16, 22, 24, and 31. You now decide to construct an interval estimate, at the 99 percent level of confidence, of the mean temperature recorded for all Canadian communities on that date. How do you do it?

◆ **Solution:**

Since you have only sample data items, you must first calculate the sample mean and sample standard deviation. The following effort gives you those values:

x	$x - \bar{x}$	$(x - \bar{x})^2$
29	4.6	21.16
16	-8.4	70.56
22	-2.4	5.76
24	-.4	.16
31	6.6	43.56
122		141.20

$$\bar{x} = \frac{122}{5} = 24.4$$

$$s = \sqrt{\frac{141.20}{(5-1)}} = \sqrt{35.3} = 5.94$$

Next, you compute your estimated standard error:

$$\hat{\sigma}_{\bar{x}} = \frac{s}{\sqrt{n}} = \frac{5.94}{\sqrt{5}} = \frac{5.94}{2.236} = 2.66$$

Recall that you are assuming the population of all such temperatures is normally distributed. This assumption is important since it justifies your use of the t-tables. (If the assumption of normality were not true, you wouldn't be justified in using t-tables, since the sample size is small.)

Using 99 percent confidence and 4 degrees of freedom, you find $t_{.005} = 4.604$. Finally, you prepare your interval estimate:

$$\bar{x} - t_{.005}\hat{\sigma}_{\bar{x}} < \mu < \bar{x} + t_{.005}\hat{\sigma}_{\bar{x}}$$
$$24.4 - 4.604(2.66) < \mu < 24.4 + 4.604(2.66)$$
$$24.4 - 12.25 < \mu < 24.4 + 12.25$$
$$12.15 < \mu < 36.65$$

FIGURE 7.9 (*a*) To obtain this MINITAB output, click on **Stat, Basic Statistics, 1-Sample t,** designate the data column in the box below **Variables,** click in the circle to the left of **Confidence interval,** to the right of **Level** enter *99,* and click **OK.** (*b*) To have the TI-83 construct a confidence interval, use the **TInterval** command on the **STAT > TESTS > 8:** menu. Before accessing the command, store the temperature data in a list. L1 is used in this example. After choosing the **TInterval** command, set the parameters as shown in screen 1. Note that by setting the **Inpt: Data,** we are having the calculator compute the mean and standard deviation from the data and then make the confidence interval. Choose **Calculate** and get the output shown in screen 2.

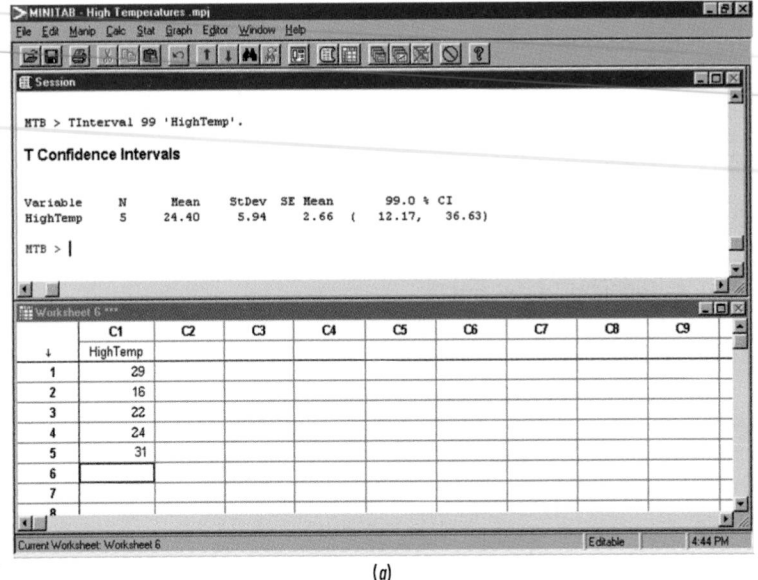

(*a*)

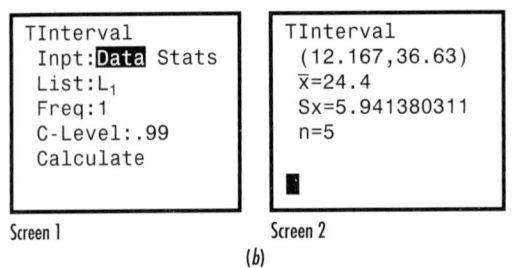

Screen 1   Screen 2

(*b*)

So you can be 99 percent confident that the mean temperature recorded for all Canadian communities on that date is between 12 and 37 degrees.◆

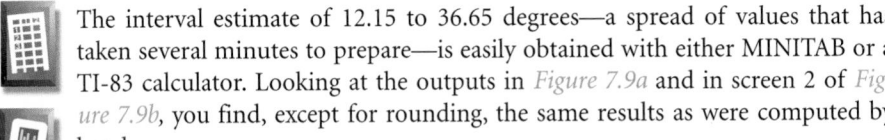

The interval estimate of 12.15 to 36.65 degrees—a spread of values that has taken several minutes to prepare—is easily obtained with either MINITAB or a TI-83 calculator. Looking at the outputs in *Figure 7.9a* and in screen 2 of *Figure 7.9b,* you find, except for rounding, the same results as were computed by hand.

The general approach to constructing an interval estimate *with an unknown σ* is summarized in *Figure 7.10.*

One last special case. In Chapter 6 we considered the finite population correction factor. This factor is used to adjust the estimate of the standard error when the sample size is more than 5 percent of the population size. While this happens infrequently in practice, the following is an example of a situation in which the finite population correction factor should be used.

☐ Example 7.9   **A Non-Wasteful Confidence Interval** The percentage of waste recycled in 29 of 58 towns with recycling facilities was calculated (Data = Recycle).

		Percentage Recycled			
12	10	12	11	13	12
18	10	33	3	10	15
12	18	20	24	5	12
14	25	11	4	14	12
26	20	17	22	11	

Construct a 90 percent confidence interval for μ = mean percentage of waste recycled in these 58 towns.

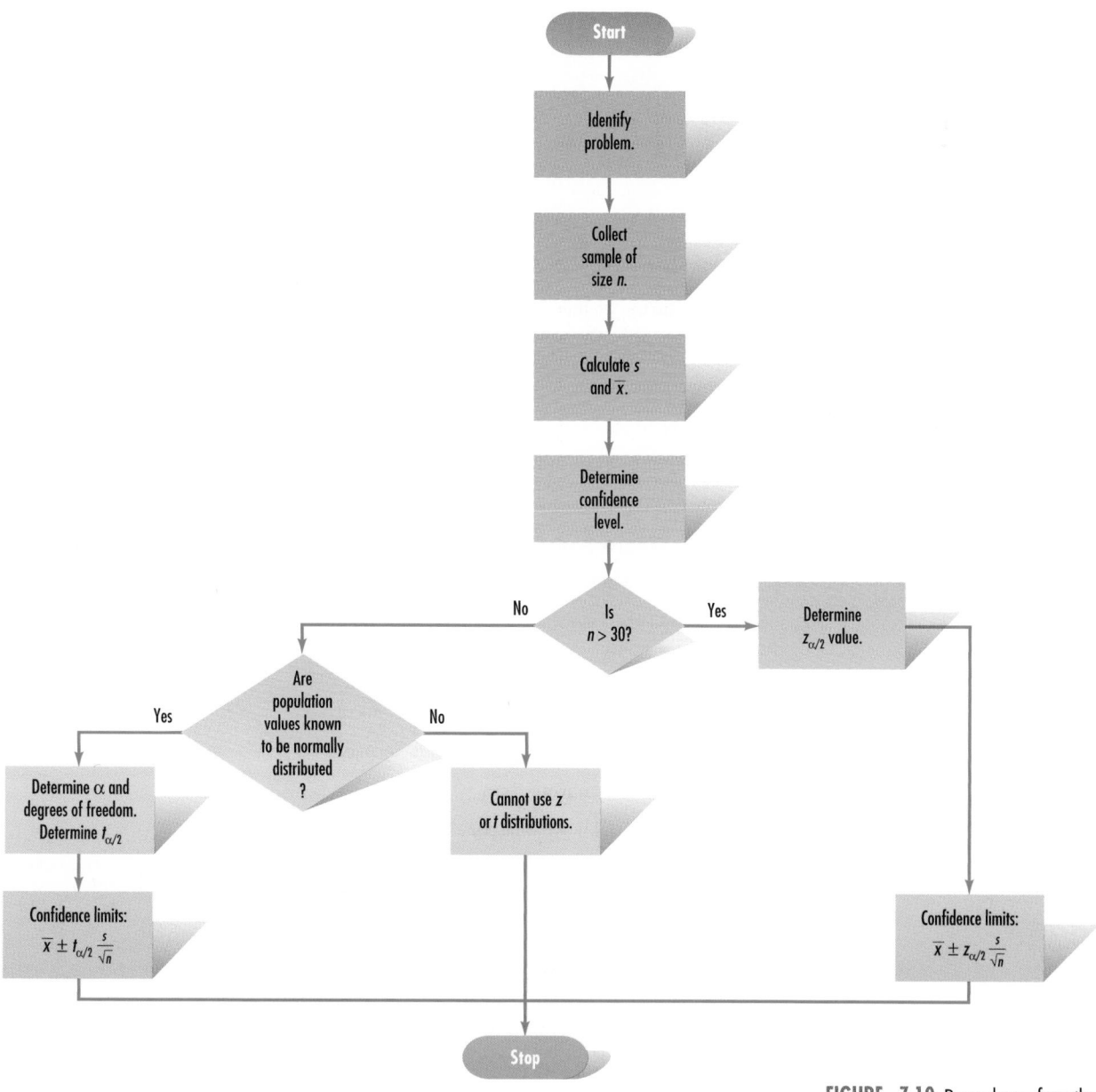

FIGURE 7.10 Procedure for the interval estimation of μ with σ unknown.

◆ **Solution:**

From the data we calculate: $\bar{x} = 14.69$, $s = 6.79$, $n = 29$.

$$\hat{\sigma}_{\bar{x}} = \frac{s}{\sqrt{n}} = \frac{6.79}{\sqrt{29}} = 1.26$$

Because we want a 90 percent confidence level, α is .10. And because the sample size is 29, there are 28 degrees of freedom. Therefore, consulting Appendix 4 under $t_{.05}$, we see the t value is 1.701. The interval estimate is

$$\bar{x} = t_{.05}\hat{\sigma}_{\bar{x}} < \mu < \bar{x} + t_{.05}\hat{\sigma}_{\bar{x}}$$
$$14.69 - 1.701(1.26) < \mu < 14.69 + 1.701(1.26)$$
$$13.43 \text{ percent} < \mu < 16.83 \text{ percent}$$

So we can be 90 percent confident that the average percentage of waste recycled in these 58 towns is between 13.43 and 16.83 percent. ◆

Self-Testing Review 7.3

23. Determine the z value for each of the following confidence levels:

   a) 86 percent.

   b) 96 percent.

   c) 98 percent.

24. Determine the t value to be used for the following situations:

   a) $n = 12$, 90 percent confidence level

   b) $n = 7$, 99 percent confidence level.

   c) $n = 15$, 95 percent confidence level.

25. For each of the following, determine if the use of a t distribution or a z distribution is needed for the construction of a 90 percent confidence interval. Find the appropriate t or z value.

   a) $n = 13$, σ is unknown and population is normal.

   b) $n = 11$, σ is known and population is normal.

   c) $n = 34$, σ is unknown.

   d) $n = 17$, σ is unknown and population is normal.

26. Given sample statistics of $\bar{x} = 75$, $s = 12$, $n = 58$, and a desired 95 percent confidence level,

   a) Find the point estimate of the population mean.

   b) Estimate the standard error of the mean.

   c) Determine the appropriate t or z value to use.

   d) Compute the error bound.

   e) Construct the 95 percent confidence interval for μ.

27. Given sample statistics of $\bar{x} = 24.7$ $s = 5.3$, $n = 18$, and a desired 99 percent confidence level (assume the population values are normally distributed),

   a) Find the point estimate of the population mean.

   b) Estimate the standard error of the mean.

   c) Determine the appropriate t or z value to use.

   d) Compute the error bound.

   e) Construct the 99 percent confidence interval for μ.

28. If it is known that $\sigma = 3.81$, the population is normally distributed, and the sample statistics are $\bar{x} = 62.7$ and $n = 17$,

   a) Find the point estimate for the population mean.

   b) Estimate the standard error of the mean.

   c) Determine the appropriate t or z value to use to get a 95 percent confidence interval.

   d) Compute the error bound at the 95 percent confidence level.

   e) Construct the 95 percent confidence interval for estimating the value of μ.

29. In order to estimate the mean time students spend on their homework each night, a professor randomly selects 20 students and finds the mean and standard deviation of this sample to be 2.3 hours and .7 hours, respectively. Assuming the population study time is normally distributed, construct a 95 percent confidence interval for the mean amount of time spent studying each night for all students.

30. A study to determine factors that would predict divorce was recently reported in the *Journal of Personality and Social Psychology*. A random sample of 222 stable couples reported the mean and standard deviation for the time they knew each other were 57.07 months and 43.46 months, respectively. Construct a 95 percent confidence interval for the mean time of all such couples.

31. A random sample of 15 patients with chronic lower back pain who participated in a recent study reported a mean duration of back pain of 17.6 months with a standard deviation of 5.0 months. Assuming the duration of back pain in the population is normally distributed, construct a 90 percent confidence interval for the mean duration of back pain for the population of such patients.

32. In a recent study published in the *Journal of Educational Research*, a random sample of 84 second-year students enrolled in a teacher preparation program were asked what they thought was the appropriate number of hours to spend in testing per week. The mean of the responses was 10.43 hours, and the standard deviation was 6.72 hours. Find a 99 percent confidence interval for the mean number of hours all second-year students in such a program believe should be spent testing each week.

33. A senior manager of a large accounting firm wants to find the mean number of hours it takes for all first-year accountants to complete an in-house training program. She randomly selects a sample of 7 first-year accountants and records their times as follows: 25, 19, 15, 25, 12, 20, 12. Find the sample mean and standard deviation and construct a 95 percent confidence interval for the population mean training time required. (Assume the population values are normally distributed.)

34. Western Trucking Company has a large number of vehicles in its fleet. To estimate the average odometer reading for its entire fleet, the dispatcher took a random sample of 6 trucks and found the sample mean and sample standard deviation to be 57,393 kilometres and 12,300 kilometres, respectively. Assuming the population of odometer readings is normally distributed, construct a 99 percent confidence interval for the mean odometer reading on all company trucks.

35. A 99 percent confidence interval for the proportion of UBC students who are regular library users was found to be from 60 percent to 70 percent. Does this mean that

a) Between 60 percent and 70 percent of the students regularly use library facilities about 99 percent of the time?

b) About 99 percent of UBC students regularly use library facilities between 60 percent and 70 percent of the time?

c) We have good reason to believe that the true proportion of UBC students who are regular library users is in the range of 60 percent to 70 percent?

d) There is a 99 percent chance that the sample proportion of library users is in the range of 60 percent to 70 percent?

36. A random sample of 36 chronic schizophrenic patients was selected, and these patients were given a card sorting test. The sample mean was 43.0 errors with a standard deviation of 25.8 errors. Assuming a normally distributed population, construct a 95 percent confidence interval for the mean score on this test that would be achieved by all such patients.

37. A random sample of 126 electronic assemblies is selected to determine the life expectancy of a certain component. The sample mean life expectancy was 648 hours, and the standard deviation was 58 hours. At the 90 percent level of confidence, estimate the true life expectancy of the population of such components.

38. Agricultural engineers need construction materials with reliable, known strengths. In a class project, J. Mehlschau examined the yielding strength of joist and plank size, grade No. 1, Hem-Fir. Agricultural engineers who use such wood believe it has yield strength that is normally distributed. Six pieces of Hem-Fir subjected to a compression machine until failure yielded the data that follow. Find the sample mean and construct a 99 percent confidence interval for the mean yielding strength of all such pieces of wood.

PSI	7,512	7,620	6,982	7,256	6,766	7,145

39. Benzene is a common component of gasoline. In a class project, C. Leung reported on data collected by the Regional Water Quality Control Board describing the benzene concentration (ppb) in groundwater near the location of a spill from a ruptured fuel tank. This benzene is a potential hazard to drinking water aquifers near the site. Calculate the sample mean and standard deviation and, assuming that the amounts of benzene in groundwater are normally distributed, construct a 90 percent confidence interval for the population mean amount of benzene in the groundwater.

Benzene				
490	120	300	230	130
123	290	68	530	250
320	270	280	450	95

40. For her master's thesis, Cynthia Collin analyzed several data sets concerning smolt size. One set of data consisted of the lengths of smolt caught by the Department of Fish and Game (Data = Smoltlen).

210.0	178.0	179.0	166.0	165.0	185.0	174.0
162.0	172.0	90.0	102.0	102.0	122.0	125.0
126.0	130.0	136.0	163.0	166.0	173.0	158.0
182.0	131.0	167.0	135.0	175.0	144.0	164.0
183.0	222.5	122.0	185.0	90.0	86.0	104.0
80.0	122.0	131.0	144.0	146.0	165.0	133.0

Construct a 90 percent confidence interval for the true mean length of smolt.

41. An institution offers different major areas of study. A survey of recent graduates from a sample of nine of these areas produced the following mean monthly salaries:

Major	Salary	Major	Salary
Physical Education	$2,000	Political Science	$2,500
Animal Science	$2,050	Chemistry	$2,666
Journalism	$2,129	Statistics	$2,800
Architecture	$2,200	Computer Science	$3,595
Accounting	$2,500		

Construct a 90 percent confidence interval for the overall mean monthly salary for all major areas.

42. The following data represent tuition fees for a sample of universities, selected randomly from the list of universities included in the *Maclean's Guide to Canadian Universities*, 2002.

University	Tuition Fee
Calgary	4,403
Dalhousie	5,424
Saskatchewan	4,033
USC	2,375
Waterloo	4,469
Winnipeg	3,566

Construct a 95 percent confidence interval for the mean tuition fee for the universities.

43. A random sample of 8 chains is selected from the top food service chains in western Canada. The following data represent sales in millions of dollars for 1999:

Name of Company	Sales	Name of Company	Sales
McDonald's	710	Robin's Donuts	55
Boston Pizza	162	Starbucks Coffee	58
Pizza Hut	90	Harvey's	18
Burger King	70	Mr. Submarine	27

Construct an 80 percent confidence interval for the mean sales of the top food service chains in 1999.

44. The Council on High Buildings and Urban Habitat, based at Leigh University, compiled a list of tallest buildings in the world (2001). A random sample of 15 buildings is selected from a list and is given below:

Building	City, Country	Year	Stories	Height (Metres)
Baiyoke Tower II	Bangkok, Thailand	1997	90	320
Central Plaza	Hong Kong	1992	78	374
Commerzbank Tower	Frankfurt, Germany	1997	56	299
Emirates Tower One	Dubai, U.A.E	2000	55	355
Empire State Building	New York, USA	1931	102	381
First Canadian Place	Toronto, Canada	1975	72	290
Kingdom Centre	Riyadh, Saudi Arabia	2000	30	345
Landmark Tower	Yokohama, Japan	1993	70	296
Petronas Tower 1	Kuala Lumpur, Malaysia	1998	88	452
Republic Plaza	Singapore	1995	66	280
Ryugyong Hotel	Pyongyang, North Korea	1995	105	300
Scotia Plaza	Toronto, Canada	1989	68	275
Sears Tower	Chicago, USA	1974	110	442
Shun Hing Square	Shenzhen, China	1996	69	384
T&C Tower	Kaosiung, Taiwan	1997	85	348

Construct a 90 percent confidence interval for the true mean height of the tallest buildings of the world.

7.4   Estimating the Population Proportion

Since the mean of the sampling distribution of proportions is equal to the population proportion, the sample proportion ($\hat{p}$) is an unbiased estimator of the population proportion (p). If the sample size is sufficiently large—that is if $n \cdot \hat{p} \geq 5$, and if $n \cdot (1 - \hat{p})$ is also ≥ 5—then the sampling distribution of $\hat{p}$ is approximately normal. Thus we are able to make probability statements about the interval estimates of p that are based on sample proportions. In this section we'll discuss only the large-sample case in the interval estimation of p since the small-sample approach is beyond the scope of this book. We use $\hat{p}$, the sample proportion, as the point estimate for p and construct the interval estimate of the population proportion as follows:

$$\underbrace{\hat{p} - z_{\alpha/2}\hat{\sigma}_{\hat{p}}}_{\substack{\text{lower confidence} \\ \text{limit}}} < p < \underbrace{\hat{p} + z_{\alpha/2}\hat{\sigma}_{\hat{p}}}_{\substack{\text{upper confidence} \\ \text{limit}}} \qquad (7.5)$$

A z value is used here in exactly the same way it was used to estimate a population mean. And when we compute a value for $\hat{\sigma}_{\hat{p}}$, we have produced an *estimate* of the standard deviation of the sampling distribution of proportions—that is, an estimate of the standard error of proportion. Thus, an unbiased estimate of the standard error of proportions may be found in this way:

$$\hat{\sigma}_{\hat{p}} = \sqrt{\frac{\hat{p}(1-\hat{p})}{n}} \qquad (7.6)$$

The estimate of the standard error is *always used* in the construction of an interval estimate. Why? Because the true standard error cannot be computed for an interval estimate of p. This fact is obvious from the following formula:

$$\sigma_{\hat{p}} = \sqrt{\frac{p(1-p)}{n}}$$

where, as you can see, the calculation of $\sigma_{\hat{p}}$ requires knowledge of p. Yet p is what we are trying to estimate! To resolve this dilemma, we must use formula 7.6.

We are now ready to show the similarity of the procedures used to estimate population means and proportions by considering the following example problems.

Example 7.10 **Fake Airbags** CBC's *Marketplace* reported that fake airbags were "a huge problem" in North America. If you're driving a used car or had your own repaired lately, you may be missing something: an airbag that works. A recent survey found that of 1,200 vehicles that had replaced airbags, 66 were fake. Estimate at the 95 percent confidence level the true proportion of vehicles having fake airbags in the population of all vehicles that have had airbags replaced.

◆ **Solution:**
We have the following data: $\hat{p} = 66/1{,}200 = .055$, $n = 1{,}200$, and the confidence level is 95 percent. The estimate of $\sigma_{\hat{p}}$ is computed as follows:

$$\hat{\sigma}_{\hat{p}} = \sqrt{\frac{\hat{p}(1-\hat{p})}{n}} = \sqrt{\frac{(.055)(.945)}{1{,}200}} = .0066$$

With a confidence level of 95 percent, the z value is $z_{.025} = 1.96$. So the interval estimate of the true proportion of vehicles having fake airbags, in the population of all vehicles that have had airbags replaced, is

$$\hat{p} - z_{.025}\hat{\sigma}_{\hat{p}} < p < \hat{p} + z_{.025}\hat{\sigma}_{\hat{p}}$$
$$.055 - 1.96(.0066) < p < .055 + 1.96(.0066)$$
$$.042 < p < .068$$

So we can be 95 percent confident that the true proportion of vehicles having fake airbags, in the population of all vehicles that have had airbags replaced, is between .042 and .068. ◆

Example 7.11 **Celebrities with Parkinson's Disease** Muhammad Ali, a three-time world boxing champion and actor Michael J. Fox, who acted in the movie *Back to the Future* are two high-profile celebrities suffering from Parkinson's disease. Researchers have found that deep-brain stimulator implants have helped patients control many of the symptoms of this disease. Suppose 50 patients with the disease are randomly selected and 8 are identified to be suitable candidates for the implant. Use a 99 percent confidence level to estimate the true proportion of Parkinson's disease patients who would be suitable candidates for the implant.

◆ **Solution:**

The data are $\hat{p} = 8/50 = .16$, $n = 50$, and the confidence level is 99 percent. The estimate of the standard error is computed as follows:

$$\hat{\sigma}_{\hat{p}} = \sqrt{\frac{\hat{p}(1 - \hat{p})}{n}} = \sqrt{\frac{(.16)(.84)}{50}} = .0518$$

With a confidence level of 99 percent, the z value is $z_{.005} = 2.575$. So the interval estimate is

$$\hat{p} - z_{.025}\hat{\sigma}_{\hat{p}} < p < \hat{p} + z_{.025}\hat{\sigma}_{\hat{p}}$$
$$.16 - 2.575(.0518) < p < .16 + 2.575(.0518)$$
$$.027 < p < .293$$

So we can be 99 percent confident that the true proportion of Parkinson's disease patients who would be suitable candidates for the implant is between .027 and .293. ◆

The general procedure for constructing an interval estimate of p in the large-sample case is summarized in *Figure 7.11*.

Example 7.12 Political polls represent one of the major uses of interval estimation of p. Let's assume that Suzanne faces a tough reelection campaign and orders a poll to learn how the voters view her candidacy. A random sample of 1,200 voters reveals that 532 are likely to vote for her, while the others polled prefer her opponent or are undecided. At the 95 percent level of confidence, what's the population proportion of voters who express a preference for Suzanne?

◆ **Solution:**

The data are $\hat{p} = 532/1,200 = .4433$, $n = 1,200$, confidence level = 95 percent. The estimate of the standard error is

$$\hat{\sigma}_{\hat{p}} = \sqrt{\frac{\hat{p}(1 - \hat{p})}{n}} = \sqrt{\frac{(.4433)(.5567)}{1,200}} = .0143$$

With a confidence level of 95 percent, the z value is $z_{.025} = 1.96$. Thus, the interval estimate is

$$\hat{p} - z_{.025}\hat{\sigma}_{\hat{p}} < p < \hat{p} + z_{.025}\hat{\sigma}_{\hat{p}}$$
$$.4433 - 1.96(.0143) < p < .4433 + 1.96(.0143)$$
$$.4153 \text{ percent} < p < .4713 \text{ percent}$$

Suzanne can be 95 percent confident that the population proportion who prefer her is less than .50—she better try to swing those undecided voters into her camp! ◆

Example 7.13 **147 Cranky People** The British Columbia Workers' Compensation Board (WCB) instituted a ban on smoking in all workplaces, effective January 1, 2000. In March 2000 the B.C. Supreme Court overturned the WCB smoking ban. If a random sample of 700 people in Burnaby, B.C., contains 147 smokers and 553 non-

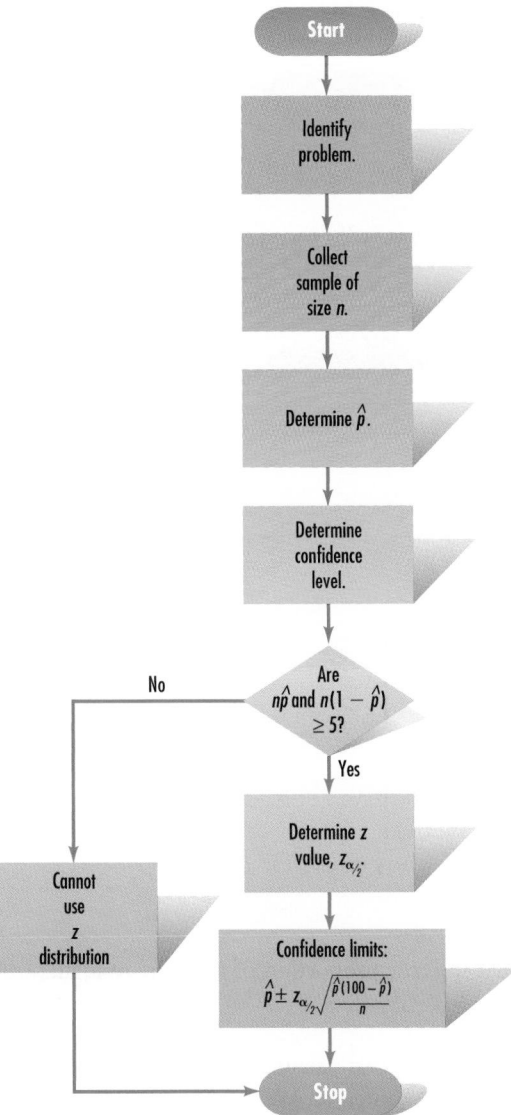

FIGURE 7.11 Procedure for interval estimation of *p* using large samples.

smokers, construct a 95 percent confidence interval for p = the true proportion of Burnaby residents who smoke.

◆ Solution:

We first calculate $\hat{p} = 147/700 = .21$. The confidence level = 95 percent, so the *z* value is $z_{.025} = 1.96$. The estimate of the standard error is

$$\hat{\sigma}_{\hat{p}} = \sqrt{\frac{\hat{p}(1 - \hat{p})}{n}} = \sqrt{\frac{(.21)(.79)}{700}} = .0154$$

The interval estimate is then constructed:

$$\hat{p} - z_{.025}\hat{\sigma}_{\hat{p}} < p < \hat{p} + z_{.025}\hat{\sigma}_{\hat{p}}$$
$$.21 - 1.96(.0154) < p < .21 + 1.96(.0154)$$
$$.1798 < p < .2402$$

FIGURE 7.12 (a) To obtain this MINITAB output, click on **Stat, Basic Statistics, 1 Proportion,** click in the circle to the left of **Summarized data,** enter 700 and 147 as **Number of trials** and **Number of successes,** respectively, click on **Options,** select 95 as the **Confidence level,** click in the box to the left of **Use test and interval based on normal distribution,** and click **OK** twice. (b) To make a confidence interval for proportions on the TI-83, use the **1-PropZInt** command on the **STAT<TESTS>A:.** In this example, there are 147 smokers out of the 700 people surveyed, so in screen 1, we fill 147 into x and 700 into n. Move the cursor to **Calculate** and press **ENTER.** The interval is shown in screen 2.

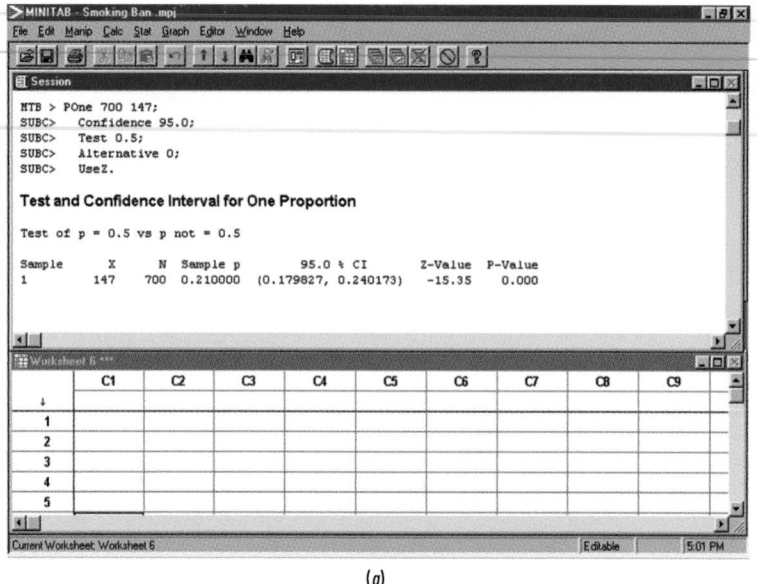

(a)

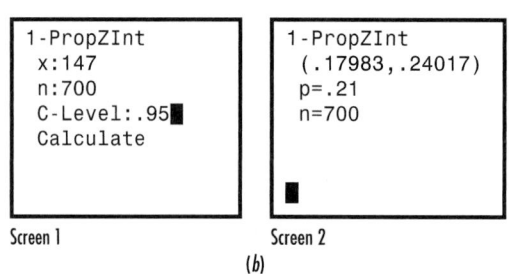

Screen 1   Screen 2

(b)

So we can be 95 percent confident that the true proportion of Burnaby residents who smoke is between .18 and .24. ◆

Once again, a computer package or a good calculator can save us some time and effort in computing a confidence interval. We used MINITAB to obtain the output in *Figure 7.12a* and a TI-83 calculator to get the result in screen 2 of *Figure 7.12b*. In each we find the same confidence interval as we obtained by hand.

Self-Testing Review 7.4

45. A typical Canadian kitchen is likely to contain many ingredients or foods that have been genetically modified. Everything from bread to tomatoes, corn and soya oil has been produced from altered food organisms. Suppose a random sample of 350 processed food items were selected from a grocery store. Two hundred and ten items contained genetically modified products. Construct a 95 percent confidence interval for the proportion of processed food items that contain genetically modified products.

46. A random sample of 864 requests for MRI (magnetic resonance imaging) scans was evaluated in a study reported in the *New England Journal of Medicine*. In 502 of these sample cases, the requesting physician had an ownership interest in the imaging facility. Form a 90 percent confidence interval for the population proportion of physicians who requested MRI scans and who had an ownership interest in the imaging facility.

47. A study was made of HIV-related risk behaviours among adolescents. Of the 76 adolescents hospitalized for psychiatric reasons in the random sample, 40 reported that they were sexually active. Form a 95 percent confidence interval for the population proportion of such hospitalized adolescents who are sexually active.

48. A fellowship program was instituted to train graduate nurses to work in intensive care units (ICUs). If a random sample of 46 nurses completes such a training program and if 27 of these nurses are currently working in an ICU, what's the 95 percent confidence interval for the population proportion of nurses who complete such a program and then later work in an ICU?

49. An article in the *New England Journal of Medicine* evaluated a syringe-exchange program. In a test of a random sample of 160 needles that were employed by injection-drug users before the exchange program was started, 108 were found to be HIV-positive. Form a 99 percent confidence interval of the population proportion of such pre-exchange needles of injection-drug users that are HIV-positive.

50. The results of a study to determine patterns of drug use in adolescents were published in the *Journal of Abnormal Psychology*. Of the 4,145 students in Grade 7 in a random sample, 124 reported using alcohol on a weekly basis. Form a 90 percent confidence interval for the percent of weekly alcohol use among all students in Grade 7.

51. A university has a large dormitory system. A vote is needed to change the system's policy of "quiet hours." In a random sample of 34 residents, 23 say they will vote in favour of the change. Construct a 95 percent confidence interval for the population proportion favouring the change in policy.

52. In a class project, C. Zimmerman used data from an article in *Environmental Progress* concerning companies' use of solvents for lithographic printing. Each company was evaluated on whether individual solvents were used safely in different situations. Of 63 evaluations that were done, the companies used the solvents safely in 40 situations. Construct a 90 percent confidence interval for the proportion of times in which the population of all such companies use the solvents safely.

53. While the skulls of most mammals are symmetrical, there are exceptions, such as odontocete whales. This is part of the normal growth pattern found throughout the taxa. Sea otters also have been noted to have naturally occurring asymmetrical skulls, with one side of the skull larger than the other. K. A. Shirley *(A Quantitative Analysis of Trends and Frequency of Asymmetry in the Skulls of the California Sea Otter, Enhydra lutris)* reported the results from measuring cranial asymmetry in 387 sea otter *Enhydra lutris* skulls. Each sea otter skull was categorized by age: pup, juvenile, and adult.

Age Class	Saggital Crest Deflects to the			Total
	Left Side	Right Side	Sides Equal	
Pups	11	3	1	15
Juveniles	61	14	21	96
Adults	86	82	108	276

a) Form a 95 percent confidence interval for the population proportion of adults whose saggital crest deflects to the left side.

b) Combining pups and juveniles, form a 95 percent confidence interval for the population proportion of non-adults whose saggital crest deflects to the left side.

54. In a class project, Po Sai Marie Yeung analyzed data found in *Marijuana Use in College* (*Youth and Society*, 1979). This paper considered the relationships that might exist between student use of marijuana and parental use of alcohol and drugs.

| | Parent | | |
Student	Neither	One	Both
Never	141	68	17
Occasional	54	44	11
Regular	40	51	19

a) For the population of students whose parents do not use alcohol or drugs, form a 90 percent confidence interval for the population proportion who never use marijuana.

b) For the population of students with at least one parent who uses alcohol or drugs, form a 90 percent confidence interval for the population percentage who never use marijuana.

55. In a computer system with many new users constantly being introduced to the system, there will be many instances of a person locking up or freezing his or her account. Additionally, more experienced users trying to bypass system limitations or restrictions can also freeze their own accounts. For a class project, J. Koepp wrote a computer program that "grabbed" a sample of computer freezes of an AIX system and broke the freezes down by college and severity level of the cause of the freeze.

College	Severe	Moderate	Standard
Agriculture	9	187	83
Architecture	10	132	27
Business	14	266	79
Engineering	64	444	214
Liberal Arts	10	265	126
Science & Math	8	145	59

a) Construct a 90 percent confidence interval for the proportion of computer freezes caused by students from the College of Engineering.

b) Construct a 90 percent confidence interval for the proportion of computer freezes that are severe.

56. The tables below summarize the results of a survey of opinions of both smokers and non-smokers on an ordinance prohibiting smoking in bars and restaurants.

| | Opinion of Ordinance for Bars | | |
	Indifferent	Support	Against
Smokers	16	20	111
Non-Smokers	90	349	114

	Opinion of Ordinance for Restaurants		
	Indifferent	**Support**	**Against**
Smokers	16	20	111
Non-Smokers	126	143	284

	Believe That the Ordinance Has Improved the Environment for Business		
	Don't Know	**No**	**Yes**
Smokers	31	27	89
Non-Smokers	97	107	349

a) Construct a 99 percent confidence interval for the proportion of smokers who are against the ban in bars.

b) For the people who support the ordinance in restaurants, construct a 95 percent confidence interval for the proportion who are smokers.

c) Construct a 90 percent confidence interval for the proportion of non-smokers who believe that the ordinance has improved the environment for business.

57. A group of 30 cyclists, 50 university students, and 50 city residents were asked how they felt about the city's support of bicycling and alternative transportation. The results are as follows.

Rating	Community	Students	Bicyclists
Excellent	3	0	0
Very good	8	3	0
Good	13	23	8
Not so good	15	15	8
Poor	9	7	11
Very poor	2	2	3

a) Construct a 90 percent confidence interval for the population proportion of community members who feel that the city's support of bicycling and alternative transportation is good or better (i.e., combine the good, very good, and excellent categories into one larger category).

b) Construct a 90 percent confidence interval for the population proportion of bicyclists who feel that the city's support of bicycling and alternative transportation is good or better.

58. A survey was given to 52 employees of Grover Beach City, not all of whom answered each question. Some of the results are summarized below. For the questions that follow, assume that this sample of Grover Beach City employees represents a sample of all municipal employees.

Number of Times Exercise/Week			
Less Than Once	**1 to 2**	**3 to 5**	**More than Five**
8	16	22	5

Level of Happiness with Job		
Very Happy	**Moderately Happy**	**Not Happy**
20	27	3

a) Construct a 95 percent confidence interval for the proportion of all municipal employees who exercise at least three times a week.

b) Construct a 95 percent confidence interval for the proportion of all municipal employees who are very happy with their job.

59. A sample of 199 recreation-centre users was taken to determine usage patterns. Some of the results are presented in the following table:

Primary Use Area/Room				
Exercise	**Gym**	**Aerobics**	**Pool**	**Racquetball**
109	25	7	39	19

Construct a 99 percent confidence interval for the proportion of users of the facility whose primary use area is the pool.

7.5   Estimating the Population Variance

We've now seen examples that show why estimates of population means and proportions are needed and how those estimates are computed. But why would an estimate of a population variance (σ^2) be needed? As you know, the variance and standard deviation are measures that show the amount of spread or scatter that exists in a data set. And it's often desirable to know the extent of this scatter so that steps can be taken to control it. It's not enough that a tire maker knows that the mean life expectancy of a line of tires is 80,000 kilometres. The manufacturer also wants to be sure that the tires produced are of a consistent quality so there isn't a wide spread in tire lifetimes. And a drug supplier has to be focused on the potency of the tablets produced. It's not enough to make tablets that have an acceptable mean strength if some tablets are unduly weak while others produce overdoses. Thus, it's understandable that manufacturers who want to produce consistent quality results will want to keep close tabs on the population variance or standard deviation.

The Chi-Square Distribution

Assuming—and this is an important caveat—that the population values are *normally distributed,* we can estimate the population variance (and thus the population standard deviation) by using a sampling distribution that is new to us.

To explain this new distribution, let's assume that we take a random sample of 20 drug tablets from a production line. Let's further assume for the moment that we know the value of the population variance (σ^2). We then compute the sample variance (s^2) and find the value for the following variable:

$$\frac{(\mathrm{df})s^2}{\sigma^2} = \frac{(n-1)s^2}{\sigma^2} = \frac{(20-1)s^2}{\sigma^2}$$

Note that in this case, df, or degrees of freedom $= n - 1$.

If we record the result of this computation, repeat the same procedure a very large number of times (a distressing thought!), and put all the trial results in a frequency distribution, the theoretical result would be a distribution called a *Chi-square (χ^2) distribution*. (The symbol for the Greek letter chi is χ, and is pronounced like the first two letters in the word kind.)

Chi-Square Distribution

When taking a sample from a population that is normally distributed, a **Chi-square distribution** is the sampling distribution for the variable $\dfrac{(\mathrm{df})s^2}{\sigma^2}$, and it has the following properties:

- Since values are obtained by using squared numbers, all χ^2 values are zero or positive—a property that's not found with z and t distributions. Thus, the scale of possible χ^2 values extends from zero indefinitely to the right in a positive direction.

- A χ^2 distribution isn't symmetrical like the z and t distributions.

- There's a different χ^2 distribution for each sample size. If we change the sample size, there's a different df (or $n - 1$ value here), and so the shape of each distribution depends on $n - 1$ or the number of degrees of freedom that exists in a sampling situation.

- The mean of any Chi-square distribution is equal to the degrees of freedom.

Figure 7.13 shows the shapes of several χ^2 probability distributions with different degrees of freedom. You'll notice that the curves with small degrees of freedom—say, from 3 to 10 df—are skewed to the right. As the df number increases, though, the

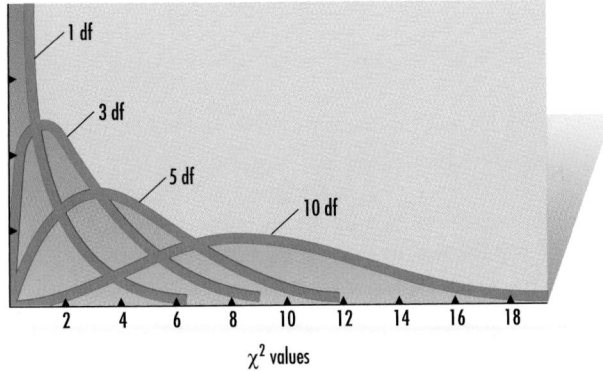

χ^2 values

FIGURE 7.13 χ^2 distributions for different degrees of freedom.

χ^2 distributions begin to look more symmetric. A table of χ^2 values is found in Appendix 6. It's organized in a way similar to the table for the t distributions so, even though there are many different χ^2 distributions, the values you'll need are all found in one table.

The Estimation Procedure

As you might expect, an interval estimate of σ^2 takes the familiar form:

lower confidence limit $< \sigma^2 <$ upper confidence limit

More specifically,

$$\underbrace{\frac{(n-1)s^2}{\chi^2_{\alpha/2}}}_{\substack{\text{lower confidence} \\ \text{limit}}} < \sigma^2 < \underbrace{\frac{(n-1)s^2}{\chi^2_{1-\alpha/2}}}_{\substack{\text{upper confidence} \\ \text{limit}}} \qquad (7.7)$$

We saw earlier that α is the chance of not including the parameter in the interval, and so it is 1.00 minus the confidence coefficient. Thus, if we are making an estimate at the 95 percent level of confidence, the $\alpha/2$ value for the lower confidence limit is .05/2 or .025, and the $1 - \alpha/2$ value for the upper confidence limit is $1 - .025$ or .975. Let's look now at the χ^2 table in Appendix 6 to see how to find the values we'll need to estimate the population variance.

If we have a sample of 20 items, what are the appropriate χ^2 values needed to make an estimate at the 95 percent level of confidence? The first (left) column of the χ^2 table gives df values, and with a sample of 20, we have $20 - 1$ or 19 degrees of freedom. The other columns give the α values. So what is the $\chi^2_{\alpha/2}$ value we need to compute the lower limit of our interval? Since $\alpha/2$ is .025, we see that the χ^2 value at the intersection of the 19 df row and the $\alpha_{.025}$ column is 32.9. And the $\chi^2_{1-\alpha/2}$ value we need to compute the upper limit of our interval is found at the intersection of the 19 df row and the $\alpha_{.975}$ column. This value is 8.91. Thus, the interval estimate would be found like this:

$$\frac{(n-1)s^2}{32.9} < \sigma^2 < \frac{(n-1)s^2}{8.91}$$

or graphically:

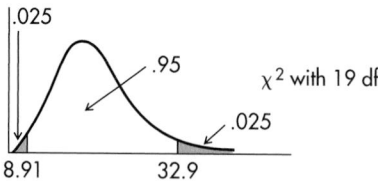

Let's summarize what you've now learned about estimating the value of σ^2 with an example.

Example 7.14　The Halloween Spook Company has a machine that's designed to manufacture candies with an average weight of 24 grams and a population standard deviation of 0.1 gram. Thus, if the machine is working properly, the population variance should be $(0.1)^2$ or .01 squared gram. To estimate the value of σ^2, an employee selected a random sample of 15 candies from a supply manufactured by the machine and found that the sample variance was 0.008 squared gram. What's the 95 percent confidence interval for the population variance? For the population standard deviation?

◆ **Solution:**
The following facts are known: $s^2 = .008$, $n = 15$, df $= 15 - 1$ or 14, and since $\alpha = .05$, $\alpha/2 - .025$, and $1 - \alpha/2 = .975$. So,

$$\frac{(n-1)s^2}{\chi^2_{.025}} < \sigma^2 < \frac{(n-1)s^2}{\chi^2_{.975}}$$

$$\frac{(14)(.008)}{26.1} < \sigma^2 < \frac{(14)(.008)}{5.63}$$

$$.0043 < \sigma^2 < .0199$$

Thus, we are 95 percent confident that the value of σ^2 lies between .0043 and .0199 squared gram. And we can take the square root of these values to find the 95 percent confidence interval for the value of σ. That is, we are 95 percent confident that the value of σ lies between $\sqrt{.0043}$ and $\sqrt{.0199}$ or between .066 and .141 gram. ◆

Example 7.15 **A Pressing Problem** In order to evaluate a weight-lifting and fitness program, each player on a football team did a one repetition, maximum-weight bench press. The weights (in pounds) pressed by the linebackers are

340 380 305 335 375 400 305 385 315

Form a 90 percent confidence interval for the standard deviation in the maximum weights pressed by the population of linebackers who go through this program. Use MINITAB or the TI-83 calculator to do the calculations.

◆ **Solution:**
Neither MINITAB nor the TI-83 calculator have a command that will directly compute the confidence interval. But MINITAB has a calculator function that will do the arithmetic and has the ability to find values from the χ^2 table. The TI-83 calculator can do the arithmetic, but must be given the χ^2 table values to compute the confidence interval. The process and results from MINITAB and the TI-83 calculator are shown in *Figures 7.14a* and *7.14b*, respectively, with the slight differences in the results caused by the number of digits used in the calculations by each. Both find that the standard deviation is 36.8084 and, squaring that, find that the sample variance is 1,354.86. Then, using critical values from the χ^2 table with df $= n - 1 = 9 - 1 = 8$, and $\alpha = 0.10$, so that $\alpha/2 = 0.05$, and $1 - \alpha/2 = 0.95$, each computes the confidence interval for the population variance with

$$\frac{(n-1)s^2}{\chi^2_{.05}} < \sigma^2 < \frac{(n-1)s^2}{\chi^2_{.95}}$$

$$\frac{8(1,354.86)}{15.51} < \sigma^2 < \frac{8(1,354.86)}{2.73}$$

$$698.8 < \sigma^2 < 3,970.3$$

Taking the square root of these values to find the 90 percent confidence interval for the value of σ, we can be 90 percent confident that the value of σ lies between $\sqrt{698.8}$ and $\sqrt{3,970.3}$ or between 26.4 and 63.0. ◆

FIGURE 7.14 (a) First enter the data into C1 and the values of $\alpha/2$ and $(1 - \alpha/2)$ into C2. Then the easiest way to obtain this MINITAB output is to type the series of commands that are in the **Session Window**. The **let** command instructs MINITAB to do the calculation that follows; the **InvCDF** command, ended with a semicolon (indicating that a subcommand follows), asks MINITAB to look up a table value; the subsequent line containing the subcommand specifies the type of table and the degrees of freedom. The confidence interval ends up in C5. (b) To use the TI-83 to make a confidence interval for the standard deviation, first calculate the sample variance, s^2. Put the data into a list (L1 is used here) and do the **1-Var Stats** command that we learned in Chapter 3. The result is shown in screen 1. Calculate s^2 as $(36.80844)^2 = 1354.86$. Next look up the critical values for the χ^2 distribution with $9 - 1 = 8$ df. With 5 percent in each tail get $\chi^2_{.05} = 2.73$ and $\chi^2_{.95} = 15.51$. The calculation of the confidence interval is done on the home screen. (See screen 2.) The result is $698.8 < \sigma^2 < 3970.3$, and to get a confidence interval for σ, take square roots to get $26.4 < \sigma < 63.0$.

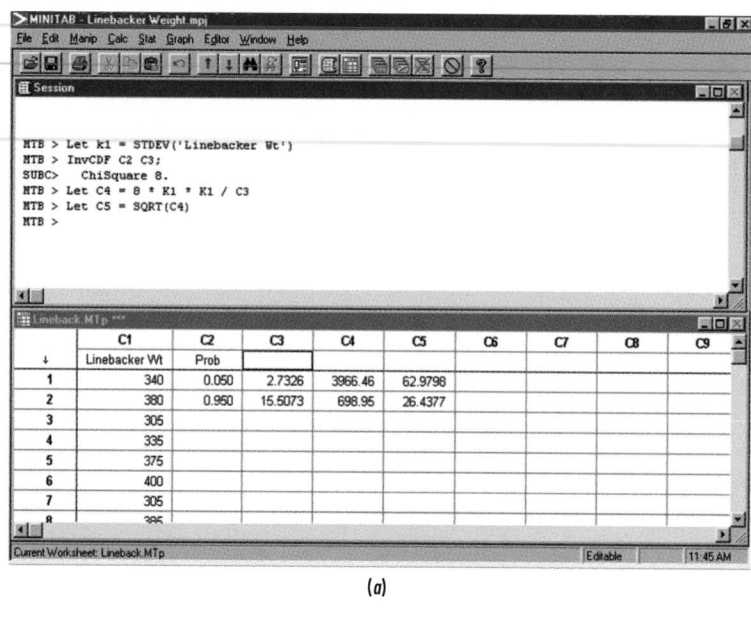

(a)

```
1-Var Stats
 x̄=348.8888889
 Σx=3140
 Σx²=1106350
 Sx=36.80843804
 σx=34.70332819
↓n=9
■
```
Screen 1

```
8*1354.86/15.51
        698.8317215
8*1354.86/2.73
        3970.285714
```
Screen 2

(b)

Self-Testing Review 7.5

60. Find the χ^2 values needed to form a 90 percent confidence interval for σ^2 when the sample size is 12.

61. Find the χ^2 values needed to form a 95 percent confidence interval for σ^2 when the sample size is 25.

62. A psychologist wants to estimate the variance of a certain verbal IQ test given to a population of bipolar patients. When the test is administered to a random sample of 27 subjects, the sample variance is 63.2. Assuming that the test scores are normal, form a 90 percent confidence interval to estimate the population variance for this test.

63. A bank manager measures the variance in waiting time for a random sample of 16 customers to be 26.8. Assuming that the waiting times are normal, form a 99 percent confidence interval for the value of σ.

64. A random sample of 14 caregivers kept diaries about their at-home patients who suffered from dementia. The sample standard deviation for the number of months these 14 had been caregivers was 34.7. Assuming for the population of all such caregivers that the number of months they have been caregivers is normal, form a 99 percent confidence interval for the population variance.

65. A pharmaceutical company is running preliminary trials for a new painkiller. A random sample of 25 subjects with migraine headaches is given the new drug. The variance in the time required for the drug to have an effect is 17.4. Construct a 95 percent confidence interval for the value of σ. What assumption is necessary for this interval to be valid?

66. Fresh tomatoes are often prepackaged in containers that average 454 grams in weight. The manager of a large supermarket would like to have information about the variation in package sizes since this influences pricing. In a random sample of 23 packages, the variance is .27. Assuming that the population of the sizes of all such packages is normally distributed, form a 99 percent confidence interval for the population variance.

67. Manufacturers of ammunition for a .38 special handgun used by law enforcement officers want to measure the variation in bullet velocity. As reported in *Guns and Ammo*, a random sample of 27 Winchester model 158 gr. bullets is fired. The mean and standard deviation for the bullet velocity (metres per second) are 266 and 4.3, respectively. Form a 99 percent confidence interval for the value of σ. What assumption is necessary for this interval to be valid?

68. The number of electronic mail messages processed by an AIX mail server was recorded each day for 22 weekdays. The results are stated below. Assume that the number of electronic mail messages has a normal distribution (Data = email).

26,749	30,986	32,444	32,907	39,168	39,015	41,367	38,899
32,397	28,594	44,557	47,717	48,122	38,981	50,601	48,845
49,544	47,883	40,787	48,998	50,701	50,529		

Form a 95 percent confidence interval for the value of σ.

69. In a class project, Patricia Reynolds states: "Triglycerides are the storage form of fatty acid in the body. In addition to being a storage fat, triglycerides also circulate in the blood along with cholesterol and other lipids." Additionally, "Measurement of serum triglyceride levels has clinical significance. Elevated serum triglyceride levels are seen in non-insulin dependent diabetes mellitus and Type 1 hyperlipidemia." The normal range of serum triglyceride levels is 35 to 165 mg/dl. A sample of students produced the following levels (Data = Triglyce):

83	163	147	86	43	76	69
200	150	168	153	176	59	
133	134	199	128	98	31	

Assuming that the population of these levels is normally distributed:

a) Form a 99 percent confidence interval for the population variance of serum triglyceride levels.

b) Form a 99 percent confidence interval for the population standard deviation of serum triglyceride levels.

7.6 Determining Sample Size to Estimate μ or p

In this chapter, the basic situation in the estimation of population means or proportions can be summarized as follows: A sample of size n is collected. The calculated values for the sample mean and standard deviation (or for the sample proportion) are available. Compute an interval estimate with a confidence level of _____ percent.

The sample was assumed to have been collected, and our task was to calculate an estimate based on the sample data given. We had to live with whatever confidence interval resulted from a specified confidence level, no matter how wide it might have been. Of course, one method of controlling the interval width is to change the confidence level, but it's improper to manipulate the confidence level so that the interval range comes out the way we want it to appear.

General Considerations About Sample Size

The precision of an estimate must often be specified before a sample is taken. For example, you may be checking the average diameter of machined parts that should not have too much error if they are to be used in finely machined equipment. In that case, you could take a sample of parts, but you would want an interval estimate with as little sampling error as possible.

We can control maximum sampling error by selecting a sample of adequate size. Remember that sampling error arises because the entire population is not studied; someone or something is always left out of the investigation. Whenever sampling is performed, we always miss some bit of information about the population that would be helpful in our estimation. If we want a high level of precision, we must sample enough of the population to provide the necessary and sufficient information. The following sections discuss the methods of determining the sample size needed to achieve a specified level of precision.

Determining the Sample Size for the Estimation of μ

Consider the following situation: Harvey, a hardware wholesaler, receives a shipment of 10,000 widgets, but before he pays for them, he wants to know if they are properly made and if they meet tolerance specifications. Let's assume he'd like to estimate the average diameter of the widgets. He also wants the estimate to be within ±0.01 cm of the true average diameter, and he wants a 95 percent confidence level for his estimate. How does he determine the sample size?

First, look at what Harvey is actually seeking. With a sample mean of $\bar{x}$, he wants the interval estimate to have *limits* that are no more than 0.01 cm *above* the point estimate and no more than 0.01 cm *below* the point estimate. That is, he wants the error bound (denoted by E) to be $E = 0.01$. And he wants this interval estimate to have a 95 percent chance of containing the true average. Thus, the desired confidence limits have been specified to be $\bar{x} \pm 0.01$ cm. Since the general form of the confidence limits is $\bar{x} \pm z_{\alpha/2}\,\sigma_{\bar{x}}$, Harvey wants $z_{.025}\sigma_{\bar{x}}$ or the error bound to equal $E = .01$ cm.

We can now find the necessary sample size by solving the equation $z_{.025}\sigma_{\bar{x}} = .01$. Since a confidence level of 95 percent is desired in our estimation of μ, the z value is $z_{.025} = 1.96$, and the formula for $\sigma_{\bar{x}}$ is

$$\sigma_{\bar{x}} = \frac{\sigma}{\sqrt{n}}$$

Therefore,

$$z_{.025}\sigma_{\bar{x}} = .01, \text{ so } 1.96\frac{\sigma}{\sqrt{n}} = .01$$

Then solving this for n, the sample size Harvey needs to estimate μ is

$$n = \left(\frac{(1.96)\sigma}{.01}\right)^2$$

Replacing 1.96 and .01 with their corresponding symbols, the more general form of this equation is

$$n = \left(\frac{(z_{\alpha/2})\sigma}{E}\right)^2 \qquad (7.8)$$

The difficulty in using the sample size formula is that we will rarely know the value of σ. Thus, it's necessary that we make an assumption about the value of the population standard deviation. In determining the sample size for an interval estimate it's always necessary to make an assumption about the value of σ.

On the basis of previous shipments, Harvey might assume that the population standard deviation of the diameter of widgets is 0.05 cm. The necessary sample size for his desired level of precision is then computed as follows:

$$n = \left(\frac{(1.96)\sigma}{.01}\right)^2 = \left(\frac{(1.96)(.05)}{.01}\right)^2 = 9.8^2 = 96.04$$

When, as usually happens, this formula gives a non-integer result, you would always round this value up to the next whole number. So Harvey should take $n = 97$ widgets to obtain his desired limits.

Figure 7.15 summarizes the general procedure for determining the sample size to estimate μ, with a specified amount of precision.

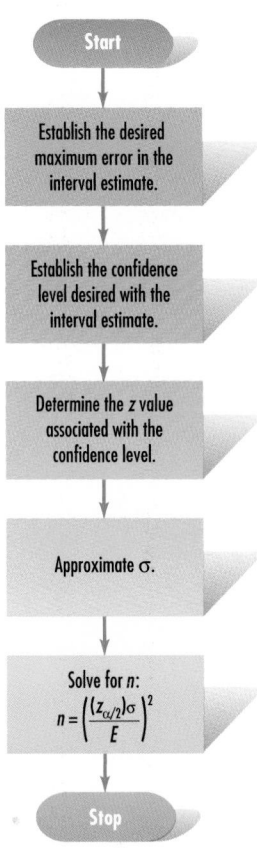

FIGURE 7.15 General procedure for determining the sample size for the estimation of μ.

Determining the Sample Size for the Estimation of p

The procedure for finding the sample size to estimate the population proportion is similar to the procedure we've just examined. You know that the interval estimate of p follows this form:

$$\hat{p} - z_{\alpha/2}\hat{\sigma}_{\hat{p}} < p < \hat{p} + z_{\alpha/2}\hat{\sigma}_{\hat{p}}$$

If we specify that p must be estimated within a certain limit, $E = error\ bound$, then we want the confidence limits to be

$$\hat{p} \pm z_{\alpha/2}\hat{\sigma}_{\hat{p}} = \hat{p} \pm E$$

This says that $E = z_{\alpha/2}\hat{\sigma}_{\hat{p}}$ and knowing that $\hat{\sigma}_{\hat{p}}$ estimates

$$\sigma_{\hat{p}} = \sqrt{\frac{p(1-p)}{n}}$$

we get

$$E = z_{\alpha/2}\sigma_{\hat{p}} = z_{\alpha/2}\sqrt{\frac{p(1-p)}{n}}$$

Solving this equation for n, you may now verify for yourself that

$$n = \frac{z_{\alpha/2}^2 p(1-p)}{E^2} \tag{7.9}$$

It's necessary at this point to approximate the value of p. The skeptics among you may wonder how it's possible to approximate p when p is what we want to estimate. Well, many times you have a rough idea of the true population proportion. For example, you may not know the true proportion of Canadian citizens who live in British Columbia, but you may know that the percentage is more than .10 but less than .25. In many cases an experienced researcher has enough knowledge about the population to approximate the true proportion. Judgment gives an approximation of the parameter, but the sample results provide an estimate of the parameter that can be objectively assessed.

What if we have no idea what the value of p might be and are unable to make any approximation of that parameter? Before answering this question, let's look at Table 7.2 and assume that we've specified a desired error bound and confidence level and our computations show that $p(1 - p) = 0.25$. Table 7.2 shows the necessary sample size under various assumptions about the population proportion. You can see the *symmetry in results*. The necessary sample size for an assumption $p = .20$ is the same as that for an assumption of $p = .80$. (A glance at column 2 of Table 7.2 will show you why this is the case.)

TABLE 7.2   ILLUSTRATION OF THE RELATIONSHIP BETWEEN THE ASSUMED VALUE OF p AND THE SAMPLE SIZE*

Assumed Value of p	p(1 − p)	$n = \dfrac{z_{\alpha/2}^2 p(1-p)}{E^2}$
(1)	(2)	(3)
0.20	(.20)(.80) = .16	400
0.40	(.40)(.60) = .24	600
0.50	(.50)(.50) = .25	625
0.60	(.60)(.40) = .24	600
0.80	(.80)(.20) = .16	400

*Given, for the purpose of this example, that $z_{\alpha/2}^2/E^2 = .25$.

As you can see in Table 7.2, the largest sample size arises when the population proportion is assumed to be .50. *When you have absolutely no idea about the true population proportion, you should assume that $p = .50$, gather the largest sample that might be needed, and obtain as much information as possible to make an estimate of p.*

Perhaps an example will help here. Suppose you are asked to estimate the proportion of students at a university who are willing to donate blood. (Canadian Blood Services is planning its schedule for the coming months, and it wants you to provide an estimate that will be within ± .05 of the true proportion.) A confidence level of 95 percent is desired. How big should the random sample be? Assume you have no idea of the true proportion.

You are given $E = .05$, and with a confidence level 95 percent you know that z is 1.96. Since you don't know the true proportion willing to donate blood, you must obtain the largest sample size possible by assuming that $p = .50$. Therefore, the necessary sample size is computed as follows:

$$n = \frac{z_{\alpha/2}^2 p(1 - p)}{E^2} = \frac{(1.96)^2 .5(1 - .5)}{(.05)^2} = \frac{.9604}{.0025} = 384.2 \text{ or } 385 \text{ students}$$

Figure 7.16 summarizes the general procedure for determining the sample size for the estimation of p.

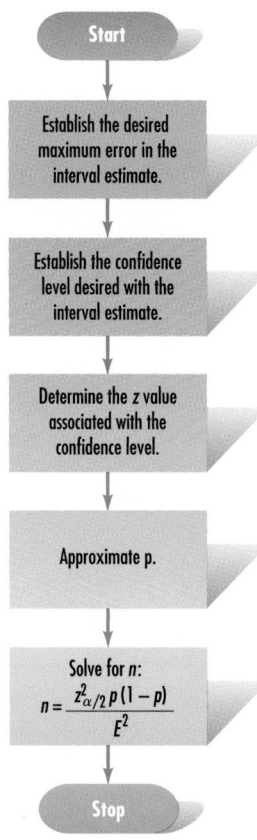

FIGURE 7.16 General procedure for determining the sample size for the estimation of p.

Self-Testing Review 7.6

70. A sociologist wishes to estimate the population mean time per week spent in caring for patients with dementia who live at home. In a preliminary random sample of 100 patients, the sample standard deviation was 68.2 hours a week. How many patients must be studied to be 95 percent confident that the sample mean is within five hours of the population mean? How many more will be needed?

71. Suppose the sociologist (see problem 70) now would like to form a 95 percent confidence interval and be within two hours of the population mean. How large a sample would now be needed?

72. Compare your results in problems 70 and 71. If all other factors remain the same, comment on the relationship between the desired accuracy and the minimum required sample size. As the amount of permissible error decreases, what happens to the required sample size?

73. A survey asked couples for the number of years they had known each other before their divorce. A preliminary random sample of 46 couples had a standard deviation of 4.346 years. How large a sample is needed to construct a 90 percent confidence interval for the mean time each couple knew each other before the divorce if the estimate is to be within .5 year of the actual time?

74. Using the data in problem 73, how large a sample is needed to construct a 95 percent confidence interval for the mean time each couple knew each other before the divorce if the estimate is to be within .5 year of the actual time?

75. Compare your results in problems 73 and 74. If all other factors remain the same, comment on the relationship between the confidence level and the minimum required sample size. As the amount of confidence increases, what happens to the required sample size?

76. A study is conducted to evaluate the proportion of infected needles used by injection-drug users.

    a) If no preliminary study is available, how large a random sample is needed to form a 95 percent confidence interval with an error bound of .05?

    b) A preliminary study of a random sample of 160 needles that were used before a needle exchange program was established found 108 to be HIV-positive. In the context of this study, use an estimate of p to determine how large a sample is needed to form a 95 percent confidence interval on the population proportion of pre-exchange-program needles that are HIV-positive.

77. A consumer wishes to estimate the proportion of processed food items that contain genetically modified (GM) products.

    a) If no preliminary study is available, how large a sample size is needed to be 95 percent confident the estimate is within .03 of p?

    b) In a preliminary study, 210 of 350 processed items contained GM products. Using this preliminary study, how large a sample is needed to construct a 95 percent confidence interval within .03 of p?

78. In a preliminary study reported in *Physical Therapy,* the sample standard deviation for the duration of a particular back pain suffered by patients was 18.0 months. How large a random sample is needed to construct a 90 percent confidence interval for the duration of such back pain for the population of back patients so that the estimate is within two months of the actual duration?

79. An accounting firm wishes to form a 90 percent confidence interval for the population mean tax refund for its clients who receive refunds. How large a random sample is needed to be within $10 of the actual amount if a preliminary study finds the standard deviation to be $42.67?

80. A preliminary sample of 512 Denver County employees was questioned in a study in the *American Journal of Public Health* to assess the prevalence of symptoms attributed to the work environment. Forty-five employees reported experiencing eye irritation. How large a random sample is needed to be 90 percent confident of being within .03 of the population proportion of those who experience eye irritation?

81. A clinical test on a random sample of 58 cardiac patients was performed to assess the increase in exercise time after 3 weeks of using the medication NORVASC. The mean and standard deviation for the increase were 62 seconds and 17 seconds, respectively. How large a sample is needed to be 99 percent confident that the sample mean is within 2 seconds of the population mean?

82. Last fall, 48 percent of the students in a university were male. Suppose we want to estimate the percentage of males who enroll next fall. Using last fall's information as a preliminary sample, how large a random sample is needed to be 99 percent confident of being within .02 of the population proportion of males who enroll next fall?

83. A class project investigated data concerning Chinook salmon. In a sample of salmon, measurements were made of the distance from the snout of the fish to the notch of the tail fin. This distance is called the fork length. The standard deviation of the sample of fork lengths was 11.675 cm. How large a random sample would be needed to estimate, with a 95 percent level of confidence, the true mean fork length of the population of all Chinook salmon, so that the estimate is within 2 cm of the actual mean fork length?

LOOKING BACK

1. Any specific value of a statistic is an estimate, and any statistic used to estimate a parameter is an estimator. An unbiased estimator is one that produces a sampling distribution that has a mean that's equal to the population parameter to be estimated. Thus, sample means, sample proportions, and sample variances are unbiased estimators of population means, proportions, and variances. The entire process of using an estimator to produce an estimate of the parameter is known as estimation.

2. A single number used to estimate a population parameter is called a point estimate, and the process of estimating with a single number is known as point estimation. Although on unbiased estimator tends towards the value of the population parameter, it's unlikely that the value of a point estimate will be exactly equal to the parameter value. Thus, an interval estimate—one that uses a spread of values to estimate a parameter—is desired over a point estimate because allowances are made for sampling error. As you've seen in this chapter, a point estimate is adjusted for sampling error to produce an interval estimate.

3. On the basis of the properties of their sampling distributions, it's possible to construct an interval estimate of μ, p, or σ^2 with some degree of certainty. The width of the interval estimate increases as the level of confidence increases, since allowance must be made for more sampling error. The level of confidence (or confidence coefficient) refers to the probability of correctly including the population parameter being estimated in the interval that is produced. The confidence levels generally used in interval estimation are 90, 95, and 99 percent. The interval estimates based on specified confidence levels are known as confidence intervals, and the upper and lower limits of the intervals are known as confidence limits.

4. The formulas needed to estimate the population mean, when σ is known or unknown and when the population is finite or infinite, are summarized in Table 7.3. You've seen that the sample size must be considered in estimation, since it affects the width of the confidence interval. If the sample size is sufficiently large (over 30), the sampling distribution of means is approximately normal, and z values are used in the estimation process. On rare occasions, z values can also be used with smaller samples if it's known that the population is normally distributed and the value of σ is also known. In most cases with smaller samples, though, if we know the population is normally distributed but we *don't* know the value of σ, the sampling distribution is approximately a t distribution. The shape of a t distribution is determined by the sample size.

5. The formulas needed to estimate the population proportion are also summarized in Table 7.3. These formulas are valid when $np \geq 5$ and when $n(1 - p)$ is also ≥ 5. The procedure for the interval estimation of p is similar to the procedure for estimating μ. Interval estimates of p values can be found almost every week in the polls published by newspapers and magazines.

6. It's often desirable to know the extent of the spread or scatter that exists in a data set so that steps can be taken to control it. When that's the case, an estimate of the population variance may be needed. If population values are

TABLE 7.3	SUMMARY OF INTERVAL ESTIMATION UNDER VARIOUS CONDITIONS			
	Estimating μ			**Estimating p**
	σ Known		**σ Unknown**	**(When $np \geq 5$ and**
$n \leq 30^*$	**$n > 30$**	**$n \leq 30^*$**	**$n > 30$**	**$n(1 - p) \geq 5$)**
$\bar{x} \pm z_{\alpha/2}\dfrac{\sigma}{\sqrt{n}}$	$\bar{x} \pm z_{\alpha/2}\dfrac{\sigma}{\sqrt{n}}$	$\bar{x} \pm t_{\alpha/2}\dfrac{s}{\sqrt{n}}$	$\bar{x} \pm z_{\alpha/2}\dfrac{s}{\sqrt{n}}$	$\hat{p} \pm z_{\alpha/2}\sqrt{\dfrac{\hat{p}(1 - \hat{p})}{n}}$

*Population values are assumed to be normally distributed.

normally distributed, the value of σ^2 can be estimated by using a Chi-square distribution. The interval estimate of σ^2 takes a familiar form:

lower confidence limit $< \sigma^2 <$ upper confidence limit

Or more specifically,

$$\frac{(n - 1)s^2}{\chi^2_{\alpha/2}} < \sigma^2 < \frac{(n - 1)s^2}{\chi^2_{1-\alpha/2}}$$

7. Discussions of how to determine the appropriate sample size when estimating the population mean or population proportion have been covered in this chapter. Determining the sample size for an interval estimate of μ requires an assumption about the value of σ. Likewise, determining the sample size to estimate the value of p requires an approximate value of p. If the researcher has absolutely no idea of the approximate value of p, then that value is assumed to be .50.

Exercises

84. Find the z value corresponding to each of the following confidence levels:

 a) 90 percent.

 b) 85 percent.

 c) 95 percent.

 d) 98 percent.

85. Find the t value corresponding to each of the following conditions:

 a) $n = 21$, 95 percent confidence level.

 b) $n = 6$, 99 percent confidence level.

 c) $n = 14$, 90 percent confidence level.

 d) $n = 4$, 95 percent confidence level.

86. In each of the following exercises, a set of conditions is given. To construct a 95 percent confidence interval for the population mean, would you use the z distribution, a t distribution, or neither? Where appropriate, determine the z or t value.

 a) $n = 47$, $\bar{x} = 83.2$, $s = 5.5$, population distribution shape unknown, σ unknown.

 b) $n – 21$, $\bar{x} = 23.1$, $s = 7.5$, population distribution shape normal, $\sigma = 7.9$.

 c) $n = 17$, $x = 3.2$, $s = 1.4$, population distribution shape normal, σ unknown.

87. In each of the following exercises, a set of conditions is given. To construct a 90 percent confidence interval for the population mean, would you use the z distribution, a t distribution, or neither? Where appropriate, determine the z or t value.

 a) $n = 16$, $\bar{x} = 733.2$, $s = 45.5$, population distribution shape normal, $\sigma = 41.7$.

 b) $n = 15$, $\bar{x} = 23.1$, $s = 7.5$, population distribution shape unknown, σ unknown.

 c) $n = 37$, $\bar{x} = 8.1$, $s = 3.9$, population distribution shape unknown, σ unknown.

88. Determine the values of x^2 needed to form the confidence intervals for the population variance for each of the following conditions:

 a) 90 percent level of confidence, $n = 22$.

 b) 95 percent level of confidence, $n = 13$.

89. Construct a 95 percent confidence interval for the population mean if $\bar{x} = 76.1$, $s = 14.2$, and the sample size is

 a) $n = 36$.

 b) $n = 49$.

 c) $n = 64$.

 d) Examine the results of problems (a) to (c). What happens to the width of a confidence interval as the sample size increases but all other conditions remain the same?

90. If $\bar{x} = 364.1$, $s = 61.7$, and $n = 100$, construct a confidence interval for μ using each of the following confidence levels:

 a) 90 percent.

 b) 95 percent.

 c) 99 percent.

 d) Using the results of problems (a) to (c), what happens to the width of the confidence interval as the level of confidence increases but all other conditions remain the same?

91. Construct a 95 percent confidence interval for the value of σ^2 if $n = 17$ and $s^2 = 31.8$.

92. Construct a 99 percent confidence interval for the value of σ^2 if $n = 24$ and $s^2 = 2.9$.

93. In 1919, a study of the four blood groups was conducted for various populations. In a random sample of 116 residents of Bougainville Island, it was observed that 74 had type A blood.

 a) What is the point estimate of the proportion of Bougainville Island residents who had type A blood?

 b) Estimate the standard error.

 c) Construct a 90 percent confidence interval for the proportion of Bougainville Island residents who had type A blood.

94. Nicholas Brendon is best known for his role as the wise-cracking Xander on televison's *Buffy the Vampire Slayer*. But a speech disorder almost thwarted the actor's rise to stardom—when he was about eight years old he realized he stuttered. According to the National Institutes of Health, more than 3 million Americans stutter. While there are several treatments, such as speech therapy and facial exercises, there is no specific cure. In a random sample of 1,000 people, it was found that 15 people stuttered.

 a) What is the point estimate of the proportion of all people who stutter?

 b) Estimate the standard error.

 c) Construct a 95 percent confidence interval for the true proportion of all people who stutter.

95. The *American Journal of Psychiatry* published the results of a study to determine if there was a possible type of brain dysfunction associated with infantile autism. Each child in the study was given a behavioural test and scored on a scale from 0 to 116, where 0 = absence of symptoms and 116 = maximum severity. (Assume the scores on this test are normally distributed.) The scores of the random sample of 21 children in the study were (Data = Behavior):

27, 35, 65, 67, 47, 46, 63, 44, 34, 51, 17, 40, 41, 60, 24, 48, 29, 73, 60, 41, 27

 a) What is the value of the point estimate you would use to estimate the mean score of *all* children with symptoms of infantile autism?

 b) Calculate the estimated standard error.

 c) Construct a 90 percent confidence interval for the mean score of all such children.

 d) Construct a 90 percent confidence interval for the population variance.

96. An issue of the *Lancet* described a study that dealt with the effects of increased inspired oxygen concentrations on exercise performance in chronic heart-failure patients. A random sample of 12 such patients was included in the study. The oxygen consumption during the exercise test (in ml/min per kg) was
9.7, 21.0, 14.3, 15.2, 12.8, 8.6, 10.9, 8.3, 19.1, 7.0, 19.5, 12.5

 a) What is the value of the point estimate of the mean amount of oxygen consumed by all such patients?

 b) Calculate the estimated standard error of the mean.

 c) Construct a 99 percent confidence interval for the population mean oxygen consumption. (Assume population values are normally distributed.)

 d) Construct a 99 percent confidence interval for the population standard deviation.

97. Royal LePage recently published a survey of Canadian house prices. The following data list the average price of standard two-storey homes in thousands of dollars for 12 randomly selected cities (we'll assume that the prices are normally distributed):

City	House Price	Property Tax
Halifax (South End), NS:	245	3,540
Charlottetown, PEI	140	2,600
Montreal (West), PQ:	295	4,300
Québec City (Chicoutimi), PQ	141	2,520
Toronto (Don Mills East), ON:	330	2,400
Ottawa (Kanata), ON	210	3,000
Winnipeg (Southdale) MB:	143	3,360
Regina (South), SK:	124	3,000
Saskatoon (West),	133	1,900
Calgary (North West), AB:	203	1,820
Edmonton (Sherwood Park), AB:	220	1,900
Vancouver (West Side) BC,	515	3,000

a) Construct a 95 percent confidence interval for the population mean price of standard two-storey houses in Canadian cities.

b) Construct a 95 percent confidence interval for the population mean property tax on standard two-storey houses in Canadian cities.

c) Construct a 95 percent confidence interval for the variance of the population of prices of standard two-storey houses in Canadian cities.

d) Construct a 95 percent confidence interval for the variance of the population of property taxes on standard two-storey houses in Canadian cities.

98. To study the characteristics of first-episode schizophrenic patients, data were collected on a random sample of 32 such patients, and these facts were reported in an issue of the *American Journal of Psychiatry*. The mean and standard deviation for the number of years of education for the patients in this sample were 12.4 years and 3.0 years, respectively. Construct a 95 percent confidence interval for the mean number of years of education for all such patients.

99. The same issue of the *American Journal of Psychiatry* reported that an IQ test was administered to a random sample of 26 chronic schizophrenic patients and the mean was found to be 97.6. For this test, the population values are known to be normally distributed with a standard deviation of 15. Construct a 90 percent confidence interval for the mean IQ of the population of chronic schizophrenic patients.

100. An issue of *SAM Advanced Management Journal* described a study that was conducted to examine the attitudes and perceptions of undergraduate business students. Of 431 business students who were in the random sample, 99 expressed an interest in international business. Form a 90 percent confidence interval for the percentage of all business students interested in international business.

101. Using the information in problem 100 to form a preliminary estimate, how large a sample would be necessary to be 90 percent confident that the sample mean is within 2 percent of the population mean?

102. A study to show expenditures in caring for patients with dementia who live at home was published in the *American Journal of Public Health*. Surveys were returned by a random sample of 141 caregivers. The caregivers reported the average number of caregiving hours a week to be 106.9 with a standard deviation of 68.2 hours. Form a confidence interval at the 90 percent level for the population mean number of caregiver hours.

103. Melanie Molberg, a physical therapist, is testing a new technique on patients who are recovering from sports injuries. To estimate the average length of time she spent with each of these patients last month, she randomly selects a sample of ten. The mean and standard deviation of her sample were 147.8 minutes and 31.2 minutes, respectively. Assuming population values are normally distributed, construct a 95 percent confidence interval for the time spent with the population of patients during the month.

104. Using the information in problem 103, form a 95 percent confidence interval for the population standard deviation for Ms. Melanie Molberg's patients.

105. In a recent study, it was found that out of 36 randomly selected subscribers to cable TV, 24 reported excellent service. Form a 90 percent confidence interval for the population percentage of subscribers who believe the service is excellent.

106. How large a sample is needed to form a 90 percent confidence interval for problem 105 and be within .05 of the population proportion?

107. The *Journal of Educational Research* has published a study in which a random sample of 281 college students took a word recall test. The mean and standard deviation scores were 58.3 and 20.5, respectively. Construct a 95 percent confidence interval for the population mean score.

108. Use the study in problem 107 for a preliminary estimate of σ. How large a sample will be necessary to be 95 percent confident of being within two units of the population mean?

109. A random sample of 64 couples in unstable marriages was part of a study (reported in the *Journal of Personality and Social Psychology*) to determine factors that would predict divorce. On a test for extroversion, the husbands had a mean and standard deviation of 24.70 and 5.14, respectively. Form a 99 percent confidence interval for the mean score on this test of all husbands in unstable marriages.

110. A study reported in *Physical Therapy* was made to compare the effect of varied training frequencies on the development of isometric lumbar torque (strength). A random sample of ten subjects with lower back pain received training every other week during this study. The mean and standard deviation for the beginning weight of this sample were 24.7 kg and 3.6 kg, respectively. Assuming that population values are normally distributed, construct a 95 percent confidence interval for the beginning population mean weight.

111. Using the study in problem 110 for a preliminary estimate of σ, how large a sample would be needed to be 95 percent confident of being within 1 kg of the population mean?

112. A mayor is running for reelection and wants to estimate the percent of voters who plan to vote for him. He instructs his staff to conduct a poll so that they are 95 percent sure their estimate will be accurate within ±3 percent. What is the minimum number of voters that must be used in the poll if no preliminary study is available?

113. An industrial engineer wishes to estimate the mean life of a calculator battery (in hours) to within two hours of the true value. Past experience has shown that the standard deviation is 15.2 hours. How large a sample should she select to be within two hours with 90 percent confidence?

114. A child psychologist wishes to estimate the mean length of time six-year-old children spend with their parents each day. Past experience has shown the standard deviation to be 127 minutes. How large a sample should he select to be within 15 minutes with 99 percent confidence?

115. A plant manager wants to form a 99 percent confidence interval to estimate the percent of defective products from the production line. She wants the estimate to be accurate within ±5 percent. What is the minimum number she needs for her sample if no preliminary study is available?

116. Data was collected on the amount of free memory during peak usage times of a campus's AIX system. The unit used was a real memory page (4,096 bytes). For the following questions, assume that the amount of free memory is normally distributed.

| 1,493 | 1,319 | 1,253 | 1,651 | 1,812 | 1,682 |
| 1,737 | 1,193 | 1,893 | 1,532 | 1,717 | 1,842 |

   a) Find the sample mean and the sample standard deviation.

   b) Form a 99 percent confidence interval for the population mean amount of free memory.

   c) Form a 99 percent confidence interval for the population variance.

   d) Form a 99 percent confidence interval for the σ.

Topics for Review and Discussion

1. What is an unbiased estimator? Why is such an estimator desirable? What are the unbiased estimators for each of the parameters μ, σ^2, and p?

2. Although a population parameter will seldom be exactly equal to a point estimate, discuss how a point estimate is used to estimate a population parameter.

3. Discuss, in your own words, the meaning of a 90 percent confidence interval.

4. What effect does an increase in the confidence level have on the width of the confidence interval?

5. What effect does an increase in the sample size have on the width of the confidence interval?

6. Under what conditions does the sampling distribution of the mean approximate a normal distribution?

7. Under what conditions is a *t* distribution used to approximate the distribution of sample means?

8. Under what conditions can we estimate the value of the population variance? What distribution is used in this estimate?

9. It is known that in using a high confidence coefficient in computing a confidence interval, there is a probability of including the population mean in the interval. What are the disadvantages in using a high confidence coefficient?

10. What should a researcher do if the interval estimate is too wide?

11. We can use the parameter $\sigma_{\bar{x}}$ in an interval estimate for μ. Why isn't it possible to use the parameter $\sigma_{\hat{p}}$ in an interval estimate for p?

Projects/Issues to Consider

1. Locate a population data set (you may use the one found for the Projects/Issues section in Chapter 6) from which you can determine the parameters μ and σ. Select a random sample of size n from this population and compute $\bar{x}$ and s.

    a) Construct a 90 percent confidence interval estimate of the population mean. Use the known value of σ. Your sample size and the shape of the distribution will determine if you use the z or a t distribution. Do you need a finite correction factor?

    b) Compare the interval estimate from part a with the known population mean. Is your population mean inside the interval you constructed? If not, why not?

2. Identify a current controversial topic and formulate a question regarding opinions on this topic. Your question may be at the local or national level, but be sure it is not stated in a biased manner. Identify the population for your question. You will form an interval estimate for the proportion of the population that responds *yes* to your question, but first determine the level of precision you want. Find the minimum sample size to achieve this level of precision and collect a sufficient number of responses. Now, form a 90 percent confidence interval for the population proportion.

3. Locate a percentage estimate achieved by polling in a recent newspaper or periodical. (These poll results are often reported as a point estimate with a statement to the effect that the results are within ±3 percentage points of the population percentage.) Use this estimate to produce a confidence interval.

4. Ask a sample of fellow students the following question: How many hours do you study in a typical week? Use the data you collected to form a 95 percent confidence interval for the mean of all students at your college. Draw a histogram of your sample. Does it appear reasonable to believe that your sample has been taken from a normal population? If not, does that affect your belief that the confidence interval is correct? Write a report summarizing your results.

5. Ask a sample of fellow students a question that can be answered *yes* or *no*. Examples include Do you plan to go to work immediately after graduation? Do you attend a religious service at least once a week? Do you regularly watch [pick your favourite show]? Use the data you collected to form a 90 percent confidence interval for the proportion of all students at your college who are in the *yes* category. How large is your interval? Is it too large to be useful? If so, what would you need to do to decrease the size of the interval? Write a report summarizing your results.

Computer/Calculator Exercises

1. Refer to Example 7.1 on page 221 and repeat the computer simulation experiment shown in *Figure 7.4a*.

    a) How many of your 15 samples produce 95 percent confidence intervals that include the population mean of 1.48 minutes?

    b) Why do your confidence intervals differ from those shown in *Figure 7.4a*?

2. Data was collected concerning the amounts of chloride, arsenic, fluoride, and phosphate (all mL/l) in Mono Basin. These minerals develop from the geothermal activity in the region and eventually could affect the quality of water. For each of these minerals, compute the sample mean and standard deviation. Then, assuming that each is normally distributed, construct a 90 percent confidence interval for the population mean amount of each mineral in the Mono Basin (Data = MonoBasn).

Chloride	Fluoride	Phosphate	Arsenic
0.0200	0.0004	0.0010	0.0200
0.0200	0.0010	0.0005	0.0200
0.0100	0.0010	0.0010	0.0200
0.0300	0.0010	0.0002	0.0400
0.0400	0.0015	0.0020	0.0600
0.0160	0.0010	0.0010	0.0320
0.0480	0.0020	0.0030	0.0800
0.0100	0.0013	0.0010	0.0120
0.2000	0.0400	0.0004	0.3500
0.0100	0.0010	0.0001	0.0700
0.0090	0.0010	0.0001	0.0900
0.0240	0.0027	0.0006	0.2600
0.0080	0.0020	0.0007	0.0500
0.0250	0.0030	0.0005	0.1600
0.1100	0.0045	0.0004	0.2200
0.0800	0.0010	0.0004	0.0020
0.0100	0.0010	0.0001	0.0009

3. A set of data called the Kodiak Island King Crab Survey Data was collected. For a selection of months, measurements at a depth of 100 m off the Alaskan coast were taken on ocean temperature, in degrees Celsius, and on ocean salinity, given in parts per thousand. The first few data points are given below (Data = Kodiakcs):

Celsius	Salinity
5.50	31.610
2.01	32.420
4.19	32.130
5.53	32.030
8.30	32.520

a) Form a 99 percent confidence interval for the population variance of the temperature.

b) Form a 90 percent confidence interval for the population standard deviation of the salinity.

4. D. Oksner, in a class project (*Relative Times of Internet Connections*), used a standard UNIX program called *ping* to measure the time (milliseconds) taken to contact and receive a reply from another computer on the Internet. He noted that local locations were not any faster than sites in Denmark and Japan. It appears that the provider and the type and quality of the connection make the difference. Assume these times represent a simple random sample of all possible connection times (Data = Internet).

1,450	310	222	680	299	157	202	525	568	447
129	253	406	331	644	822	461	292	204	396
684	517	322	536	343	259	526	288	330	262
205	294	496	1,043	366	511				

a) Form a 95 percent confidence interval for the population mean time taken to contact and receive a reply from another computer on the Internet.

b) Form a 95 percent confidence interval for the population variance.

5. In a class project, data was collected from a sample of 59 students from a graduating class of 429 business administration majors. One variable was GPA (Data = BusGPA).

GPA					
2.547	2.622	2.803	3.138	3.424	2.896
2.895	3.371	2.708	3.591	3.554	3.322
3.617	3.142	3.054	2.975	3.147	4.000
3.721	3.334	2.646	3.539	2.586	3.213
3.044	2.800	3.544	3.273	3.598	3.700
3.558	3.488	2.517	2.991	2.859	3.066
3.350	3.656	3.450	2.458	2.913	3.052
3.045	3.448	2.914	2.754	3.251	2.450
3.763	2.830	2.832	3.181	2.890	2.620
3.236	3.654	3.527	3.694	2.883	

a) Form a 95 percent confidence interval for the true mean GPA of the 429 business administration majors.

b) Form a 95 percent confidence interval for the value of σ.

6. An article in the *Journal of Materials in Civil Engineering* gave the following observations on the longitudinal compressive strength (Mpa) of the 1/4-in. MMFG series 500/525 plate material of 20 mm specimen (Data = Platempa):

255	256	259	260	260	261	261	261	262
263	264	266	266	267	267	267	268	268
268	269	269	269	270	270	271	272	273
274	274	275	276	277	279	279	279	279
280	280	280	281	282	282	283	283	283
284	287	287	287	289	290	296		

a) Form a 99 percent confidence interval for the population mean longitudinal compressive strength (Mpa) of the 1/4 in. MMFG series.

b) Form a 99 percent confidence interval for the population variance.

7. In a previously mentioned project, Travis Greenley analyzed the number of sit-ups from an Army Physical Fitness Test (APFT). The data also included the number of push-ups and the times in a two-mile run. The first few data pairs are below (Data = APFTPup2):

Push-Ups	2-Mile Run
60	960
49	900
51	971
76	908
56	1,080
86	829

a) Form a 90 percent confidence interval for the population mean number of push-ups done in two minutes on the Army Physical Fitness Test.

b) Form a 90 percent confidence interval for the population variance of the push-ups.

c) Form a 90 percent confidence interval for the population mean of the times in a two-mile run on the APFT.

d) Form a 90 percent confidence interval for the value of σ for the two-mile run times.

8. Computer network usage gives system administrators helpful information in deciding when to expand and upgrade equipment. In a class project, (*Electrical Engineering Computer Network Usage,* 1996), E. Willard looked at a random sample of the number of users on the Electrical Engineering Department's computer network during its peak usage periods (Data = EENetwrk).

Number of Users on the Electrical Engineering Computer Network

20	12	17	10	13	11	14	9	6	14
8	8	25	11	22	18	8	13	4	23
26	15	13	35	14	14	20	18	12	21

a) Form a 95 percent confidence interval for the population mean.

b) Form a 95 percent confidence interval for the population variance.

9. Data was collected on shrubs at Swanton's farm. Measurements were made of height (centimetres), age (months) and bark thickness (millimetres) (Data = Swanton).

Height	Age	Bark	Height	Age	Bark
122.00	20	1.1	164.00	40	2.3
193.50	36	2.8	203.25	52	2.0
166.50	18	2.0	174.00	30	2.5
82.00	10	1.2	159.00	22	3.0
133.50	21	2.0	205.00	42	2.6
156.00	29	1.4	223.50	45	4.3
172.50	51	1.8	195.00	54	4.0
81.00	11	1.1	232.50	39	2.2
148.00	26	2.5	190.50	36	3.5
113.00	12	1.5	100.00	8	1.4
84.00	13	1.4			

a) Form a 90 percent confidence interval for the population mean height of the shrubs.

b) Form a 90 percent confidence interval for the value of σ of the heights of the shrubs.

c) Form a 95 percent confidence interval for the population mean age of the shrubs.

d) Form a 95 percent confidence interval for the value of σ of the age of the shrubs.

e) Form a 99 percent confidence interval for the population mean bark thickness of the shrubs.

f) Form a 99 percent confidence interval for the value of σ of the bark thickness of the shrubs.

10. Use the World Wide Web to access the DASL data sets in the "confidence interval" category at DASLCInt. Select the data set that most appeals to you and find the mean and standard deviation of the data. Assuming that the data you selected follows a normal distribution, form a 99 percent confidence interval for the mean of the population from which the data was taken.

CHAPTER 8

Testing Hypotheses: One-Sample Procedures

LOOKING AHEAD

You'll learn procedures in this chapter to help you decide if sample results *support* a hypothesis about a parameter value or if the results show that the hypothesis should be *rejected*. That is, from our examination of sampling concepts, we can figure out what type of sample results should happen if the hypothesized population value is correct. If the sample results differ substantially from what we expect, the difference is called a statistically significant difference, and this difference is the basis for rejecting the hypothesis being tested.

But we're getting ahead of ourselves. Before the chapter asks you to test hypotheses and make decisions, it outlines a general hypothesis-testing procedure for you to use to conduct one-sample hypothesis tests of means, proportions, and variances. (In later chapters, we'll look at hypothesis-testing procedures that involve two or more samples.)

Thus, after studying this chapter, you should be able to

- Explain the necessary steps in the general hypothesis-testing procedure.

- Perform one-sample hypothesis tests of means (both one- and two-tailed versions) when the population standard deviation is known, as well as when it's not available.

- Perform one-sample hypothesis tests of proportions for both one- and two-tailed testing situations.

- Perform one-sample hypothesis tests of variances for both one- and two-tailed testing situations.

8.1　The Hypothesis-Testing Procedure in General

We saw in the last chapter that when we have an estimation situation, the value of a population parameter is unknown, and sample results are employed to provide some insight about the true value. In this chapter, though, the sample results are used for a different purpose. Although the exact value of a parameter may still be unknown, there's often some idea or hypothesis about its true value. Sample results may bolster the hypothesis, or they may indicate the assumption is untenable. For example, Dean Vicki Schneider may state that the average IQ of the students at her university is 130. This statement may be an assumption on her part, and there should be some way of testing her claim. One possible method of checking involves sampling. If a random sample of these students produces an average IQ of 104, it's easy to reject the hypothesis that the true average is 130 because of the large discrepancy between the sample mean and the hypothesized value of the population mean. Similarly, if the sample mean is 131, the dean's statement appears reasonable. Unfortunately, life's decisions are not always as clear-cut as this. Often, the difference between the value of the sample statistic and the hypothesized parameter is neither too large nor too small, and the correct decision is less obvious. Suppose, for example, the average IQ of a sample is 136; or suppose it's 122. Does either value warrant rejection of the statement that $\mu = 130$? Obviously, the decision process must be based on some sort of criterion.

Before we present the formal steps in the hypothesis-testing procedure, let's consider another example. Suppose the mayor of a town states that the average per capita income of the town's citizens is $40,000, and you have a statistician friend—Alan Jonat—who is hired by the town council to verify or discredit the mayor's claim. Obviously, Alan's knowledge of sampling variation tells him that even if the true mean is $40,000 as stated, a sample mean will most likely not equal the parameter value. Alan realizes there will probably be a difference between the sample mean and the hypothesized population value even when the hypothesized value is the true population mean. The immediate question confronting him is how large or significant should the difference between the value of $\bar{x}$ and the hypothesized population value be to provide sufficient reason to dismiss the mayor's claims? Is a difference in values of $100 significant? Is a difference of $1,000 significant? Our look at hypothesis testing will try to answer these types of questions.

Still Another Look at the Sampling Distribution of Means

Let's look at *Figure 8.1*, which depicts a sampling distribution of means where (1) the true mean μ is actually equal to the hypothesized value (μ_0) of $40,000 and (2) the standard error is equal to $200. *In other words, we are assuming that the mayor is actually correct and μ is indeed $40,000.* (Of course, Alan and the town council aren't aware of this fact.) Suppose further that Alan takes a sample of townspeople, with the result that the sample mean per capita income is equal to $40,200. Is it reasonable for Alan to expect this result with a μ of $40,000 and a $\sigma_{\bar{x}}$ of $200? That is, how likely is it that a $\bar{x}$ of $40,200 will occur in this situation? As a more general question, what are the chances of Alan's getting a sample mean that differs from the μ_0 of $40,000 by ±$200?

Since the sampling distribution in *Figure 8.1* is approximately normal, Alan can check the likelihood that a sample mean is between $39,800 and $40,200 by seeing how many standard errors from the value of $\mu = $40,000 a difference of $200 represents. In terms of z values, how far does $40,200 or $39,800 lie from the true and hypothesized popu-

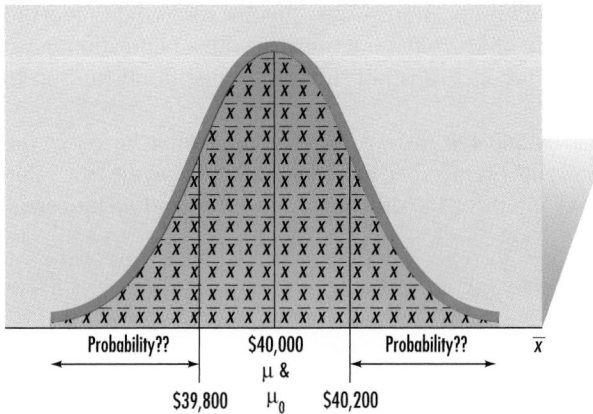

FIGURE 8.1 A normally shaped sampling distribution where the assumed mean and the true mean happen to be of equal value.

Where $\sigma_{\bar{x}} = \$200$

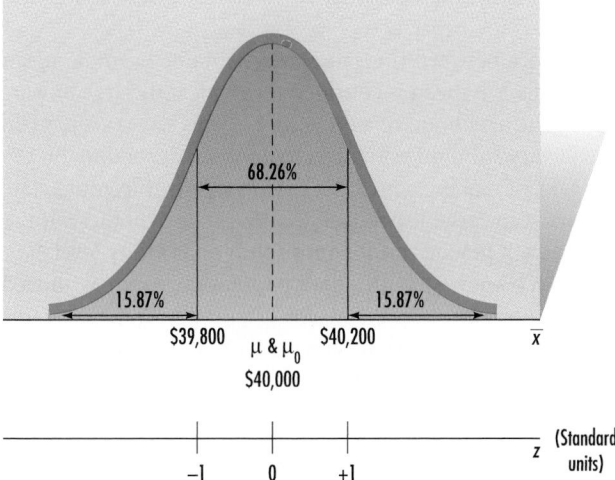

FIGURE 8.2 Illustration of the likelihood of obtaining an $\bar{x}$ that differs from the true mean by one standard error or more.

Where $\sigma_{\bar{x}} = \$200$

lation mean of $40,000—that is, what's the standardized difference or the number of *standard units*? Alan can calculate the standard units in this way:

$$z = \frac{\bar{x} - \mu_0}{\sigma_{\bar{x}}}$$

$$z = \frac{\$40,200 - \$40,000}{\$200} \quad \text{and} \quad z = \frac{\$39,800 - \$40,000}{\$200}$$

$$= 1.00 \qquad\qquad\qquad = -1.00$$

Thus, we can see that if a sample mean in our example differs from the hypothesized value by $200, it differs by one standard unit or one standard error. Consulting the *z* table in Appendix 2, we note that the area under one side of the distribution that corresponds to a *z* value of 1.00 is .3413, and the total area between – 1.00 and +1.00 is .3413 + .3413 = .6826. This means that there's a .1587 chance that the value of $\bar{x}$ may be more than one standard error above the mean and another .1587 chance that the value of $\bar{x}$ will be more than one standard error below the mean. All this is demonstrated in *Figure 8.2*, where it's shown that there's a total chance of 31.74 percent that

$\bar{x}$ will differ from μ by one standard unit or more. Consequently, Alan could report to the town council that a sample mean of $40,200 is not unusual with a population mean of $40,000, and a $200 difference such as this is not sufficiently significant for him to reject the mayor's claim.

Suppose Alan's sample mean is $40,400 instead of $40,200. Would he reject the mayor's claim with this sample result? (Remember, he really doesn't know the true value of the population mean.) Converting this $400 difference between $\bar{x}$ and μ_0 into standard units, we get

$$z = \frac{\bar{x} - \mu_0}{\sigma_{\bar{x}}} = \frac{\$40,400 - \$40,000}{\$200} = 2.00$$

Thus, the total chance that a $\bar{x}$ will differ from our true mean of $40,000 by two or more standard errors is only approximately 4.6 percent, as shown in *Figure 8.3*. Given such a low chance of obtaining a sample mean of $40,400, Alan would likely be justified in rejecting the mayor's claim. Now, there's sufficient statistical evidence for him to conclude that the mayor's claim is incorrect.

As you can now see, the difference between the value of an obtained sample mean and a hypothesized value of a population mean is considered significantly large to warrant rejection of the hypothesis if the likelihood of a difference of this size is very small. The criterion of "very small" will vary from one situation to another, depending on the risk the researcher is willing to take of making a mistake. For now, it's sufficient to state that all hypothesis tests must have some established rule that rejects a hypothesis if the likelihood of a value of $\bar{x}$ falls below a predetermined minimum probability level.

Unfortunately, since Alan doesn't know that the true population mean is indeed $40,000, he may justifiably but erroneously reject the mayor's claim if he obtains a sample mean of $40,400. As a matter of fact, if he establishes a rule that any sample mean value that differs from the hypothesized mean of $40,000 by two or more standard errors in either direction of the sampling distribution will cause the hypothesis to be rejected, then, if the true mean is indeed $40,000, he will erroneously reject the mayor's claim 4.6 percent of the time if he makes a large number of tests. In other words, even

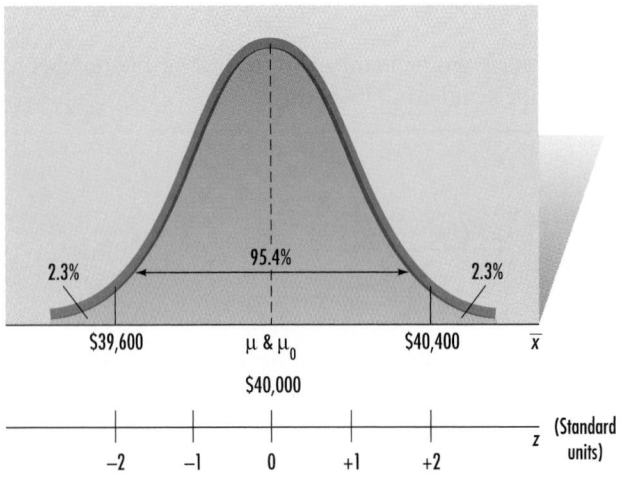

FIGURE 8.3 Illustration of the likelihood of obtaining an $\bar{x}$ that differs from the true mean by two or more standard errors.

when the true mean is equal to the hypothesized value, occasionally a sample mean will fall into the unlikely portion of the sampling distribution and lead to an erroneous decision to reject the hypothesized value as the true value. In short, the predetermined minimum likelihood of a sample mean is also the risk of rejecting a hypothesis that is actually true.

With this basic example in mind, we're now ready to study the formal steps in the classical (or traditional) hypothesis-testing procedure.

Steps in the Classical Hypothesis-Testing Procedure

There are seven steps in this testing procedure, and we'll encounter these same seven steps repeatedly in the remainder of this book.

Step 1: State the Null and Alternative Hypotheses
The first step in traditional hypothesis testing is to specifically note the hypotheses to be tested *before* sampling.

> This assumption to be tested is known as the **null hypothesis,** and the symbol for the null hypothesis is H_0.

Suppose we want to test the hypothesis that the population mean is equal to 100. The format of this hypothesis is

$H_0: \mu = 100$

As we've seen earlier, the hypothesized value of the population mean when used in calculations is identified by the symbol μ_0.

It's important to note here that the null hypothesis is the one that contains the *equality* relation—that is, H_0 states that some parameter (mean, proportion, variance) is *equal to* a specified value. A test is often carried out for the purpose of trying to show that H_0 *isn't* true. For example, a researcher may hope that the population mean life expectancy of a new type of automobile battery will exceed the 60-month mean life expectancy of a currently sold product. But in conducting a test of the new battery, H_0 is that the population mean life expectancy is equal to 60 months. The researcher's hope in this test is that the sample results will show a higher mean life expectancy and thus won't support H_0.

If the sample results don't support the null hypothesis, we must obviously conclude something else.

> The conclusion that is accepted contingent on the rejection of the null hypothesis is known as the **alternative hypothesis,** and the symbol for the alternative hypothesis is H_1.

There are three possible alternative hypotheses to the null hypothesis previously stated:

$H_1: \mu \neq 100$
$H_1: \mu > 100$
$H_1: \mu < 100$

The selection of an alternative hypothesis depends on the nature of the problem, and later sections of this chapter discuss these alternative hypotheses. (The researcher carrying out the test of the new type of automobile battery would like to have reason to reject H_0 that $\mu = 60$ months in favour of H_1 that $\mu > 60$ months.) As with the null hypothesis, the alternative hypothesis should be stated prior to actual sampling.

Step 2: Select the Level of Significance Having noted the null and alternative hypotheses, the second step is to establish a criterion for when to reject the null hypothesis. If the true mean is actually the hypothesized value, from the sampling distribution of the sample means, we know that a small difference between a sample mean and μ is more likely than a large difference and an extremely large difference is unlikely. The question is, How large does the difference between $\bar{x}$ and μ_0 need to be for us to believe that μ_0 is not correct? We base the decision on probability. If the difference is unlikely, below some predetermined minimum probability level, we will reject H_0. In our previous example involving the mayor's claim, a difference between $\bar{x}$ and μ_0 with a likelihood of only 4.6 percent or less was considered unlikely, and so Alan felt there was sufficient reason to reject the hypothesis. In that case, a 4.6 percent chance of occurrence was the predetermined minimum probability level.

As noted earlier, if the true mean is indeed equal to the hypothesized value, the predetermined minimum probability level is also the risk of erroneously rejecting the null hypothesis when that hypothesis is true. Therefore, the next step in the hypothesis-testing procedure is to state this level of risk of rejecting a true null hypothesis.

> This risk of erroneous rejection of H_0 is known as the **level of significance,** which is denoted by the Greek letter α (alpha).

Of course, the costlier it is to mistakenly reject a true null hypothesis—maybe because you might be sued and lose a lot of money—the smaller α should be. Thus, the value of α is small, usually .01 or .05. Technically, α is known as the risk of a **type I error**—that is, the risk that a true null hypothesis will be rejected. When we erroneously fail to reject a false null hypothesis, it's known as a **type II error.** When we decrease the probability of a type I error, we raise the probability of a type II error. We'll concentrate on the role of the type I error; a thorough treatment of type II errors is beyond the scope of this book.

In summary, whenever a statistical hypothesis is rejected or not rejected on the basis of a sample, there is always the risk of making a wrong decision. In reality, H_0 may or may not be true, and H_0 may or may not be rejected, so there are four possible outcomes. Schematically, the four possible outcomes are

	H_0 is True	H_0 is False
H_0 is rejected	Type I Error	Correct Decision
H_0 is not rejected	Correct Decision	Type 2 Error

Note that there are two types of correct decisions and two types of incorrect decisions. Consider an analogy with a courtroom trial, where H_0 is the statement "the person is not guilty" and H_1 is the statement "the person is guilty." The trial process may result in either of two correct decisions or either of two errors as illustrated below.

	H_0 is True (Person Is Not Guilty)	H_0 is False (Person Is Guilty)
H_0 is Rejected (person is found guilty)	Type 1 Error	Correct Decision
H_0 is not Rejected (person is not found guilty)	Correct Decision	Type 2 Error

Step 3: Determine the Test Distribution to Use Once the level of significance is chosen, it's then necessary to select the correct probability distribution to use for the particular test. In this chapter, as in Chapter 7, we'll focus on the standard normal (z), t, and Chi-square (χ^2) distributions. In later chapters we'll see that other probability distribution options are possible, but for now, here are our options. We'll use the z distribution in hypothesis tests of *means and proportions* when the sample size (n) is sufficiently large. We can also use the z distribution in tests of means when we have a smaller sample *if* two conditions are met: (1) it's known that the population values are normally distributed and (2) the value of the population standard deviation is known. (This is just a restatement of the rules graphically presented in *Figure 7.8*, page 229.) If n is ≤ 30 and the population values are known to be normally distributed, but the value of σ is unknown, then a t distribution is needed. When we are concerned with one-sample hypothesis tests of variances, if the population involved is normally distributed, we use the Chi-square distributions introduced in Chapter 7. Once the appropriate distribution is selected, we will know what type of sample statistic should be used as the basis of our hypothesis-testing decision. This is called the *test statistic*.

> The sample statistic whose value is the basis of the hypothesis-testing decision is called the **test statistic.**

Step 4: Define the Rejection or Critical Region Once the appropriate test statistic is determined, it's then possible to move to the next step. Suppose in a test using the z distribution that the level of significance (the risk of erroneous rejection of the null hypothesis) is chosen to be $\alpha = .05$. This means the null hypothesis will be rejected if the difference expressed in standard units between $\bar{x}$ and μ_0 has only a 5 percent or less chance of occurring. Since in many cases the null hypothesis can be rejected if the value of $\bar{x}$ is either too high or too low, we may want a .025 chance of erroneous rejection in each tail of the sampling distribution if the true mean is equal to the hypothesized value. Using the same notation as in Chapter 7, the z value with a tail area of .025 will be denoted $z_{.025}$ or, more generally, $z_{\alpha/2}$. In this situation, an α value of .05 represents the *total* risk of error. *Figure 8.4* shows how the normal curve is partitioned. With .025 in each tail, the remaining area in each half of the sampling distribution is .4750 (.5000 − .0250). Appendix 2 shows the z value for an area figure of .4750 is $z_{.025} = 1.96$.

What does the partitioning of the normal curve in *Figure 8.4* mean? *Figure 8.5* shows that if a sample mean differs from the hypothetical mean by 1.96 or more standard errors in either direction, there's sufficient reason to reject the null hypothesis at the .05 level of significance. Thus, a z value of 1.96, called the critical value of the test, represents the value in standard units at which the difference between $\bar{x}$ and μ_0 becomes significant enough to raise doubt that the null hypothesis is true. A **significant difference** is a difference between $\bar{x}$ and μ_0 that leads to the rejection of the null hypothesis.

FIGURE 8.4 With a total desired
risk of erroneous rejection of a true
null hypothesis of .05, the standardized difference between × and
μ_0 becomes significant at + 1.96 or
−1.96.

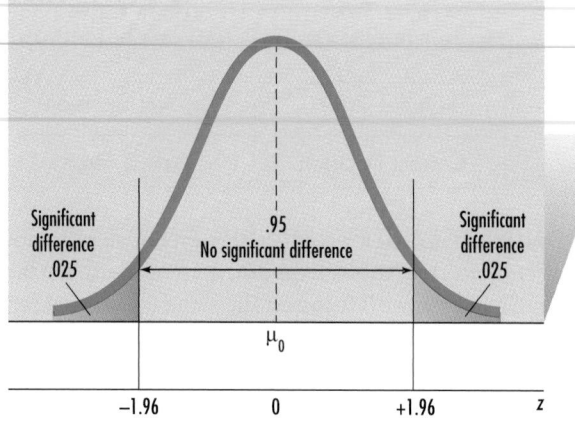

FIGURE 8.5 Construction of rejection region with a significance level
of .05.

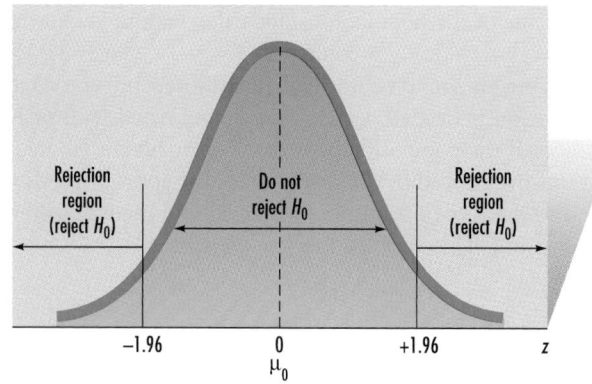

> The **rejection region** (or **critical region**) is thus that part of the sampling distri-
> bution—equal in total area to the level of significance—that's specified as being
> unlikely to contain the value of a test statistic if H_0 is true. A point at the start or
> boundary of the rejection region is called a **critical value** of the test.

After the level of significance is stated and the proper test distribution is selected, the
fourth step in our procedure is to find the critical value(s) for the rejection region
of the test statistic. If the difference between an obtained $\bar{x}$ and the assumed μ_0 has a
value that falls into the rejection region, the null hypothesis is rejected. If the difference
doesn't fall into the critical region, of course, the null hypothesis is not rejected. You
might have noticed that we have not said that we *accept* a null hypothesis; rather we
have used phrases such as "fail to reject the null hypothesis" or "the null hypothesis is
not rejected." This is because a test *never proves* with any certainty that a null hypothesis is true. Rather, a test merely fails to provide sufficient statistical evidence for rejecting a null hypothesis. The only standard of truth is the population parameter, and
since the true value of that parameter is unknown, the assumption can never be proven.
Thus, by saying we *fail to reject* the null hypothesis, rather than proving that the hypothesized parameter value is true, we are implying that we merely have not been able
to find compelling evidence that it is untrue. A similar analogy can be found in a crim-

inal trial when a jury renders a not-guilty verdict. The jurors may not know for sure if the defendant is innocent of the charges, but there isn't enough evidence to cause them to convict the defendant.

Step 5: State the Decision Rule After we've stated the hypotheses, selected the level of significance, determined the test distribution to use, and defined the rejection region, the fifth step is to prepare a *decision rule*.

> A **decision rule** is a formal statement that clearly states the appropriate conclusion to be reached about the null hypothesis based on the value of the test statistic.

The general format of a decision rule is

Reject H_0 in favour of H_1 if the value of the test statistic falls into the rejection region. Otherwise, fail to reject H_0.

Step 6: Make the Necessary Computations After all the ground rules have been laid out for the test, the next step is the actual data analysis. A sample of items is collected, the sample statistic(s) are computed, and an estimate of the parameter is calculated. Assuming that we're testing a hypothesis about the value of the population mean, we first calculate the value of a sample mean. To convert the difference between $\bar{x}$ and μ_0 into a standardized value, it's also necessary to compute the standard error of the mean. Then the standardized difference between the sample mean and the hypothesized parameter is the test statistic:

$$z = \frac{\bar{x} - \mu_0}{\sigma_{\bar{x}}} \tag{8.1}$$

Step 7: Make a Statistical Decision *If the value of the test statistic falls into the rejection region, the null hypothesis is rejected.* For example, *Figure 8.6* shows the rejection region of a normal curve with $\alpha = .01$. Referring to the z table, a total risk of 1 percent corresponds to z critical values of -2.575 and $+2.575$. Suppose a sample produced a test statistic of $z = 2.60$. Since z falls into the rejection region, there's sufficient reason to reject the null hypothesis, and the risk of erroneous rejection is only 1 percent.

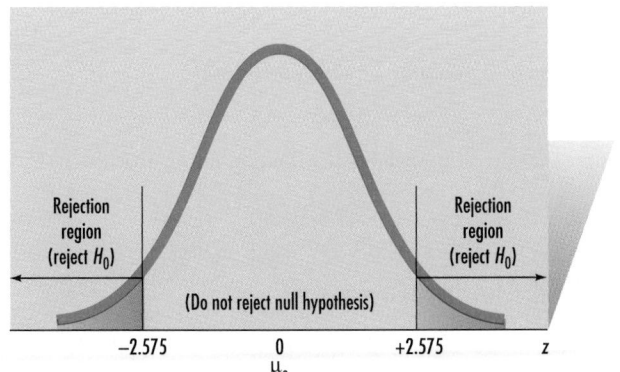

FIGURE 8.6 Rejection region with $\alpha = .01$.

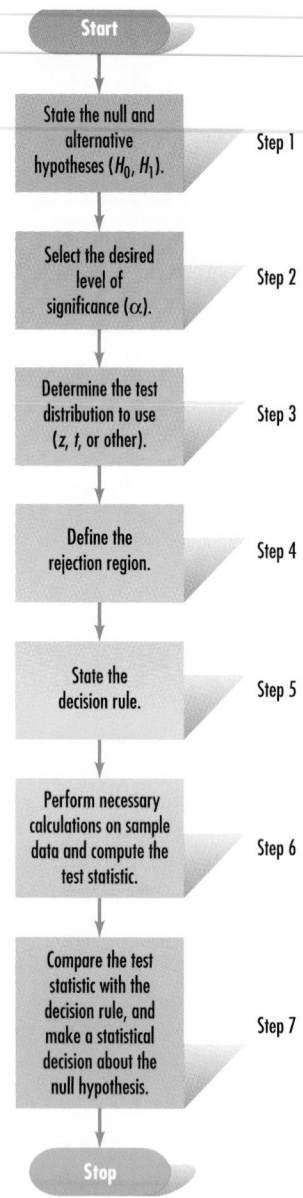

FIGURE 8.7 Classical seven-step hypothesis-testing procedure.

At this point, you may be dizzy with definitions and procedural steps. To help you sort out your head, *Figure 8.7* summarizes the general seven-step procedure for a classical hypothesis test.

Managerial Decisions and Statistical Decisions: A Caution

Let's conclude this section on a non-statistical note. Although statistical laws give us objective ways to assess hypotheses, a statistical conclusion doesn't represent the final word in decision making. Consumers of statistical reports use quantitative results as one form of input in a complex network of factors that affect an ultimate decision. But decision making is full of uncertainty, and although statistical results serve to reduce and control some of this uncertainty, they don't completely eliminate doubt. Problems may be quantified and a result obtained, but the solution is only as good as the input that has gone into structuring the problem.

Thus, statistical results, although objectively determined, shouldn't be blindly accepted. Other situational factors must also be considered. For example, a statistical test may tell a production manager that a machine probably isn't producing as much as she had assumed. But this result doesn't tell her what action to take. She may replace the machine, fix it, or leave it in its present condition. The ultimate decision is made by considering the available money for replacement, the repair record of the machine, the availability of new machines, and so on. Thus, the statistical conclusion is not necessarily the managerial conclusion; it's simply one factor that must be considered in the context of the whole problem.

Self-Testing Review 8.1

1. If a sample has 57 members, what is the chance that the mean of this sample will fall 1.96 or more standard errors from the true population mean?

2. If a sample has 14 members and the population is normally distributed but we don't know the population standard deviation, what is the chance that the mean of this sample will fall 2.65 or more standard errors from the true population mean?

3. If a sample has 22 members and we know the population is normally distributed with a standard deviation of 62.9, what's the chance that the mean of this sample will fall 2.33 or more standard errors from the true population mean?

4. What is a type I error?

5. What is a type II error?

6. What is the relevance of the level of significance of a hypothesis test?

7. What is a null hypothesis?

8. Why is it important to know the correct probability distribution for a particular test?

9. What is a critical value?

10. What is a test statistic?

11. Describe the seven steps in classical hypothesis testing.

12. What is an alternative hypothesis?

13. If the null hypothesis is $H_0: \mu = 18$, state three possible alternative hypotheses.

14. For each of the following situations, formulate a null and an alternative hypothesis:

   a) The population mean IQ is 100. A psychologist wants to test the hypothesis that the mean IQ for alcoholics is different than 100.

   b) An industrial engineer wants to test the hypothesis that the mean length of the steel beams being manufactured is 3.2 m.

   c) Last year the mean sales per week in a large department store were $85,492. A manager wants to test the hypothesis that sales have increased since he was promoted.

   d) A consumer advocate claims that the mean price for a cellular phone is not $300.

15. A vocational counsellor claims that the average score on a Life Roles Inventory Scale for the importance of lifestyle in choosing a career is less than 14.09.

16. A physician claims that the mean cost for an MRI test is less than $1,000.

8.2 One-Sample Hypothesis Tests of Means

It's time now to look at one-sample testing procedures for means under various conditions. You'll recall that there are three possible alternative hypotheses. The choice of which alternative to use for a test depends on factors that we'll consider in this section.

Classical Two-Tailed Tests When σ Is Known

If the null and alternative hypotheses are in this format,

$H_0: \mu = $ *hypothesized value*
$H_1: \mu \neq $ *hypothesized value*

and if the null hypothesis is rejected, then the conclusion is simply that the population mean doesn't equal the hypothesized value. It doesn't matter if the true value is likely to be more or less than the hypothesized value. The only conclusion is that the true and hypothesized values aren't likely to be the same.

The nature of the above hypotheses requires a *two-tailed test.*

> A **two-tailed test** is one that rejects the null hypothesis if the test statistic is significantly *higher or lower* than the hypothesized value of the population parameter.

With a two-tailed test, therefore, the rejection region has two parts, as shown in *Figure 8.8.* Since the hypothesis may be rejected with a sample value that's too high or too low, the total risk of error in rejecting μ_0 is evenly distributed in each tail. That is, the area in *each* part of the rejection region is $\alpha/2$.

When the value of σ is known and either $n > 30$ or the population is normally distributed so that the sampling distribution of the sample mean is normally or approximately normally distributed, the critical values or boundaries of the rejection region

FIGURE 8.8 Illustration of a rejection region for a two-tailed test with $\alpha = .05$.

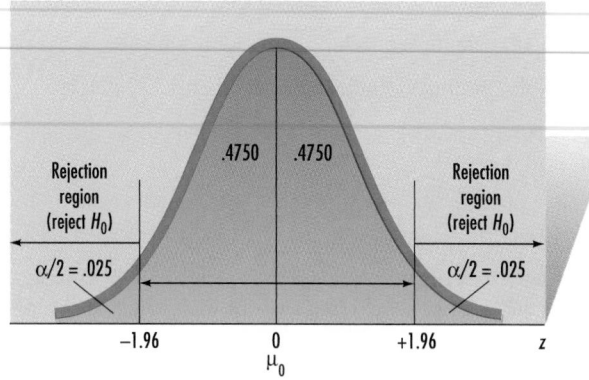

are found through the use of the z table. These critical values are determined by the z value corresponding to the probability $.5000 - \alpha/2$. For example, with a two-tailed test and $\alpha = .05$, the area in each tail is .025. Looking up the z value that corresponds to an area figure of $.5000 - .05/2$ or .4750, we find the critical values of the rejection region are $-z_{.025} = -1.96$ and $z_{.025} = +1.96$ (see *Figure 8.8*).

The appropriate decision rule in this example for a two-tailed test using the z distribution is

Reject H_0 in favour of H_1 if $z < -1.96$ or $z > +1.96$. Otherwise, fail to reject H_0.

(What if z is exactly 1.96? In this and other similar situations throughout the book, we'll interpret the decision rule to exclude 1.96 from the rejection region. A value of 1.97, of course, falls in the rejection region.)

The following examples show the use of two-tailed tests when σ is known. (In the first three problems, we'll label the seven steps in the classical hypothesis testing procedure that were identified in the preceding pages.)

◻ **Example 8.1**   Kate Flower, president of the Kate and Edith Cake Company, says that the mean number of cakes sold daily is 1,500. An employee wants to test the accuracy of Kate's claim. A random sample of 36 days shows that the mean daily sales was 1,450 cakes. Using a level of significance of $\alpha = .01$ and assuming $\sigma = 120$ cakes, what should the worker conclude?

◆ **Solution:**

Hypotheses (Step 1):

H_0: $\mu = 1,500$ cakes
H_1: $\mu \neq 1,500$ cakes

The level of significance of .01 *(Step 2)* is given in the problem, and this is a two-tailed test because a sample mean that is significantly too high or too low is sufficient to reject the null hypothesis. The interest of this test is only whether or not $\mu = 1,500$; no other conclusion is to be drawn.

The z distribution is used here *(Step 3)* because $n > 30$ and σ is known. And with $\alpha = .01$, the risk of erroneous rejection is .005 in each tail. This means that the chance of correctly deciding in favour of H_0 on one side of the normal curve is .4950. Consulting the z table, the z critical value corresponding to an area of .4950 is $z_{.005} = 2.575$. (The rejection region for this problem *(Step 4)* is illustrated in *Figure 8.9*.)

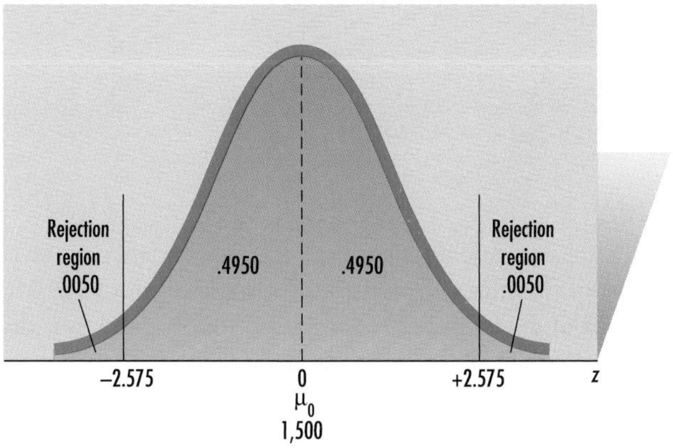

FIGURE 8.9 Illustration of a two-tailed rejection region using $\alpha = .01$.

Under these circumstances, the decision rule *(Step 5)* is stated as follows:

Reject H_0 in favour of H_1 if $z < -2.575$ or $z > +2.575$. Otherwise, fail to reject H_0.

The computation of the test statistic *(Step 6)* is:

$$z = \frac{\bar{x} - \mu_0}{\sigma_{\bar{x}}} = \frac{\bar{x} - \mu_0}{\sigma/\sqrt{n}} = \frac{1,450 - 1,500}{120/\sqrt{36}} = -2.5$$

Conclusion (Step 7):

Since $z = -2.5$, which is between ± 2.575, the null hypothesis cannot be rejected at the .01 level of significance. That is, Kate's claim that cake sales average 1,500 daily cannot be rejected at the .01 level. This does not prove that the K & E Cake Company makes an average of exactly 1,500 cakes daily. Rather, it simply says it is feasible that the mean is around 1,500. ◆

Example 8.2   An insurance executive asserts that the mean amount paid by his firm for personal injury claims resulting from automobile accidents is $18,500. An actuary wants to check the accuracy of this assertion and is allowed to sample randomly 36 cases involving personal injury. The sample mean is $19,415, and past years' data indicate that $\sigma = \$2,600$. Test the executive's belief with $\alpha = .05$.

◆ **Solution:**

Hypotheses (Step 1):

H_0: $\mu = \$18,500$
H_1: $\mu \neq \$18,500$

The level of significance to use *(Step 2)* is given in the problem, and this is a two-tailed test because the actuary is interested in deciding only if the true mean is different from $18,500, not in how it differs from $18,500.

Since $n > 30$ and σ is given, the z table *(Step 3)* is used. With $\alpha = .05$, there's a risk of .025 in each tail. The z value needed for an area of $.5000 - .0250$ or .4750 is 1.96, and hence ± 1.96 are the z critical values that define the rejection region *(Step 4)*. Therefore, the decision rule *(Step 5)* is

Reject H_0 in favour of H_1 if $z < -1.96$ or $z > +1.96$. Otherwise, fail to reject H_0.

The test statistic is calculated as follows *(Step 6)*:

$$z = \frac{\bar{x} - \mu_0}{\sigma_{\bar{x}}} = \frac{\bar{x} - \mu_0}{\sigma/\sqrt{n}} = \frac{\$19{,}415 - \$18{,}500}{\$2{,}600/\sqrt{36}} = \frac{\$915}{\$433.33} = 2.11$$

Conclusion (Step 7):

Since the value of the test statistic falls beyond +1.96, there's enough evidence to reject the null hypothesis at the .05 level of significance. That is, the sample mean of $19,415 lies 2.11 standard errors to the right of the hypothesized mean of $18,500, and thus the sample mean falls into the rejection region. Whenever a test is run at $\alpha = .05$, as the actuary selected here, there is only a 5 percent chance that a true null hypothesis will be rejected. So the actuary has strong (statistically significant) evidence that she should not trust the claim of the insurance executive that the mean amount paid by the firm for this type of claim is $18,500. ◆

Example 8.3   **Statistical process control** is a name given to sampling techniques that are used to monitor a controlled production process and to signal when that process fails to behave in the desired way. Let's assume your summer job includes checking the output of an automatic machine that produces thousands of bolts each hour. This machine, when properly adjusted, makes bolts with a mean diameter of 14.00 mm. That is, the value of μ should be 14.00 mm. Bolts that vary too much in either direction from this mean diameter aren't suitable for their intended use. It's known from past experience that the value of σ is 0.15 mm, and it's also known that the machine makes bolts with diameters that are normally distributed about the population mean. You take a random sample of 6 bolts from the machine's output each hour, and your latest sample has bolts with the following diameters (in mm): 14.15, 13.85, 13.95, 14.20, 14.30, and 14.35. At the .01 level, does it appear that the machine is properly adjusted?

◆ **Solution:**

Hypotheses (Step 1):

H_0: $\mu = 14.00$ mm
H_1: $\mu \neq 14.00$ mm

This is a two-tailed test because bolts that vary significantly in either direction can't be used for their primary purpose.

The level of significance is .01 *(Step 2)*. You can use the z distribution in this case *(Step 3)*, even though n is small, because the value of σ is known and because you also know that the population is normally distributed, With $\alpha = .01$, the corresponding z critical values are ±2.575 *(Step 4)*. Thus, you establish the following decision rule *(Step 5)*:

Reject H_0 in favour of H_1 if $z < -2.575$ or $z > +2.575$. Otherwise, fail to reject H_0.

To calculate the value of the test statistic, you must first find the value of the mean of your sample of six bolts. You find this mean, as follows:

$$\frac{14.15 + 13.85 + 13.95 + 14.20 + 14.30 + 14.35}{6} = 14.1333 \text{ mm}$$

Now, you compute the test statistic *(Step 6)*:

$$z = \frac{\bar{x} - \mu_0}{\sigma_{\bar{x}}} = \frac{\bar{x} - \mu_0}{\sigma/\sqrt{n}} = \frac{14.1333 - 14.00}{.15/\sqrt{6}} = \frac{.1333}{.0612} = 2.18$$

Conclusion (Step 7):

Since *z* falls between ± 2.575, you fail to reject the null hypothesis, at the .01 level of significance, that the population mean is 14 mm. Based on this test, there is no statistically significant evidence that the machine is operating improperly. ◆

All the calculations we just did can be tedious and are likely to have an occasional error. We will see in the next section how to get MINITAB and a TI-83 calculator to do these calculations for us.

A *p*-Value Approach to Hypothesis Testing

We've now looked at three examples that have followed the classical hypothesis-testing procedure. There is another way to conduct such tests, which uses what is called a *p-value* (or probability-value) testing approach. Most of the steps used in a *p*-value hypothesis test are the same as those we've been following in using the classical procedure, but there are also a few differences. Let's consider the problem situation in Example 8.3 again, but this time we'll use a *p*-value approach to see if the bolt-making machine is properly adjusted.

Steps in the *p*-Value Procedure

Step 1: State the Null and Alternative Hypotheses In our example problem,

H_0: $\mu = 14.00$ mm
H_1: $\mu \neq 14.00$ mm

As you can see, this first step is the same in the classical and *p*-value procedures.

Step 2: Select the Level of Significance In our example, α is .01, and, again, this second step is the same in traditional and *p*-value tests. (We'll see in a moment, though, that some researchers who use the *p*-value approach may omit this step.)

Step 3: Determine the Test Distribution to Use The *z* distribution is correct for our example, and there is still no difference between classical and *p*-value tests.

Step 4: State the Decision Rule The classical step of defining the rejection (or critical) region is omitted in a *p*-value test, and a decision rule may be formulated next. The decision rule is stated as follows:

Reject H_0 if the *p*-value is less than α. Otherwise, fail to reject H_0.

Thus, in our Example 8.3 problem, we'll reject H_0 if the *p*-value is less than .01. Note, however, that some researchers who prefer to use a *p*-value hypothesis test don't select a level of significance, and they don't specify a decision rule. Rather, they merely report the p-value(s) produced by their studies and leave the interpretations to those who read their reports in professional journals. When that approach is used, a published p-value of less than 0.01 is considered to be a very strong statistical argument for rejecting H_0, and a p-value of from 0.01 to 0.05 may give readers sufficient reason to doubt the validity of H_0.

Step 5: Compute the Test Statistic There's no difference between classical and p-value methods here. We've seen that the test statistic for our Example 8.3 problem is

$$z = \frac{\bar{x} - \mu_0}{\sigma_{\bar{x}}} = \frac{\bar{x} - \mu_0}{\sigma/\sqrt{n}} = \frac{14.1333 - 14.00}{.15/\sqrt{6}} = \frac{.1333}{.0612} = 2.18$$

Step 6: Compute the Appropriate p-Value It's helpful here to sketch the correct probability distribution—the z distribution in this example—for the case when H_0 is true and locate the value of the test statistic z on the sketch. For our Example 8.3 problem, which is concerned with both tails of the probability distribution, such a sketch is shown in *Figure 8.10*. As you can see, the p-value is the total area in each tail of the probability distribution beyond the z value of 2.18 and its negative, −2.18. The area between 0 (the z value of μ_0) and the z value of +2.18 is found to be .4854 in the normal table in Appendix 2. And the same area, of course, is found between 0 and a z value of −2.18. So in the *left tail:*

probability that $z < -2.18$ if H_0 is true $= .5000 - .4854 = .0146$

And in the *right tail:*

probability that $z > +2.18$ if H_0 is true $= .5000 - .4584 = .0146$

What meanings can we attach to these values of .0146? Well, as you've seen in earlier discussions, the probability that a sample mean will fall 2.18 or more standard errors

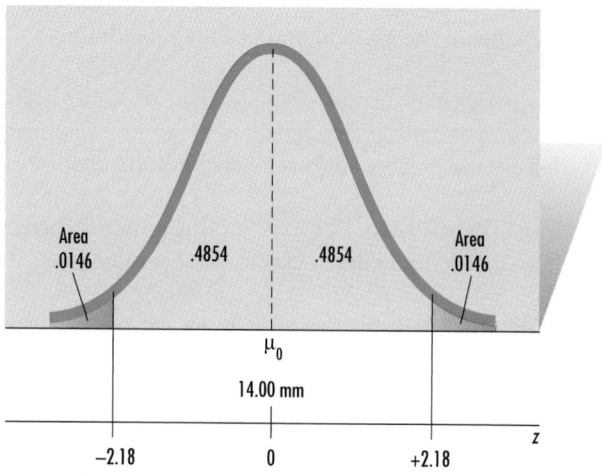

FIGURE 8.10 Illustration of a p-value for a two-tailed test using the data in Example 8.3.

p-value = 2(area in right tail)
= 2(.0146) = .0292

to the right of a population mean is .0146, and, of course, the probability that a sample mean will be 2.18 or more standard errors to the left of a population mean is also .0146. Thus, to compute the probability or *p*-value that a sample mean will fall into either the right-tail *or* left-tail area beyond 2.18 standard errors in a two-tailed test using the normal probability distribution, we employ this formula:

$$p\text{-value (two-tailed)} = P(z < -|z|) + P(z > |z|) = 2 \times P(z > |z|) \qquad (8.2)$$

where $|z|$ = the absolute value (ignore the signs) of the test statistic.

And in our Example 8.3 problem, the *p*-value we are looking for is

$$p\text{-value (two tailed)} = P(z < -|z|) + P(z > |z|)$$
$$= 0.146 + 0.146 = 0.292 \text{ or approximately } .03$$

To summarize, then,

> The **p-value** of a hypothesis test is the probability of obtaining a difference between the test statistic and the hypothetical population parameter that is at least as extreme as the one actually observed, assuming H_0 is true. The smaller the *p*-value, the stronger the case against H_0.

Step 7: Make a Statistical Decision Since the computed *p*-value of .03 is greater than the level of significance of .01, we fail to reject the null hypothesis. In our example, the *p*-value of .03 tells us that a sample with a mean at least this far from 14.00 could be expected to happen 3 percent of the time when the value of μ is 14.00 mm. As noted earlier, though, if we hadn't selected a level of significance in advance, a *p*-value of .03 might be interpreted by some as sufficient reason to doubt the validity of our hypothesis that the population mean is 14.00 mm.

You've spent some time following the computations needed to conduct classical and *p*-value hypothesis tests of the sample bolt data presented in Example 8.3. But computer statistical packages and statistical calculators can easily handle such tasks. *Figure 8.11a* and both screen 2 and screen 3 of *Figure 8.11b* show the results of using MINITAB and a TI-83 calculator to do our hypothesis test computations. Other than slight differences caused by rounding and reporting the results to a different number of significant digits, we again get $z = 2.18$ and a *p*-value of .03.

Classical One-Tailed Tests When σ Is Known

Many times it's not enough to simply test that the true value is *not equal* to the hypothesized value. If the null hypothesis isn't tenable, we may be concerned only if the true value is either probably higher than the hypothesized value or probably lower than the hypothesized value, but not both. For example, suppose it is safe for medical technicians to work with contaminated materials no more than an average of 15 minutes

FIGURE 8.11 (*a*) To obtain the MINITAB output, click on **Stat, Basic Statistics, 1-Sample Z.** In this window, enter the data column in the **Variables** box, click in the circle next to the **Test mean** box and supply the value of μ_0 (= 14), click in the **Sigma** box and enter the value of σ (= .15), and click on **OK.** (*b*) To form the hypothesis test in Example 8.3 on the TI-83, use the **Z-Test** command on the **STAT > TESTS.** Put the data into a list. **L1** is used here. Access the command and set the parameters as shown in screen 1. Choose **Calculate** and get the results in screen 2. If we perform the test again choosing **Draw** instead of **Calculate,** we get screen 3. This shows the same values and the sketch.

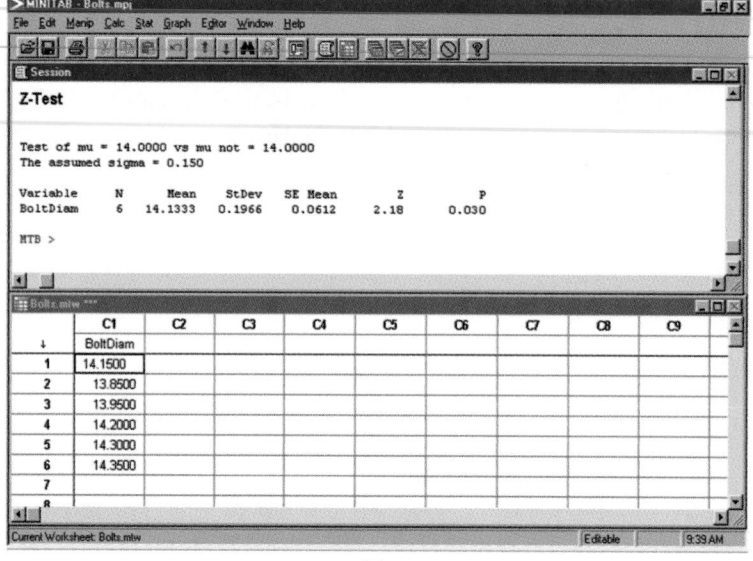

(*a*)

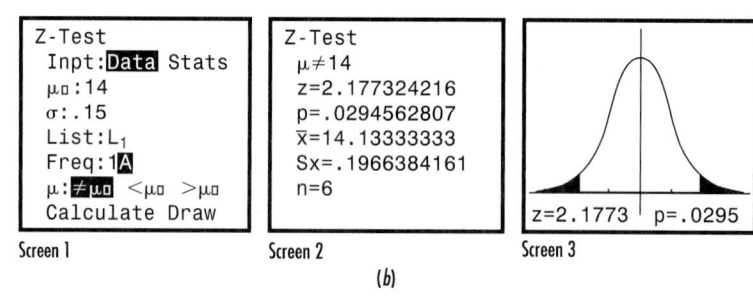

Screen 1   Screen 2   Screen 3

(*b*)

per day. In this case, we would be concerned only if the mean exceeds 15 minutes per day and would want to test the null hypothesis

H_0: $\mu = 15$ minutes

against an alternative hypothesis,

H_1: $\mu > 15$ minutes

Consider a second example. Suppose you are working for a drug firm that currently markets a muscle relaxant that has a mean time-to-relief of 15 minutes. A company chemist claims she has developed a new formulation that works faster. To evaluate her claim, you would want to test the null hypothesis

H_0: $\mu = 15$ minutes

against an alternative hypothesis,

H_1: $\mu < 15$ minutes

In situations such as demonstrated by these two examples, the null hypothesis is still

H_0: μ = hypothesized value

But the alternative hypothesis is one of the following:

H_1: μ > hypothesized value

or

H_1: μ < hypothesized value

The nature of either alternative hypothesis indicates a *one-tailed test.*

> In a **one-tailed test,** the rejection region is only one tail of the sampling distribution, and the null hypothesis is rejected only if the value of a test statistic falls into this tail. If the alternative hypothesis is H_1: parameter > hypothesized value so that the rejection region is in the right tail of the sampling distribution, then the one-tailed test is also known as a **right-tailed test;** but if the alternative hypothesis is H_1: parameter < hypothesized value so that the rejection region is in the left tail, then the one-tailed test is a **left-tailed test.**

Right-Tailed Tests When the alternative hypothesis is

H_1: μ > hypothesized value

the rejection region is in the right tail of the sampling distribution, and the null hypothesis is rejected only if the value of a sample mean is significantly higher than the hypothesized value. In such a test, the attention is focused on rejecting H_0 solely on the basis that the true value might be greater than the hypothesized value. So we should use a right-tailed test only when we are unconcerned if the true value is actually less than the hypothesized value.

If you're confused by the previous paragraph, consider this analogy. Suppose you and a friend are guessing a third person's age. Your friend hypothesizes that the third party is exactly 20 years old, but you believe that he is older. Finally, you ask the third person, "Are you more than 20 years old?" He says no. As a result, you cannot reject your friend's assertion, but his opinion may be wrong because you didn't ask the person if he was less than 20 years old. However, if your interest in the third person's age is based on whether it is legal to serve him alcohol in a province where the legal drinking age is 21, you probably would not care if he was younger than 20 anyway. The non-rejection of H_0 in a right-tailed test is similar to this analogy.

Left-Tailed Tests When the alternative hypothesis is

H_1: μ < hypothesized value

we're interested in seeing if the true value is *less* than the hypothesized value. In this case, H_0 is rejected only if the value of a sample mean is *significantly low*. In a left-tailed test, H_0 isn't rejected if the true value is likely to be more than the hypothesized value.

FIGURE 8.12 Illustration of the rejection regions for left-tailed and right-tailed tests.

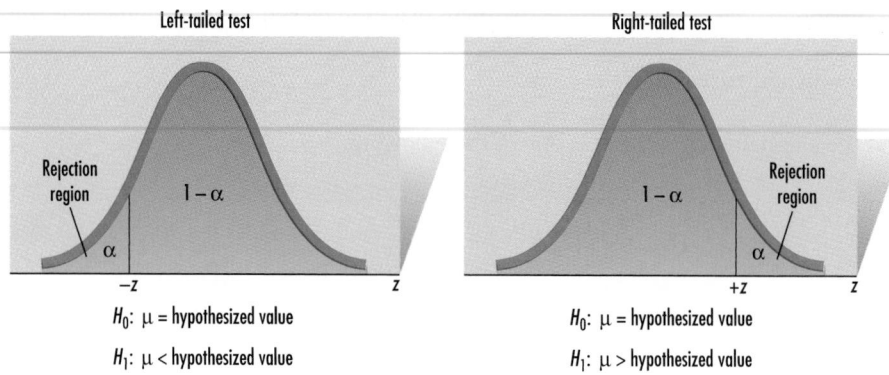

FIGURE 8.13 Rejection for a left-tailed test at the .05 level of significance.

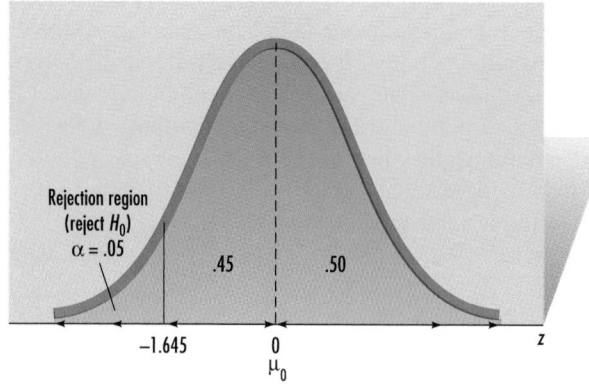

The distinctions between left- and right-tailed tests are shown in *Figure 8.12*.

Level of Significance Considerations The level of significance (α) is the total risk of erroneously rejecting H_0 when it's actually true. In a two-tailed test, the total risk is evenly divided between each tail. But in a one-tailed test, an area in the single tail is assigned the total risk or α. If the z distribution is applicable, the correct z critical value is thus determined by the one-tailed probability of $.5000 - \alpha$. For example, if the level of significance is .05 for a left-tailed test, the boundary of the rejection region is a z critical value of -1.645 (see *Figure 8.13*). This critical value is denoted $-z_{.05}$, or, more generally, $-z_\alpha$.

Decision Rule Statements If a z distribution is to be used, the decision rule for a *left-tailed test* takes this form:

Reject H_0 in favour of H_1 if $z < -z$ critical value $(-z_\alpha)$. Otherwise, fail to reject H_0.

The decision rule for a *right-tailed test* is

Reject H_0 in favour of H_1 if $z > z$ critical value (z_α). Otherwise, fail to reject H_0.

The test statistic is computed the same way for a one-tailed test as for a two-tailed test.

Let's look now at the following examples, where a one-tailed test is applicable and where the value of α is known.

Example 8.4   Valerie Lyons, a production supervisor at a chemical company, wants to be sure that the Super-Duper can is filled with an average of 454 grams of product. If the mean volume is significantly less than 454 grams, customers (and regulatory agencies) will likely complain, prompting undesirable publicity. The physical size of the can doesn't allow a mean volume significantly above 454 grams. A random sample of 36 cans shows a sample mean of 442 grams. Production records show that σ is 8 grams. Use this to conduct a hypothesis test with $\alpha = .01$.

◆ **Solution:**
Hypotheses (Step 1):

H_0: $\mu = 454$ grams
H_1: $\mu < 454$ grams

The nature of the problem is such that if the null hypothesis is rejected, Valerie will conclude that the population mean is too low.
We know that $\alpha = .01$ *(Step 2)*, and with $n > 30$ and with σ known, the z distribution is used *(Step 3)*. Thus, with $\alpha = .01$, and with a left-tailed test, the rejection region begins at a z critical value of $-z_{.01} = -2.33$ *(Step 4)*. Therefore, the decision rule *(Step 5)* is

Reject H_0 in favour of H_1 if $z < -2.33$ (remember that $-2.34 < -2.33$). Otherwise, fail to reject H_0.

The test statistic is computed as follows *(Step 6)*:

$$z = \frac{\bar{x} - \mu_0}{\sigma_{\bar{x}}} = \frac{\bar{x} - \mu_0}{\sigma/\sqrt{n}} = \frac{442 - 454}{8/\sqrt{36}} = -9.00$$

Conclusion (Step 7):
Since $z < -2.33$, Valerie must reject H_0 and rush to correct the filling process. It's virtually impossible that a sample selected from a sampling distribution that has a true mean of 454 grams will have a sample mean located 9.00 standard errors to the left of the true mean! ◆

Example 8.5   Jeff Kuhn, a perfume distributor, believes that the mean cost to process a sales order is $13.25. Alia Adam, cost controller, fears that the average cost of processing is more than that. She is interested in taking action if costs are high, but she can accept the situation if the actual mean cost is below the hypothesized value. A random sample of 100 orders has a sample mean of $13.35. Assuming the value of σ is its historical value of $0.50, conduct a test at the .01 level of significance.

◆ **Solution:**
Hypotheses (Step 1):

H_0:$\mu = \$13.25$ cost
H_1: $\mu > \$13.25$ cost

This is a right-tailed test because only a significantly high sample mean value will lead Alia to reject the null hypothesis. With $\alpha = .01$ *(Step 2)*, and with $n > 30$, the z distribution is applicable *(Step 3)*, and the correct z critical value is $z_{.01} = 2.33$ *(Step 4)*.

Decision Rule (Step 5):

Reject H_0 in favour of H_1 if $z > 2.33$. Otherwise, fail to reject H_0.

Test Statistic (Step 6):

$$z = \frac{\bar{x} - \mu_0}{\sigma_{\bar{x}}} = \frac{\bar{x} - \mu_0}{\sigma/\sqrt{n}} = \frac{\$13.35 - \$13.25}{\$0.50/\sqrt{100}} = 2.00$$

Conclusion (Step 7):

Since $z < 2.33$, Ms. Adam will fail to reject the null hypothesis that the mean cost is $13.25. She has insufficient reason to reject Mr. Kuhn's statement at the .01 level of significance. ◆

A *p*-Value One-Tailed Test

A two-tailed *p*-value hypothesis test was presented a few pages earlier. Let's use the data in Example 8.5 now to show how a one-tailed *p*-value test is conducted.

The first steps to conduct the test in Example 8.5 don't change. The hypotheses *(Step 1)* for this right-tailed test are still

H_0: $\mu = \$13.25$ cost
H_1: $\mu > \$13.25$ cost

The level of significance (α) remains .01 *(Step 2)*, and we'll still use the z distribution *(Step 3)* to carry out this test. Our decision rule is identical to what it would be for a two-tailed test when using *p*-values *(Step 4)*:

Reject H_0 if the *p*-value is less than .01. Otherwise, fail to reject H_0.

The computation of the test statistic doesn't change *(Step 5)*:

$$z = \frac{\bar{x} - \mu_0}{\sigma_{\bar{x}}} = \frac{\bar{x} - \mu_0}{\sigma/\sqrt{n}} = \frac{\$13.35 - \$13.25}{\$0.50/\sqrt{100}} = 2.00$$

To compute the appropriate *p*-value *(Step 6)* for a one-tailed test when the z distribution is used, we select *one* of these formulas:

p-value (right-tailed test) = $P(z >$ calculated value of the test statistic)	
$= P(z > z)$	(8.3)
p-value (left-tailed test) = $P(z <$ calculated value of the test statistic)	
$= P(z < z)$	(8.4)

Since this is a right-tailed test, our *p*-value is

p-value (right-tailed test) = $P(z > z) = P(z > 2.00)$
$= .5000 - .4772$ (Use Appendix 2 to find that the area
between 0 and a z value of 2.00 is .4772.)
$= .0228$

Since the computed p-value of .0228 is greater than the level of significance of .01, we fail to reject H_0, and Ms. Adam again has insufficient evidence to doubt Mr. Kuhn's statement that the mean cost to process a sales order is $13.25 *(Step 7)*. Our p-value of .0228 tells us that a sample with a mean of $13.35 or larger could be expected to happen 2.28 percent of the time when the value of μ is $13.25. Of course, if this test had been conducted with $\alpha = .05$, we would have rejected H_0.

Classical Two-Tailed Tests When σ Is Unknown

Up to now, we've been working hypothesis tests with σ known. But as you saw in Chapter 7, knowledge of σ is rare. Usually, the sample standard deviation (s) is used in the testing procedure.

With σ unknown, the following aspects of the traditional hypothesis testing procedure are affected:

1. The correct sampling distribution can no longer be assumed to be approximately normally shaped if n is 30 or less.

2. In the computation of the test statistic, an estimated standard error—$\hat{\sigma}_{\bar{x}}$—must be used instead of $\sigma_{\bar{x}}$.

When σ is unknown, we may still perform a hypothesis test if either the sample size is large ($n > 30$) or if the population is normally distributed. In either case, the t distribution is the appropriate distribution to use for a test on a population mean. The t critical value(s) used as the boundary of a rejection region depends on the level of significance and the degrees of freedom (which are $n - 1$ for the tests in this chapter). For example, suppose you are making a two-tailed test at the .05 level of significance with a sample size of 16. In the t table in Appendix 4, the t value with 15 degrees of freedom is 2.131. That is, $t_{\alpha/2}$ or $t_{.025} = 2.131$. The t table is set up to show the rejection region in one tail. When $n > 30$, as the critical values for the z distribution and the t distribution are very similar, we will use the z distribution to perform the test in this large sample case.

As we shall see in the following examples, the seven-step testing procedure is the same with an unknown σ as with a given σ, with the exceptions that (1) the proper test distribution (z or t) must be used and (2) the correct method of calculating the test statistic must be followed.

■ Example 8.6   J. C. Daly, co-owner of the J-T Bar, believes his business sells an average of 17 bottles of Border Ale daily. His partner thinks this estimate is wrong. A random sample of 36 days shows a mean sales of 15 bottles and a sample standard deviation (s) of 4 bottles. Test the accuracy of Daly's opinion at the .10 level of significance.

◆ **Solution:**

Hypotheses (Step 1):

H_0: $\mu = 17$ bottles
H_1: $\mu \neq 17$ bottles

This is a two-tailed test because we wish to assess only the validity of Daly's belief. The level of significance *(Step 2)* is .10. With $n = 36$, the sampling distribution approximates the normal distribution, and thus the z distribution applies *(Step 3)*.

Since this is a two-tailed test and $\alpha = .10$, the risk of error in each tail is .05. The z critical value corresponding to $.5000 - .05 = .45$ is $z_{.05} = 1.645$ *(Step 4)*.

Decision Rule (Step 5):

Reject H_0 in favour of H_1 if $z < -1.645$ or $z > +1.645$. Otherwise, fail to reject H_0.

With $s = 4$ and $n = 36$, $\hat{\sigma}_{\bar{x}}$ is estimated in the following manner:

$$\hat{\sigma}_{\bar{x}} = \frac{s}{\sqrt{n}} = \frac{4}{\sqrt{36}} = .667$$

Test Statistic (Step 6):

$$z = \frac{\bar{x} - \mu_0}{\hat{\sigma}_{\bar{x}}} \tag{8.5}$$

$$= \frac{15 - 17}{.667} = -3.00$$

Conclusion (Step 7):

Since $z < -1.645$, it's necessary to reject Daly's claim at the .10 level of significance. There is statistically significant evidence that the mean amount of Border Ale sold differs from 17 bottles per day. ◆

Example 8.7   The height of female adults in Biglandia is normally distributed, and a journal article claims that the mean height of these females is 163 cm. To test this claim, a sociologist takes a random sample of 16 Biglandia women and finds that the mean is 160 cm and the standard deviation is 6.4 cm. Can the claim made in the article be rejected at the .05 level of significance?

◆ **Solution:**

Hypotheses (Step 1):

H_0: $\mu = 163$ cm
H_1: $\mu \neq 163$ cm

The nature of the problem indicates a two-tailed test, and for a significance level of .05 *(Step 2)*, there will be a .025 risk of erroneous rejection in each tail. The t distribution is applicable because the population heights are normally distributed and the sample size is only 16 *(Step 3)*. With 15 degrees of freedom and a .025 risk in each tail, $t_{.025} = 2.131$ *(Step 4)*.

Decision Rule (Step 5):

Reject H_0 in favour of H_1 if $t > -2.131$ or $t < +2.131$. Otherwise, fail to reject H_0.

Test Statistic (Step 6):

$$t = \frac{\bar{x} - \mu_0}{\hat{\sigma}_{\bar{x}}} = \frac{\bar{x} - \mu_0}{s/\sqrt{n}} = \frac{160 - 163}{6.4/\sqrt{16}} = \frac{-3.0}{1.6} = -1.88$$

Conclusion (Step 7):

Since *t* falls between ±2.131, there is insufficient reason to reject the article's statement at the .05 level of significance. It is feasible that the mean height of female adults in Biglandia is 163 cm. ◆

Example 8.8   Let's go back to the problem in Example 8.3 and change some assumptions. Let's suppose the bolts made by the automatic machine are normally distributed and should still have a mean diameter of 14.00 mm. If bolts vary significantly in either direction from this standard, they aren't suitable for their intended use. But let's assume now that the value of σ isn't known, and we must instead calculate a sample standard deviation. As before, the latest sample has 6 bolts with the following diameters (in mm): 14.15, 13.85, 13.95, 14.20, 14.30, and 14.35. Our previous decision was that the bolt machine was operating properly. Is that decision still the correct one at the .01 level?

◆ **Solution:**
Hypotheses (Step 1):

H_0: $\mu = 14.00$ mm
H_1: $\mu \neq 14.00$ mm

This is still a two-tailed test, and $\alpha = .01$ *(Step 2)*, but we must now use the *t* distribution *(Step 3)* because the sample size is only six and we don't know σ. With 5 degrees of freedom and a .005 risk in each tail, $t_{.005} = 4.032$ *(Step 4)*.

Decision Rule (Step 5):

Reject H_0 in favour of H_1 if $t < -4.032$ or $t > +4.032$. Otherwise, fail to reject H_0.

The value of *s* must be computed as follows (remember from Example 8.3 that $\bar{x} = 14.1333$):

x	$(x - \bar{x})$	$(x - \bar{x})^2$
14.15	.0167	.00028
13.85	−.2833	.08026
13.95	−.1833	.03360
14.20	.0667	.00445
14.30	.1667	.02779
14.35	.2167	.04696
		.19334

$$s = \sqrt{\frac{\Sigma(x - \bar{x})^2}{n - 1}} = \sqrt{\frac{.19334}{5}} = .1966$$

Test Statistic (Step 6):

$$t = \frac{\bar{x} - \mu_0}{\hat{\sigma}_{\bar{x}}} = \frac{\bar{x} - \mu_0}{s/\sqrt{n}} = \frac{14.1333 - 14.00}{.1966/\sqrt{6}} = \frac{.1333}{.0803} = -1.66$$

Conclusion (Step 7):

Since t falls between ±4.032, we'll fail to reject H_0 and continue to think, as in Example 8.3, that the machine is in adjustment. The sample results were such that we came close to rejecting H_0 in Example 8.3, but not this time because the t distribution is flatter than the z distribution with thicker tails and because s in this example is larger than the assumed σ in Example 8.3. ◆

p-Value Test Using the t Distribution

The p-value approach is also used to conduct tests when σ is unknown and when the t distribution must then be used. Let's look again at Example 8.8. As you know by now, the hypotheses, level of significance, and test distribution to use (the t distribution in this case) remain unchanged when p-value tests are employed.

Our decision rule for Example 8.8 is now

Reject H_0 if the p-value is $< .01$. Otherwise, fail to reject H_0.

The *test statistic* is still the same 1.66 computed in Example 8.8. And to compute the p-value for this two-tailed test using the t distribution, the following formula applies:

$$p\text{-value (two tailed)} = P(t < -|t|) + P(t > |t|)$$
$$= P(t < -|1.66|) + P(t > |1.66|)$$

We're looking now for the probability of getting a t value that exceeds 1.66 in each tail of the t distribution that has 5 degrees of freedom. Unfortunately, we hit a snag at this point in our attempt to find the exact p-value because of deficiencies in our t table in Appendix 4. Since that table includes only a limited number of α values— remember there are different t distributions for each degree of freedom—the best we can do is find the table values *on the 5-df row* that are closest to our t value of 1.66. These table values are 1.476 and 2.015. The t value of 1.476 separates 10 percent of the area in each tail from the middle 80 percent of the distribution. And the t value of 2.015 separates 5 percent of the area *in each tail* from the middle 90 percent of the distribution. Thus, $t = 1.66$ corresponds to a probability value of between .05 and .10, and so

$$p\text{-value (two tailed)} = P(t < -|1.66|) + P(t > |1.66|)$$
$$= (.05 \text{ to } .10) + (.05 \text{ to } .10)$$
$$= .10 \text{ to } .20$$

that is, $0.10 < p\text{-value} < 0.20$

Since the p-value figure (somewhere between .10 and .20) is certainly greater than the α value of .01, we fail to reject H_0 that $\mu - 14.00$ mm.

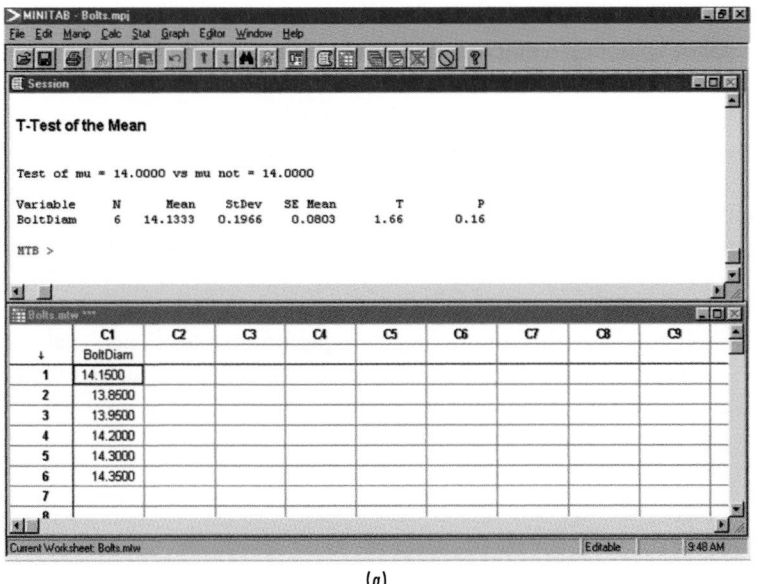

(a)

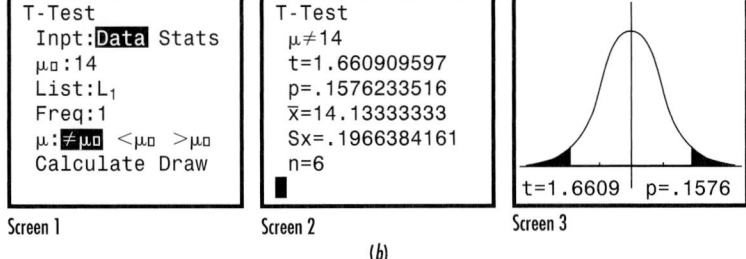

Screen 1   Screen 2   Screen 3

(b)

FIGURE 8.14 (a) To obtain the MINITAB output, click on **Stat, Basic Statistics, 1-Sample t.** In this window, enter the data column in the **Variables** box, click in the circle next to the **Test mean** box and supply the value of μ_0, (14 in this example), and click on **OK.** (b) To use the TI-83 to do the calculations for the hypothesis test in Example 8.8, first put the data into a list. **L1** is used here. Access the **T-Test** command from the **STAT<TESTS** menu, and set the parameters for the test as shown in screen 1. Choose **Calculate** and get the results in screen 2. If we perform the test again choosing **Draw** instead of **Calculate,** we get screen 3. This shows the same values and the sketch.

The completion of the hypothesis test in Example 8.8 required tedious calculations to find the sample mean and standard deviation. But, as in Example 8.3, our computing chores can be turned over to a statistical software package or a statistical calculator, and the same results can be achieved in seconds. *Figure 8.14a* shows the MINITAB output from this example, while screen 2 and screen 3 of *Figure 8.14b* give the results of using a TI-83 to obtain the values we've already computed. And now the mystery of where the *p*-value lies between .10 and .20 is solved! As you can see, the *p*-value is .16 (or .1576). The greater use in recent years of *p*-value tests is due in part to the ease with which computer software and calculators can supply such results.

Example 8.9   **How Much Jam Is Jammed into a Jam Jar?** The label on Ol-lieberry jam jars lists a fill of 269 grams. A sample of jars was selected and the contents were weighed. The results are listed below. Using the *p*-value approach and $\mu = .05$, does it appear that the mean fill of the population of all weights is 269 grams?

Fill Weight				
276.45	270.02	273.03	265.50	274.93
269.44	277.73	272.73	274.55	269.00

◆ **Solution:**

Because filling too low is dishonest and bad business, and because filling too high is expensive and may overflow the jar and make a mess, we will run a two-tailed test.

Hypotheses (Step 1):

H_0 $\mu = 269$ grams
H_1: $\mu \neq 269$ grams

We have already chosen $\alpha = .05$ *(Step 2)*. Because the sample size is only ten and we don't know σ, we will use the t distribution *(Step 3)* to perform the test. This is valid if the population values are normally distributed. Experience with this and similar filling situations indicates that this is a reasonable assumption.

Decision Rule (Step 4):

Reject H_0 if the p-value is $< .05$, Otherwise, fail to reject H_0.

 We used both MINITAB (see *Figure 8.15a*) and a TI-83 calculator (see screen 2 and screen 3 of *Figure 8.15b*) to compute the test statistic *(Step 5)* and the p-value *(Step 6)*.

Conclusion (Step 7):

Because the p-value $= .021 < .05$, H_0 is rejected. It appears that the label is misleading, though, since the jam jars seem to be overfilled in a way that probably won't upset the consumer. ◆

Classical One-Tailed Tests When σ Is Unknown

The following examples are one-tailed tests made when σ is unknown. *It's assumed in these examples that the population values are normally distributed.* You'll notice that the testing procedure is essentially unchanged.

Example 8.10   The manager of the Granite Rock Company believes that the average truckload delivered weighs 2,500 kilograms. A shareholder, Adil Ali, argues that this is an inflated figure to lure new investors. Mr. Ali randomly samples the records of 25 loads and finds the mean load to be 2,460 kilograms with a standard deviation (s) of 250 kilograms. Can Adil reject the manager's claim using a significance level of .05?

◆ **Solution:**
Hypotheses (Step 1):

H_0: $\mu = 2,500$ kilograms
H_1: $\mu < 2,500$ kilograms

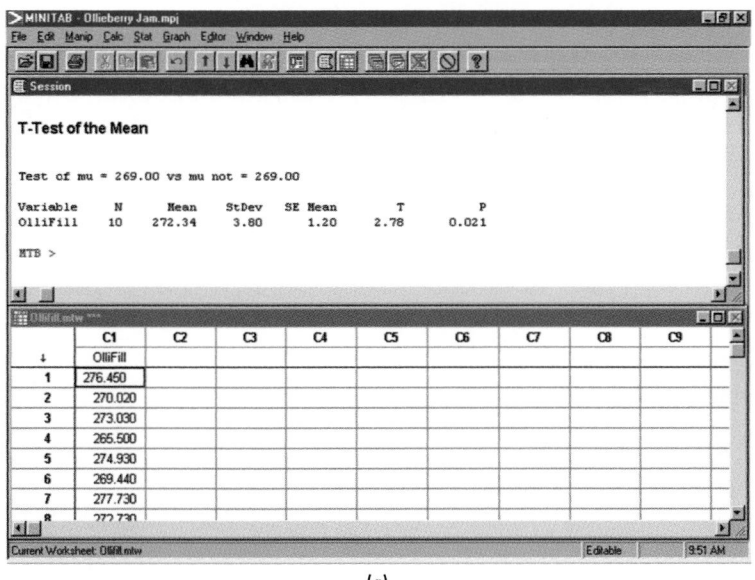

(a)

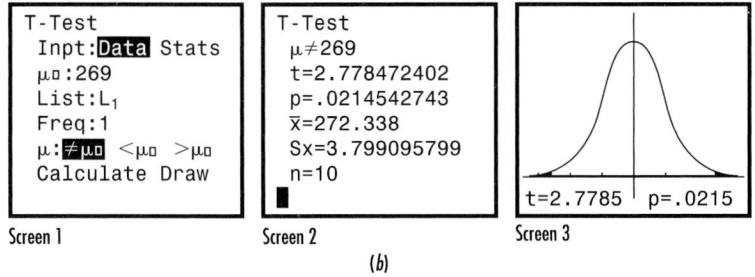

Screen 1   Screen 2   Screen 3

(b)

FIGURE 8.15 (a) MINITAB *t*-test output of Ollieberry jam data. (b) TI-83 screens for Ollieberry jam data.

This is a left-tailed test because Adil is worried only that the mean of 2,500 kilograms is inflated. And since this is a one-tailed test, the area in the single tail of the rejection region is equal to the significance level of .05 *(Step 2)*.

With $n = 25$, the *t* distribution applies *(Step 3)*, there are 24 degrees of freedom, and $t_{.05} = 1.711$ *(Step 4)*.

Decision Rule (Step 5):

Reject H_0 in favour of H_1 if $t < -1.711$. Otherwise, fail to reject H_0.

Test Statistic (Step 6):

$$t = \frac{\bar{x} - \mu_0}{\hat{\sigma}_{\bar{x}}} = \frac{\bar{x} - \mu_0}{s/\sqrt{n}} = \frac{2,460 - 2,500}{250/\sqrt{25}} = \frac{-40}{50} = -.80$$

Conclusion (Step 7):

Since $t > -1.711$, there's no significant reason for Mr. Ali to doubt the manager's claim. It's quite possible that a sample could be selected with a mean located only $-.80$ standard error from a true mean. ◆

☐ **Example 8.11**   Harry N. Fox, owner of the HNF Employment Agency, believes that the agency receives an average of 16 complaints per month from companies that hire the agency's people. Naaz Noble, an interviewer, is concerned that the true mean is higher than Harry believes. If Harry's hypothesis is an understatement, something must be done about the agency's employee screening procedures. A sample of 10 months yields an average of 18 complaints with a standard deviation of 3 complaints. Conduct a test at the .01 level.

◆ **Solution:**
Hypotheses (Step 1):

H_0: $\mu = 16$ complaints per month
H_1: $\mu > 16$ complaints per month

Because Naaz is concerned only about the possibility that the mean number of complaints is over 16, this is a *right-tailed test.*
    With $n = 10$ and $\alpha = .01$ *(Step 2)*, the t critical value *(Step 3)* with 9 degrees of freedom is $t_{.01} = 2.821$ *(Step 4)*.

Decision Rule (Step 5):

Reject H_0 in favour of H_1 if $\textbf{\textit{t}} > 2.821$. Otherwise, fail to reject H_0.

Test Statistic (Step 6):

$$t = \frac{\bar{x} - \mu_0}{\hat{\sigma}_{\bar{x}}} = \frac{\bar{x} - \mu_0}{s/\sqrt{n}} = \frac{18 - 16}{3/\sqrt{10}} = \frac{2}{.95} = 2.11$$

Conclusion (Step 7):
Since $t < 2.821$, there's insufficient reason at the .01 level of significance to reject Harry's hypothesis. ◆

☐ **Example 8.12**   We've seen how the MINITAB statistical program and the TI-83 calculator process two-tailed z and t tests in earlier examples. But one-tailed tests are also handled with ease. Let's suppose that Naaz isn't satisfied with the results obtained in the preceding example and decides to sample another ten-month period. The sample gave the following complaint data: 20, 14, 12, 24, 17, 22, 13, 16, 15, and 19.

◆ **Solution:**
Hypotheses (Step 1):

H_0: $\mu = 16$ complaints per month
H^1: $\mu > 16$ complaints per month

And at the .01 level *(Step 2)*, a t critical value *(Step 3)* of 2.821 *(Step 4)* is still needed.

Decision Rule (Step 5):

Reject H_0 in favour of H_1 if $\textbf{\textit{t}} > 2.821$. Otherwise, fail to reject H_0.

The sample mean and sample standard deviation are found as follows:

x	$(x - \bar{x})$	$(x - \bar{x})^2$
20	2.8	7.84
14	−3.2	10.24
12	−5.2	27.04
24	6.8	46.24
17	−.2	.04
22	4.8	23.04
13	−4.2	17.64
16	−1.2	1.44
15	−2.2	4.84
19	1.8	3.24
172		141.60

$$\bar{x} = \frac{\sum x}{n} = \frac{172}{10} = 17.2$$

$$s = \sqrt{\frac{\sum(x - \bar{x})^2}{n - 1}} = \sqrt{\frac{141.60}{9}} = 3.967$$

With $s = 3.967$, we can now compute the test statistic:

Test Statistic (Step 6):

$$t = \frac{\bar{x} - \mu_0}{\hat{\sigma}_{\bar{x}}} = \frac{\bar{x} - \mu_0}{s/\sqrt{n}} = \frac{17.2 - 16}{3.967/\sqrt{10}} = \frac{1.2}{1.254} = .96$$

Conclusion (Step 7):

Since $t < 2.821$, we fail to reject H_0. There's still insufficient reason to doubt Harry's claim. ◆

All of these results are duplicated in the MINITAB computer output shown in *Figure 8.16a* and in the TI-83 calculator screens 2 and 3 of *Figure 8.16b*. As you can see, these both compute the value of the test statistic and also produce the *p*-value for the test. This *p*-value is obtained by using the formula:

$$p\text{-value (right-tailed test)} = P(t > t) = P(t > .96)$$

Again, we can't find the exact *p*-value for this example from Appendix 4, but *Figure 8.16a* and *Figure 8.16b* both tell us it is .18. And since .18 > .01, we know that Naaz should fail to reject H_0.

We've now discussed one-sample hypothesis tests of means under various conditions. The classical testing procedure is similar under all conditions, and the testing differences that exist are reflected in the differences that appear in the decision rules. These differences are summarized in Table 8.1. The *p*-value testing procedure uses the same decision rules in all tests (reject H_0 if the *p*-value is < α. Otherwise, fail to reject H_0).

FIGURE 8.16 (*a*) The steps are identical to those used to perform the *t* test in Figures 8.14 and 8.15 except we need to tell MINITAB that we are doing a right-tailed test. To do so, click on the down arrow to the right of the **Alternative** box and click on **greater than.** (*b*) To use the TI-83 to do the calculations for Example 8.11, first put the data into a list. L1 is used here. Access the **T-Test** command from the **STAT**>**TESTS** menu, and set the parameters for the test as shown in screen 1. Choose $>\mu_0$ to make the calculator do the one-sided hypothesis test. Choose **Calculate** and get the results in screen 2. If we perform the test again choosing **Draw** instead of **Calculate,** we get screen 3. This shows the same values and the sketch.

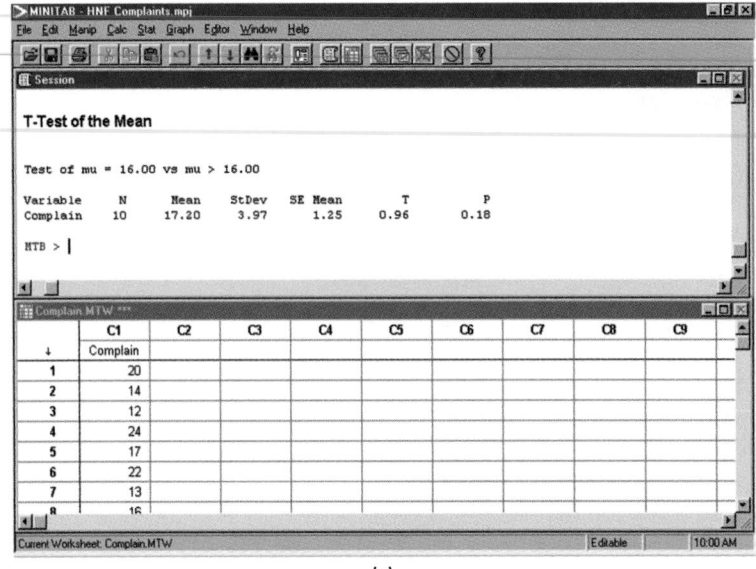

(*a*)

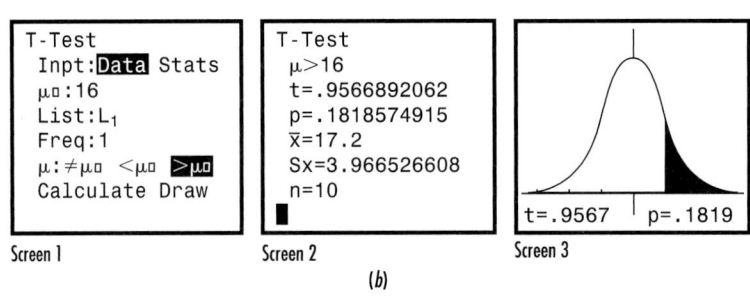

(*b*)

TABLE 8.1 DECISION RULES UNDER VARIOUS CONDITIONS WITH CLASSICAL HYPOTHESIS TESTING OF MEANS

$n > 30$, σ **Known and Population Values Known to Be Normally Distributed**	$n \le 30$, σ **Unknown, and Population Values Known to Be Normally Distributed**
TWO-TAILED TEST Reject H_0 in favour of H_1 if $\mathbf{z} > +z_{\alpha/2}$ or $z < -z_{\alpha/2}$. Otherwise, fail to reject H_0.	Reject H_0 in favour of H_1 if $t > +t_{\alpha/2}$ or $\boldsymbol{t} < -t_{\alpha/2}$. Otherwise, fail to reject H_0.
LEFT-TAILED TEST Reject H_0 in favour of H_1 if $\mathbf{z} < -z_\alpha$. Otherwise, fail to reject H_0.	Reject H_0 in favour of H_1 if $\boldsymbol{t} < -t_\alpha$. Otherwise, fail to reject H_0.
RIGHT-TAILED TEST Reject H_0 in favour of H_1 if $\mathbf{z} > +z_\alpha$. Otherwise fail to reject H_0.	Reject H_0 in favour of H_1 if $\boldsymbol{t} > +t_\alpha$. Otherwise, fail to reject H_0.

One problem we have ignored is the assumption of normality. In the small sample case, $n \leq 30$, to have a valid test or confidence interval, we assume that we have taken a random sample from a normal population. Is it possible to determine if that assumption is reasonable? The answer is yes. In fact, there are several methods, but the details are beyond the scope of this text. So what we have done is employ MINITAB to demonstrate the type of test that is possible. The following graph was produced by MINITAB for the complaint data of the previous example. The null hypothesis being tested is that the sample has been taken from a normal population, and the alternative is that the sample has been taken from a non-normal population. If the data are from a normal population, the points that you see on the graph should be relatively straight, that is, close to the red line. MINITAB eliminates any need for making a judgment concerning whether the data are close to the line—it prints the p-value for this test of normality. As the p-value is .871—larger than any reasonable level of significance—we would decide in favour of the null hypothesis and conclude that it was reasonable to believe the sample was from a normal population.

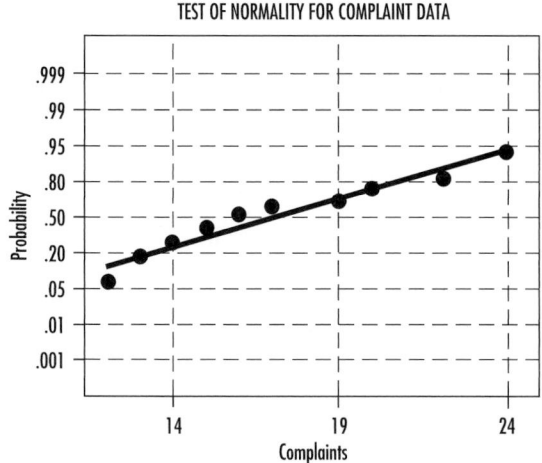

If we reject the hypothesis that the sample was from a normal population, there are other options available. You may be able to select a larger sample and use a large-sample procedure that does not rely on the assumption of normality. Or, you may be able to use a non-parametric test to answer your questions. These tests, appearing in Chapter 13, require fewer assumptions than the tests considered so far.

Let's look at one more example.

Example 8.13 **Chemotherapy and Red Blood Cells** In a class project, Jodi Sauer discussed mean corpuscular volume (MCV) or the average volume of erythrocytes (red blood cells). This volume is measured in microscopic units called femtoliters (fl). The mean MCV for the general population without known medical problems is 90 fl. It has been suspected that many chemotherapy drugs used to treat cancer cause elevated MCV levels. The MCV counts that follow were obtained from a sample of 92 patients. Does this data support the idea that chemotherapy drugs cause an elevated MCV? Test using the p-value approach and $\alpha = .01$ (Data = MCV).

MCV					
90.7	97.6	101.9	65.6	105.5	90.6
91.0	97.5	94.6	89.0	94.2	107.7
97.3	95.7	94.1	98.8	96.6	91.6
89.5	94.8	93.8	79.7	96.8	94.0
102.2	97.0	97.7	92.8	90.8	96.3
86.4	93.6	89.4	91.2	95.2	103.7
83.6	104.3	101.4	98.4	101.0	86.5
100.2	96.8	86.9	90.5	80.9	101.9
103.1	90.7	68.4	103.4	91.2	97.1
91.9	90.6	87.9	101.5	93.4	100.8
101.5	86.3	90.4	90.1	80.0	94.8
90.6	100.2	99.7	86.7	89.2	86.0
68.1	89.2	90.4	92.7	87.4	77.1
88.4	85.8	97.9	88.9	87.0	95.1
93.2	99.2	95.6	90.4	86.0	94.6
90.4	94.2				

◆ Solution:

Because we are concerned only with elevated levels of MCV, we will run a right-tailed test.

Hypotheses (Step 1):

H_0: μ = 90 fl
H_1: μ > 90 fl

We set the level of significance at α = .01 *(Step 2)*. Because the sample size is 92, we can use the *z* distribution *(Step 3)* to perform the test.

Decision Rule (Step 4):

Reject H_0 if the *p*-value is < .01. Otherwise, fail to reject H_0.

We used both MINITAB and a TI-83 calculator to compute the test statistic *(Step 5)* and associated *p*-value *(Step 6)*. The results are found in *Figure 8.17a* and screens 2 and 3 of *Figure 8.17b*, respectively. In each, with σ unknown, we used the one-sample *t* rather than the one-sample *z* procedure. There is a good reason for this. Remember, up to now, we have used the *z* distribution as an approximation of the *t* distribution whenever *n* > 30. This is because the test statistic is approximately normally distributed and the table of the *z* distribution is more complete than the table of the *t* distribution. However, the test statistic actually has the shape of a *t* distribution with 92 − 1 = 91 degrees of freedom (which, with so many degrees of freedom, is approximately normal). Both MINITAB and the TI-83 calculator are not limited by our tables and can compute any desired *t* values. So by asking for the one sample *t* rather than the one sample *z*, we are actually asking for the more appropriate procedure to be done.

Conclusion (Step 7):

Because *p*-value = .0006 < .01, H_0 is rejected. It appears that the MCV is elevated for patients undergoing chemotherapy. ◆

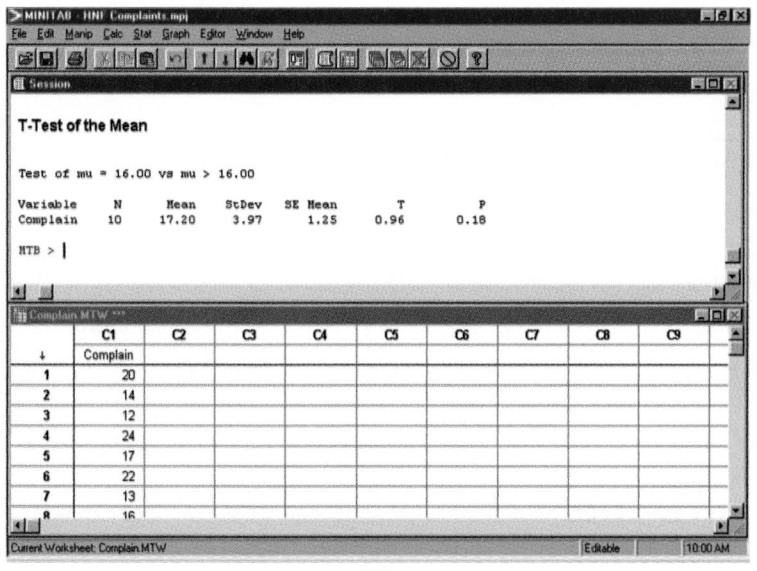

(*a*)

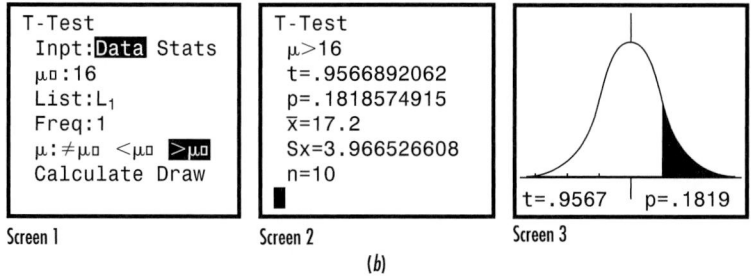

Screen 1   Screen 2   Screen 3

(*b*)

FIGURE 8.17 (*a*) MINITAB *t* test of MCV data. (*b*) TI-83 calculator screens of MCV data. Note that the *p*-value is reported in scientific or exponential notation. If that is unfamiliar, it simply indicates the decimal place should be moved the number of places indicated by the number to the right of E, with zeros inserted if necessary. So, 6.3262947E-4 is .00063262947.

Self-Testing Review 8.2

17. Assume $n > 30$ or σ is known and the population distribution is normal. Determine the critical z value(s) for each of the following types of hypothesis tests:

    a) Right-tailed test, $\alpha = .01$.

    b) Two-tailed test, $\alpha = .05$.

    c) Left-tailed test, $\alpha = .05$.

18. Determine the critical t value(s) to be used for the following tests:

    a) $n = 13$, left-tailed test, $\alpha = .05$.

    b) $n = 21$, two-tailed test, $\alpha = .01$.

    c) $n - 9$, right-tailed test, $\alpha = .05$.

19. For each of the following, determine if the use of a t or z distribution is appropriate for the hypothesis test. Find the critical t or z value(s).

    a) $n = 19$, σ is unknown and population distribution is normal, left-tailed test, $\alpha = .05$.

    b) $n = 11$, σ is known and population distribution is normal, right-tailed test, $\sigma = .01$.

c) $n = 34$, σ is unknown, two-tailed test, $\alpha = .01$.

d) $n = 12$, σ is unknown and population distribution is normal, left-tailed test, $\alpha = .05$.

20. What is the meaning of the term p-value for a right-tailed hypothesis test? What is the meaning for a left-tailed test? For a two-tailed test?

21. How does a p-value procedure differ from the classical hypothesis-testing procedure?

22. The level of significance for a test is .05, and the p-value is .07. What is the decision? (Do you reject or fail to reject the null hypothesis?)

23. The level of significance for a test is .01, and the p-value is .004. What is the decision?

24. The p-value for a test is .23. What decision is made at the .05 level of significance? At the .01 level?

25. The p-value for a test is .002. What decision is made at the .05 level of significance. At the .01 level?

26. The p-value for a test is .02. What decision is made at the .05 level of significance? At the .01 level?

27. For each of the following, use the seven-step classical hypothesis-testing procedure (and where necessary, assume the population is normally distributed):

a) Test the claim that μ is equal to 50 at the .05 level of significance. Use sample data of $n = 45$, $\bar{x} = 48.3$, $\sigma = 5.1$.

b) Test the claim that μ is more than 231 at the .01 level of significance. Use sample data of $n = 18$, $\bar{x} = 235.3$, $s = 15.7$.

c) Test the claim that μ is lower than 1,500 at the .05 level of significance. Use sample data of $n = 62$, $\bar{x} = 1,483$, $\sigma = 51.3$.

28. A survey conducted on January 30, 2003, for Wal-Mart reported that on average, people planned to spend $51 on the purchase of a Valentine's Day gift that year. A survey of 40 people after Valentine's day in 2003 found they had spent an average of $64 with a standard deviation of $18. Test the hypothesis at the .05 level that the population mean expenditure on Valentine's day gifts in 2003 was higher than $51.

29. A survey recently reported that the mean national annual expenditure for inpatient and outpatient services of all persons over 64 years of age was $5,423. If a random sample of 352 persons over age 64 living in Sudbury had an average expense of $5,516, with a standard deviation of $979, can we conclude that the mean inpatient and outpatient expense of all Sudbury residents over age 64 is higher than the national average of $5,423? Use the .01 level of significance.

30. According to the *Career Development Quarterly,* men completing a Life Roles Inventory questionnaire have a mean response of 15.08 on their evaluation of the importance of opportunity for advancement. A random sample of 27 women responded to the same questionnaire with a mean response of 14.44 and a standard deviation of 3.32. Assuming a normally distributed population, test the hypothesis that women rate advancement lower in importance than do men in career decision making. Use the .01 level of significance.

31. A large number of students were taught calculus using a new method of teaching. The new method emphasized interactive computer labs, cooperative learning, and extensive writing. These students then wrote the same final exam as students taught using traditional methods. The possible score on problem 1 on this exam was 0 to 4. The population of all students taught with traditional methods received a mean score of 1.30 for problem 1. The mean and standard deviation of a random sample of 41 scores made by students who were taught using the new method were 1.87 and 1.58 respectively. Test the hypothesis that the mean score on problem 1 made by the population of all students taught using the new method is higher than 1.30. Use the .05 level of significance.

32. An article describing research on the subject of the role of touch on consumer behaviour appeared in the *Journal of Consumer Research*. The mean and standard deviation of the ratings of a random sample of 124 diners who were touched by male servers were 3.07 and 1.08, respectively. (The rating scale was +4 for extremely good service, 0 for neutral service, and –4 for extremely poor service.) Test the hypothesis that the population mean rating of male servers who touch their customers is three. Use the .05 level of significance.

33. According to *Management Accounting*, salary figures for certified management accountants (CMAs) who are in the field less than 1 year are normally distributed with a mean of $31,129. Suppose a random sample of 15 first-year CMAs in Edmonton produces a mean salary of $32,379, with a standard deviation of $1,797. Test the hypothesis that the mean for all Edmonton first-year CMAs is not equal to $31,129. Use the .05 level of significance.

34. In 1993, *Consumer Reports* gave the following prices for a sample of 19 cellular phones:

$499 279 669 550 207 600 399 100 235 467
 200 235 489 300 299 200 200 249 249

Assuming a normally distributed population, test the hypothesis at the .05 level that the population mean price for cellular phones at the time of this survey was more than $300.

35. The *American Heart Journal* reports that the mean arterial blood pressure (mm Hg) for a control population of patients with congestive heart failure is 84.2. A study was made to assess the effect of Captopril on patients with congestive heart failure. A random sample of 29 patients who took Captopril had a mean arterial blood pressure of 69.1 with a standard deviation of 15.62. Assuming the data are normally distributed, test the hypothesis at the .01 level that the population mean arterial blood pressure for patients who take Captopril is less than 84.2.

36. In problems (a)–(d), use the *p*-value method for the hypothesis tests.

a) A study to examine how well marital dissolution was predicted by husbands' and wives' personality scores was recently published in the *Journal of Personality and Social Psychology*. The mean rating on a scale for "neuroticism" for wives in stable marriages was 19.43. Do wives in unstable marriages differ? A random sample of 64 wives in unstable marriages had a mean score of 29.85 with a standard deviation of 24.17. Test the hypothesis that wives in unstable marriages have a neuroticism rating greater than 19.43. Use the .01 level of significance.

b) Transcutaneous electrical nerve stimulation (TENS) devices are frequently used in the management of acute and chronic pain. An important component of the TENS system is the skin electrode. A study reported in the *Journal of Physical Therapy* was made to determine conductive differences among electrodes used with TENS devices. A random sample of 11 electrodes in the low-impedance group produced impedance measures (in ohms) of

1,200 1,200 1,000 1,600 1,400 1,400 1,200 1,700 1,600 1,300 1,600

Assuming a population of normally distributed values, test the hypothesis that the population mean impedance measure for all such electrodes is 1,400. Use the .05 level of significance.

c) Normal subjects have a mean of 46.3 on the Stroop Color-Word Test. A study of 32 first-episode schizophrenic patients reported in the *American Journal of Psychiatry* had a mean of 32.78 and standard deviation of 10.8 on this test. Test the hypothesis at the .05 level that the population mean score for first-episode schizophrenic patients on this test is 46.3.

d) It is thought that marketing executives are generally satisfied with their jobs. The *Journal of Marketing* recently published the results of a survey in which there were responses from 216 marketing executives. On a Likert scale of 1 to 5 (where 1 = extremely dissatisfied, and 5 = extremely satisfied), the mean response of this random sample was 3.78 with a standard deviation of 1.65. Test the hypothesis at the .01 level that the mean response of all such executives is equal to 3.9 against the alternative that the mean response is less than 3.9.

37. A biology student reported on an experiment in which he took 40 butterflies capable of flight early in the morning and measured their resting inactivity period (RIP). It has been theorized that butterflies that fly early in the morning would have a shorter mean RIP, as this behaviour is thought to be a thermoregulatory mechanism. The RIP for the population of all butterflies is believed to be 133 seconds. Test the hypothesis at the .10 level that the population of all butterflies capable of flight early in the morning has a mean RIP less than 133 seconds (Data = RIP).

		RIP (sec)		
117	52	132	125	98
132	152	103	120	77
140	155	156	75	145
181	115	102	66	102
86	156	134	112	124
92	93	124	142	124
177	148	148	187	170
64	85	167	121	167

38. An engineering student examined the minimum bursting pressure of a certain type and size of PVC irrigation pipe. The manufacturer claims a mean bursting pressure of more than 350 psi. A sample of ten such pipes was experimentally determined to have the following bursting pressures:

401   359   383   427   414   415   389   463   394   428

Test to see if the manufacturer's claim appears true. Use a level of significance of .05.

39. A project manager collected data in order to check the quality of ceramic turbine blades. The data consisted of measurements on the maximum principal stress on the blades, an indicator of possible impact failure for the component:

Maximum Principal Stress (MPa)					
4,468	5,364	2,047	2,240	3,978	4,102
1,399	2,020	1,503	2,585	2,213	2,571

One project required a mean greater than 2,650 MPa. Using a level of significance of .01, test to see if the mean maximum principal stress of all such ceramic turbine blades would satisfy the requirements of the project.

40. Due to the increased demand for Internet access, many systems require upgrades in router, servers, or even cable to higher and faster mediums to accommodate the load. An Internet service provider wanted to see if the mean number of hits to a server exceeds 38,000/day. He took a sample of $n = 31$ days and found the number of hits each day:

Hits

19,168	49,033	45,847	31,713	38,323	47,446
50,297	35,495	44,660	39,731	46,326	35,122
38,515	29,814	50,956	50,459	37,664	20,059
41,275	24,468	25,041	37,891	45,934	48,439
46,506	41,103	47,372	49,140	42,273	40,837
35,937					

Using a level of significance of .10, test to see if the mean number of hits on all days to this server exceeds 38,000/day (Data = ServeHit).

41. The use of polymers in medicine, especially in the area of drug delivery, is one of the fastest growing areas of polymer chemistry. A researcher conducted an experiment in which different formulations were used in a delivery device. A sample was taken from one formulation on the first total drug reading (mg):

603	534	542	591	610	489	516	570	596	654

The desired result was for the mean of this amount to exceed 450 mg. Using a level of significance of .05, test to see if the formulation appears to be delivering the desired mean.

42. All electrical and electronic devices vary in quality, even if manufactured in the same way. An electrician tested the capacitance (in μF or 1×10^{-6} Farads) of 30 capacitors using a Wavetech multimeter:

0.342	0.309	0.335	0.333	0.327	0.346
0.321	0.346	0.334	0.322	0.322	0.326
0.334	0.341	0.321	0.343	0.315	0.341
0.345	0.314	0.348	0.337	0.311	0.352
0.329	0.337	0.324	0.339	0.331	0.313

The nominal value of the capacitors, as determined by the manufacturer, is .33 μF. Test the hypothesis at the .05 level that the population mean of the capacitance is .33 μF (Data = Capacitn).

43. M. Wells obtained carbon monoxide readings in the air over a region. Regulations set the maximum safe level of carbon monoxide at 20 ppm. Using a level of .01, test to see if the mean carbon monoxide in the air over this region is less than the maximum safe level of 20 ppm (Data = CarbMono).

Carbon Monoxide (ppm)

6	13	10	13	12	12	23	11
12	11	8	7	18	9	15	21
10	13	4	7	10	5	7	

8.3 One-Sample Hypothesis Tests of Proportions

The classical seven-step hypothesis-testing procedure for proportions in the large-sample case is essentially the same one used for testing means with a large sample size. (As in Chapter 7, this section discusses only the large-sample proportion testing case where $np \geq 5$ and where $n(1 - p)$ is also ≥ 5. The complexity of the small-sample case is beyond the scope of this book.)

The only significant change in conducting a classical test of proportions rather than a test of means is in the computation of the test statistic. The test statistic for proportions is computed as follows:

$$z = \frac{\hat{p} - p_0}{\sigma_{\hat{p}}} \tag{8.6}$$

where p_0 = hypothesized value of the population proportion.

You may recall from Chapter 6 that the correct value of the standard error of proportion is found with this formula:

$$\sigma_{\hat{p}} = \sqrt{\frac{p(1 - p)}{n}}$$

Of course, we don't know the population proportion (p) now; if we did, we wouldn't be making a test! But we'll use the hypothesized value of p, in computing the standard error. That way, if our hypothesis is true, we'll calculate the correct value of $\sigma_{\hat{p}}$. Thus, $\sigma_{\hat{p}}$ is found as follows:

$$\sigma_{\hat{p}} = \sqrt{\frac{p_0(1 - p_0)}{n}} \tag{8.7}$$

To demonstrate the traditional testing procedure for proportions, let's first examine a two-tailed test situation and then look at one-tailed test examples.

Classical Two-Tailed Testing

Example 8.14   The editor of a newspaper, the *Weekly Daily*, has written that 25 percent of the university students in the paper's circulation area read newspapers daily. A random sample of 200 of these university students shows that 45 of them are daily readers of newspapers. At the .05 level, is the editor's statement likely to be true?

◆ **Solution:**
Hypotheses (Step 1):

H_0: $p = .25$
H_1: $p \neq .25$

This is a two-tailed test because we are interested in seeing if the editor's claim of 25 percent is true; if untrue, we don't care how it is so. We know that $\alpha = .05$ *(Step 2)*. With $np > 5$ [it's $(200)(.225)$ or 45], and with $n(1 - p)$ also ≥ 5 [it's $(200)(.775)$ or 155], the z distribution is used *(Step 3)* to determine the rejection region. With $\alpha = .05$, there is an area of .025 in each tail of the rejection region, and so the correct z values are $\pm z_{.025} = 1.96$ *(Step 4)*.

Decision Rule (Step 5):

Reject H_0 in favour of H_1 if $z < -1.96$ or $z > +1.96$. Otherwise, fail to reject H_0.

With a hypothesized value of .25, the standard error of proportion is

$$\sigma_{\hat{p}} = \sqrt{\frac{p_0(1 - p_0)}{n}} = \sqrt{\frac{(.25)(.75)}{200}} = .031$$

Test Statistic (Step 6):

$$z = \frac{\hat{p} - p_0}{\sigma_{\hat{p}}} = \frac{.225 - .25}{.031} = -.81$$

Conclusion (Step 7):

Since z falls between ± 1.96, we fail to reject H_0. There's not enough evidence to reject the editor's assertion. ◆

Classical One-Tailed Testing

Example 8.15 The manager of the Big-Wig Executive Hair Stylists, Hugo Brandt, has advertised that 90 percent of the firm's customers are satisfied with the company's services. Polly Tanquary, a consumer activist, feels that this is an exaggerated statement that might require legal action. In a random sample of 150 of the company's clients, 132 said they were satisfied. What should be concluded if a test is conducted at the .05 level of significance?

◆ **Solution:**

Hypotheses (Step 1):

H_0: $p = .90$
H_1: $p < .90$

This is a *left-tailed test* because Polly Tanquary is concerned only that the statement about 90 percent being satisfied is exaggerated—she certainly wouldn't be worried if Big-Wig's claim is too modest. With the .05 level of significance *(Step 2)*, the z distribution is used *(Step 3)* and the rejection region is bounded by a z critical value of $-z_{.05} = -1.645$ *(Step 4)*.

Decision Rule (Step 5):

Reject H_0 in favour of H_1 if $z < -1.645$, Otherwise, fail to reject H_0.

STATISTICS IN ACTION

With $p_0 = .90$ and $n = 150$, the standard error of proportion is

$$\sigma_{\hat{p}} = \sqrt{\frac{p_0(1 - p_0)}{n}} = \sqrt{\frac{(.90)(.10)}{150}} = .024$$

Test Statistic (Step 6):

$$z = \frac{\hat{p} - p_0}{\sigma_{\hat{p}}} = \frac{.88 - .90}{.024} = -.83$$

Conclusion (Step 7):

Since z is not less than -1.645, H_0 is not rejected. There's insufficient reason for Polly to doubt Hugo's claim. ◆

■ **Example 8.16**   A Patent Medicine Company supervisor assumes that the bottling machine is operating properly if only .05 of the processed bottles are not full. A random sample of 100 bottles had 7 bottles that weren't full. Using a significance level of .01, conduct a test to see if the machine is operating properly.

◆ **Solution:**

Hypotheses (Step 1):

H_0: $p = .05$ not full
H_1: $p > .05$ not full

This is a right-tailed test because the supervisor is concerned only that the true proportion might be more than anticipated. With a .01 level *(Step 2)*, the z critical value *(Step 3)* is $z_{.01} = 2.33$ *(Step 4)*, and therefore the decision rule is as follows:

Decision Rule (Step 5):

Reject H_0 in favour of H_1 if $z > 2.33$. Otherwise, fail to reject H_0.

With $p_0 = .05$ and $n = 100$, the standard error of proportion is

$$\sigma_{\hat{p}} = \sqrt{\frac{p_0(1 - p_0)}{n}} = \sqrt{\frac{(.05)(.95)}{100}} = .0218$$

Test Statistic (Step 6):

$$z = \frac{\hat{p} - p_0}{\sigma_{\hat{p}}} = \frac{.07 - .05}{.0218} = .92$$

Conclusion (Step 7):

Since z is less than 2.33, H_0 is not rejected. It does not appear that the machine is operating improperly. ◆

p-Value Tests of Proportions

The classical approach was used to make the two- and one-tailed tests of proportions we've now considered. But we could easily have conducted a *p*-value test for each example by following the seven *p*-value steps outlined earlier. Without repeating all the details again, the appropriate *p*-value for Example 8.14 (a two-tailed test in which the calculated value of the test statistic was $z = -.81$) is

$$p\text{-value (two tailed)} = P(z < -|z|) + P(z > |z|)$$
$$= P(z < -|-.81|) + P(z > |-.81|)$$
$$= P(z < -.81) + P(z > .81)$$
$$= .209 + .209 = .418$$

And the conclusion is that since .418 is much greater than $\alpha = .05$, we fail to reject H_0 and the editor's opinion.

For Example 8.16 (a right-tailed test with $z = .92$), the *p*-value is

$$p\text{-value (right-tailed test)} = P(z > |z|)$$
$$= P(z > |.92|)$$
$$= P(z > .92)$$
$$= .1788$$

Again, the conclusion is that since .1788 > .01, we fail to reject H_0 that the machine is operating as expected.

Example 8.17   An Exercise on Exercise A student group involved in facilities planning wanted to see if more than 50 percent of the people who work out at a recreation centre use the exercise room. A sample of 199 recreation centre users showed that 109 of them, or 54.8 percent, used the exercise room. At a level of significance of .01, does it appear more than 50 percent of the people who work out at the centre use the exercise room?

Let *p*% denote the true percentage of all recreation centre users who use the exercise room.

◆ **Solution:**
Hypotheses (Step 1):

H_0: *p*% = 50 percent (or, $p = .050$)
H_1: *p*% > 50 percent (or, $p > 0.50$)

This is a right-tailed test because the student group wanted to know if the percentage was *greater than* 50 percent. We have selected $\alpha = .01$ *(Step 2)*. With $n\hat{p} \geq 5$ [it's (199)(.5477) or 108.99], and with $n(1 - \hat{p})$ also ≥ 5 [it's (199)(.4523) or 90.01], the *z* distribution is used *(Step 3)* to determine the rejection region. We are going to use the *p*-value approach, so with $\alpha = .01$, the decision rule is *(Step 4)*

Reject H_0 if the *p*-value is less than .01. Otherwise, fail to reject H_0.

FIGURE 8.18 (*a*) To obtain this MINITAB output, click on **Stat, Basic Statistics,** and **1 Proportion.** Click in the circle next to **Summarized data,** enter the number of trials, **199,** the number of successes, **109,** and then click on the **Options** button. In the **Options** window, ignore the **Confidence Level** box (MINITAB will both compute a confidence interval for π and perform hypothesis test calculations, but here we are interested only in the hypothesis test). Enter **.50** in the **Test proportion** box, specify **greater than** in the **Alternative** box, and click in the box next to **Use test and interval based on normal distribution.** Then click on **OK** twice. (*b*) To obtain the TI-83 calculator results, access the **1-PropZTest** command from the **STAT>TESTS** menu, and set the parameters for the test as shown in screen **1.** Choose **Calculate** and get the results in screen **2.** If we perform the test again choosing **Draw** instead of **Calculate,** we get screen **3.** This shows the some values and the sketch.

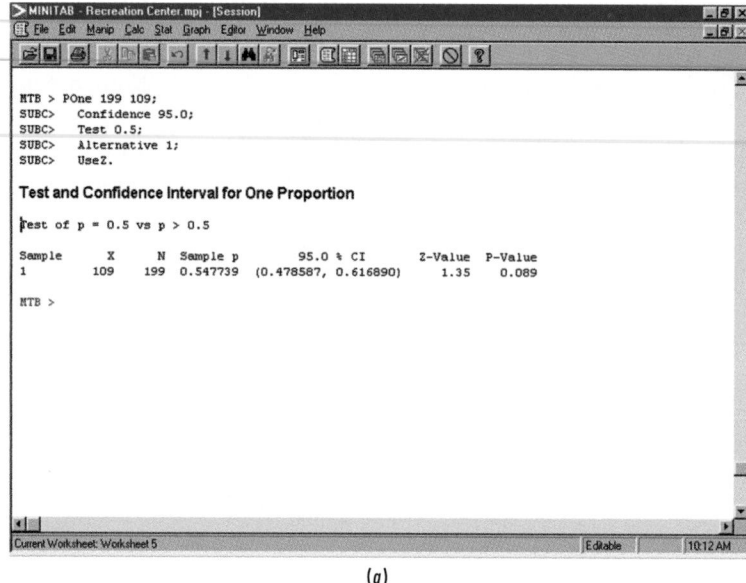

(*a*)

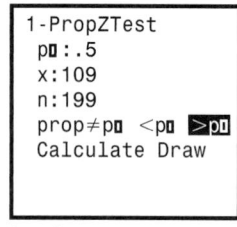

Screen 1

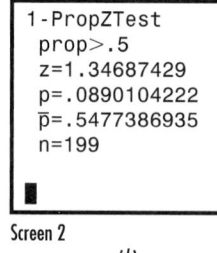

Screen 2

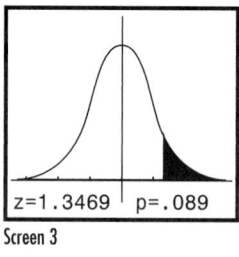

Screen 3

(*b*)

We let MINITAB and a TI-83 calculator compute the test statistic (*Step 5*) and calculate the *p*-value (*Step 6*). The results are in *Figure 8.18a* and screens 2 and 3 of *Figure 8.18b*. Because the *p*-value is .089 > .01, our conclusion (*Step 7*) is to fail to reject H_0. There's not enough evidence to conclude that more than 50 percent of the people who work out at the centre use the exercise room. ◆

Self-Testing Review 8.3

44. Test the hypothesis that $p > .35$, given a random sample of 114 in which 42 are successes. Use the .01 level of significance.

45. Test the hypothesis that $p = .05$, given a random sample of 84 in which 11 are successes. Use the .05 level of significance.

46. Researchers are interested in the return rate of questionnaires sent out for a study. Some believe this rate is 50 percent. As part of a *Journal of Consumer Research* study to determine the motivation of compulsive buyers, a random sample of 808 such buyers received a questionnaire accompanied by two cover letters. A total of 388 of these questionnaires were completed and returned. Test the hypothesis at the .05 level that the return rate for the population of such buyers is less than 50 percent.

47. It is widely thought that there is a high incidence of disability among the homeless population. A random sample of 87 homeless people not living in shelters contained 67 who were disabled in one or more categories (such as substance abuse, psychiatric disability, or medical disability). Test the hypothesis that over 0.75 of all homeless people not living in shelters have one or more types of disability. Use the .01 level of significance.

48. A study in the *Journal of Abnormal Psychology* dealt with a random sample of 1,710 high school students. Of these students, 150 had suffered from an anxiety disorder at one time in their lives. Test the hypothesis at the .01 level that more than 6 percent of all high school students have suffered from some type of anxiety disorder.

49. Social workers claim that 15 percent of all the beds in homeless shelters are designated for families. It was found in a random sample that 196 of 1,395 shelter beds were reserved for families. At the .01 level, test the hypothesis that beds for families are 15 percent of the total beds available.

50. In a telephone poll of 1,368 people in the United States, 1,163 responded in favour of the following question: "Would you favour or oppose a national law that required a seven-day waiting period between the time a person applied to buy a handgun and the time it was sold to them?" Test the hypothesis at the .05 level that more than 80 percent of all citizens are in favour of the seven-day waiting period.

51. Statistics Canada reported that 30.3 percent of all Canadian households are heated by electricity. If a random sample of 337 Manitoba households contains 73 that are heated by electricity, can it be concluded that the true proportion of all households in Manitoba that are heated by electricity is less than .303? Use the .01 level of significance.

52. Law enforcement officers know that a high percentage of robberies are committed by those with a history of drug and/or alcohol abuse. The *Journal of Research in Crime and Delinquency* recently reported that in a random sample of 96 robberies, 46 were found to be related in some way to drugs and/or alcohol. Test the hypothesis that over 40 percent of all robberies committed are related to drugs and/or alcohol. Use the .05 level of significance.

53. It has been postulated that a student is more likely to smoke marijuana if both parents use alcohol and drugs. For a class project, Po Sai Marie Yeung found data related to this question in *Marijuana Use in College* (Youth and Society, 1979). This paper reported that among 47 students whose parents use alcohol and drugs, 30 occasionally or regularly smoke marijuana. Test the hypothesis that more than 50 percent of the population of students whose parents use alcohol and drugs smoke marijuana occasionally or regularly. Use the .10 level of significance.

54. A random sample of households was selected from each of the provinces listed below. It was noted whether or not each household had air conditioning (AC). The results are as follows:

Province	Without AC	With AC
Manitoba	118	49
Saskatchewan	121	22
Alberta	356	21

Test the hypothesis at the .05 level that

   a) More than 20 percent of all Manitoba households have air conditioning.

   b) Twenty percent of all Saskatchewan households have air conditioning.

   c) Less than 20 percent of all Alberta households have air conditioning.

55. In a study of the plans of 26 female recreation administration majors, it was reported that 10 of the 26 planned to go to graduate school. Using the p-value method, test the hypothesis that more than 20 percent of all female recreation administration majors plan to go to graduate school. Use a level of significance of .10.

56. McIntyre et al. in "Dexamethasone as Adjunctive Therapy in Bacterial Meningitis" (*Journal of the American Medical Association*), looked at a number of studies that evaluated the use of dexamethasone as protection against hearing loss in childhood *Haemophilus influenzae,* type B (Hib), meningitis. Part of the data included a report on the number of cases of meningitis that were caused by Hib in various locations, four of which follow. It was thought by one of the authors that, while it was accepted that 80 percent of the cases of meningitis were caused by Hib in the past, this rate was going down.

Study	*Haemophilus influenzae,* Type B	Total
Costa Rica	79	101
Switzerland	67	115
Canada	57	101
U.S.	83	143

(Note: In the questions that follow, many of the steps are identical.) Using a level of significance of .05, test the hypothesis that the percentage of cases of meningitis that were caused by Hib is less than 80 percent:

    a) In the Costa Rican population.

    b) In the Swiss population.

    c) In the Canadian population.

    d) In the U.S. population.

57. Physicians claim a population success rate of 60 percent in the treatment of non-Hodgkin's lymphoma with a regimen called COPA. In a study reported in the *New England Journal of Medicine,* 79 patients from a random sample of 127 patients in the COPA regimen had survived after 2 years. Test the hypothesis at the .01 level that the survival rate of the population using the COPA regimen is 60 percent.

58. The Plastic Surgery Information Service provides information on various aspects of plastic surgery. One table at *PSRecon* gives the distribution for reconstructive procedures in 1996. It reports that 28 percent of such surgeries were for tumour removal. A 1998 sample reported that 82 of 222 reconstructive procedures were for tumour removal. Use this sample to test that the percent of reconstructive procedures that are tumour removals in 1998 is 28. Use the p-value method and a level of significance of .05.

8.4 One-Sample Hypothesis Tests of Variances and Standard Deviations

As you know, dispersion is measured by the variance and standard deviation. And as you saw in Chapter 7, it's often desirable to know the amount of dispersion that exists in a data set so that steps may be taken to control the extent of this spread or scatter. Thus, procedures have been devised to test hypotheses about population variances or population standard deviations (the same steps are used in either case) by those who seek to produce consistent results. Let's look now at these procedures.

Classical Two-Tailed Testing

Assuming we know that *the values in the population we are testing are normally distributed*, we can then follow our familiar seven steps to test a hypothesis about the population variance (σ^2) or standard deviation (σ). Let's first consider an example problem, and then we'll outline these steps.

Example 8.18 Suppose that your summer job duties now include checking the output of a new automatic machine that makes gears that are used in a customer's product. Gear diameters can't vary too much from the specified value or they will be either too loose or too tight to work as they should. Other machines in the plant can produce the same gears, and when they are operating properly, the population standard deviation for the diameter of the gears they make is .002 cm. You want to test the new machine to see if the standard deviation of its output is equal to that of the other machines. It is reasonable to assume that the population of outputs is normally distributed. You take a random sample of 11 gears and find that the sample standard deviation is .0028 cm. Is there evidence that the new machine is producing gears with a standard deviation that isn't .002?

◆ **Solution:**
Step 1: State the Null and Alternative Hypotheses In our example,

H_0: $\sigma = .002$ cm
H_0: $\sigma \neq .002$ cm

This is a *two-tailed test* because we want to see if the output of the new machine produces gears with σ of .002 cm. We're interested in knowing if there's a significant difference in the size of σ in either direction from .002.

Step 2: Select the Level of Significance We'll conduct this test at the .05 level.

Step 3: Determine the Test Distribution to Use As long as the values in the population are normally distributed, we use the Chi-square (χ^2) distribution to make tests of variances/standard deviations. As you saw in Chapter 7 (and in *Figure 7.11*), when sampling from a normal population, a χ^2 distribution is the sampling distribution for the variable

$$\frac{(n-1)s^2}{\sigma^2}$$

which extends from zero indefinitely to the right in a positive direction, isn't symmetrical, and changes with each change in sample size. The table of χ^2 values we'll use is Appendix 6.

Step 4: Define the Critical Regions For a two-tailed test, the rejection region consists of values of the test statistic $> \chi^2_{\alpha/2}$ or $< \chi^2_{1-\alpha/2}$. For our example, $\chi^2_{\alpha/2}$ is $\chi^2_{.05/2}$ or $\chi^2_{.025}$. The χ^2 value in Appendix 6 under the .025 column and in the 10-df (degrees of freedom) row is 20.5. (Remember that we have a sample of 11, so the df figure is

FIGURE 8.19 Chi-square values for a two-tailed test when $\alpha = .05$ and df = 10.

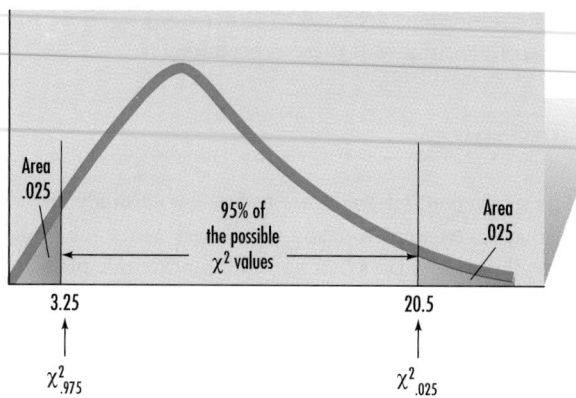

$11 - 1$ or 10.) And $\chi^2_{1-\alpha/2}$ is $\chi^2_{1-.05/2}$ or $\chi^2_{.975}$. The table value for $\chi^2_{.975}$ with 10 df is 3.25. *Figure 8.19* shows the critical region.

Step 5: State the Decision Rule Using χ^2 to denote the test statistic, the decision rule is

Reject H_0 in favour of H_1 if $\chi^2 > 20.5$ or $\chi^2 < 3.25$. Otherwise, fail to reject H_0.

Step 6: Compute the Test Statistic The test statistic formula is

$$\chi^2 = \frac{(n - 1)s^2}{\sigma_0^2} \tag{8.8}$$

where σ_0^2 = the hypothesized population variance

And in our example problem,

$$\chi^2 = \frac{(n - 1)s^2}{\sigma_0^2} = \frac{(11 - 1)(.0028)^2}{(.002)^2} = 19.6$$

Step 7: Make the Statistical Decision Since $\chi^2 = 19.6$ falls between 3.25 and 20.5, we fail to reject the null hypothesis that the σ is .002 cm and decide that the new machine is producing gears with a value of σ that is consistent with those made by the other machines. ◆

Classical One-Tailed Testing

Example 8.19 A drug company makes tablets to help control a certain disorder, and the process that produces these tablets is considered out of control if the standard deviation of the tablet weights exceeds .0125 mg. The company believes that the tablet weights are normally distributed. A random sample of 20 tablets taken during a routine periodic check produced a sample standard deviation of .0190 mg. At the .05 level, is this evidence that the tablet production process is out of control?

◆ **Solution:**

Hypotheses (Step 1):

H_0: $\sigma = .0125$ mg
H_1: $\sigma > .0125$ mg

This is a right-tailed test because the concern is that the value of σ not exceed .0125 mg. We know that $\alpha = .05$ *(Step 2)*, and we know to use a χ^2 distribution in our test *(Step 3)*. In our right-tailed test example, χ_α^2 is the table value in Appendix 6 that is at the intersection of the 19-df row and the .05 α column. That critical value is 30.1 *(Step 4)*. The decision rule for a right-tailed test is determined as follows:

Reject H_0 in favour of H_1 if $\chi^2 > \chi_\alpha^2$. Otherwise, fail to reject H_0.

Decision Rule (Step 5):

Reject H_0 in favour of H_1 if $\chi^2 > 30.1$. Otherwise, fail to reject H_0.

Test Statistic (Step 6):

$$\chi^2 = \frac{(n-1)s^2}{\sigma_0^2} = \frac{(20-1)(.0190)^2}{(.0125)^2} = 43.9$$

Conclusion (Step 7):

Since 43.9 is greater than the Chi-square table value of 30.1 at the .05 level, we must reject the null hypothesis. The tablet production process doesn't seem to be in control, and it must be corrected immediately. ◆

p-Value Tests of Variances/Standard Deviations

The *p*-value approach can be easily substituted for the classical method we've just used to test hypotheses about variances/standard deviations. But the χ^2 table (like the *t* table) is limited in the number of α values it can present. Thus, we usually can't find a specific *p*-value of interest, but instead must place the test *p*-value within some range. In Example 8.19, which we've just considered, the *p*-value of interest is

$$p\text{-value (right-tailed test)} = P(\chi^2 > \chi^2)$$
$$= P(\chi^2 > 43.9)$$

And in the 19-df row of Appendix 6 we find that $\chi^2 = 43.9$ falls beyond the highest table value of 38.6, so we know the *p*-value is less than 0.005. As with other *p*-value tests, the decision rule is to reject H_0 if the *p*-value $< \alpha$. Since our *p*-value here is less than .005 and since $\alpha = .05$, we know to reject H_0. Computer programs, of course, easily produce *p*-values for hypothesis tests of variances and standard deviations.

Example 8.20 **Pinging around the World** An information technologist used a standard UNIX program called *ping* to measure the time (milliseconds) taken to contact and receive a reply from another computer on the Internet. He noted that other nearby locations were not any faster than sites in Denmark and Japan. It appears that the provider and the type and quality of the connection are more important than location. Assuming that the population of connection times is normally distributed, use the data to test if the population standard deviation is less than 300 milliseconds at $\alpha = .05$ (Data = Internet).

1,450	310	222	680	299	157	202	525	568	447	129	253
406	331	644	822	461	292	204	396	684	517	322	536
343	259	526	288	330	262	205	294	496	1,043	366	511

◆ **Solution:**

Hypotheses (Step 1):

H_0: $\sigma = 300$ milliseconds
H_1: $\sigma < 300$ milliseconds

This is a *left-tailed test* because we want to know if σ is less than 300 milliseconds. We selected $\alpha = .05$ *(Step 2)* and will use a χ^2 distribution in our test *(Step 3)*. For a left-tailed test, $\chi^2_{1-\alpha}$ is $\chi^2_{.95}$; with $36 - 1 = 35$ df, the table value is approximately halfway between the table values with 30 and 40 df, 22.5 *(Step 4)*. The decision rule *(Step 5)* for a left-tailed test is

Reject H_0 in favour of H_1 if $\chi^2 < \chi^2_{1-\alpha} = 22.5$. Otherwise, fail to reject H_0.

To calculate the test statistic, we first compute $s^2 = 68,382.9$. Then the test statistic is *(Step 6)*:

$$\chi^2 = \frac{(n-1)s^2}{\sigma^2_0} = \frac{(36-1)(68,382.9)}{300^2} = 26.6$$

Conclusion (Step 7):

Since 26.6 is greater than 22.5, we fail to reject the null hypothesis. There is insufficient evidence to demonstrate that the standard deviation of the connect time is less than 300 milliseconds. ◆

Self-Testing Review 8.4

59. Determine the appropriate χ^2 critical values to use for a test of variance, given the following:

    a) $n = 12$, $\alpha = .05$, H_0: $\sigma^2 = 63.4$, H_1: $\sigma^2 < 63.4$.

    b) $n = 7$, $\alpha = .01$, H_0: $\sigma^2 = 23.91$, H_1: $\sigma^2 \neq 23.91$.

    c) $n = 24$, $\alpha = .01$, H_0: $\sigma^2 = 742$, H_1: $\sigma^2 > 742$.

60. Assuming the population involved is normally distributed, test the hypothesis that the population variance is 85. Use the .01 level of significance. The given statistics are $\bar{x} = 25$, $s^2 = 78$, $n = 16$.

61. Assuming the population involved is normally distributed, test the hypothesis that the value of σ is more than 4.26. Use the .05 level of significance. The given statistics are $\bar{x} = 649$, $s^2 = 5.317$, $n = 24$.

62. For years it was estimated that the waiting time for the Dare-Devil ride in Happy Times Amusement Park had a standard deviation of 4.2 minutes. This summer a new snake-type waiting line is introduced. It's found that for a random sample of 27 customers, the waiting time has a standard deviation of 3.9 minutes. Assuming the waiting times are normally distributed, test the hypothesis at the .05 level that, with the new waiting line, the population standard deviation is less than 4.2 minutes.

63. According to an issue of *Management Accounting,* the mean salary for all certified management accountants (CMAs) is $75,080. Suppose the salaries are normally distributed. If a random sample of 17 Ottawa CMAs has a mean salary of $73,973 with a standard deviation of $862, test the hypothesis at the .01 level that the population standard deviation for all Ottawa CMAs is less than $1,500.

64. A new machine dispenses oil into 8 litre containers. In a random sample of 16 containers, the variance is .35. Assuming the fill amounts are normally distributed, test the hypothesis at the .01 level that the variance is less than .50.

65. Normal subjects have a population mean of 20.9 on the Logical Memory Test. A recent study in the *American Journal of Psychiatry* showed that a random sample of 12 first-episode schizophrenic patients had a mean of 12.8 and a standard deviation of 6.98 on this test. Suppose the scores on this test are normally distributed. At the .01 level, can we conclude that the variance on this test for all first-episode schizophrenic patients is greater than 40?

66. A random sample of 24 university students spent a mean time of 148 minutes watching TV on a weekday. The standard deviation was 113 minutes. Suppose the times are normally distributed. Test the hypothesis at the .05 level that the standard deviation for the time all university students watch TV on a weekday is more than 90 minutes.

67. A calculator battery has a population mean life of 80 hours. A random sample of 21 calculators was tested, and it was found that the variance in battery life span was 4.1. Assuming the battery life is normally distributed, at the .05 level, test the hypothesis that the population variance is less than 9.

68. A study was made to evaluate the use of a Dacron ligament device in the surgical treatment of knee ailments. A Tegner activity scale is used to evaluate functional knee activity levels before and after knee surgery, and the scale ranges from 0 to 10, where 10 = the capabilities of a professional athlete, and 0 = total incapacity. Five years after the surgery using the Dacron device, a random sample of 8 patients had a mean Tegner score of 5.0 and a standard deviation of 2.0. Suppose the Tegner scores are approximately normal (as the scores are integers between 0 and 10, they could not be exactly normal). Test the hypothesis at the .05 level that 5 years after such surgery the population variance for the Tegner score is more than 3.5.

69. Milk obtained from cows has an average fat composition of 4.0 percent. In *Causes of MilkFat Test Variation* at *DHIA* (Extension Circular #340, College of Agricultural Sciences, Pennsylvania State University), Heald, Scibilia, and Barnard reported on the results of a DHIA (Dairy Herd Improvement Assoc.) analysis on raw milk to determine the percentage of fat composition. Thirty-one days of data on the differences in the percent of milk fat from the monthly average follow:

Difference in Milk Fat				
0.152	−0.048	0.152	−0.048	−0.548
0.052	0.652	−0.048	0.352	0.352
0.052	0.152	0.248	−0.348	0.052
−0.448	0.352	−0.048	−0.248	0.052
−0.248	−0.048	−0.048	−0.348	−0.148
0.352	−0.048	0.252	0.052	−0.148
0.052				

Assuming these numbers represent a sample from a normally distributed population, use this data to see if the population standard deviation of these differences exceeds .100 (Data = MilkFat).

70. Scientists interested in the natural environment have attempted to construct computer models of the Earth that are able to predict climate and weather. In a class project, N. French reported on a data set found in the journal *Remote Sensing of the Environment*. Part of it included the errors made by computer models trying to predict surface temperature at various environmental conditions. The errors (°K) made by a sample of one of the models (°K) follow:

−1.99	1.37	−0.80	−0.25	0.27	0.76
1.24	1.69	2.13	2.56	2.97	3.42

Assuming the population is normally distributed, test the hypothesis at the .01 level that the standard deviation is greater than 1.00 (°K).

71. For a class project, J. Koepp collected data on the amount of free memory during peak usage times of the campus's AIX system. The unit used was a real-memory page (4,096 bytes), and the results from a sample of $n = 12$ were

1,493	1,319	1,253	1,651	1,812	1,682
1,737	1,193	1,893	1,532	1,717	1,842

Suppose the free memory is normally distributed. Using a level of .05, test if the standard deviation in the population of free memory during peak usage times is 100.

LOOKING BACK

1. Statisticians often take a sample to confirm or reject some hypothesis made about the value of a parameter. The assumption about the value of this parameter is called the null hypothesis. The conclusion that's accepted if sample results fail to support the null hypothesis is called the alternative hypothesis. Stating these hypotheses prior to sampling is the *first step* in any hypothesis-testing procedure.

2. Having noted the null and alternative hypotheses, the *second step* in the classical testing procedure is to establish a criterion for rejection of the null hypothesis. This criterion is called the level of significance—the risk of rejecting a true H_0. If a true hypothesis is rejected, a type I error is made, and if a false hypothesis is not rejected, a type II error is made. This step is usually—but not always—followed by those who use the *p*-value approach to hypothesis testing.

3. The *third step* in classical and *p*-value testing procedures is to select the correct probability distribution to use for the test. In a tests of means, if $n > 30$ or the value of σ is known and the population values are normally distributed, then the *z* table is used. However, when $n < 30$ and the population values

are normally distributed but σ is unknown, then the t distribution table is needed. In a test of proportions, the z distribution is used as long as both $n\hat{p}$ and $n(1 - \hat{p})$ are at least 5. The Chi-square distribution is used in tests of variances/standard deviations for normal populations. Once the correct test distribution is known, it's then possible to move to a *fourth step* in the classical procedure. This step is to establish the rejection region—that part of the sampling distribution (equal in total area to the level of significance) that's specified as being unlikely to contain a sample statistic if H_0 is true. If the difference between an obtained sample statistic and the assumed parameter has a value that falls into a rejection region, H_0 is rejected.

4. The *fifth step* in the classical testing procedure is to prepare a decision rule—a formal statement that clearly states the conclusion to be reached about H_0 on the basis of sample results. This step is also found in p-value tests. After all these steps have been completed, the *sixth step* is the actual data analysis. Sampling is done, and the value of the test statistic is computed. Finally, the *seventh* (and last) *step* is to make the statistical decision. If the test statistic falls into a rejection region, H_0 is rejected; otherwise, it is not rejected.

5. One-sample hypothesis tests of means, proportions, or variances/standard deviations are two-tailed or one-tailed. In a two-tailed test, the alternative hypothesis claims that the value of the population parameter is either higher or lower than the value stated in H_0. With a two-tailed test, the rejection region has two parts. The alternative hypothesis in a right-tailed test is that the true parameter value is greater than the parameter value given in H_0. The alternative hypothesis in a left-tailed test is that the true parameter value is less than the parameter value given in H_0. Both one- and two-tailed tests of hypotheses about population means, proportions, and variances/standard deviations are presented in this chapter. Several examples are computed by hand to show the procedures used and are then repeated using a statistical software package and calculator. Both classical and p-value hypothesis tests are demonstrated. The final decisions made with either approach are identical when α is specified in advance of the test.

Exercises

72. Test the hypothesis at the .05 level of significance that the population mean is greater than 7. Use the following sample statistics to make your decision: $\bar{x} = 8.1$, $s = 2.3$, $n = 84$.

73. Test the hypothesis at the .05 level of significance that the population mean is 58. Use the following sample statistics to make your decision, and assume the population values are normally distributed: $\bar{x} = 55.93$, $s = 5.2$, $n = 24$.

74. Test the hypothesis at the .01 level of significance that the population proportion is less than 0.75. Use the following sample data to make your decision: Out of 639, 452 were successes.

75. Test the hypothesis at the .01 level of significance that the population standard deviation is 85.2. Use the following sample statistics to make your decision: $\bar{x} = 55.93$, $s = 81.7$, $n = 28$.

76. A population of normal subjects has a mean of 20.9 on the Logical Memory Test. A study reported in the *American Journal of Psychiatry* of a random sample of 32 first-episode schizophrenic patients had a mean of 12.8 on this test and a standard deviation of 6.98. Test the hypothesis at the .01 level that the mean score for all first-episode schizophrenic patients on the Logical Memory Test is 20.9.

77. A consumer found the following prices for a sample of digital cameras:

$499	279	669	550	207	600	399	100	235	467
249	200	235	489	300	299	200	200	249	

Test the hypothesis at the .05 level that the population standard deviation for the cost of a digital camera is more than $150. What assumption is necessary about the population of prices for the test to be valid?

78. Two years ago, the population proportion of nursing-home residents who had behavioural problems was 0.48. A random sample of 6,629 nursing-home residents taken this year found that 1,392 had behavioural problems. Test the hypothesis at the .01 level that less than 0.48 of all nursing-home residents now have behavioural problems.

79. Among a random sample of 94 television shows, 48 depicted at least one act of violence. Test the hypothesis at the .01 level that the proportion of all shows on television that depict violence is higher than 0.50.

80. The mean score on a 10-item calculus concepts test (where each item was scored from 0 to 3 points) for all students enrolled in a traditional calculus course at a university was 9.64. A random sample of 41 students in a Project CALC calculus course is given the same test, and the mean and standard deviation for this sample are 11.52 and 7.06, respectively. Test the hypothesis at the .05 level that the mean score for all Project CALC students on this test is higher than 9.64.

81. In a *Journal of Marketing* survey of a random sample of 216 sales executives, the mean response on a question asking how often they experienced tension at their jobs was 1.79, and the standard deviation was .60. (Responses were measured on a Likert scale of 1 to 5, where 1 represented never tense, and 5 meant always tense.) Test the hypothesis at the .01 level that the population mean response from sales executives on the question of job tension is equal to 2.

82. In a random sample of 1,192 students, it was found that French was the dominant language for 357 of these students. Test the hypothesis at the .05 level that 30 percent of all such students have French as their dominant language.

83. The former manager of the jewellery department at Lacy's Department Store claimed that the mean daily sales was $2,150. Heather Stiles is hired as the new department manager. Having taken a statistics course, Heather randomly selects seven days and finds that the daily sales figures are

---

$1,198   2,080   1,130   1,510   2,821   2,777   4,977

Assuming the sales data are normally distributed, test the hypothesis that the mean daily sales is higher than $2,150. Use the .01 level of significance.

84. *Career Development Quarterly* reported the results of a study in which men and women completed a Life Roles Inventory questionnaire. As a part of this study, each participant was asked to rate the importance of good working conditions in the selection of a career. The mean response for the women was 14.91. On the same question, a random sample of 26 men responded with an average rating of 13.75 and a standard deviation of 3.26. Assuming the response data are normally distributed, test the hypothesis at the .05 level that men rate the importance of good working conditions lower than do women in career decision making.

85. Use the sample statistics from problem 84 and test the hypothesis that the standard deviation value for all men responding to the Life Roles Inventory questionnaire is greater than 2. Use the .05 level of significance.

86. A study to assess the effect of Captopril on patients with congestive heart failure was reported in the *American Heart Journal*. A random sample of 29 patients who took Captopril had a mean arterial blood pressure of 69.1 (mm Hg) with a variance of 15.62. Assuming such blood pressures are normally distributed, test the hypothesis at the .01 level that the population variance for patients who take Captopril is less than 16.

87. An article in the *New England Journal of Medicine* reported that a sample of 273 patients with medical back problems requested MRI scans. The mean cost for this sample was $981, and the standard deviation was $231. Test the hypothesis at the .01 level that the mean cost for an MRI for the population of self-referred patients with back problems is equal to $1,000.

88. Syringe-exchange programs represent one attempt to slow the spread of HIV infection among injection drug users. A study found that 68 percent of a random sample of syringes that were not distributed by an exchange program were HIV positive. After the syringe program was underway, 338 needles were tested, and 164 were found to be HIV positive. Test the hypothesis at the .05 level that the percent of HIV infection in all needles used by injection drug users was lower than 68 percent after the exchange program was in operation.

89. A study to examine how well marital dissolution is predicted by husbands' and wives' personality scores was published in the *Journal of Personality and Social Psychology*. The mean rating on a scale for "Agreeableness" for husbands in stable marriages was 27.37. Do husbands in unstable marriages have a different rating on this scale? A random sample of 64 husbands in unstable marriages had a mean score of 27.29 with a standard deviation of 3.75. Test the hypothesis at the .01 level that the population mean agreeableness rating of husbands in unstable marriages is different than 27.37.

90. As reported in the *Journal of Consumer Research*, the "change-of-intention score" is a self-reported measure on a scale of −9 to +9. Six customers randomly selected at the May Company reported a mean 4.17 change-of-intention score for name brand items after learning of a 20 percent discount in the price of the items. The standard deviation was .32. Assuming population scores are normally distributed, test the hypothesis at the .05 level that with a 20 percent discount, the population mean change-of-intention value is 4.5.

91. Transcutaneous electrical nerve stimulation (TENS) devices are frequently used in management of acute and chronic pain. An important component of the TENS system is the skin electrode. A study in the *Journal of Physical Therapy* was made to determine conductive differences among electrodes used with TENS devices. A random sample of 11 electrodes in the low-impedance group produced impedance measures (in ohms) of

1,200	1,200	1,000	1,600	1,400	1,400
1,200	1,700	1,600	1,300	1,600	

Assuming the population of such measures is normally distributed, test the hypothesis that the population variance for the impedance measure for all such electrodes is less than 50,000. Use the .05 level of significance.

92. The standard deviation for the waiting time for a random sample of 15 customers at a credit union was 1.7 minutes. Assuming the population of waiting times is normally distributed, test the hypothesis at the .01 level that the population variance is more than 1.5 minutes.

93. *USA Today* published the results of a survey to see how well the characters on TV reflect real-life people. In the U.S. population, 7 percent of all females are redheads. In a random sample of 1,263 females on television, 139 had red hair. Test the hypothesis at the .05 level that the percentage of females who are redheads is higher on television than in real life.

94. The *Journal of Educational Psychology* reported that a random sample of 281 people had a mean score of 58.3 on a test of word recall. The standard deviation was 20.5. Test the hypothesis at the .01 level that the population mean score on this test is 55.

95. Know-It-All Consultants, Ltd., has stated in its promotional brochure that the mean cost for its advice is $5,600 per client. Assume a random sample of 36 clients had a sample mean of $5,750 with a sample standard deviation of $175. Conduct a test of the consultants' claim at the .05 level.

96. A professor believes that only 33 percent of a college's students have a job while attending school. A student, Robert Ng, thinks the professor has underestimated the zeal of his peers. A random sample of 49 students showed that 17 of them worked after school. At the .01 level, determine who is likely to be correct.

97. A hospital receives a large shipment of vials of serum. These vials are supposed to contain 50 mg of serum each, and it's undesirable for the contents to be either above or below that value. A random sample of 24 vials shows a mean content of 49.25 mg. Assume the population is normally distributed and it's known that the population standard deviation will be about 2 mg. At the .01 level, should the hospital reject the shipment?

98. Let's assume you make scaffolds and buy ropes for them from the Hemphill Rope Company. The strength values of these ropes are normally distributed. A random sample of 26 ropes from a new shipment has a sample mean breaking strength of 427 kg with a sample standard deviation of 5 kg. The company specifications require that the mean breaking strength be at least 430 kg. At the .05 level, would you reject the shipment?

99. A light bulb manufacturer claims her bulbs have a population mean life of 1,000 hours. Is this claim justified at the .05 level if a random sample of 25 bulbs has a sample mean of 994 hours with a standard deviation of 30 hours? Assume the population life expectancy of the bulbs is normally distributed.

100. A fertilizer distributor has been selling fertilizer in 20 kg bags for several months. The population weight is normally distributed with a standard deviation weight of .60 kg. A customer, Ms. Duthie, believes she has been sold underweight bags and is thinking of reporting the distributor. To support her hunch, Ms. Duthie buys 4 bags of fertilizer at random and finds that the average weight is 19.65 kg. At the .05 level, does Duthie have a case against the distributor?

101. The diameter measure of parts produced by an automatic machine is normally distributed, and when the machine is properly adjusted, these parts have a mean diameter of 50 mm. It's undesirable for parts to vary significantly in either direction from this mean value. A random sample of ten parts is used to check on machine operation. The sample mean is 50.02 mm, and the sample standard deviation is .024 mm. At the .05 level, is the machine in adjustment?

102. The Speak-Easy Company produces speaker components for stereo systems. The weights of these components are normally distributed, but they should generally weigh about 26 grams. Weight deviations in either direction from this standard are undesirable. In a recent quality control check, a random sample of 12 components taken from a large lot had a sample mean of 25.8 g, and the sample standard deviation was 0.35 g. At the .10 level, do the components in the lot meet quality standards?

103. Melvin claims his average golf score is 75. Melvin lies a lot, so you observe his game for a random sample of 9 rounds and find that the sample mean is 80 strokes with a sample standard deviation of 4 strokes. At the .01 level, should you reject Melvin's claim? Assume that Melvin's game scores are normally distributed.

104. An MLA claims that 60 percent of the population in her constituency are in favour of passing a strict gun control law, but a hunting club member believes the percentage is much less than that. You take a random sample of 200 people in the constituency and find that 116 favour a strict law. At the .01 level, which person—the MLA or the club member—appears to be right?

105. To meet design specifications, steel rods produced in a factory must have a mean diameter of 1.5 cm. (It's undesirable for the rods to vary in either direction from this standard.) The population of diameters is known to be normally distributed with a standard deviation of .01 cm. Samples of 20 rods are taken each hour, and the sample mean diameters are computed. In the latest sample, the mean diameter is 1.5005 cm. At the .05 level, is the production process in control?

106. Light bulbs with a stated mean lifetime of 750 hours have been sitting in a warehouse for years. A sample of ten bulbs is selected at random and destructively tested. The sample mean and standard deviation values are found to be 710 and 40 hours, respectively. At the .10 level, has the prolonged storage significantly reduced the life expectancies of these bulbs? Assume the life expectancy of the bulbs in the population is normally distributed.

107. Suppose steel rods with normally distributed breaking strengths are used in the manufacture of bench presses. A random sample of 13 rods taken from a new shipment has a sample mean breaking strength of 1,975 kg with a sample standard deviation of 40 kg. The manufacturing specifications require that the mean breaking strength be at least 2,000 kg. At the .05 level, should the shipment be rejected?

108. For the shipment described in problem 107, test the hypothesis at the .05 level that the population variance is less than 2,000.

109. A contractor claims its consulting services cost the government an average of $10,000 per consultation. A random sample of 15 consultation fees is examined, and it's found that the sample mean is $10,575. The standard deviation of this sample is $600. If the population of consulting fees is normally distributed, is there sufficient evidence at the .05 level to suggest that the contractor averages more than $10,000 per consultation?

110. The table that follows gives the distribution of the maximum wind speed of 1,293 tornadoes.

Wind Speed (km/h)	Number
110 or less	696
111 to 180	411
181 to 250	129
251 to 320	43
321 to 390	13
391 to 460	1

Using a level of significance of .01, test the hypothesis that 50 percent of the population of tornadoes have wind speeds of 110 km/h or less.

111. In construction, it is necessary to use materials with reliable, known strengths. Joist and plank size, grade No. 1, Hem-Fir wood is commonly used in agricultural structures, and agricultural engineers who use such wood believe it has yield strength that is normally distributed with $\mu = 7,000$ psi and

$\sigma = 875$ psi. Suppose it is reasonable to assume the population of such strengths is normally distributed. In a class project, J. Mehlschau examined the yielding strength of such Hem-Fir. Six pieces were subjected to a compression machine until failure with the results:

7,512	7,620	6,982	7,256	6,766	7,145

a) Assuming $\sigma = 875$ psi, test the hypothesis at the .05 level that the population mean yielding strength of this type of wood is less than 7,000 psi.

b) Even if the mean strength is large enough for construction purposes, the standard deviation should also be small. Otherwise, while there would be pieces of wood much stronger than necessary, there would also be pieces too weak for construction. (Reminds us of the joke about the statistician with one foot in boiling water and the other in a bucket of ice who said "on the average" he felt fine.) Test the hypothesis that σ is no more than 875 psi, using a level of significance of .05.

112. Suppose that last year, 83.1 percent of tummy tucks were done on people between 19 and 34 years old. In a sample of 157 people having a tummy tuck this year, 113 were between 19 and 34 years old. Use this information to test to see if the percentage this year is different from last year. Use a level of significance of .05.

113. A computer science student sampled 22 weekdays and wrote a computer program to determine the number of electronic mail messages processed by an AIX mail server each day (Data = email).

26,749	30,986	32,444	32,907	39,168	39,015
41,367	38,899	32,397	28,594	44,557	47,717
48,122	38,981	50,601	48,845	49,544	47,883
40,787	48,998	50,701	50,529		

Suppose it is reasonable to assume the population of the number of electronic mail messages processed by an AIX mail server each day is normally distributed.

a) The system is designed to handle a mean of less than 50,000 electronic mail messages per day. Using a level of significance of .01, test the hypothesis that the demand on the mail server is within the design limit.

b) A steady rather than sporadic number of electronic mail messages is better for the performance of the system. Using a level of significance of .01, test the hypothesis that the standard deviation of the demand on the mail server is no more than 5,000.

114. The measurement of serum triglyceride levels has clinical significance. The normal range of serum triglyceride levels is 35 to 165 mg/dl. This implies that, if the population of serum triglyceride levels is normal, the mean is approximately 100 mg/dl and the standard deviation is around 30 mg/dl. A sample of teenagers produced the following levels (Data = Triglyce).

83	163	147	86	43	76	69
200	150	168	153	176	59	
133	134	199	128	98	31	

a) Using a level of significance of .05, test the hypothesis that the population of serum triglyceride levels of teenagers has a mean of 100 mg/dl.

b) Using a level of significance of .05, test the hypothesis that the population of serum triglyceride levels of teenagers has a standard deviation of 30 mg/dl.

115. According to 2001 Canadian Census data, 45.9 percent of the population of Vancouver were landed immigrants (people granted the right to live in Canada permanently), 49.4 percent of the population of Toronto were landed immigrants, and 27.6 percent of the population of Montreal were landed immigrants.

a) This year, a random sample of 200 Vancouver residents contained 82 landed immigrants. At the .10 level of significance, is this evidence that the percentage of landed immigrants in Vancouver has decreased?

b) This year, a random sample of 150 Toronto residents contained 85 landed immigrants. At the .10 level of significance, is this evidence that the percentage of landed immigrants in Toronto has changed?

c) This year, a random sample of 450 Montreal residents contained 99 landed immigrants. At the .10 level of signif-

icance, is this evidence that the percentage of landed immigrants in Montreal has increased?

116. In a class project, D. Rogers obtained 14 concrete cylinders produced by students and designed to have a compressive strength of 3,500 psi. He measured the compressive strengths with the following results:

3,423	3,376	3,304	3,601	3,078	3,747	3,603
3,720	3,597	3,794	3,322	3,319	3,497	3,575

Assuming the population of such strengths is normally distributed, use this sample to test the hypothesis that the mean compressive strength of all such concrete cylinders is 3,500 psi.

117. The data that follow represents the median monthly salary made by a sample of university graduates one year after graduation, broken down by randomly selected majors:

Degree	Salary
Physical education	$2,000
Animal science	$2,050
Journalism	$2,129
Architecture	$2,200
Accounting	$2,500
Political science	$2,500
Chemistry	$2,666
Statistics	$2,800
Computer science	$3,595

In the previous year, the population mean had been $2,100. Test, using a level of significance of .05, that the population mean is greater for the population of all the newer graduates.

Topics for Review and Discussion

1. Discuss the types of hypotheses used in a statistical test. How can you always tell which is the null hypothesis?

2. Identify and discuss the seven steps in the classical hypothesis-testing method.

3. Decisions made in hypothesis testing are not guaranteed to be the correct ones. Discuss the possible types of errors an expert statistician (such as you) could make.

4. Discuss the concept of the level of significance. What role does it play in a right-tailed test? In a left-tailed test? In a two-tailed test?

5. What is the importance of the rejection region in classical hypothesis testing?

6. What is a test statistic?

7. Which test distribution is used for a test of the population mean when a large sample is available? When a small sample is used?

8. Which test distribution is used for a test for the population proportion?

9. What test distribution is used to test a population variance?

10. What is a p-value?

11. Identify and discuss the steps in p-value hypothesis testing.

Projects/Issues to Consider

1. Formulate a pair of hypotheses about an appropriate measurable quantity for the population of students at your school. (Suggestions include the mean number of kilometres they travel to get to school, the mean number of credit hours they are taking this term, their average height, how many hours a night they spend on homework, and so on.) Decide on a level of significance. Collect sample data and complete the test. Write a paragraph discussing your methodology and your findings.

2. Formulate a pair of hypotheses for the population of students at your school that involves a proportion. This could be

the proportion of those favouring a certain issue, the proportion of the student body that are business majors, and so on. Decide on a level of significance, collect a sample, and perform a hypothesis test. Write a paragraph describing your findings and include your methodology in this paragraph.

3. Formulate a pair of hypotheses about a variance. Collect sample data and perform a hypothesis test. Write a paragraph describing your methodology and your findings.

Computer/Calculator Exercises

1. Alan Shi analyzed data he had collected for a project. It consisted of the maximum pit depth of cold rolling steel used in a radiator's circulating system (Data = PitDepth).

Maximum Pit Depth (mm)

0.254	0.388	0.166	0.218	0.408	0.205
0.208	0.291	0.246	0.253	0.306	0.149
0.348	0.395	0.226	0.185	0.370	0.168
0.415	0.408	0.362	0.454	0.178	0.148
0.229	0.306	0.227	0.326	0.240	0.131
0.272	0.301	0.252	0.309	0.407	0.145

a) Test the hypothesis at the .10 level that the population mean maximum pit depth is less than .30 mm.

b) Using a level of significance of .10, test to see if the standard deviation of the maximum pit depth is greater than .10.

2. In the field of computers, one area of growing importance is downtime. For a class project, R. Vilhauer contacted a company and gained access to the time, in a year, that the company's computer systems or networks were down due to problems such as hardware malfunction (Data = Downtime).

Downtime (hr)

56.00	32.25	49.00	10.00	123.00	76.50
59.75	32.83	57.50	14.20	100.60	48.75
37.50	23.90	41.23	78.33	39.75	28.17
51.70	47.20	93.80	22.71	46.20	15.20
223.00	1.00	150.20	59.34	44.62	51.80
32.70	44.63	62.38	50.90	40.80	45.00
86.30	51.50	54.10	33.70	58.20	28.17
23.78					

a) Assuming the computer systems of this company represent a sample of all such systems, test the hypothesis that mean downtime of this population is more than 50 hours per year. Use a level of significance of .10.

b) Using a level of significance of .10, test the hypothesis that the standard deviation of the population is 25 hours per year.

3. Determining computer network usage gives system administrators a useful figure in deciding when to expand and upgrade equipment. In a class project E. Willard looked at a random sample of the number of users on the Electrical Engineering Department's computer network during its peak usage periods (Data = EENetwrk).

Number of Users on the Electrical Engineering Computer Network

20	12	17	10	13	11	14	9	6	14
8	8	25	11	22	18	8	13	4	23
26	15	13	35	14	14	20	18	12	21

a) Test the hypothesis that the mean of the population of users on the electrical engineering computer network is 12. Use a level of significance of .05.

b) Using a level of significance of .50, test the hypothesis that the standard deviation of the population is 10.

 4. Use the World Wide Web to access the DASL data set described at DASLSped and located at DASLMich. The abstract on the former page describes the hypothesis that can be tested. Do as that page asks, that is, test the hypothesis that the true mean is 734.5 for each of the five trials and for all 100 observations combined.

5. On the Internet, "America's Career Infonet" at <u>ACI</u> contains a wealth of information on many careers. At that location, categories called **Job Families** are listed. Once you select one of these categories and click on **Next,** a list of occupations appears. Selecting one of these and clicking on **Search** shows information that includes the number employed in that occupation in a recent year, the projected growth in that occupation (percent), and the median weekly earnings. We are going to run an experiment on your ability to guess. To orient yourself, click on some of the occupations and look at the type of numbers given on those pages. Then go through the following process. Pick an occupation. Before clicking on *Search*, write a guess for number employed, project growth, and median weekly earnings. Then find out if you were over or under in your guesses. Repeat this until you have 25 in each category (some occupations are missing some information, usually the median weekly salary). Once you have your 3 sets of 25 guesses, use them to test $H_0: p = .5$ for each; that is, test that your guesses are unbiased. Pick your own level of significance and summarize your findings in the form of a report.

6. On the information page of *World Factbook* at <u>Wrld-Fact</u>, the following information is given: "The World Factbook is prepared by the Central Intelligence Agency for the use of U.S. Government officials, and the style, format, coverage, and content are designed to meet their specific requirements. Information was provided by the American Geophysical Union, Bureau of the Census, Central Intelligence Agency, Defense Intelligence Agency, Defense Nuclear Agency, Department of State, Foreign Broadcast Information Service, Maritime Administration, National Imagery and Mapping Agency, National Maritime Intelligence Center, National Science Foundation (Antarctic Sciences Section), Office of Insular Affairs, U.S. Board on Geographic Names, U.S. Coast Guard, and other public and private sources." Information is given about individual countries at <u>CntryFac</u>. We are going to try to help you evaluate your knowledge of the world by performing a few hypothesis tests.

a) Under the category *Age structure,* country populations are broken down into age categories. Before checking any countries, guess the mean percentage for all countries that would be in the category 0 to 14 years. Randomly select 5 countries and use that data to do a hypothesis test of $H_0: \mu =$ *your guess* at $\alpha = .05$.

b) Under the category *Population growth rate,* the percent increase in the population is given. Before checking any countries, guess what the average of this is. Randomly select 10 countries and use that data to do a hypothesis test of $H_0: \mu =$ *your guess* at $\alpha = .05$.

c) Under the category *Sex ratio,* the ratio of male to female births is given. Randomly select 20 countries and use that data to do a hypothesis test that the ratio is 1 (equal number of male and female births) at $\alpha = .05$.

7. The Statistics Canada home page has links to the Canadian Socio-Economic Information Management System at <u>CANSIM</u>. Click on **The State,** then **Government,** then **Employment and average weekly earnings (including overtime), public administration and all industries, Canada, the provinces and territories.** Under **List of Tables,** select **Average Weekly Earnings** at <u>CanAWE</u>. You will see a table that gives the average weekly earnings for each province of people in public administration, broken down by federal, provincial, and local.

a) Considering this to be a sample of salaries, test the hypothesis that the mean salary of federal employees is greater than $750 at $\alpha = .01$.

b) Considering this to be a sample of salaries, test the hypothesis that the mean salary of provincial employees is equal to $750 at $\alpha = .01$.

c) Considering this to be a sample of salaries, test the hypothesis that the mean salary of local employees is less than $750 at $\alpha = .01$.

CHAPTER 9

Inference: Two-Sample Procedures

LOOKING AHEAD

In this chapter we'll use the data obtained from two samples taken from different populations. The estimation and hypothesis-testing concepts introduced in Chapters 7 and 8 are used to compare (1) two population variances, (2) two population means, and (3) two population proportions. (Since the results obtained in comparing two variances may be needed during an analysis of two means, we'll consider variances first in this chapter.)

Thus, after studying this chapter, you should be able to

- Explain the purpose of two-sample hypothesis tests of variances, means, and proportions.

- Understand the procedures to be followed in conducting these tests of variances, means, and proportions.

- Understand the need for and distinguish between independent and dependent samples.

- Perform the necessary computations and make the appropriate statistical decisions in two-sample hypothesis-testing situations.

- Explain the uses of confidence intervals in the estimation of differences for two means and for two proportions.

- Construct confidence intervals for differences of two means or of two proportions at different levels of confidence.

9.1 Hypothesis Tests of Two Variances

Some General Thoughts

Decision makers often want to see if two populations are similar or different with respect to some characteristic. For example, an instructor may want to know if male professors receive higher salaries than female professors for the same teaching load. Or a psychologist may want to see if an experimental group responds differently than a control group to an experimental stimulus. Or the purchasing agent of a firm that manufactures cooling towers may need to know if the cooling fan motors of one supplier are more durable than those of another vendor. In short, there are many situations that require groups to be compared on the basis of a given trait.

Chapter 7 gave us methods to estimate the value of a parameter; Chapter 8 showed us ways to test the validity of a hypothesized value of a parameter. In either case, there was only a single value of the parameter in which we were interested. In this chapter, though, we're concerned with the parameters of two different populations. We'll learn how to test if the two parameters are the same and, for means and proportions, how to estimate the amount by which the two parameters are likely to differ. So we are not primarily interested in estimating the *distinct values* of the parameter; rather, the topic of interest is the *relative values* of the parameters. That is, does one population appear to possess more or less of a trait than the other? Our purpose in this chapter, then, is to use the data from two samples to evaluate the difference between the parameters of two populations.

Two-Variance Testing: Purpose and Assumptions

Our purpose in this section is to use sample variances (s_1^2 and s_2^2) to arrive at conclusions about the corresponding population variances (σ_1^2 and σ_2^2). Thus, we'll take random samples from two populations, compute the variance for each sample data set, and use the results obtained as the basis for comparing the population variances (and standard deviations).

The following two assumptions must be true if the testing procedure we'll follow is to produce valid results:

1. The data in the two populations we sample must be *normally distributed.*

2. The data source (persons, objects, and so on) in the first population must be *independent* of the data source in the second population. Thus, we assume that *independent samples* are used.

> Two samples are said to be **independent samples** if the data sources used to generate the data sets from the two populations are unrelated to each other. If, however, the same (or related) data sources are used to generate the data sets for each population, then the samples taken from each population are said to be **dependent samples.**

If our populations consist of two groups of students in two separate sections of a statistics course, and if we randomly select samples from each population and test the knowledge in both classes, then we have independent samples. But if we test the knowledge of a sample of statistics students *before* they take an intensive review course and retest the same students *after* the course is completed to evaluate the difference in scores for each student, then we have dependent samples. Such "before-and-after" tests usually involve dependent samples. There are ways to handle such situations (as we'll soon see), but the procedure to test two variances described in this section requires independent samples.

The Testing Procedure

The procedure used to test hypotheses about the variances of two populations follows the seven familiar steps outlined in Chapter 8. We'll focus on the *classical procedure* in this chapter and we'll give an example of the *p*-value approach.

Step 1: State the Null and Alternative Hypothesis The *null hypothesis* in a test of two variances is that there's *no difference* in the variability of the two populations. That is,

$$H_0: \sigma_1^2 = \sigma_2^2$$

The *alternative hypothesis* is either that there is a significant difference between the population variances or that one variance identified by the analyst is greater than the other. Thus, the alternative hypothesis takes one of these familiar forms:

$$H_1: \sigma_1^2 \neq \sigma_2^2$$
$$H_1: \sigma_1^2 > \sigma_2^2$$
$$H_1: \sigma_1^2 < \sigma_2^2$$

Step 2: Select the Level of Significance The analyst must choose the value of α.

Step 3: Determine the Test Distribution to Use We've used the z, t, and χ^2 probability distributions at different times in Chapters 7 and 8. But now we must consider a new distribution. To get a feel for this new distribution, let's assume the null hypothesis is true, and σ_1^2 does equal σ_2^2. In at case, the ratio $\sigma_1^2/\sigma_2^2 = 1$. And if H_0 is true and if we compute variances for the samples taken from each population, then the ratio s_1^2/s_2^2 should also yield a result that doesn't deviate too far from a value of 1.

Of course, sampling variation can be expected to cause some disparity in the two sample variances even when H_0 is true. But how much disparity is reasonable—that is, how far from 1 can the ratio stray before it should be concluded that H_0 isn't true? The answer to this question is found through the use of F *distribution*.

F distribution

An **F distribution** is the sampling distribution for the variable s_1^2/s_2^2 when samples are taken independently from two normally distributed populations for which s_1^2/s_2^2, and it has the following properties:

- There are no negative values in an *F* distribution, so the scale of possible *F* values extends from 0 to the right in a positive direction.

- An **F distribution** isn't symmetrical like the *z* or *t* distributions; rather, it is skewed to the right like a χ_2 distribution.

- There are many **F** distributions, and each one is determined by the numerator and denominator degrees of freedom, which, in turn, depend on the number of samples and the number of observations in the samples. Thus, the *F* distribution used to compare two samples of size 8 and 9 is different from the ones used to compare samples of 9 and 10, 6 and 7, 15 and 16, and so on.

Figure 9.1 shows the general shape of *F* distributions. The *F* distribution values we'll need for our two-variance testing procedure are given in the tables in Appendix 5. To use these tables to look up the critical *F* values we need, we must know three things:

1. The *level of significance* (specified in *Step 2* of our testing procedure).

2. The *degrees of freedom* (df) for the sample variance used in the *numerator of* our test statistic s_1^2/s_2^2. To use the *F* tables in Appendix 5 if our alternative hypothesis is H_1: $\sigma_1^2 \neq \sigma_2^2$, *we specify that the sample with the largest sample variance is designated as sample 1,* and this larger variance is always used in the numerator of our test statistic. If we want a one-tailed test, the simplest way to run the test is to always designate the alternative hypothesis as H_1: $\sigma_2^2 > \sigma_2^2$ (this might require us to interchange sample 1 and sample 2 so that $s_1^2 > s_2^2$). The test statistic will be $F = s_1^2/s_2^2$. In either case, the degrees of freedom for the numerator, then, is $n_1 - 1$.

3. The *degrees of freedom* (df) for the sample used in the *denominator* of our test statistic. This value is $n_2 - 1$.

Step 4: Define the Rejection or Critical Region Let's assume we're conducting a two-tailed test at the .05 level of significance. There are 10 items in sample 1 (which is chosen as sample 1 because it has a larger sample variance than sample 2), and 11 items in sample 2. The .025 areas in each tail of the *F* distribution (a total of .05) make up the rejection region. To find the critical *F* value we need in this case, we look in Appendix 5 and locate the "critical values" table for $\alpha = .025$ (these are one-tailed tables).

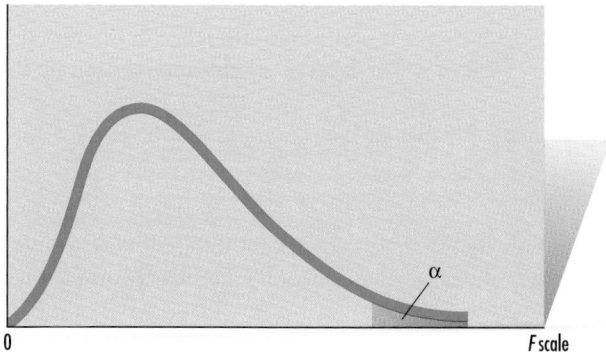

0   *F* scale

FIGURE 9.1 The general shape of *F* distributions.

As you've seen, to use the F distribution tables in Appendix 5, you must also know the df values for numerator and denominator. In our example, $df_{num} = 10 - 1$ or 9, and $df_{den} = 11 - 1$ or 10. You'll notice in Appendix 5 that the table *columns* correspond to degrees of freedom in the numerator, and the *rows* represent degrees of freedom in the denominator. So in the table for $\alpha = .025$, the critical F value found at the intersection of the column numbered 9 and the row numbered 10 is 3.78. Thus, a test statistic with a value that exceeds 3.78 in this case falls into the rejection region.

Step 5: State the Decision Rule We can now state the decision rule for this situation as follows:

Reject H_0 in favour of H_1 if the test statistic $F > 3.78$. Otherwise, fail to reject H_0.

Step 6: Compute the Test Statistic The formula needed to compute the test statistic F is

$$F = \frac{s_1^2}{s_2^2} \tag{9.1}$$

Step 7: Make the Statistical Decision If F is greater than 3.78 in this instance, the null hypothesis that $\sigma_1^2 = \sigma_2^2$ is rejected. Otherwise, we fail to reject H_0.

Now let's look at an example problem and follow the steps we've just outlined.

☐ Example 9.1   Two experimental diets designed to add weight to malnourished adults in developing countries are being tested. It's assumed that each diet will produce weight gains that are normally distributed. Although factors such as the average weight gain produced by each diet and each diet's cost per serving are obviously important, the dietitian in charge of the testing also wants to know if there is a significant difference in the variability of the weight gains produced by each diet.

◆ Solution:

To test this variability, the first diet (A) is given to eight malnourished adults, and the second diet (B) is supplied to nine malnourished adults. The weight gains for diet A (in kilograms) after a six-week period are

4.1   4.3   6.0   5.6   8.5   7.9   5.1   4.9

The gains (in kilograms) made by those fed diet B during the same time are

7.3   6.7   8.3   7.0   6.6   6.8   9.2   7.6   5.9

Table 9.1 presents these two sample data sets and shows the computation of the sample variance values.

The dietitian's interest now is to see if there's a significant difference in the variability of the weight gains produced by each diet. The level of significance chosen by the dietitian is .05.

The following null hypothesis *(Step 1)* is that such a difference doesn't exist:

H_0: $\sigma_1^2 = \sigma_2^2$

The alternative hypothesis is simply that there is a significant difference between the population variances. Thus, the alternative hypothesis takes the familiar two-tailed test form:

H_0: $\sigma_1^2 \neq \sigma_2^2$

TABLE 9.1 WEIGHT GAIN (IN KILOGRAMS)

Diet A			Diet B		
x	$(x - \bar{x})$	$(x - \bar{x})^2$	x	$(x - \bar{x})$	$(x - \bar{x})^2$
4.1	−1.7	2.89	7.3	.03	.0009
4.3	−1.5	2.25	6.7	−.57	.3249
6.0	.2	.04	8.3	1.03	1.0609
5.6	−.2	.04	7.0	−.27	.0729
8.5	2.7	7.29	6.6	−.67	.4489
7.9	2.1	4.41	6.8	−.47	.2209
5.1	−.7	.49	9.2	1.93	3.7249
4.9	−.9	.81	7.6	.33	.1089
46.4	.0	18.22	5.9	−1.37	1.8769
			65.4	0	7.8401

$$\bar{x}_1 = \frac{\Sigma x}{n} = \frac{46.4}{8} = 5.80 \text{ kilograms} \qquad \bar{x}_2 = \frac{\Sigma x}{n} = \frac{65.4}{9} = 7.27 \text{ kilograms}$$

$$s_1^2 = \frac{\Sigma(x - \bar{x})^2}{n - 1} = \frac{18.22}{8 - 1} = 2.6029 \qquad s_2^2 = \frac{\Sigma(x - \bar{x})^2}{n - 1} = \frac{7.8401}{9 - 1} = .9800$$

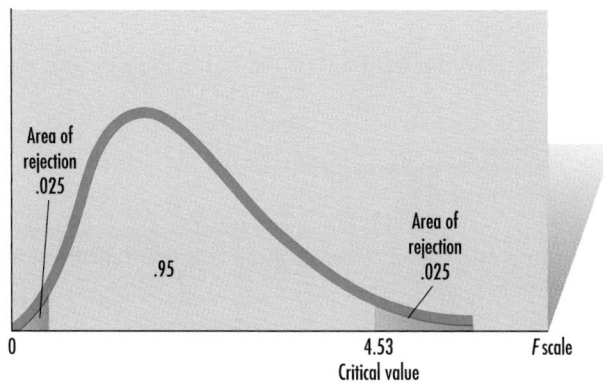

FIGURE 9.2 The critical *F* value of 4.53 defines the rejection region of the *F* distribution with 7 degrees of freedom in the numerator and 8 degrees of freedom in the denominator, at $\alpha = .05$.

The dietitian specifies that $\alpha = .05$ *(Step 2)*, and, of course, we'll use the *F* distribution in this test *(Step 3)*. As you can see in Table 9.1, sample 1 with the larger variance of 2.6029 consists of the 8 adults fed diet A, and sample 2 with the smaller variance of .9800 is the 9 adults receiving diet B. Thus, the size of sample 1 is 8 ($n_1 - 8$), and the size of sample 2 is 9 ($n_2 = 9$). The degrees of freedom for the numerator, then, is $n_1 - 1$, or 8 − 1, or 7, and the degrees of freedom for the denominator is $n_2 - 1$, or 9 − 1, or 8.

Figure 9.2 shows the rejection region for our test involving diets A and B. With $\alpha = .05$, and with a two-tailed test (remember, H_1: $\sigma_1^2 \neq \sigma_2^2$), we need to find the appropriate *F* critical value that separates the .025 area in the right tail from the rest of the distribution. Now you can see why we stipulated earlier that the sample with the largest variance is always labelled sample 1 and that the larger sample variance is always placed in the numerator of the test statistic. When set up in this way, the computed statistic will always be 1 or greater, and we need only find the *F* value that separates the

2.5 percent of the area in the right tail from the remaining 97.5 percent of the area. Thus, in the table for $\alpha = .025$, the critical F value *(Step 4)* found at the intersection of the column numbered 7 and the row numbered 8 is 4.53 (see *Figure 9.2*).

We can now state the decision rule for our example as follows *(Step 5)*:

Reject H_0 in favour of H_1 if $F > 4.53$. Otherwise, fail to reject H_0.

And from Table 9.1 we see that $s_1^2 = 2.6029$ and $s_2^2 = .9800$. Thus, our test statistic *(Step 6)* is

$$F = \frac{s_1^2}{s_2^2} = \frac{2.6029}{.9800} = 2.656$$

Since $F = 2.656$ is less than 4.53, we fail to reject the null hypothesis that $\sigma_1^2 = \sigma_2^2$ *(Step 7)*. There doesn't appear to be a significant difference in the variability of the weight gains produced by the two experimental diets. ◆

Suppose a recent article has claimed that the effectiveness of the first diet depends on the physiology of the dieters and this could possibly cause greater variation in the weight gain amounts than the second diet. Because of this, the dietitian wants to conduct a *one-tailed test* so that the alternative hypothesis reads

$$H_1: \sigma_1^2 > \sigma_2^2$$

In this case, the entire α value of .05 is in the right tail of the F distribution, and the decision rule is

Reject H_0 in favour of H_1 if $F > 3.50$ (.05 table, $df_{num} = 7$, $df_{den} = 8$). Otherwise, fail to reject H_0.

Since $F = 2.656 < 3.50$, the decision is still to fail to reject H_0 in this one-tailed test at the .05 level. ◆

Example 9.2 **Sit-up for Variation?** In Chapter 7, we looked at the number of sit-ups done by several classes that took an Army Physical Fitness Test (APFT). We've reproduced the data below but now have the data broken down by gender of the participants. Using the p-value approach and $\alpha = .05$, does it appear that the variance in the number of sit-ups done by the population of females is the same as that of the males (Data = APFTSitx)?

Females		Males				
75	103	38	61	92	64	47
86	26	30	64	92	66	66
80	50	68	60	58	73	39
63	14	87	100	70	71	75
60	26	95	61	68	95	90
83	43	71	87	57	67	56
		51	88	61		

◆ Solution:

As we are looking for any difference in the variances, we will run a two-tailed test. The hypotheses are *(Step 1)*:

$H_0: \sigma_1^2 = \sigma_2^2$
$H_1: \sigma_1^2 \neq \sigma_2^2$

We have chosen $\alpha = .05$ *(Step 2)*, and, assuming the number of sit-ups done by the populations of females and males are normal, we'll use the F distribution to run the test *(Step 3)*. Our decision rule *(Step 4)* is

Reject H_0 if the p-value is $< .05$. Otherwise, fail to reject H_0.

We used MINITAB (see *Figure 9.3a*) and the TI-83 calculator (see *Figure 9.3b*) to compute the test statistic *(Step 5)* and the p-value *(Step 6)*. (Note: Some of the MINITAB output you receive will be unfamiliar—you should look at the test statistic and p-value given under the heading *F-Test* [*normal distribution*]). We see that the test statistic's value is 2.509 and the p-value is .042. Therefore, because p-value $= .042 < .05$, our conclusion *(Step 7)* is to reject H_0. It appears that the variance in the number of sit-ups done by the population of females is different from that of males. ◆

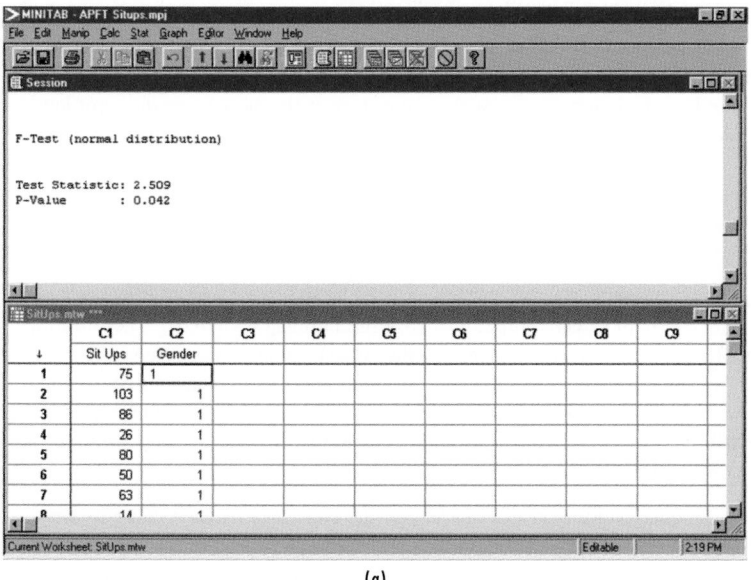

(a)

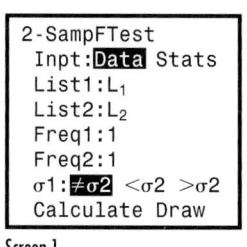

Screen 1

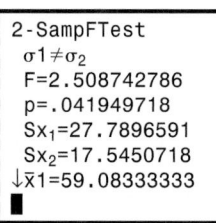

Screen 2

(b)

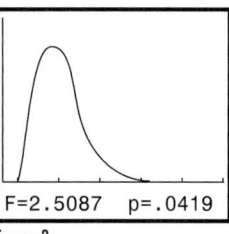

Screen 3

FIGURE 9.3 (*a*) To obtain this MINITAB output, we need to enter two columns of data: the first column containing the number of sit-ups for each student and the second column an indicator of gender (we used 1 to indicate females and 2 to indicate males). Next, access the **Homogeneity (Equality)** of **Variance** window by clicking on **Stat, ANOVA,** and **Homogeneity of Variance.** In this window, enter *Sit Ups* in the Response box, *Gender* in the **Factors** box, and click on **OK.** (*b*) To use the TI-83 to do the calculations of the test statistic and the *p*-value, put the data for females into one list and the data for males into another list. We will use L1 for females and L2 for males. Choose the **2-SampFTest** from the **Tests** menu. Complete the parameters for the test as shown in screen 1. Calculate and Draw can then be used to get screens 2 and 3.

Self-Testing Review 9.1

1. What are the two necessary conditions that must be satisfied if the testing procedure for equal variances is to produce valid results?

2. Use a right-tailed test and test the equality of population variances at the .01 level of significance given the following data: For sample A, $n - 21$, $s^2 = 35.43$, and $\bar{x} = 67.47$. And for sample B, $n = 13$, $s^2 = 48.91$, and $\bar{x} = 307.84$.

3. Use a two-tailed test and test the equality of population variances at the .05 level of significance given the following data: For sample A, $n = 16$, $s^2 = 457.21$, and $\bar{x} = 247.16$. And for sample B, $n = 7$, $s^2 = 99.08$, and $\bar{x} = 247.27$.

4. The length of time customers at Shop N Pay must wait in line before they can leave the checkout station with their purchases is measured. For a random sample of 7 customers, the sample variance is 17.84 min^2. The competition down the street, Buy Fair, uses a different type of checkout system. The length of time 25 customers wait in line at Buy Fair is measured and the variance is 15.93 min^2. Assuming these times are normally distributed, test the hypothesis at the .05 level that there is less population variance at Buy Fair.

5. On-the-Ball, Inc., makes ball bearings that are used in tractors and other equipment. On the 8-to-4 shift, a random sample of 16 ball bearings is selected, and the diameters are measured. The variance is 17.39 mm^2. Later, a random sample of 13 ball bearings is selected from the 4-to-midnight shift, and the variance for the diameter measures is found to be 12.83 mm^2. Assuming these diameters are normally distributed, test the hypothesis at the .05 level that the population variances for the two shifts are equal.

6. When offered a 20 percent discount, a random sample of 6 customers at the May Company reported a mean of 4.17 on a "change-of-intention-to-buy" scale (that goes from –9 to +9) with a standard deviation of .32. At the same store at the 30 percent discount level, a random sample of 7 customers reported a mean of 4.00 and standard deviation of .08 for their intention-to-buy scores. Assume the population of scores on this scale is normally distributed. Test the hypothesis at the .05 level that at this May Company store there's no difference in variance in the intention-to-buy scale when a discount rate is 20 percent versus when it is 30 percent.

7. A pharmaceutical company makes a *Weight-Away* tablet that is advertised to control appetite for ten hours. It is in direct competition with the popular *Fatnomore*. The duration of time each tablet is effective was measured in clinical tests. A random sample of 14 people who tested *Weight-Away* had a variance of 3.92 hrs^2. For a similar sample of 7 people who tested *Fatnomore*, the variance was 7.21 hrs^2. Assume the population of duration times is normally distributed. Test the hypothesis at the .05 level that the population variances for both products are equal.

8. A machine is designed to fill bags of cement, and the bags state that the contents weigh 18 kg. When the conveyer belt that the bags travel on was set at a speed of 5 cm per second, a random sample of 28 bags had a variance of 1.3. The production manager decided to speed up the conveyor belt to 12 cm per second. When this was done, a random sample of 16 bags had a variance of 4.9. Assume the population of cement fill amounts is normally distributed. Test the hypothesis at the .05 level that when the conveyor belt is set at the faster speed, the population variance in the amount of cement in the bags will be greater.

9. As mentioned in Chapter 8, scientists have attempted to construct computer models to predict climate and weather. In a class project, N. French reported on a data set found in the journal *Remote Sensing of the Environment*. Three computer models tried to predict surface temperature at various environmental conditions. The errors made by two of the models ($°K$) follow:

Error	
Model 2	**Model 3**
0.53	1.51
0.22	0.78
−0.09	0.06
−0.39	−0.64
−0.69	−1.31
−0.97	−1.96
−1.26	−2.60
−1.53	−3.22
−1.80	−3.82
−2.06	−4.42
−2.32	−4.99
−2.58	−5.56

Assuming these errors are normally distributed, test the hypothesis at the .05 level that the two computer models have the same population variances (Data = TempMod2).

10. An aqueduct has three pumping plants along its route. When concrete is placed at such construction sites, sample cylinders are filled with some of the concrete and, after curing, tested for compressive strength (psi). For a class project, B. Stewart presented such data from two of the pumping plants, Polonio Pass and Devil's Den:

Polonio Pass				**Devil's Den**			
3,520	4,670	3,780	3,880	4,700	3,550	4,750	3,600
3,470	3,770	3,420	3,690	4,610	4,010	4,100	4,030
4,090	3,950	4,030	5,210	4,470	3,940	3,550	5,330
4,380	3,600	4,020	4,380	4,915	4,090	3,830	5,460
4,210	3,660	4,600	5,200	4,900	3,960	3,950	3,760

Assume the population of compressive strengths is normally distributed. Test the hypothesis at the .10 level that the two pumping plants have the same population variances (Data = PumpPlnt)

11. Twenty alkaline and 20 heavy-duty RadioShack batteries were placed individually in a circuit consisting of two flashlight bulbs wired in parallel, a switch, a battery holder, and a Hewlett-Packard 427-A analog DC voltmeter. Each battery was drained to a reference failure voltage of 0.9 volts and the time to failure (min.) was measured:

Alkaline				**Heavy-Duty**			
105	141	147	148	29	22	22	27
140	143	108	125	26	17	22	23
116	139	146	134	23	27	23	24
140	149	142	140	22	25	22	26

Assume the population of times to failure is normally distributed. Test the hypothesis at the .05 level that the two types of batteries have the same population variances (Data = Battery).

12. A researcher compared the rate of forest regeneration of abandoned pastures and sugar cane fields in Central Eastern Ecuador. The data included the total accumulated biomass at three locations within each field. Such data for two fields follow:

Field	Biomass		
Pasture	54,577	44,891	39,658
Sugar cane	45,923	25,214	104,196

Assume the population of the total accumulated biomass is normally distributed. Test the hypothesis at the .05 level that the population variance of the accumulated biomass for sugar cane fields is greater than that of pastures.

13. In a class project, Mariah Paone described an experiment that compared two groups of ten coleus plants. Both groups were grown in hydroponic solutions in a greenhouse. One set was grown in a standard hydroponic solution, while the second set was grown in a hydroponic solution treated with added nitrogen. The 10-week growth (in cm) was recorded:

Standard		Nitrogen	
20.5	21.0	25.0	24.5
21.0	23.5	23.5	25.0
22.5	23.0	25.5	24.5
21.5	22.0	23.0	23.5
20.0	24.0	24.0	24.0

Assuming these growth amounts are normally distributed, test the hypothesis at the .05 level that the two hydroponic solutions have the same population variances (Data = Coleus).

14. Contamination of silicon wafer surfaces with particles and surface chemical oxidation have been shown to degrade device yield. In "A Portable Nitrogen Purged Microenvironment: Design Specification and Preliminary Field Test Data" (*Data PROCEEDINGS—Institute of Environmental Sciences*), C. W. Draper, et al. describe a nitrogen-purged portable microenvironment. Ten wafers receiving a standard clean in a cleanroom were compared to five wafers receiving a megasonics clean and transported through a non-clean environment in the microenvironment. Defects were measured on two vernier patterns/wafer.

Standard	Megasonic
53	26
193	90
113	546
640	90
800	120
140	
85	
658	
140	
140	

Test the hypothesis at the .10 level that the two methods have the same population variances. What assumption is necessary for this test to be valid (Data = Megsonic)?

15. In a class project mentioned earlier in this chapter involving the number of sit-ups done on an Army Physical Fitness Test (APFT), measurements were also taken on times (sec.) in a two-mile run (Data = APFT2Mlx).

Two-Mile Run						
Female		**Male**				
1,080	1,063	960	863	692	723	899
1,042	1,159	900	803	855	806	1,073
911	1,165	971	1,147	1,245	834	834
1,084	1,208	908	741	831	817	905
1,043	1,194	829	898	737	966	945
901		998	879	890	1,029	1,055
		887	874			

Assuming the times on the two-mile run are normally distributed, test the hypothesis at the .05 level that the times in two-mile run for females and males have the same population variances.

9.2 Inferences about Two Means

We've just looked at a way to do a hypothesis test for the equality of two variances. In this section and the next, we will see how to test for the equality of two means and of two proportions and how to construct confidence intervals for the difference in the values of two means and of two proportions. Our approach will be to examine each hypothesis test in some detail and follow that with a brief introduction to the corresponding confidence interval. As many of the ideas, conditions, and details concerning estimation are identical to those of hypothesis testing, this should be the easiest way for you to learn both topics and recognize the relation between the two.

In the previous section, we looked at a single testing procedure that allowed us to arrive at a decision about two population variances. That procedure assumed that (1) the data in the two populations were normally distributed, and (2) independent samples were used.

In considering inferences about two means, we'll continue to assume that each sample is either taken from a normally distributed population or that the sample size is large, that is, $n > 30$. But instead of a single procedure to follow, there are now several possible paths to take, as you can see in *Figure 9.4*. Of course, only one of the four procedures labelled in *Figure 9.4* is used in any given test, and thus only one of the paths is followed to conduct that test. "Well, fine," you may be thinking, "but how do I pick the right path through that maze in *Figure 9.4*?" The answer to your reasonable question is that you begin at the "Start" symbol at the top of *Figure 9.4* and consider each of the questions raised in the four diamond-shaped decision symbols until you've arrived at the correct test procedure to use. Thus,

- You'll follow *Procedure 1* to conduct a paired *t* test if you have two *dependent* samples taken from normally distributed populations.

- You'll follow *Procedure 2* and use the *z* distribution to conduct the test if you have independent random samples from normally distributed populations with known σ_1 and σ_2, or if the sizes of both random samples exceed 30.

STATISTICS IN ACTION

It Was Worth a Try

A total of 2,235 women at four Latin American health centres were thought to have a higher than average risk of delivering a low-birth-weight infant. Of these women, 1,115 were randomly assigned to an intervention program that provided four to six home visits from a nurse or social worker in addition to routine prenatal care. The remaining 1,120 received only routine prenatal care. There was little difference in the weights of the children born to the two groups The study concluded that interventions designed to provide psychological support and health education during high-risk pregnancies are unlikely to reduce the incidence of low birth weight among infants.

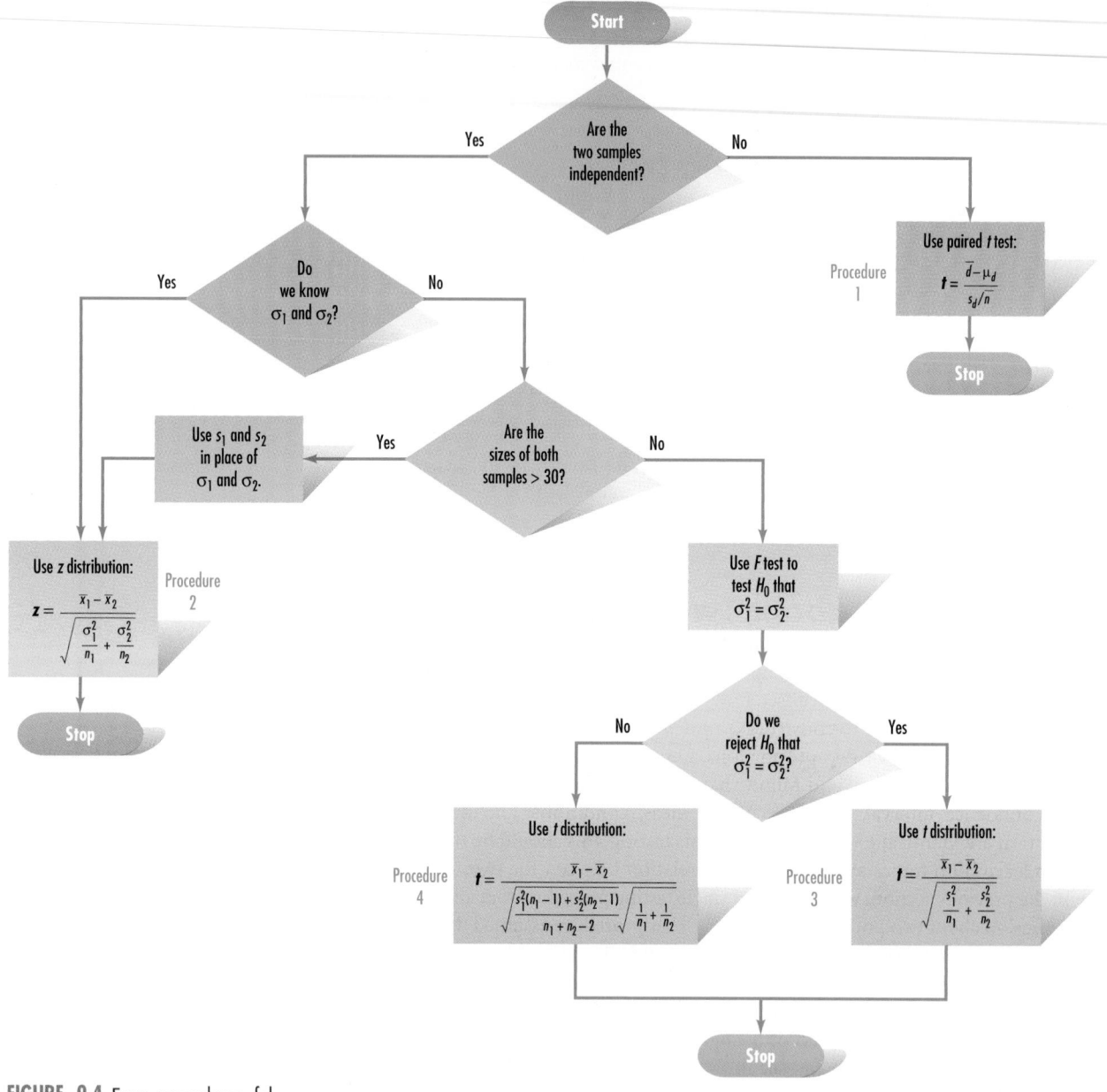

FIGURE 9.4 Four procedures followed to conduct hypothesis tests about the means of two normally distributed populations. The correct procedure to use in a given situation depends on the answers to the questions posed in the four diamond-shaped decision symbols.

- If σ_1 and σ_2 are unknown and either or both of the sample sizes are small, however, you first use the F test we've just studied to test the null hypothesis that $\sigma_1^2 = \sigma_2^2$. If the result of that F test is to *reject* H_0 that $\sigma_1^2 = \sigma_2^2$, then you'll use the t distribution and *Procedure 3* to conduct the test.

- If the result of the F test is to *fail to reject* H_0 that $\sigma_1^2 = \sigma_2^2$, then you'll use the t distribution and *Procedure 4* to conduct the test.

Let's now consider two-sample hypothesis testing examples using each of these four procedures. Although details vary, you'll be relieved to know that the same familiar seven steps are used in each testing procedure. After examining each test, we'll then look at the corresponding confidence interval.

Procedure 1A: The Paired t Test for Dependent Populations

Example 9.3   An industrial engineer is evaluating a new technique to assemble air compressors. If there's a difference in the number of compressors that can be assembled when the existing procedure is used and when the new technique is followed, she will recommend that the company use the approach that results in the greatest worker productivity. A sample of eight employees is selected at random, and the number of compressors they each produce in one week using the existing procedure is recorded. The same eight workers are then trained to use the new technique, and their output for one week is then noted. (Since the same workers are used to produce each sample, the samples are dependent.) The engineer's data are given in the first three columns of Table 9.2. She will run a hypothesis test at the .05 level of significance to determine if the data indicate that the new technique has caused a change in the mean number of compressors assembled.

◆ **Solution:**

The paired t test for dependent samples follows the same procedures used in Chapter 8 when the t distribution is employed in one-sample hypothesis tests of means. But now the test is applied to the *differences between paired values*. These differences form a single set of observations, and our testing effort follows the results from Chapter 8.

This path begins with a statement of the null and alternative hypotheses *(Step 1)*. The null hypothesis is that the population mean output using the existing method is equal to the population mean output obtained with the new technique. In other words, H_0 is that the mean difference (μ_d) between existing and new production methods is zero. Thus, the null hypothesis can be stated in this way:

$H_0: \mu_d = 0$

TABLE 9.2   SAMPLE DATA BEFORE AND AFTER THE USE OF A NEW COMPRESSOR ASSEMBLY TECHNIQUE, AND CALCULATIONS NEEDED FOR A PAIRED t TEST

Employee	Production after New Method (x_1)	Production before New Method (x_2)	Difference $(x_1 - x_2)$ (d)	$(d - \bar{d})$	$(d - \bar{d})^2$
A	85	80	5	3	9
B	84	88	−4	−6	36
C	80	76	4	2	4
D	93	90	3	1	1
E	83	74	9	7	49
F	71	70	1	−1	1
G	79	81	−2	−4	16
H	83	83	0	−2	−4
			16	0	120

$$\bar{d} = \frac{\Sigma d}{n_{pairs}} = \frac{16}{8} = 2.00$$

$$s_d = \sqrt{\frac{\Sigma (d - \bar{d})^2}{n - 1}} = \sqrt{\frac{120}{8 - 1}} = \sqrt{17.143} = 4.14$$

And the alternative hypothesis is that there is a mean difference between production methods:

$H_1: \mu_d \neq 0$

The next move is to select the level of significance *(Step 2)*, and the engineer wants to conduct this test at the .05 level of significance. *Step 3* is to determine the test distribution to use, and since the samples are small and the name of this test is the paired *t* test, it's no surprise that we'll use the *t* distribution. *Step 4* is to define the rejection or critical region. With a *two-tailed test* here, there's a .025 region in each tail of the *t* distribution. And the $t_{.025}$ critical value with $n - 1$, or $8 - 1$, or 7 degrees of freedom is found in Appendix 4 to be 2.365. Note that *n* in a paired *t* test represents the number of pairs of data. *Step 5* is to state the decision rule. The decision rule here is

Reject H_0 in favour of H_1 if $t < -2.365$ or $t > +2.365$. Otherwise, fail to reject H_0.

We next *(Step 6)* compute the test statistic. You'll recall from Chapter 8 that when the *t* distribution is used in one-sample hypothesis tests of means, the test statistic (or *t* value) is found with this formula:

$$t = \frac{\bar{x} - \mu_0}{\hat{\sigma}_{\bar{x}}} = \frac{\bar{x} - \mu_0}{s/\sqrt{n}}$$

The difference between a sample mean and a hypothetical population mean is found, and this difference is then divided by an estimated standard error to get a standardized value. Except for the fact that we're dealing with paired differences now, the following test statistic formula follows exactly the same approach:

$$t = \frac{\bar{d} - \mu_d}{s_d/\sqrt{n}} \tag{9.2}$$

Instead of a sample mean ($\bar{x}$) and hypothetical population mean (μ_0) in the numerator of the test statistic, we use the mean of the differences between the sample pairs ($\bar{d}$, which is equal to $\Sigma d/n_{\text{pairs}}$) and the hypothetical difference between the two population means (μ_d), which is equal to zero if the null hypothesis is true. And in the denominator, we now use the standard deviation of the paired sample *d* values (s_d) and the square root of the *number of pairs* of data (n_{pairs}). The value of s_d is found with this formula:

$$s_d = \sqrt{\frac{\Sigma(d - \bar{d})^2}{n - 1}} \tag{9.3}$$

As you can see in Table 9.2, the value of $\bar{d}$ is 2.00, and the s_d value is 4.14. Thus,

$$t = \frac{\bar{d} - \mu_d}{s_d/\sqrt{n}} = \frac{2.00 - 0}{4.14/\sqrt{8}} = \frac{2.00}{1.464} = 1.37$$

Step 7 is to make the statistical decision. Since $t = 1.37$ is between the t critical values of ±2.365, we fail to reject the null hypothesis that the mean difference in production methods is zero. The engineer can't conclude that one assembly method is better than the other. ◆

Suppose in the previous example the new technique required more costly equipment so that the engineer would recommend switching to the new technique only if the new technique produced a greater average output. The engineer would then want to conduct a *one-tailed test* in which the alternative hypothesis reads

$H_1: \mu_d > 0$

In this case, the entire α value is in the right tail of the t distribution. Thus, if we are making a paired t test with 8 paired observations at the .05 level, the $t_{.05}$ value with $n - 1$, or $8 - 1$, or 7 df is 1.895. And the decision rule is

Reject H_0 in favour of H_1 if $t > 1.895$. Otherwise, fail to reject H_0.

We would then calculate the test statistic and make the statistical decision just as we did for a two-tailed test. You might note that the engineer did a right-tailed test. But if the engineer had obtained the differences of the paired date by calculating *existing minus new* rather than *new minus existing*, the resulting hypothesis test would have been left tailed. However, the decision would be the same. The moral is to consider which way the subtractions are done when performing a one-tailed test on differences.

Example 9.4 **A Yawner of an Experiment** A researcher asked 16 subjects to perform several tasks before and after 24 hours of sleep deprivation. One task involved the subjects lifting weights until muscle failure. Below is a count of the number of bench presses done before and after 24 hours of sleep deprivation. We want to see if there is enough evidence, at a level of significance of 0.01, to show that the population mean number of bench presses is less after the sleep deprivation (Data = Sleepbp).

Subject	Bench Press Pre	Post
1	19	19
2	11	10
3	9	8
4	51	51
5	60	58
6	23	21
7	20	17
8	32	28
9	16	16
10	11	9
11	26	22
12	45	40
13	26	20
14	10	7
15	8	6
16	15	11

◆ Solution:

We start, as always, with the null and alternative hypotheses *(Step 1)*. We need to be a little careful here. We are planning to perform a one-tailed test. However, whether we run a right-tailed or left-tailed test depends on how we do the calculation of the difference. Here, we decided to compute

Difference = Pre − Post

That being the case, if sleep deprivation causes a decrease in the mean number of bench presses, this will be a positive difference. Thus the null and alternative hypotheses are

H_0: $\mu_d = 0$
H_1: $\mu_d > 0$

(Note: If we had defined the difference as Post minus Pre, the direction of H_1 would reverse; that is, we would have a left-tailed rather than a right-tailed test. However, everything else would also reverse and *we would reach exactly the same decision.* The point is, while it doesn't matter which way we define the difference, once it is defined, we must be careful to follow through correctly.)

We have chosen $\alpha = .01$ *(Step 2)*, and, assuming that the values in the population of differences in the number of bench presses are normally distributed, we'll use the t distribution to run the test *(Step 3)*. Using the p-value approach, our decision rule *(Step 4)* is

Reject H_0 if the p-value < .01. Otherwise, fail to reject H_0.

 We used MINITAB (see *Figure 9.5a*) and the TI-83 calculator (see *Figure 9.5b*) to compute the test statistic *(Step 5)* and the p-value *(Step 6)* of the test. Because the p-value each gives us (.000 from MINITAB and .000041 by the TI-83) are both < .01, our conclusion *(Step 7)* is to reject H_0. There is strong evidence that sleep deprivation does cause a decrease in the true mean number of bench presses. ◆

Procedure 1B: The Confidence Interval for Dependent Populations

While often we want to perform a hypothesis test on the value of a mean difference, other times we simply want to estimate it. Under the same conditions that allow us to do a test, we may also construct a confidence interval for the mean difference, μ_d:

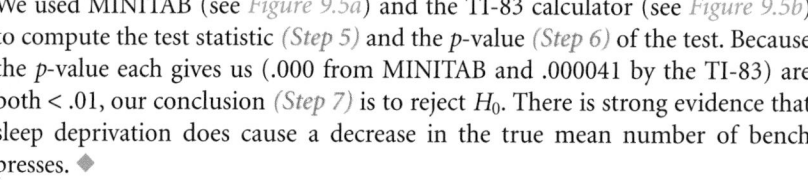

$$\bar{d} - t_{\alpha/2}\frac{s_d}{\sqrt{n}} < \mu_d < \bar{d} + t_{\alpha/2}\frac{s_d}{\sqrt{n}} \tag{9.4}$$

Example 9.5   Suppose the industrial engineer from Example 9.3 wants to estimate the population mean difference (μ_d) between existing and new assembly methods of air compressors. Use that sample to obtain a 95 percent confidence interval.

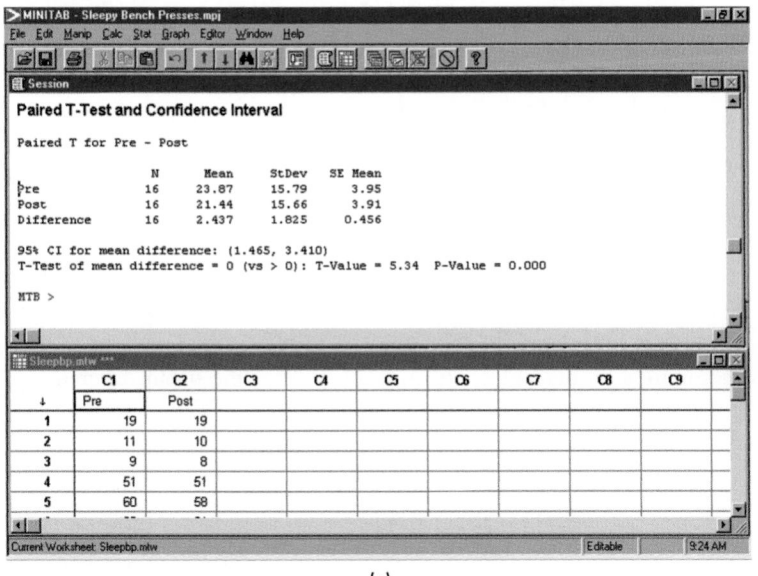

(a)

FIGURE 9.5 (a) To obtain this MINITAB output, click on **Stat, Basic Statistics,** Paired t, enter *Pre* in the box to the right of **First sample** and *Post* in the box to the right of **Second Sample,** and click OK. (b) To perform the calculations for a paired *t* test on the TI-83, use the **T-Test** that we used in Chapter 8. However, we must first get the differences into a list. To do this, put the PRE data into **L1** and the POST data into **L2**. On the home screen, enter **L1-L2 STO L3**. This will store the differences into **L3.** You may verify that the differences are in **L3** by going to the **STAT> Edit** menu. Next perform the T-Test on L3. See screen 1 for the setup and screen 2 for the results.

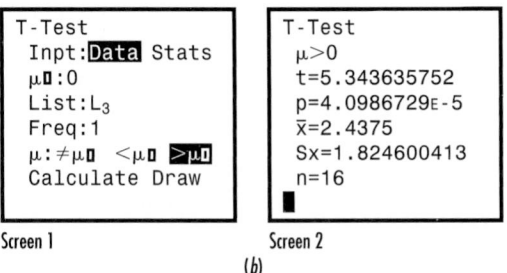

Screen 1   Screen 2
(b)

◆ Solution:

We would use the same value from the *t* distribution as in Example 9.3, $t_{.025}$ with 7 degrees of freedom, 2.365. As we saw in Table 9.2, the value of $\bar{d}$ is 2.00, and the s_d value is 4.14. So the confidence interval is

$$\bar{d} - t_{\alpha/2}\,\frac{s_d}{\sqrt{n}} < \mu_d < \bar{d} + t_{\alpha/2}\,\frac{s_d}{\sqrt{n}}$$

$$2.00 - 2.365\left(\frac{4.14}{\sqrt{8}}\right) < \mu_d < 2.00 + 2.365\left(\frac{4.14}{\sqrt{8}}\right)$$

$$2.00 - 3.46 < \mu_d < 2.00 + 3.46$$

$$2.00 - 3.46 < \mu_d < 5.46$$

We conclude that the difference in the mean number of air compressors assembled is somewhere between − 1.46 (1.46 more by the *existing* method) and 5.46 (5.46 more by the *new* method). That is, it is not clear which method is better than the other—perhaps there is no difference at all. This agrees with our hypothesis testing decision that the engineer can't conclude that one assembly method is better than the other. If our interval did not include zero, that is, if the end points were both negative or both positive, then we *could* conclude that the two methods differ. In that case, the null hypothesis in Example 9.3 would have been rejected. ◆

FIGURE 9.6 To make a confidence interval for the true mean difference in the bench press example, we will use the **TInterval** command that we used in Chapter 7. We still have the differences in L3. Screen 1 shows the settings for the interval, and screen 2 shows the results.

```
TInterval
 Inpt:Data Stats
 List:L₃
 Freq:1
 C-Level:.95
 Calculate
```

Screen 1

```
TInterval
 (1.4652,3.4098)
 x̄=2.4375
 Sx=1.824600413
 n=16
```

Screen 2

■ **Example 9.6**   **Pressing the Example** Use MINITAB and the TI-83 calculator to compute a 95 percent confidence interval for the mean difference in Example 9.4, the bench press example.

◆ **Solution:**

MINITAB has already obtained a 95 percent confidence interval in *Figure 9.5a*. A similar result is produced by the TI-83 calculator in screen 2 of *Figure 9.6*. Both indicate that the 95 percent confidence interval is $1.465 < \mu_d < 3.410$. That is, we can be 95 percent confident there is a decrease of between 1.465 and 3.410 in the true mean number of bench presses done without sleep, agreeing with our hypothesis test decision. ◆

Procedure 2A: The *z* Test for Independent Populations

A *z* test is used when

1. The samples are taken independently from two populations, and

2. Either
   (*a*) Both populations are normal and the values of σ_1 and σ_2 are known,
   or
   (*b*) The size of both samples exceeds 30. (The large sample sizes will make the test statistic approximately normal even when the populations are not normal and the population variances are not known.)

When both of these two conditions are met, *Step 1* in the testing procedure is (surprise!) to formulate the null and alternative hypothesis. The *null hypothesis* is

$H_0: \mu_1 = \mu_2$

This hypothesis states that the true mean of the first population is equal to the true mean of the second population. The three possible alternative hypotheses are, as before, two-tailed, right-tailed, and left-tailed, that is,

$H_1: \mu_1 \neq \mu_2$
$H_1: \mu_1 > \mu_2$
$H_1: \mu_1 < \mu_2$

When the null hypothesis states that the true mean of group 1 is equal to the true mean of group 2 ($\mu_1 = \mu_2$), it's essentially saying that the *difference between the parameters of the two groups is zero*—that is, $\mu_1 - \mu_2 = 0$. This idea makes it possible for us to visualize another type of sampling distribution.

The Sampling Distribution of the Differences between Sample Means A conceptual schematic of this new sampling distribution is shown in *Figure 9.7*. Distribution A in *Figure 9.7* is the sampling distribution of the sample means for population 1, and distribution B is the corresponding sampling distribution for population 2. Each of these theoretical distributions is developed from the means of all the possible samples of a given size that can be drawn from a population. Now if we were to select a single sample mean from distribution A and another sample mean from distribution B, we could subtract the value of the second mean from the value of the first mean and get a difference—that is, $\bar{x}_1 - \bar{x}_2$ = difference. This difference is either a negative or positive value, as shown in the examples between distributions A and B in *Figure 9.7*.

We could theoretically continue to select sample means from each population and continue to compute differences. If we then constructed a frequency distribution of *all the sample differences,* we would have distribution C in *Figure 9.7*, which is the **sampling distribution of the differences between sample means.** And, as noted in *Figure 9.7*, if H_0 is true if μ_1 is equal to μ_2, then the value of the mean of the sampling distribution of the differences ($\mu_{\bar{x}_1 - \bar{x}_2}$) is $\mu_1 - \mu_2 = 0$. In short, the negative differences and the positive differences cancel, and the mean is zero.

Even if the mean of the sampling distribution of differences is zero, though, the characteristics of the sampling distribution of differences allows the value of $\bar{x}_1 - \bar{x}_2$ to deviate from zero. If the parameters are truly equal and if random samples are taken from the two populations, it's unlikely that the difference of $\bar{x}_1 - \bar{x}_2$ will equal zero exactly; there will usually be some sampling variation. But if the true means are equal, the likelihood of an extremely large difference between $\bar{x}_1$ and $\bar{x}_2$ is small, especially

FIGURE 9.7 Conceptual schematic of the sampling distribution of the differences between sample means.

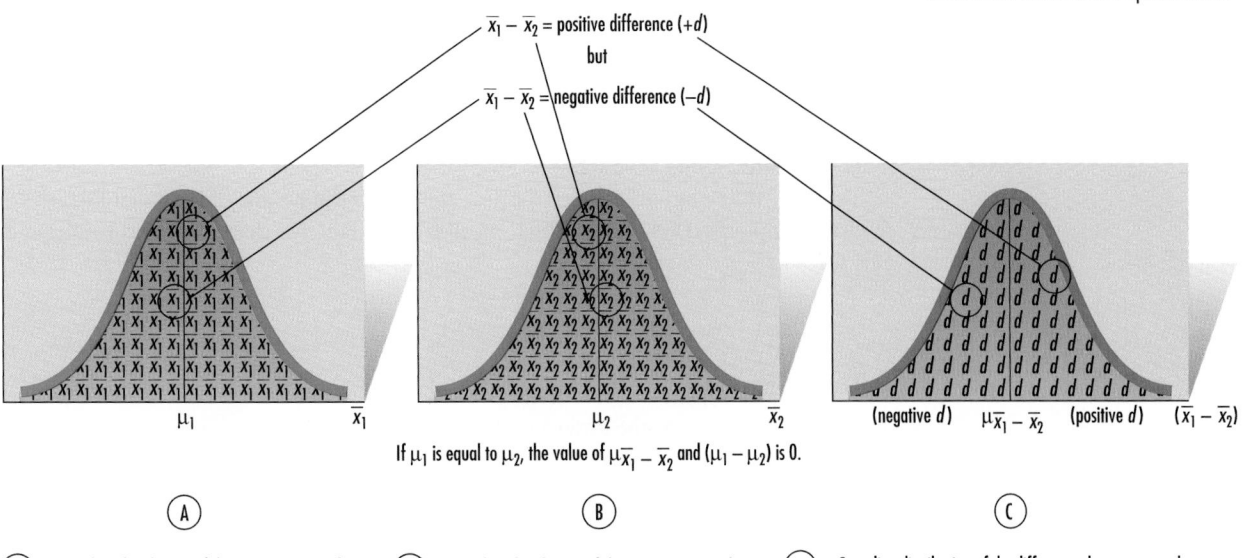

$\bar{x}_1 - \bar{x}_2$ = positive difference $(+d)$
but
$\bar{x}_1 - \bar{x}_2$ = negative difference $(-d)$

If μ_1 is equal to μ_2, the value of $\mu_{\bar{x}_1 - \bar{x}_2}$ and $(\mu_1 - \mu_2)$ is 0.

(A) = Sampling distribution of the means — population 1 (B) = Sampling distribution of the means — population 2 (C) = Sampling distribution of the differences between sample means

FIGURE 9.8 The sampling differences between means when σ_1 and σ_2 are known or when n_1 and n_2 are both > 30.

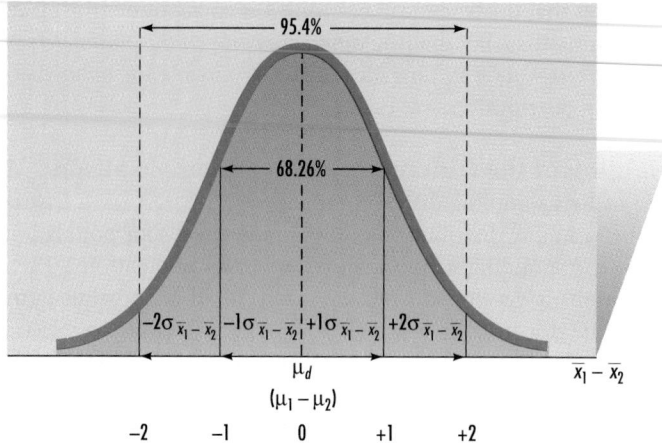

in two large samples. Thus, if an extremely large difference occurs between $\bar{x}_1$ and $\bar{x}_2$, it's justifiable to conclude that the true means of the two populations aren't equal. The immediate problem, of course, is to figure out when the difference between samples is so large that the null hypothesis can be rejected.

If we know that both populations are normally distributed or if we take a large sample from each population, the shape of the sampling distribution of the differences between means is normal or, in the large sample case, approximately normal. Thus, the middle 68.26 percent of the differences in that sampling distribution are found within 1 standard deviation of the mean, and 2 standard deviations to either side of the mean accounts for 95.44 percent of the differences. The standard deviation of the sampling distribution of differences is called the **standard error of the difference between means** and is identified by the symbol $\sigma_{\bar{x}_1 - \bar{x}_2}$ (see *Figure 9.8*).

Now that we've considered these theoretical concepts, we can briefly summarize the remaining six steps in our z test for independent samples. *Step 2* is to pick a level of significance, and we've just seen that the appropriate test distribution to use *(Step 3)* is the z distribution. The process of establishing a rejection region *(Step 4)* and stating a decision rule *(Step 5)* is exactly the same here as in Chapter 8, when the z distribution was applicable. For example, with a two-tailed test and a .05 level of significance, the z critical values for the boundaries of the rejection region are ± 1.96. For a left-tailed test and a .05 level, the z value is -1.645.

Just as in other hypothesis tests, a test statistic (z) must also be calculated *(Step 6)* for two-sample tests of means. You'll recall from Chapter 8 that one z was found with this formula:

$$z = \frac{\bar{x} - \mu_0}{\sigma_{\bar{x}}}$$

That is, the statistic was the difference between actual and hypothetical values expressed in number of standard errors. Now, our test statistic uses the standardized difference between $\bar{x}_1$ and $\bar{x}_2$ and is computed as follows:

$$z = \frac{(\bar{x}_1 - \bar{x}_2) - (\mu_1 - \mu_2)}{\sigma_{\bar{x}_1 - \bar{x}_2}} \quad \text{or} \quad z = \frac{(\bar{x}_1 - \bar{x}_2)}{\sigma_{\bar{x}_1 - \bar{x}_2}} \tag{9.5}$$

since $\mu_1 = \mu_2$ is assumed to be zero if H_0 is true. And (if it's known that we have two independently drawn random samples with known population standard deviations) the standard error of the difference is computed as follows:

$$\sigma_{\bar{x}_1 - \bar{x}_2} = \sqrt{\frac{\sigma_1^2}{n_1} + \frac{\sigma_2^2}{n_2}} \tag{9.6}$$

When σ_1^2 and σ_2^2 are unknown, but n_1 and n_2 both exceed 30 we can substitute s_1^2 and s_2^2 for σ_1^2 and σ_2^2. Because of the Central Limit Theorem, the test statistic will be approximately normal, and we can perform a valid test. Once the test statistic is computed, we compare its value to the decision rule to reach a conclusion *(Step 7)*.

Let's now took at the following examples, which illustrate two-tailed and one-tailed tests.

Example 9.7 **Two-Tailed Testing When σ_1 and σ_2 Are Known** The Russ Trate Traffic Signal Company has decided to install new types of microprocessors in its traffic light assemblies so that these units can more efficiently monitor and control traffic flows. Microprocessors from two suppliers are judged to be suitable for the application. To have more than one source of supply, the Trate Company prefers to buy microprocessors from both suppliers, provided there's no significant difference in durability. A random sample of 35 computer assemblies of brand A and a sample of 32 computers of brand B are tested. The mean time between failure (MTBF) for the brand A computers is found to be 2,800 hours, and the MTBF for the brand B units is found to be 2,750 hours. Information from industry sources indicates that the population standard deviation is 200 hours for brand A and 180 hours for brand B. At the .05 level of significance, is there a difference in durability?

◆ **Solution:**
Hypotheses (Step 1):

$H_0: \mu_1 = \mu_2$
$H_1: \mu_1 \neq \mu_2$

Since the Trate Company is interested only in seeing if there is any difference between the two brands, this is a two-tailed test. Also, the level of significance is specified at the .05 level *(Step 2)*, and the knowledge of the population standard deviations (and the large sample sizes) enable us to use the z distribution *(Step 3)*. Thus, the rejection region is bounded by z critical values = ±1.96 *(Step 4)*, and the decision rule *(Step 5)* is

Reject H_0 in favour of H_1 if $z < -1.96$ or $z > +1.96$. Otherwise, fail to reject H_0.

With $\sigma_1 = 200$ hours, $n_1 = 35$, $\sigma_2 = 180$ hours, and $n_2 = 32$,

$$\sigma_{\bar{x}_1 - \bar{x}_2} = \sqrt{\frac{\sigma_1^2}{n_1} + \frac{\sigma_2^2}{n_2}} = \sqrt{\frac{200^2}{35} + \frac{180^2}{32}} = 46.43 \text{ hours}$$

Therefore, the test statistic *(Step 6)* is

$$z = \frac{(\bar{x}_1 - \bar{x}_2)}{\sigma_{\bar{x}_1 - \bar{x}_2}} = \frac{2,800 - 2,750}{46.43} = 1.08$$

Conclusion (Step 7):

Since the test statistic does not fall within the rejection region, we can conclude that there's no significant difference in the durability of the two microcomputer brands. ◆

Example 9.8   **One-Tailed Testing When σ_1 and σ_2 Are Known** Discount Stores Corporation owns outlet A and outlet B. For the past year, outlet A has spent more dollars advertising casual slacks than outlet B. The corporation's advertising manager wants to see whether the advertising has resulted in more sales for outlet A. A random sample of 36 days at outlet A had a mean of 170 slacks sold daily. A random sample of 36 days at outlet B had a mean sales of 165 slacks. Assuming $\sigma_1^2 = 36$ and $\sigma_2^2 = 25$, what can be concluded if a test is conducted at the .05 level of significance?

◆ **Solution:**

Hypotheses (Step 1):

H_0: $\mu_1 = \mu_2$
H_1: $\mu_1 > \mu_2$

This is a *right-tailed test* because the manager wants to see if the sales performance of outlet A is better than the performance of outlet B. With a .05 level *(Step 2)*, the z value *(Step 3)* that bounds the rejection region is $z_{.05} = 1.645$ *(Step 4)*. Thus, the decision rule *(Step 5)* is

Reject H_0 in favour of H_1 if $z > 1.645$. Otherwise, fail to reject H_0.

The test statistic *(Step 6)* is:

$$z = \frac{(\bar{x}_1 - \bar{x}_2)}{\sigma_{\bar{x}_1 - \bar{x}_2}} = \frac{170 - 165}{\sqrt{\dfrac{36}{36} + \dfrac{25}{36}}} = \frac{5}{1.3017} = 3.84$$

Conclusion (Step 7):

Since $z > 1.645$, there's sufficient reason to believe that outlet A has sold more slacks than outlet B. ◆

When the population standard deviations are unknown—the usual situation—and when the samples from both populations are large (> 30), then the sample standard deviations are used to estimate the population values. That is, $s_1 = \sigma_1$ and $s_2 = \sigma_2$.

An estimated standard error of the difference between means is then computed as follows:

$$\hat{\sigma}_{\bar{x}_1 - \bar{x}_2} = \sqrt{\frac{s_1^2}{n_1} + \frac{s_2^2}{n_2}} \tag{9.7}$$

Example 9.9   **Two-Tailed Testing When σ_1 and σ_2 Are Unknown** Dr. K. M. Svoboda, a psychologist, administered IQ tests to see if there was a difference in the scores produced by a population of business majors and a population of psychology majors. A random sample of 40 business majors had a mean score of 131 with a standard deviation of 15. The random sample of 36 psychology majors had a mean of 126 and a standard deviation of 17. At the .01 level of significance, is there a difference?

◆ **Solution:**
Hypotheses (Step 1):

$H_0: \mu_1 = \mu_2$
$H_1: \mu_1 \neq \mu_2$

Since Dr. Svoboda is interested only in judging the equality or non-equality between the two groups, this is a two-tailed test. The .01 level is specified *(Step 2)*, and since our sample sizes are large, the z distribution is used *(Step 3)*. Thus, the rejection region is bounded by $z = -2.575$ and $z = +2.575$ *(Step 4)*, and the decision rule *(Step 5)* is

Reject H_0 in favour of H_1 if $z < -2.575$ or $z > +2.575$. Otherwise, fail to reject H_0.

With $s_1 = 15$, $n_1 = 40$, $s_2 = 17$, and $n_2 = 36$, the test statistic *(Step 6)* is

$$z = \frac{\bar{x}_1 - \bar{x}_2}{\sqrt{\dfrac{s_1^2}{n_1} + \dfrac{s_2^2}{n_2}}} = \frac{131 - 126}{\sqrt{\dfrac{15^2}{40} + \dfrac{17^2}{36}}} = \frac{5}{3.695} = 1.35$$

Conclusion (Step 7):

Since the test statistic falls between ± 2.575, we can conclude that there is not a significant difference in the IQ scores of the two groups. ◆

Example 9.10 **One-Tailed Testing When σ_1 and σ_2 Are Unknown** A Chamber of Commerce manager is seeking to attract new industry to his area. One argument he has been using is that average wages paid for a particular type of job are lower than in other parts of the nation. A rather skeptical company president assigns his brother-in-law the task of testing this claim. A random sample of 60 workers (group 1) performing the particular job in the chamber manager's area is taken, and the sample mean is found to be $9.75 per hour with a sample standard deviation of $2.00 per hour. Another random sample of 50 workers (group 2) taken in a different region produced a sample mean of $10.25 per hour with a sample standard deviation of $1.25 per hour. At the .01 level, what report should the brother-in-law give to the president?

◆ **Solution:**
Hypotheses (Step 1):

$H_0: \mu_1 = \mu_2$
$H_1: \mu_1 < \mu_2$

This is a one-tailed test because the validity of the chamber manager's claim is being evaluated—that is, that the mean wages paid in his area are less than in other areas. At the .01 level *(Step 2)*, the z critical value *(Step 3)* that bounds the rejection region is $-z_{.01} = -2.33$ *(Step 4)*. Thus, the decision rule *(Step 5)* is

Reject H_0 in favour of H_1 if $z < -2.33$. Otherwise, fail to reject H_0.

With $s_1 = \$2.00$, $n_1 = 60$, $s_2 = \$1.25$, and $n_2 = 50$, the test statistic *(Step 6)* is

$$z = \frac{\bar{x}_1 - \bar{x}_2}{\sqrt{\dfrac{s_1^2}{n_1} + \dfrac{s_2^2}{n_2}}} = \frac{\$9.75 - \$10.25}{\sqrt{\dfrac{\$2.00^2}{60} + \dfrac{\$1.25^2}{50}}} = \frac{-\$0.50}{\$0.313} = -1.60$$

Conclusion (Step 7):

Since z does not fall into the rejection region, the chamber manager's claim is not sup-ported by the sample results at the .01 level. The brother-in-law is relieved to report that the test results do not contradict the president's doubts. ◆

Procedure 2B: The Confidence Interval for Independent Populations

We want to be able to estimate the difference between two population means, $\mu_1 - \mu_2$, using a confidence interval. We can do so if the conditions under which it is valid to do a hypothesis test are satisfied—that is, we have either independent samples from normal populations with known variances or independent samples that are large (both greater than 30). Then the confidence interval is calculated with

$$(\bar{x}_1 - \bar{x}_2) - z_{\alpha/2}\sigma_{\bar{x}_1 - \bar{x}_2} < \mu_1 - \mu_2 < (\bar{x}_1 - \bar{x}_2) + z_{\alpha/2}\sigma_{\bar{x}_1 - \bar{x}_2} \qquad (9.8)$$

Example 9.11   In Example 9.9, Dr. K. M. Svoboda looked at the difference in the IQ scores produced by a population of business majors and a population of psychol-ogy majors. Dr. Svoboda found that $x_1 = 131$, $\bar{x}_2 = 126$, and $\sigma_{\bar{x}_1 - \bar{x}_2} = 3.695$. Use this in-formation to obtain a 99 percent confidence interval for $\mu_1 - \mu_2$.

◆ **Solution:**

The hopefully now familiar value from the z distribution for 95 percent confidence is 2.575. The confidence interval is

$(\bar{x}_1 - \bar{x}_2) - z_{\alpha/2}\sigma_{\bar{x}_1 - \bar{x}_2} < \mu_1 - \mu_2 < (\bar{x}_1 - \bar{x}_2) + z_{\alpha/2}\sigma_{\bar{x}_1 - \bar{x}_2}$
$(131 - 126) - (2.575)(3.695) < \mu_1 - \mu_2 < (131 - 126) + (2.575)(3.695)$
$5 - 9.51 < \mu_1 - \mu_2 < 5 + 9.51$
$-4.51 < \mu_1 - \mu_2 < 14.51$

The confidence interval indicates the difference of the means could be either negative or positive. Therefore, it is also possible the difference is zero or, more simply, there is no difference between the means, agreeing with the hypothesis-testing results of Ex-ample 9.9. ◆

Example 9.12   **Something Fishy, Part Two?** In Chapter 3 we investigated, through graphical techniques, the idea that the mean lengths (mm) of fish differ by gender (the sample data are reproduced on the next page). Test that supposition with a hypothesis test using a level of significance of .01 and the p-value approach (Data = Dvrsole2).

Female							
292	316	327	334	337	341	342	345
349	350	351	355	356	357	357	360
361	362	363	364	366	366	369	373
375	376	379	380	382	384	385	386
388	389	390	393	394	400	405	412
442	457						

Male							
331	339	339	340	341	346	347	358
364	366	370	371	371	371	373	374
381	381	384	386	387	387	388	389
390	392	393	394	395	397	398	398
398	403	404	405	408	409	410	410
411	412	413	414	415	417	419	419
420	420	421	423	425	427	436	439
439	451						

◆ **Solution:**

Because we are looking for any difference, the null and alternative hypotheses *(Step 1)* are

$H_0: \mu_1 = \mu_2$
$H_1: \mu_1 \neq \mu_2$

We have selected $\alpha = .01$ *(Step 2)*. Because both samples contain more than 30 observations, we will substitute the values of sample variances for the population variances and use the normal distribution to run the test *(Step 3)*. With the *p*-value approach, our decision rule *(Step 4)* is

Reject H_0 if the *p*-value is $< .01$. Otherwise, fail to reject H_0.

We again used MINITAB (*Figure 9.9a*) and the TI-83 calculator (screen 2 of *Figure 9.9b*) to calculate the test statistic *(Step 5)* and the *p*-value *(Step 6)*. (Notice that we did a *t* test rather than a *z* test—as in the one sample case, whenever the population variances are unknown, we are really doing a *t* test—but the *z* and *t* distributions and their critical values are so close with large samples that it doesn't make much difference [no pun intended] anyway). Because the *p*-value is .0001 < .01, our conclusion *(Step 7)* is to reject H_0. There is significant evidence that there is a difference in the mean lengths of male and female fish. Additionally, the MINITAB two-sample output automatically includes a confidence interval (with the one-sample program, you had to pick either the confidence interval or the hypothesis test), while the interval could also be calculated by a TI-83 calculator. The 95 percent confidence interval is

$-35.9 < \mu_1 - \mu_2 < -12.1$

FIGURE 9.9 (a) There are two ways to obtain this MINITAB output. Both require that we access the **2-Sample t** window by clicking on **Stat Basic Statistics, 2-Sample t.** If the data for the male and female fish are in different columns, click on **Samples in different columns** and enter the columns in the appropriate rectangles; if all the lengths are in one column, click on **Samples in one column,** enter the lengths as **Samples** and the genders as **Subscripts,** and click OK. (b) To use the TI-83 to calculate the test statistic and the p-value for the data, put the female lengths into one list and put the male lengths into another list. We have the females in L1 and the males in L2. Choose the **2-SampTTest** from the **TESTS** menu. Screen 1 shows the setup for the test. Choose **Calculate** from the test screen. The results are shown in screen 2.

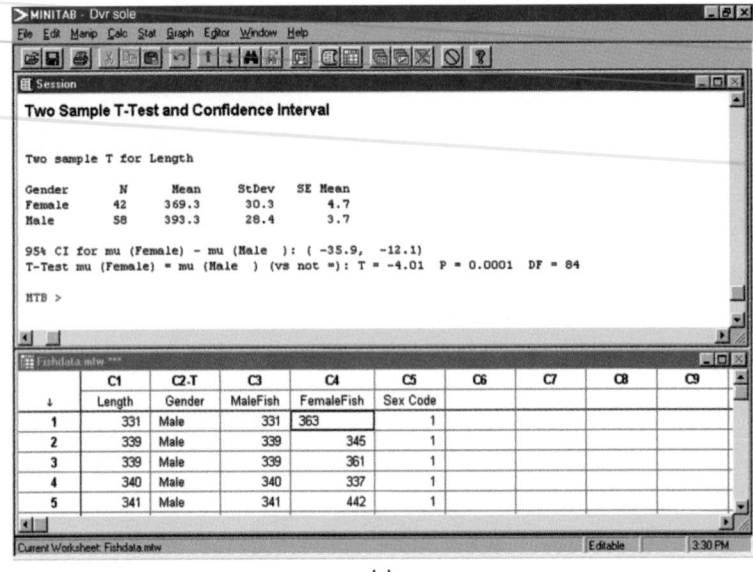

(a)

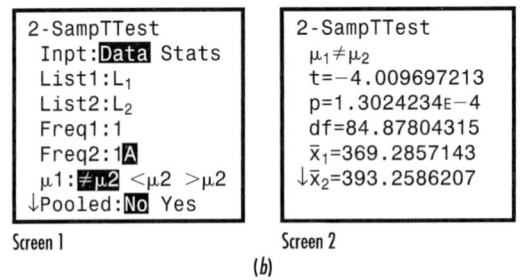

Screen 1   Screen 2
(b)

So it looks like the mean length of the population of male fish is greater than the mean of the population of females by between 12.1 and 35.9 mm. We say the mean length of the males is greater because the confidence interval limits are negative numbers and our difference is $\mu_1 - \mu_2$, where μ_2 is the mean of the males. If we had reversed the definition, that is, if we had used μ_1 to represent the mean of the males and μ_2 the mean of the females, our confidence interval would have been

$$12.1 < \mu_1 - \mu_2 < 35.9$$

and we would reach the same conclusion. ◆

Example 9.13 **Hydroseed the Deerweed, Indeed** In a class project (*Comparison of Width of Lotus Scoparius on Two Experimental Test Plots*), Susi Bernstein presented the widths (mm) of deerweed in two locations. The first location was not treated with hydroseed, while the second was. Test the hypothesis at a level of .01 that the hydroseeding increases the mean width of deerweed (Data = HydrSeed).

No Hydroseed			Hydroseed		
0.07	0.02	0.38	0.29	0.85	0.42
0.05	0.03	0.02	0.33	0.04	0.41
0.04	0.02	0.01	0.29	0.16	0.15
0.07	0.48	0.01	0.59	0.62	0.69
0.05	0.02	0.02	0.13	0.98	0.29
0.24	0.45	2.21	1.18	0.26	0.44
0.02	0.39	0.55	0.19	0.25	1.02
0.98	0.03	0.62	0.47	0.22	0.53
0.05	0.22	0.12	0.48	0.12	0.88
0.02	0.13	0.13	0.04	0.01	0.46
0.41	0.17	0.18	1.01	0.06	0.21
0.02	0.11	0.06	0.03	0.31	1.25
0.03	0.16	0.02	0.11	0.14	1.54
0.18	0.16	0.27	0.06	0.08	1.90
0.05	0.05	0.16	0.01	0.96	0.92
0.03	0.09	0.72	0.01	0.13	0.58
1.06	0.03	0.50	0.53	0.17	0.32
0.09	0.20	0.91	0.10	0.48	0.68
0.04	0.48	0.02	0.08	0.12	0.59
0.05	0.01	0.40	0.07		

◆ **Solution:**

Because we are looking to see if the hydroseed increases the mean width, we test *(Step 1)*

$H_0: \mu_1 = \mu_2$
$H_1: \mu_1 < \mu_2$

We have decided on $\alpha = .01$ *(Step 2)*. With the large sample sizes, we will use the normal distribution to perform the test *(Step 3)*. Our decision rule *(Step 4)* is

Reject H_0 if the *p*-value is < .01. Otherwise, fail to reject H_0.

Using MINITAB and the TI-83 calculator to do the computations *(Step 5)*, we get the output of *Figure 9.10a* and screen 2 of *Figure 9.10b*. Because the *p*-value *(Step 6)* is .0030 < .01, our conclusion *(Step 7)* is to reject H_0. There is strong evidence that the hydroseeding increases the mean width of deerweed. ◆

Procedure 3A: Small-Sample *t* Test for Independent Populations When $\sigma_1 \neq \sigma_2$

As you can see in *Figure 9.4*, the following conditions must be met before Procedure 3 can be applied:

1. The two samples are taken from two independent, normally distributed populations.

2. The values of σ_1 and σ_2 are unknown.

FIGURE 9.10 (a) MINITAB two-sample *t* test of deerweed data. (b) TI-83 two-sample *t* test of deerweed data.

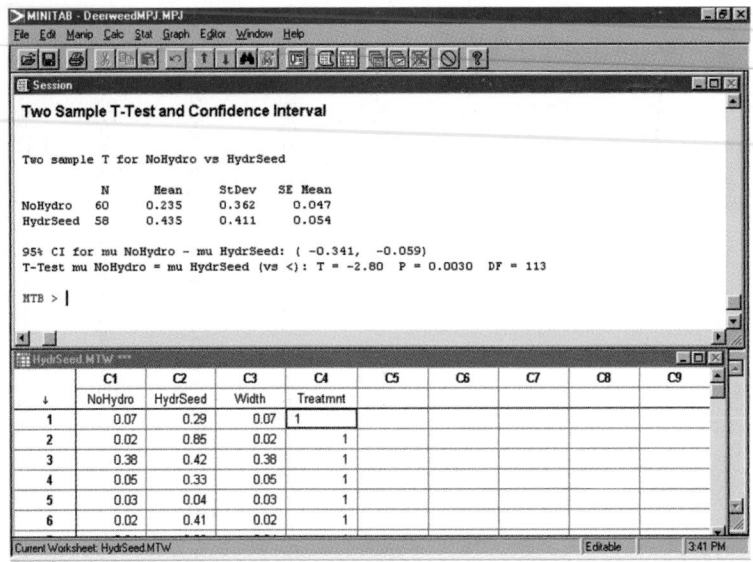

(a)

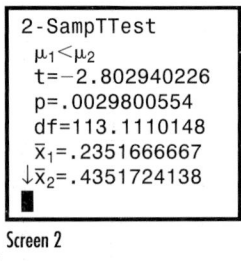

Screen 1   Screen 2

(b)

3. The size of n_1 or n, is small (≤ 30).

4. An *F* test leads to the conclusion that σ^2_1 and σ^2_2 are likely to be *different* (*unequal*).

When these conditions are met, the *t* test steps followed in Procedure 3 closely parallel those we've just followed to conduct one- and two-tailed tests. Since that's the case, we need not consider as many examples in this section.

Example 9.14   An apartment rental agent tells the personnel manager of a firm thinking of building a plant in the agent's city that the mean rental rates for two-bedroom apartments are the same in sectors A and B of the city. To test this claim, the personnel manager randomly samples apartment complexes in each sector and obtains the following data:

Sector A	Sector B
$\bar{x}_1 = \$595$	$\bar{x}_2 = \$580$
$n_1 = 10$	$n_2 = 12$
$s_1 = \$62$	$s_2 = \$32$
$s_1^2 = 3{,}844$	$s_2^2 = 1{,}024$

What can the personnel manager conclude about the agent's claim at the .5 level?

◆ **Solution:**

Since the two samples are small and come from independent populations with unknown population standard deviations, we must first conduct an F test to see if σ_1^2 and σ_2^2 are likely to be different. Sector A has the largest variance, so that value becomes s_1^2, and the variance in sector B is identified as s_2^2. All other values in sectors A and B have similar subscripts. The hypotheses *(Step 1)* for our F test are

H_0: $\sigma_1^2 = \sigma_2^2$
H_1: $\sigma_1^2 \neq \sigma_2^2$

With $\alpha = .05$ *(Step 2)*, and with $n_1 - 1$, or $10 - 1$, or 9 degrees of freedom in the numerator, and with $n_2 - 1$, or $12 - 1$, or 11 degrees of freedom in the denominator, the critical F value *(Step 3)* in Appendix 5 is found in the table for $\alpha = .025$ at the intersection of the column numbered 9 and the row numbered 11. This critical F value is 3.59 *(Step 4)*. Thus, thus decision rule *(Step 5)* for our F test is

Reject H_0 in favour of H_1 if $F > 3.59$. Otherwise, fail to reject H_0.

The test statistic for our F test *(Step 6)* is

$$F = \frac{s_1^2}{s_2^2} = \frac{3,844}{1,024} = 3.754$$

Conclusion of our F test *(Step 7)*: Since $F = 3.754 > 3.59$, we reject the null hypothesis and conclude that σ_1^2 and σ_2^2 are likely to be different.

The results of this preliminary F test clear the way for us to use Procedure 3 to test the rental agent's claim that the rental rates for two-bedroom apartments are the same in sectors A and B.

Hypotheses (Step 1):

H_0: $\mu_1 = \mu_2$
H_1: $\mu_1 \neq \mu_2$

This is a two-tailed test since we are merely trying to validate the agent's claim. The personnel manager specifies that $\alpha = .05$ *(Step 2)*. With small samples and unknown population standard deviations, the t distribution must be used *(Step 3)*. With $\alpha = .05$ and with a two-tailed test, we need $\pm t_{.025}$ critical values for the boundaries of the rejection region. To find those values in Appendix 4, though, we must know the degrees of freedom (df), In this Procedure 3 test, *the df figure is the smaller of $n_1 - 1$ or $n_2 - 1$.* Thus, the df figure we need is $n_1 - 1$, or $10 - 1$, or 9. And so the $t_{.025}$ critical values that bound the rejection region are ±2.262 *(Step 4)*.

The decision rule *(Step 5)* is

Reject H_0 in favour of H_1 if $t < -2.262$ or $t > +2.262$. Otherwise, fail to reject H_0.

The test statistic for this Procedure 3 test is computed in a familiar way, and it's frequently used, but it produces only approximate results. However, no better test has been devised to satisfy the conditions spelled out at the beginning of this section. The formula for this test statistic is

$$t = \frac{\bar{x}_1 - \bar{x}_2}{\sqrt{\dfrac{s_1^2}{n_1} + \dfrac{s_2^2}{n_2}}} \qquad (9.9)$$

With $s_1^2 = 3,844$, $n_1 = 10$, $s_2^2 = 1,024$, and $n_2 = 12$, the test statistic *(Step 6)* is

$$t = \frac{\bar{x}_1 - \bar{x}_2}{\sqrt{\dfrac{s_1^2}{n_1} + \dfrac{s_2^2}{n_2}}} = \frac{\$595 - \$580}{\sqrt{\dfrac{3,844}{10} + \dfrac{1,024}{12}}} = \frac{\$15}{21,673} = .692$$

Conclusion (Step 7):

Since $t = .692$ falls between ± 2.262, we fail to reject the null hypothesis. The rental agent appears to be making a reasonable statement when she says that mean rates for two-bedroom apartments are the same in sectors A and B. ◆

What if this had been a *one-tailed test?* What if the test is to see if rates are higher in sector A than in sector B? In that case, the alternative hypothesis is

H_1: $\mu_1 > \mu_2$

and the decision rule is

Reject H_0 in favour of H_1 if $t > 1.833$ ($t_{.05}$, df = 9). Otherwise, fail to reject H_0.

The computed value of t remains .692 in a one-tailed test, and, in this case, the statistical decision is still to fail to reject the null hypothesis because $.692 < 1.833$.

Procedure 3B: Small-Sample Confidence Interval for Independent Populations When $\sigma_1 \neq \sigma_2$

To compute a confidence interval for this situation, we can use

$$(\bar{x}_1 - \bar{x}_2) - t_{\alpha/2}\sqrt{\left(\frac{s_1^2}{n_1}\right) + \left(\frac{s_2^2}{n_2}\right)} < \mu_1 - \mu_2 < (\bar{x}_1 - \bar{x}_2) + t_{\alpha/2}\sqrt{\left(\frac{s_1^2}{n_1}\right) + \left(\frac{s_2^2}{n_2}\right)} \qquad (9.10)$$

Here, calculating a 95 percent confidence interval for the samples of Example 9.14, we need $t_{\alpha/2} = t_{.025}$ (df = 9) = 2.262, the same value we used in our two-sided .05 level test. Then, using the previous calculation results, we compute

$\$15 - 2.262(21.673) < \mu_1 - \mu_2 < 15 + 2.262(21.673)$
$\$15 - 49.02 < \mu_1 - \mu_2 < 15 + 49.02$
$-\$34.02 < \mu_1 - \mu_2 < 64.02$

We would conclude that the difference in the mean rental rates could be anywhere from $34.02 higher in sector B to $64.02 higher in sector A. So it is possible that the difference is zero, agreeing with the hypothesis test results.

■ **Example 9.15**   **Socialism up in Smoke?** In *Mortality from Smoking Worldwide* (British Medical Bulletin, 1996), Peto et al. estimate the number and proportion of deaths due to smoking in 44 developed countries. They divided these into OECD (Organization for European Collaboration and Development) countries and former socialist countries. Samples from both groups yielded the following data on the percentage of females from each country whose death was related to smoking.

OECD Country	Percent	Former Socialist Country	Percent
Canada	14		
Denmark	15	Armenia	3
Germany	3	Czech Rep.	5
Ireland	16	Moldova	3
Italy	4	Poland	5
Japan	5	Romania	3
Spain	0	Slovakia	3
Sweden	4	Turkmenistan	0
USA	17	Yugoslavia	4

Using a level of .05, does it appear there is a difference in the mean female smoking mortality rate between OECD and former socialist countries (Data = SmokeSoc)?

◆ **Solution:**

To decide on the testing procedure to use in comparing the means, we first test

$H_0: \sigma_1^2 = \sigma_2^2$
$H_1: \sigma_1^2 \neq \sigma_2^2$

We used both MINITAB and a TI-83 calculator to do the calculations, obtaining the results in *Figure 9.11a* and screen 2 of *Figure 9.11b*, respectively. Because the *p*-value = .001 < .05, we reject the null hypothesis and conclude that there is a difference in the variances of the two populations. With that in mind, we are now ready to test

$H_0: \mu_1 = \mu_2$
$H_1: \mu_1 \neq \mu_2$

We will use MINITAB and the TI-83 calculator again to do the calculations, but with one proviso. Because of a different approach in determining the degrees of freedom, both MINITAB and the TI-83 calculator will yield a slightly different result than if we were to do the calculations by hand. These differences won't concern us—just use the results you get with whichever method you choose for a problem. The MINITAB output is in *Figure 9.12*, while screen 4 of *Figure 9.11b* contains the results obtained by the TI-83 Calculator. Since *p*-value = .042 < .05, H_0 is rejected. It appears that there is a difference in the mean female smoking mortality rate between OECD and former

FIGURE 9.11 (*a*) MINITAB test of equal variances for smoking data. (*b*) Put the OECD mortality rates into one list and put the former socialist rates into another list. We have the OECD mortality rates in L1 and the former socialist rates in L2. We will first test the equality of variances using **2-SampFTest** from the **Tests** menu. Provide the inputs for the test as shown in screen 1. The test statistic *F* = 17.8 and the *p*-value is .001. Thus we have strong evidence that the variances are not equal. So in the two-sample *t* test, we will not pool the variances. Choose the **2-SampTTest** from the **TESTS** menu. Screen 3 shows the setup for the test. Choose **Calculate** from the test screen. The results are shown in screen 4. To make a 95 percent confidence interval for the difference in means, we can choose **2-SampTInt** from the **TESTS** menu. Screen 5 shows the setup, and screen 6 shows the results.

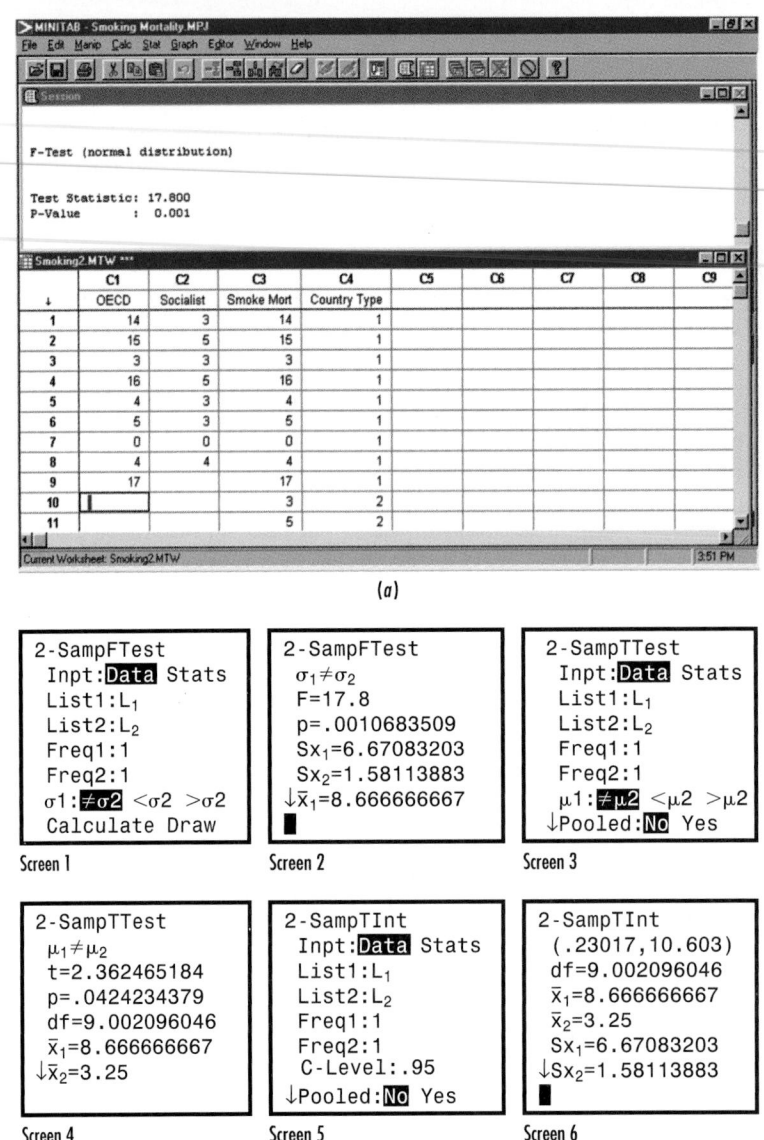

FIGURE 9.12 MINITAB test of equal means for smoking data.

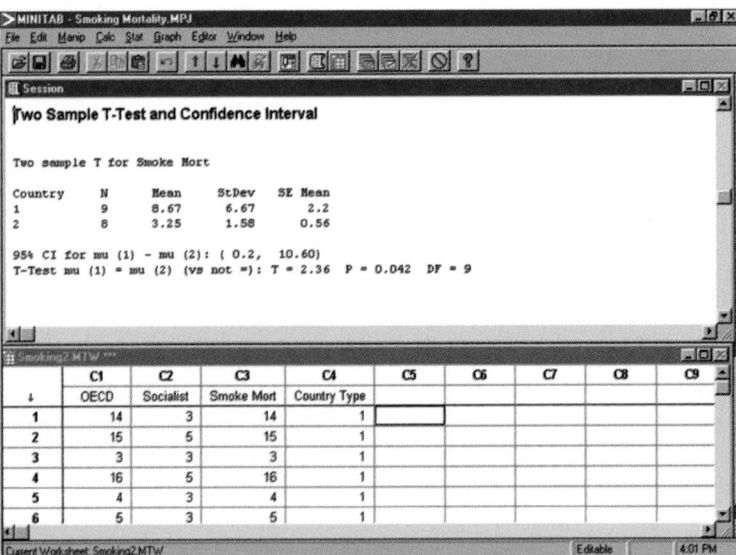

socialist countries. Moreover, the 95 percent confidence interval found in *Figure 9.12* and screen 6 of *Figure 9.11b*

$$0.2 < \mu_1 - \mu_2 < 10.6$$

indicates that the mean mortality rate is greater for females in the OECD countries by between 0.2 and 10.6 percent. ◆

Procedure 4A: Small-Sample t Test for Independent Populations When $\sigma_1 = \sigma_2$

As shown in *Figure 9.4*, the following conditions must be met if Procedure 4 is to be used:

1. The two samples are taken from two independent, normally distributed populations.

2. The values of σ_1 and σ_2 are unknown.

3. The size of n_1 or n_2 is small (≤ 30).

4. An F test leads to the conclusion that σ_1^2 and σ_2^2 are likely to be equal.

When these conditions are met, the seven t test steps followed in Procedure 4 also parallel those we've already considered. The null hypothesis *(Step 1)* for Procedure 4 remains

$$H_0: \mu_1 = \mu_2$$

And the alternative is one of the following:

$$H_1: \mu_1 \neq \mu_2$$
$$H_1: \mu_1 > \mu_2$$
$$H_1: \mu_1 < \mu_2$$

A level of significance must be specified *(Step 2)*, and values from the t table are used *(Step 3)* when we define the rejection region. The degrees of freedom value needed in Procedure 4 to use the t table when two small samples are tested is found with this formula:

$$df = n_1 + n_2 - 2$$

Thus, if there are 14 items in sample one and 16 items in sample two, our df value is $(14 + 16 - 2)$ or 28. If we are making a *two-tailed test* at the .05 level of significance with these samples, then our t value is 2.048 *(Step 4)*, and our decision rule *(Step 5)* is

Reject H_0 in favour of H_1 if $t < -2.048$ or $t > +2.048$. Otherwise, fail to reject H_0.

Before we can compute the test statistic, we must first calculate the estimated standard error of the difference between means. Since we assume that an F test has been made and the result supports the assumption that the unknown population variances (and standard deviations) are equal, an estimate of the population standard deviation is found by pooling, or combining, information from the two samples. The formula for the pooled standard deviation is

$$s_p = \sqrt{\frac{s_1^2(n_1 - 1) + s_2^2(n_2 - 1)}{n_1 + n_2 - 2}}$$

And the formula for the estimated standard error is

$$\hat{\sigma}_{\bar{x}_1 - \bar{x}_2} = s_p\sqrt{\frac{1}{n_1} + \frac{1}{n_2}}$$

These formulas can be combined in the test statistic formula as follows:

$$t = \frac{\bar{x}_1 - \bar{x}_2}{s_p\sqrt{\frac{1}{n_1} + \frac{1}{n_2}}} = \frac{\bar{x}_1 - \bar{x}_2}{\hat{\sigma}_{\bar{x}_1 - \bar{x}_2}} \tag{9.11}$$

This formula is then used to compute the test statistic *(Step 6)*, and a statistical decision *(Step 7)* is made.

Now let's look at an example.

Example 9.16   Let's revisit Example 9.1 and consider again the case of the two experimental diets designed to add weight to malnourished adults in developing countries. Table 9.1 on page 329 presents the weight gains made by the eight adults who were fed diet A and the nine adults who received diet B. As you can see in Table 9.1, the relevant data are

Diet A	Diet B
$\bar{x}_1 = 5.80$ kg	$\bar{x}_2 = 7.27$ kg
$n_1 = 8$	$n_2 = 9$
$s_1^2 = 2.6029$	$s_2^2 = .9800$

We've already used the F test in Example 9.1 and decided in favour of the hypothesis that $\sigma_1^2 = \sigma_2^2$. Now, let's suppose the dietitian wants to conduct a test at the .05 level to see if there's a significant difference in the mean weight gained by the two groups.

◆ **Solution:**
Following the steps in Procedure 4, as the dietitian is interested in testing for any difference in weight gain, the hypotheses *(Step 1)* are

$H_0: \mu_1 = \mu_2$
$H_1: \mu_1 \neq \mu_2$

A .05 level is specified *(Step 2)*, the t distribution must be used *(Step 3)*, and the rejection region is based on t critical values with df = 15 and α = .05. These t values are ±2.131 *(Step 4)*.

The decision rule *(Step 5)* is

Reject H_0 in favour of H_1 if $t < -2.131$ or $t > +2.131$. Otherwise, fail to reject H_0.

The test statistic *(Step 6)* is

$$t = \frac{\bar{x}_1 - \bar{x}_2}{\sqrt{\dfrac{s_1^2(n_1 - 1) + s_2^2(n_2 - 1)}{n_1 + n_2 - 2}}\sqrt{\dfrac{1}{n_1} + \dfrac{1}{n_2}}} = \frac{5.80 - 7.27}{\sqrt{\dfrac{2.6029(7) + .9800(8)}{15}}\sqrt{\dfrac{1}{8} + \dfrac{1}{9}}}$$

$$= \frac{-1.47}{1.32(.4859)} = \frac{-1.47}{.6414} = -2.29$$

Conclusion (Step 7):

Because $-2.29 < -2.131$, reject the null hypothesis. The population mean weight gain of diet A isn't equal to the gain of diet B at the .05 level. ◆

Procedure 4B: Small-Sample Confidence Interval for Independent Populations When $\sigma_1 = \sigma_2$

To calculate a confidence interval for this equal variance case, we use

$$(\bar{x}_1 - \bar{x}_2) - t_{\alpha/2}\hat{\sigma}_{\bar{x}_1 - \bar{x}_2} < \mu_1 - \mu_2 < (\bar{x}_1 - \bar{x}_2) + t_{\alpha/2}\hat{\sigma}_{\bar{x}_1 - \bar{x}_2} \qquad (9.12)$$

A 95 percent confidence interval for the previous example would use the same *t* value as the hypothesis test, 2.131. Thus, a confidence interval is

$-1.47 - 2.131(.6414) < \mu_1 - \mu_2 < -1.47 + 2.131(.6414)$
$-1.47 - 1.37 < \mu_1 - \mu_2 < -1.47 + 1.37$
$-2.84 < \mu_1 - \mu_2 < -0.10$

We can be 95 percent confident that the mean weight gain for diet B is greater than that of diet A by between 0.10 and 2.84 kg.

Example 9.17   **Pushing on with Push-Ups** One last time, we'll take a look at the results from the class that took the Army Physical Fitness Test (APFT). Following are observations on the number of push-ups done in two minutes, broken down by gender. We will test at a level of .05 to see if there is any difference in the mean number of push-ups done by the populations of females and males (Data = APFTPupx).

Push-Ups						
Female		**Male**				
56	55	60	62	82	78	40
58	15	49	72	77	68	52
56	43	51	42	43	82	40
41	47	76	82	53	57	75
33	35	86	72	64	80	82
49	42	73	80	43	62	72
		59	85	59		

◆ **Solution:**

Because we have $n_1 = 12 < 30$, this is a small sample. So to select the testing procedure to use, we test

$$H_0: \sigma_1^2 = \sigma_2^2$$
$$H_1: \sigma_1^2 \neq \sigma_2^2$$

Figure 9.13a is MINITAB output for this exercise; the top portion gives the *p*-value for this test. Screen 2 of *Figure 9.13b* gives the corresponding value obtained by a TI-83 calculator. Because the *p*-value = .571 > .05, we fail to reject the null hypothesis and decide there is insufficient evidence to indicate a dif-

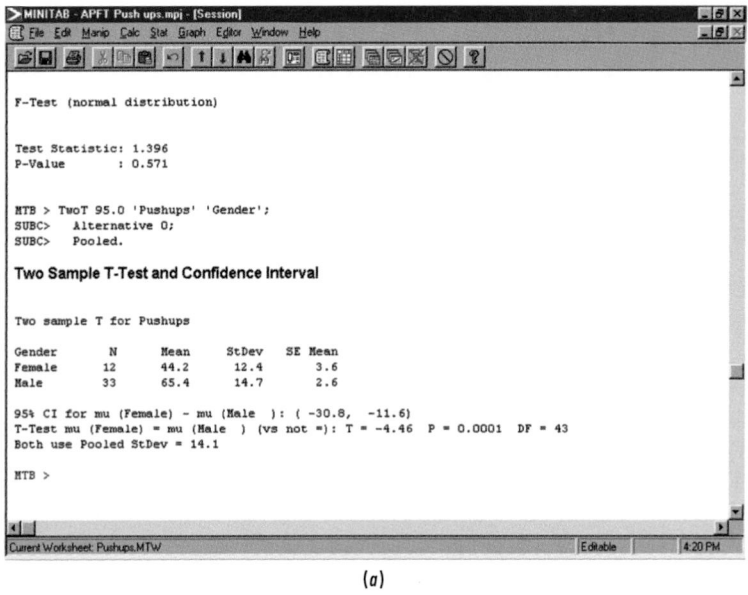

FIGURE 9.13 (*a*) Two-sample *t* MINITAB output for push-up example. The only extra step in the **2-Sample** *t* procedure needed to obtain this output is to check in the box next to **Assume equal variances** before clicking **OK.** (*b*) We have put the number of push-ups for females in L1 and the number of push-ups for males in L2. We first test the equality of variances using **2-SampFTest** from the **TESTS** menu. Provide the inputs for the test as shown in screen 1. Screen 2 gives the results. The test statistic **F** = .716, and the *p*-value is .570. Thus we fail to reject H_0 and decide that there is insufficient evidence to indicate that variances are different. So in the two-sample *t* test, we will pool the variances. Choose the **2-SampTTest** from the **TESTS** menu. Screen 3 shows the setup for the test. Choose **Calculate** from the test screen. The results are shown in screen 4. To make a 95 percent confidence interval for the difference in means we can choose **2-SampTInt** from the **TESTS** menu. Screen 5 shows the setup, and screen 6 shows the results.

(*b*)

ference in the variances of the two populations. So we will use the test statistic involving the pooled standard deviation to test

$H_0: \mu_1 = \mu_2$
$H_1: \mu_1 \neq \mu_2$

The bottom portion of *Figure 9.13a* and screen 4 of *Figure 9.13b* give the results for this test. Since this *p*-value = .0001 is less than .05, H_0 is rejected. It appears that there is a difference in the mean number of push-ups done by the populations of males and females taking the APFT. The 95 percent confidence interval given by MINITAB in *Figure 9.13a* and by the TI-83 calculator in screen 6 of *Figure 9.13b* is

$-30.8 < \mu_1 - \mu_2 < -11.6$

This indicates that the mean number of push-ups done by males is greater than the number for females by between 11.6 and 30.8. ◆

Self-Testing Review 9.2

16. Four tests were discussed in this section: the paired *t* test, the *z* test, the *t* test for populations with equal variances, and the *t* test for populations with unequal variances. For each of these tests, what assumptions must be satisfied to produce useful results?

17. An *American Journal of Public Health* study dealt with the type of care given to the disabled elderly. After short-term hospital stays, a random sample of 110 disabled elderly subjects were assigned to an experimental group that offered physician-led primary home care on a 24-hour basis. Another sample of 73 disabled elderly subjects in a control group were offered ordinary care. After 6 months, the experimental group of 110 had a mean and standard deviation of 24.1 and 5.24, respectively, on the MMSE (mini-mental-state examination, where scores range from 0 to 30). The control group of 73 had a mean and standard deviation on the same test of 23.9 and 6.29, respectively. At the .05 level, test the hypothesis that a population receiving the experimental treatment would do significantly better on the MMSE exam than one receiving ordinary care.

18. Using the statistics given in problem 17 construct a 95 percent confidence interval for the difference in the population means between subjects receiving experimental and ordinary care.

19. The "perceived discount" or PD, is measured as follows: PD = (perceived regular price – perceived sale price)/perceived regular price. A study to see if the PD for "high-image" stores is higher than the PD for stores with generally lower prices was published in the *Journal of Consumer Research*. At Nordstrom's (a high-image store), the mean PD for a random sample of 44 customers for name-brand items on sale was 38.08, and the standard deviation was .84. At the May Company, the mean PD for a random sample of 47 customers for similar sale items was 35.60 with a standard deviation of .79. Test the hypothesis at the .01 level that the population PD at Nordstrom's is higher than the population PD at the May Company.

20. An experiment was conducted to evaluate the effectiveness of a work-site health promotion program in reducing obesity as measured by a body mass index (BMI). A random sample of 16 work sites received classes on weight control combined with payroll incentives. Another sample of 16 work sites served as a control and received no classes or incentives. The following data represent the mean BMI for the *control group* before and after the experiment.

The mean BMI for each site in the control group before the experiment:

26.50 26.07 25.37 27.41 25.39 25.40 25.79 26.34
26.52 26.08 26.45 25.90 25.51 25.67 25.44 27.04

The mean BMI for each site in the control group after two years:

26.06 26.40 25.53 26.28 25.39 25.69 26.12 26.24
26.53 26.37 26.22 26.42 25.57 24.94 25.95 26.47

Test the hypothesis at the .01 level that there was no difference in BMI for the control group before and after the treatment. Assume the mean change in BMI is normally distributed (Data = BMI Cntrl).

21. The following data lists the net worth (in billions of dollars) and ages of two random samples of billionaires in 2002, the first from Europe and the second from North America.

For the European sample the values were

Name	Net Worth	Source	Age
J. Quandt	18.4	BMW	74
C. de Carvalho	4.3	Heineken	47
G. Agnelli	2.3	Fiat	81
M. Ferrero	1.7	chocolates	75
M. Hilti	1.1	power tools	55
I. Kamprad	13.4	Ikea	75
N. Hayek	2.4	Swatch	73
K. Kristiansen	2.1	Lego	54
E. Bernat	1.2	lollipops	78
A. Kudelski	1.0	software	42

For the North American sample the values were

Name	Net Worth	Source	Age
W. Gates	52.8	Microsoft	46
M. Dell	11.1	Dell	37
P. Knight	5.7	Nike	64
B. Marcus	3.0	Home Depot	72
H. McCain	1.5	French fries	74
J. Walton	20.7	Walmart	56
J. Mars	9.0	candy	65
W. Wrigley Jr.	3.4	chewing gum	39
G. Lucas	3.0	movies	57
D. Fisher	1.5	Gap	71

a) Test the hypothesis at the .05 level that the population mean net worth of billionaires is higher in North America than in Europe. Before doing so, test for the equality of the population variances at the .05 level to determine the appropriate t test to use. What assumptions are necessary for either test?

b) Test the hypothesis at the .05 level that the population mean age of billionaires is the same in North America and Europe. Before doing so, test for the equality of the population variances at the .05 level to determine the appropriate *t* test to use. What assumptions are necessary for either test?

22. A study reported in the *Journal of Consumer Research* dealt with the influence of touch on consumers' evaluations of service. Experimenters were trained as servers in a restaurant. In alternating hours, the servers either touched or did not touch the diners. The mean and standard deviation of ratings given by a random sample of 32 female diners who were touched were 2.84 and 1.10 respectively. A random sample of 35 female diners who were not touched gave mean and standard deviation ratings of 2.21 and 0.82 respectively. Construct a 95 percent confidence interval for the difference in the population mean ratings for female diners touched and not touched by their servers.

23. A study in the *American Journal of Public Health* dealt with a randomly selected group of 264 primary caregivers. These caregivers were interviewed and asked to keep diaries for six months. Diaries were returned by 141 caregivers, and 123 did not return diaries. The mean and standard deviation of the time spent in working as a caregiver for the sample of caregivers who returned diaries were 42.0 months and 34.7 months, respectively. Of the sample who didn't return diaries, the mean and standard deviation for the number of months working as a caregiver were 37.2 and 33.4, respectively. Test the hypothesis at the .05 level that the population mean time spent working as a caregiver is the same for the two groups.

24. Using the statistics given in problem 23, construct a 95 percent confidence interval for the difference in the population mean time spent working as a caregiver for the two groups.

25. An engineer wanted to compare drill bits made of high speed steel and carbide. She designed an experiment in which both types of bits were used in a drill press to drill through eight pieces of concrete with different characteristics. The time (in seconds) needed by each bit to drill through the pieces are as follows:

Concrete Type	High-Speed Steel	Carbide
A	340	167
B	120	90
C	290	79
D	100	56
E	178	94
F	138	95
G	174	99
H	642	184

Assuming both populations are normally distributed, test the hypothesis at the .05 level that the population mean time needed for the high-speed steel bits to drill through the concrete is significantly greater than the mean time for the carbide bits.

26. A salesperson wants to compare two product-presentation methods. One method involves the use of slides, graphs, and other stationary images; the other involves an interactive display combined with a videotape. She wants to see if there is a difference in the average amount people are willing to spend on the product depending on the type of presentation they view. She uses the methods on separate groups of five. After viewing their presentation, the first group was willing to pay an average $340 with a standard deviation of $85; the second group was willing to pay an average of $440 with a standard deviation of $160. Test, using a level of significance of 0.01, to see if the mean amount associated with one of the methods is greater than the other. Before doing so, test for the equality of the population variances at the .02 level to determine the appropriate *t* test to use. What assumptions are necessary for either test?

27. An experiment reported in the *American Journal of Public Health* was conducted to evaluate the effectiveness of a work-site health promotion program in reducing obesity as measured by a body mass index (BMI). A random sample of 16 work sites received classes on weight control combined with payroll incentives. Another sample of 16 work sites served as a control and received no classes or incentives. The following data represents the mean BMI for each site in the control group after two years:

26.06   26.40   25.53   26.28   25.39   25.69   26.12   26.24
26.53   26.37   26.22   26.42   25.57   24.94   25.95   26.47

The mean BMI for each site in the treatment group after two years is

26.02   25.87   25.02   25.46   25.70   26.10   26.24   26.57
24.57   25.18   26.84   26.31   26.22   25.61   26.42   25.16

Test the hypothesis at the .05 level that after 2 years there was no difference in the population mean BMIs between the treatment group and the control group. To select the appropriate procedure, first test for the equality of the population variances at the .05 level. Assume both populations are normally distributed (Data = BMI2year).

28. A study is made that involves individual measures of neuropsychological functioning for random samples of chronic schizophrenic patients and for normal subjects. The 25 schizophrenic patients had a mean of 93.2 on the Wide Range Achievement Test (WRAT) and a standard deviation of 16.8. The 25 normal subjects had a mean WRAT score of 107.8 with a standard deviation of 11.6. Assume both populations are normally distributed. Test the hypothesis at the .01 level that there's no difference in the population WRAT scores for the two groups.

29. A test was conducted to determine the effectiveness of using an anti-inflammatory cream on delayed-onset muscle soreness. A random sample of ten patients is treated with the cream on one arm and with a placebo on the other (control) arm. After four days, a measure of muscle soreness is then taken for each patient on each arm. The results are

Control Arm	Treated Arm
46	2
22	32
10	30
14	3
26	14
29	32
29	2
47	39
20	18
13	2

Using a paired t procedure, test the hypothesis at the .01 level that there is less soreness in the treated arm (Data = Soreness).

30. Using the statistics given in problem 29, construct a 95 percent confidence interval for the mean difference in muscle soreness between arms treated with the cream and with a placebo.

31. How well can divorce be predicted by a wife's personality score? In a study reported in the *Journal of Personality and Social Psychology,* a follow-up was made of a random group of 286 couples 5 years after their marriage. It was found that 222 couples remained together and 64 had dissolved their marriages. As newlyweds, all wives in the study group (and husbands, too, but that's another question) were given a personality test and were then rated on "dysfunctional beliefs." For the wives in the sample of couples who remained together, the mean rating for dysfunctional beliefs was 49.53, and the standard deviation was 12.62. For the 64 divorced wives, the mean dysfunctional beliefs score was 53.73 with a standard deviation of 4.74. Test the hypothesis at the .05 level that there's no significant difference in the mean dysfunctional beliefs scores for the populations of women considered in the problem.

32. A study was published in the *American Journal of Psychology* that dealt with the effect of Lorazepam on brain glucose metabolism. In this study, there were random samples of 13 normal subjects and 10 alcoholic subjects. The verbal IQ for the normal subjects was 116 with a standard deviation of 23. The verbal IQ for the alcoholic sample was 109 with a standard deviation of 13. Assume both populations are normally distributed. Test the hypothesis at the .05 level that the population mean IQ of alcoholics is lower than that of normal subjects, using the appropriate *t* test.

33. Using the information given in problem 32, construct a 95 percent confidence interval for the difference in the population mean IQ of normal and alcoholic subjects.

34. In the study cited in problem 32 of the effect of Lorazepam on brain glucose metabolism, five of the alcoholic subjects were given Lorazepam, and five were given a placebo. Brain metabolic values (μ mol/100g/min) were determined. At the thalamus (a part of the brain), the mean metabolic value for the subjects receiving a placebo was 40.7, and the standard deviation was 4. For the subjects receiving Lorazepam, the mean metabolic value was 34.5, and the standard deviation was 7. Test the hypothesis at the .01 level that population mean metabolic rates measured at the thalamus are no different for alcoholics given a placebo and those given Lorazepam, using the appropriate *t* test. What assumptions are necessary for the test?

35. Using the information given in problem 34, construct a 99 percent confidence interval for the difference in the population mean metabolic rate of subjects receiving a placebo and subjects receiving Lorazepam.

36. Many amputees participate in a variety of athletic activities, so there's a demand for prosthetic legs that will improve their athletic performance. Different types of artificial limbs designed for those who have had one leg amputated below the knee were compared against each other and against an intact flesh-and-bone counterpart in an issue of *Physical Therapy*. In one segment of the study, the duration of single limb support (SLS) while walking on a Solid Ankle Cushion Heel prosthetic leg was compared with the duration of SLS for a patient's intact leg. In 10 trials of the artificial leg, the mean duration of SLS was .32 seconds, and the standard deviation was .00027 seconds. Ten trials were also made on the natural leg, and the mean duration of SLS was .41 seconds, and the standard deviation was .00018 seconds. Test the hypothesis at the .05 level that there's no difference in the population mean duration of SLS between the prosthetic leg and the natural leg, using the appropriate *t* test. What assumption is necessary for this test?

37. A measure of the right atrial pressure (mm Hg) was made for cardiac patients who were given Captopril and for those given Nitroprusside. The random sample of 21 patients given Captopril had a right atrial pressure of 7.8 mm Hg, and a standard deviation of 1.4 mm Hg. For the 21 patients given Nitroprusside, the mean right atrial pressure was 6.6 mm Hg, and the standard deviation was 1.6 mm Hg. Test the hypothesis at the .01 level that there's no difference in the population mean right atrial pressure between the two groups, using the appropriate *t* test. Assume both populations are normally distributed.

38. Do men and women have different values when choosing a career? The following random sample data from a Career Development Quarterly study give the result of responses by males and females to a Life Roles Inventory questionnaire. Use the paired *t* test at the .01 level to see if the ratings are different for men and women. Assume the population of differences is normally distributed (Data = LifeRole).

Value	Male Rating	Female Rating
Ability utilization	16.69	17.17
Achievement	16.76	17.17
Advancement	15.88	14.44
Aesthetics	13.31	13.75
Altruism	14.95	16.49
Authority	14.61	14.51
Autonomy	15.79	16.37
Creativity	14.89	14.82
Economics	16.31	16.25
Lifestyle	14.09	14.45
Personal development	17.31	18.02
Physical activity	14.18	13.97
Prestige	15.34	15.79
Risk	10.34	9.47
Social interaction	12.65	13.82
Social relations	15.44	16.93
Variety	13.06	13.96
Working conditions	13.75	14.91
Cultural identity	12.76	13.48
Physical prowess	9.49	8.51

39. An article in *Criminal Justice and Behavior* claims that an intellectual imbalance of performance IQ (P) with verbal IQ (V)—such that $P > V$—is a useful predictor of the probability of becoming delinquent. A random sample of 157 "high $P > V$" delinquents had a mean delinquency score of 255.7 with a standard deviation of 30.7, and a random sample of 356 "low $P > V$" delinquents had a mean delinquency store of 195 with a standard deviation of 41.8. Test the hypothesis at the .01 level that there is no difference in the mean delinquency scores for these two populations.

40. When offered a 20 percent discount, a random sample of 6 customers at the May Company reported a mean of 4.17 on a "change-of-intention-to-buy" scale and a standard deviation of .32. When offered a 30 percent discount, a random sample of 7 customers reported a mean of 4.00 and a standard deviation of .08 for their "change-of-intention-to-buy" scores. Test the hypothesis at the .01 level that at this May Company store, there's a different population mean value on the intention-to-buy scale when a 20 percent discount rate is offered and when the rate is 30 percent. Before doing so, test for the equality of the population variances at the .01 level in order to determine the appropriate test to use. (You may have already done this test in Self-Testing Review 9.1, problem 6.) What assumptions are necessary for either test?

41. Using the information given in problem 40, construct a 99 percent confidence interval for the difference in the population mean value on the intention-to-buy scale when a 20 percent discount rate is offered and when the rate is 30 percent.

42. An agent for professional athletes is interested in branching into new sports for possible clients. Part of his preparatory work includes a comparison of the mean incomes of two groups he could possibly represent, jai alai players and professional bowlers. He takes a sample of 37 jai alai players and 52 professional bowlers and finds that the mean incomes for the two groups, respectively, are $73,000 and $89,000, while the standard deviations are $11,000 and $21,000. Construct a 95 percent confidence interval for the difference in the population mean incomes of the two groups.

43. For many companies, their brand name and what it represents are an important asset—the basis of competitive advantage and of future-earning streams. In a class project, a student collected data on peoples' opinions about two film brands, Kodak, a popular North American brand, and Fuji, a popular Japanese brand whose name recognition is less in Canada. She collected data under two conditions. In the first, 30 subjects were shown similar prices for the two brands (Kodak $4.19 and Fuji $4.09), while in the second, 27 subjects were shown prices markedly different (Kodak $4.19 and Fuji $2.99). She asked questions on film quality, reliability, reputation, value, whether the film was a worthwhile buy, was being sold at a reasonable price, and if the person intended to purchase the film. (Note: High scores designate high ratings.)

| | Similar Prices | | | |
| | Kodak | | Fuji | |
	Mean	S.D.	Mean	S.D.
Quality	4.10	0.80	3.73	0.94
Reliability	4.27	0.83	3.73	1.17
Reputation	4.67	0.66	3.67	0.92
Value	3.80	0.92	3.87	1.04
Worthwhile buy	4.03	1.03	3.73	1.20
Reasonable price	3.33	1.06	3.90	1.09
Intend to buy	3.97	1.00	3.53	1.25

| | Dissimilar Prices | | | |
| | Kodak | | Fuji | |
	Mean	S.D.	Mean	S.D.
Quality	4.59	0.64	4.22	0.97
Reliability	4.56	0.58	4.37	0.74
Reputation	4.78	0.42	4.44	0.80
Value	3.96	1.02	4.41	0.64
Worthwhile buy	4.00	0.78	4.15	0.72
Reasonable price	2.51	0.94	4.44	0.75
Intend to buy	3.29	1.03	4.07	0.83

Assume the populations involved are normally distributed for the questions that follow.

a) For each of the 7 variables, test the hypothesis at the .05 level that the population variances for the Kodak and Fuji film are equal when people are shown similar prices. (Note: Because of the constant sample sizes, the decision rule will be the same for all these tests).

b) For each of the 7 variables, test the hypothesis at the .05 level that the population means for the Kodak and Fuji film are equal when people are shown similar prices.

c) For each of the 7 variables, construct a 95 percent confidence interval for the difference in the population means for the Kodak and Fuji film when people are shown similar prices.

d) Repeat problems (a) to (c) for the situation in which people are shown markedly different prices. Compare the results for similar and dissimilar prices.

44. Twenty-four cans of cola—six Coke, six Diet Coke, six Pepsi, and six Diet Pepsi—were studied. The contents of each can of cola were emptied into a clean chemistry beaker (which was weighed prior to each measurement to obtain a fair weight) and weighed on a digital scale with weight to the nearest hundredth of a gram. A 12-ounce can is supposed to contain 355 ml, and 355 ml of pure water should weigh 355 g. Diet cola has a specific gravity similar to water and so should weigh 355 g. Regular cola contains dissolved sugar and hence should weigh more (Data = Cola).

Coke	Pepsi	Diet Coke	Diet Pepsi
367.78	362.10	351.17	354.42
367.43	365.55	355.21	357.37
368.87	372.77	352.47	352.73
369.82	365.47	353.61	349.46
368.85	378.23	352.70	355.28
370.32	367.71	354.53	355.91

Assume the populations involved are normally distributed for the questions that follow.

a) Test the hypothesis at the .05 level that the population variances for the weights of Coke and Diet Coke are equal.

b) Test the hypothesis at the .05 level that the population means for the weights of Coke and Diet Coke are equal.

c) Construct a 95 percent confidence interval for the difference in the population mean weights of Coke and Diet Coke.

d) Test the hypothesis at the .05 level that the population variances for the weights of Pepsi and Diet Pepsi are equal.

e) Test the hypothesis at the .05 level that the population means for the weights of Pepsi and Diet Pepsi are equal.

f) Construct a 95 percent confidence interval for the difference in the population mean weights of Pepsi and Diet Pepsi.

45. The following data represent the three-mile (split) and five-mile (final) times, in minutes, for male cross-country runners from the Universities of Nebraska and Colorado at the Big 12 Cross-Country meet held in Ames, Iowa, during Fall 1996 (Data = XCountry).

Nebraska		Colorado	
3 Mile	5 Mile	3 Mile	5 Mile
14.85	24.87	15.15	25.40
14.85	25.07	15.43	25.82
15.30	25.63	15.43	25.87
15.38	26.27	15.43	25.87
15.63	26.53	15.73	26.08
15.65	26.47	15.80	26.10
15.70	26.60	15.80	26.40
15.73	26.83	15.82	27.00
		16.40	27.53

Assume the populations involved are normally distributed for the questions that follow:

a) Test the hypothesis at the .05 level that the population variances for the three-mile times of Nebraska and Colorado are equal.

b) Test the hypothesis at the .05 level that the population means for the three-mile times of Nebraska and Colorado are equal.

c) Construct a 95 percent confidence interval for $\mu_1 - \mu_2$.

d) Repeat Exercises (a) to (c) for the five-mile times and compare the results with those of the three-mile times.

46. An experiment compared the performances of electronic and magnetic ballasts used in fluorescent lighting. The variables compared included ballast efficiency factor (foot-candles/watt), light output (foot-candles), total harmonic distortion (percent), power factor (watts), and the temperature of the lamp and ballasts (Celsius) themselves (Data = Ballast).

Type	BEF	LO	THD	PF	Lamp	Bist
Mag	0.480	43	12.6	0.991	37.8	33.0
Mag	0.490	42	15.6	0.988	40.4	33.2
Mag	0.483	43	11.5	0.975	34.7	37.0
Mag	0.482	42	16.1	0.987	38.8	35.3
Elec	0.583	40	26.6	0.959	30.6	27.5
Elec	0.571	41	16.0	0.988	32.2	28.8
Elec	0.564	41	23.4	0.966	30.6	27.2
Elec	0.516	40	9.8	0.958	37.5	28.9
Elec	0.548	39	14.9	0.951	29.7	30.7
Elec	0.588	41	32.0	0.952	35.9	20.4

Assume the populations involved are normally distributed for the questions that follow.

a) For each of the six variables, test the hypothesis at the .05 level that the population variances for electronic and magnetic ballasts used in fluorescent lighting are equal. (Note: Because of the constant sample sizes, the decision rule will be the same for all these tests.)

b) For each of the six variables, test the hypothesis at the .05 level that the population means for electronic and magnetic ballasts used in fluorescent lighting are equal.

c) For each of the six variables, construct a 95 percent confidence interval for the difference in the population means for electronic and magnetic ballasts.

47. In Problem 10, Self-Testing Review 9.1, we looked at a data set from two pumping stations along the route of an aqueduct. It contained the compressive strength (psi) of concrete cylinders used on the sites. When testing for equal population variances, the p-value of the test statistic was .689. Test the hypothesis at the .01 level that the concrete cylinders at the two pumping plants have equal population means (Data = PumpPlnt).

Polonio Pass				Devil's Den			
3,520	4,670	3,780	3,880	4,700	3,550	4,750	3,600
3,470	3,770	3,420	3,690	4,610	4,010	4,100	4,030
4,090	3,950	4,030	5,210	4,470	3,940	3,550	5,330
4,380	3,600	4,020	4,380	4,915	4,090	3,830	5,460
4,210	3,660	4,600	5,200	4,900	3,960	3,950	3,760

48. The following data, taken from the Statistics Canada 2001 Census, represent the average total income of male and female residents for a random sample of Canadian cities for 2001 (Data = CityIncome).

City	Male	Female
Calgary	45,306	26,573
Charlottetown	29,212	21,472
Fredericton	33,799	22,827
Halifax	37,279	25,034
London	39,387	25,138
Moncton	32,290	21,014
Montreal	31,277	23,926
Niagara Falls	35,234	21,912
Regina	35,926	24,208
St. John's	35,190	23,514
Toronto	45,010	30,175
Vancouver	39,423	28,103
Winnipeg	34,796	23,143

Source: Statistics Canada.

Construct a 95 percent confidence interval for the difference in the population mean income of male residents and female residents, where these differences are assumed to be a sample taken from a normal population.

49. In problem 11, Self-Testing Review 9.1, 20 alkaline and 20 heavy-duty RadioShack batteries were drained and the times to failure (min) were observed:

Alkaline				Heavy-Duty			
105	141	147	148	29	22	22	27
140	143	108	125	26	17	22	23
116	139	146	134	23	27	23	24
140	149	142	140	22	25	22	26

The hypothesis test that the two types of batteries have equal population variances yielded a p-value of .000. Construct a 95 percent confidence interval for the difference in the mean time to failure between the populations of alkaline and heavy-duty batteries (Data = Battery).

50. In problem 13, Self-Testing Review 9.1, we compared the growth of two groups of ten coleus plants, one grown in a standard hydrophonic solution, the other in a hydrophonic solution treated with added nitrogen. The ten-week growth (cms) was recorded;

Standard		Nitrogen	
20.5	21.0	25.0	24.5
21.0	23.5	23.5	25.0
22.5	23.0	25.5	24.5
21.5	22.0	23.0	23.5
20.0	24.0	24.0	24.0

Testing the hypothesis that the two hydrophonic solutions have equal population variances, we obtain a *p*-value of .138. Test the hypothesis at the .05 level that the two hydrophonic solutions have equal population means (Data = Coleus).

51. The data that follow represent the mean monthly salary made by university graduates one year after graduation, broken down by a sample of majors over a two-year span (Data = CPSlrydf).

Year	English	Account	Arch	MIS	Com Sci	Mech Eng	Journal	Poli Sci
94–95	2,150	2,500	2,000	3,155	3,229	3,000	1,917	2,408
95–96	2,000	2,500	2,200	3,316	3,595	3,250	2,129	2,500

Year	Soc Sci	Chem	Math	Phys Ed	Stat	Animal Sci	Crop Sci	Home Ec
94–95	1,812	2,300	2,806	1,708	3,000	1,600	2,175	1,700
95–96	1,863	2,666	2,708	2,000	2,800	2,050	2,141	2,000

Assuming these differences are a sample from a normal population, estimate the change in the mean salary using a 90 percent confidence interval.

52. In problem 14, Self-Testing Review 9.1, we looked at the defects on silicon wafer surfaces that received either a standard or megasonic cleaning:

Standard	Megasonic
53	26
193	90
113	546
640	90
800	120
140	
85	
658	
140	
140	

Testing the hypothesis that the two methods have the same population variance, we obtain a *p*-value of .593. Test the hypothesis at the .10 level that the two methods have the same population mean number of defects (Data = Megsonic).

53. In problem 15, Self-Testing Review 9.1, we tested the hypothesis at the .05 level that the times (sec.) for females and males in a two-mile run on an Army Physical Fitness Test (APFT) have the same population variances. The *p*-value for the test was .624. Now test the hypothesis at the .05 level that the times for females and males in a 2-mile run have equal population means (Data = APFT2Mlx).

Two-Mile Run						
Female				**Male**		
1,080	1,063	960	863	692	723	899
1,042	1,159	900	803	855	806	1,073
911	1,165	971	1,147	1,245	834	834
1,084	1,208	908	741	831	817	905
1,043	1,194	829	898	737	966	945
901		998	879	890	1,029	1,055
		887	874			

54. A recent study investigated the time required for men and women to complete a doctoral degree, after completing a bachelor's degree. The table below gives the median time (both the number of years registered in graduate school and the total or "real" number of years) between obtaining the bachelor's and doctoral degrees. A sample of fields of study yielded the following data.

Field	**Men**		**Women**	
	Reg	Total	Reg	Total
Physics	6.68	7.76	7.04	8.38
Math	6.66	8.58	6.76	8.42
Comp sci	6.81	9.34	7.87	11.19
Ag sci	6.54	10.71	6.73	10.50
Bio sci	6.78	8.56	6.71	8.54
Psych	7.13	9.87	7.23	10.02
Soc sci	7.55	10.53	8.06	11.73

Assume the populations of differences involved are normally distributed for the questions that follow:

a) Using a paired t procedure, test the hypothesis at the .05 level that there is no difference in the mean registered time between degrees for males and females.

b) Construct a 95 percent confidence interval for the difference in the mean registered time between degrees for males and females.

c) Using a paired t procedure, test the hypothesis at the .05 level that there is no difference in the mean total time between degrees for males and females.

d) Construct a 95 percent confidence interval for the difference in the mean total time between degrees for males and females.

55. Interested in the price of gas or diesel fuel in Canada? M J Ervin and Associates Inc. reported the following prices as of July 16, 2002.

City	Location	Regular Gas	Diesel
Calgary	West	68.7	58.9
Charlottetown	East	67.4	62.6
Edmonton	West	68.4	54.0
Halifax	East	73.9	68.2
Kamloops	West	64.9	58.7
Lethbridge	West	69.0	57.9
London	East	69.9	61.4
Montreal	East	75.7	68.1
Ottawa	East	66.4	59.7
Prince George	West	73.9	59.9
Regina	West	75.9	61.2
Saskatoon	West	75.9	62.1
Sault Ste. Marie	East	69.5	64.3
St. Catharines	East	67.4	63.9
Saint John	East	72.8	68.4
St. John's	East	77.8	74.6
Sudbury	East	69.0	61.9
Thunder Bay	East	73.0	63.7
Toronto	East	70.8	62.0
Vancouver	West	71.3	63.1
Victoria	West	78.3	64.7
Windsor	East	68.0	58.7
Winnipeg	West	70.2	59.5
Yellowknife	West	89.9	79.4

Assume the populations involved are normally distributed for the questions that follow.

a) Test the hypothesis at the .05 level that the population variances of gas prices are equal for the West and East.

b) Test the hypothesis at the .05 level that the population means of gas prices are equal for the West and East.

c) Construct a 95 percent confidence interval for $\mu_1 - \mu_2$, the difference between the mean price of gas in the West and East.

d) Test the hypothesis at the .10 level that the population variances of diesel prices are equal for the West and East.

e) Test the hypothesis at the .10 level that the population means of diesel prices are equal for the West and East.

f) Construct a 90 percent confidence interval for $\mu_1 - \mu_2$, the difference between the mean price of diesel in the West and East.

56. In hydraulic engineering, it is important to be able to take accurate measurements on flow or discharge. For a class project, B. Stewart collected discharge data using two different methods. One type of measuring device used in closed conduits is a rotameter, a device placed inside a pipe. The second method is known as the Weigh Tank method and involves timing how long it takes to fill a container of known volume. Sample data were collected on ten pairs of flow rates (m³/sec) (Data = FlowRate)

Rotameter	Weigh Tank
0.0002920	0.0002940
0.0002330	0.0002340
0.0001830	0.0001840
0.0001420	0.0001430
0.0001170	0.0001120
0.0000917	0.0000951
0.0002670	0.0002590
0.0002500	0.0002730
0.0002170	0.0001980
0.0001670	0.0001660

Using a paired t procedure, test the hypothesis at the .10 level that the means of the two methods are equal.

57. In two class projects, students analyzed data concerning the melting point of cheese, an important characteristic for the marketability of any new cheese. The diameter of the cheese is measured, the cheese is heated at a specific temperature and time, and then the diameter is remeasured. The difference in the diameters (cm) is the melting value. The following data are measurements taken on pairs of cheese samples with the same fat content heated both by a microwave and a conventional oven:

Microwave	Conventional
0.88	0.75
1.31	1.94
1.40	1.98
1.25	1.63
1.13	1.25
1.00	1.25

a) Would you need to test for the equality of variances for this data before doing a hypothesis test? Why or why not?

b) Using a paired t procedure, test the hypothesis at the .01 level that the conventional oven yields a higher mean melting point.

c) Construct a 99 percent confidence interval for the mean difference in the melting points of the two oven types. What assumption is necessary for the validity of this interval?

58. Patrick Madigan examined the relation between systolic and diastolic blood pressure and heart recovery rate. Each person in the experiment exercised on a stationary bike until they reached 65 percent of their maximum heart rate. Then the time (sec) for each to recover their normal rate was observed (Data = Recovery).

Gender	Systolic	Diastolic	Recovery
M	118	82	183
M	110	70	140
M	118	80	451
F	116	70	131
M	126	68	149
F	112	62	154
F	124	70	183
F	108	62	135
M	122	82	384

Assume the populations involved are normally distributed for the questions that follow.

a) For systolic and diastolic blood pressure and the heart recovery rate, test the hypothesis at the .05 level that the population variances for females and males are equal.

b) For systolic and diastolic blood pressure and the heart recovery rate, test the hypothesis at the .05 level that the population means for females and males are equal.

9.3 Inferences about Two Proportions

In the previous section, we examined methods of making inferences about two means. This, of course, involves working with numerical data. In this section, we will look at ways of comparing two populations when attribute data are involved. When this is the case, we want to be able to make inferences about population proportions.

Hypothesis Testing of Two Proportions

There are two assumptions that must be met to carry out the seven-step testing procedure described in this section:

1. The two samples are taken from two independent populations.

2. The samples taken from each population are sufficiently large. That is, for each sample $np \geq 5$ and $n(1 - p) \geq 5$.

The purpose of conducting two-sample hypothesis tests of proportions is to see, through the use of sample data, if there's a statistically significant difference between the proportions of successes of two populations. The null hypothesis in such tests of the differences between proportions is

H_0: $p_1 = p_2$

The alternative hypothesis can be two-tailed, right-tailed, or left-tailed:

H_1: $p_1 \neq p_2$
H_1: $p_1 > p_2$
H_1: $p_1 < p_2$

STATISTICS IN ACTION

Not Up My Nose You Don't ...

A year-long study of smokers was conducted at the Maudsley Hospital in London. A group of 227 smokers received 4 weeks of therapy designed to help them give up their habit. Half of the group were given an experimental nasal spray containing nicotine, and the other half were given a spray containing a placebo. One-fourth of those using the experimental spray and one-tenth of those using the placebo spray gave up smoking during the trial.

The Sampling Distribution of the Differences between Sample Proportions The **sampling distribution of the differences between sample proportions** is theoretically analogous to the sampling distribution of the differences between sample means. The mean of the sampling distribution of the differences between proportions is zero *if* the null hypothesis is true—that is, if $p_1 = p_2$. If the sample size of each group is large, the shape of the sampling distribution is approximately normal. The standard deviation of the sampling distribution of the differences between proportions, which is called the **standard error of the difference between proportions,** is calculated as follows:

$$\sigma_{\hat{p}_1 - \hat{p}_2} = \sqrt{\frac{p_1(1 - p_1)}{n_1} + \frac{p_2(1 - p_2)}{n_2}}$$

Unfortunately, the computation of $\sigma_{\hat{p}_1 - \hat{p}_2}$ requires a knowledge of the parameters. If these values were known in the first place, there would be no need to conduct a test! Therefore, *in tests of differences between proportions, and in the construction of a confidence interval for the difference between proportions,* $\sigma_{\hat{p}_1 - \hat{p}_2}$ *is always unknown, and must be estimated.*

When testing the hypothesis that $p_1 = p_2$, we will use a pooled estimate, $\hat{p}$, to estimate the common value of p_1 and p_2, where the pooled estimate is obtained by dividing the total number of successes $(x_1 + x_2)$ for the two samples, by the total number of observations $(n_1 + n_2)$, that is,

$$\hat{p} = \frac{x_1 + x_2}{n_1 + n_2} = \frac{n_1\hat{p}_1 + n_2\hat{p}_2}{n_1 + n_2}$$

Our estimate for $\sigma_{\hat{p}_1 - \hat{p}_2}$ is then

$$\sqrt{\frac{\hat{p}(1 - \hat{p})}{n_1} + \frac{\hat{p}(1 - \hat{p})}{n_2}} = \sqrt{\hat{p}(1 - \hat{p})\left(\frac{1}{n_1} + \frac{1}{n_2}\right)},$$

and the test statistic is

$$z = \frac{(\hat{p}_1 - \hat{p}_2) - (p_1 - p_2)}{\sqrt{\hat{p}(1 - \hat{p})\left(\frac{1}{n_1} + \frac{1}{n_2}\right)}} \text{ or } \frac{(\hat{p}_1 - \hat{p}_2)}{\sqrt{\hat{p}(1 - \hat{p})\left(\frac{1}{n_1} + \frac{1}{n_2}\right)}} \qquad (9.13)$$

since $p_1 - p_2$ will equal zero if the null hypothesis is true.

The general seven-step procedure for testing the differences between proportions is not any different than the z test for differences between means. Consequently, there's little need here for an extended further discussion. The following is an example of a two-tailed test.

Example 9.18 Wayne Mitchell, candidate for public office, feels that male voters as well as female voters have the same opinion of him. A random sample of 36 male voters showed that 12 of these voters favoured his election. Thus, $\hat{p}_1$ is 12/36 or 0.3333. And it was found in a random sample of 50 female voters that 18 were Wayne's supporters. So $\hat{p}_2$ is 18/50 or 0.36. Test the validity of Wayne's assumption, using a significance level of .05.

◆ Solution:

Hypotheses (Step 1):

H_0: $p_1 = p_2$
H_1: $p_1 \neq p_2$

This is a two-tailed test because Wayne is interested only in the equality or non-equality of the proportion of favourable opinions between males and females. The .05 level is specified *(Step 2)*, the z distribution is applicable *(Step 3)*, and the rejection region is bounded by critical z values = ±1.96 *(Step 4)*.

The decision rule *(Step 5)* is

Reject H_0 in favour of H_1 if $z < -1.96$ or $z > +1.96$. Otherwise, fail to reject H_0.

(Step 6) z is calculated as follows.

$$\hat{p} = \frac{x_1 + x_2}{n_1 + n_2} = \frac{12 + 18}{36 + 50} = \frac{30}{86} = 0.3488, \text{ and}$$

$$z = \frac{\hat{p}_1 - \hat{p}_2}{\sqrt{\hat{p}(1 - \hat{p})\left(\frac{1}{n_1} + \frac{1}{n_2}\right)}} = \frac{0.3333 - 0.3600}{\sqrt{0.3488(1 - 0.3488)\left(\frac{1}{36} + \frac{1}{50}\right)}} = \frac{-0.0267}{0.1042} = -.26.$$

Conclusion (Step 7):

Since $z = -.26$ is between ±1.96, there is no reason to reject Wayne Mitchell's claim. Apparently, both genders have about the same low opinion of Wayne!

Had this been a *one-tailed test* to see if male voters were significantly less responsive to Wayne's message than female voters, the alternative hypothesis would be

H_1: $p_1 < p_2$

And the decision rule would become

Reject H_0 in favour of H_1 if $z < -1.645$. Otherwise, fail to reject H_0.

The value of the test statistic, *z,* would remain unchanged, and the conclusion would still be to fail to reject the null hypothesis. ◆

Confidence Interval for the Difference of Two Proportions

To compute a confidence interval for the difference in population proportions, $p_1 - p_2$ in the large, independent sample case, we estimate $\sigma_{\hat{p}_1 - \hat{p}_2}$ by using $\hat{\sigma}_{\hat{p}_1 - \hat{p}_2}$, where

$$\hat{\sigma}_{\hat{p}_1 - \hat{p}_2} = \sqrt{\frac{\hat{p}_1(1 - \hat{p}_1)}{n_1} + \frac{\hat{p}_2(1 - \hat{p}_2)}{n_2}}.$$

STATISTICS IN ACTION

But I'm Compelled ...
A *Journal of Consumer Research* study assessed the characteristics of compulsive buyers and compared them with the characteristics of general consumers. There was no discernible difference in the household incomes of these groups. But while gender was about equally represented in the study (48.3 percent men and 51.7 percent women), compulsive buyers were heavily skewed toward female respondents (92 percent).

The confidence interval is

$$(\hat{p}_1 - \hat{p}_2) - z_{\alpha/2}\hat{\sigma}_{\hat{p}_1 - \hat{p}_2} < (\hat{p}_1 - \hat{p}_2) + z_{\alpha/2}\hat{\sigma}_{\hat{p}_1 - \hat{p}_2} \qquad (9.14)$$

lower limit   upper limit
of estimate   of estimate

Example 9.19 Suppose in Example 9.18, candidate Wayne Mitchell had wanted to obtain a 90 percent confidence interval for $p_1 - p_2$. Compute the interval for him.

◆ **Solution:**

In that example, $p_1 = .3333$ of $n_1 = 36$ male voters favoured his election while for females it was $\hat{p}_2 = .36$ of 50 female voters. Our best estimate for $\sigma_{\hat{p}_1 - \hat{p}_2}$ is

$$\hat{\sigma}_{\hat{p}_1 - \hat{p}_2} = \sqrt{\frac{\hat{p}_1(1 - \hat{p}_1)}{n_1} + \frac{\hat{p}_2(1 - \hat{p}_2)}{n_2}} = \sqrt{\frac{.3333(.6666)}{36} + \frac{.36(.64)}{50}} = .1038$$

Additionally, the appropriate z value for a 90 percent confidence interval is $z_{.05} = 1.645$. Thus, the confidence interval is

$$(\hat{p}_1 - \hat{p}_2) - z_{.05}\,\hat{\sigma}_{\hat{p}_1 - \hat{p}_2} < p_1 - p_2 < (\hat{p}_1 - \hat{p}_2) + z_{.05}\,\hat{\sigma}_{\hat{p}_1 - \hat{p}_2}$$
$$(.3333 - .36) - 1.645(.1038) < p_1 - p_2 < (.3333 - .36) + 1.645(.1038)$$
$$-.0267 - .1708 < p_1 - p_2 < -.0267 + .1708$$
$$-.1975 < p_1 - p_2 < .1441, \text{ or to two decimals,}$$
$$-.20 < p_1 - p_2 < .14$$

So, with 90 percent confidence, all we can say is that the proportion of females who prefer Mitchell might be up to .14 (or 14 percent) higher, or down to .20 (or 20 percent) lower, than the proportion of males who prefer Mitchell, or anything in between. This confidence interval gives no indication that Mitchell is preferred by one gender more than the other, agreeing with the hypothesis test result. ◆

Example 9.20 **Same Percentage of Messers and Mmes in MIS?** In a class project, Rebecca Just presented the majors and genders of a sample of 199 business administration majors. Of 101 males, 18 were majoring in management information science (MIS); of 98 females, 29 were majoring in MIS. Using the p-value approach and a level of .05, is there a difference in the population proportions of males and females who major in MIS?

◆ **Solution:**

Hypotheses (Step 1):

H_0: $p_1 = p_2$
H_1: $p_1 \neq p_2$

We have selected the .05 level for the test *(Step 2)*. The sample proportions are $\hat{p}_1 = 18/101 = .178$ and $\hat{p}_2 = 29/98 = .296$. The z distribution is applicable *(Step 3)* because

$$n_1\hat{p}_1 = 101(.178) = 18 \quad n_1(1 - \hat{p}_1) = 101(.822) = 83$$
$$n_2\hat{p}_2 = 98(.2965) = 29 \quad n_2(1 - \hat{p}_2) = 98(.704) = 69$$

are all greater than 5. Using the *p*-value approach, our decision rule *(Step 4)* is

Reject H_0 if the *p*-value is < .05. Otherwise, fail to reject H_0.

Using MINITAB to do the calculations *(Step 5)*, we obtain the output of *Figure 9.14a*. The *p*-value *(Step 6)* is .049 < .05, so we reject the null hypothesis in favour of the alternative and conclude *(Step 7)* that there is evidence of a difference in the proportions of males and females who major in MIS. (The TI-83 calculator gives a slightly different result (see *Figure 9.14b*). The *p*-value is 0.051, different from the *p*-value obtained by MINITAB of 0.049. This small difference is caused by the TI-83 and MINITAB using different methods for estimating the standard error. Both methods are reasonable, and usually the difference is not enough to worry about. Based on the 95 percent confidence interval in the MINITAB output, we would estimate that MIS is chosen as a major more often by females by between 0 and 23.5 percent. ◆

We should mention again that, just as with differences of means, it does not matter which group is the first and which is the second. If, in this example, we had chosen p_1 to be the proportion for females and p_2 the proportion for males, the hypothesis test would have reached the same conclusion, and the confidence interval, though between two positive rather than negative values, would have the same interpretation. We just need to be aware of our choice and follow through in our logic and interpretations.

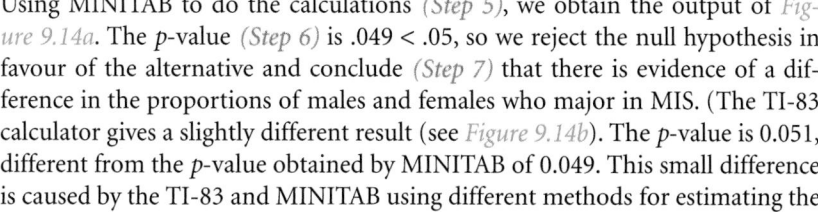

(a)

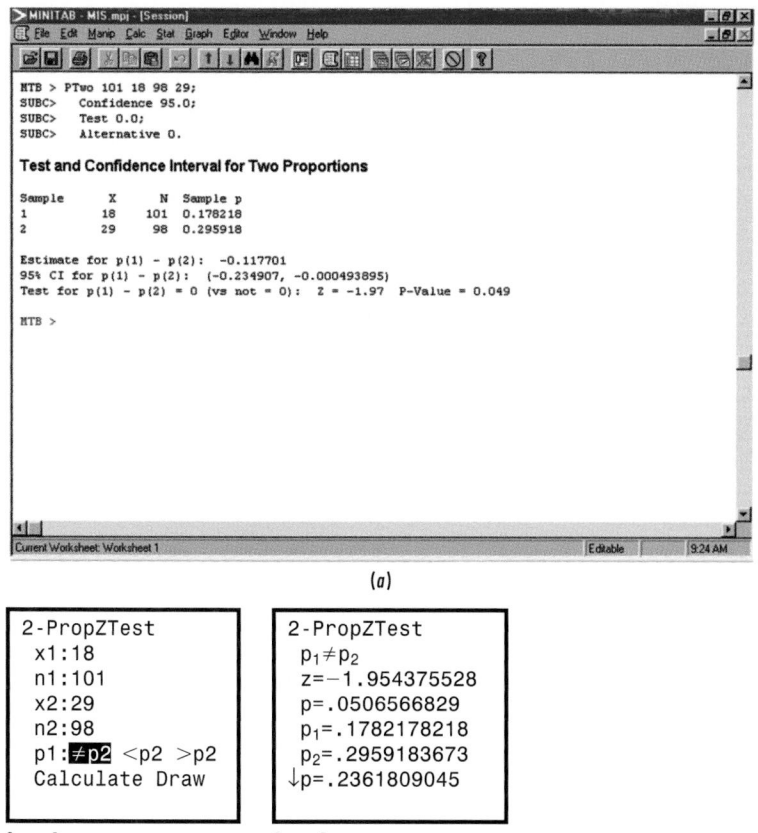

(b)

FIGURE 9.14 (*a*) To obtain this MINITAB output, click on **Stat, Basic Statistics, 2 Proportions.** Next click on **Summarized data,** enter the number of trials and successes for the two samples, follow by clicking on the **Options** button. In that window, enter the confidence level for a confidence interval and the alternative hypothesis for a hypothesis test. Then click **OK** twice. (*b*) Choose the **2-PropZTest** from the **TESTS** menu. Screen 1 shows how to set up the test, and screen 2 shows the results.

STATISTICS IN ACTION

Not Heartening News for Ladies

In an Associated Press article published July 30, 1998, it was reported that "women are significantly more likely to die after heart bypass surgery than men even if the men are just as old and sick when they go under the knife." Previously it was thought that the reason women have a higher fatality rate was that they are in worse health by the time they reach surgery. However, Dr. Fred Edwards, the study's author and a cardiac surgeon, accessed the Society of Thoracic Surgeons' national database for the medical records of 344,000 patients—97,000 of them women—who had heart bypasses between 1994 and 1996. When he compared men and women with identical risk factors, more women died each time, sometimes at twice the rate of men.

Self-Testing Review 9.3

59. A study in the *American Journal of Public Health* reported that out of a random sample of 512 Denver employees, 292 reported they experienced headaches. And of a sample of 281 Adams County employees, 172 reported they experienced headaches. Test the hypothesis at the .01 level that there's no difference in the population proportion of employees who experience headaches at the two locations.

60. A doctor believes she has discovered a better treatment for acne. She treats 32 of her patients by her new method and discovers 18 patients found it successful. In a second random sample of size 36, the patients were treated by the old method. In this case 18 patients found it successful. At the .05 level of significance, can the doctor conclude that the new method is better than the old method?

61. Humour is commonly used as an advertising tool in the United States, but researchers know little about its use in foreign markets. One type of humour found in ads is the showing of situations in which there are expected/unexpected contrasts. In a *Journal of Marketing* study, a random sample of 36 U.S. ads showed that 16 contained an expected/unexpected contrast. In Germany, a sample of 36 ads had 18 with expected/unexpected contrasts. Test the hypothesis at the .01 level that there is a different population proportion of ads that have expected/unexpected contrasts in the two nations.

62. Using the information given in problem 61, construct a 99 percent confidence interval for the difference in the population proportion of ads that have expected/unexpected contrasts in the two nations.

63. A study of psychological disorders and how they affect high school students was published in the *Journal of Abnormal Psychology*. In a random sample of 891 females in the study, 16 had attention-deficit hyperactivity. And in the random sample of 819 males, 37 had attention-deficit hyperactivity. Test the hypothesis at the .01 level that males have a greater population proportion of attention-deficit hyperactivity.

64. In a study reported in the *American Journal of Psychiatry,* the characteristics of a random sample of 17 patients with major depression were compared with the characteristics of a random sample of 47 patients without depression. The study found that 8 of the patients with major depression had a family history of psychiatric disorder, while 23 of those without depression had a family history of psychiatric disorder. Test the hypothesis at the .01 level that the population proportion of patients with a family history of psychiatric disorder is the same for patients with and without major depression.

65. Using the information given in problem 64, construct a 99 percent confidence interval for the difference in the population proportion of patients with a family history of psychiatric disorder for patients with and without major depression.

66. The *Journal of Research in Crime and Delinquency* has published a study on the situational characteristics of crimes. In a random sample of 96 robberies, 36 were committed by people who acted alone. And in a random sample of 69 assaults, 39 were committed by people who acted alone. Test the hypothesis at the .05 level that the population proportion of crimes committed by people acting alone is the same for robbery and assault.

67. Using the information given in problem 66, construct a 95 percent confidence interval for the difference in the population proportion of crimes committed by people acting alone for robbery and assault.

68. In a study reported in the *American Journal of Psychiatry,* the responses regarding HIV risk behaviour of a random sample of 76 hospitalized adolescents in a psychiatric facility were compared with the responses of a random sample of 802 school-based adolescents in the same city. Seven of the hospitalized adolescents reported using injection drugs while 29 of the school group reported the same behaviour. Test the hypothesis at the .01 level that injection drug use among the population of psychiatrically hospitalized adolescents is greater than it is among the population of school-based adolescents.

69. During the last flu season, a random sample of 200 people who were given a flu shot showed that 7 still caught the flu. In another random sample of 400 people who were not given a flu shot, there were 29 people who caught the flu. At the .05 level of significance, can we conclude that the true proportion of all people with a flu shot who catch the flu is less than the true proportion of all people without a flu shot who catch the flu?

70. Using the information given in problem 69, construct a 95 percent confidence interval for the difference in the population proportion of all people with a flu shot who catch the flu and the population proportion of all people without a flu shot who catch flu.

71. A study in the *New England Journal of Medicine* sought to learn if the risk of neural-tube birth defects could be decreased by mothers taking multivitamins in the period preceding delivery. It was found that in a random sample of 2,394 women who were given vitamins, there were 67 congenital malformations in the babies they delivered. There were 2,310 women in a control group who were given placebos, and among this group there were 109 congenital malformations. Test the hypothesis at the .01 level that the population proportion of birth defects is equal for the group given vitamins and the group not given vitamins.

72. A study in the *American Journal of Psychiatry* used random samples of 202 nicotine-dependent people and 192 non-dependent people to see if nicotine-dependent people had a greater vulnerability to psychiatric disorders. In the nicotine-dependent group, 169 were currently smoking, and in the non-dependent group, 123 were smoking. Test the hypothesis at the .05 level that the population proportion of those who are still smoking is higher in the nicotine-dependent group.

73. Using the information given in problem 72, construct a 95 percent confidence interval for the difference in the population proportion for the two groups.

74. In a class project, Joe Woolman worked with data from a process qualification of semi-conductor equipment at a site in Japan. Tools used to remove photoresist from silicon wafers were tested on 250 wafers for several companies and the number of wafers that passed inspection noted. The results for two of the companies follow:

Process	Pass	Fail
Applied	234	16
GaSonics	221	29

a) Test the hypothesis at the .10 level that the population proportion of wafers that pass inspection are the same for the two companies.

b) Construct a 90 percent confidence interval for the difference in the population proportions of wafers that pass inspection for the two companies.

75. A survey was conducted of university students who played video, computer or Internet games. When random samples of 550 males and 520 females who played such games were asked "Which do you play the most?" the results were as follows:

	Video Games	Computer Games	Internet Games
Male	46%	32%	22%
Female	30%	45%	25%

a) At the 0.05 level of significance, can we conclude that the population percentage of all female student gamers who mostly play Internet games is higher than the population percentage of all male student gamers who mostly play Internet games?

b) Construct a 95 percent confidence interval for the difference in the population percentages of male and female gamers who mostly play computer games.

c) At the 0.05 level of significance, can we conclude that the population percentage of all male student gamers who mostly play video games is higher than the population percentage of all female student gamers who mostly play video games?

d) Construct a 95 percent confidence interval for the difference in the population percentages of male and female gamers who mostly play video games.

76. Brad Brewster (*An Evaluation of a Bike Lane Project in San Luis Obispo, Ca.,* Cal Poly Senior Project) described a survey in which people were asked their opinion of SLO's support of bicycling and alternative transportation. Of 30 cyclists, 8 felt positive about SLO's support, while of 50 city residents, 24 felt positive.

a) Test the hypothesis at the .10 level that the population percentages of cyclists and city residents who felt positive towards SLO's support of bicycling and alternative transportation are the same.

b) Construct a 90 percent confidence interval for the difference in the population percentage of cyclists and city residents who feel positive towards SLO's support of bicycling and alternative transportation.

77. McIntyre et al. in "Dexamethasone as Adjunctive Therapy in Bacterial Meningitis" (*Journal of the American Medical Association*) looked at a number of studies that evaluated the use of dexamethasone as protection against hearing loss in childhood *Haemophilus influenza,* type B (Hib), meningitis.

a) Part of the paper reported that in Canada, 57 of 101 cases of meningitis were caused by Hib, while in the United States, 83 of 143 cases were caused by Hib. Test at a level of .05 the hypothesis that the population percentages of cases of meningitis caused by Hib in Canada and the United States are the same.

b) The paper reported that in 260 cases of meningitis treated with dexamethasone, 8 patients suffered severe hearing loss. In 233 cases of meningitis not treated with dexamethasone, 27 patients suffered severe hearing loss. Test at a level of .01 the hypothesis that, for people with meningitis, treatment with dexamethasone decreases the percentage of incidence of severe hearing loss.

c) The paper also reported that in 390 cases of meningitis treated with dexamethasone, 25 patients suffered neurological deficits other than hearing loss. In 367 cases of meningitis not treated with dexamethasone, 38 patients suffered neurological deficits other than hearing loss. Test at a level of .10 the hypothesis that, for people with meningitis, treatment with dexamethasone decreases the percentage of incidence of neurological deficits other than hearing loss.

78. Unseasonal rains in the Deccan plateau of India in 1995 led to damaged maize and sorghum crops in some villages. In "A Foodborne Disease Outbreak Due to the Consumption of Moldy Sorghum and Maize Containing Fumonisin Mycotoxins" (*Clinical Toxocology,* 1997), Bhat, Shetty, Amruth, and Sudershan showed that consumption of these grains led to a food-borne disease whose symptoms included abdominal pain, borborygmi, and diarrhea. Data taken from that paper follow:

Village	Population	
	Affected	**Not Affected**
Atkur Thanda	278	25
Athkur	320	118
Kalkoda	234	53
Yacharam	122	233
Total	1424	449

Age	Sex	Affected	Not Affected
1 to 6	Boys	5	26
	Girls	7	21
7 to 17	Boys	375	121
	Girls	321	124
>18	Boys	328	132
	Girls	289	124
Total		1,325	548

a) Test the hypothesis at the .05 level that there is no difference in the population percentages of affected people in Athkur and Kalkoda.

b) Construct a 95 percent confidence interval for the difference in the population percentages of affected people in Atkur Thanda and Yacharam.

c) For children 1 to 6, test the hypothesis at the .10 level that there is no difference in the population percentages of affected boys and girls.

d) For children 7 to 17, construct a 90 percent confidence interval for the difference in the population percentages of affected boys and girls.

e) For people over 18, test the hypothesis at the .01 level that the population percentage of affected males is greater than the population percentage of females.

L O O K I N G B A C K

1. You've seen in this chapter how to evaluate two populations to see if they're likely to be similar or different with respect to some characteristic. Our interest isn't in looking at the magnitude of the parameters; rather, our concern is to see if one population appears to possess more or less of a trait than the other. The prerequisites to making inferences about two variances, two means, and two proportions that are discussed in this chapter are spelled out when the tests and confidence intervals are introduced.

STATISTICS IN ACTION

"The Pill" and Ovarian Cancer

An August 13, 1998, an Associated Press article described a study in the *New England Journal of Medicine* that reported: "Birth control pills appear to cut the chances of ovarian cancer in half among women who inherit a faulty gene that puts them at high risk for the disease." While it was known that the pill reduces the risk of ovarian cancer, it was not known if the pill reduced the risk for women with bad genes, called BRCA1 and BRCA2. Dr. Steven A. Narod of Women's College Hospital in Toronto described the study in which 207 women with ovarian cancer resulting from defective BRCA1 and BRCA2 were compared to 161 of their sisters, some of whom also had genetic mutations. The study found that those who had used birth control pills had an overall 50 percent lower risk of ovarian cancer and, if they had used the pill for more than 6 years, the risk was 60 percent lower. However, "The same genetic defects also cause breast cancer, and the pill also carries a slightly higher risk of this kind of cancer in women without the bad genes." Narod said his research has turned up no sign that birth control pills significantly increase the chance of breast cancer in women with the BRCA defects, but "that possibility exists."

2. We've used testing procedures to make relative comparisons between two population variances, two population means, and two population proportions. The null hypothesis to be tested in these situations is that the two parameters are equal. That is, there's no significant difference between the two parameters. The alternative hypothesis may be either one-tailed or two-tailed depending on the logic of the situation.

3. An F distribution is the sampling distribution used to make tests of two variances, z and t distributions are used in making inferences about means, and the z distribution is used in making inferences about proportions. The same basic seven-step testing procedure (state the hypotheses, select the level of significance, determine the correct test distribution, define the critical region, state the decision rule, compute the test statistic, and make the statistical decision) is used in all the tests outlined in this chapter. Likewise, similar interpretations are given to confidence intervals on the difference between two means and two proportions.

4. Only one procedure is discussed for tests of two variances and for tests or confidence intervals on two proportions. But four procedures are used to make inferences about two means. The choice of the correct procedure to use depends on the answers to the questions raised in the four diamond-shaped decision symbols found in Figure 9.4. Examples of each of these procedures are given and discussed in the chapter.

Exercises

79. A study reported in the *Journal of Consumer Research* sought to learn the effect of touching on customer behaviour. Shoppers were approached at random by three male and three female experimenters as they entered a store, and the shoppers were handed a catalogue. During alternate one-hour periods, the experimenter either touched the subject lightly on the upper arm or did not. There were 17 in the group who were touched and 16 in the no-touch group. The mean and standard deviation of the shopping time for the shoppers who were touched were 22.11 minutes and 4.74 minutes, respectively. For the no-touch group, the mean and standard deviation times were 13.56 and 5.67, respectively. Assuming both populations are normally distributed, test the hypothesis at the .05 level that the population variances are equal for both groups.

80. Using the statistics given in problem 79, test the hypothesis at the .05 level that the population mean time spent shopping by those who were touched is significantly greater than the similar time spent by those who were not touched.

81. An *American Journal of Public Health* study dealt with the type of care given to disabled elderly people. After short-term hospital stays, a random sample of 110 disabled elderly subjects were assigned to an experimental group that offered physician-led primary home care on a 24-hour basis. Another sample of 73 disabled elderly subjects in a control group were offered ordinary care. After 6 months, the experimental group of 110 used a mean of 4.2 drugs with a standard deviation of 2.10 drugs. The control group of 73 used a mean of 4.6 drugs with a standard deviation of 3.15. At the .01 level, test the hypothesis that the population represented by the experimental group needed fewer drugs.

82. Using the information given in problem 81, construct a 99 percent confidence interval for the difference in the population means of the amounts of drugs used by the experimental and control groups.

83. One appeal by mail for new members of a political party brought 412 responses to 5,000 letters. After a radio campaign, another, more expensive, mail solicitation brought 311 responses to 3,000 letters. At the .05 level of significance, do the data indicate that the second, more expensive solicitation was more effective than the less expensive solicitation?

84. A random sample of 8 pairs of identical 12-year-old twins took part in a study to see if vitamins helped their attention spans. For each pair, twin A was given a placebo, and twin B received a special vitamin supplement. A psychologist then determined the length of time (in minutes) each remained with a puzzle. The results were

Twin A	Twin B
34	29
18	42
39	33
31	40
28	38
26	40
28	27
22	15

Use a paired t procedure to test the hypothesis at the .05 level that the vitamin supplement gives recipients a longer attention span.

85. Using the information given in problem 84, construct a 95 percent confidence interval for the difference in the population means of the attention spans of twins given the placebo and the vitamin supplement.

86. A study in the *American Journal of Public Health* dealt with a randomly selected group of 264 primary caregivers. These caregivers were interviewed and asked to keep diaries for six months. Diaries were returned by 141 caregivers, and 123 did not return diaries. Of those who returned diaries, the average years of education was 13.9, and the standard deviation was 2.9 years. Of those who did not return diaries, the average years of education was 13.5, and the standard deviation was 3.2 years. Test the hypothesis at the .05 level that there was no difference in the education of the population of caregivers who fell into these two groups.

87. A researcher claims that the percentage of patients who show signs of cognitive impairment is different for patients who are restrained and those who are unrestrained. A random sample of 5,834 nursing home patients who are restrained finds that 2,519 show no signs of cognitive impairment. Another random sample of 4,110 patients who are unrestrained finds that 2,983 show no signs of cognitive impairment. Test the researcher's claim at the .05 level of significance.

88. An experiment was conducted over a three-year period to evaluate the effectiveness of a work-site health promotion program in reducing obesity. Before the trial was run, the mean and standard deviation of body mass index (BMI), a measure of obesity, were determined in each work site. For the random sample of 16 work sites in the treatment group (the group receiving classes on weight control), the mean and standard deviation for BMI (kg/m^2) were 25.58 and .81, respectively. For the random sample of 16 work sites in the control group (the group not receiving any weight control instruction), the mean and standard deviation were 25.80 and .99, respectively. Assume both populations are normally distributed. Test the hypothesis at the .05 level that there was no difference in the population variance of the BMI between the groups of work sites before the trial was run.

89. Use the statistics from problem 88 and test the hypothesis at the .01 level that there's no difference in the population mean BMI between the two groups of work sites.

90. Use the statistics from problem 88 to construct a 99 percent confidence interval for the difference in the population mean BMI between the two groups of work sites.

91. A programmer recently received a new processor for his PC. He is interested in estimating the average amount of time saved by this processor. To do this he issues four different commands with and without the new processor and determines how much time was required for each. Use the results in the following table (time is in msec) to obtain the appropriate 95 percent confidence interval, assuming the differences in times are normally distributed.

Command	1	2	3	4
Without processor	200	190	173	151
With processor	198	180	171	149

92. An article in *Teaching of Psychology* compared attitudes toward nuclear disarmament (AND) scores of teachers who have discussed nuclear disarmament issues in any course against the AND scores of those teachers who have not discussed the issue. For the random sample of 72 teachers who have discussed this issue, the mean on the AND questionnaire was 77.04 with a standard deviation of 13.28. For the random sample of 55 teachers who have not discussed this issue, the mean AND score was 69.33 with a standard deviation of 13.52. Test the hypothesis at the .01 level that population attitudes towards nuclear disarmament are different for the two groups of teachers.

93. A study to see how well marital dissolution was predicted by the personality scores of husbands and wives was published in the *Journal of Personality and Social Psychology*. A random selection of 286 newlywed couples was made. After 5 years, 222 couples remained together and 64 had dissolved their marriages. The mean age of the husband in the 222 stable marriages was 30.47, and the standard deviation was 7.65. For the 64 divorced couples, the mean age of the husband was 29.64, and the standard deviation was 6.83. Test the hypothesis at the .01 level that there's no difference in the population mean age of the husband in the two types of couples.

94. Using the statistics given in problem 93, construct a 99 percent confidence interval for the difference in the population mean ages of the husbands in the two types of couples.

95. A study reported in the *American Journal of Sports Medicine* was undertaken to find the optimum type of knee surgery for patients with anterior cruciate ligament injuries. Two types of surgeries were performed. For Technique A (anatomic location of the graft through a drill hole on the femur), surgery was successful for 22 out of the random sample of 30 patients. For Technique B (modified over-the-top reconstruction), 32 out of a random sample of 54 surgeries were successful. Compute a 99 percent confidence interval for the difference between the percentages of successful surgeries for the two techniques.

96. Some professors of education claim there's a significant difference of opinion about testing and test uses between preservice and inservice teachers. In a study reported in the *Journal of Educational Research*, random samples from both groups were asked their opinion on this statement: "Standardized tests serve a useful purpose." (The response scale ranged from 1 = strongly agree to 6 = strongly disagree.) The 84 preservice sophomore education majors had a mean response of 4.02 with a standard deviation of .83, while the 32 inservice teachers responded to the statement with a mean of 2.93 and a standard deviation of .97. Test the professors' claim at the .01 level.

97. Using the information given in problem 96, construct a 99 percent confidence interval for the difference in the population mean responses of the preservice and inservice teachers.

98. The following data, taken from the Statistics Canada 2001 Census, represents the average total income of male and female residents for a random sample of Canadian cities for 2001:

City	Male	Female
Brandon	30,974	19,453
Edmonton	37,355	23,013
Hamilton	39,788	24,704
Moncton	32,290	21,014
Moose Jaw	31,471	19,740
Québec City	31,539	22,964
Saint John	32,003	20,207
Saskatoon	34,575	21,396
Sudbury	37,317	24,397
Victoria	30,451	24,530

Source: Statistics Canada.

Use this data to compute a 99 percent confidence interval for the amount by which the mean total income of the male residents exceeds that of the female residents. What assumption is necessary for this confidence interval to be valid?

99. A Project CALC course is quite different from a traditional calculus course because it emphasizes interactive computer laboratories, co-operative learning, and extensive student writing. A final exam was given to a random sample of 46 students in a traditional course who scored a mean of 9.64 and a standard deviation of 5.21 on a portion of the exam involving concepts. For the same portion of the test, 41 Project CALC students scored a mean of 11.52 and a standard deviation of 7.07. Test the hypothesis at the .05 level that the population mean score for Project CALC students is higher than the mean score for the traditional students.

100. In an *American Journal of Psychology* study of the characteristics of alcoholics, there were random samples of 12 normal subjects and 10 alcoholic subjects. The normal subjects had a mean score of 1 with a standard deviation of 0.6 on the Hamilton Rating Scale for Depression. For the alcoholic subjects, the mean rating on the same scale was 6 with a standard deviation of 3. Assume the populations are normal with variances not equal, and test the hypothesis at the .01 level that alcoholics have a higher population mean rating on the Hamilton scale than do normal subjects.

101. A study compared the step length in meters of amputees using a solid ankle cushion heel (SACH) prosthesis with those using a Carbon Copy II (CC II) device. For the random sample of 10 using SACH, the mean step length was .764 m, and the standard deviation was .0011 m. For the sample of 10 using CC II, the mean step length was .766 m, and the standard deviation was .00054 m. Assume both populations are normally distributed. Test the hypothesis at the .05 level that the population variances for the two types of prosthetic feet are equal.

102. Use the data from problem 101 to test the hypothesis that there's no difference in the population mean step length between the two types of prosthetic feet. Use the .01 level.

103. The *Journal of Research in Crime and Delinquency* published a study on the situational characteristics of crimes. In a random sample of 96 robberies, 46 were related in some way to drugs or alcohol. And in a random sample of 69 assaults, 43 were related to drugs or alcohol. Test the hypothesis at the .05 level that the population percentage of robberies related to drugs or alcohol is lower than that for assaults.

104. Using the information given in problem 103, construct a 95 percent confidence interval for the difference in the population percentages of robberies and assaults that are related to drugs or alcohol.

105. The mean heart rate (beats per minute, or bpm) for a random sample of 31 patients with congestive heart failure who were given Captopril was 75.2 bpm, and the standard deviation was 2.7 bpm. The random sample of 31 patients who were given Nitroprusside had a mean heart rate of 77.4 bpm and a standard deviation of 2.4 bpm. Test the hypothesis at the .01 level that there's no difference in heart rate for the population of patients given Captopril and those given Nitroprusside.

106. A study on psychological disorders and how they affect high school students was published in the *Journal of Abnormal Psychology*. Out of a random sample of 891 females in the study, 12 had an eating disorder. Of the random sample of 819 males, 1 had an eating disorder. Why would it be inappropriate to use these samples to test to see if there is a difference in the percentages of males and females who have eating disorders?

107. Random samples of 26 men and 27 women responded to a questionnaire designed to determine the value of various activities in their lives. A comparison of the mean scores on a scale for each activity is as follows:

Activity	Men	Women
Studying	34.34	34.85
Working	43.95	44.31
Community	30.58	31.92
Home/Family	44.80	46.55
Leisure	39.42	40.39

Use the paired *t* procedure to test the hypothesis at the .01 level that there's no difference in the values of these activities in men and women.

108. Using the information given in problem 108, construct a 99 percent confidence interval for the difference in the mean population values of these activities in men and women.

109. Syringe-exchange programs represent one attempt to slow the spread of HIV infection among injection-drug users. In a study reported in the *New England Journal of Medicine*, a random sample of 160 needles was tested for the HIV virus, and 108 were found to be positive. A year later, after the introduction of a syringe-exchange program, a sample of 338 needles was tested, and 164 were found to be HIV positive. Test the hypothesis at the .05 level that the population percentage of HIV positive needles used by injection-drug users was lower after the exchange program was in operation.

110. An article in *Criminal Justice and Behavior* claims that an intellectual imbalance of performance IQ (P) with verbal IQ (V)—such that $P > V$—is a useful predictor of the probability of becoming delinquent. A random sample of 269 male juvenile delinquents were classified in the low $P > V$ group, and a sample of 253 were classified in the high $P > V$ group. In a full-scale IQ test, the boys in the low $P > V$ group had a mean of 90.57 with a standard deviation of 16.1. For the high $P > V$ group, the mean IQ was 96.51 with a standard deviation of 11.4. Test the hypothesis at the .05 level that there's no difference between the population mean IQ scores for these groups.

111. A random sample of 21 students who stayed home and commuted to their schools had a mean GPA of 2.685 with a standard deviation of .792. A random sample of 21 students who went away to school had a mean GPA of 2.480 and a standard deviation of .689. Assuming the GPAs are normally distributed for the populations from which these samples were taken, at the .05 level, are the population variances for the two groups equal?

112. Do students who stay at home and commute to school have better GPAs than their friends who go away to school? Test the hypothesis at the .05 level that students who stay at home have a higher population mean GPA than those who go away. Use the data from problem 111.

113. A double-blind study is one in which neither doctor nor patient know who is receiving a drug and who is receiving a placebo. In such a study of 118 patients with mild to moderate heart difficulty, the mean change in total exercise time (in seconds) for the random sample of 60 patients given a placebo was 22 seconds, and the standard deviation was 13 seconds. For the experimental group of 58 patients given NORVASC, the mean change in total exercise time was 62 seconds with a standard deviation of 17 seconds. Test the hypothesis at the .01 level that NORVASC significantly improves the population mean exercise time.

114. Let's look again at the double-blind study discussed in problem 113. Out of the 60 patients who received a placebo, 17 had symptomatic improvement. Of the 58 patients given NORVASC, 32 had significant improvement. Test the hypothesis at the .01 level that the population percentage of patients who use NORVASC and experienced improvement is significantly greater than those who were given a placebo.

115. A brewery operated two wastewater plants that treated municipal and brewery wastewater. For a class project, C. Zimmerman compared four different labs that analyzed this wastewater. This analysis included assaying the discharge for mercury, silver, cadmium, lead, and copper (all in mcg/l). The brewery staff suspected that some labs were using improper techniques, causing inconsistent results and false positives for dangerous amounts of these elements in the water. To check, the four labs were sent similar samples of water to analyze. Following are the results from two of the labs (Data = Brewery1).

Mercury	Lab 3	Lab 4
	0.80	0.50
	0.70	0.90
	0.70	0.90
	0.80	0.70
	0.70	0.70
	0.70	0.60
	0.70	0.70

Silver	Lab 3	Lab 4
	0.60	0.20
	0.70	0.50
	0.60	0.80
	0.50	0.70
	0.60	0.70
	0.60	0.60
	0.60	0.60

Cadmium	Lab 3	Lab 4
	0.70	0.80
	0.50	0.80
	0.80	0.70
	0.70	0.80
	0.80	0.70
	0.80	0.80
	0.80	0.70

Lead	Lab 3	Lab 4
	6.0	4.2
	9.0	3.5
	8.0	3.6
	4.0	3.7
	8.0	4.1
	8.0	4.1
	7.0	3.5

Copper	Lab 3	Lab 4
	5	10
	9	12
	5	11
	8	22
	9	23
	8	13
	5	17

Assume all the populations involved are normally distributed for the questions that follow.

a) Test the hypothesis at the .10 level that the population variances are the same for mercury.

b) Test the hypothesis at the .10 level that population means are the same for mercury.

c) Test the hypothesis at the .05 level that the population variance of silver for Lab 4 is greater than that of Lab 3.

d) Test the hypothesis at the .05 level that the population variances are the same for cadmium.

e) Test the hypothesis at the .05 level that the population means are the same for cadmium.

f) Test the hypothesis at the .02 level that the population variances are the same for lead.

g) Test the hypothesis at the .02 level that the population means are the same for lead.

h) Test the hypothesis at the .01 level that the population variance of copper for Lab 4 is greater than that of Lab 3.

116. In a class project, T. Miao reported on a data set she had collected from Strawberry Creek. She questioned whether the upstream pH, with little human contact, would differ from downstream pH, where human contact is the rule. She took a sample of ten readings from the two locations (Data = StrawCrk).

Upstream	Downstream
5.81	7.20
6.00	6.99
2.32	7.41
6.90	7.30
7.25	6.59
7.43	6.78
6.79	5.93
7.89	7.00
6.58	7.62
7.64	7.86

Assume both the populations are normally distributed.

a) Test the hypothesis at the .10 level that the population variances for pH at the two locations are equal.

b) Test the hypothesis at the .10 level that the population means for pH at the two locations are equal.

117. A random sample of households was selected from each of the provinces listed below. It was noted whether or not each household had air conditioning (AC). The results are as follows:

Province	Without AC	With AC
Manitoba	118	49
Saskatchewan	121	22

a) Test the hypothesis at the .01 level that there is no difference in the population percentages of households that have air conditioning for the two provinces.

b) Construct a 99 percent confidence interval for the difference in the population percentages of households that have air conditioning for the two provinces.

118. In a class project, Brian Patterson extracted data on the lengths of brook trout from "Mercury Concentrations in Maine Sport Fishes" from the 1997 volume of *Transactions of the American Fisheries Society.* There were two groups, wild and stocked, and the measurements (cm) on their lengths are as follows (Data = BrookTrt):

Wild		Stocked	
18.0	28.4	18.2	30.5
18.7	29.3	18.3	31.8
18.8	29.5	18.5	34.7
20.0	29.8	19.7	36.0
20.1	30.2	19.8	39.1
20.5	31.0	20.3	
21.7	31.5	21.8	
22.2	32.2	24.2	
22.8	33.5	24.5	
23.5	33.6	25.0	
25.0	34.0	25.6	
26.3	34.1	28.9	
26.9	35.4	29.3	
27.2	35.5	29.7	
28.3	39.0	29.8	

Assume both populations of lengths are normally distributed for the questions that follow.

a) Test the hypothesis at the .05 level that the population variances for the lengths of wild and stocked trout are equal.

b) Test the hypothesis at the .05 level that the population means for the lengths of wild and stocked trout are equal.

c) Compute a 95 percent confidence interval for $\mu_1 - \mu_2$

119. Random samples of 50 male and 50 female students were asked about aspects of and alternatives to the current dry-campus policy.

Should the Campus Remain Dry?		
Gender	Yes	No
Male	20	30
Female	25	25

Should There Be Alcohol-Tolerant Zones?		
Gender	Yes	No
Male	39	11
Female	32	18

Would You Support a Pub on Campus?		
Gender	Yes	No
Male	32	18
Female	32	18

Would a Pub be a Health/Safety Risk?		
Gender	Yes	No
Male	16	34
Female	23	27

Should Pres. Allow Exceptions to Policy?		
Gender	Yes	No
Male	28	22
Female	31	19

a) For each of the questions, test the hypothesis at the .05 level that there is no difference in the population percentage of males and females who answered yes to that question.

b) For each of the questions, construct a 95 percent confidence interval for the difference in the population percentage of males and females who answered yes to that question.

120. In "Impaired Vasopressin Suppression and Enhanced Atrial Natriuretic Hormone Release Following an Acute Water Load in Primary Adosteronism by Kimura et al. (*European Journal of Endocrinology,* 1997), a study was carried out involving 12 patients with aldosterone-producing adenomas before and after adrenalectomy. All patients had high blood pressure, took antihypertensive drugs, and showed a tendency towards hypernatraemia. Profiles of these patients with primary aldosteronism were taken at admission and two months after the operation. Some of the variables reported in the study include systolic blood pressure (SBP in mm Hg), diastolic blood pressure (DBP in mm Hg), serum Na concentration (SNa in mmol/l), serum K concentration (SK in mmol/l), and plasma aldosterone concentration (PAC in pmol/l) (Data = AldConc).

	Admission				
Patient	SBP	DBP	SNa	SK	PAC
1	160	90	149	2.7	560
2	164	104	147	3.0	720
3	152	88	145	4.0	680
4	150	86	144	3.7	1,020
5	136	76	144	4.0	1,450
6	140	80	146	2.1	4,290
7	122	80	140	3.9	720
8	154	80	144	3.3	400
9	192	110	143	4.1	760
10	188	98	144	3.0	940
11	148	98	142	4.1	550
12	152	96	144	2.1	2,240

After Removal of Adrenal Tumour(s)					
Patient	SBP	DBP	SNa	SK	PAC
1	108	88	144	5.4	70
2	130	80	142	5.5	170
3	130	82	144	4.8	90
4	140	88	145	4.3	50
5	152	90	140	5.0	100
6	140	70	144	3.3	740
7	130	80	140	4.4	210
8	146	90	141	4.3	100
9	126	70	141	4.7	70
10	162	90	142	3.7	80
11	110	70	139	4.8	110
12	140	88	141	4.1	120

Assume all the populations involved are normally distributed for the questions that follow.

a) For each of the 5 variables, test the hypothesis at the .05 level that the population means are the same before and after the operation.

b) For each of the 5 variables, construct a 95 percent confidence intervals for the mean difference in the populations.

121. Katherine Lukey examined the perceptions of postgraduate lifestyle qualities of two majors. Several questions from a survey of 26 recreation administration and 12 architecture female majors are summarized in the following tables:

Dating Habits	R.A.	Arch.
Dating on and off	9	1
Dating steadily	8	7
Living with significant other	2	1
Not dating	7	3

Education Plans	R.A.	Arch.
Won't complete college	1	0
Bachelor degree	15	5
Some post-graduate work	0	2
Complete master's	7	5
Complete doctorate	3	0

Marriage Plans	R.A.	Arch.
Never	0	0
Don't know	4	0
Within a year of graduation	2	0
Two to three years	5	3
Four to five years	12	6
More than five years	2	1
Already married	1	2

Number of Children	R.A.	Arch.
None	2	1
Don't know	4	0
One	2	0
Two	8	11
Three or more	10	0

a) Test the hypothesis at the .10 level that there is no difference in the population percentage of female recreation administration and architecture majors who date steadily.

b) Construct a 90 percent confidence interval for the difference in the population percentages of female recreation administration and architecture majors who plan to complete a master's or doctorate degree.

c) Test the hypothesis at the .05 level that there is no difference in the population percentage of female recreation administration and architecture majors who plan to marry in four to five years.

d) Why would it be invalid to construct a confidence interval for the difference in the population percentage of female recreation administration and architecture majors who plan to have two children?

122. In a class project based on data collected for her master's thesis (1997), Cynthia Collin presented the mean smolt length (mm) of samples at two locations for four age categories of smolt. Age is denoted by how many years a fish spent in freshwater and ocean water on the left and right side of the backslash, respectively:

Age	Waddell Creek	Gualala River
1\1	400	403
2\1	466	523
1\2	643	657
2\2	665	702

a) Using a paired *t* procedure, test the hypothesis at the .01 level that the mean smolt length is greater for the population of Gualala River than for the population at Waddell Creek. What assumption is necessary for this test to be valid?

b) Construct a 99 percent confidence interval for the difference in the mean smolt lengths.

123. Mark Gonsalves examined the effects of a low-fat diet, low-intensity aerobic exercise program over a five-week period. Sixteen volunteers were divided into two groups of eight, one group acting as a control, while the other participated in the five-week program. Measurements were taken on body fat percentage before and after the program (Data = LowFat).

Experimental		Control	
Pretest	**Posttest**	**Pretest**	**Posttest**
23.67	24.60	27.79	28.01
18.62	18.53	25.59	25.42
35.79	36.01	21.53	21.67
22.66	22.53	25.25	26.03
18.74	18.59	17.49	17.91
22.25	22.03	25.34	25.25
19.95	19.25	19.59	20.19
14.61	14.06	21.40	21.67

Assume the populations involved are normally distributed for the questions that follow.

a) Using a paired *t* procedure, test the hypothesis at the .05 level that the mean body fat percentage decreases for the population of participants in a low-fat diet, low-intensity aerobic exercise program over a five-week period.

b) Construct a 95 percent confidence interval for the change in the mean body fat percentage of the population of participants in a low-fat diet, low-intensity aerobic exercise program over a five-week period.

c) Calculate the changes in the body fat percentage of the control group.

d) Test the hypothesis at the .05 level that the population variances of the body fat percentage changes for the experimental and control groups are equal.

e) Test the hypothesis at the .05 level that the population mean of the body fat percentage changes is greater for the experimental than the control group.

Topics for Review and Discussion

1. Explain the purpose of two-sample hypothesis tests of variances, means, and proportions.

2. For the two-sample test of variances, what are the necessary assumptions that must be made about the population if the test is to yield usable results?

3. Compare and contrast the four types of two-sample inferences about means discussed in this chapter. For each, describe the necessary assumptions.

4. The paired *t* test actually uses the techniques discussed in Chapter 8. Why is this statement true?

5. What is a sampling distribution of the differences between sample means? How is such a distribution created?

6. When will the mean of the sampling distribution of the differences between sample means be equal to zero?

a) What assumptions are necessary to make any inferences about the difference of two proportions?

b) What is a sampling distribution of the differences between sample proportions? How is such a distribution created?

c) When will the mean of the sampling distribution of the differences between sample proportions be equal to zero?

7. Why is it necessary to use an estimated standard error of the differences between proportions when making an inference about population proportion differences?

8. When is it more appropriate to compute a confidence interval rather than perform a test on the difference between two means or proportions?

Projects/Issues to Consider

1. Go to the library and look through sources that relate to a field that interests you. Locate a source in which there's raw data from two samples. First analyze the type of test that could be done to test the hypothesis that the population means are equal. Then perform the test. Discuss your findings.

2. Locate a library source that involves qualitative data and that gives percentage information from two samples. Perform a hypothesis test about the appropriate population percentages.

3. Log on to the Internet and find the home page of an organization that has links to data sets or data libraries. Select a data set in which there's raw data from two samples. First analyze the type of test that could be done to test the hypothesis that the population means are equal. Then perform the test. Discuss your findings.

4. Log on to the Internet and find the home page of an organization that has links to data sets or data libraries. Select a data set that involves qualitative data and that gives percentage information from two samples. Perform a hypothesis test about the appropriate population percentages.

5. Identify a current issue—one about which people have differing opinions. Now compose a question about this issue and identify two populations (these could be male/female, student/non-student, undergraduate/graduate student, over age 25/under age 25, smoker/non-smoker, and so on) from which you will select samples and record responses. Perform a test to see if the proportions who have a particular view on this issue in the two populations are likely to be different. Discuss your methodology and results.

6. Take a sample of 25 male and 25 female students. Ask them how many hours they watch television in a typical week. Test to see if there is a difference in the means for the two populations. Does it appear that you have performed a valid test? Discuss your methodology and results.

7. Take a sample of 20 students. Ask them to tell you their average marks at high school and at university. Test to see if their university average is less than their high school average. Write a report discussing your methodology and results.

Computer/Calculator Exercises

1. In a class project, Jodi Sauer reported that hemoglobin (Hgb), a quaternary blood protein that transports oxygen in the blood to different tissues, varies in level based on sex and age. Medical journals report that normal adult Hgb levels in men are between 14 and 18 g/ml while women are reported to have levels between 12 and 16 g/ml. To examine the validity of these results, she obtained a sample of the Hgb levels of 151 males and 174 females, The first few lines of data follow (Data = Hemoglob).

Male Hgb	Female Hgb
14.5	10.7
13.6	10.8
12.8	9.2
16.5	11.9
12.2	12.7

a) Test the hypothesis at the .05 level that the population variances for males and females are equal.

b) Test to see if the mean adult Hgb level is higher for the population of males than females. Use a level of .05.

c) Compute a 95 percent confidence interval for $\mu_1 - \mu_2$.

2. In a class project, Eddie Grannis stated, "The giant freshwater prawn (*Macrobrachium rosenbergii*) is an animal that exhibits a wide variation of growth patterns depending on its environment. Water quality, water temperature, diet, stocking density, and available hiding surfaces are influential growth factors." Students divided a group of these prawns into two groups and placed them in different aquaria. After 25 days, their weight in grams was recorded (Data = Prawns).

Tank 1				Tank 2			
0.85	1.11	1.43	0.92	1.47	0.70	1.11	1.60
0.94	0.66	1.39	1.21	0.64	0.70	1.28	0.83
0.82	0.76	0.93	1.96	0.79	0.84	0.69	0.78
1.19	1.02	1.54	1.43	1.95	1.00	1.18	1.20
0.52	1.03	1.72	1.55	0.82	0.69	2.08	1.35
1.14	0.93	1.52	1.29	0.94	1.24	0.68	1.86
0.76	0.88	1.28	1.30	0.71	1.31	1.31	1.44
1.59	1.24			0.94	0.82		

a) Test the hypothesis at the .10 level that the population variances for the two different aquaria are equal.

b) Test to see if the population mean weights differ between the two aquaria. Use a level of .10.

c) Compute a 90 percent confidence interval for $\mu_1 - \mu_2$.

3. In "Greenhouse Screening of Corn Gluten Meal as a Natural Control Product for Broadleaf and Grass Weeds" (*HortScience*, 1995), Bingaman and Christians described an experiment in which the application of corn gluten meal (CGM) as a weed control product was evaluated. One portion of their data described the reduction in survival, relative to the control, of 22 varieties of weeds based on application of different amounts of CGM. Part of the results are in the following table (Data = CGMSurvl).

324 g(m2)	649 g(m2)
60	81
31	35
49	63
78	99
80	95
66	33
82	88
85	85
75	94
75	90
63	54
37	78
51	70
56	53
97	95
0	20
87	96
42	43
51	85
0	18
6	29
43	65

Test the hypothesis at the .05 level that increased amounts of CGM cause a greater mean reduction in survival.

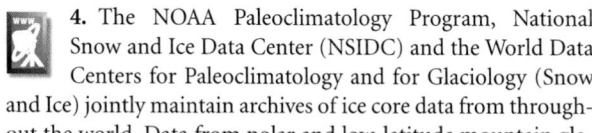 **4.** The NOAA Paleoclimatology Program, National Snow and Ice Data Center (NSIDC) and the World Data Centers for Paleoclimatology and for Glaciology (Snow and Ice) jointly maintain archives of ice core data from throughout the world. Data from polar and low-latitude mountain glaciers and ice caps are archived. The data at NSIDC includes such information as temperature in degrees Celsius, salinity in parts per thousand, depth in metres, and conductivity for different locations. Using a .05 level, compare the means of one of these variables for two locations.

5. In a class project based on data collected for her master's thesis, Cynthia Collin presented several data sets concerning smolt size. One of these included two sets of smolt lengths (mm). The first contains the lengths of smolt caught by the Department of Fish and Game. The second set consists of back-calculated estimates of lengths based on characteristics of the fish (Data = SmoltBck).

Fish and Game			Back Calculated	
210	126	183	210.39	231.07
178	130	222	134.56	193.85
179	136	122	134.56	320.68
166	163	185	211.77	247.61
165	166	90	217.28	210.39
185	173	86	217.28	199.36
174	158	104	184.20	189.71
162	182	80	196.60	264.16
172	131	122	182.82	244.86
90	167	131	302.76	327.57
102	135	144	265.54	244.86
102	175	146	203.50	279.32
122	144	165	202.12	253.13
125	164	133	272.43	199.36

a) Test the hypothesis at the .05 level that the population variances for the caught and back-calculated lengths are equal.

b) Test to see if the means of the populations of caught and back-calculated smolt lengths are equal. Use a level of .05.

6. A typical cement facility uses a synthetic polymer to filter out dust particles that may be airborne due to coking and cement processes. In order to achieve acceptable ambient air conditions, it is necessary to direct the exhaust from the various cement processes to a baghouse (think of it as a large vacuum-cleaner element). Since the filters in the baghouse undergo harsh conditions, they do not last long. In a class project, D. Isham used data found in the *Journal of the Air and Waste Management Association*, which compared the lifetimes (days) of polymer filters to nomex-type filters (Data = Baghouse).

Polymer					Nomex				
35	25	28	26	31	33	32	30	30	33
34	31	29	33	33	32	32	31	31	29
31	27	31	33	28	29	30	33	27	27
28	30	33	29	31	32	32	28	27	30
26	29	35	32	30	26	30	34	31	26
33	30	29	33		28	28	28	28	

Assume both populations are normally distributed.

a) Test the hypothesis at the .05 level that the population variances for the lifetimes of polymer and nomex filters are equal.

b) Test the hypothesis at the .05 level that the population means for the lifetimes of polymer and nomex filters are equal.

7. The following data set is part of a larger set kindly provided by Jeff Tupen of TENERA, Inc. Jeff has spent years working on *Alia carinata*, or the carinate dove shell. The data set below contains morphometric shell variables (first six in mm, last two in degrees) measured from the shelled gastropod *Alia carinata* from a benthic habitat (subtidal benthic hard bottom, i.e., a rocky subtidal benchrock outcropping in approximately 10 m) (Data = Alia1).

Sex	Shell Height	Shell Width	Spire Height	Spire Width	Aperature Height	Aperature Width	Shell Angle	Spire Angle
f	7.01	3.31	2.50	1.98	3.02	1.45	42.0	44.5
f	6.53	3.12	2.23	1.80	2.81	1.25	46.5	47.0
f	7.57	3.62	2.74	2.24	3.04	1.60	45.5	43.0
f	6.55	3.37	2.35	1.93	2.70	1.33	51.5	49.5
f	6.96	3.44	2.60	2.08	3.06	1.41	46.0	44.0
f	7.52	3.59	2.59	2.24	3.15	1.33	47.5	49.0
f	6.99	3.34	2.64	2.08	2.82	1.32	42.5	42.5
f	7.14	3.61	2.28	2.07	3.06	1.46	49.0	47.5
f	7.01	3.35	2.28	2.02	2.90	1.47	45.5	47.5
m	7.62	3.68	2.96	2.27	3.00	1.45	44.0	42.0
m	7.72	3.84	2.75	2.34	3.00	1.43	48.5	50.0
m	7.37	3.67	2.72	2.03	2.94	1.46	44.0	42.0
m	8.69	4.16	2.94	2.57	3.57	1.59	46.5	50.0
m	7.32	3.65	2.58	2.10	3.03	1.46	46.5	44.0
f	7.06	3.63	2.44	2.19	2.98	1.42	48.0	50.0
m	6.68	3.25	2.30	2.00	2.76	1.31	46.0	48.0
m	8.28	3.91	2.98	2.43	3.29	1.54	42.5	42.0
m	7.21	3.66	2.61	2.13	3.14	1.50	48.0	44.5
m	7.24	3.80	2.54	2.21	2.93	1.52	51.0	51.5
m	7.11	3.66	2.48	2.11	2.90	1.32	47.5	45.0
f	7.52	3.56	2.77	2.08	3.04	1.55	43.5	42.0
m	7.39	3.58	2.60	2.04	2.85	1.40	42.0	40.0
m	7.70	3.76	2.85	2.15	3.08	1.51	46.0	45.5
m	7.70	3.51	2.78	2.27	3.25	1.54	43.0	47.0
f	7.39	3.65	2.72	2.20	3.00	1.49	45.0	43.0
m	7.49	3.95	2.59	2.26	3.10	1.54	49.0	50.0
f	7.49	3.46	2.62	2.05	3.20	1.32	41.0	42.5
f	7.19	3.52	2.41	2.23	3.14	1.48	46.0	48.5
f	6.91	3.43	2.58	2.16	2.97	1.43	48.0	49.5
m	8.41	3.88	3.13	2.33	3.19	1.65	43.0	44.5

a) For each of the 8 variables, test the hypothesis at the .05 level that the population variances for female and male *Alia carinata* are equal. (Note: Because of the constant sample sizes, the decision rule will be the same for all these tests).

b) For each of the 8 variables, test the hypothesis at the .05 level that the population means for female and male *Alia carinata* are equal.

c) For each of the 8 variables, construct a 95 percent confidence interval for the difference in the population means for female and male *Alia carinata*.

8. For a class project, Rick Tanguay recorded the circumference (cm) of the arms and legs of right- and left-handed individuals. His contention was that the mean circumference of the arms and legs of right-handed individuals, being left-hemisphere dominant, would be greater on the left side, and the reverse would be true for left-handed individuals (Data = Left-Rght).

Left Leg	Right Leg	Left Arm	Right Arm
	Right-Handed		
62.1	60.7	25.9	27.2
62.3	59.3	26.5	26.3
61.3	59.4	26.1	24.0
61.4	61.6	24.3	24.5
61.3	61.7	24.4	27.1
61.1	60.0	25.8	24.2
60.5	58.5	25.3	26.1
61.0	62.4	27.1	28.3
63.3	59.4	25.1	26.1
63.3	59.8	25.3	25.2
60.1	61.6	25.7	25.8
60.4	60.5	26.7	25.1
62.6	60.7	27.9	24.1
62.8	60.0	26.5	25.8
63.0	60.3	25.9	25.8
	Left-Handed		
61.2	62.8	24.1	27.0
61.6	62.9	22.9	26.3
60.5	60.1	25.5	27.8
59.3	61.0	25.1	25.0
60.0	59.0	26.6	26.0
60.5	61.9	27.7	27.6
59.3	60.0	26.8	26.7
60.6	61.7	26.0	26.2
61.8	62.6	25.0	26.5
59.6	61.1	24.6	26.1
61.4	60.6	25.4	26.1
62.2	60.3	24.8	25.3
60.8	62.0	26.1	26.3
60.2	60.3	27.0	25.6
60.5	58.6	24.6	25.2
60.8	61.1	24.1	24.6
60.9	60.8	24.5	24.8

Assume the populations involved are normally distributed for the questions that follow.

a) Using a paired t procedure, test the hypothesis for the population of right-handed people that the mean circumference of the left leg is greater than that of the right. Use a level of significance of .10.

b) Using a paired t procedure, test the hypothesis for the population of right-handed people that the mean circumference of the left arm is greater than that of the right. Use a level of significance of .10.

c) Using a paired t procedure, test the hypothesis for the population of left-handed people that the mean circumfer-

ence of the right leg is greater than that of the left. Use a level of significance of .10.

d) Using a paired t procedure, test the hypothesis for the population of left-handed people that the mean circumference of the right arm is greater than that of the left. Use a level of significance of .10.

e) Using a paired t procedure, test the hypothesis for the combined population of right- and left-handed people that the mean circumference of the opposite (left for right-handed, right for left-handed) leg is greater than that of the non-opposite leg. Use a level of significance of .10.

f) Using a paired t procedure, test the hypothesis for the combined population of right- and left-handed people that the mean circumference of the opposite (left for right-handed, right for left-handed) arm is greater than that of the non-opposite arm. Use a level of significance of .10.

9. In a class project, Patricia Reynolds states, "Percentage body fat (body composition) is a good way of assessing physical fitness and aids in determining optimal health. Body fat can be determined by such methods as hydrostatic weighing, skin-fold calipers and bioelectrical impedance analysis (BIA). BIA is a convenient, non-invasive and reliable method to assess body composition." Ms. Reynolds took 30 students in an experimental nutrition class and used BIA to measure their body fat both at the start of the quarter and, to see if any of the concepts of good nutrition learned in the class had any immediate effect, again at the end of the quarter (Data = BodyFat).

Pre	Post	Pre	Post
19	19	25	22
22	23	30	30
27	26	23	23
25	23	18	18
24	23	22	19
18	20	24	23
24	24	14	14
25	26	15	16
21	21	15	13
17	16	18	20
18	17	21	23
27	24	23	21
28	28	20	20
16	17	21	21
15	18	19	19

Test at a level of .10 the hypothesis that the mean percentage of body fat for the population of students in such an experimental nutrition class would go down.

10. The University of California, San Diego, maintains a "Social Sciences Data Collection" Web site at <u>SocSciDC</u> that includes the results of multiple Field (California) polls. Examine one of the poll results and construct a 95 percent confidence interval for the population percentage involved.

11. The *Home Office Research and Statistics Directorate UK* produces information on crime in the United Kingdom. Summary information over recent years by type of crime is given at <u>UKCrime</u>. Assuming the numbers on this page represent a sample of all crime in the U.K. test the hypothesis at the .05 level that there has been no change in the percentage of burglaries in the two most recent years.

 12. Use the World Wide Web to access DASL at <u>DASLMeth</u>. Click on *Two-sample t test* and select one of the stories.

a) Test the hypothesis of no difference between the two population means using a level of .05.

b) Construct a 95 percent confidence interval for the difference of the two population means.

13. Use the World Wide Web to access DASL at <u>DASLMeth</u>. Click on *Pooled t test* and select one of the stories.

a) Test the hypothesis of no difference between the two population means using a level of .01.

b) Construct a 99 percent confidence interval for the difference of the two population means.

 14. Use the World Wide Web to access DASL at <u>DASLMeth</u>. Click on *Paired t test* and select one of the stories.

a) Test the hypothesis that the population mean difference is zero using a level of .10.

b) Construct a 90 percent confidence interval for the population mean difference.

 15. Use the World Wide Web to access *WWW Virtual Library: Beer and Brewing* at <u>Beerbrew</u>. Click on *Beer Alcohol & Calories FAQ*. Take a random sample of ten regular beers and five light beers.

a) Test at a level of .05 the hypothesis that the population mean amount of alcohol of regular beer is greater than that of light beer.

b) Construct a 95 percent confidence interval for the mean difference in the amounts of alcohol in regular and light beer.

c) Test at a level of .05 the hypothesis that the population mean number of calories in regular beer is greater than that of light beer.

d) Construct a 95 percent confidence interval for the mean difference in the number of calories in regular and light beer.

 16. Use the World Wide Web to access *WWW Virtual Library: Agricultural Economics* at <u>AgriEcon</u>. Click on *Data on the Web*. There you will find links to many data sets. Find one or more that will allow you to answer the following questions. You may need to use an attribute variable to define your populations (e.g., gender, continent, type of organization, etc.).

a) Finding a data set with two or more populations sampled independently, test at a level of .10 the hypothesis that the means of a numerical variable for two of these populations are equal.

b) Finding a data set with two or more populations sampled dependently or in pairs, test at a level of .01 the hypothesis that the population mean difference of a numerical variable equals zero.

c) Finding a data set with two or more populations sampled independently, construct a 95 percent confidence interval for the difference in the percentages of an attribute variable for two of these populations.

 17. Use the World Wide Web to access *Statistics Canada* at <u>StCanada</u>. Click on your preferred language, then on *Canadian Statistics*. There you will find links to many data sets. Find one or more that will allow you to answer the following questions. You may need to use an attribute variable to define your populations (e.g., gender, continent, type of organization, etc.).

a) Finding a data set with two or more populations sampled independently, construct a 95 percent confidence interval for the difference in the means of a numerical variable for two of these populations.

b) Finding a data set with two or more populations sampled dependently or in pairs, construct a 99 percent confidence interval for the mean difference of a numerical variable for two populations sampled dependently.

c) Finding a data set with two or more populations sampled independently, test at a level of .10 the hypothesis that the percentages of an attribute variable for two of these populations are equal.

 18. Use the World Wide Web to access *The World Bank Group* home page at <u>WrldBank</u>. Click on *World Development Indicators* twice, then *Selected Tables*. You will find tables from the *World Development Indicators Book*. Find one or more that will allow you to answer the following questions. You may need to use an attribute variable to define your populations (e.g., gender, continent, type of organization, etc.).

a) Finding a data set with two or more populations sampled independently, test at a level of .05 the hypothesis that the means of a numerical variable for two of these populations are equal.

b) Finding a data set with two or more populations sampled dependently or in pairs, construct a 90 percent confidence interval for the mean difference of a numerical variable for two populations sampled dependently.

c) Finding a data set with two or more populations sampled independently, test at a level of .01 the hypothesis that the percentages of an attribute variable for two of these populations are equal.

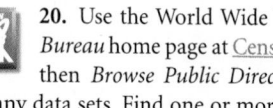 **19.** STAT-USA, an agency in the Economics and Statistics Administration, U.S. Department of Commerce, maintains a home page at STATUSA. From there, you can access many different data sets. Find one or more that will allow you to answer the following questions. You may need to use an attribute variable to define your populations (e.g., gender, continent, type of organization, etc.).

a) Finding a data set with two or more populations sampled independently, construct a 99 percent confidence interval for the difference in the means of a numerical variable for two of these populations.

b) Finding a data set with two or more populations sampled dependently or in pairs, test at a level of .05 the hypothesis that the population mean difference of a numerical variable equals zero.

c) Finding a data set with two or more populations sampled independently, construct a 90 percent confidence interval for the difference in the percentages of an attribute variable for two of these populations.

20. Use the World Wide Web to access the *U.S. Census Bureau* home page at CensusBu. Click on *Access Tools* and then *Browse Public Directories and Files.* You will find many data sets. Find one or more that will allow you to answer the following questions. You may need to use an attribute variable to define your populations (e.g., gender, continent, type of organization, etc.).

a) Finding a data set with two or more populations sampled independently, test at a level of .01 the hypothesis that the means of a numerical variable for two of these populations are equal.

b) Finding a data set with two or more populations sampled dependently or in pairs, test at a level of .10 the hypothesis that the population mean difference of a numerical variable equals zero.

c) Finding a data set with two or more populations sampled independently, construct a 95 percent confidence interval for the difference in the percentages of an attribute variable for two of these populations.

CHAPTER 10

Analysis of Variance

LOOKING AHEAD

You saw in Chapter 9 (and in Figure 9.4, page 336) that there are three hypothesis-testing procedures that may be used to see if there's likely to be a significant difference between the means of two independent populations. Now, in this chapter, you'll learn a testing technique called analysis of variance (often abbreviated ANOVA) that can be used, for example, to help a manager evaluate the performance of three (or more) employees to see if any performance level is different from the others. Using ANOVA techniques, a physical therapist can evaluate the results of four treatments for lower back problems to see if one or more is different from the others. And a marketing executive can see if there's a difference in sales productivity in the five company regions.

We'll first consider the assumptions and procedural steps associated with the ANOVA technique. Next, we'll present an example that uses the ANOVA testing procedure to arrive at a statistical decision. And finally, we'll see how computers can be used to make short work of the ANOVA testing process.

Thus, after studying this chapter, you should be able to

- Explain the purpose of analysis of variance and identify the assumptions that underlie the ANOVA technique.

- Describe the ANOVA hypothesis-testing procedure.

- Use the ANOVA testing procedure and the F distributions tables to arrive at statistical decisions about the means of three or more populations.

- Decide which means differ by using Fisher's least significant difference method.

10.1 Analysis of Variance: Purpose and Procedure

Purpose and Assumptions

Analysis of variance (ANOVA) is the name given to the approach that allows us to use sample data to see if the values of two or more unknown population means are likely to be different. If exactly two means are compared, the ANOVA procedure discussed in this chapter gives the same results obtained with the two-sample procedure for testing small samples that was outlined in Section 9.2, Procedure 4A, on page 357. Our purpose in this chapter, though, isn't to generate more two-sample tests. Rather, our focus now is to look at situations where the need is to compare three or more unknown population means.

An initial step is to define the terminology used. First, the **response** is the variable of interest to be measured in the experiment. We also refer to the response as the **dependent variable.** For example, the response might be the number of customers served, the lifetime of a battery pack, or the yield of a canola crop. The intent is usually to determine the effect of one or more variables (called independent variables) on the response. These variables, such as brand of battery, or type of fertilizer, are usually referred to as the factors in the experiment. **Factors** are the variables whose effect on the response is to be investigated. Factors may be quantitative (such as amount of fertilizer), or qualitative (such as brand of fertilizer). The **levels** of a factor are the values of the factors that are used in the experiment. For example, the levels of the brand of fertilizer might be A, B, C, or D and the levels of the amount of fertilizer might be 100, 105, or 110 kg/ha. The **treatments** of an experiment are the factor-level combinations used. When a *single factor* is used, the treatments are the levels of the factor. When two or more factors are used, such as brand of fertilizer, and amount of fertilizer, the treatments are the brand-amount combinations used. If the brand has four levels and the amount has three levels, then there are a total of $4 \times 3 = 12$ treatments.

In sections 10.1, 10.2 and 10.3, we'll consider experiments involving a single factor. Our focus, there, is on a one-way ANOVA test of means. In Section 10.4, we'll consider experiments involving two factors. Our focus there will be on two-way ANOVA tests.

As you've learned in earlier chapters, statistical techniques generally involve assumptions that must be valid if the techniques are to be correctly applied. In the case of analysis of variance, the *following assumptions must be true:*

1. The populations under study have *normal* distributions.

2. The samples are drawn *randomly,* and each sample is *independent* of the other samples.

3. The populations from which the sample values are obtained all have the same unknown population variance (σ^2). That is, this third assumption is

$$\sigma_1^2 = \sigma_2^2 = \sigma_3^2 = \cdots = \sigma_k^2$$

where k = number of populations.

These assumptions deserve some attention. The ANOVA procedures described in this chapter have been shown to produce reasonably reliable results even for approximately mound-shaped distributions. (If the samples are independent but the distributions are

very non-normal, we can use the Krushkal-Wallis test presented in Section 13-5 on page 602.) It has been shown that as long as the sample sizes are similar, the largest variance can be up to nine times the smallest, and the results of ANOVA will generally still be reliable.

The Procedural Steps for an ANOVA Test

As you certainly know by now, a hypothesis-testing procedure begins with a statement of the hypotheses to be tested, and it concludes when a statistical decision is made. The testing procedure for ANOVA is no different, and it follows seven familiar steps.

Step 1: State the Null and Alternative Hypotheses   The null hypothesis in analysis of variance is that the independent samples are drawn from different populations with the same mean. In other words, the null hypothesis is always

$H_0: \mu_1 = \mu_2 = \mu_3 = \cdots = \mu_k$. That is, H_0: All population means are equal.

where k = the number of populations under study

And the alternative hypothesis in any analysis of variance is

H_1: Not all population means are equal.

A careful reading of the alternative hypothesis shows that if H_0 is rejected in favour of H_1, you can conclude that at least one population mean differs from the other population means. But the analysis of variance test cannot tell you exactly how many population means differ, nor will it give you exact information about which means differ. For example, six populations could be under study, and if only one population mean differs from the other five means, which are equal, H_0 may be rejected in favour of the alternative hypothesis.

   But if H_0 is true and if the three assumptions listed previously are valid, the net effect is conceptually equal to the case where all the samples are picked from the one population shown in *Figure 10.1a*. But if H_0 turns out to be false and if the three assumptions still remain valid, the population means will not all be equal. In this event, the samples in an application might be taken from populations such as those shown in *Figure 10.1b*. Of course, these populations are still normally distributed, and they still have the same variance.

Step 2: Select the Level of Significance   A criterion for rejection of H_0 is necessary, and tests are typically made where α is specified to be .01 or .05.

Step 3: Determine the Test Distribution to Use   An F distribution is used in an ANOVA test. You'll recall that the properties and shapes of F distributions were introduced in Chapter 9 in the discussion of hypothesis tests of two variances. To summarize here, an F distribution is skewed to the right and has a scale starting at 0 and extending to the right. There are many F distributions, and each one is determined by the numerator and denominator degrees of freedom, which depend on the number of samples and the number of observations in the samples. The F distribution tables are found in Appendix 5.

If H_0 is true, we have

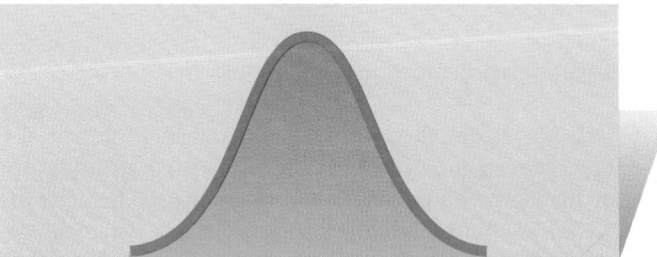

k number of normal populations with
$\mu_1 = \mu_2 = \mu_3 = \ldots = \mu_k$
$\sigma_1^2 = \sigma_2^2 = \sigma_3^2 = \ldots = \sigma_k^2$

(a)

If H_0 is not true, we may have

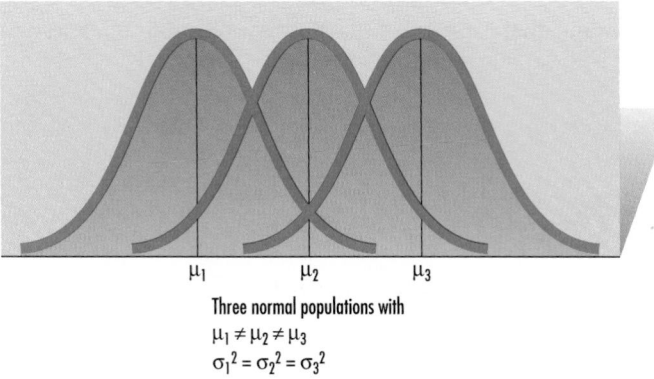

$\mu_1 \qquad \mu_2 \qquad \mu_3$

Three normal populations with
$\mu_1 \neq \mu_2 \neq \mu_3$
$\sigma_1^2 = \sigma_2^2 = \sigma_3^2$

(b)

FIGURE 10.1 (a) Illustrates several populations when H_0 is true. (b) Illustrates several populations when H_0 is not true.

Step 4: Define Rejection or Critical Region You may remember from Chapter 9 that to find the critical F value that is the boundary of the rejection area, we need to know three things:

1. The level of significance (specified in Step 2 in our procedure).

2. The degrees of freedom for the numerator (df_{num}) of the test statistic (F). The value of df_{num} is

$$df_{num} = k - 1 \qquad (10.1)$$

where $k =$ the number of samples

Thus, if we have taken random and independent samples from three populations, $df_{num} = 3 - 1$, or 2.

3. The degrees of freedom for the denominator (df_{den}) of the test statistic. The value of df_{den} is

$$df_{den} = T - k \qquad (10.2)$$

where T = the total number of items in all samples, or $n_1 + n_2 + n_3 + \cdots + n_k$
k = the number of samples

So if we have three samples with seven items in the first sample, nine in the second, and eight in the third, $df_{den} = (7 + 9 + 8) - 3 = 21$.

If we know that $\alpha = .05$, $df_{num} = 2$, and $df_{den} = 21$, then we can find the critical F value that starts the rejection region in an ANOVA test. In using the F tables in Appendix 5, we must first locate the table with the relevant α. (With $\alpha = .05$ here, it's the first table in that appendix.) Next, we must locate the critical value of F where the degrees of freedom for the numerator (found at the top of the columns) and the degrees of freedom for the denominator (shown to the left of the rows) intersect. In this example, the critical F value (where we've included subscripts to indicate the items needed to locate the critical value) is

$$F_{2,21,\alpha=.05} = 3.47$$

Thus, a test statistic with a value that exceeds 3.47 in this case falls into the rejection region.

Step 5: State the Decision Rule In a situation where $\alpha = .05$, $df_{num} = 2$, and $df_{den} = 21$, the decision rule is

Reject H_0 in favour of H_1 if $\mathbf{F} > 3.47$. Otherwise, fail to reject H_0.

Step 6: Compute the Test Statistic The test statistic (or F value) is found with this formula:

$$\mathbf{F} = \frac{\hat{\sigma}^2_{between}}{\hat{\sigma}^2_{within}} \qquad (10.3)$$

As you can see, the test statistic consists of two estimates of the population variance (σ^2). Two independent computational methods are used to produce these estimates. (We'll consider the $\hat{\sigma}^2_{within}$ estimate first, but, as you'll see later, it's not necessary for this value to be computed first in the ANOVA procedure.)

The $\hat{\sigma}^2_{within}$ estimate of σ^2 remains appropriate regardless of any differences between population means. In other words, the means of the several populations may differ, but this estimate of σ^2 isn't affected by the possible fact that H_0 is false. Although any one of the sample variances (s^2) could be used as this estimate of σ^2, the variances of all the samples are usually pooled and averaged to estimate σ^2 because of the greater amount of data thus considered. Therefore, in the ANOVA procedure, a variance from each sample is computed, and the sample variances are then pooled to produce a value for $\hat{\sigma}^2_{within}$. Any deviation of this estimate from the population variance is due to random error present in any sampling situation. (Keep that word *error* in mind—we'll refer to it later.) The formula for $\hat{\sigma}^2_{within}$ (regardless of whether the samples are of equal size or not) is

$$\hat{\sigma}^2_{within} = \frac{\sum d_1^2 + \sum d_2^2 + \sum d_3^2 + \cdots + \sum d_k^2}{T - k} \qquad (10.4)$$

where $\sum d_1^2 =$ the sum of the squared differences—that is, $\sum(x_1 - \bar{x}_1)^2$—for the first sample

$\sum d_2^2 =$ the sum of the squared differences—that is, $\sum(x_2 - \bar{x}_2)^2$—for the second sample, and so on

$T =$ total number of all items in all samples $(n_1 + n_2 + n_3 + \cdots + n_k)$

$k =$ number of samples

Since, as noted previously, the $\hat{\sigma}$ estimate isn't affected by the possible fact that H_0 is false, this computed value cannot, by itself, be used to test the validity of H_0. As you've seen in the test statistic formula, a second element—$\hat{\sigma}^2_{between}$—is also needed.

The second method used to estimate σ^2—the $\hat{\sigma}^2_{between}$ procedure—results in an appropriate estimate of σ^2 if, and only if, the population means are equal. This approach produces an estimate that contains the effects of any differences between the population means. If there are no differences between means, this computed estimate of σ^2 shouldn't differ too much from $\hat{\sigma}^2_{within}$ (which is now used as a standard against which this second estimate is evaluated). This $\hat{\sigma}^2_{between}$ method of estimating σ^2 is based on the variation between the sample means and is founded on the Central Limit Theorem.

If the null hypothesis is true, then, as we saw in *Figure 10.1a*, it's as though all the samples are selected from the same normal population distribution with the same μ. And as we saw in Chapter 6, and as the Central Limit Theorem tells us, if the population is normally distributed, the distribution of the sample means is also normal. Furthermore, you'll remember that the standard deviation of this sampling distribution—the standard error of the sample means—is found by this basic formula:

$$\sigma_{\bar{x}} = \frac{\sigma}{\sqrt{n}}$$

Now, if we square both sides of this basic equation, we get

$$\sigma_{\bar{x}}^2 = \frac{\sigma^2}{n}$$

which can be manipulated by multiplying both sides by n to yield the population variance

$$n\sigma_{\bar{x}}^2 = \sigma^2$$

Thus, if we knew the square of the standard error ($\sigma_{\bar{x}}^2$), we could compute the precise value of σ^2 merely by multiplying $\sigma_{\bar{x}}^2$ by the sample size.

Without going into further details, we can simply summarize here and supply the formulas needed to effectively (1) compute an estimate of the square of the standard error ($\hat{\sigma}_{\bar{x}}^2$) and (2) multiply this estimate by the sample size to effect an estimate of σ^2. This second way to estimate σ^2 produces a value for $\hat{\sigma}^2_{between}$. This estimate of σ^2 has merit if (and only if) H_0 is true. If H_0 is false, this estimates a quantity that is larger than σ^2 that is based on factor differences among the samples (keep that word *factor* in mind, too, because we'll also get back to it later).

There are two formulas needed to compute a value for $\hat{\sigma}^2_{\text{between}}$. First, a **grand mean** $(\overline{\overline{X}})$—the mean of all the values in all the samples—is required:

$$\overline{\overline{X}} = \frac{\text{total of all sample items}}{\text{number of items from all samples}} = \frac{n_1\overline{x}_1 + n_2\overline{x}_2 + \cdots + n_k\overline{x}_k}{n_1 + n_2 + \cdots + n_k} \qquad (10.5)$$

where n_1 = number of items in sample 1
n_2 = number of items in sample 2
n_k = number of items in sample k
$\overline{x}_1$ = mean of sample 1
$\overline{x}_2$ = mean of sample 2
$\overline{x}_k$ = mean of sample k

And then we can produce $\hat{\sigma}^2_{\text{between}}$ with this formula:

$$\hat{\sigma}^2_{\text{between}} = \frac{n_1(\overline{x}_1 - \overline{\overline{X}})^2 + n_2(\overline{x}_2 - \overline{\overline{X}})^2 + \cdots + n_k(\overline{x}_k - \overline{\overline{X}})^2}{k - 1} \qquad (10.6)$$

where k = number of samples

In summary, then, if H_0 is true, the $\hat{\sigma}^2_{\text{between}}$ value should be a good estimate of the population variance, and it should be approximately the same as the $\hat{\sigma}^2_{\text{within}}$ value. Ideally, of course, if H_0 is true, then

$$F = \frac{\hat{\sigma}^2_{\text{between}}}{\hat{\sigma}^2_{\text{within}}} = 1.00$$

But we know that sampling variation makes this an unlikely result, even when H_0 is true. Should there be a significant difference between $\hat{\sigma}^2_{\text{within}}$ and $\hat{\sigma}^2_{\text{between}}$, however, it may be concluded that this difference is the result of at least one difference between the population means.

Step 7: Make the Statistical Decision   If, as noted previously in our decision-rule step, we have a critical F value of 3.47 and if our two computed estimates of σ^2 yield similar values that produce a test statistic that is > 3.47, then we will reject the null hypothesis that the means of the three populations sampled are equal. Otherwise, we will fail to reject the null hypothesis.

Self-Testing Review 10.1

1. What necessary assumptions must be met for an analysis of variance test to be valid?

2. What are the null and alternative hypotheses in any ANOVA test

3. Discuss the concepts of $\hat{\sigma}^2_{\text{within}}$ and $\hat{\sigma}^2_{\text{between}}$. How is each computed? Which is a pooled variance?

4. What is the grand mean $(\overline{\overline{X}})$? How can it be computed?

5. Which measure—$\hat{\sigma}^2_{\text{within}}$ or $\hat{\sigma}^2_{\text{between}}$—is an estimate of σ^2 if (and only if) the null hypothesis is true?

6. Why is an ANOVA test always a right-tailed test?

7. How is the critical region determined in an ANOVA test? What do you need to know before finding the critical F value?

8. Find the critical F value for an ANOVA test if $\alpha = .01$ and if there are 6 samples with a total of 35 items in all of the samples.

9. Find the critical F value for an ANOVA test if $\alpha = .05$ and if there are 4 samples with a total of 44 items in all of the samples.

10. Find the critical F value for an ANOVA test if $\alpha = .01$ and if there are 3 samples with a total of 29 items in all of the samples.

11. What is F if $\hat{\sigma}^2_{\text{between}} = 35.7$ and $\hat{\sigma}^2_{\text{within}} = 14.6$?

12. What is F if $\hat{\sigma}^2_{\text{between}} = 215.23$ and $\hat{\sigma}^2_{\text{within}} = 73.81$?

13. The following are true/false questions:

   a) When the null hypothesis is rejected, it may be concluded that no two population means are equal.

   b) If the null hypothesis is true, $\hat{\sigma}^2_{\text{between}}$ must equal $\hat{\sigma}^2_{\text{within}}$.

   c) The $\hat{\sigma}^2_{\text{between}}$ value is used as a pooled variance.

10.2 An ANOVA Example

☐ **Example 10.1**   Callie Fisk, vice president of the Nickel and Dime Savings Bank, is reviewing employee performance for possible salary increases. In evaluating tellers, Callie decides that an important performance criterion is the number of customers served each day. She expects that each teller should handle approximately the same number of customers daily. Otherwise, each teller should be rewarded or penalized accordingly. How does Callie compare the tellers?

◆ **Solution:**

For each teller, Callie randomly selects six business days when the teller is stationed at the window nearest the entrance. Customer traffic for each teller during these days is recorded. The variable of interest, then, is the number of customers served, while the factor that might affect this variable is the teller involved. The sample (or teller) data follow:

Customer Traffic Data		
Teller 1 **Ms. Munny**	**Teller 2** **Mr. Coyne**	**Teller 3** **Mr. Sentz**
45	55	54
56	50	61
47	53	54
51	59	58
50	58	52
45	49	51

The null hypothesis *(Step 1)* is that the three tellers each serve the same average number of customers per day. That is, Ms. Munny, Mr. Coyne, and Mr. Sentz are assumed to have the same workload, Thus,

$H_0: \mu_1 = \mu_2 = \mu_3$, or H_0: All population means are equal

The alternative hypothesis is that not all the tellers are handling the same average number of customers per day. That is, at least one of the tellers is performing much better than the others, or, perhaps, at least one of the tellers is not performing up to the standards of the others. Thus,

H_1: Not all the population means are equal

Let's assume Callie believes that there should be at most a 5 percent chance of erroneously rejecting a true H_0. Thus, she specifies a level of significance of .05 *(Step 2)*.

Callie knows, of course, to use an F distribution in her test *(Step 3)*, and her next step is to define the rejection or critical region. The df_{num} value is $k - 1$, or $3 - 1$, or 2, and the df_{den} value is $T - k$, or $18 - 3$, or 15. So, with $\alpha = .05$, $df_{num} = 2$, and $df_{den} = 15$, the critical F value in this ANOVA test is $F_{2,15,\alpha=.05} = 3.68$ *(Step 4)*.

The decision rule *(Step 5)* is

Reject H_0 in favour of H_1 if $F > 3.68$. Otherwise, fail to reject H_0.

The next step *(Step 6)* is to compute the test statistic. Since the formula for the test statistic (F value) is

$$F = \frac{\hat{\sigma}^2_{between}}{\hat{\sigma}^2_{within}}$$

we (and Callie) must first calculate the numerator and denominator values for this formula.

The following procedure is carried out to compute $\hat{\sigma}^2_{between}$ (the numerator of F).

1. A mean is computed from the sample data for each teller. The sample means are shown in Table 10.1 and have been designated $\bar{x}_1$, $\bar{x}_2$, and $\bar{x}_3$ for tellers 1, 2, and 3, respectively.

2. The grand mean is computed next:

$$\bar{\bar{X}} = \frac{n_1\bar{x}_1 + n_2\bar{x}_2 + \cdots + n_k\bar{x}_k}{n_1 + n_2 + \cdots + n_k} = \frac{6(49) + 6(54) + 6(55)}{6 + 6 + 6} = \frac{948}{18} = 52.67$$

3. After these easy steps, we are now ready to determine the value of $\hat{\sigma}^2_{between}$:

$$\hat{\sigma}^2_{between} = \frac{n_1(\bar{x}_1 - \bar{\bar{X}})^2 + n_2(\bar{x}_2 - \bar{\bar{X}})^2 + n_3(\bar{x}_3 - \bar{\bar{X}})^2}{k - 1}$$

$$= \frac{6(49 - 52.67)^2 + 6(54 - 52.67)^2 + 6(55 - 52.67)^2}{3 - 1}$$

$$= \frac{6(13.469) + 6(1.769) + 6(5.429)}{2} = \frac{124.00}{2} = 62.0$$

TABLE 10.1   DATA USED IN COMPUTING $\hat{\sigma}^2_{between}$

	Customer Traffic Data		
Day	Teller 1 Ms. Munny	Teller 2 Mr. Coyne	Teller 3 Mr. Sentz
1	45	55	54
2	56	50	61
3	47	53	54
4	51	59	58
5	50	58	52
6	45	49	51
Total	294	324	330
	$\bar{x}_1 = 49$	$\bar{x}_2 = 54$	$\bar{x}_3 = 55$

$$\bar{\bar{X}} = \frac{n_1\bar{x}_1 + n_2\bar{x}_2 + \cdots + n_k\bar{x}_k}{n_1 + n_2 + \cdots + n_k} = \frac{6(49) + 6(54) + 6(55)}{6 + 6 + 6} = \frac{948}{18} = 52.67$$

$$\begin{aligned}\hat{\sigma}^2_{between} &= \frac{n_1(\bar{x}_1 - \bar{\bar{X}})^2 + n_2(\bar{x}_2 - \bar{\bar{X}})^2 + n_3(\bar{x}_3 - \bar{\bar{X}})^2}{k - 1}\\[4pt] &= \frac{6(49 - 52.67)^2 + 6(54 - 52.67)^2 + 6(55 - 52.67)^2}{3 - 1}\\[4pt] &= \frac{6(13.469) + 6(1.769) + 6(5.429)}{2} = \frac{124.00}{2} = 62.0\end{aligned}$$

We can see that the total computed by using the squared differences of the sample means about $\bar{\bar{X}}$ is 124.00. This total of 124 is often called a *sum of squares between value,* as we'll see later. The computed value for $\hat{\sigma}^2_{between}$ is 62.0, and this figure is often called a *mean squares between* that's based on the factor being considered. This 62.0 value is an appropriate estimate of σ^2 *if, and only if,* the null hypothesis is true.

The procedure for computing $\hat{\sigma}^2_{between}$ by focusing on the variance between sample means is summarized in *Figure 10.2.*

We now have a value for $\hat{\sigma}^2_{between}$, the numerator of our test statistic, but we still need to find the denominator, $\hat{\sigma}^2_{within}$. The following procedure is carried out to compute $\hat{\sigma}^2_{within}$:

1. For *each sample,* we compute the *deviation* between each value within the sample and the mean of that sample—that is, compute $x - \bar{x}$ for every value in each sample. Table 10.2 shows the deviation computations for each teller. For teller 1, Ms. Munny, the average customer traffic ($\bar{x}_1$) is 49. Thus, the deviation for day 1 is $45 - 49$, or -4; the deviation for day 2 is $56 - 49 = 7$; and so forth.

2. After the deviation of each observation from its sample mean is computed, each deviation is squared—that is, $(x - \bar{x})^2$. These squared deviations are summed—$\sum(x - \bar{x})^2$—and the sums are labelled $\sum d^2$. That is, $\sum(x - \bar{x})^2 = \sum d^2$. For tellers 1, 2, and 3, the sums of the squared deviations are 90, 84, and 72, respectively. (Alternative Calculation: Since the variance of a sample is $s^2 = \dfrac{\sum d^2}{n - 1}$, we have $\sum d^2 = (n - 1)s^2$.

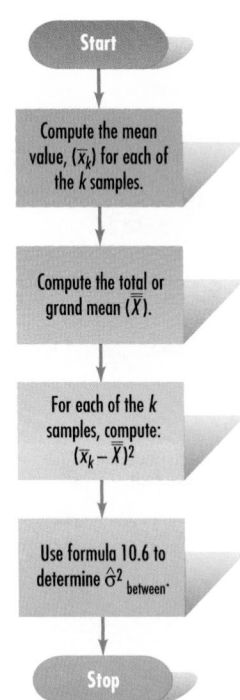

FIGURE 10.2 Procedure for the computation of $\hat{\sigma}^2_{between}$ (the "MS factor").

TABLE 10.2   DATA USED IN COMPUTING $\hat{\sigma}^2_{within}$

	Teller 1 Ms. Munny			Teller 2 Mr. Coyne			Teller 3 Mr Sentz		
Day	x_1	$x_1 - \bar{x}_1$	$(x_1 - \bar{x}_1)^2$	x_2	$x_2 - \bar{x}_2$	$(x_2 - \bar{x}_2)^2$	x_3	$x_3 - \bar{x}_3$	$(x_3 - \bar{x}_3)^2$
1	45	−4	16	55	1	1	54	−1	1
2	56	7	49	50	−4	16	61	6	36
3	47	−2	4	53	−1	1	54	−1	1
4	51	2	4	59	5	25	58	3	9
5	50	1	1	58	4	16	52	−3	9
6	45	−4	16	49	−5	25	51	−4	16
	294		$\Sigma d_1^2 = 90$	324		$\Sigma d_2^2 = 84$	330		$\Sigma d_3^2 = 72$
	$\bar{x}_1 = 49$			$\bar{x}_2 = 54$			$\bar{x}_3 = 55$		

$$\hat{\sigma}^2_{within} \quad \frac{90 + 84 + 72}{18 - 3} = \frac{246}{15} = 16.4$$

Using a calculator, we could first compute $s_1^2 = 18$, $s_2^2 = 16.8$, and $s_3^2 = 14.4$. Then $\Sigma d_1^2 = 5(18) = 90$, $\Sigma d_2^2 = 5(16.8) = 84$, and $\Sigma d_3^2 = 5(14.4) = 72$.) This total of 246 is also often called a *sum of squares within value,* as we'll see later.

3. The sum of squares figure of 246 is then divided by the quantity $T - k$, where T is the total number of sample items, or 18 in this example, and k is the number of samples (3). Thus, $T - k = 15$.

Finally, as you can see in Table 10.2, $\hat{\sigma}^2_{within}$ is conveniently computed as follows, using formula 10.4:

$$\hat{\sigma}^2_{within} = \frac{\Sigma d_1^2 + \Sigma d_2^2 + \Sigma d_3^2}{T - k} = \frac{90 + 84 + 72}{18 - 3} = \frac{246}{15} = 16.4$$

This estimate of σ^2 is also referred to as a *mean squares within,* and any deviation of this value from the true σ^2 is due to random error. *Figure 10.3* summarizes the procedure used to compute $\hat{\sigma}^2_{within}$.

Now that we've computed $\hat{\sigma}^2_{between}$ and $\hat{\sigma}^2_{within}$, we're ready to form a ratio of two population variance estimates and calculate the test statistic as follows:

$$F = \frac{\hat{\sigma}^2_{between}}{\hat{\sigma}^2_{within}} = \frac{62.0}{16.4} = 3.78$$

The final step now is to make the statistical decision *(Step 7)*. Since the **F** = 3.78 and since the critical table value = 3.68, Callie should conclude that H_0 is unlikely and decide in favour of the alternative hypothesis. At least one of the tellers among Munny, Coyne, and Sentz is likely to be handling more or fewer customers than the others. Additional analysis is needed to precisely define the nature of the difference in work performance. We will demonstrate how to do this in the next section with the help of the computer. ◆

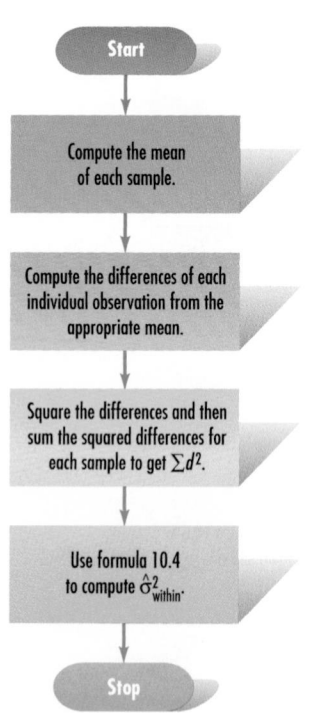

FIGURE 10.3 Procedure for the computation of $\hat{\sigma}^2_{within}$ (the "MS error").

Self-Testing Review 10.2

For all the exercises in this section, assume the populations involved are normally distributed with equal variances.

14. Language comprehension appears to decline with advancing age. A study in *Applied Psycholinguistics* sought to determine which factors contribute significantly to comprehension difficulty. A randomly selected group of paid volunteers was recruited through advertising in local newspapers, and these people agreed to have their hearing tested. The following data represent the pure-tone average (in db HTL) for the subjects who were separated into different age groups (30s, 50s, 60s, and 70s). Test the hypothesis at the .05 level that the population mean hearing level is the same for all age groups (Data = Hearing).

Thirties	Fifties	Sixties	Seventies
9	9	19	18
13	5	8	22
5	8	14	24
5	3	26	
10	15		

15. After taking an introductory class in statistics, students were asked a series of questions to determine their opinions on the quality of the class, where a high score indicated that the students thought the class was worthwhile. This particular class included only forestry, ecology, and water resources majors. The following data represent a sample of responses from each of the three majors (Data = TestOpin):

Forestry Resources	Ecology	Water
11	10	3
9	4	6
19	0	2
18	13	9
8	18	1
	14	7
		2
		5

Test the hypothesis at the .05 level that the population mean responses for the three majors are equal.

16. A career counsellor claims that there is no difference in career decision-making skills among students in various school districts. A test to determine career decision-making skills is given to random samples of people in three different districts. The results of this test are shown below. Test the counsellor's claim at the .01 level (Data = CareerSk).

District 1	District 2	District 3
17	12	13
9	10	14
13	15	14
16	13	15
12		15
		14

STATISTICS IN ACTION

Full Moon Madness?

Q. My sister is an emergency room nurse and is convinced that the full moon has an influence on people. Do you think that's true?

—Anonymous

A. The word "lunatic" comes from "lunar," which means "of or relating to the moon." One study found that 80 percent of emergency room nurses and 64 percent of physicians believe the moon affects their patients. However, studies designed to confirm this widespread conviction don't necessarily support it. When researchers at a mental health centre tracked psychiatric hospital admissions in search of a lunar effect, they found only a tiny insignificant blip when the moon was full (DrWeil.com, 18 April 2000).

17. A large accounting firm wants to see if the accuracy of its employees is related to the school from which the employees graduated. Seven accountants representing four schools were randomly selected, and the number of errors committed by each accountant over a two-week period was recorded as follows (Data = AcctgErr):

School A	School B	School C	School D
14	17	19	23
16	16	20	12
17	18	22	21
13	15	21	10
22	16	18	9
9	12	19	15
10	14	15	16

Conduct an ANOVA test at the .01 level. Is there a significant difference in accuracy?

18. A track coach has learned of two new training techniques that are designed to reduce the time required to run a mile. Three random samples of runners have been selected for the experiment: Group A trained under the old approach, group B under one of the new techniques, and group C under the other new technique. After a month of training, each runner was timed in a mile run. The data are as follows (times in minutes) (Data = MileRun):

Group A	Group B	Group C
4.81	4.43	4.38
4.62	4.50	4.29
5.02	4.32	4.33
4.65	4.37	4.36
	4.41	

Conduct an ANOVA test at the .05 level to see if the population mean times for all those using the three methods are equal.

19. Ms. Anne Breen, a first-year middle-school teacher, claims that television-viewing habits are the same for all students in the different middle-school grades. She questioned a random sample of middle-school students about how many minutes they watch TV each day after school until bedtime, and produced the following data (Data = TVGrades):

Sixth Grade	Seventh Grade	Eighth Grade
459	115	272
311	153	88
152	201	374
293	30	178

Test Ms. Breen's claim at the .05 level.

20. The Tackey Toy Company plans to install special battery packs in its new line of Tackey robots. Three suppliers can produce packs with equal prices that meet Tackey's needs. But

Tackey managers want to examine the data on the life expectancy of each brand before selecting a supplier. A random sample of five battery packs is selected from each vendor, and the useful life of each battery pack (in hours) is determined. Use the following data to make a statistical decision at the .05 level. Is there a significant difference in the population life expectancy of the different brands of battery packs (Data = Tackpack)?

Lifelong	Neverstop	Everrun
144	168	184
136	150	172
146	142	168
134	166	187
150	136	176

21. The director of information systems for an insurance claim centre is trying to select the best computer-sorting algorithms for handling new claims. The output that follows resulted from an experiment in which 6 sorting algorithms were used to sort 24 sets of 20,000 random records. Each algorithm was used four times and the completion times were recorded for each run.

Trideck	Quick	Meld	Bubble	Hande	Dorf
720	551	534	498	853	390
543	543	876	476	468	378
664	468	762	399	587	534
542	345	640	367	666	289

At the .01 level, is there a significant difference in the mean completion times for the six sorting algorithms (Data = Sorting)?

22. A large retailer must make a choice between three sales locations in a shopping mall. The retailer wants to see if the mean daily traffic count is the same for all locations. Unable to be at three places at the same time, she selects 21 weekdays and randomly chooses 7 days for each location to station herself and count the daily traffic. The following data are the result:

Location 1	Location 2	Location 3
643	249	458
542	404	513
537	564	475
484	745	536
464	353	364
369	647	738
478	351	594

At the .05 level, is there a significant difference in the population mean traffic count at the three locations (Data = MallLoc)?

23. For a class project, six students prepared popcorn in a similar fashion using identical amounts of three oils. Afterwards, they counted the number of unpopped kernels, with the results as follow (Data = Popcorn):

Vegetable	Canola	Safflower
336	544	381
453	577	404
468	498	504
516	631	428

At the .05 level, is there a significant difference in the mean number of unpopped kernels?

24. A major distributor of cameras suspects that consumers are insensitive to price changes for the highest-quality camera. To test this suspicion, 16 retail outlets are randomly divided into groups of 4 and asked to sell the camera at 1 of 4 predetermined prices. The number of cameras sold in a week are as follows (Data = PriceCam):

Price 1	Price 2	Price 3	Price 4
3	5	10	8
5	4	9	4
7	6	4	5
4	7	5	7

What conclusions can be made about the population mean selling price at the .05 level of significance?

10.3 The One-Way ANOVA Table and Computers to the Rescue

The One-Way ANOVA Table

It's often desirable to place the computations of the last several pages in a **one-way ANOVA table**—a summary listing of the values needed to produce an ANOVA test. Table 10.3 shows the general format of this type of ANOVA table. The first column lists the source, or type, of variation. As we've seen, this variation is measured between samples—the **factor variation**—and within samples—the **error variation.** (The word *treatment* is often substituted for the word *factor* because many ANOVA techniques originated in agricultural research where the concern was with the different treatments—for example, different fertilizers or seeds—that could be applied to the soil.) Column 2 in Table 10.3 shows the degrees of freedom associated with each source of variation (the df values we've computed earlier).

Column 3 in Table 10.3 records the sum of squares (SS) figures computed during our $\hat{\sigma}^2_{between}$ and $\hat{\sigma}^2_{within}$ calculations. (You'll remember that these terms were mentioned earlier.) The fourth column is labelled **mean of squares (MS)**—the designation in an

TABLE 10.3   THE FORMAT OF A GENERAL ONE-WAY ANOVA TABLE

Source of Variation	Degrees of Freedom (df)	Sum of Squares (SS)	Mean of Squares (MS)	Computed F Value (F)
Between samples (factor variation)	$k - 1$	SS between (SSB) or SS factor	$\hat{\sigma}^2_{between}$ (MS factor)	$\dfrac{\hat{\sigma}^2_{between}}{\hat{\sigma}^2_{within}}$
Within samples (error variation)	$T - k$	SS within (SSW) or SS error	$\hat{\sigma}^2_{within}$ (MS error)	
Total	$T - 1$	SSB + SSW		

ANOVA table for our computed values of $\hat{\sigma}^2_{between}$ and $\hat{\sigma}^2_{within}$. The $\hat{\sigma}^2_{between}$ value is often called **MS factor** (or **MS treatment**), and the $\hat{\sigma}^2_{within}$ value is often referred to as **MS error.** Finally, column 5 presents the computed F value (**F**) which, we've seen, is $\hat{\sigma}^2_{between}/\hat{\sigma}^2_{within}$ (or MS factor/MS error).

Computers to the Rescue

The MINITAB statistical package makes short work of the procedures we've considered in this chapter. Additionally, it provides us with a method, if the null hypothesis of equal population means is rejected, of deciding which pairs of means are different. This is known as Fisher's procedure and will be discussed in the next few examples.

Example 10.2   Redo the hypothesis test of the bank teller example using MINITAB.

◆ **Solution:**

MINITAB was used to generate the output in *Figure 10.4*. In *Figure 10.4a*, we have an ANOVA table for our three tellers. In the column labelled **F**, we find the previously calculated value of the test statistic, **F** = 3.78. Even better, just to the right in the column labelled *P*, we find that the *p*-value of the test statistic is .047. Using the *p*-value approach to hypothesis testing, the decision rule is to reject H_0 in favour of H_1 if the *p*-value $< \alpha$. Otherwise, we fail to reject H_0. Since the *p*-value of .047 is less than .05, we know to reject the null hypothesis at the 5 percent level of significance, agreeing with the result in Example 10.1. ◆

A set of 95 percent confidence intervals for individual population means are produced below the ANOVA table. While these might be informative about the individual means considered one at a time, they really don't allow us to figure out which pairs of means are significantly different. And when the F test is significant, indicating that at least one of the means is different from the rest, we certainly would like to be able to answer the question, Which means are different? We can use Fisher's procedure, sometimes called Fisher's least significant difference or Fisher's LSD to address that question.

FIGURE 10.4 (a) To obtain the ANOVA table, click on **Stat, ANOVA, One-way,** enter the column of data in the box next to **Response,** and enter a column with the names of the tellers in the box next to **Factor.** (b) To obtain Fisher's comparisons, in the **ANOVA** window, click on **Comparisons,** check on **Fisher's** procedure with the selected level of significance, and click **OK** twice.

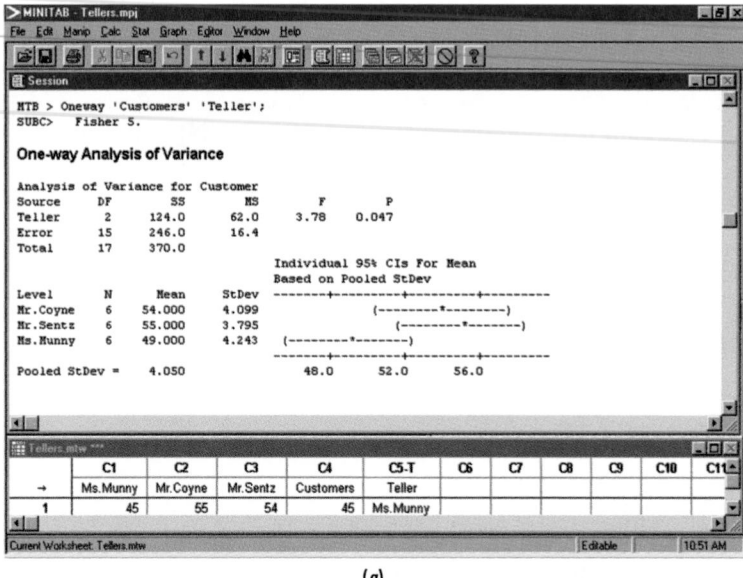

(a)

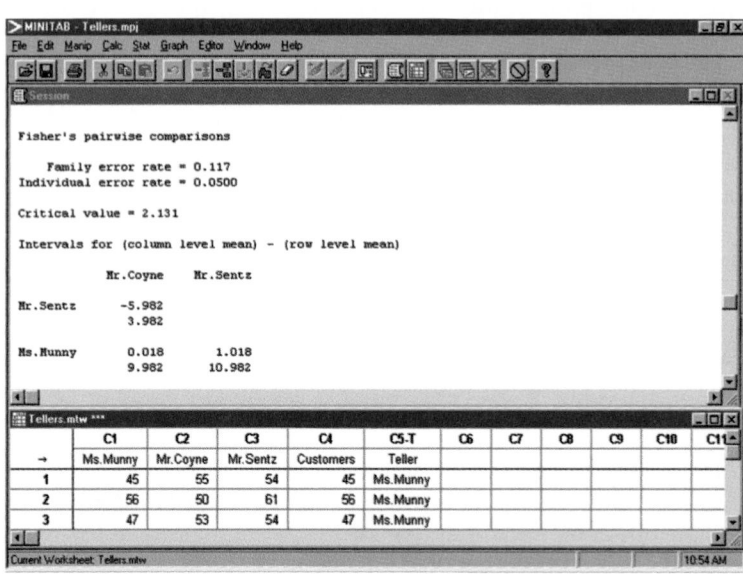

(b)

Example 10.3   Use Fisher's procedure to decide which pairs of bank tellers handle a different number of mean clients per day.

◆ **Solution:**

The results of Fisher's procedure are on the MINITAB output of *Figure 10.4b.* Under the heading *Intervals for (column level mean)—(row level mean),* there are confidence intervals for the difference between every pair of population means. For example, under the column heading of *Mr. Sentz* and the row heading of *Ms. Munny,* we have a 95 percent confidence interval for the difference in the population mean for Mr. Sentz less the population mean for Ms. Munny, namely, between 1.018 and 10.982 clients per day. Let's look at that confidence interval. Because the interval's limits are both positive, there is a strong indication that the difference is positive. Believing that the difference is positive, we would say that the mean number of clients handled by Mr. Sentz is greater than the mean number of clients handled by Ms. Munny. If the confidence interval's limits had both been negative, we would again have decided there was a significant difference in the means, except now we would decide that Ms. Munny handled a greater mean number of clients. However, if the lower limit is negative and the upper limit positive, then 0 is in the interval, indicating it is possible that there is no difference in the mean number of clients the two tellers handle. In this case, we would conclude that there is insufficient evidence to show a difference between the two population means. Again referring to *Figure 10.4b*, we see that both confidence intervals involving Ms. Munny consist only of positive values. In both of these intervals, it is Ms. Munny's mean that is being subtracted from the other teller's mean; this indicates that her mean is significantly lower than the mean for either of the other two tellers. However, the confidence interval for the difference between Mr. Coyne and Mr. Sentz, going from a negative to positive limit, indicates that there is insufficient evidence to demonstrate a significant difference between these two tellers. In summary, we would decide that the average number of customers per day that Ms. Munny handles is less than either Mr. Coyne or Mr. Sentz, but there is little evidence of a difference between Mr. Coyne and Mr. Sentz. ◆

Congratulations! You've just about made it through a rather detailed section. Let's finish with two more brief examples.

Example 10.4 The Real Thing Weighs More?
Twenty-four cans of cola—six Coke, six Diet Coke, six Pepsi, and six Diet Pepsi—were studied. The contents of each can of cola were emptied into a clean chemistry beaker (which was weighed prior to each measurement to obtain a fair weight) and weighed on a digital scale with weight measured to the nearest hundredth of a gram. Analyze the data using a level of significance of .05 throughout (Data = Cola).

Coke	Pepsi	Diet Coke	Diet Pepsi
367.78	362.10	351.17	354.42
367.43	365.55	355.21	357.37
368.87	372.77	352.47	352.73
369.82	365.47	353.61	349.46
368.85	378.23	352.70	355.28
370.32	367.71	354.53	355.91

◆ **Solution:**

Using MINITAB and a TI-83 calculator to do the computations, we obtain the output in *Figures 10.5a* and *b* the TI-83 screens of *Figure 10.5c*. The p-value of .000 found in *Figure 10.5a* and screen 1 of *Figure 10.5c* is strong evidence that we should not reject H_0 in favour of H_1 at the 5 percent level of significance. Examining Fisher's pairwise comparisons of *Figure 10.5b*, the two confidence intervals that have positive limits indicate that the mean weight of the cans of Coke is significantly greater than the mean weight of the cans of Diet Coke and of Diet Pepsi. The two confidence intervals that have negative limits indicate that the mean weight of the cans of Pepsi is also significantly greater than the mean weight of the cans of Diet Coke and of Diet Pepsi. This makes sense. A 12-ounce can is supposed to contain 355 ml. And 355 ml of pure water should weigh 355 g. Diet cola

FIGURE 10.5 (a)(b) MINITAB ANOVA output for the cola data. (c) To perform the ANOVA on the TI-83, first put the data into lists. In this example, we use L1 for Coke, L2 for Pepsi, L3 for Diet Coke, L4 for Diet Pepsi. Access the **ANOVA** command from the **STAT**>**TESTS** menu. (It is choice F.) Then paste the command on the home screen and enter the lists separated by commas: ANOVA (L1,L2,L3,L4). Press **ENTER** to get the results shown in screens 1 and 2. Confidence intervals could be calculated for the individual means using the **TInterval** command from Chapter 7. To match the MINITAB intervals, use the pooled standard deviation, Sxp.

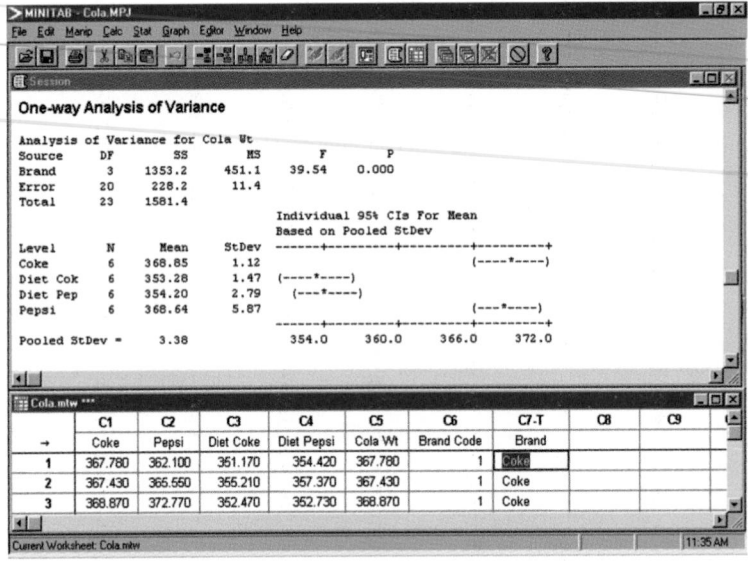

(a)

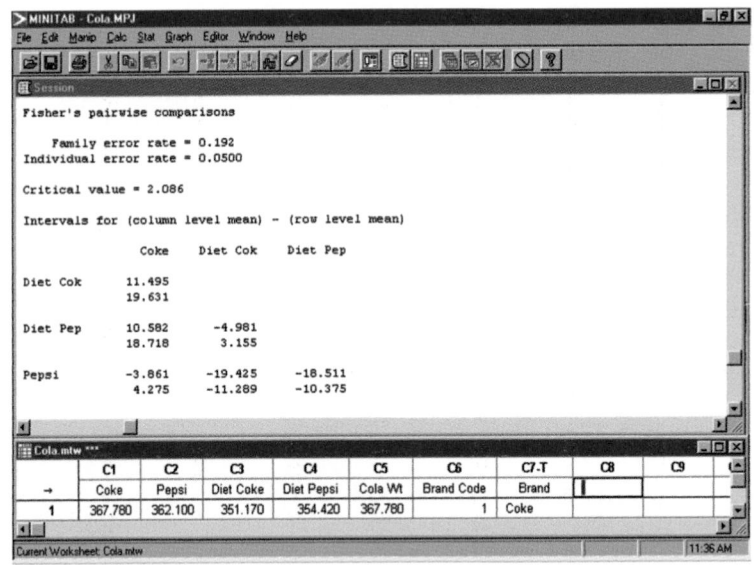

(b)

```
One-way ANOVA          One-way ANOVA
 F=39.5371331         ↑ MS=451.076911
 p=1.3489173E-8        Error
 Factor                 df=20
  df=3                  SS=228.178867
  SS=1353.23073         MS=11.4089433
↓ MS=451.076911         Sxp=3.37771274
```

Screen 1   Screen 2

(c)

has a specific gravity similar to water and so should weigh 355 g. Regular cola contains dissolved sugar and hence weighs more. This is a physical explanation for what turns out to be a statistically significant difference. ◆

Example 10.5 As a class project, Ryan gathered the following data on the total gross incomes for samples of movies in the years 2000, 2001, and 2002. At the .01 level of significance, is there any significant difference in the mean gross income in the three years (Data = Moviesgross)?

2000 Movies	Total Gross
Cast Away	233.57
Crouching Tiger, Hidden Dragon	128.027
Dinosaur	137.7
Dr. Seuss' How the Grinch Stole Christmas	260.031
Erin Brockovich	125.549
Gladiator	187.671
Meet the Parents	166.225
Mission: Impossible 2	215.345
Scary Movie	156.997
The Perfect Storm	182.595
What Lies Beneath	155.37
What Women Want	182.737
X-Men	157.3

2001 Movies	Total Gross	2002 Movies	Total Gross
A Beautiful Mind	170.709	Austin Powers in Goldmember	213.079
American Pie 2	145.065	Die Another Day	153.761
Black Hawk Down	108.585	Harry Potter and the	
Dr. Dolittle 2	112.891	Chamber of Secrets	252.098
Hannibal	164.978	Ice Age	176.233
Harry Potter and the		Lilo & Stitch	145.772
Sorcerer's Stone	317.558	Men in Black II	190.419
Jurassic Park III	181.166	Minority Report	131.976
Lara Croft: Tomb Raider	131.144	My Big Fat Greek Wedding	227.899
Monsters, Inc.	255.746	Scooby-Doo	153.244
Ocean's Eleven	183.349	Signs	227.746
Pearl Harbor	198.474	Spider-Man	403.706
Planet of the Apes	179.996	Star Wars: Episode II—	
Rush Hour 2	226.138	Attack of the Clones	310.302
Shrek	267.652	The Lord of the Rings:	
Spy Kids	112.692	The Two Towers	261.032
The Fast and the Furious	144.512	The Santa Clause 2	138.278
The Lord of the Rings:		XXX	141.204
The Fellowship of the Ring	313.322		
The Mummy Returns	201.95		
The Princess Diaries	108.245		
Vanilla Sky	100.539		

FIGURE 10.6 MINITAB output for movies data

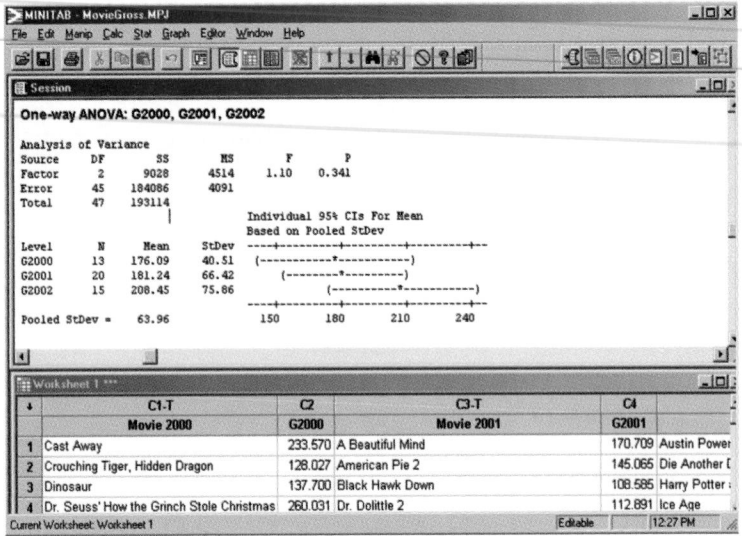

◆ **Solution:**

 Once again letting MINITAB do the work, we get the output in *Figure 10.6*. The *p*-value of .341 > .01 does not give a significant indication of a difference in the mean gross income in the three years. That being the case, there is no justification for using Fisher's procedure to compare the means—we have already decided that there appears to be no difference. ◆

Self-Testing Review 10.3

For all the exercises in this section, assume the populations involved are normally distributed with equal variances.

 25. A college bicycling club has four groups using different training programs. These groups are group 1 = distance cycling, group 2 = sprint cycling, group 3 = combination distance/sprint cycling, and group 4 = combination cycling/weight lifting. The following data represent the times (min.) required for each member of the four groups to ride a loop that included a 7 percent uphill grade (Data = BikeTrai):

Group 1	Group 2	Group 3	Group 4
84	56	70	47
93	78	59	73
83	56	78	104
61	61	53	71
121		104	69
67		110	99
		40	

When supplied with this data set, MINITAB produces the following output:

```
Analysis of Variance
Source   DF      SS      MS       F         p
Factor    3    1220     407     0.87     0.473
Error    19    8868     467
Total    22   10088
                          Individual 95% CIs For Mean
                          Based on Pooled StDev
Level     N    Mean    StDev   ----------+---------+---------+------
Group 1   6   84.83    21.28                     (---------*---------)
Group 2   4   62.75    10.44   (---------*---------)
Group 3   7   73.43    25.97              (---------*---------)
Group 4   6   77.17    21.11              (---------*---------)
                                ----------+---------+---------+------
Pooled StDev =         21.60             60        80       100
```

a) What does the term *factor* mean in the MINITAB output? What other term has been used to designate the same meaning?

b) What does the term *error* mean?

c) Interpret the degrees of freedom (df) entries in the MINITAB output, and explain how they are computed.

d) How is the SS error computed?

e) How is the SS factor computed?

f) What is another name for the MS error?

g) What is another name for the MS factor?

h) What is the test statistic, and how is it computed from the ANOVA table entries?

i) Interpret the *p*-value in the MINITAB output, and make the statistical decision at the .05 level.

j) A "Level" heading is used in the output. What's the meaning of this label?

k) What is the meaning of the pooled standard deviation shown in the MINITAB output?

l) What information is easily available from the bottom half of the MINITAB output?

m) Why would it be inappropriate to examine the results of Fisher's procedure for this data set?

26. The following gives market-share data in four locations:

Loc. 1	Loc. 2	Loc. 3	Loc. 4
28.42	10.81	17.78	32.25
23.00	12.83	13.58	22.75
29.00	10.66	18.50	27.45
28.79	10.11	18.37	11.79

When supplied with this data set, MINITAB produces the following output:

```
Analysis of Variance on MrktShar
Source     DF     SS      MS        F        p
Location    3    614.3   204.8     8.92    0.002
Error      12    275.4    22.9
Total      15    889.7
                            Individual 95% CIs For Mean
                            Based on Pooled StDev
   Level   N    Mean    StDev  ---+---------+---------+---------+---
       1   4  27.302   2.878                            (-----*-----)
       2   4  11.102   1.190   (-----*-----)
       3   4  17.058   2.339           (-----*-----)
       4   4  23.560   8.753                  (-----*-----)
                               ---+---------+---------+---------+---
Pooled StDev = 4.790              8.0      16.0      24.0      32.0

Fisher's pairwise comparisons

    Family error rate = 0.184
Individual error rate = 0.0500

Critical value = 2.179

Intervals for (column level mean) - (row level mean)
                    1          2          3
       2        8.819
               23.581

       3        2.864    -13.336
               17.626      1.426

       4       -3.638    -19.838    -13.883
               11.123     -5.077      0.878
```

a) Explain the df entries, and tell how they are computed.

b) What is the test statistic, and how is it computed from the table entries?

c) Interpret the p-value, and make the statistical decision at the .05 level.

d) Use the Fisher's pairwise comparisons portion of the output to decide which means are significantly different at the .05 level.

 27. Consider the following MINITAB ANOVA output:

```
Analysis of Variance
Source     DF     SS      MS        F        p
Factor      3    491.6   163.9     6.56    0.006
Error      13    324.6    25.0
Total      16    816.2
                            Individual 95% CIs For Mean
                            Based on Pooled StDev
Level       N    Mean    StDev  ------+---------+---------+---------+
Thirties    5   8.400   3.435   (------*------)
Fifties     5   8.000   4.583   (-----*------)
Sixties     4  16.750   7.632                (-------*-------)
Seventies   3  21.333   3.055                       (-------*-------)
                               ------+---------+---------+---------+
Pooled StDev = 4.997              7.0      14.0      21.0      28.0
```

a) How many different factors are considered?

b) How many values are in each factor group, and what is the total number of values?

c) How would you compute the various df entries?

d) How are the MS entries computed?

e) What two values in the table do you need to compute the test statistic?

f) What is the p-value for this test? Interpret it and tell what decision you would make from it.

g) Based on your decision on H_0, would you want to use Fisher's procedure on this problem?

 28. The MINITAB output that follows resulted from an experiment in which the scores on a test of racial prejudice were compared for three members of each of four ethnic groups.

```
Analysis of Variance
Source       DF        SS          MS         F         p
EthGroup      3      2092.9       697.6      7.56     0.010
Error         8       738.0        92.3
Total        11      2830.9
```

a) How would you compute the various df entries?

b) How are the MS entries computed?

c) What two values in the table do you need to compute the test statistic?

d) What is the p-value for this test? Using a level of significance of .05, what decision would you make from it?

e) Based on your decision on H_0, would you want to use Fisher's procedure on this problem?

 29. Upon release of the movie *Spiderman*, a fan of old comic books wanted to compare the mean prices of past issues of *Amazing Spiderman, Uncanny X-Men*, and *Fantastic Four* comics. Taking a random sample from each group, he found the following prices:

Amazing Spiderman

Issue	desc.	price	Issue	desc.	price
344	1st Cleus Kasady	9	426	Ock's Corpse Stolen	2
212	1st Hydro-Man	8	290	Peter Proposes to MJ	5
271	1st Manslaughter	5	223	Red Ghost	7
192	24 hours till Doomsday	8	336	Return Sinister Six	3
323	Captain America	6	357	Sidekicks Revenge	2.5
428	Dr. Octopus	2	431	vs. Carnage	2
401	Mark of Kaine	2	235	vs. Tarantula	7
313	McFarlane Art	8	351	vs. Tri-Sentinel	2.5
257	MJ Knows Identity	6	374	vs. Venom	2.5
440	Molten Man	2			

Uncanny X-Men			Fantastic Four		
Issue	desc.	price	Issue	desc.	price
155	1st Brood	6	163	Finale	7
227	Fall of the Mutants	5	307	Goodbye	3
300	Foil Cover	6	185	Here There Be Witches	6
364	Hunt for Xavier	2.5	294	Hero Worship	3
240	Inferno	5	367	Infinity War	2.25
277	Jim Lee Art	4	363	Innerverse	2.25
179	Morlocks	5	300	Marriage Human Torch	3
154	Return Corsair	6	313	Mole Man	3
361	Return Gambit	2.5	154	Mystery Mask	10
269	Return Rogue	5	348	New FF	3
251	Siege Perilous	5	206	The Death of FF	4
			192	The Screaming Wind	6
			401	vs. Maximus	2.25
			170	vs. Power Man	7

This data produces the following MINITAB output:

```
Analysis of Variance
Source    DF     SS     MS      F        p
Factor     2   0.90   0.45    0.09    0.916
Error     41 208.67   5.09
Total     43 209.56
                            Individual 95% CIs For Mean
                            Based on Pooled StDev
Level      N   Mean   StDev  -+---------+---------+---------+-----
Amazing   19  4.711  2.573        (------------*------------)
Uncanny   11  4.727  1.252        (---------------*---------------)
Fantastic 14  4.411  2.383     (-----------*-----------)
                            -+---------+---------+---------+-----
Pooled StDev = 2.256          3.20      4.00      4.80      5.60
```

a) How would you compute the various df entries?

b) How are the MS entries computed?

c) What two values in the table do you need to compute the test statistic?

d) What is the p-value for this test? Interpret it and tell what decision you would make from it.

e) Based on your decision on H_0, would you want to use Fisher's procedure on this problem?

30. Fill in the missing entries for the following ANOVA table:

```
Analysis of Variance
Source          DF        SS         MS         F
Factor           3       73.6        C?         E?
Error           A?       816.1       D?
Total           15       B?
```

a) A =

b) B =

c) C =

d) D =

e) E =

f) What decision should be made about the equality of the population means at the .01 level?

31. Fill in the missing entries for the following ANOVA table:

```
Analysis of Variance
Source        DF          SS          MS          F
Factor        A?          363.6       C?          E?
Error         12          727.3       D?
Total         14          B?
```

a) A =

b) B =

c) C =

d) D =

e) E =

f) What decision should be made about the equality of the population means at the .01 level?

32. In a class project, J. Wertz compared the compressive strengths of five different concrete mixes. The first mix was a standard concrete mix designed for a compressive strength of 38 Mpa (1 Mpa = 145.04 psi); the second and third mixes have the same mix ratio, but 25 percent and 35 percent, respectively, of the fine aggregate (sand) was replaced with discarded (dirty) foundry sand; the fourth and fifth are like the second and third except they use new (clean) foundry sand. The 28-day compressive strength data for hardened concrete (15-cm × 30-cm cylinder) follow (Data = Concrete):

Normal	25 Percent Dirty	35 Percent Dirty	25 Percent Clean	35 Percent Clean
43.0	32.3	30.2	44.4	43.0
44.5	32.3	30.7	41.5	44.6
44.0	36.2	31.1	44.9	42.6

a) Produce an ANOVA table for this data set.

b) Test the hypothesis at the .01 level that the population mean strengths are the same for the 5 mixes.

c) If H_0 is rejected, use Fisher's procedure at the .01 level to determine which means are significantly different.

33. The use of polymers in medicine, especially in the area of drug delivery, is one of the fastest-growing areas of polymer chemistry. In a class project, B. McClure described an experiment in which four different formulations were used in a delivery device. The data collected was the first total drug reading (mg) on each sample (Data = Polymer):

0.0 cc	0.5 cc	1.0 cc	2.0 cc
703	573	529	603
735	602	682	534
731	589	565	542
638	688	590	591
673	604	524	610
621	661	492	489
598	503	534	516
581	493	515	570
659	647	548	596
580	537	650	654

a) Produce an ANOVA table for this data set.

b) Test the hypothesis at the .05 level that the population mean drug readings are the same for the four formulations.

c) If H_0 is rejected, use Fisher's procedure at the .05 level to determine which means are significantly different.

34. In a class project, M. Parmar compared the mean reflectance of different sputtering machines (larger numbers are better). A sputtering machine is used for metalization on wafers in the semiconductor industry. Parmar gathered this data while working for a technology firm (Data = Sputter):

Sputtering Machine		
Anelva 1013	**Anelva 1051**	**Endura 5500**
88.8	90.2	94.8
90.2	91.7	93.5
91.3	90.0	90.9
89.5	90.9	94.2
90.3	92.5	94.1

a) Produce an ANOVA table for this data set.

b) Test the hypothesis at the .01 level that the population mean reflectances are the same for the three machines.

c) If H_0 is rejected, use Fisher's procedure at the .01 level to determine which means are significantly different.

35. The following data show the amount spent in dollars for 60 people, 20 paying cash, 20 paying by cheque, and 20 paying by credit card at a department store (Data = Target):

Cash	Cheque	Credit
7.27	44.57	24.22
3.14	3.58	82.27
5.30	14.71	77.24
2.70	113.13	26.25
1.05	42.38	18.01
0.89	16.44	59.34
7.63	22.15	57.24
13.48	10.59	17.48
4.23	27.54	45.08
4.05	22.00	16.03
13.44	25.44	42.11
36.57	6.12	39.86
19.96	19.09	7.40
2.47	18.87	23.15
11.65	11.88	64.33
6.49	50.53	46.36
14.70	50.82	17.94
2.06	46.36	6.44
24.44	6.15	30.70
2.67	39.70	21.29

a) Produce an ANOVA table for this data set.

b) Test the hypothesis at the .05 level that the population mean amounts spent are the same for the three methods of payment.

c) If H_0 is rejected, use Fisher's procedure at the .05 level to determine which means are significantly different.

36. In 2003, a collector of HotWheels model cars collected the following samples of prices (in dollars) of various cars that were in the original packaging, for the years 1995, 1996, and 1997.

1995 Car Name	Price	1996 Car Name	Price	1997 Car Name	Price
Classic Cobra	8	Fire Eater	6	'80s Corvette	4
Camaro Racer	12	'55 Chevy	4	Spittin' Image 2	5
Mercedes SL	4	Bywayman	45	VW Bug	60
Ferrari 355	10	Pizza Vette	24	Nissan Truck	30
Power Rocket	5	Kenworth T600	12	Stealth	4
Big Chill	7	Hydroplane	6	Baja Bug	15
Fire Eater	6	'80s Camaro Z-28	4	Avus Quattro	20
Zender Fact 4	23	Porsche 930	4		
'59 Caddy	40				

a) Produce an ANOVA table for this data set.

b) Test the hypothesis at the .05 level that the population mean prices are the same for the three years.

10.4   Two-Way Analysis of Variance

The analysis of variance technique shown in sections 10.1, 10.2, and 10.3 is called a **one-way analysis of variance** since there is only one independent variable or factor. A **two-way analysis of variance** is an extension of the one-way analysis of variance since it involves two independent variables or factors. Suppose for example, we wish to determine whether the yield of a canola crop is affected by either or both, the brand of fertilizer and the amount of fertilizer.

We could perform two one-way ANOVA tests, one comparing means of different brands, and another comparing means using different amounts of fertilizer. Alternatively, there are several reasons we may want to use a two-way ANOVA procedure instead:

- First, it enables us to study the interaction of the factors. That is, the same amount of two different brands may produce different effects on the yield. This type of effect can be determined only if both factors are used simultaneously.

- Second, a savings of time and effort result. Usually fewer observations are needed than the number required to perform two one-way analyses.

- Third, the conclusions reached have broader application. This is because the behaviour of each factor is studied in conjunction with different levels of other factors. Thus the results are more useful than those obtained by holding other factors constant.

The following is intended to provide a brief introduction to the two-way analysis of variance procedure.

Example 10.6   A movie industry analyst wishes to determine whether there are any significant differences in the mean gross incomes of movies for the years 2000, 2001, and 2002, and also wishes to determine whether there is any significant difference between the mean gross income of movies with ratings G/PG and those with an R rating. In this example, gross income (in millions of dollars) is the dependent variable, and there are two factors or independent variables. The first factor is the year and the second factor is the movie rating. The first factor has three levels (2000, 2001, and 2002) while the second factor two has two levels (Ratings G/PG and R). Therefore, there are $3 \times 2 = 6$ treatments.

The analyst then selects a random sample of, say, three movies from each of the six populations involved. The results are given in the table below. The analyst compares gross income of movies depending on the year and the ratings using a two-way analysis of variance procedure.

Movie	Gross Income	Rating	Year
Dr. Seuss' How the Grinch Stole Christmas	260.031	G	2000
What Women Want	182.737	G	2000
Meet the Parents	166.225	G	2000
Gladiator	187.671	R	2000
Scary Movie	156.997	R	2000
Erin Brockovich	125.549	R	2000

Movie	Gross Income	Rating	Year
Shrek	267.652	G	2001
Ocean's Eleven	183.349	G	2001
Hannibal	164.978	G	2001
Vanilla Sky	100.539	R	2001
The Fast and the Furious	144.512	R	2001
American Pie 2	145.065	R	2001
The Lord of the Rings: The Two Towers	261.032	G	2002
My Big Fat Greek Wedding	227.899	G	2002
Scooby-Doo	153.244	G	2002
8 Mile	115.27	R	2002
Red Dragon	92.93	R	2002
Blade II	81.645	R	2002

◆ **Solution:**

In this example, there are three sets of hypotheses to be tested. There is one for the interaction, and one for each factor, called the **main effects**.

1. H_0: The factors "rating of a movie" and "year the movie was produced" do not interact to affect the gross income of the movie.

   H_1: The factors "rating of a movie" and "year the movie was produced" do interact to affect the gross income of the movie.

2. H_0: There is no difference in the mean gross income of movies in the years 2000, 2001, and 2002.

   H_1: There is a difference in the mean gross income of movies in the years 2000, 2001, and 2002.

3. H_0: There is no difference in the mean gross income of movies with ratings G/PG and R.

   H_1: There is a difference in the mean gross income of movies with ratings G/PG and R.

If there is an interaction effect present, it means that both the rating of a movie and the year the movie was produced affect the gross income and that the movie rating affects the gross income differently in different years.

The computational procedure for the two-way ANOVA is quite lengthy, so we will assume that a software package is being used. MINITAB was used to generate Figure 10.7, and the following is a summary of the output:

Two-way ANOVA: Total Gross versus Year, Rating

```
Analysis of Variance for Total Gross
Source          DF          SS          MS         F         P
Year             2       1,805         903      0.52     0.609
Rating           1      28,558      28,558     16.37     0.002
Interaction      2       3,844       1,922      1.10     0.364
Error           12      20,928       1,744
Total           17      55,135
```

FIGURE 10.7 To obtain the ANOVA table, click **Stat**, ANOVA, two-way, in the two-way Analysis of Variance dialog box, select **Total Gross** (C2). Select **Year** (C4) into the "Row Factor" box. Select **Rating** (C3-T) into the "Column Factor" box. Click **OK** in the Two-way Analysis of Variance box.

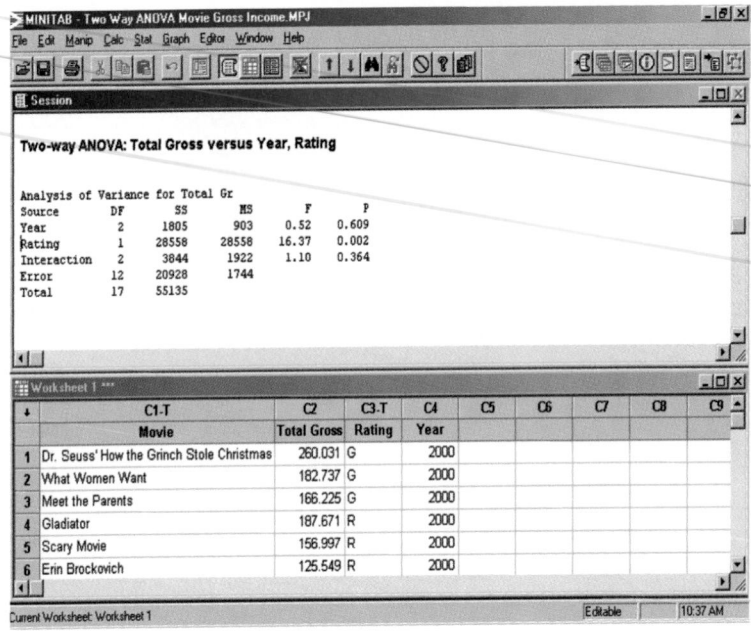

For testing the first set of hypotheses, (H_0: interaction not present ... , versus H_1: interaction present ...) we note that the test statistics is $F = 1.10$ and the p-value is 0.364. Using a .05 level of significance, we fail to reject H_0, since 0.364 is not less than .05. Thus we cannot conclude that interaction is present in this example.

For testing the second set of hypotheses, (H_0: There is no difference in the mean gross income of movies in the years 2000, 2001, and 2002, versus H_1: There is a difference in the mean gross income of movies in the years 2000, 2001, and 2002), we note that the test statistics is $F = 0.52$ and the p-value is 0.609. Using a .05 level of significance, we fail to reject H_0, since 0.609 is not less than .05. Thus we cannot conclude the mean gross incomes for the years 2000, 2001, and 2002 are different.

For testing the third set of hypotheses, (H_0: There is no difference in the mean gross income of movies with ratings G/PG and R, versus H_1: There is a difference in the mean gross income of movies with ratings G/PG and R), we note that the test statistics is $F = 16.37$ and the p-value is 0.002. Using a .05 level of significance, we reject H_0, since 0.002 is less than .05. Thus we can conclude that the mean gross incomes of movies with ratings G/PG and R are different. ◆

As seen in this example, MINITAB and most other statistical software summarize the results of a two-way analysis of variance in a table. When an experiment has two factors, say, A and B with levels a and b respectively, then there are **a** × **b** treatments under consideration. Suppose for each treatment, a random sample of **r** observations are selected. Then there are a total of **n** = **r** × **a** × **b** observations obtained. The format of a general two-way ANOVA table (Table 10.4) is similar to the one discussed in Section 10.3 for a one-way ANOVA. Since there are two factors (A and B) under consideration, the source of variations are then due to factor A, factor B, interaction of factors A and B, and the error. The total sum of squares (SST) is then the sum of squares (SS) of the above variations. That is

$$SST = SS(\text{Factor A}) + SS(\text{Factor B}) + SS(\text{Interaction A} \times \text{B}) + SS(\text{Error})$$

TABLE 10.4 THE FORMAT OF A GENERAL TWO-WAY ANOVA

Source of Variation	Degrees of Freedom (df)	Sum of Squares (SS)	Mean of Squares (MS)	Computed F Value (F)
Factor A	$a - 1$	SS_A	$MS_A = SS_A/(a - 1)$	MS_A/MS_E
Factor B	$b - 1$	SS_B	$MS_B = SS_B/(b - 1)$	MS_B/MS_E
Interaction $A \times B$	$(a - 1)(b - 1)$	$SS_A \times B$	$MS_A \times B = SS_A \times B/((a - 1)(b - 1))$	$MS_{A \times B}/MS_E$
Error	$n - ab$	SS_E	$MS_E = SS_E/(n - ab)$	
Total	$n - 1$	SST		

and in an abbreviated form as

$$SST = SS_A + SS_B + SS_{A \times B} + SS_E$$

As in one-way ANOVA, we must make sure that the following assumptions are satisfied before we attempt to apply two-way analysis of variance.

Assumptions for the Two-Way Analysis of Variance

1. The populations from which the samples were obtained must be normally or approximately normally distributed.

2. The samples must be independent.

3. The variances of the populations from which the samples were selected must be equal.

4. The random samples for each treatment must be equal in size.

In general, there are three sets of hypotheses that could be tested. There is one for the interaction and one for each factor, or independent variable. The hypotheses are as follows:

1. H_0: There is no interaction effect between the factors.

   H_1: There is an interaction effect between the factors.

2. H_0: There are no effects from factor A. (That is, the means at each level of factor A are all equal.)

   H_1: There are effects from factor A. (That is, the means at each level of factor A are not all equal.)

3. H_0: There are no effects from factor B. (That is, the means at each level of factor B are all equal.)

   H_1: There are effects from factor B. (That is, the means at each level of factor A are not all equal.)

If interaction is found to be present, the differences between the treatment means can be further investigated, not by comparing the means for each factor individually, but rather by pairwise comparisons of all treatment means. Tests similar to Fisher's procedure used in one-way ANOVA are available but are beyond the scope of this book.

Randomized Block Design

We saw in Chapter 9 that when two means are to be compared, a paired t test is sometimes more effective than one involving two independent samples. This is because effective pairing can considerably reduce the amount of variation due to extraneous factors in which we are not interested. A similar reduction in extraneous variation can be made when comparing more than two means. The randomized block design is an extension of the paired t test, and is used to compare the means of two or more populations. It is an alternative to the one-way ANOVA procedure.

Suppose an agricultural scientist wants to compare the average yield of four different varieties of wheat, and has 20 plots of land available for planting. If 5 of these plots are randomly selected and planted with variety 1, 5 of the remaining 15 plots are selected for variety 2, and so on, the result is a *completely randomized experiment,* and the data should be analyzed using the one-way ANOVA. The disadvantage of this experiment is that the plots of land may have considerably different soil conditions, moisture, temperature, etc., and a separate assessment of differences between varieties will not be possible (plot differences are confounded with variety differences).

Here is an alternative experiment. Consider separating the 20 plots into 5 groups, with each group consisting of 4 plots. Within each group, the plots are as alike as possible with respect to soil conditions, moisture, temperature, etc. Then within each group, one plot is randomly selected for variety 1, a second plot is randomly chosen for variety 2, and so on. The homogeneous groups are called *blocks,* and the random allocation of varieties within each block as described results in a *randomized block experiment.* Since the growing conditions for each block would now be more homogeneous, the variations in yield recorded would be mostly due to variations in wheat variety rather than due to variations in other factors. We then may test the null hypothesis H_0: The mean yield is the same for each variety grown, against the alternative hypothesis H_1: The mean yield is not the same for each variety grown.

> Suppose that experimental units are first separated into groups consisting of a units in such a way that the units within each group are as similar as possible. Within any particular group, the treatments are then randomly allocated so that each unit in a group receives a different treatment. The groups are often called **blocks,** and the experimental design is referred to as a **randomized block design.**

A randomized block design enables us to compare two or more population means. Suppose we wish to compare a population means using b blocks. There are $a \times b$ measurements to be obtained. The key to analyzing data from a randomized block experiment is to represent SST, which measures total variation, as the sum of three components:

SST = SS(Factor A) + SS(Block) + SS(Error)

Or, in abbreviated form

$$SST = SS_A + SS_{Block} + SS_E$$

TABLE 10.5 THE FORMAT OF A GENERAL RANDOMIZED BLOCK DESIGN ANOVA TABLE

Source of Variation	Degrees of Freedom (df)	Sum of Squares (SS)	Mean of Squares (MS)	Computed F Value (F)
Factor A	$a - 1$	SS_A	$MS_A = SS_A/(a - 1)$	MS_A/MS_E
Blocks	$b - 1$	SS_{Block}	$MS_{Block} = SS_{Block}/(b - 1)$	MS_{Block}/MS_E
Error	$(a - 1)(b - 1)$	SS_E	$MS_E - SS_E/((a - 1)(b - 1))$	
Total	$ab - 1$	SST		

A randomized block experiment is a special case of a two-factor experiment, in which one factor, blocks, is created solely to control for extraneous variation.

The format of a general ANOVA table (Table 10.5) for the randomized block design is similar to the one discussed for a two-way ANOVA, without interaction.

The hypotheses of interest and assumptions required for a randomized block design are similar to those required for a completely randomized experiment.

Assumptions and Hypotheses

The single observation made on any particular treatment in a given block is assumed to be selected from a normal distribution. The variance of this distribution is the same for each block-treatment combination.

The hypotheses of interest are the following:

H_0: The mean value is the same for each treatment.
H_1: The mean value is not the same for each treatment.

■ **Example 10.7** **Is Crime on the Increase in Canadian Cities?** The Insurance Corporation of British Columbia (ICBC) recently reported that the crime rate had increased in most BC cities over the last few years. Is this also true for cities across Canada? A random sample of 15 Canadian cities is selected and the crime rate (number of crimes per 100,000 of population) as reported by Statistics Canada for the years 1999, 2000, and 2001 are as given below. Each city represents a block.

	Crime Rate for the Years				Crime Rate for the Years		
	1999	2000	2001		1999	2000	2001
Calgary	7,554	7,115	7,137	Sudbury	6,514	6,784	7,535
Edmonton	8,533	8,377	9,032	Thunder Bay	9,109	8,900	8,602
Halifax	9,551	9,249	9,354	Toronto	5,385	5,290	5,343
Hamilton	6,743	6,565	7,102	Vancouver	11,562	11,210	11,314
London	8,581	8,721	7,894	Victoria	11,865	10,594	9,996
Montréal	7,171	7,234	6,830	Windsor	6,595	7,086	7,374
Regina	15,191	14,769	16,387	Winnipeg	9,763	10,377	10,947
Saint John	7,367	6,277	6,612				

FIGURE 10.8 To obtain the ANOVA table, click **STAT,** ANOVA, two-way, in the two-way Analysis of Variance dialog box, select **CRIMERATE** (C2) into the Response box. Select **YEAR** (C3) into the "Row Factor" box and check the "Display Means" check box. Select **CITIES** (C1-T) into "Column Factor" box and check the "Display Means" check box. Check the "Fit additive model" check box. Click OK in the "Two-way Analysis of Variance" dialog box.

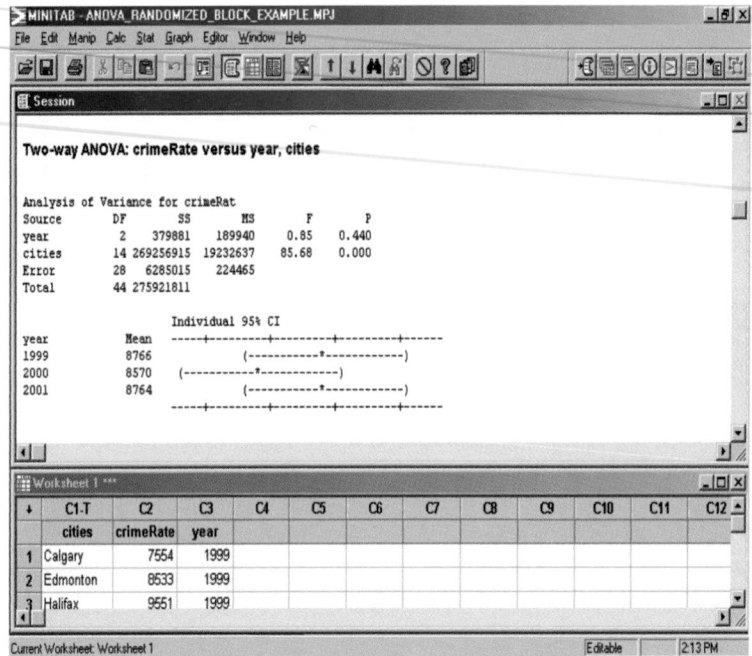

◆ Solution:

We are interested in testing

H_0: The mean crime rate for Canadian cities was the same in each of the years 1999, 2000, and 2001.

H_1: The mean crime rate for Canadian cities was not the same in each of the years 1999, 2000, and 2001.

The computations for the randomized block experiment are performed using a two-way ANOVA procedure, without interaction. MINITAB was used to generate the output if *Figure 10.8*.

For testing the hypotheses, (H_0: The mean crime rate for Canadian cities was the same in each of the years 1999, 2000, and 2001, vs. H_1: The mean crime rate for Canadian cities was not the same in each of the years 1999, 2000, and 2001), we note that the test statistics is $F = 0.85$ and the *p*-value is 0.440. Using a .05 level of significance, we fail to reject H_0, since 0.440 is not less than .05. Thus we cannot conclude that the mean crime rate for Canadian cities changed during the years 1999, 2000, and 2001. ◆

Self-Testing Review 10.4

37. A Healthy Life Style Group wishes to see whether there is a difference in weight loss in using a high-protein diet or a high-carbohydrate diet. Five members are randomly assigned to each of the diet programs according to sex. After four weeks on the diet, the weight losses of the members are determined. The weight losses in kilograms are shown below.

	High Protein	High Carbohydrate
Male	5.1, 4.7, 2.6, 8.5, 6.6	7.1, 9.5, 9.4, 5.9, 10.2
Female	8.2, 9.6, 10.1, 9.4, 11.8	15.5, 17.2, 16.1, 9.7, 12.6

Use a two-way ANOVA procedure with $\alpha = 0.05$ to answer the following questions.

a) Do the factors "diet" and "sex" significantly interact to affect the amount of weight lost?

b) Is there a significant difference between the mean weight loss using the high-protein diet and the mean weight loss using the high-carbohydrate diet?

c) Is there a significant difference between the mean weight loss of males and the mean weight loss of females?

38. An Agricultural Research Institute is interested in comparing the yield of three varieties of canola planted with three different types of fertilizers. Four research plots are randomly assigned to each variety of canola and type of fertilizer. The yield of canola in bushels per acre is recorded for each plot and is given below:

		Type of Canola		
		1	2	3
		49	47	39
	1	33	30	19
		19	12	31
		23	20	28
		48	53	43
Fertilizer	2	18	32	67
		30	37	60
		21	45	74
		55	65	34
	3	44	63	66
		35	51	58
		18	74	68

Use a two-way ANOVA procedure with $\alpha = 0.05$ to answer the following questions.

a) Do the factors "type of canola" and "fertilizer" significantly interact to affect the yield?

b) Are there any significant differences between the mean yields of the three types of canola?

c) Are there any significant differences between the mean yields using the three types of fertilizer?

39. The partially completed ANOVA table given here is for a two-way ANOVA experiment.

Source	df	SS	MS	F
A	4		.6	
B	3	1.5		
A × B			.4	
Error				
Total	59	12.87		

a) Give the number of levels for each factor.

b) How many observations were collected for each factor-level combination?

c) Complete the ANOVA table.

d) What sets of hypotheses can you test from this table?

40. The partially complete ANOVA table given here is for a two-way ANOVA experiment.

Source	df	SS	MS	F
A			1.2	
B	2	1.5		
A × B	4		.8	
Error	27			
Total		8.9		

a) Give the number of levels for each factor.

b) How many observations were collected for each factor-level combination?

c) Complete the ANOVA table.

d) What sets of hypotheses can you test from this table?

41. Suppose a researcher from an animal feed company is interested in comparing the mean weight gains of pigs when fed three types of feeds. He knows that the weight gained by the pigs is not only due to the type of feed used but also depends on the genetic makeup of the pigs. Therefore, in order to reduce variation of this kind to be introduced in the data, he randomly selects five litters of pigs with three or more piglets in each litter. Three pigs are randomly selected from each litter. Each of the three-litter mates is assigned randomly a type of feed. The pigs are individually housed and fed. The gains, in kilograms, after 30 days are recorded for each pig. The data are presented below:

Feed	Litter							
	1	2	3	4	5	6	7	8
A	28	18	17	22	22	26	24	19
B	23	18	13	19	21	22	26	24
C	25	19	24	23	22	29	27	25

At the .05 level of significance, can we conclude that the mean weight gain is same for all three feed types?

42. An agricultural scientist wants to compare three varieties of wheat for yield. Since the yield depends on the soil conditions, moisture, and other factors beside the variety of the wheat, the scientist selects three-acre plots in five localities that differ considerably regarding conditions. For plots in each location, one variety is randomly assigned to each plot. After the harvest the yield bushels per acre is recorded for each plot. The data are given below:

Location	Variety 1	Variety 2	Variety 3
1	42	43	32
2	47	45	39
3	43	42	29
4	40	45	28
5	48	49	35

At the .05 level significance, can we conclude that the mean yield is same for all three varieties?

LOOKING BACK

1. The purpose of the one-way ANOVA technique discussed in this chapter is to enable a decision maker to compare three or more independent sample means to see if there are statistically significant differences between the means of the populations from which the samples are taken. The following three assumptions must be true before the ANOVA technique can be applied to a decision-making situation: (1) the population distributions approximate the normal distribution, (2) the samples are random and independent of each other, and (3) the variances of all populations are equal.

2. As is the case with other hypothesis-testing procedures, we follow a seven-step procedure to complete an ANOVA test. This test begins with a statement of the null and alternative hypotheses (*Step 1*); it then requires that the test be made at a suitable level of significance (*Step 2*). An *F* distribution is used in an ANOVA test (*Step 3*). Three things must be known to find the *F* value in Appendix 5 that is on the boundary of the rejection area (*Step 4*). These three items are (*a*) the level of significance, (*b*) the degrees of freedom for the numerator of the test statistic, and (*c*) the degrees of freedom for the denominator of the test statistic. When these three items are determined, the critical *F* value for the test can be found, and the decision rule can be formulated (*Step 5*).

3. Finding the test statistic (*Step 6*) requires that two estimates of the population variance be computed by using two independent computational methods. In one approach—the one that produces $\hat{\sigma}^2_{within}$—the population variance is estimated by computing the variances found in each sample. These sample variances are pooled and averaged to get an estimate of σ^2. Any deviation of this estimate from the true population variance is due to random sampling error. In the other approach, $\hat{\sigma}^2_{between}$, an estimate of σ^2 is found by measuring the variation between the sample means. This estimate of σ^2 has merit if, and only if, H_0 is true. Any deviation of this estimate from the value of σ^2 is due to factor differences among the samples. The two estimates of σ^2 are then used to compute the test statistic (or *F* value). Ideally, if H_0 is true, this statistic will have a value of 1.00 since the two estimates of σ^2 will yield the same results. Realistically, however, sampling variation will normally cause the test statistic to differ from 1.00 even when H_0 is true. Once the test statistic (*F*) is computed, a statistical decision (*Step 7*) can be made. If the computed *F* value ≤ the appropriate *F* table value at a specified level of confidence, the null hypothesis is not rejected. But if the *F* value is found to exceed the table value, the ANOVA test concludes with the rejection of the null hypothesis. At that point, usually a method such as Fisher's least significant difference is used to determine which pairs of means are significantly different.

4. It's often desirable to prepare a one-way ANOVA table—a summary listing of the values needed to produce an ANOVA test. The first column of this table lists the sources of variation, and subsequent columns show degrees of freedom, sum of squares (SS) figures, mean squares (MS) values (the $\hat{\sigma}^2_{between}$ and $\hat{\sigma}^2_{within}$ calculations), and the computed test (*F*) statistic. Statistical software packages typically display ANOVA output in this table format.

5. A two-way analysis of variance is an extension of the one-way analysis of variance since it involves two independent variables or factors. In general, there are three sets of hypotheses that could be tested. There is one for the

interaction and one for each factor, or independent variable. The computational procedure for the two-way ANOVA is lengthy, so we use a software package. The software package produces a p-value for each set of hypotheses being tested. We reject the null hypothesis if the p-value is less than the level of significance selected.

6. The randomized block design is an extension of the paired t test, and is used to compare the means of two or more populations.
   It is an alternative to the one-way ANOVA procedure. A randomized block experiment is considered as a special case of a two-factor experiment, in which one factor, blocks, is created to control for extraneous variation.

Exercises

For all the exercises in this section, assume the populations involved are normally distributed with equal variances.

43. Find the critical F value for each of the following situations:

   a) $\alpha = .05$, $df_{num} = 5$, and $df_{den} = 8$.

   b) $\alpha = .05$, $df_{num} = 5$, and $df_{den} = 20$.

   c) $\alpha = .05$, $df_{num} = 5$, and $df_{den} = 30$.

44. Examine your answers for problem 43. What can you conclude about the critical F value when all other conditions remain the same and the df_{den} increases?

45. Find the critical F value for each of the following situations:

   a) $\alpha = .01$, $df_{num} = 5$, and $df_{den} = 25$.

   b) $\alpha = .01$, $df_{num} = 7$, and $df_{den} = 25$.

   c) $\alpha = .01$, $df_{num} = 10$, and $df_{den} = 25$.

46. Examine your answers for problem 45. What can you conclude about the critical F value when all other conditions remain the same and the df_{num} increases?

47. Find the critical F value for each of these situations:

   a) $\alpha = .05$, $df_{num} = 8$, and $df_{den} = 15$.

   b) $\alpha = .01$, $df_{num} = 5$, and $df_{den} = 20$.

48. In a test to see if mental skills vary for different age groups, a random sample of subjects in their 30s, 50s, 60s, and 70s were given a "digits backward" test. (A psychologist reads a sequence of digits and each subject is asked to recite the digits in reverse order.) The following data represent the number of digits correctly recited by each subject (Data = Digits):

Thirties	Fifties	Sixties	Seventies
4	3	4	5
5	5	7	3
6	3	7	7
8	7	4	
6	7		

Test the hypothesis at the .01 level that the population means for all four age groups are equal.

49. A study compared the effect of various training frequencies on the development of strength. Participants were randomly selected from four training groups. Those in group 1 worked out once every other week, those in group 2 had a weekly workout, group 3 participants met twice a week, and group 4 members worked out three times a week. The following data represent a multitask measurement of strength for each of the participants (Data = StrngFrq):

Group 1	Group 2	Group 3	Group 4
27	39	37	24
50	36	28	53
43	47	44	51
31	51	36	51
37		30	45
37		27	65
		44	

Test the hypothesis at the .05 level that the population mean strengths for the participants of the four groups are equal.

50. Maria Reed, the marketing director for a pasta manufacturer, claims that the height of the shelves on which her product is displayed will affect the sales volume. With the cooperation of 15 retail stores, an experiment is carried out. In five randomly selected stores, the product is placed at eye level on the shelves. In another five, the product is displayed at waist level, and in the third five, the product is placed at knee level. The number of pasta packages sold in a week is recorded below (Data = Pasta):

Eye Level	Waist Level	Knee Level
98	106	103
106	105	95
111	98	87
85	93	94
108	96	92

At the .01 level, is there a significant difference in the population mean sales based on the shelf location of the product?

51. A career counsellor claims there is no difference in mean career decision-making attitudes among the population of students from various socioeconomic classes. The results of scores from an attitudes test given to random samples of students are as follows (Data = SocEcAtt):

Lower	Middle	Upper
32	45	38
36	42	38
40	34	31
32	42	41
33	29	
37	33	
	34	

Test the counsellor's claim at the .01 level.

52. A marketing expert wants to compare case sales of three brands of detergent to see if there's a difference in market share of these products. Stores are randomly selected and asked to monitor their sales (in cases) of one of the brands for two weeks. The following data have been gathered (Data = Detergnt):

Brand A	Brand B	Brand C
32.5	27.5	15.5
27.7	27.7	12.5
18.4	30.3	18.9
37.7	13.7	15.8
21.7	5.7	15.1

What should the marketing expert conclude at the .05 level?

53. Children considered "at risk" readers are placed into one of three experimental reading-recovery programs. After six weeks in the program, each is presented with a passage to read. The number of errors made by individuals in each group is given in the following data (Data = ReadingR):

Moody	Lindavic	Bell
4	7	6
2	6	9
5	11	7
9	11	10
3	6	

Test the hypothesis at the .01 level that the population mean number of errors for all three groups is the same.

54. Scores on measures of emotional distress have been reported in the *American Journal of Psychiatry* for random samples of nicotine-dependent smokers, non-dependent smokers, and non-smokers. These scores are shown as follows (Data = Smokemot):

Nico-Dependent	Non-Dependent	Non-Smokers
87	58	86
141	50	68
128	44	72
63	97	63
47	80	79
47	63	73
	55	72

Test the hypothesis at the .01 level that there's no difference in the population mean scores for the three groups.

55. The sales manager of Floppydisk Software wants to see if a dress code will have an effect on sales. In an experiment, salespersons were randomly selected to wear business suits, casual outfits, or jeans when visiting prospective clients. The following sales (in thousands of dollars) for a four-week period have been recorded (Data = DressCod):

Suits		Casual		Jeans	
$26	$33	$19	$25	$22	$29
37	40	24	24	33	31
41		31	29	34	
35		28	32	19	
29		23		25	

Is there a significant difference at the .05 level in the population mean sales for the three groups?

56. The following questions refer to this MINITAB ANOVA output:

```
Analysis of Variance
Source        DF        SS        MS        F         p
Factor         3       2.08      0.69      0.22     0.884
Error         13      41.80      3.22
Total         16      43.88
                                    Individual 95% CIs For Mean
                                    Based on Pooled StDev
Level         N       Mean      StDev   --+---------+---------+---------+----
Thirties      5       5.800     1.483               (----------*----------)
Fifties       5       5.000     2.000      (----------*----------)
Sixties       4       5.500     1.732         (-----------*------------)
Seventies     3       5.000     2.000   (--------------*-------------)
                                        --+---------+---------+---------+----
Pooled StDev =          1.793           3.0       4.5       6.0       7.5
```

a) What does the term *factor* mean in the output? What other term has been used to designate the same meaning?

b) What does the term *error* mean?

c) Interpret the degrees of freedom (df) entries in the output, and explain how they are computed.

d) How is the SS error computed?

e) How is the SS factor computed?

f) What is another name for the MS error?

g) What is another name for the MS factor?

h) What is the test statistic, and how is it computed from the ANOVA table entries?

i) Interpret the *p*-value in the output, and make the statistical decision at the .05 level.

j) A level heading is used in the output. What's the meaning of this label?

k) What information is easily available from the bottom half of the output?

l) Would we want to use Fisher's procedure on this data set?

m) What is the meaning of the pooled standard deviation shown in the output?

57. Use the following MINITAB ANOVA output to answer these questions:

```
Analysis of Variance
Source        DF        SS        MS        F         p
Factor         2      62.36     31.18      5.92     0.009
Error         21     110.60      5.27
Total         23     172.96
                                    Individual 95% CIs For Mean
                                    Based on Pooled StDev
Level         N       Mean      StDev   -------+---------+---------+---------
Summer        7       4.571     1.512   (--------*--------)
Fall          9       8.111     3.180                     (-------*-------)
Spring        8       5.000     1.512      (-------*-------)
                                        -------+---------+---------+---------
Pooled StDev =          2.295              4.0       6.0       8.0
```

a) Explain the df entries, and tell how they are computed.

b) What is the test statistic, and how is it computed from the table entries?

c) Interpret the p-value; and make the statistical decision at the .05 level.

d) Would we want to use Fisher's procedure on this data set?

58. Fill in the missing entries for the ANOVA table below:

```
Analysis of Variance
Source     DF      SS       MS      F
Factor     2       1515     C?      E?
Error      A?      10750    D?
Total      19      B?
```

a) A =

b) B =

c) C =

d) D =

e) E =

f) What decision should be made about the equality of the population means at the .05 level?

59. Fill in the missing entries for the ANOVA table below:

```
Analysis of Variance
Source     DF      SS       MS      F
Factor     3       B?       C?      E?
Error      20      43.33    D?
Total      A?      51.83
```

a) A =

b) B =

c) C =

d) D =

e) E =

f) What decision should be made about the equality of the population means at the .01 level?

60. In a class project, Susi Bernstein presented measurements on the widths (mm) of buckwheat in a location near a granite mine that was hydroseeded subsequent to mining. Because of possible differences in width due to placement on the slope, the data included an indication of placement on the slope (1 = top, 2 = middle, 3 = bottom 1/3 of the plot) (Data = BuckwhtW):

Top	Middle	Bottom
10.0	2.5	17.0
6.0	0.4	5.0
3.0	0.5	4.0
130.0	1.2	11.5
18.0	1.2	2.0
6.5	1.0	2.0
11.0	1.3	11.0
9.0	0.5	
2.0	1.0	
5.0	13.0	

a) Produce an ANOVA table for this data set.

b) Test the hypothesis at the .01 level that the population mean widths are the same for the three placements.

c) If H_0 is rejected, use Fisher's procedure at the .01 level to determine which means are significantly different.

61. Phototoxicity, pesticide-induced injury to plants, can be caused by insufficient testing before the pesticide is marketed. Dr. Mark Shelton collected data using four treatments, namely a control, Marathon 1G, one tablet of Acephate 15 percent, and two tablets of Acephate 15 percent. These were placed on hibiscus plants, and the number of unopened buds was used as a measure of phototoxicity (Data = Hibiscus):

Control	Marathon	1 Tab Acephate	2 Tab Acephate
3	4	3	3
5	9	8	5
3	11	4	5
4	7	5	5
3	8	2	2
3	8	5	3
6	5	3	3
5	3	2	4
3	3	2	2
3	9	3	4
5	5	2	3
2	7	3	6
3	4	5	4
3	6	3	4
3	5	5	8
4	2	3	6

a) Produce an ANOVA table for this data set.

b) Test the hypothesis at the .05 level that the population mean number of unopened buds are the same for the 4 treatments.

c) If H_0 is rejected, use Fisher's procedure at the .05 level to determine which means are significantly different.

62. In a class project, W. Beard explored the effects of various amounts of fly ash in high-strength concrete. Data found in the *ACI Materials Journal* gave the compressive strength of 28-day-old samples of 4,000 psi specified strength concrete using from 0 to 60 percent high-calcium fly ash (class C) (Data = FlyAsh):

Percent Fly Ash					
0	**20**	**30**	**40**	**50**	**60**
4,779	5,189	5,110	5,995	5,746	4,895
4,706	5,140	5,685	5,628	5,719	5,030
4,350	4,976	5,618	5,897	5,782	4,648

a) Produce an ANOVA table for this data set.

b) Test the hypothesis at the .01 level that the population mean strengths are the same for the six amounts of fly ash.

c) If H_0 is rejected, use Fisher's procedure at the .01 level to determine which means are significantly different.

63. A high school is interested in introducing interactive mathematics educational software into the classrooms. In an experiment to see whether the type of software and students' experience with video games affect their math test scores, random samples of five students each are taught mathematics using various combinations of software and video game experience. The students were tested after one week of instruction. The following table gives their math test scores:

		Software Used		
		A	**B**	**C**
	None	71	74	45
		64	72	76
		64	81	58
		57	72	70
		79	68	63
	Some	82	61	59
		91	54	66
Video		70	71	51
Game		69	71	78
Experience		73	69	84
	Moderate	68	70	70
		87	90	85
		72	73	75
		66	75	71
		60	71	61
	Lots	80	51	70
		72	65	71
		58	64	72
		68	53	64
		63	55	66

Use a two-way ANOVA procedure with $\alpha = 0.05$ to answer the following questions.

a) Do the factors "software used" and "video game experience" significantly interact to affect math test scores?

b) Are there any significant differences between the mean test scores of students using the three different types of software?

c) Can we conclude that the mean test scores of students are different for at least two of the levels of video game experience?

64. Many students listen to music when they are studying. A psychology student wanted to determine whether listening to different kinds of music produces different mean scores on memory recall tests. He randomly selected one student who majored in science, one who majored in engineering, one who majored in education, and one who majored in arts. The students were each given memory recall tests after studying a piece of literature while listening to classical music, a piece of literature while listening to easy listening music, and a piece of literature while listening to blues music. The following are the test scores of the students:

Student	Classical	Easy Listening	Blues
1	75	80	65
2	65	78	70
3	80	90	75
4	60	65	45

Can it be concluded that listening to different kinds of music produces different mean scores on memory recall tests? Use a .05 level of significance.

Topics for Review and Discussion

1. Discuss the hypotheses in an analysis of variance test.

2. What are the three assumptions that must be met if the ANOVA test is to produce useful results?

3. Discuss the meaning of the decision to reject the null hypothesis.

4. Discuss the two different methods used in ANOVA to estimate the population variance. Which is an estimate of σ^2 regardless of the truth of the null hypothesis? Which is a valid estimate if, and only if, the null hypothesis is true?

5. "If the test statistic is less than or equal to 1, the null hypothesis will never be rejected." Give the rationale behind this statement.

6. Identify the columns and rows used in an ANOVA table and discuss the meaning of the values that are entered in each cell.

7. Discuss the p-value approach to ANOVA testing.

8. Discuss how to use Fisher's procedure to compare means.

Projects/Issues to Consider

1. Go to the library and locate a periodical of interest to you that describes an ANOVA test. Discuss the meaning of the terms used in the article.

2. Do some research and investigate a variable that could be measured for three or more groups. (Some examples are games won by the teams in the different NHL divisions; number of credits for first-, second-, third-, and fourth-year students at your school; prices of stocks on the various exchanges; and so on.) Once you have sample values for each factor, perform an ANOVA test. Discuss your methodology and your results.

3. Access the Internet and locate a site that contains data appropriate to an ANOVA. Do the ANOVA test and, if appropriate, use Fisher's procedure to determine which means are significantly different. Write a report summarizing your results.

4. Take a sample of students divided into four groups: 1 = females who have a job during the school year; 2 = females who do not have a job during the school year; 3 = males who have a job during the school year; and 4 = males who do not have a job during the school year. Ask the members of your sample a question that requires a numerical response (e.g., What is your GPA? or How many times in a month do you go out on a date? or How much time in a week do you study?). Do the ANOVA test on these responses and, if appropriate, use Fisher's procedure to determine which means are significantly different. Write a report summarizing your results.

Computer/Calculator Exercises

For all the exercises in this section, assume the populations involved are normally distributed with equal variances.

1. In "Greenhouse Screening of Corn Gluten Meal as a Natural Control Product for Broadleaf and Grass Weeds" (*HortScience*, 1995), Bingaman and Christians described an experiment in which the application of corn gluten meal (CGM) as a weed control product was evaluated. One portion of their data described the reduction in survival, relative to the control, of weeds. The results are in the following table (Data = CGMSurv2):

Percent Reduction Quantity of CGM

324 g(m^2)	649 g(m^2)	973 g(m^2)
60	81	72
31	35	41
49	63	63
78	99	100
80	95	96
66	33	94

Percent Reduction Quantity of CGM

324 g(m^2)	649 g(m^2)	973 g(m^2)
82	88	99
85	85	96
75	94	97
75	90	100
63	54	83
37	78	100
51	70	82
56	53	92
97	95	100
0	20	71
87	96	99
42	43	51
51	85	97
0	18	35
6	29	79
43	65	78

a) Produce an ANOVA table for this data set.

b) Test the hypothesis at the .01 level that the population mean reductions are the same for the three amounts of CGM.

c) If H_0 is rejected, use Fisher's procedure at the .01 level to determine which means are significantly different.

2. Data were collected on a sample of students from a graduating class of business administration majors. Part of the data consists of the concentration, university GPA, and high school GPA of 44 majors, and a few example lines of data follow (Data = BusGPAs):

Concentr	ConcCode	Col GPA	HS GPA
MIS	1	2.547	3.30
MIS	1	2.895	3.39
FIM	2	3.617	3.71
MGT	3	3.721	3.86
MIS	1	3.044	3.58
MM	4	3.558	4.04
HRM	5	3.350	4.05

a) Produce an ANOVA table for college GPA.

b) Test the hypothesis at the .10 level that the population mean college GPAs are the same for the seven concentrations.

c) If H_0 is rejected, use Fisher's procedure at the .10 level to determine which means are significantly different.

d) Produce an ANOVA table for high school GPA.

e) Test the hypothesis at the .10 level that the population mean high school GPAs are the same for the seven concentrations.

f) If H_0 is rejected, use Fisher's procedure at the .10 level to determine which means are significantly different.

3. In a class project, William Wilkie, an instructor for an engineering lab course at Cuesta College that involves eight different experiments, considered the distribution of grades in the worksheets for each experiment. While there is also a lab report that goes with each experiment, the worksheet involves key concepts and gives the student an opportunity to work with thought-provoking questions and, because of this, is considered to be a better measure of learning. Wilkie wanted to examine the grades to see if there is a significant difference in the worksheet grades so he could adjust his future teaching and testing emphases (Data = EngLab):

Lab 1	Lab 2	Lab 3	Lab 4	Lab 5	Lab 6	Lab 7	Lab 8
20	19	19.5	20	20	18	19	20
18.5	17.5	19.5	20	20	19	19	20
20	16	19	19	19	19	20	18
17	18	19.5	20	18.5	18	19	20
18.5	16.5	19.5	20	20	18	19	20
20	15	20	18	20	19	20	20
18	19	19	19	20	19	16.5	20
20	18	20	20	20	19	16	18
17	20	20	20	20	19	20	20
20	17.5	19.5	19.5	19.5	20	20	20
20	17	20	20	20	19	19	20
19	19	20	19.5	20	20	19	18
19	18	20	20	20	19	18	20
18	18	20	20	20	19	16	20
17.5	18	20	19.5	20	19	20	18
17	16.5	19.5	18	20	20	18	18
17	19	19	19	20	20	16.5	20
19	18	20	19	20	19	16	18
17	17.5	19.5	20	20	19	18	20
17	19	20	19.5	20	20	19	20
18	18	20	19	20	19	16	18
	17	19		20	20	20	20
	19				19	16	

a) Produce an ANOVA table for this data set.

b) Test the hypothesis at the .05 level that the population mean grades are the same for the eight experiments.

c) If H_0 is rejected, use Fisher's procedure at the .05 level to determine which means are significantly different.

4. Often structural engineers are interested in finding the safety factors of older bridges in order to estimate their capacity and life expectancy. In a class project, B. Yu examined a report, "Safety Analysis of Suspension-Bridges Cables: Williamsburg Bridge" (*Journal of Structural Engineers*), that presented a methodology to estimate the current safety factor of suspension cables. The tensile strength—the maximum force that the wire is able to withstand before permanent plastic deformation occurs in the wire—was determined for individual wires that make up the cable. Part of the data follows in which ten measurements are taken upon each wire (Data = Wires):

IB3	IF4	IG4	IH2	IA4	IF1	1C2	ID2	IG2	IC4
26.1312	27.3886	28.6727	28.9993	28.9911	27.9250	28.4384	22.3971	29.8204	28.8817
25.7393	27.3542	28.6995	27.7400	28.9361	27.1455	28.0756	25.5473	27.7038	29.4408
26.0385	27.2589	28.5273	28.4535	29.2038	29.2977	28.2062	24.8356	29.1419	28.9819
25.6414	27.5543	28.3226	28.6897	29.0281	28.3971	28.1555	25.5928	28.5591	29.3027
25.3678	27.5298	28.5121	27.9492	28.7565	27.8106	28.5681	25.0349	28.8764	29.0935
25.8641	27.3116	28.6416	29.1690	29.2474	27.9334	28.1721	27.4626	28.0602	28.7556
25.9669	27.5371	28.5888	28.5398	29.0712	27.3217	28.1322	23.6698	28.2932	29.4688
25.7754	27.4359	28,5926	29.2668	29.0612	27.4500	28.1867	24.7550	29.1790	28.9226
25.5610	27.1807	28.7679	27.7827	29.0719	28.4733	28.6079	25.9276	28.9345	28.7565
26.0176	27.2393	28.4270	28.2377	29.0328	27.4008	28.1455	24.7471	30.0529	29.3187

a) Produce an ANOVA table for this data set.

b) Test the hypothesis at the .05 level that the population mean tensile strengths are the same for the ten wires.

c) If H_0 is rejected, use Fisher's procedure at the .05 level to determine which means are significantly different.

5. As part of an investigation into the possible effects of landfill on groundwater chemistry, the following measurements of conductivity, hardness, and chloride were made on water from several local water wells (Data = LOCondty, LOHardns, LOChlord):

Conductivity (μ hos/cm)					
MW-6	MW-7	MW-8	MW-9	MW-10	MW-11
1,220	1,680	1,325	1,810	970	1,350
1,130	1,900	1,150	1,700	1,150	1,350
1,400	1,700	1,300	1,725	1,100	1,250
1,400	1,600	1,400	1,500	1,010	1,250
1,625	1,580	1,360	1,725	880	1,300
1,670	1,620	1,340	1,700	975	1,230
2,100	1,700	1,250	2,000	1,300	1,250
1,070	1,840	1,360	1,900	1,050	1,130
1,622	1,772	1,417	2,040	1,116	1,300

Hardness (mg/L)				
MW-7	MW-8	MW-9	MW-10	MW-11
908	692	1,170	245	334
1,180	706	1,120	242	327
930	789	1,110	252	326
833	742	885	256	306
960	780	1,130	254	294
871	776	840	270	290
913	739	1,320	256	291
1,040	782	1,130	268	268
918	736	1,080	246	294

Chloride ($\mu\gamma$/L)					
MW-6	MW-7	MW-8	MW-9	MW-10	MW-11
310	192	99	169	215	164
323	202	98	162	215	146
338	150	98	154	215	137
323	130	95	115	214	133
396	148	106	178	225	134
407	136	98	119	218	130
410	182	103	223	218	127
374	170	103	163	211	120
279	149	96	165	258	118

a) Produce an ANOVA table for conductivity.

b) Test the hypothesis at the .10 level that the population mean conductivity readings are the same for the six wells.

c) If H_0 is rejected, use Fisher's procedure at the .10 level to determine which means are significantly different.

d) Produce an ANOVA table for hardness.

e) Test the hypothesis at the .05 level that the population mean hardness readings are the same for the five wells.

f) If H_0 is rejected, use Fisher's procedure at the .05 level to determine which means are significantly different.

g) Produce an ANOVA table for chloride.

h) Test the hypothesis at the .01 level that the population mean chloride readings are the same for the six wells.

i) If H_0 is rejected, use Fisher's procedure at the .01 level to determine which means are significantly different.

6. The data set and description of this exercise were kindly provided by Jeff Tupen of TENERA, Inc. Jeff has spent years working on *Alia carinata*, or the carinate dove shell. His data set contains morphometric shell variables measured from the shelled gastropod *Alia carinata* from four habitats: B = Benthic (subtidal benthic hard bottom, i.e., a rocky subtidal benchrock outcropping in approximately 10 m); G = Gastroclonium (intertidal [+ 1 m] *Gastroclonium subarticulatum*, hollow branch seaweed); M = Macrocystis (*Macrocystis pyrifera*, giant kelp surface canopies); Z = Zostera (*Zostera marina*, eelgrass). A few lines of data (first six variables in millimetres, last two in degrees) follow (Data = Alia2):

Habitat	Shell Height	Shell Width	Spire Height	Spire Width	Aperature Height	Aperature Width	Shell Angle	Spire Angle
B	7.01	3.31	2.50	1.98	3.02	1.45	42.0	44.5
B	6.53	3.12	2.23	1.80	2.81	1.25	46.5	47.0
B	7.57	3.62	2.74	2.24	3.04	1.60	45.5	43.0
M	6.86	3.45	2.21	1.90	2.90	1.53	50.5	52.0
M	7.49	3.54	2.54	2.01	3.11	1.37	45.5	45.0
G	7.06	3.42	2.23	2.00	3.13	1.58	44.0	45.5
Z	6.48	3.51	1.94	1.77	2.91	1.49	55.5	56.0
Z	6.81	3.59	2.24	2.04	2.90	1.54	52.0	51.0

a) Produce an ANOVA table for each variable of this data set.

b) Test the hypothesis at the .05 level that the population means are the same for each of these variables.

c) For each time the H_0 is rejected, use Fisher's procedure at the .05 level to determine which means are significantly different.

7. Use the World Wide Web to access DASL at DASLMeth. Click on *ANOVA* and select one of the stories.

a) Produce an ANOVA table for the data set.

b) Test the hypothesis at the .05 level that the population means are the same.

c) If H_0 is rejected, use Fisher's procedure at the .05 level to determine which means are significantly different.

8. Use the World Wide Web to access The Food and Agriculture Organization of the United Nations at UNFAO.

There are links to many data sets at that site. Select one that has a quantitative response and an attribute variable that can be used to define groups.

a) Produce an ANOVA table for the data set.

b) Test the hypothesis at the .05 level that the population means are the same for the groups.

c) If H_0 is rejected, use Fisher's procedure at the .05 level to determine which group means are significantly different.

9. Use the World Wide Web to access FedStats: Regional Statistics at FedStReg. There are links to many data sets at that site. Select one that has a quantitative response and an attribute variable that can be used to define groups.

a) Produce an ANOVA table for the data set.

b) Test the hypothesis at the .05 level that the population means are the same for the groups.

c) If H_0 is rejected, use Fisher's procedure at the .05 level to determine which group means are significantly different.

CHAPTER 11

Chi-Square Tests: Goodness-of-Fit and Contingency Table Methods

LOOKING AHEAD

In this chapter you'll learn how to evaluate the market response to a new product and how to compare injuries in different sports. In the early pages, we'll first present an overview of the purpose of two types of hypothesis tests that use the Chi-square probability distributions. This orientation leads us to a discussion of the procedural steps needed to conduct such tests. Then, we'll follow these procedural steps to carry out goodness-of-fit and contingency table hypothesis tests.

Thus, after studying this chapter, you should be able to

- Explain the purpose of the (a) goodness-of-fit test and (b) contingency table test.

- Describe the steps needed to carry out such hypothesis tests.

- Use these procedural steps to arrive at statistical decisions when goodness-of-fit and contingency table tests are made.

11.1   Chi-Square Testing: Purpose and Procedure

Purpose and Assumptions

You saw in Chapter 3 that a variable of interest is typically obtained by counting or by using some measuring device. In this chapter we'll concentrate on techniques that can be used for attribute or qualitative data and that involve counting the data items that fall into selected testing categories. And we'll be dealing with two types of hypothesis tests—the goodness-of-fit and contingency table tests—that focus on count data.

The Goodness-of-Fit Test   In Chapter 5 we saw that in a *binomial experiment* the same action (trial) is repeated a fixed number of times under identical conditions, and each action is independent of the others. For each trial there are only two possible outcomes (success or failure). Now, though, our interest in conducting a goodness-of-fit test is to evaluate a *multinomial experiment* in which there can be more than two possible outcomes for each trial.

> A **multinomial experiment** is one that consists of a fixed number of identical and independent trials, the outcome for each trial falls into only one of the several (or k) possible categories or classes, and the probability that a single trial will result in a specified outcome remains the same throughout the experiment. In a multinomial experiment involving n repeated independent trials, where p_k denotes the probability that the outcome of any one trial is of type k, the probability of obtaining x_1 outcomes of type 1, x_2 outcomes of type 2, ... , and x_k outcomes of type k, (where $x_1 + x_2 + \cdots + x_k = n$), is given by $p(x_1, x_2, \ldots, x_k) = \frac{n!}{x_1! \, x_2! \ldots x_k!} p_1^{x_1} p_2^{x_2} \cdots p_k^{x_k}$. This distribution is called the multinomial distribution.

Often, we will be interested in seeing if the probability of an outcome falling into each category follows a particular probability distribution. Thus, a **goodness-of-fit test** is one that's used to see if the distribution of the observed outcomes of the sample trials supports a hypothesized population distribution.

For example, a researcher can use a goodness-of-fit test to see if a new product is likely to have altered the market shares commanded by competing products. Or a political pollster might use p_1, p_2, p_3, and p_4 to represent the proportion of all voters who will vote Liberal, NDP, Conservative, or Other in the next election, and then test the hypothesis that $p_1 = .55$, $p_2 = .15$, $p_3 = .20$, and $p_4 = .10$.

In a goodness-of-fit test, then, our purpose is to establish a hypothesis about how we think the data items will be distributed into the different categories of interest. Then we'll conduct a test to see if the observed results conform to the results that would be expected if our hypothesis is true. The *assumptions in a goodness-of-fit test are*

1. The sample is a simple random sample, and frequency counts are obtained for the possible k classes or cells.

2. The expected frequency for each of the k categories is at least five.

The Contingency Table Tests   You saw in Chapter 4 that a *contingency table* is one that shows all the classifications of the variables being studied—that is, it accounts for all contingencies in a particular situation. In this chapter we'll use a contingency table to see if two classification variables are likely to be independent. Each cell in a contingency table is at the intersection of a row and a column. The rows represent one classification category, and the columns represent another such category.

Thus, for our present needs, the table contains values that are grouped in row-variable and column-variable ways.

> A **contingency table test for independence** is one that tests the hypothesis that the data in a single sample are cross-classified in independent ways.

For example, a medical school researcher may use a contingency table test to evaluate the change in the condition of patients (one variable) according to the drug treatments they have received (the other variable). Or a political scientist may classify a sample of voters by location of residence (one variable) and preference for candidates seeking office (the other variable).

The *assumptions in a contingency table test for independence are*

1. The sample data items are obtained through random selection.

2. The expected frequency for each cell in the table is at least five.

> A **contingency table test for homogeneity of proportions** is one that tests the hypothesis that the proportion of elements of each type is the same in several different populations.

In this situation, samples are selected from several different populations. The sample sizes are specified in advance, so that either the row totals or the column totals are known before the samples are selected. For example, a political pollster may want to decide whether the distribution of Liberal, NDP, Conservative, and Other voters is the same in B.C. Alberta, and Ontario. The pollster may decide to determine the voting preferences of a sample of 300 B.C. voters, a second sample of 200 Alberta voters, and a third sample of 500 Ontario voters. The results could then be classified according to province of residence (one variable) and voting preference (the second variable).

The assumptions in a contingency table test for homogeneity of proportions are

1. Each sample is obtained through random selection.

2. The expected frequency for each cell is at least five.

Self-Testing Review 11.1

1. What is a multinomial experiment?

2. What is the objective of a goodness-of-fit test?

3. List the assumptions in a goodness-of-fit test.

4. What is the objective of a contingency table test for independence?

5. List the assumptions in a contingency table test for homogeneity.

11.2 The Goodness-of-Fit Test

We've seen that the goodness-of-fit test is used to see if a population under study "fits" or follows one with given probability distribution values. For example, such a test may be used to decide whether the sample data follows a normal, binomial, Poisson, or uniform probability distribution.

The Procedural Steps for the Goodness-of-Fit Test

Once again, our topic is a hypothesis-testing procedure, and once again we follow a familiar seven-step process that begins with a statement of the hypotheses to be tested and concludes when a statistical decision is made.

Step 1: State the Null and Alternative Hypotheses The null hypothesis for a goodness-of-fit test is essentially that the population being analyzed fits some specified probability distribution pattern. This pattern can vary, of course, according to the logic of the experiment. The alternative hypothesis, then, is simply that the population doesn't fit the specified distribution. For example, in one test, H_0 might be that the population distribution is uniform. A **uniform distribution** is one in which all the possible categories for the outcomes are considered to have an equal or uniform probability. Thus, if an experiment with a hypothesized uniform distribution has k categories, each category should contain $100/k$ percent of all the sample outcomes. The alternative hypothesis in this case is that the population distribution is *not* uniform. Or the null hypothesis in a goodness-of-fit test could be that the population percentage breakdown of four possible blood types A, B, O, and AB is 42 percent, 10 percent, 45 percent, and 3 percent, respectively. The alternative hypothesis in such a test is that at least one of the stated percentages isn't supported by the test results.

Step 2: Select the Level of Significance This step doesn't differ from similar steps in other tests. A criterion for rejection of H_0 is necessary, and an α value of .01 or .05 is typically used.

Step 3: Determine the Test Distribution to Use The goodness-of-fit is based on the Chi-square probability distribution introduced in Chapter 7. To summarize here, a χ^2 distribution has the following properties:

- The scale of possible χ^2 values extends from zero indefinitely to the right.

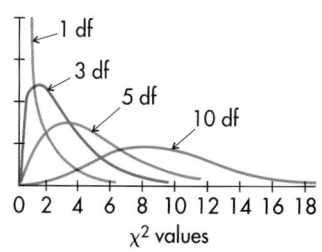

FIGURE 11.1 χ^2 distributions for different degrees of freedom.

- A χ^2 distribution is not symmetrical, and a different one is used for each change in the number of degrees of freedom that can exist in a sampling situation (see *Figure 11.1*).

The Chi-square table we'll use in this chapter is found in Appendix 6.

Step 4: Define the Rejection or Critical Region We must know the Chi-square value that is the boundary of the area of rejection in a goodness-of-fit test. To find this critical χ^2 value, we must know two things:

1. *The level of significance* (specified in *Step 2* of our procedure).

2. *The degrees of freedom* (df). In a goodness-of-fit test, the value of df is

$$\text{df (goodness-of-fit)} = k - 1 \qquad (11.1)$$

where k = the number of possible outcomes in the experiment

Let's suppose that we are making a goodness-of-fit test at the .05 level, and there are four possible outcomes in our experiment. In that case, the critical χ^2 value can be found in Appendix 6 under the column labelled .05. (You'll be pleased to know that the rejection region in all goodness-of-fit and contingency table tests is found only in the *right tail* of the χ^2 distribution.) To find the cell in the .05 column that we need, we must also know the proper df row to use. With four possible outcomes, df $= k - 1$, or $4 - 1$, or 3. Thus, the critical χ^2 value for our test is 7.81 (.05 column, df 3 row).

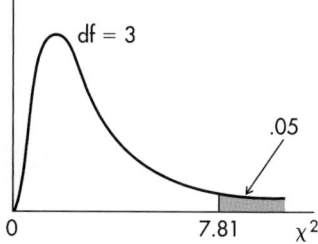

Step 5: State the Decision Rule The general form of the decision rule for the goodness-of-fit test is

Reject H_0 in favour of H_1 if the test statistic $\chi^2 > \chi^2$ critical value found in *Step 4* above. Otherwise, fail to reject H_0.

Thus, for our goodness-of-fit test at the .05 level with four possible outcomes, the decision rule is

Reject H_0 in favour of H_1 if $\chi^2 > 7.81$. Otherwise, fail to reject H_0.

Step 6: Compute the Test Statistic The test statistic is a Chi-square test statistic.

$$\chi^2 = \Sigma\left[\frac{(O - E)^2}{E}\right] \qquad (11.2)$$

where O = an *observed* (sample) frequency
            E = an *expected* (hypothesized) frequency if H_0 is true

The O, or observed, values are found in the problem (sample) data set, and the E, or expected values, are computed to conform to the null hypothesis that is being tested. If the observed frequencies or counts and the expected frequencies are identical, formula 11.3 shows us that the test statistic is zero. From the standpoint of verifying the null hypothesis, a computed test statistic of zero is ideal since our sample data will be exactly what we had expected. But you're sophisticated enough by now in matters statistical to know that it's very unlikely that the O and E values in an application will be identical even when H_0 is true. Sampling variation will, after all, usually cause some discrepancy between the O and E values.

Step 7: Make the Statistical Decision   If the test statistic computed in *Step 6* exceeds the Chi-square critical value specified in the decision rule *(Step 5)*, then it falls into the rejection region (see *Figure 11.2*), and H_0 is rejected. If, however, χ^2 falls below this χ^2 value, then the null hypothesis cannot be rejected.

The following example shows how χ^2 concepts can be used to test the goodness-of-fit between sample data and a uniform distribution. The test for goodness-of-fit between sample data and a uniform distribution is the simplest, and it is quite useful.

Example 11.1   The Bitter Bottling Company has developed "Featherweight," the cola with fewer calories and less taste. To evaluate this new product, the marketing manager gives a taste test to a random sample of 300 people. Each person in the sample tastes Featherweight and four other diet cola brands. To avoid bias, the actual brand labels are replaced by the letters A, B, C, D, and E. The results of the sample are shown in the following table:

Results of Bitter Bottling's Taste Test

Brand	Number Preferring Brand (O)
A	50
B	65
C	45
D	70
E	70
	300

Let's now follow our familiar seven-step testing procedure to evaluate Featherweight.

◆ **Solution:**

Step 1: State the Null and Alternative Hypotheses   The hypotheses are H_0: The population distribution is uniform—that is, each of the cola brands is preferred by an equal percentage of the population.

H_1: The population distribution is *not* uniform—that is, the taste preference frequencies are not equal.

Step 2: Select the Level of Significance Let's assume that Bitter's marketing manager wants to conduct the test at the .05 level of significance.

Step 3: Determine the Test Distribution to Use We know to use a χ^2 distribution as long as all the E values are at least five.

Step 4: Define the Rejection or Critical Region The level of significance is .05, and the df value is $k-1$, or $5-1$, or 4. Thus, the critical χ^2 table value that is the boundary of the rejection region is found in the table in Appendix 6 at the intersection of the .05 column and the 4-df row. This table value is 9.49.

Step 5: State the Decision Rule The decision rule is

Reject H_0 in favour of H_1 if $\chi^2 > 9.49$. Otherwise, fail to reject H_0.

Step 6: Compute the Test Statistic
The observed frequencies (O) are given in our sample data set. And four additional columns useful for our computations are added to this data set in Table 11.1. If the null hypothesis is true, we would expect an equal or uniform number of people to prefer each of the five cola brands. That is, if there's no significant difference in taste preference, then one-fifth, or 20 percent, of the tasters should prefer brand A, 20 percent should prefer brand B, and so on. Thus, the E value for each brand should be 20 percent of 300, or 60.

As we've seen, the appropriate formula for our test statistic is

$$\chi^2 = \Sigma\left[\frac{(O-E)^2}{E}\right]$$

Table 11.1 shows the computation of the test statistic for this goodness-of-fit example problem. The steps to compute the test statistic are

1. Subtract the E value from the O value—that is, $O-E$—and record the difference (as shown in the fourth column of Table 11.1). As a check of your math, note that $\Sigma(O-E)$ must equal zero, and note as well that $\Sigma O = \Sigma E$.

TABLE 11.1 COMPUTATION OF THE TEST RATIO FOR EXAMPLE 11.1

Brand	Number Preferring (O)	E	$O-E$	$(O-E)^2$	$\dfrac{(O-E)^2}{E}$
A	50	60	−10	100	1.667
B	65	60	5	25	.417
C	45	60	−15	225	3.750
D	70	60	10	100	1.667
E	70	60	10	100	1.667
	300	300	0		9.168

$$\chi^2 = \Sigma\left[\frac{(O-E)^2}{E}\right] = 9.168$$

FIGURE 11.2 MINITAB calculation of goodness-of-fit test statistic.

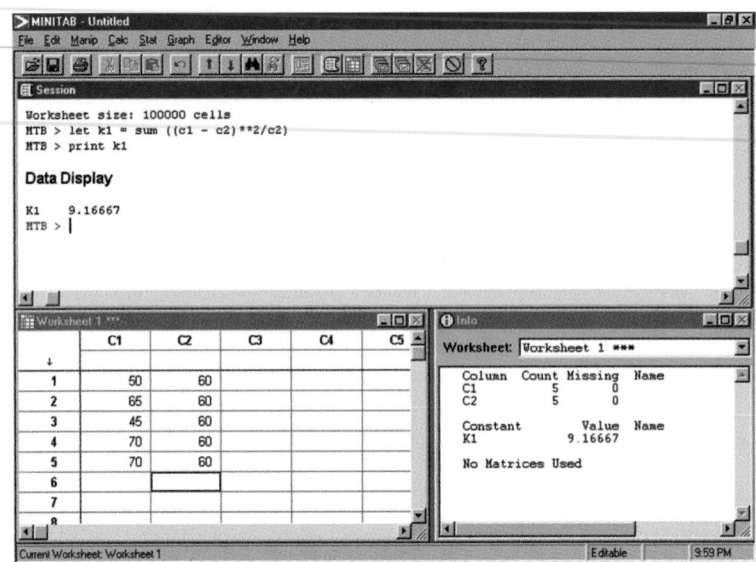

2. To eliminate negative values, square the $O - E$ differences to get $(O - E)^2$ (fifth column, Table 11.1).

3. Divide each of these squared differences—$(O - E)^2$—by the E value to get $(O - E)^2/E$ (last column, Table 11.1).

4. Add the $(O - E)^2/E$ values to get the computed test statistic value (total of last column, Table 11.1). As you can see, the test statistic is 9.168.

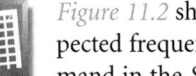 *Figure 11.2* shows how a MINITAB software user can supply observed and expected frequencies and calculate the value of the test statistic by a simple command in the *Session Window*. The computed value is placed in the constant $k1$, which then can be viewed either by typing the session command "print k1" or simply viewed in the *Info Window* (in *Figure 11.2* we have done both).

Step 7: Make the Statistical Decision We fail to reject our H_0 because the test statistic 9.168 (9.16667 by MINITAB) is less than 9.49. At the .05 level, we cannot reject the hypothesis that all the cola brands are preferred by an equal percentage of the population. We must conclude that at the .05 level we do not have significant evidence that Featherweight is better (or worse) tasting than the other brands. ◆

Example 11.2   Suppose that Adam Shaw, a management consultant, is hired to evaluate the market response to a new and improved irrigation pump developed by Delta Corporation. Two other companies—Alpha Products and Beta Industries—supply competitive pumps. For some time, Alpha has controlled 50 percent of this market, Beta has had 30 percent of the market, and Delta has had a 20 percent market share. Adam's assignment now is to see if Delta's new pump is likely to cause a shift in these market percentages.

Adam assembles a random sample of 200 pump users who are familiar with Delta's new product and with the competing equipment. The purchase preferences of these 200 users is as follows:

Product Evaluated	Number Preferring (O)
Alpha's pump	74
Beta's pump	62
Delta's new pump	64
	200

What conclusions can Adam draw from this survey response?

◆ **Solution:**

Step 1: State the Null and Alternative Hypotheses The null hypothesis is that the new pump has no effect on the market shares controlled by the three companies. That is,

H_0: The population market share percentages are Alpha = 50, Beta = 30, and Delta = 20.

The alternative hypothesis is

H_1: The population market share percentages are no longer as specified in H_0.

Step 2: Select the Level of Significance Let's assume Adam wants to make this test at the .01 level of significance.

Step 3: Determine the Test Distribution to Use Adam correctly employs the Chi-square distribution.

Step 4: Define the Rejection or Critical Region The level of significance is .01, and the df value is $k - 1$, or $3 - 1$, or 2. Thus, the χ^2 critical value is found in Appendix 6 at the intersection of the .01 column and the 2-df row. This table value is 9.21.

Step 5: State the Decision Rule The decision rule is

Reject H_0 in favour of H_1 if $\chi^2 > 9.21$. Otherwise, fail to reject H_0.

Step 6: Compute the Test Statistic The observed frequencies (O) are given in Adam's sample data set. And four additional columns are added to this data set in Table 11.2. *If the null hypothesis is true,* the expected number (E) preferring each pump is shown in the column labelled E of Table 11.2. Thus, Adam would expect that 50 percent of the 200 pump users, or 100 users, would prefer the Alpha product, 60 users would be expected to opt for the Beta pump, and the remaining 40 users would be expected to favour Delta's new offering. With the observed and expected values now available, Adam can compute the test statistic as shown in Table 11.2.

Step 7: Make the Statistical Decision Since the test statistic of 21.23 is greater than the Chi-square table value of 9.21, Adam must reject H_0 that the population market share percentage controlled by the three companies remains unchanged. Adam can happily report to his client that the introduction of Delta's new pump has apparently altered the market share structure. Although the χ^2 test itself doesn't support any further conclusions, an examination of Adam's data suggests that Delta's new product

TABLE 11.2   ADAM SHAW'S WORKSHEET TO COMPUTE THE TEST RATIO FOR THE PUMP PREFERENCE DATA IN EXAMPLE 11.2

Product Evaluated	Number Preferring (O)	E	$O - E$	$(O - E)^2$	$\dfrac{(O - E)^2}{E}$
Alpha's pump	74	100	−26	676	6.76
Beta's pump	62	60	2	4	.07
Delta's new pump	64	40	24	576	14.40
	200	200	0		21.23

$$\chi^2 = \Sigma \left[\frac{(O - E)^2}{E} \right] = 21.23$$

Face-to-face interviews are often used to gather data for market-research and demographic studies.

© Jeff Greenberg/MR/Visuals Unlimited

will increase its market share at Alpha's expense (at least until Alpha makes its own χ^2 test and rushes to bring out its new version). ◆

Example 11.3   **A Recreational Exercise** The percentages of first-, second-, third-, and fourth-year students enrolled at a university are 18, 13, 21, and 48 percent, respectively. A sample of 170 students using the gymnasium were asked their year of study. The results are

Year of Study			
1st	2nd	3rd	4th
30	28	37	75

Using a level of significance of .05, test to see if the percentages of first-, second-, third-, and fourth-year students who use the gymnasium are equal to the percentages enrolled at the university.

◆ **Solution:**

The hypotheses are

H_0: The population year of study percentages are first = 18, second = 13, third = 21, and fourth = 48.
H_1: The population year of study percentages are not as specified in H_0.

We have decided to do this test at the .05 level of significance, and it is clear we should use the Chi-square distribution with a df value of $k - 1 = 4 - 1 = 3$. We will use both MINITAB and a TI-83 calculator to compute the test statistic and generate a p-value for this test, so the decision rule is

Reject H_0 in favour of H_1 if p-value < .05. Otherwise, fail to reject H_0.

MINITAB (*Figure 11.3a*) and the TI-83 calculator (screen 3 of *Figure 11.3b*) calculated the value of the test statistic as $\chi^2 = 2.168$, with an associated p-value of .538. As this p-value is not less than .05, we fail to reject H_0. At the .05 level, there is insufficient evidence to indicate that the distribution of the class levels of the users of the gymnasium differs from the distribution of the university class levels. ◆

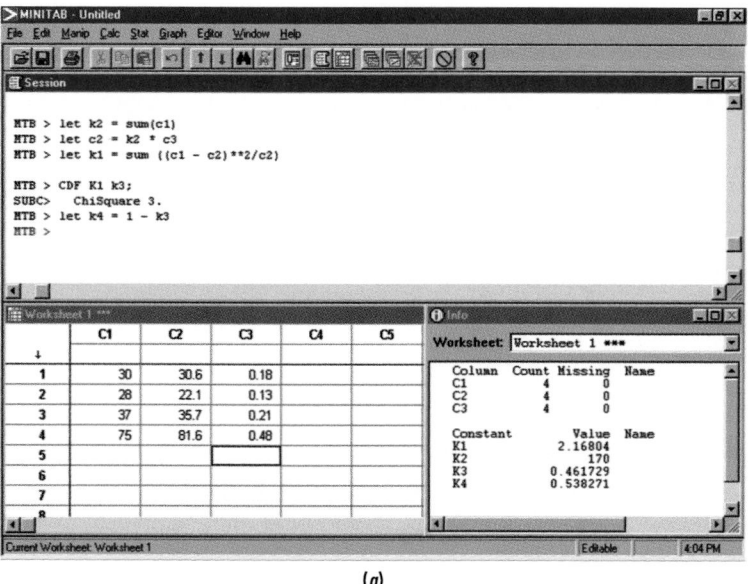

(a)

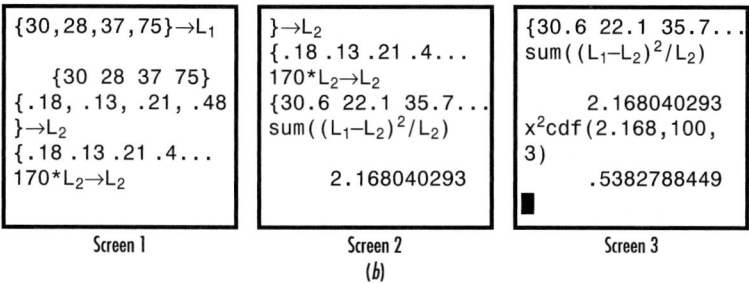

Screen 1   Screen 2   Screen 3

(b)

FIGURE 11.3 (a) To calculate the test statistic, we first entered the observed frequencies into C1 and the enrollment percentages into C3. Then we multiplied the total of C1 by the percentages in C3 to compute the E values, which we put into C2. (Note the first two lines in the **Session** window and the resulting columns of the **Worksheet.**) Using the same "let" command as in Figure 11.2, we calculate 2.168 as the test statistic and place that value into the constant $k1$. The last three lines in the **Session** window use MINITAB commands to calculate the p-value, which is placed into $k4$ and can be read in the **Info Window.** (b) To perform the test, enter the observed frequencies into L1 and the percentages claimed in the null hypothesis into L2. This may be done on the home screen as shown in screen 1 or using **STAT** > **Edit** as we have done before. To get the expected frequencies, enter 170*L2 → L2. This puts the expected frequencies into L2. To calculate the χ^2 statistic on the home screen, enter **sum** $((L1 - L2)^2/L2)$ and press **ENTER.** Recall that **sum** is a command on the **LISTS**>**MATH** menu. To get the p-value, we use the χ^2 cdf command on the **DISTR** menu. The syntax is χ^2**cdf (Low, upper, df).** In screen 3 we used 100 as an upper endpoint of the interval somewhat arbitrarily—any large number will do. The df is $4 - 1 = 3$. In screen 3 you can see the value of the test statistic and its associate p-value.

Self-Testing Review 11.2

6. The personnel director for a large insurance company claims there has been a change in the level of education of management personnel in the last five years. Research shows that five years ago the highest level of education for 15 percent of the managers was a high school diploma; for 64 percent, it was a college degree; for 8 percent, it was some graduate school; and for 13 percent, it was a master's degree or higher. A recent random sample of 216 of today's managers yielded the following results:

Highest Level of Education	Number of Managers
High school diploma	19
College degree	132
Graduate school	30
Master's degree or higher	35

At the .01 level, does a goodness-of-fit test indicate that there has been a change in the level of education for the management population in the last five years?

7. In 1987 10 percent of nursing home residents were younger than 65, 13 percent of residents were between 65 and less than 75, 32 percent were between 75 and less than 84, and 45 percent were 84 and older. The following data are from a recent random sample of 6,629 nursing home residents:

Age	Current Number
Younger than 65	398
65 and <75	663
75 and <84	2,254
84 and over	3,314

At the .05 level, has the age distribution of all nursing home residents changed since 1987?

8. The production manager at a food products plant claims that absenteeism among workers is more common on some weekdays than on others. The following sample data were recorded last week:

Day	Number Absent
Monday	24
Tuesday	17
Wednesday	15
Thursday	19
Friday	25

Test the hypothesis at the .05 level that absences occur uniformly over the five days.

9. A botanist checking for dominant and recessive traits interbreeds two types of plants and expects four classes of hybrid results to appear in the Mendelian ratio of 9:3:3:1 (56.25 percent, 18.75 percent, 18.75 percent, and 6.25 percent). The results of her experiment show that there are 860 plants of one class, 350 of another, 300 of a third, and 90 of a fourth class. Test the hypothesis at the .05 level that her results are in accordance with the Mendelian ratio.

10. There are four branches of a local bank. Last year, branch A handled 28.42 percent of all transactions, branch B had 21.81 percent of these transactions, branch C had 17.81 percent, and branch D had 31.96 percent. A new shopping mall has recently opened, and the vice president of the bank wants to see if this opening has produced any changes in the distribution of transactions. The transactions for a week selected at random after the mall opening were

Branch	Transactions
A	583
B	749
C	427
D	732

Test the hypothesis at the .01 level that the distribution of transactions has changed after the construction of the new mall.

11. A random sampling of police records shows the following number of crimes were committed in a mid-sized city for each day of the week:

Day	Number of Crimes
Sunday	74
Monday	63
Tuesday	57
Wednesday	68
Thursday	79
Friday	98
Saturday	119

Test the hypothesis at the .05 level that there is a uniform distribution in the number of crimes committed each day of the week.

12. A few years ago it was known that 37.6 percent of first-year college students had applied to no college other than the one they were attending, 14.7 percent had applied to one other school, 15.8 percent had applied to two others, 13.7 percent to three others, and 18.2 percent had applied to four or more other schools. A guidance counsellor is now investigating the attitudes and characteristics of first-year students. A random sample of 308 first-year students were asked for the number of colleges they applied to other than the one they were attending, and the responses were as follows:

Other Colleges Applied to	Number of Students
0	85
1	47
2	58
3	37
4 or more	81

Test the hypothesis at the .05 level that the sample distribution fits the one spelled out above.

13. Having decided that a giraffe was a silly mascot, the students at a university have decided to replace the giraffe with a new mascot. The dean of students thinks that half of the students favour a snail as the new school mascot, one-third favour a squid, while the remainder favour a clam. A random sample of 60 students yielded the following:

Favourite	Snail	Squid	Clam
Number	20	25	15

Does this sample fit the idea of the dean of students at the .05 level?

14. In February 2003, CTV News reported that a 14-year-old Vancouver girl will likely face years of constructive surgery after being viciously mauled by two dogs. "The right side of her face was shredded," said plastic surgeon James Boyle. Prompted by this incident, a concerned parent, determined to learn more about attacks by dogs, found the following data, reported by the Canadian Hospitals Injury Reporting and Prevention Program (CHIRPP) from a sample of 1,237 injuries associated with Dog Bites and Dog attacks. (The time of day at which the injury occurred was recorded for only 1,030 of the injuries.)

Time at Which Injury Occurred

	Number
8 A.M. to noon	127
Noon to 4 P.M.	250
4 P.M to 8 P.M.	405
8 P.M. to midnight	223
Midnight to 8 A.M	25
Total	1,030

Day During Which Injury Occurred

	Number
Sunday	230
Monday	161
Tuesday	138
Wednesday	147
Thursday	154
Friday	153
Saturday	254
Total	1,237

Season During Which Injury Occurred

	Number
Spring (March–May)	332
Summer (June–August)	467
Fall (September–November)	265
Winter (December–February)	173
Total	1,237

a) Test the hypothesis at the .01 level that of all dog attacks on people in Canada, 10 percent occur in the time period 8 A.M. to noon, 25 percent occur between noon and 4 P.M., 40 percent occur between 4 P.M. and 8 P.M., 20 percent occur between 8 P.M. and midnight, and 5 percent occur between midnight and 8 A.M.

b) Test the hypothesis at the .05 level that of all dog attacks on people in Canada 1/9 occur on each weekday (Monday to Friday), and 2/9 occur on each of Saturday and Sunday.

c) Test the hypothesis at the .10 level that dog attacks on people in Canada occur uniformly over the four seasons.

15. Carson Ackerman asked a sample of students their preferred workout time. He obtained the following responses:

Time	Number
Morning	6
Afternoon	13
Evening	26

Using a goodness-of-fit test at the .05 level, test to see if the workout times are preferred uniformly.

16. Carol Morris asked a random sample of students their preferred soft drink from among Coke, Pepsi, and 7-Up. Her results are in the following table:

Soft Drink	Number
Coke	26
Pepsi	18
7-Up	10

Test the hypothesis at the .01 level that the three soft drinks are equally preferred by the population of students.

17. For a class project, Shannon Beckwith reported on a survey. This survey was done to inquire on working women's form of physical activity. Over 1,000 women responded, selecting one of the following as their primary source of physical exercise, with the resulting percentages:

Working Women	
Primary Source of Physical Exercise	**Percentage**
Yoga	12.5
Running	37.2
Power walking	22.1
Aerobics	11.5
Bicycling	10.8
No physical exercise	5.9

A survey of 100 randomly selected female students resulted in the following preferences:

Female Students	
Primary Source of Physical Exercise	**Percentage**
Yoga	6
Running	46
Power walking	3
Aerobics	18
Bicycling	22
No physical exercise	5

Using a goodness-of-fit test at the .05 level, is the frequency distribution for female students the same as for these 1,000 working women?

11.3 The Contingency Table Tests

The concept of independent variables was discussed in Chapter 4. You'll recall that two variables are independent if the occurrence (or non-occurrence) of one doesn't affect the chances of the occurrence of the other. How, you may have wondered then, is it possible to tell if two variables are independent? Additionally, in Chapter 9 we

considered ways of comparing the proportion of elements of each type in two different populations. You may have wondered then how to compare the proportion of elements of each type in more than two populations. Well, the following examples show how χ^2 concepts can be used in a contingency table test to see if two variables under study are likely to be cross-classified independently, and also to see if the proportions of elements of each type are the same in more than two populations.

The Procedural Steps for the Contingency Table Tests

Once again, we follow the familiar seven-step process that begins with a statement of the hypotheses to be tested and concludes when a statistical decision is made.

Step 1: State the Null and Alternative Hypotheses The null hypothesis for a contingency table test for independence is that the two variables under study are independent. The alternative hypothesis in this text is that the two variables are not independent—that is, one variable is dependent on (or related to) the other.

The null hypothesis for a contingency table test for homogeneity of proportions is that the proportion of elements of each type is the same in each of several different populations. The alternative hypothesis in this test is that at least one proportion is different from the others.

Note that if the data consists of a contingency table where members of a single sample are classified according to two criteria of classification, the appropriate test is the test for independence. If the data consists of a contingency table where members of several samples (of predetermined sizes) are classified according to type of element as well as which population is being sampled, the appropriate test is the test for homogeneity of proportions.

Step 2: Select the Level of Significance This step doesn't differ from similar steps in other tests. A criterion for rejection of H_0 is necessary, and an α value of .01 or .05 is typically used.

Step 3: Determine the Test Distribution to Use Contingency table tests are also based on the Chi-square probability distributions introduced in Chapter 7, and summarized in Section 11.2:

Step 4: Define the Rejection or Critical Region We must know the Chi-square value that is the boundary of the area of rejection in contingency table tests. To find this critical χ^2 value, we must know two things:

1. *The level of significance* (specified in *Step 2* of our procedure).

2. *The degrees of freedom.* In *contingency table tests,* the value of df is

$$\text{df (contingency table)} = (r-1)(c-1) \tag{11.3}$$

where r = number of rows in the table
c = number of columns in the table

Now, let's assume we are performing a contingency table test at the .01 level, and our contingency table has two rows and three columns—that is, we have a 2×3 table. The df value we need is $(r - 1)(c - 1)$, or $(2 - 1)(3 - 1)$, or 2. And the critical χ^2 value at the intersection of the 2 df row and the .01 column in Appendix 6 is 9.21.

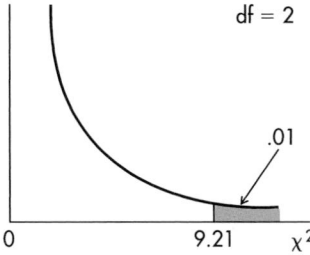

Step 5: State the Decision Rule The general form of the decision rule for contingency table tests is

Reject H_0 in favour of H_1 if the test statistic $\chi^2 > \chi^2$ critical value found in *Step 4* above. Otherwise, fail to reject H_0.

For our 2×3 contingency table test at the .01 level, the decision rule is

Reject H_0 in favour of H_1 if $\chi^2 > 9.21$. Otherwise, fail to reject H_0.

Step 6: Compute the Test Statistic The test statistic here is also a Chi-square test statistic.

$$\chi^2 = \Sigma \left[\frac{(O - E)^2}{E} \right] \qquad (11.4)$$

where $O =$ an *observed* (sample) frequency
        $E =$ an *expected* (hypothesized) frequency if H_0 is true

As in the Goodness-of-Fit Test, the O, or observed, values are found in the problem (sample) data set, and the E, or expected values, are computed to conform to the null hypothesis that is being tested.

Step 7: Make the Statistical Decision If the test statistic computed in *Step 6* exceeds the Chi-square critical value specified in the decision rule (*Step 5*), then it falls into the rejection region, and H_0 is rejected. If, however, χ^2 falls below this χ^2 value, then the null hypothesis cannot be rejected.

Example 11.4 **Contingency Table Test for Independence—Bicycling, Trampolining, Inline Skating—Injuries** The CBC television program *Marketplace* reported that "a growing number of children are hurting themselves on backyard trampolines. And those injuries are more likely to be serious than those suffered during other activities." To investigate this conclusion, a sample of data was obtained from the Canadian Hospitals Injuries Reporting and Prevention Program (CHIRPP) on injuries sustained in three sports in Canada—bicycling, trampolining, and inline skating. This data is summarized in Table 11.3. As you can see, the samples of injuries are cross-classified according to sport and injury type. The objective is to determine if the type of injury is independent of the sport involved.

TABLE 11.3 SAMPLE OF INJURIES CLASSIFIED BY SPORT AND TYPE OF INJURY

| | Sport | | | |
	Bicycling	Trampolining	Inline Skating	Total
Injury Type				
Fracture	266	267	456	989
Open Wound	51	30	74	155
Other	261	252	427	940
Total	578	549	957	2,084

◆ **Solution:**

Step 1: State the Null and Alternative Hypotheses

H_0: The type of injury is independent of the sport involved.
H_1: The type of injury depends on the sport involved.

Step 2: Select the Level of Significance Let's use $\alpha = .05$

Step 3: Determine the Test Distribution to Use We use the χ^2 distribution (as long as the expected values are at least five.)

Step 4: Define the Rejection or Critical Region Since the contingency table has three rows and three columns, the degrees of freedom is $(3 - 1)(3 - 1) = 4$. Using $\alpha = .05$ and df = 4, we find (from Appendix 6) the critical χ^2 value is 9.49.

Step 5: State the Decision Rule The decision rule is

Reject H_0 in favour of H_1 if $\chi^2 > 9.49$. Otherwise, fail to reject H_0.

Step 6: Compute the Test Statistic The observed or O values are given in Table 11.3. We also need the expected (E) values to compute the test statistic. You'll recall from Chapter 4 that two variables, say F and B, are independent if and only if their joint probability [P(F and B)] is equal to the product $P(F) \times P(B)$. If H_0 is true that type of injury and sport involved are independent, then we should be able to compute the probability that any one injury is a fracture and occurs in bicycling by multiplying the individual probabilities of P(fracture) × P(occurs in bicycling). This $P(F) \times P(B) = (989/2,084) \times (578/2,084) = .13162$. Thus if the variables are independent, the probability is .13162 that any one injury is a fracture and occurs in bicycling. Since there are a total of 2,084 injuries in all, the expected number that are fractures occurring in bicycling would be 2,084(.13162) or 274.30 if H_0 is true. And if the type of injury is independent of the sport involved, we could follow the above procedure to compute the expected number of fractures in the other two sports.

Another way to view the same procedure is to consider that a total of 2,084 injuries were examined, and 989 of these injuries were fractures. Since the 989 fractures is 47.46 percent of the total, we would expect 47.46 percent of the injuries in each of the three sports to be fractures if H_0 is true. Thus, of the 578 bicycling injuries, we would expect 47.46 percent (or 274.30) to be fractures, and of the 549 trampolining injuries, we would expect 47.46 percent (or 260.54) to be fractures, and of the 957 inline skating injuries, we would expect 47.46 percent (or 454.16) to be fractures.

The same analysis can also be used to compute the E values for open wounds and other types of injuries. (Since 155/2,084 or 7.44 percent of all injuries examined were open wounds, for example, we would expect that 7.44 percent of the 578 bicycling injuries, or about 42.99, would be open wounds.) But the computations of the E values are even easier to follow if we refer to the contingency table in Table 11.3 and compute the expected frequencies for each cell in the table. A cell is formed by the intersection of a row and a column. Since there are three rows and three columns in Table 11.3, there are $3 \times 3 = 9$ cells. (Tables with r rows and c columns are often referred to as $r \times c$ tables; in our example, we have a 3×3 table.)

The expected values may be computed for each cell of a contingency table by the following formula:

$$E = \frac{(\text{row total}) (\text{column total})}{\text{grand total}} \qquad (11.5)$$

The use of this formula may be illustrated by computing the number of injuries that would be expected to be fractures occurring while bicycling, if H_0 is true. From Table 11.3, you can see that the total for the row in which this cell is located is 989, the total for the column for this cell is 578, and the grand total is 2,084. Thus, the E value for the cell is computed as follows:

$$E = \frac{(989)(578)}{2,084} = 274.30$$

The same procedure can be used to get the E values for all the other cells of the table. Table 11.4 duplicates all the observed frequencies of Table 11.3 and shows the E values for each cell in parentheses.

Note that the total of the expected values in each row must equal the total of the observed values in the row. And the total of the expected values in each column must equal the total of the observed values in the column. That is, the sum of expected number of fracture injuries in the three sports is $274.30 + 260.54 + 454.16 = 989$, and the sum of the expected number of all types of bicycling injuries is $274.30 + 42.99 + 260.71$, and so on. Thus, if you know the row total for fractures equals 989, and if

TABLE 11.4 OBSERVED AND EXPECTED FREQUENCIES

Injury Type	Bicycling	Trampolining	Inline Skating	Total
Fracture	266 (274.30)	267 (260.54)	456 (454.16)	989
Open Wound	51 (42.99)	30 (40.83)	74 (71.18)	155
Other	261 (260.71)	252 (247.63)	427 (431.66)	940
Total	578	549	957	2,084

TABLE 11.5   COMPUTATION OF THE TEST STATISTIC

Row-Column (Cell)	O	E	$O - E$	$(O - E)^2$	$\dfrac{(O - E)^2}{E}$
1-1	266	274.30	–8.3	68.890	.251
1-2	267	260.54	6.46	41.732	.160
1-3	456	454.16	1.84	3.386	.007
2-1	51	42.99	8.01	64.160	1.492
2-2	30	40.83	–10.83	117.289	2.873
2-3	74	71.18	2.82	7.952	.112
3-1	261	260.71	0.29	0.084	.000
3-2	252	247.63	4.37	19.097	.077
3-3	427	431.66	–4.66	21.716	.050
	2084	2084.00	0		5.022

$$\chi^s = \left[\frac{(O - E)^2}{E} \right] = 5.022$$

STATISTICS IN ACTION

Where Are You on the Obesity Chart?

Heart disease, cancer, arthritis, and Type II diabetes have been linked to obesity. Statistics Canada reported the percentage distribution of Body Mass Index of Canadians for 2000/01. Body mass index (BMI) is

$$BMI = \frac{weight\ (kg)}{(height\ (m))^2}$$

Un—underweight (BMI under 18.5)
Ac—acceptable weight (BMI 18.5–24.9)
Ov—overweight (BMI 25.0–29.9)
Ob—obese (BMI 30.0 or higher)
M—men
W—women

The percentages of Canadians in each classification were reported as follows:

Age/ Sex	Un (%)	Ac (%)	Ov (%)	Ob (%)
20–24				
M	2.8	63.6	25.3	7.7
W	10	66.6	14.7	7.3
25–34				
M	1.4	46.6	36.7	14.6
W	5.3	60	20.8	11.6
35–44				
M	0.9	40.5	41.9	16
W	4.2	56.4	23.4	13.3
45–54				
M	0.6	36.1	43.2	19.7
W	2.2	48.3	30.4	16.1
55–64				
M	0.7	35.2	45.1	18.4
W	1.6	42.4	34	19

Source: Statistics Canada, Canadian Community Health Survey, 2000/01, http://statcan.ca/english/freepub/82-221-XIE100502/tables/html/1225.htm.

you have two of the three expected values in the row (say 274.30 and 260.54), you can easily find the third expected value as follows: 2,084 – (274.30 + 260.54) = 454.16.

Now that we have all the E values for our contingency table, we are ready to calculate the test statistic. Table 11.5 shows this computation. The columns labelled O and E in Table 11.5 reproduce the data from Table 11.4 in a more convenient format. As a check of your arithmetic, note that $\sum O = \sum E$.

The steps to compute the test statistic are

1. Subtract each E value from the corresponding O value—that is $O - E$—for each cell in the contingency table, and record the difference (as shown in the column labelled $O - E$ of Table 11.5). As another check of your math, note also that $\sum(O - E)$ must equal zero.

2. Square the $O - E$ differences to get $(O - E)^2$ (penultimate column, Table 11.5).

3. Divide each of these squared differences—$(O - E)^2$—by the E value for each cell to get $(O - E)^2/E$ (last column, Table 11.5).

4. Add the $(O - E)^2/E$ values to get the computed test statistic value (total of the last column, Table 11.5). As you can see, the value of the test statistic is 5.022.

Step 7: Make the Statistical Decision   Since our test statistic of 5.022 is not greater than 9.49, we fail to reject H_0. Thus, at the .05 level of significance, we do not have sufficient evidence to conclude that the type of injury depends on the sport involved. ◆

Computers and Calculators Make It Easy

In virtually every case in this book where we've encountered a standardized test on procedure that requires numerous calculations, we've also located a program in a statistical software package or a procedure from a powerful calculator that takes over the chore of carrying out those computations. Thus, you'll not be surprised now to learn that

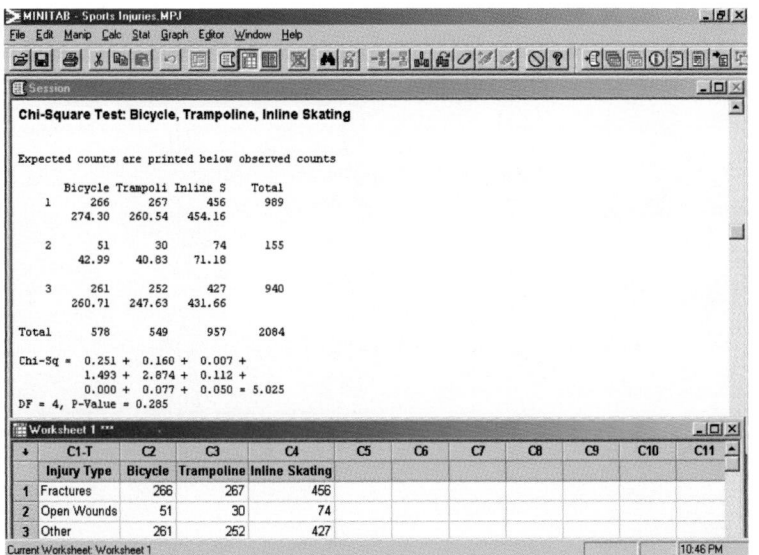

FIGURE 11.4 To obtain this MINITAB output, the injury types are stored in column C1-T and the number of bicycling fractures, open wounds, and other injuries are stored in that order in Column 2 (C2) of a MINITAB worksheet, just as they were shown in Table 11.3. The data for the other two sports are similarly stored in columns 3 and 4. Then click on **Stat, Tables, Chi-Square Test,** enter the columns to be analyzed in the box below **Columns containing the Table,** and click **OK.**

programs are readily available to process contingency table tests. We'll look at a MINITAB program next and a TI-83 procedure as part of Example 11.5.

Figure 11.4 shows the MINITAB output for the example problem we've just considered. The software produces (1) the observed and expected frequencies identical to those found in Table 11.4, (2) the results in the last column of Table 11.5 and its total, which is the computed test statistic, (3) the degrees of freedom (four in this exercise), and (4) the p-value of the test statistic. Although we could now look for the χ^2 table value, the p-value approach makes that unnecessary. Because the p-value of .032 is less than .05, we reject H_0, agreeing with the statistical decision previously reached.

A summary of the steps in a contingency table test is outlined in *Figure 11.5*.

Example 11.5   **Contingency Table Test for Homogeneity of Proportions—Someone to Hug?** A Canadian National Population Health Survey of Canadians over the age of 12 reported that 76 percent of males and 81 percent of females indicated that they do have someone to hug as part of their social support.

Assuming these estimates were based on random samples of 400 males and 400 females, we may reconstruct the following contingency table:

TABLE 11.6   SOMEONE TO HUG?

	Yes	No
Male	304	96
Female	324	76

Source: Statistics Canada, Health Reports, 2001 Annual Report, Catalogue no. 82-003-XIE Vol. 12 No. 3.

At the .05 level of significance, can we conclude that the proportion of Canadian males over the age of 12 who have someone to hug is different than the proportion of Canadian females over the age of 12 who have someone to hug?

FIGURE 11.5 Steps in a contingency table test.

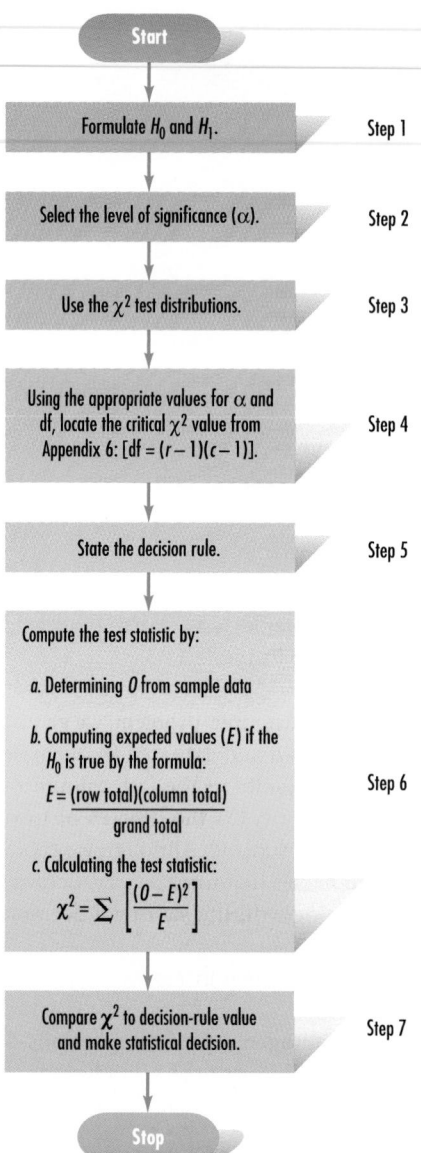

Start

Formulate H_0 and H_1.   Step 1

Select the level of significance (α).   Step 2

Use the χ^2 test distributions.   Step 3

Using the appropriate values for α and df, locate the critical χ^2 value from Appendix 6: [df $= (r-1)(c-1)$].   Step 4

State the decision rule.   Step 5

Compute the test statistic by:

a. Determining O from sample data

b. Computing expected values (E) if the H_0 is true by the formula: Step 6

$$E = \frac{\text{(row total)(column total)}}{\text{grand total}}$$

c. Calculating the test statistic:

$$\chi^2 = \sum \left[\frac{(O-E)^2}{E} \right]$$

Compare χ^2 to decision-rule value and make statistical decision.   Step 7

Stop

◆ Solution:

Let p_1 and p_2 denote the true proportion of all Canadian males, females, respectively, over the age of 12 who have someone to hug.

Step 1: State the Null and Alternative Hypotheses

H_0: $p_1 = p_2$
H_1: $p_1 \neq p_2$

Step 2: Select the Level of Significance Again we use $\alpha = .05$.

Step 3: Determine the Test Distribution to Use We again use the χ^2 distribution (as long as the expected values are at least five.)

Step 4: Define the Rejection or Critical Region Since the contingency table has two rows and two columns, the degrees of freedom is $(2 - 1)(2 - 1) = 1$. Using $\alpha = .05$ and df = 1, we find (from Appendix 6) the critical χ^2 value is 3.84.

Step 5: State the Decision Rule The decision rule is

Reject H_0 in favour of H_1 if $\chi^2 > 3.84$. Otherwise, fail to reject H_0.

Step 6: Compute the Test Statistic The observed or O values are given in Table 11.6. We also need the expected (E) values to compute the test statistic. Note that if H_0 is true, that is if $p_1 = p_2$, then our best estimate for the common proportion of all Canadians over the age of 12 who have someone to hug is $628/800 = 0.785$. Thus, in a sample of 400 males, we would expect to find $400 (0.785) = 314$ who have someone to hug, and in a sample of 400 females we would also expect to find 314 who have someone to hug. In a similar manner, we may obtain the E values for the other cells of the table. Note that this procedure for calculating the E values is equivalent to the procedure used in the contingency table test for independence, namely

$$E = \frac{\text{(row total) (column total)}}{\text{grand total}}$$

For example, the E value in the first row and first column is

$$E = \frac{(400)(628)}{800} = 314$$

Table 11.7 summarizes all observed and expected frequencies.

Now that we have all the E values for our contingency table, we are ready to calculate the test statistic. Table 11.8 shows this computation. The columns labelled O and E in Table 11.8 reproduce the data from Table 11.7 in a more convenient format. As a check of your arithmetic, note that $\sum O = \sum E$.

The steps to compute the test statistic are

1. Subtract each E value from the corresponding O value—that is $O - E$—for each cell in the contingency table, and record the difference (as shown in the column labelled ($O - E$ of Table 11.8). As another check of your math, note also that $\sum(O - E)$ must equal zero.

TABLE 11.7 OBSERVED AND EXPECTED FREQUENCIES

	Someone to Hug?		
	Yes	No	Total
Male	304	96	400
	(314)	(86)	
Female	324	76	400
	(314)	(86)	
Total	628	172	800

TABLE 11.8   COMPUTATION OF THE TEST STATISTIC

Row-Column (Cell)	O	E	$O - E$	$(O - E)^2$	$\dfrac{(O - E)^2}{E}$
1-1	304	314	−10	100	0.3185
1-2	96	86	10	100	1.1628
2-1	324	314	10	100	0.3185
2-2	76	86	−10	100	1.1628
	800	800	0		2.9626

$$\chi^s = \Sigma\left[\frac{(O - E)^2}{E}\right] = 2.9626$$

2. Square the $O - E$ differences to get $(O - E)^2$ (penultimate column, Table 11.8).

3. Divide each of these squared differences—$(O - E)^2$—by the E value for each cell to get $(O - E)^2/E$ (last column, Table 11.8).

4. Add the $(O - E)^2/E$ values to get the computed test statistic value (total of the last column, Table 11.8). As you can see, the value of the test statistic is 2.9626.

Step 7: Make the Statistical Decision Since our test statistic of 2.9626 is not greater than 3.84, we fail to reject H_0. Thus, at the .05 level of significance, no, we do not have enough evidence to conclude that the proportion of Canadian males over the age of 12 who have someone to hug is different than the proportion of Canadian females over the age of 12 who have someone to hug.

We also used both MINITAB and a TI-83 calculator to do the computations. Having entered the observations into columns named YES and NO, then performing steps to do a χ^2 test, we obtain the MINITAB output in *Figure 11.6a*. Using a TI-83, after entering the data into a matrix as shown in screen l of *Figure 11.6b*, we obtain the results of screen 2. The p-value is .085. Therefore, at the .05 level, since .085 is not less than .05, we again fail to reject H_0. ◆

Self-Testing Review 11.3

18. To meet the needs of their students, schools have students take the Language Assessment Scales (LAS) Test to determine their dominant or strongest language. The results of a random sample of kindergarten and first-grade students are as follows:

Dominant Language	Kindergarten	First Grade	Total
English	160	197	357
French	75	92	167
Mixed	284	348	632
Bilingual	16	20	36
Total	535	657	1,192

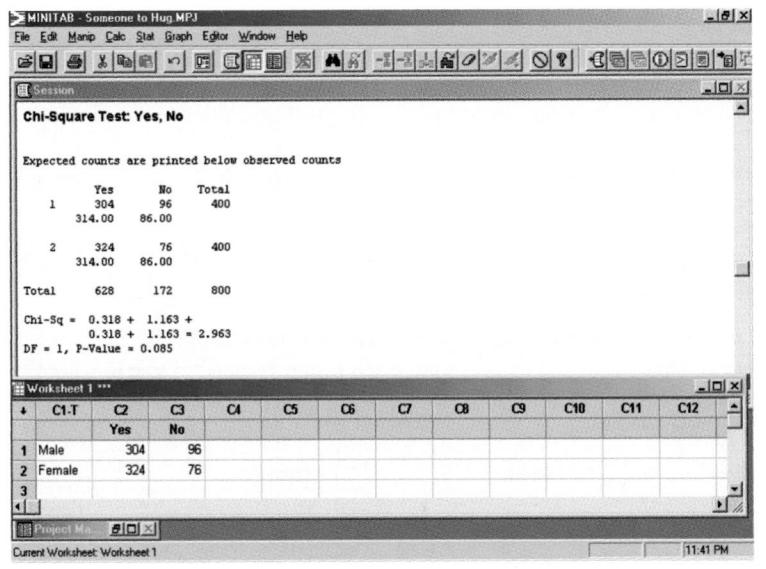

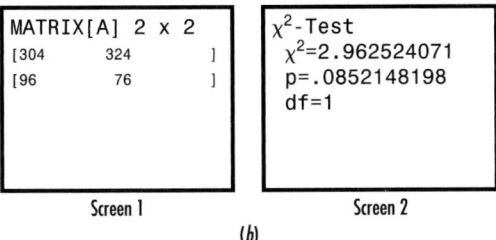

Screen 1   Screen 2

(b)

FIGURE 11.6 (*a*) MINITAB output for sex versus Response data. (*b*) To use the TI-83 to test if sex and having someone to hug are independent, we first need to enter the observed frequency data in a matrix. Press the **MATRX** key, move to the **EDIT** menu, and select matrix [A]. Then enter the info as shown in screen 1. Choose χ^2 **TEST** from the **STAT>TESTS** menu. The data has been placed in matrix [A] and the expected values will be stored in matrix [B]. If you want to use other matrix names, access them from the **MATRX>NAMES** menu. Choose **Calculate.** The results are shown in screen 2.

At the .01 level, is language dominance in the region independent of school grade?

19. The output that follows resulted from using MINITAB to analyze data collected on the religion and political party (1 = Liberal, 2 = New Democrat, 3 = Other) of a random sample of Canadians.

	Protstnt	Catholic	Islam	Other	Total
1	31	19	3	4	57
	17.46	21.09	10.21	8.24	
2	19	27	14	3	63
	19.30	23.31	11.29	9.10	
3	3	18	14	18	53
	16.24	19.61	9.50	7.66	
Total	53	64	31	25	173

ChiSq = 10.495 + 0.206 + 5.095 + 2.179 +
        0.005 + 0.585 + 0.651 + 4.093 +
        10.791 + 0.132 + 2.135 + 13.962 = 50.330

df = 6, p = 0.000

At the .05 level, test the hypothesis that religion and political party are independent.

20. To study the traits of heredity, randomly selected samples of 135 pairs of identical twins and 527 pairs of fraternal twins were assessed for mental retardation. Records were kept as to whether the pairs were concordant (both retarded or both not retarded) or discordant (one retarded and the other not retarded). The data were

**Long-Term Effects
of the Pill**

A study published in the *British Medical Journal*, described in a January 6, 1999, Associated Press article, actually had good news about taking birth control pills. The study involved 46,000 British women tracked for 25 years, and it found that ten years after they stopped taking the Pill, women's chances of dying from cancer, stroke, and other side effects were the same as those of women who had never taken it. Although scientists had long known that women are at a slightly elevated risk of cervical cancer, breast cancer, stroke, and other circulatory system diseases while taking the pill, the long-term effects were uncertain. Valerie Beral, director of the Imperial Cancer Research Fund's cancer epidemiology unit in Oxford University said, "We can reassure women that if they stopped the pill ten or more years ago, if they get some illness it's not because they took the pill when they were young." Interestingly, the findings also showed it was just as safe to take the pill for more than ten years as it was to take it for two years—the average length women take it.

Twin Type	Concordant	Discordant	Total
Identical	129	6	135
Fraternal	195	332	527
Total	324	338	662

At the .01 level, test the hypothesis that the percentage of concordance for the mental retardation trait is the same for both types of twins.

21. A random sample of high school students were given a questionnaire to learn their perceptions of school. When males and females were asked if they planned to stay in school, the responses were as follows:

Stay in School	Male	Female	Total
Yes	76	118	194
No	37	157	194
Total	113	275	388

Test the hypothesis at the .05 level that the decision to remain in school is independent of sex for high school students.

22. A random sample of physicians were cross-classified according to career choice and year of graduation. The results are as follows:

Career Choice	Graduates 1993–97	Graduates 1998–2002	Total
Family medicine	8,597	9,605	18,202
Internal medicine	8,591	10,672	19,263
Pediatrics	3,962	4,755	8,717
Total	21,150	25,032	46,182

Test the hypothesis at the .01 level that the type of career choice made by graduating physicians is independent of the date of graduation.

23. After the introduction of a new federal budget, a survey was taken to see if people thought they would be paying a little more in taxes, a lot more, or no more to the government. The following responses, classified by income, were obtained from this random sample:

Income	A Little More	A Lot More	No More	Didn't Know	Total
Under $40,000	65	30	50	5	150
40,000 < 50,000	154	77	90	14	335
50,000 < 70,000	180	111	38	18	347
Over 70,000	72	63	33	3	171
Total	471	281	211	40	1,003

Test the hypothesis at the .05 level that income level and the population's opinion about the tax consequences of this budget are independent.

24. Janet Mitchell took a survey of 71 male and 74 female students and asked, "In your relationship, who spends more on herself or himself?" The information she gathered is described in the following contingency table:

Spends More	Male	Female	Total
Females	29	33	62
Males	21	30	51
Neither	21	11	32
Total	71	74	73

At the .05 level, are the population percentages of opinions on who spends more in a relationship the same for males and females?

25. A study to determine optimal time after injury for ligament reconstruction was reported in the *American Journal of Sports Medicine*. Time from injury to surgery was established as acute, subacute, and chronic. Subjects in these randomly selected groups were cross-categorized as to whether their knee cartilage was normal, needed replacement, or needed repair. Results were recorded as follows:

Time Group	Normal Cartilage	Cartilage Replacement	Cartilage Repair	Total
Acute	12	21	14	47
Subacute	4	5	6	15
Chronic	2	16	11	29
Total	18	42	21	81

Test the hypothesis at the .05 level that for the population of ligament replacement patients, time after injury and before surgery and cartilage condition are independent.

26. The following table classifies the members of a large police force according to ethnic group and sex:

Group	Male	Female	Total
Indian	47	11	58
Asian	249	48	297
Black	531	120	651
Hispanic	701	120	821
White	8,144	1,574	9,718
Total	9, 672	1,873	11,545

Test the hypothesis at the .01 level that for this police force, sex and ethnic group are independent.

27. Amanda Bernal took a survey of 400 students and determined the college in which each was enrolled and whether or not the students had participated in high school sports. The information she gathered is in the following contingency table:

College	Yes	No	Total
Math & Science	58	15	73
Business	51	52	103
Agriculture	42	28	70
Engineering	32	39	71
Architecture	29	54	83
Total	212	188	400

Test the hypothesis at the .05 level that college is independent of whether or not a student had participated in high school sports.

28. Courtney Adams took random samples of 124 female and 155 male students and asked if they were pro-abortion, anti-abortion, or not sure/no opinion. The information she gathered is described in the following contingency table:

Opinion	Women	Men	Total
Pro-abortion	63	52	115
Anti-abortion	46	69	115
Not sure/No opinion	15	34	49
Total	124	155	279

Test the hypothesis at the .01 level that the proportions of responses in the categories Pro-abortion, Anti-abortion, and Not sure/no opinion are the same for men and women.

29. Natalie Bailey asked 14 male and 18 female intercollegiate swimmers, "Are the male swimmers more dedicated than the female swimmers?" The results are presented in the following contingency table:

Sex	Yes	No	Total
Male	9	5	14
Female	5	13	18
Total	14	18	32

At the .10 level, is the answer to this question independent of sex?

30. Kristine Milliken took random samples of 40 male and 40 female students and asked them to select their preferred food from among pizza, chicken, and pasta. The information she gathered is described in the following contingency table:

Sex	Pizza	Chicken	Pasta	Total
Male	18	13	9	40
Female	11	7	22	40
Total	29	20	31	80

Test the hypothesis at the .05 level that the percentages of males who prefer pizza, chicken, and pasta are equal to the percentages of females who prefer pizza, chicken, and pasta.

31. Michael Bruce investigated the relationship between area of a restaurant (dining room or bar) and type of alcohol consumed. He did this by taking a random sample of days at the restaurant and, for both the dining room and bar, determining the number of days in which the sales of beer, of wine, and of liquor exceeded $200. The information he collected is in the following contingency table:

Location	Beer	Wine	Liquor	Total
Dining Room	18	26	8	52
Bar	24	7	30	61
Total	42	33	38	113

Test the hypothesis at the .01 level that the type of alcohol consumed is independent of the location in the restaurant.

32. Karen Ames examined data she found in "Ability of Primary Care Physicians to Recognize Physical Findings Associated with HIV." Primary care physicians were asked to identify three common physical findings associated with HIV infection: Kaposi's sarcoma, oral hairy leukoplakia, and diffuse lymphadenopathy. The results she presented follow:

Diagnosis	Sarcoma	Leukoplakia	Lymphadenopathy	Total
Correct	23	22	23	68
Incorrect	66	75	110	251
Total	89	97	133	319

Source: Statistics Canada, Catalogue 82-003.

Test the hypothesis at the .05 level that the ability to reach a correct diagnosis is independent of the type of ailment.

33. Statistics Canada recently obtained samples of Canadians aged 18 or older from various health regions in Canada. Sample members were asked to report the state of their health.

a) Partial results from several provincial capitals are shown below.

Health Region	Sample Size	Number Reporting Fair or Poor Health
Toronto	2,295	308
Winnipeg	1,878	242
Edmonton	1,891	227
Victoria	1,113	148

At the .05 level test the hypothesis that the population percentage having fair or poor health is the same in all four health regions.

b) Partial results from health regions in the Vancouver area are shown below.

Health Region	Sample Size	Number Reporting Fair or Poor Health
Vancouver	1,200	167
Burnaby	791	105
North Shore	767	53
Richmond	731	104

At the .10 level, test the hypothesis that the population percentage having fair or poor health is the same in all four health regions.

34. Po Sai Marie Yeung analyzed data found in "Marijuana Use in College." This paper considered the relationships that might exist between student use of marijuana and parental use of alcohol and drugs. The table that follows reports the rate of student use of marijuana and the number of their parents who were regular users of alcohol and drugs.

Student	Parent		
	Neither	One	Both
Never	141	68	17
Occasional	54	44	11
Regular	40	51	19

Test the hypothesis at the .01 level that student use of marijuana is independent of parental use of alcohol and drugs.

35. Random samples of 150 adults were selected from six Canadian provinces. Those selected were cross-classified according to marital status and province of residence. The results were as follows:

	Alberta	British Columbia	Manitoba	Ontario	Québec	Saskatchewan
Single	49	47	48	46	61	47
Married	76	74	76	79	59	77
Separated	7	8	5	6	5	5
Divorced	11	12	10	10	15	10
Widowed	7	9	11	9	10	11
	150	150	150	150	150	150

Are the six provinces homogeneous with respect to the legal marital status of their residents? Use $\alpha = 0.05$.

LOOKING BACK

1. A goodness-of-fit test is conducted to evaluate a multinomial experiment in which there are more than two possible outcomes for each trial. Such a test is used to see if the distribution of the observed outcomes of the sample trials supports a hypothesized population distribution. The researcher establishes a hypothesis about how he or she thinks the data items will be distributed into the different testing categories of interest. Then the test is carried out to see if the observed results conform to the results that would be expected if the hypothesis is true. The assumptions in a goodness-of-fit test are that the sample is a random sample, frequency counts are obtained for the possible k cells, and the expected frequency is at least five for each of the k categories.

2. The contingency table tests considered in this chapter deal with two classification variables. Each cell in a contingency table is at the intersection of a row and a column. The rows represent one classification category, and the columns represent another such category. Thus, a contingency table test of independence is one that tests the hypothesis that the data are cross-classified in independent ways. A contingency table test for homogeneity of proportions is one that tests the hypothesis that the proportion of elements of each type is the same in several different populations. The assumptions in contingency table tests are that the sample data items are obtained through random selection and the expected frequency for each cell in the table is at least five.

3. A familiar seven-step hypothesis-testing procedure is used to carry out both the goodness-of-fit and contingency table tests. In this procedure, the null and alternative hypotheses are established (*Step 1*), the level of significance is specified (*Step 2*), and an appropriate Chi-square distribution is used (*Step 3*) to define the rejection or critical region (*Step 4*), which allows the analyst to formulate a decision rule (*Step 5*). A test statistic is then computed (*Step 6*) for the goodness-of-fit or contingency table test, and the statistical decision (*Step 7*) is then possible.

Exercises

36. Participants in a consumer product research study were given four types of orange juice to sample and were asked to rate the taste quality for each type of juice. A random sample of 30 subjects received one brand to drink at a time. Five minutes elapsed between consecutive juice samples, during which time the subjects were asked to eat a cracker. The following table shows the preferences:

Brand	Number Preferring
A	10
B	8
C	5
D	7

At the .01 level, test the hypothesis that there was an equal preference for each brand (a uniform distribution).

37. Alan Dunton examined the ability of female and male students to do 40 or more push-ups in 60 seconds at the end of a 2-hour workout. The results he obtained are in the following contingency table:

40+ Push-ups	Male	Female	Total
Yes	17	11	28
No	5	15	20
Total	22	26	48

Test the hypothesis at the .05 level that the proportion of students who are able to do 40 or more push-ups in 60 seconds at the end of a 2-hour workout is the same for males and females.

38. Are marital status and race independent variables for those who have legal abortions? Use the following sample data to test the independence of these variables at the .01 level.

Marital Status	White	Non-White	Total
Married	68	31	99
Unmarried	279	141	420
Total	347	172	519

39. The following table is a summary of data on vehicle collisions taken from an SGI report, *2001 Saskatchewan Traffic Accident Facts:*

Time of Day	Weekday (Mon. to Fri.)	Weekend Day (Sat. or Sun.)	Total
12 to 3 A.M.	763	792	1,555
3 to 6 A.M.	469	545	1,014
6 to 9 A.M.	2,261	431	2,692
9 A.M. to 12 P.M.	2,636	791	3,427
12 to 3 P.M.	3,620	1,032	4,652
3 to 6 P.M.	4,787	1,148	5,935
6 to 9 P.M.	3,201	1,070	4,271
9 P.M. to 12 A.M.	2,251	945	3,196
Total	19,988	6,754	26,742

Test the hypothesis at the .05 level that, in Saskatchewan, the time of day of a collision is independent of whether or not the day is a weekday.

40. A politician running for office is planning his campaign strategy on the issue of gun control and wants to know if there is a significant difference in the percentage of voters who favour the issue in districts A, B, C. Random samples of voters from the three districts yield the following data:

District	In Favour	Opposed	Total
A	89	46	135
B	65	45	110
C	60	50	110
Total	214	141	355

Test the hypothesis at the .01 level that there is no difference in the percentage favouring gun control in the 3 districts.

41. To gauge the opinion of workers about a proposed change in the union constitution, the union's executive committee sent questionnaires to random samples of members in three locals. The survey results are as follows:

Opinion	Local X	Local Y	Local Z	Total
Favour change	17	23	10	50
Oppose change	9	13	8	30
No response	4	4	12	20
Total	30	40	30	100

At the .05 level, is there a significant difference in the reactions of the workers in the 3 locals to the proposed change?

42. The production manager of a company that does steel plating has collected the following data during a randomly selected 24-hour period:

Shift	Number of Defects
8 A.M. to 4 P.M.	27
4 P.M. to midnight	35
Midnight to 8 A.M.	49

At the .01 level, are the defects uniformly distributed among the shifts?

43. In studies of traits of heredity, randomly selected samples of 135 pairs of identical twins and 527 pairs of fraternal twins were assessed for left- or right-handedness. Records were kept as to whether a pair of twins were concordant (both left- or both right-handed) or discordant (one left- and the other right-handed). The data were

Twin Type	Concordant	Discordant	Total
Identical	107	28	135
Fraternal	406	121	527
Total	513	149	662

At the .0l level, is the proportion of concordance for the handedness trait the same for both types of twins?

44. In clinical trials, 103 of the randomly selected patients discontinued using NORVASC or a placebo because of adverse effects. Test the hypothesis at the .01 level that the type of adverse effect and the dosage level are independent variables.

Adverse Event	5-mg Dose	10-mg Dose	Placebo	Total
Edema	9	29	5	43
Dizziness	10	9	9	28
Flushing or palpitation	8	19	5	32
Total	27	57	19	103

Criteria for Admission	Inpatients	Outpatients	Total
Physiologic instability	128	88	216
Dehydration	103	26	129
Severe complications	100	7	107
Meets more than one criterion	196	113	309
Total	527	234	761

45. To meet the needs of their students, schools have students take the Language Assessment Scales (LAS) Test to determine their dominant reading language. The results of a random sample of first- and second-grade students in a particular region are as follows:

Grade	French Reading	Engish Reading	Total
First	242	293	535
Second	295	362	657
Total	537	655	1,192

At the .01 level, is the primary reading language independent of grade?

46. An automobile sales manager in Edmonton claims that on 20 percent of the selling days, no cars are sold; on 30 percent of the selling days, one car is sold; on 30 percent of the days, 2 cars are sold; on 15 percent of the days, 3 cars are sold; and on 5 percent of the days, 4 or more cars are sold. In a recently sampled period, the following sales results were achieved:

Number Sold per Day	Number of Days
0	8
1	11
2	10
3	6
4 or more	6

Test the hypothesis at the .05 level that the population distribution for the number of cars sold each day fits the one claimed by the sales manager.

47. A children's hospital in Ontario has certain criteria that are used to admit as inpatients or outpatients those who have contracted measles. These criteria and a random sample of patients admitted in the inpatient and outpatient categories are shown in the following table:

At the .05 level, is inpatient/outpatient status independent of the criteria for admission?

48. According to geneticists, the distribution of blood type in the general population is 42 percent type A, 10 percent type B, 3 percent type AB, and 45 percent type O. A study of the four blood groups was conducted for various populations. In a sample of 116 residents in 18 villages on Bougainville Island, it was observed that 74 were type A, 12 were type B, 11 were type AB, and 19 were type O. At the .01 level, did the distribution on Bougainville Island fit that of the general population?

49. Christina Sawatzky took a random sample of 77 students and asked them to select their preferred vacation location from among France, Bali, and Australia. The information she gathered is described in the following contingency table:

Sex	France	Bali	Australia	Total
Male	3	16	22	41
Female	12	15	9	36
Total	15	31	31	77

Test the hypothesis at the .05 level that the selection of the preferred vacation location is independent of gender.

50. A student took random samples of 25 male and 25 female students and asked them to select their preferred restaurant between Tim Hortons and Burger King. His results are in the following contingency table:

Sex	Tim Hortons	Burger King	Total
Male	7	18	25
Female	20	5	25
Total	27	23	50

Test the hypothesis at the .05 level that the proportion of males who prefer Burger King is equal to the proportion of females who prefer Burger King.

51. The 2000/01 Canadian Community Health Survey reported the following percentages of Canadians aged 15 or older in the various categories listed:

Physical Activity	Aboriginal	Non-Aboriginal
Active	23.3	21.8
Moderately Active	22.6	23.5
Inactive	54.1	54.7

Body Mass Index	Aboriginal	Non-Aboriginal
Acceptable or underweight	41.8	54.3
Overweight	33.5	31.7
Obese	24.7	14.0

Source: Statistics Canada, Canadian Community Health Survey, 2000/01.

Assume these percentages are based on a sample of 1,000 Aboriginals and 3,000 Non-Aboriginals. (The sample sizes were not mentioned in the report.)

a) At the .05 level of significance, can it be concluded that the Aboriginal population and the Non-Aboriginal population are homogeneous with respect to physical activity?

b) At the .05 level of significance, can it be concluded that the Aboriginal population and the Non-Aboriginal population are homogeneous with respect to body mass index?

52. *Figure 11.7* contains a MINITAB printout for a test of independence.

a) What is the total number in the sample?

b) How many categories are there for each variable?

c) What is the number of degrees of freedom for this test, and how could you compute it without this printout?

d) What is the value of the test statistic?

e) Find the cell (row and column intersection) that contributed the most to this test statistic value.

f) With $\alpha = .05$, what decision is made?

53. *Figure 11.8* contains a MINITAB printout for a test of independence.

a) What is the total number in the sample?

b) How many categories are there for each variable?

c) What is the number of degrees of freedom for this test, and how could you compute it without this printout?

d) What is the value of the test statistic?

e) With $\alpha = 01$, what decision is made?

54. *Figure 11.9* contains a MINITAB printout to answer the questions below.

a) What is the total number in the sample?

b) How many categories are there for each variable?

c) What is the number of degrees of freedom for this test, and how could you compute it without this printout?

d) What is the value of the test statistic?

e) What decision should be made at $\alpha = .05$?

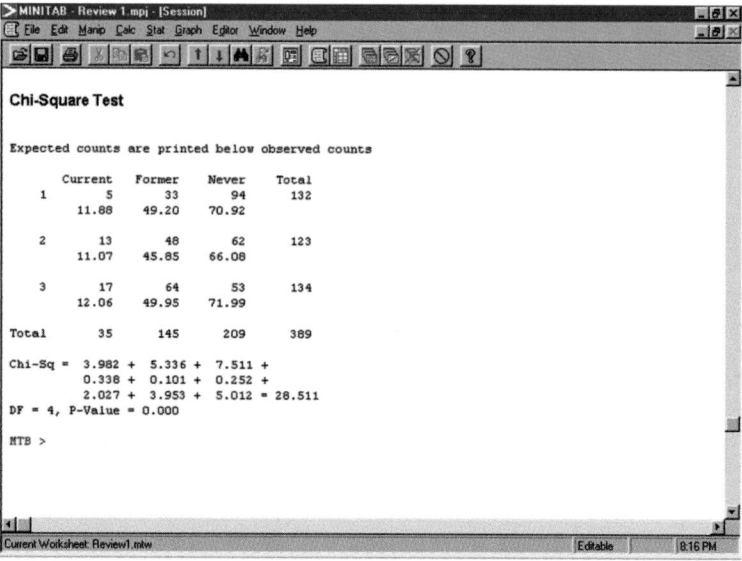

FIGURE 11.7 MINITAB printout for question 52.

FIGURE 11.8 MINITAB output for question 53.

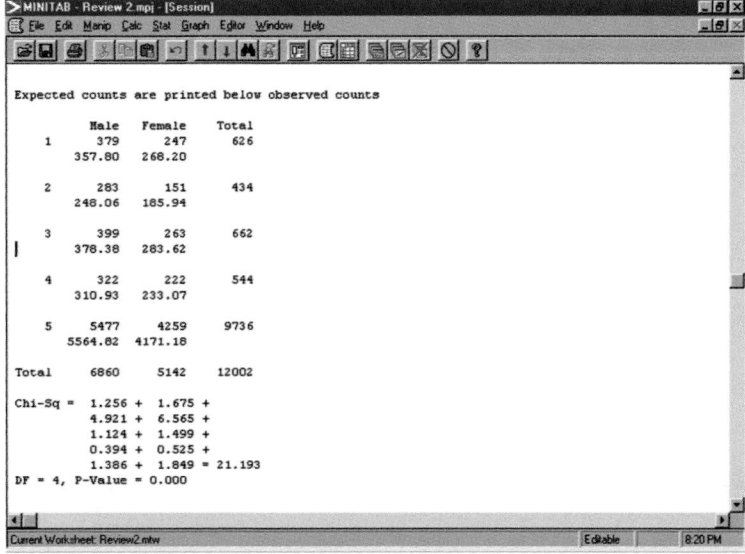

FIGURE 11.9 MINITAB output for question 54.

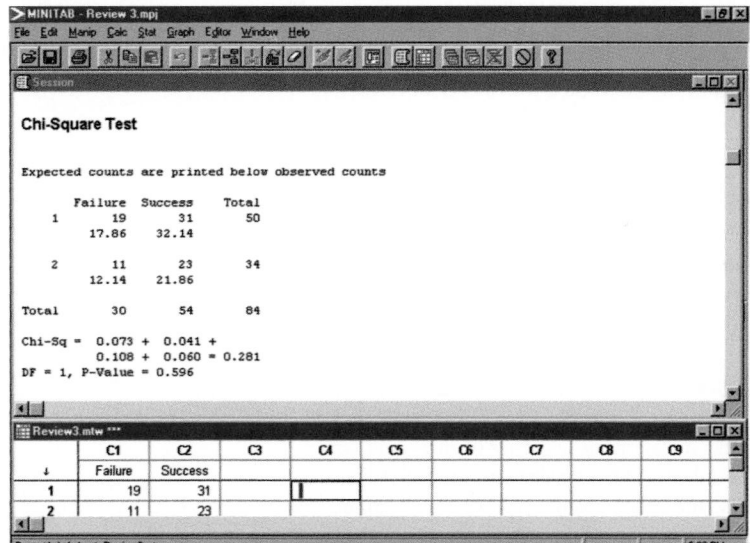

Topics for Review and Discussion

1. What are the similarities and differences between the test for goodness-of-fit and the contingency table procedure that tests to see if the data are cross-classified in independent ways?

2. Examine the formula used to compute the test statistic and discuss the significance of a χ^2 value of zero.

3. Even if the null hypothesis is true, why is it unlikely that the computed test statistic will be zero?

4. Discuss the purpose of a goodness-of-fit test. List three possible situations where this test would be of use.

5. Discuss the purpose of a contingency table test for independence of variables. List three practical applications for this test.

6. How do the tests examined in this chapter differ from those in Chapters 8, 9, and 10? (Hint: Compare the types of data used in each chapter.)

Projects/Issues to Consider

1. You may wish to identify a variable that can be subdivided into three or more categories, or you may choose to focus on a controversial issue with three or more possible opinions. Obtain counts or responses on your campus or elsewhere for your variable or issue. Establish hypotheses about the probability distribution of the possible outcomes, and then perform a goodness-of-fit test. Discuss your results in a class report.

2. a) You'll need to repeat a multinomial experiment 100 times. For example, you can roll a die and note the top surface after each roll; draw a card from a standard deck, note the suit, and replace it; or even write A, B, C, and D on an equal number of equal-sized slips of paper, and then draw one slip at a time, note the letter, and replace it. Before carrying out your experiment, though, you should establish hypotheses about the probability distribution of the outcomes. Finally, use the goodness-of-fit test and discuss the results obtained.

b) If you worked with a die, try "loading" the die (use tape or glue on one face). Then, redo the goodness-of-fit test with the loaded die. If you worked with a deck of cards, try

altering the deck by, for example, removing seven of the cards in the heart suit and redoing the goodness-of-fit test. And if you worked with slips of paper, change the distribution of slips, and repeat your test procedure.

c) Compare the results of parts *a* and *b* in a class report.

3. First, select a current and controversial issue, and then establish response categories. For example, these categories could be "agree," "disagree," or "don't know." Next, split those you will question into two or more groups (male/female, French/English/Swedish, British Columbia/Alberta/Saskatchewan, and so on). Then create a questionnaire that will elicit a response and that will also place the person into his or her proper group. Organize your responses into a contingency table, and perform a test of the independence of the variables. Discuss your results in a class report.

4. Locate a journal article in which a Chi-square test either has been used or could be used. In either case, describe the data categories and discuss how the test was (or could be) set up to either test for goodness-of-fit or for the independence of variables.

Computer/Calculator Exercises

1. The Florida Museum of Natural History Ichthyology Collection (George H. Burgess, curator) home page, located at *FlaFish*, contains links to numerous databases. If you click on *Shark Research* and on that page find *Trends in Worldwide Shark Attacks* and then click on *Attacking Species of Sharks,* you will access a table containing a contingency table of species of shark versus type of attack. To determine if species of shark and type of attack are independent, form a smaller contingency table of species: white, tiger, and other, against type of attack: unprovoked, provoked, and other (since there are totals in the original table, you can calculate the O values for both "other" categories by subtraction). Using your software to do all calculations, perform the test using a level of significance of .05.

2. A new strain of whitefly—silverleaf whitefly—is jeopardizing many agricultural crops, including tomatoes. Some tomato growers use whitefly parasites as a means of controlling this pest. Since these parasites are greatly affected by leaf morphology and biochemistry, it is possible that certain varieties of tomato are more hospitable to parasites than others. Christa Conforti analyzed the effect of tomato plant variety as hosts to whitefly parasites. Her aim was to determine if there is a relationship between tomato variety and the amount of whitefly parasitization. Christa ran a greenhouse experiment, releasing whitefly parasites on tomato plants with a natural infestation of silverleaf whitefly. After five weeks, leaflets were examined under a microscope to determine if whitefly nymphs were parasitized or unparasitized.

Tomato Variety	Parasitized	Unparasitized
9000	165	172
90295	68	13
95495	369	142
Agora	184	121
Avalon	219	692
Blitz	26	22
Cabarnet	36	20
Graziella	180	40
RCH51279	241	159
Trust	314	458

Using your software to do all calculations, perform a level .05 test to see if tomato variety and whitefly parasitization are independent.

3. Awareness of the possible effects of carcinogenic substances has increased efforts to reduce exposure to such substances. In "Reducing Carcinogens in Public Schools: A Non-regulatory Approach by a Regulatory Agency" survey data are given concerning whether school districts have disposed of, are scheduled to dispose of, or still use various carcinogens.

	Disposed	Plan to Dispose	Still in Use
Benzene	281	56	115
Lead chromate	147	59	31
Asbestos	114	45	58
Sodium dichromate	80	67	44
Arsenic trioxide	32	17	7
Arsenic	28	16	11
Sodium arsenate	15	15	9
Other	36	12	8

Using your software to do all calculations, perform a level .01 test to see if the actions of the school districts are independent of the type of carcinogen.

4. A random sample of 1,935 HIV-positive people was cross-classified according to age and sex. The results are as follows.

Age	Male	Female	Total
0 to 12	20	4	24
13 to 19	53	4	57
20 to 29	643	48	691
30 to 39	677	25	702
40 to 49	320	11	331
50 to 59	93	3	96
60+	30	4	34
Total	1,836	99	1,935

Using your software to do all calculations, perform a level .05 test to see if, for the population of people who are HIV positive, age and sex are independent.

5. The enrollment at a large university is given below, classified according to area of study and sex.

Area of Study	Men	Women
Agriculture	1,751	1,753
Architecture	962	517
Business	1,407	1,021
Engineering	3,365	705
Liberal Arts	1,089	1,980
Science and Math	881	1,049
Teacher Education	101	281

Using your software to do all calculations, perform a level .01 test to see if choice of study area and sex are independent.

6. McIntyre et al. in "Dexamethasone as Adjunctive Therapy in Bacterial Meningitis" looked at a number of studies that evaluated the use of dexamethasone as protection against hearing loss in childhood *Haemophilus influenzae*, type B (Hib), meningitis. One aspect of the study reported on the causative agents of the bacterial meningitis by location.

	Causative Organisms in Dexamethasone Trials			
Study	*Haemophilus influenzae,* Type B	*Streptococcus pneumoniae*	*Neisseria meningitidis*	Total
Dallas 1	77	10	7	100
Dallas 2	77	7	10	100
Dallas 3	45	9	4	60
Costa Rica	79	8	2	101
Switzerland	67	11	28	115
Canada	57	13	18	101
U.S.	83	33	24	143
Finland	29	6	21	58
Mozambique	12	25	11	70
Total	526	122	125	848

Using your software to do all calculations, perform a level .05 test to see if the causative agents of the bacterial meningitis are independent of location.

 7. In the Statlib Datasets Archive at <u>DASLSets</u>, click on *Irish.ed*, a data set submitted to Statlib by Adrian E. Raftery. You will find a longitudinal educational transition data set for a sample of 500 Irish students. The variables include sex, whether the student had taken a "leaving certificate," and type of school. Paste the data set into your software. Using your software to do all calculations, perform a level .05 test to see if

a) Sex is independent of whether a student had taken a "leaving certificate."

b) Sex is independent of type of school.

c) Whether a student had taken a "leaving certificate" is independent of type of school.

8. In the Statlib Datasets Archive at <u>DASLSets</u>, click on *Plasma Retinol*, a data set submitted to Statlib by D. W. Nierenberg, T. A. Stukel, M. R. Karagas, and the Micronutrient Study Group. This data file (*n* = 315) investigates the relationship between personal characteristics and dietary factors and plasma concentrations of retinol, beta-carotene, and other carotenoids. It includes the variable sex (1 = male, 2 = female), smoking status (1 = never, 2 = former, 3 = current smoker), and vitamin use (1 = yes, fairly often; 2 = yes, not often; 3 = no). Paste the data set into your software. Using your software to do all calculations, perform a level .01 test to see if

a) Sex is independent of smoking status.

b) Sex is independent of vitamin use.

c) Smoking status is independent of vitamin use.

9. On the Internet, access the Data & Story Library at <u>DASL</u> and click on *List all methods*. On the new screen, click on *Chi-Square test*. From the choices, pick the data set that you find the most interesting, and download it to your software. Use the software to conduct a contingency table test at a level of .05.

CHAPTER 12

Linear Regression and Correlation

LOOKING AHEAD

In this chapter you'll see how statistical techniques can be used to help a manager make a hiring decision, and you'll see how an executive can arrive at sales forecasts for her company. We'll consider equations in this chapter that describe the relationship that exists between two or more variables. Such equations are usually solved with the help of modern computers or calculators. The name given to the study methodology that uses these modern tools is *regression analysis*—an anachronistic term dating to Sir Francis Galton's nineteenth-century study of the relationship between parents' heights and children's heights. Since Galton found that the stature of the offspring of very short or very tall parents tended to "regress" toward the mean population height, he was legitimately engaged in a regression analysis. Subsequent studies, of course, had nothing to do with Galton's regression analysis, but the name has stuck.

First, we'll examine some introductory concepts. Next, we'll focus on simple linear regression analysis and some relationship tests and prediction intervals that may be prepared in such an analysis. The focus then shifts to simple linear correlation analysis. Finally, we'll consider multiple linear regression and correlation topics.

Thus, after studying this chapter, you should be able to

- Explain the purposes of regression and correlation analysis.

- Compute and interpret the meaning of regression equations and standard errors of estimate for simple linear and multiple linear regression analysis situations and then use these measures to prepare interval estimates of the mean and individual values of the dependent variable for forecasting purposes.

- Compute and explain the meaning of the coefficients of determination and correlation when simple linear and multiple linear correlation analysis techniques are used.

12.1   **Introductory Concepts**

It's often necessary to prepare a **forecast**—an expectation of what the future holds—before a decision can be made. For example, it may be necessary to predict revenues before a budget can be prepared. And a university must predict enrollment before making up class schedules. These and other decisions can be made easier if a relationship can be established between the variable to be predicted and some other variable that is either known or is significantly easier to anticipate.

For our purposes, the term **relationship** means that changes in two or more variables are associated with each other. For example, we might find a high degree of relationship between the consumption of natural gas and the number of cold days during the winter, or between a change in the price of a product and consumer demand for the product. That is, we might logically expect a change (increase) in the number of cold days to be accompanied by a change (increase) in the consumption of natural gas, or a change (increase) in the price of a product to be accompanied by a change (decrease) in the demand for the product.

STATISTICS IN ACTION

Too Many Sails in the Sunset

An Australian sailor uses a statistical software program to collect and analyze volumes of data on temperature, wind velocity, wind direction, barometric pressure, and a host of other variables. His goal is to predict the weather on the day of a sailing race more accurately than his competitors, and his analysis helps him decide which sails to bring aboard the day of the race (too many sails and the boat is too heavy; too few sails and the right sail could be left behind).

Regression and Correlation Analysis: A Preview

The tools of regression analysis and correlation analysis have been developed to study and measure the statistical relationship that exists between two or more variables. The terms **simple regression** and **simple correlation** refer to those studies dealing with just two variables. When three or more variables are considered, the study deals with **multiple regression** and **multiple correlation.**

In regression analysis, an estimating or predicting equation is developed to describe the pattern or functional nature of the relationship that exists between the variables. As the name implies, an analyst prepares an **estimating** (or **regression**) **equation** to make estimates of values of one variable from given values of the other(s).

> The **dependent** (or **response**) **variable** is the variable to be estimated; it is customarily plotted on the vertical, or *y*, axis of a graph and is therefore identified by the symbol *y*.

> An **independent** (or **explanatory**) **variable** (*one in the simple regression/correlation case, two or more in multiple regression/correlation*) is one that presumably exerts an influence on or explains variations in the dependent variable. In simple regression/correlation, the independent variable is customarily plotted on the horizontal, or *x*, axis and is therefore identified by the symbol *x*.

Let's assume that Hiram N. Hess, personnel manager of the Tackey Toy Manufacturing Company, finds that there's a close and logical relationship between the productive output of employees in a certain department of the company and their earlier performance on an aptitude test. Thus, *if* Hiram computes an estimating, or regression, equation (as we'll do in a few pages) and *if* he has the aptitude test score of a job application, *then* he may use his estimating equation to predict the future output (the dependent variable) of the applicant based on test results (the independent variable). Included in the techniques used to make estimates of the dependent variable are regression analysis procedures that measure the dependability of these measures.

In **correlation analysis,** the purpose is to measure the strength or closeness of the relationship between the variables. In other words, regression analysis asks, "What is the pattern of the existing relationship?" and correlation analysis asks, "How strong is the relationship described in the regression equation?" Although it's possible to be concerned only with regression analysis or only with an analysis of correlation, the two are typically considered together.

To summarize, in the following pages we'll concentrate on three main tasks (the first two of which are a part of regression analysis):

1. Computing the regression, or estimating, equation and then using it to provide an estimate of the value of the dependent or response variable y when given one or more values of the independent or explanatory variable(s) x.

2. Computing measures that show the possible errors that may be involved in using the estimating equation as a basis for forecasting.

3. Preparing measures that show the closeness of the association or correlation that exists between the variables.

A Logical Relationship: The First Step

Your sales last year just paralleled the sales of rum cokes in Rio de Janeiro, as modified by the sum of the last digits of all new telephone numbers in Toronto. So, why bother with surveys of your own market? Just [get] the data from Canada and Brazil.—*Lydia Strong*

STATISTICS IN ACTION

I Grieve

Bill Illing, a director of employee services, has used statistical software to investigate the handling of employee grievances. His study involved dependent variables such as the number of grievances filed per month against middle and top managers. His independent variables included the managers involved in the grievance, the presence or absence of a collective bargaining agreement when the grievance was filed, and the presence or absence of an "employee involvement" program when the grievance was filed. The results of the study helped managers improve their negotiating skills, and it helped them do a better job of resolving employee grievances.

Two variables or series may move together for several reasons. And analysts may correctly assume a causal relationship in their interpretation of correlation measures. But just because two variables are associated in a statistical sense does not guarantee the existence of a causal relationship. In other words, the existence of a causal relationship, usually does imply correlation, but, as the previous quote adequately shows, statistical correlation alone does not in any way prove causality. (If you believe that it does, you should indeed use the data from Canada and Brazil!)

Causal relationships may fit into cause-and-effect or common-cause categories. A **cause-and-effect relationship** exists if a change in one variable produces a change in another variable. For example, an increase in the temperature of a chemical process may cause a decrease in the yield of the process, and an increase in the level of production output may cause an increase in total production cost. Alternatively, two series may vary together because of a **common-cause factor** that impacts both series in the same way. One could probably find a close relationship between jewellery sales and compact disk sales, but one of these series is not the cause and the other the effect. Rather, changes in both series are probably a result of changes in consumer income.

Of course, as we saw in the quote at the beginning of this section, some relationships are purely accidental. So if a relationship were found between furniture sales in Canada and the average temperature in Sweden, for example, it would be a meaningless exercise to analyze the data. In an interesting paper, Mark Nicolich showed that over a number of years there was a very strong relationship between increasing wine consumption and decreasing SAT scores. Relationships such as these are known as *spurious correlations* (unless, of course, a goodly portion of the wine was consumed the evening before the SAT exam).

Probably the first step in the study of regression and correlation, therefore, is to see if *a logical relationship* may exist between the variables to support further analysis. Unfortunately, presenting a summary of many types of variables, and the forces at work on those variables, is beyond the scope of this book. Fortunately, though, such a summary is to be found in the psychology, economics, biology, business, and other courses that you've taken or will take. It's only through the use of reason and judgment (along with the application of knowledge about the variables and the forces at work) that an analysis may assume causality, whether cause and effect or common cause. Yet without this assumption, there's not much point in proceeding with regression and correlation analyses.

Other students (not you) sometimes go to one of two extremes at about this point in their introduction to regression and correlation: (1) They fail to realize the importance of seeing if a logical relationship exists, and they mechanically apply the statistical procedures in the following pages and arrive at possibly spurious correlations to which they erroneously assign interpretations of causality. Or (2) they think that since one cannot prove causality from correlation, it's necessary to conclude that there's no connection at all between correlation and causality. You, of course, will avoid either of these extremes.

The Scatter Diagram

Let's assume that a logical relationship may exist between two variables. To support further analysis, the next step, then, is to use a graph to plot the available data. This graph—called a **scatter diagram**—shows plotted points. Each point represents a study member for which we have an *x* (independent or explanatory) value and a *y* (dependent or response) value. The *scatter diagram serves two purposes:* (1) It helps us see if there's a useful relationship between the two variables, and (2) it helps us determine the type of equation to use to describe the relationship.

We can illustrate the purposes of a scatter diagram by using the data in Table 12.1. This figure gives us the output for a time period in dozens of units (the dependent, or response, variable) and the aptitude test results (the independent, or explanatory, variable) for eight employees in a department of the Tackey Toy Manufacturing Company. If the aptitude test does what it's supposed to do, it's reasonable to assume that employees with higher aptitude scores will be among the higher producers. Our group of eight employees represents a small sample of workers. We've kept the employee count

TABLE 12.1   OUTPUT AND APTITUDE TEST RESULTS OF EIGHT EMPLOYEES
OF TACKEY TOY MANUFACTURING COMPANY

Employee	Aptitude Test Results (*x*)	Output (Dozens of Units) (*y*)
A	6	30
B	9	49
C	3	18
D	8	42
E	7	39
F	5	25
G	8	41
H	10	52

FIGURE 12.1 Scatter diagram. (*Source:* Table 12.1).

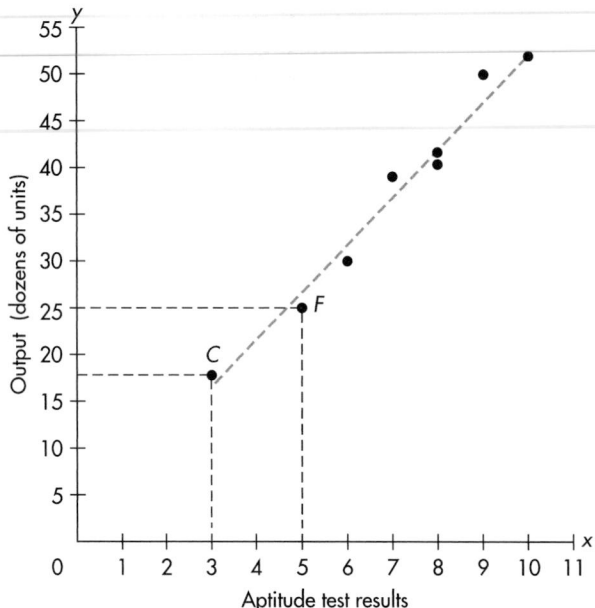

small and the data simple, though, to minimize the computational effort necessary in later sections. In a real-world problem, you will usually work with larger samples.

The data for each employee represent *one* point on the scatter diagram shown in *Figure 12.1*. The points representing employees C and F are labelled to show you how the pairs of observations for the employees are used to prepare the points on the chart. As you'll notice in *Figure 12.1*, the eight points form a path that can be approximated by a *straight line*. Thus, there appears to be a **linear relationship** between the variables. And a high degree of relationship is indicated by the fact that the points are all close to this straight-line path. You'll also notice there's a **positive** (or **direct**) **relationship** between the variables—that is, as aptitude test results *increase,* output also *increases.* Of course, it's quite possible for variables to have a **negative** (or **inverse**) **relationship** (as the *x* value increases, the *y* value decreases).

Statistical software packages and calculators with graphics capabilities can easily create scatter diagrams. We used MINITAB (see *Figure 12.2a*) and a TI-83 (see screen 2 of *Figure 12.2b*) to prepare scatter diagrams for the same data set used to produce *Figure 12.1*. The eight points must still follow a positive straight-line pattern; any differences in appearance is caused by slightly different choices being made for the scales of the axes.

Figure 12.3 summarizes some possible scatter diagram forms. *Figures 12.3a, b, and c* show the positive and negative linear patterns we've been considering. We'll consider only linear relationships in this chapter's computations. However, relationships need not be linear, as shown in *Figures 12.3d* to *f*. In *Figure 12.3f*, the variables might be family income and age of the head of the household. (Income tends to rise for a period and then fall off when retirement age is reached.) Finally, it's possible that a scatter diagram such as the one in *Figure 12.3g* might show *no relationship* at all between the variables.

☐ **Example 12.1**   **Regressing Pressing** A weight-lifting program was created for football players. As part of the program's evaluation, players were given a one repeti-

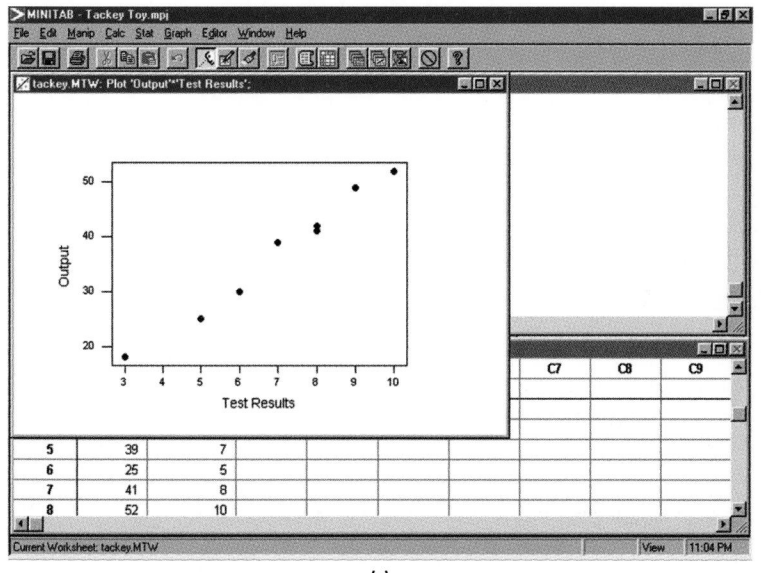

(a)

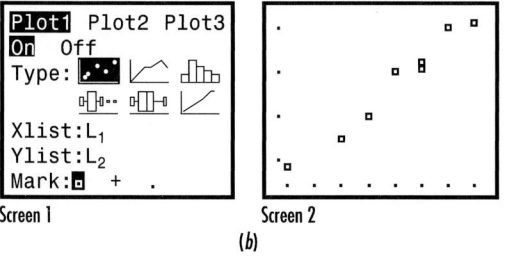

Screen 1   Screen 2
(b)

FIGURE 12.2 (*a*) To obtain this MINITAB output, click on **Graph, Plot,** enter *Output* as **Y** and *Test Results* as **X,** and click **OK.** (*b*) To make this scatter plot, enter the aptitude test results into **L1** and the output into list **L2.** Access the **STAT PLOT** menu and choose plot 1. Set the plot up as shown in screen 1. Next set the window so that the points can all be seen. For example, set the window as

Xmin = 2.5, Xmax = 10.5,
Xscl = 1
Ymin = 15, Ymax = 55, Yscl = 10

Press **Graph** and you get the plot shown in screen 2. Note that **TRACE** will allow you to see the coordinates of the data points.

tion, maximum weight bench press in the spring and again in the fall. The results for the players in one program follow (Data = BnchPrss):

Fall Bench	Spring Bench	Fall Bench	Spring Bench
385	385	315	275
405	370	275	285
315	305	425	425
325	275	365	375
365	315	465	455
340	315	475	485
380	355	430	405
305	300	315	315
335	315	315	295
375	315	405	365
400	375	365	390
305	295	305	265
385	345	275	255
315	315	265	270
360	335	360	315
305	285	335	335
295	295	325	295
265	265		

FIGURE 12.3 Scatter diagram forms.

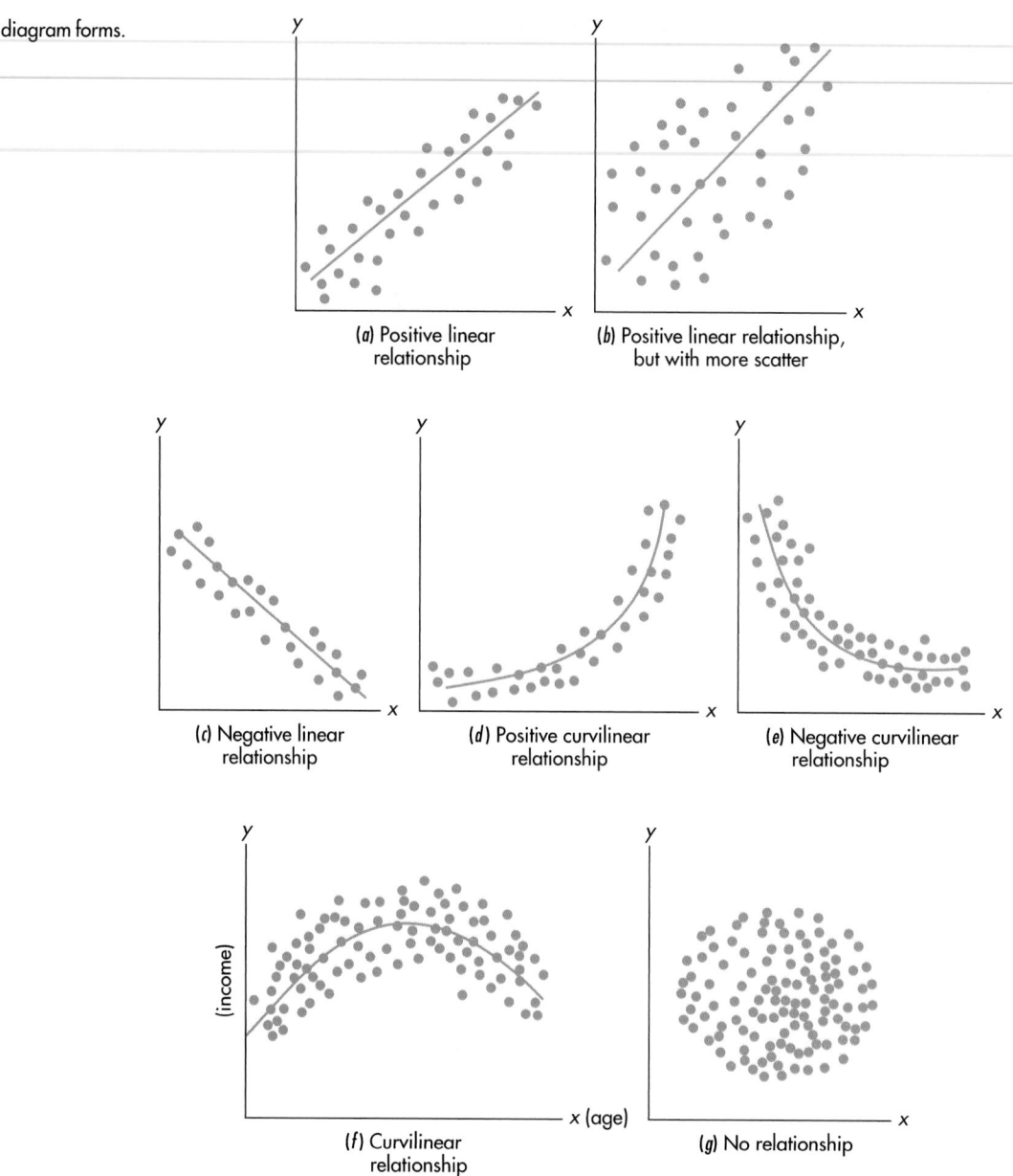

(a) Positive linear relationship

(b) Positive linear relationship, but with more scatter

(c) Negative linear relationship

(d) Positive curvilinear relationship

(e) Negative curvilinear relationship

(f) Curvilinear relationship

(g) No relationship

Generate a scatter diagram for this sample and see if it appears that there is a linear relationship between the weights lifted in the spring and the following fall.

◆ **Solution:**

MINITAB was used to generate the scatter diagram of *Figure 12.4*. There is obviously a linear relationship between the spring and fall weights. ◆

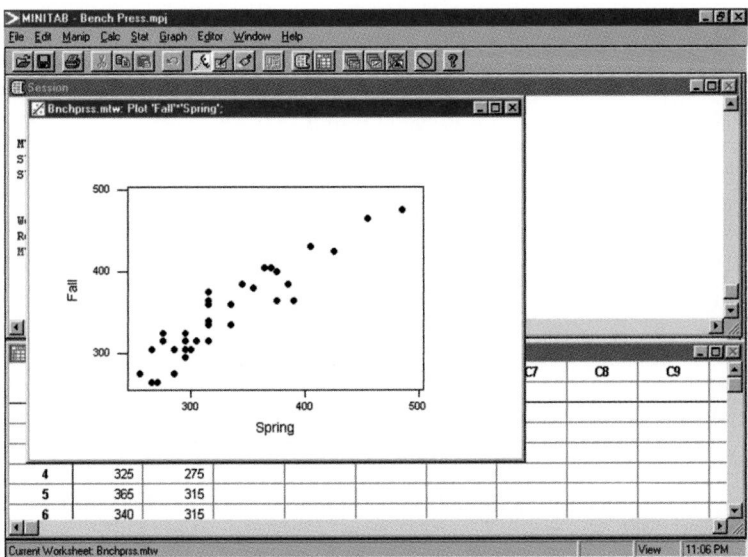

FIGURE 12.4 MINITAB scatter diagram of bench press data.

Self-Testing Review 12.1

1. What is the purpose of linear regression analysis?

2. Discuss the roles of the dependent (response) variable and the independent (explanatory) variable(s).

3. What is correlation analysis?

For each of the following scatter diagrams, determine if there is (*a*) a positive linear relationship, (*b*) a negative linear relationship, or (*c*) no linear relationship.

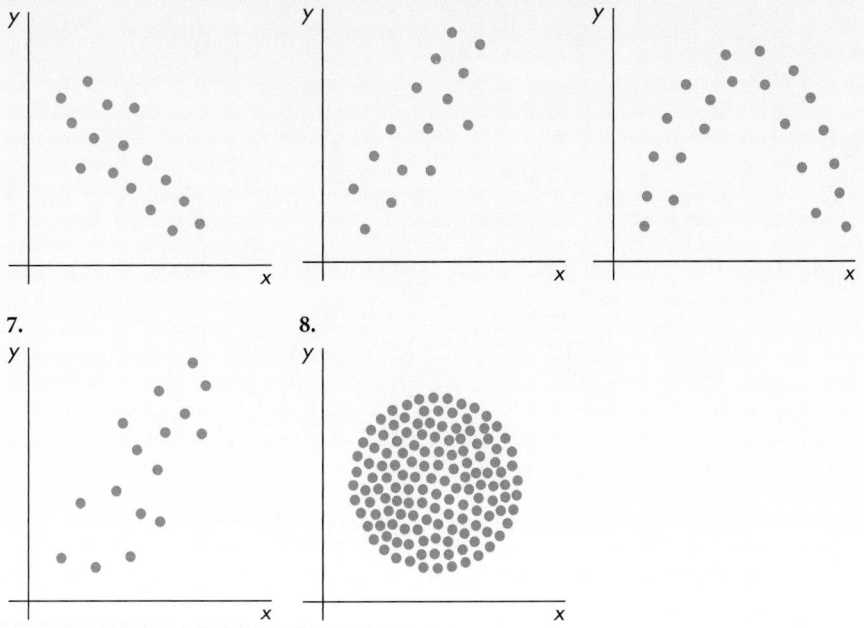

9. For each of the following data pairs, do you think there would tend to be a positive linear relationship, a negative linear relationship, or no relationship?

a) x = the height of twin A, and y = the height of twin B.

b) x = the number of hours in safety training, and y = the number of accidents.

c) x = a person's IQ, and y = the number of books the person read last year.

d) x = a person's IQ, and y = the person's height.

e) x = the height of a male, and y = the shoe size of the male.

f) x = the hours a student watches television per week, and y = the student's grade point average.

g) x = the dollar amount of sales to customers, and y = the bonus received.

h) x = a person's income, and y = the dollars the person spent for clothing.

10. Draw a scatter diagram for each of the following data pairs. State if you think there's a positive linear relationship, a negative linear relationship, or no linear relationship.

a) We'll let x = the number of radio ads aired per week by an automobile dealership, and y = the number of automobiles sold per week by the dealership.

x	3	16	7	4	15	7	8	5
y	4	40	16	9	38	16	17	10

b) Let x = a grade six student's IQ score, and y = the hours spent watching TV each week.

x	125	116	97	114	85	107	105
y	5	14	30	16	41	25	21

c) Let x = a child's age, and y = the number of visits the child makes to a doctor during the year.

x	5	6	8	14	15	7	8	12
y	9	2	12	17	9	16	6	15

d) Let x = the number of days a patient is hospitalized, and y = the age of the patient.

x	1	6	2	4	5	3
y	15	75	27	3	15	15

12.2 Simple Linear Regression Analysis

The straight line in the scatter diagram in *Figure 12.1* that describes the relationship between the variables is called a **regression** (or **estimating**) **line.** We've seen in the Looking Ahead section that Sir Francis Galton's study showed that the height of the children of tall parents tended to regress (or move back) toward the average height of the population. Galton called the line describing this relationship a *line of regression.* The word *regression* has stuck with us, but other words such as *estimating* or *predictive* are probably more apt.

The Linear Regression Equation

We'll compute an estimating or regression equation in this section to describe the relationship between the variables. Our interest here is limited to an analysis of **simple linear regression** of y on x—that is, to the case in which the relationship between two variables can be adequately described by a straight line.

The Straight-Line Equation *Figure 12.5a* shows a straight line (identified by the symbol $\hat{y}$) of the type that we'll soon be computing. To define this line, we must know two things about it. First, we must know the value of the y *intercept*—that is, the value (read on the y axis) of a in *Figure 12.5a* when x is equal to zero. And second, we need to know the *slope of the line* (b). This slope, as shown in *Figure 12.5a*, is found by

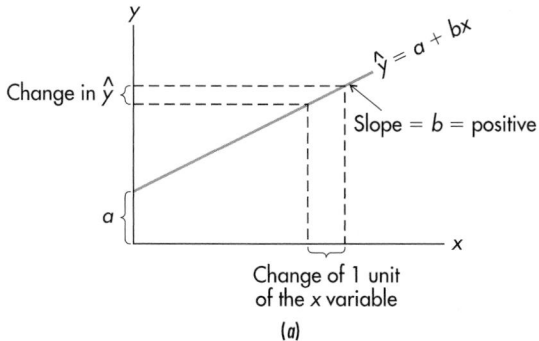

(a)

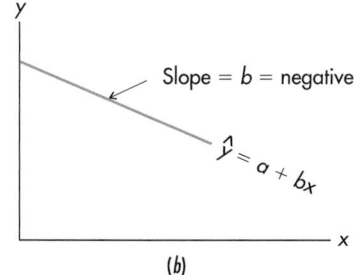

(b)

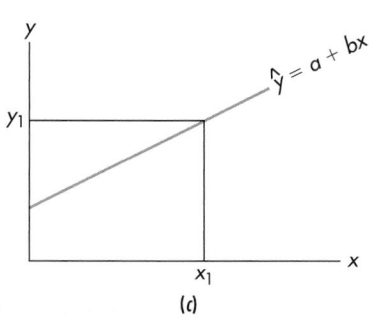

(c)

FIGURE 12.5 Graphs of regression lines.

(1) measuring a change of one unit of the x variable, and (2) measuring the corresponding change in $\hat{y}$ on the y axis. In *Figure 12.5a*, the slope of the line has a *positive* value; in *Figure 12.5b*, the slope has a *negative* value. In both cases, however, the formula for $\hat{y}$ (and the formula that we will use to compute the straight-line equation) is:

$$\hat{y} = a + bx \tag{12.1}$$

where $\hat{y}$ = a computed estimate of the dependent variable
           a = the y intercept or the value of $\hat{y}$ when x is equal to zero
           b = the slope of the regression line, or the increase or decrease in $\hat{y}$ for each change of one unit of x
           x = a given value of the independent variable

Thus, if we selected a value of the independent or explanatory variable x_1 as shown in *Figure 12.5c*, drew a vertical line up to the regression line $\hat{y}$, and then drew a horizontal line to the y axis, the value of y_1 would be an estimate of the dependent or response variable y, given the value of the independent variable x_1.

Properties of the Linear Regression Line   There are two properties of the linear regression line. The first of these properties is demonstrated in *Figure 12.6*, which shows the regression line fitted to the scatter diagram data that are plotted on a graph. Each point on the scatter diagram represents a value for x and y. The regression line $\hat{y}$ is drawn in a straight line through these points. Sometimes the $\hat{y}$ value for a given value of x is greater than the y value, and sometimes $\hat{y}$ is less than y for a given x quantity. But the fact is that the regression line is fitted to the data in the scatter diagram in such a way that the *positive* deviations of the scatter points *above* the line in the diagram cancel out the *negative* deviations of the scatter points *below* the line, and the resulting sum is zero (see *Figure 12.6*). Thus, the *first property* of the regression line is

$$\Sigma(y - \hat{y}) = 0$$

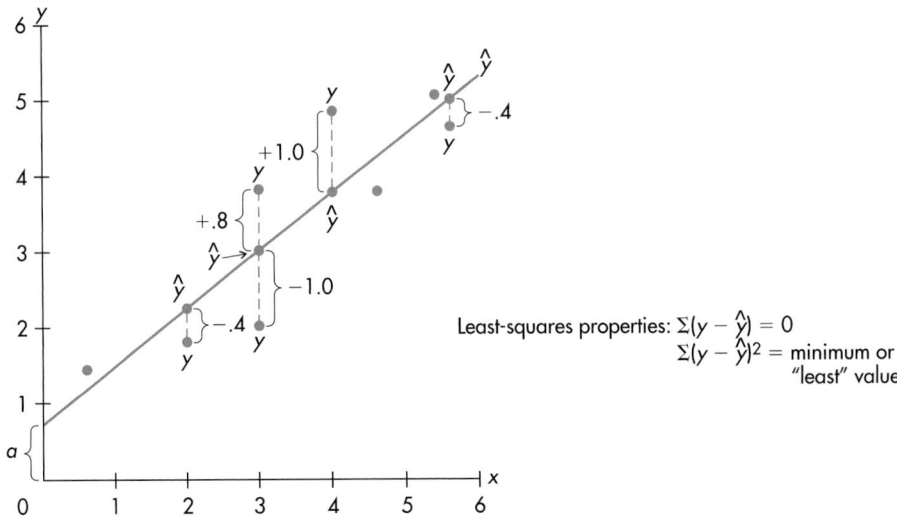

FIGURE 12.6 Regression line fitted to the scatter diagram.

And the sum of the *squares* of the deviations is less than would be the case if any other straight line were substituted for the $\hat{y}$ line and the process of computing and squaring deviations were carried out. In other words, the *second property* is

$\Sigma(y - \hat{y})^2$ = a minimum, or "least," value

And so the name **method of least squares** is used to describe the approach we'll follow to fit a straight line to a linear regression data set.

The values of a and b in the regression equation are computed with the following formulas:

$$b = \frac{n(\Sigma\, xy) - (\Sigma\, x)(\Sigma\, y)}{n(\Sigma\, x^2) - (\Sigma\, x)^2} \qquad (12.2)$$

where n = number of paired observations
   $(\Sigma\, x^2)$ = the sum of all the values in an x^2 column
   $(\Sigma\, x)^2$ = the square of the sum of an x column

$$a = \bar{y} - b\bar{x} \qquad (12.3)$$

where $\bar{y}$ = the mean of the y variable
   $\bar{x}$ = the mean of the x variable

The linear regression line always passes through the point at the intersection of $\bar{y}$ and $\bar{x}$.

Computing the Linear Regression Equation We're now ready to find the regression equation for the data presented in Table 12.1. A worksheet for computing the values required to solve for b and a (using formulas 12.2 and 12.3) is given in Table 12.2. A y^2 column is also included in Table 12.2. We don't need that column to

TABLE 12.2 WORKSHEET FOR COMPUTING b AND a

Employee	Aptitude Test Results (x)	Output (Dozens of Units) (y)	xy	x²	y²
A	6	30	180	36	900
B	9	49	441	81	2,401
C	3	18	54	9	324
D	8	42	336	64	1,764
E	7	39	273	49	1,521
F	5	25	125	25	625
G	8	41	328	64	1,681
H	10	52	520	100	2,704
Total	56	296	2,257	428	11,920

$$\bar{x} = \frac{\Sigma\, x}{n} = \frac{56}{8} = 7 \qquad \bar{y} = \frac{\Sigma\, y}{n} = \frac{296}{8} = 37$$

FIGURE 12.7 To obtain this graph, click on **Stat, Regression, Fitted Line Plot,** enter *Output* in the box to the right of **Response (Y)** and *Test Results* in the box to the right of **Predictor (X),** and click **OK.**

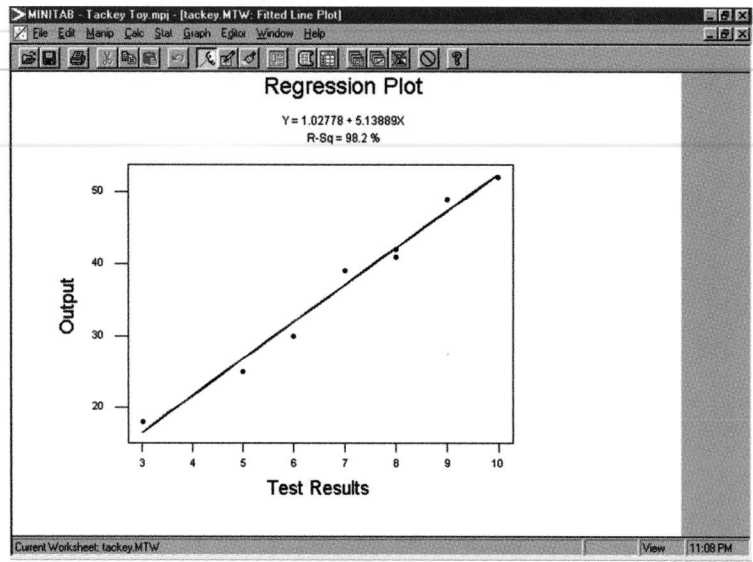

calculate the regression equation, but we'll use it later. The values of *b* and *a* are found as follows:

$$b = \frac{n(\sum xy) - (\sum x)(\sum y)}{n(\sum x^2) - (\sum x^2)} = \frac{8(2,257) - (56)(296)}{8(428) - (56)^2} = \frac{1,480}{288} = 5.1389$$

$$a = \bar{y} - b\bar{x} = 37 - (5.1389)(7) = 1.0277$$

Therefore, the regression equation that describes the relationship between the output of our sample of Tackey Toy employees and their aptitude test results is

$$\hat{y} = 1.0277 + 5.1389(x)$$

 As you might expect, statistical software can eliminate the need to do these tedious calculations by hand. MINITAB offers several ways to obtain the least squares regression line. The output in *Figure 12.7* is the result of using MINITAB's **Fitted Line Plot.** It prepares a scatter diagram that includes a plot of the estimated regression line, its equation, and something we'll discuss soon, the coefficient of determination (denoted as r^2).

An Alternative

Regression analysis is a commonly applied tool in the social and physical sciences, and it is used to forecast future business and economic results. An alternative forecasting approach would be for you to sit in a trance on a tripod above a chasm that emitted noxious vapors and make oracular utterances for someone to record. This was the approach used by the Greeks in ancient Delphi.

Making Preliminary Predictions with the Regression Equation

There was once a young manager named Hess
Whose forecasts were always a mess.
So his boss did appear,
And in voice loud and clear,
Said, "Hess, son, try regression, or consider another career!"

The primary use of the regression equation is to estimate values of the dependent variable given values of the independent variable. Suppose, for example, that the unfortunate Hiram Hess, personnel manager for Tackey Toys, is considering hiring an appli-

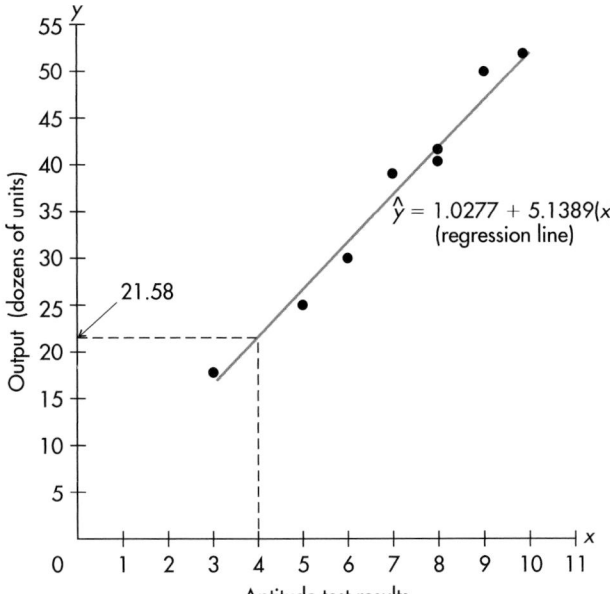

FIGURE 12.8 Graphical illustration of a predicted value.

cant who scored a four on the aptitude test. The supervisor of the department wants someone hired who can produce an average of 30 dozen units. Of course, it's not possible to tell exactly what the applicant's future production might be, but Hiram can use the equation computed in the preceding section to arrive at a preliminary estimate or forecast of the average amount of output produced by those who score a four on the aptitude test. How? By simply substituting 4 for x in the regression equation. The estimate is computed as follows:

$$\hat{y} = 1.0277 + 5.1389(4) = 1.0277 + 20.556 = 21.58 \text{ dozen units of output}$$

This prediction is shown graphically in *Figure 12.8*.

But some words of caution are needed here. First, we do not yet know how dependable our estimate is likely to be (that's the subject of the next section). And second, when we make an estimate from a regression equation, it's incorrect to extend this estimate beyond the range of the original observations. There's no way of knowing what the nature of the regression equation will be if we encounter values of the dependent variable larger or smaller than those we've observed. For example, in our Tackey Toy situation it's ridiculous to assume that an employee's output will increase indefinitely as his or her test results increase. There's obviously some upper limit to aptitude test scores, and regardless of aptitude, the speed of productive equipment and physical endurance also set a limit to productive output. Since the largest value of x we observed is 10, we can place no reliance on estimates that might be made of the output of employees who have test scores of, say, 15 or 16.

The Standard Error of Estimate

When predicting from a regression equation, the question arises, How dependable is the estimate? Obviously, an important factor in gauging dependability is the closeness of the relationship between the variables. Let's look at *Figure 12.9* and assume that both

FIGURE 12.9 Varying degrees of spread or scatter.

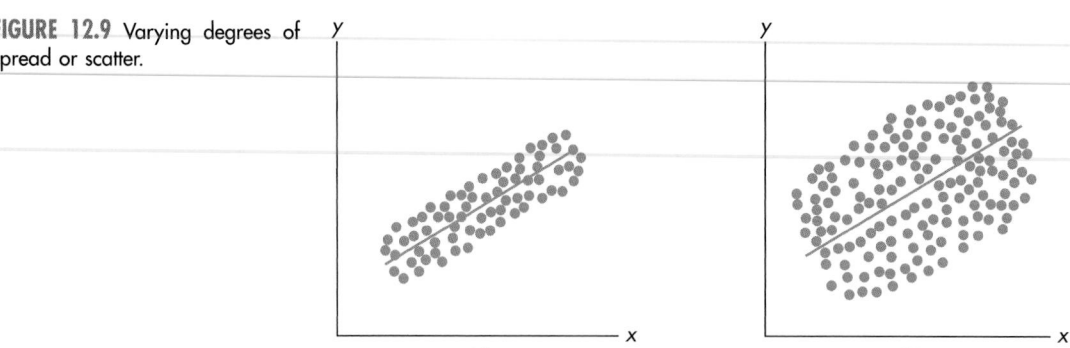

(a)   (b)

scatter diagrams have the same scales for the variables and the same regression line. When the points in a scatter diagram are closely spaced around the regression line, as they are in *Figure 12.9a*, it's logical to assume that an estimate based on that relationship will probably be more dependable than an estimate based on a regression line such as that shown in *Figure 12.9b*, where the scatter is greater. Therefore, if we had a measure of the extent of the spread, or scatter, of the points around the regression line, we would be in a better position to judge the dependability of estimates made using the line.

You'll not be surprised to learn that we do have a measure that indicates the extent of the spread, scatter, or dispersion of the points about the regression line. From an estimating standpoint, *the smaller this measure is, the more dependable the prediction is likely to be.* (The numerical value of this measure for *Figure 12.9a* is smaller than the value for *Figure 12.9b* because the dispersion is smaller in *Figure 12.9a*.) The name of this measure is the **standard error of estimate** (the symbol is $s_{y.x}$), and, as the name implies, it's used to qualify the estimate made with the regression equation by indicating the extent of the possible variation (or error) that may be present.

Computation of $s_{y.x}$ In more precise terms, *the standard error of estimate is a standard deviation that measures the scatter of the observed values around the regression line.* Thus, one formula that may be used to compute the standard error of estimate naturally bears a striking resemblance to the formula used to compute the standard deviation for ungrouped data. The primary difference between the two formulas lies in the fact that the standard deviation is measured from the mean ($\bar{y}$), while the standard error of estimate is measured from the regression line ($\hat{y}$). Both the mean and the regression line, of course, indicate central tendency—the difference being, in regression, the mean of y depends on the value of x. The formula for the standard error of estimate is

$$s_{y.x} = \sqrt{\frac{\Sigma(y - \hat{y})^2}{n - 2}}$$

(12.4)

The $n - 2$ in the denominator is used in this case because our sample data are used to estimate two parameters, the true slope and intercept, but we'll omit a detailed explanation of degrees of freedom.

In using formula 12.4, we must compute a value for $\hat{y}$ for each value of x by substituting each x value into the regression equation $\hat{y} = 1.0277 + 5.1389(x)$. We must then compute the difference between these $\hat{y}$ values and the corresponding observed values of y. Table 12.3 shows a worksheet for calculating the standard error of estimate for our Tackey Toy example. The standard error of estimate is calculated as follows:

TABLE 12.3 WORKSHEET FOR COMPUTING $s_{y.x}$

Employee	Aptitude Test Results (x)	Output (Dozens of Units) (y)	$(\hat{y})$	$(y - \hat{y})$	$(y - \hat{y})^2$
A	6	30	31.86	−1.86	3.4596
B	9	49	47.28	1.72	2.9584
C	3	18	16.44	1.56	2.4336
D	8	42	42.14	−0.14	0.0196
E	7	39	37.00	2.00	4.0000
F	5	25	26.72	−1.72	2.9584
G	8	41	42.14	−1.14	1.2996
H	10	52	52.42	−0.42	.1764
Total	56	296*	296.00*	0.00	17.3056

*Note that the sums of y and $\hat{y}$ are equal. This must always be true if $\Sigma(y - \hat{y}) = 0$.

$$s_{y.x} = \sqrt{\frac{\Sigma(y - \hat{y})^2}{n - 2}} = \sqrt{\frac{17.3056}{6}} = \sqrt{2.884}$$

= 1.698 dozens of units of output. (The value of $s_{y.x}$ will always be expressed in the units of the y variable.)

Although it's helpful to use formula 12.4 to explain the nature of $s_{y.x}$, a much easier formula to apply is

$$s_{y.x} = \sqrt{\frac{\Sigma(y^2) - a(\Sigma y) - b(\Sigma xy)}{n - 2}} \qquad (12.5)$$

You'll notice that all the values needed for this formula are available from Table 12.2, which was used to prepare the regression equation. Using the values from Table 12.2

$$s_{y.x} = \sqrt{\frac{\Sigma(y^2) - a(\Sigma y) - b(\Sigma xy)}{n - 2}} = \sqrt{\frac{(11,920) - 1.0277(296) - 5.1389(2,257)}{6}}$$

$$= \sqrt{\frac{17.304}{6}} = \sqrt{2.884} = 1.698 \text{ dozens of units of output—the same result}$$
obtained when using formula 12.4

Self-Testing Review 12.2

11. The manager of an automobile dealership wishes to investigate the relationship between the number of radio ads aired per week and the number of automobiles sold. A random sample of the records for eight weeks produces the following data pairs where x is the number of radio ads aired and y is the number of automobiles sold.

x	3	16	7	4	15	7	8	5
y	4	40	16	9	38	16	17	10

a) Find $\sum x$, $\sum x^2$, and $(\sum x)^2$.

b) Find $\sum y$, $\sum y^2$, and $(\sum y)^2$.

c) Find $\sum xy$.

d) Find $\bar{x}$ and $\bar{y}$.

e) Find b and a.

f) Write the equation for the line of regression.

g) Predict the number of automobiles sold per week when six radio ads are aired.

h) Predict the number of automobiles sold per week when three radio ads are aired.

i) Calculate the standard error of estimate.

12. A sixth-grade teacher believes there is a relationship between her students' IQ scores and the hours they spend watching television each week. The following table represents a random sample of data, where $x =$ the IQ score of a student in grade 6, and $y =$ the hours spent watching TV each week:

x	125	116	97	114	85	107	105
y	5	14	30	16	41	25	21

a) Find $\sum x$, $\sum x^2$, and $(\sum x)^2$.

b) Find $\sum y$, $\sum y^2$, and $(\sum y)^2$.

c) Find $\sum xy$.

d) Find $\bar{x}$ and $\bar{y}$.

e) Find b and a.

f) Write the equation for the line of regression.

g) Predict the number of hours of TV watching for a student in grade 6 with an IQ of 91.

h) Predict the number of hours of TV watching for a student in grade 6 with an IQ of 125.

i) Calculate the standard error of estimate.

13. The Rip-Off Vending Machine Company operates coffee vending machines in office buildings. The company wants to study the relationship, if any, that exists between the number of cups of coffee sold per day and the number of people working in each building. Sample data for this study were collected by the company and are presented below:

Number of People Working at Location (x)	Number of Cups of Coffee Sold (y)
5	10
6	20
14	30
19	40
15	30
11	20
18	40
22	40
26	50

a) Find $\sum x$, $\sum x^2$, and $(\sum x)^2$.

b) Find $\sum y$, $\sum y^2$, and $(\sum y)^2$.

c) Find $\sum xy$.

d) Find $\bar{x}$ and $\bar{y}$.

e) Find b and a.

f) Write the equation for the line of regression.

g) Predict the number of cups of coffee for a building with 17 employees.

h) Predict the number of cups of coffee for a building with five employees.

i) Calculate the standard error of estimate.

14. The following data represent the three-mile (split) and five-mile (final) times, in minutes, for male cross-country runners from Nebraska and Colorado at the Big 12 cross-country meet held in Ames, Iowa. For the analysis that follows, combine the data from the Nebraska and Colorado runners (Data = XCountry):

Nebraska		Colorado	
3 Mile	5 Mile	3 Mile	5 Mile
14.85	24.87	15.15	25.40
14.85	25.07	15.43	25.82
15.30	25.63	15.43	25.87
15.38	26.27	15.43	25.87
15.63	26.53	15.73	26.08
15.65	26.47	15.80	26.10
15.70	26.60	15.80	26.40
15.73	26.83	15.82	27.00
		16.40	27.53

a) Find b and a.

b) Write the equation for the line of regression.

c) Predict the 5-mile time for a person whose 3-mile time is 15.0 minutes.

d) Predict the 5-mile time for a person whose 3-mile time is 15.8 minutes.

e) Calculate the standard error of estimate.

15. M. Parmar studied the accuracy of a function generator. She did so by comparing the dial frequency to the actual frequency of the generator. She wanted to see how well the dial setting predicted the true frequency (Data = FundGen).

Frequency (Hz)					
Dial	Actual	Dial	Actual	Dial	Actual
100	112	800	827	5,000	5,069
200	210	900	945	6,000	6,077
300	318	1,000	1,060	7,000	7,130
400	421	2,000	2,031	8,000	8,210
500	516	3,000	3,042	9,000	9,218
600	630	4,000	4,072	10,000	12,021
700	728				

a) Find b and a.

b) Write the equation for the line of regression.

c) Predict the actual frequency for a dial setting of 300 Hz.

d) Predict the actual frequency for a dial setting of 6,500 Hz.

e) Calculate the standard error of estimate.

12.3 Statistical Inference in Simple Linear Regression Analysis

Simple Linear Regression Model

In order to make statistical inferences using simple regression analysis techniques, there are several underlying assumptions that must apply. These assumptions are

1. Corresponding to each possible value of X, there is a distribution of possible values of Y, where the means of all such Y-distributions fall in a straight line; that is $\mu_{y.x} = E(Y) = A + BX$ for some unknown parameters A and B.

2. For each X, the distribution of Y values is normally distributed. To check the validity of this assumption, a test for normality is performed; one such test is discussed in Section 12.5.

3. Each of the distributions of Y values has the same standard deviation σ. That's why in *Figure 12.10* the normal curves are drawn with the same width, or *spread*. Statisticians call this condition **homoscedasticity,** where *homo* means "same" and *scedastic* means "scatter."

4. Each Y value in these distributions is independent of the others.

The following is a summary of the model.

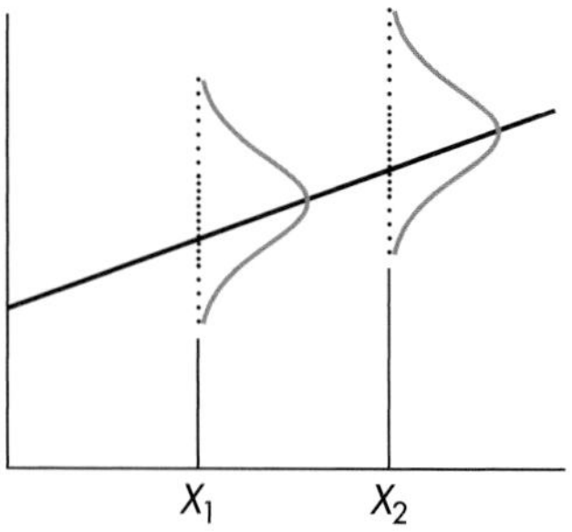

FIGURE 12.10 When statistical inferences are drawn using a regression model, a basic assumption is that for each possible value of X, there's a set of Y values that is normally distributed about the regression line.

Straight-Line Regression Model

For the Population

Mean: $\mu_{y.x} = E(Y) = A + BX$
Individual Value: $Y_i = A + BX_i + \varepsilon_i$

where
Y = dependent (or response) variable
X = independent (or explanatory) variable
A = y-intercept of the line
B = slope of the line
ε (epsilon) = random error component

The errors ε_i are assumed to follow a normal distribution with mean 0 and standard deviation σ.

For the Sample

Mean: $\hat{y} = a + bx$
Individual value: $y_i = a + bx + \varepsilon_i = \hat{y} + \varepsilon_i$

where $\varepsilon_i = y_i - \hat{y}$ and is called the *residual* for the individual i.

The mean of the residuals is 0, and the residuals may be used to estimate the common population standard deviation σ. The sample statistics a and b estimate the population parameters A and B.

Does a True Relationship Exist?

Hiram Hess now has a regression equation that gives him a central line through his sample data set. He also has a standard error of estimate that measures the scatter of the observed values of y about the regression line. It appears that there's a close relationship between aptitude test results and employee output. But appearances can sometimes be deceiving.

What if each point in the scatter diagram in *Figure 12.11a* shows how a Tackey production employee scored on the aptitude test and then performed later on the job? What if *Figure 12.11a* represents the entire population of production employees? If that were true, there's obviously no relationship between X and Y (the symbols we'll use for the population independent and dependent variables), and the slope of the population regression line (which we'll represent with the symbol B) has a value of zero. Perhaps Hiram was unfortunate enough to draw the misleading sample (represented by the black dots) shown in *Figure 12.11b*. The positive slope of Hiram's sample regression equation indicates a relationship, but a true relationship doesn't exist if B is zero. What can Hiram do about this dilemma? He can conduct a hypothesis test using many of the same concepts we've examined in earlier chapters.

A t Test for Slope

Let's now use the model for simple linear regression and our familiar seven-step hypothesis-testing procedure to test the value of B, the slope of the population regression line.

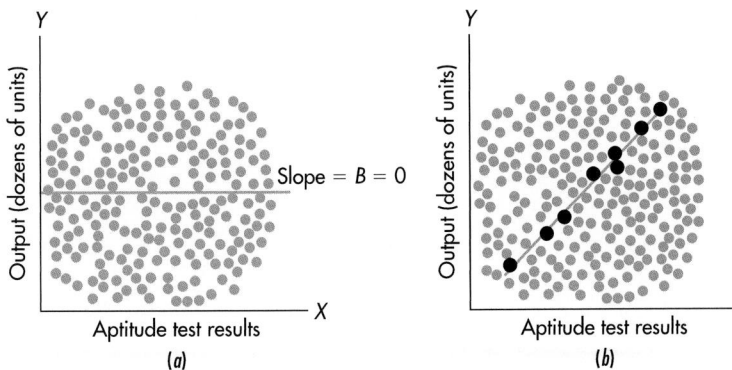

FIGURE 12.11 (a) What if this is the scatter diagram for all Tackey production workers? (b) Hiram's sample could suggest a relationship that doesn't exist in the population.

Step 1: Formulate the Null and Alternative Hypotheses Hiram's interest is to see if a true relationship exists between the X and Y variables. If no relationship exists between test results and output, the value of B (the slope of the population regression line) is zero. Thus, the *null hypothesis* to be tested is

H_0: $B = 0$

And the *alternative hypothesis* is

H_1: $B \neq 0$

Step 2: Select the Level of Significance Hiram elects to conduct his test at the .05 level.

Step 3: Determine the Test Distribution to Use With the assumptions we've outlined, and with a small sample, it's appropriate to use the t distributions table in Appendix 4.

Step 4: Define the Rejection or Critical Region The boundaries of the rejection region are determined by the t critical value corresponding to $t_{\alpha/2}$ and $n - 2$ degrees of freedom (df). In this case, the t value in the .025 column and the $8 - 2$, or 6, df row is 2.447.

Step 5: State the Decision Rule The decision rule is

Reject H_0 in favour of H_1 if the standardized difference between the sample slope (b) and the hypothesized population slope of 0 falls into the rejection region, that is, $t > 2.447$ or < -2.447. Otherwise, fail to reject H_0.

Step 6: Compute the Test Statistic The test statistic for a t test for slope is found with this formula:

$$t = \frac{b - 0}{s_b} = \frac{b}{s_b} \qquad (12.6)$$

where b = slope of the sample regression equation
   s_b = an estimated standard error value—that is, an estimate of the standard deviation of the sampling distribution of all b values that could be calculated if repeated samples of size n were taken

The following formula can be used to calculate s_b:

$$s_b = \frac{s_{y.x}}{\sqrt{\Sigma(x^2) - (\Sigma x)^2/n}} \qquad (12.7)$$

where n = the number of paired observations in the sample

To compute the test statistic for our example, we first calculate s_b (using the data found in Table 12.2 and in earlier computations):

$$s_b = \frac{s_{y.x}}{\sqrt{\Sigma(x^2) - (\Sigma x)^2/n}} = \frac{1.698}{\sqrt{428 - (56)^2/8}} = \frac{1.698}{6} = .283$$

Then the test statistic is

$$t = \frac{b}{s_b} = \frac{5.1389}{.283} = 18.159$$

Step 7: Make the Statistical Decision Since $t = 18.159$ is much greater than the t value of 2.447, we reject the null hypothesis that $B = 0$. This means that we decide in favour of the alternative hypothesis that there is a non-zero slope to the population regression, and that a meaningful regression relationship does exist between Hiram's aptitude test scores and employee output. To Hiram's relief, the possibility described in *Figure 12.11a* apparently doesn't apply in this case. We can support this conclusion in another way by calculating a 95 percent confidence interval for the value of B as follows:

$$b - t_{\alpha/2}(s_b) < B < b + t_{\alpha/2}(s_b)$$
$$5.1389 - 2.447(.283) < B < 5.1389 + 2.447(.283)$$
$$5.1389 - .6925 < B < 5.1389 + .6925$$
$$4.45 < B < 5.83$$

Thus, we're 95 percent confident that the true population slope isn't zero, but rather has a value between 4.45 and 5.83.

The confidence interval and t-test for regression slope are summarized in the box below.

Confidence Interval and *t*-Test for Regression Slope

The **confidence interval for the slope *B*** is

$$b \pm t_{\alpha/2}(s_b)$$

To test the hypothesis H_0: $B = 0$, compute the **test statistic**

$$t = \frac{b}{s_b}$$

The **degrees of freedom** are $n - 2$.

Deliverance from Detail

You can now compute a regression equation and standard error of estimate, and you can use values of b and $s_{y.x}$ to conduct a t test to see if a true relationship is likely to exist between the x and y variables. You've dealt with many details in the last few pages, so you'll be pleased to know that many of these details can

FIGURE 12.12 To obtain this MINITAB output, click on **Stat, Regression, Regression,** enter *Output* in the box to the right of **Response** and *Test Results* In the box to the right of **Predictors,** then click on **Options.** In the **Options** window, enter 4 in the box below **Prediction Intervals for new observations** (we'll use the output from this in a few pages), then click on **OK** twice.

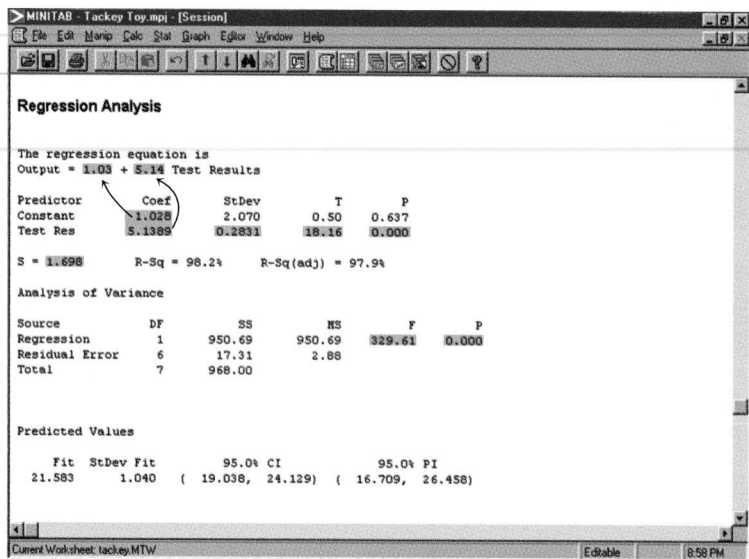

easily be turned over to a statistical software package. We used MINITAB to do regression calculations for the data in our example problem—that is, for the output units produced and the aptitude test result figures of the eight Tackey Toy employees. We haven't yet considered some of the measures MINITAB has produced in *Figure 12.12*, although we will later. For now, we've highlighted the following familiar values that we've computed in previous pages (minor variations are due to rounding):

$a = 1.0277$ or 1.028 or 1.03
$b = 5.1389$ or 5.14
$s_{y.x} = 1.698$
$s_b = .283$ or $.2831$
t for t test $= 18.159$ or 18.16

We know from Chapter 8 that if the p-value is less than the level of significance (.05 in our t test), we reject H_0 (that $B = 0$). The p-value of 0.000 in *Figure 12.12* leads to that conclusion. The probability of getting a value of the test statistic as extreme as 18.16 is 0.000 when the sample comes from a population with a slope of zero, so Hiram is virtually certain that the population slope isn't zero.

An Analysis of Variance Test

You'll notice that *Figure 12.12* also has a section labelled "Analysis of Variance." Another way to test for the presence of slope in the population regression line is to use the analysis of variance (ANOVA) concepts presented in Chapter 10. An ANOVA test gives the same results as the t test we've just examined when you want to see if a true relationship exists between the x and y variables in a simple linear regression situation. If that's the case, then you may wonder why we bother with another testing procedure. It is because the t test and the ANOVA procedure test different hypotheses in multiple regression situations where there's more than one independent or predictor variable to consider.

The ANOVA table format in *Figure 12.12* follows the one described in Table 10.3, page 413. We'll see how the sum of squares (SS) and mean square (MS) values are found in a few pages. But first, let's look at the essence of the ANOVA test. This test also begins with a statement of the null and alternative hypotheses *(Step 1)*. Without going into unnecessary details, the ANOVA hypotheses are equivalent to those of the *t* test:

H_0: There's no linear relationship between X and Y
H_1: There is such a relationship

You'll recall that Hiram has specified a .05 level of significance *(Step 2)*. The test distribution to use *(Step 3)* is one of the F distributions found in Appendix 5. To find the boundary that defines the rejection region *(Step 4)*, Hiram must know the level of significance (spelled out in Step 2) and the degrees of freedom for both the numerator and denominator of the test statistic that will be computed in Step 6. The df values in Hiram's example problem are

$$df_{num} = m = 1$$
$$df_{den} = (n - m - 1) = 6$$

where m = the number of independent variables; always 1 in simple linear regression
n = the number of paired observations

Thus, the critical F table value that starts the rejection region is 5.99 ($F_{1,6,\alpha=.05}$).
The decision rule *(Step 5)* in this ANOVA test is

Reject H_0 in favour of the H_1 if $F > 5.99$. Otherwise, fail to reject H_0.

After the computer has calculated the SS and MS values shown in *Figure 12.12*, it uses these figures to compute a test statistic (F value) *(Step 6)*. This F value is 329.61 and is shown in our computer printout. Since $F = 329.61$ is far greater than the table F value of 5.99, H_0 is rejected *(Step 7)*. The probability that Hiram's sample could generate an F of 329.61 or more if the sample came from a population that had a slope of zero is 0.000, the same *p*-value as in the *t* test.

Example 12.2 **Pressing Regressing** Returning to the spring and fall bench pressing abilities of football players, suppose we want to use a regression equation to predict the weight pressed in the fall based on the weight pressed in the spring. Test to see if there is evidence that the population slope is not zero at a level of significance of .05.

◆ **Solution**
The hypotheses are

H_0: $B = 0$
H_1: $B \neq 0$

We will conduct this test at the .05 level and, with the usual assumptions, use the *t* distribution. MINITAB will allow us to use the *p*-value approach, and, therefore, we have the following decision rule:

Reject H_0 in favour of H_1 if the *p*-value $< .05$. Otherwise, fail to reject H_0.

FIGURE 12.13 (a) MINITAB regression output for the bench press data. (b) Enter the spring bench press data into L1 and the fall data into L2. We will first calculate the linear regression equation for the fall bench press weight in terms of the spring bench press weight. From the **STAT>CALC** menu, choose option **8 LinReg(a + bx).** After the command is pasted onto the home screen, enter L1, L2 to calculate the regression equation. The results are shown in screen 1. Thus, the regression equation is Fall = 49.25 + .904*Spring. Note if you want to see the correlation coefficient r, before doing the regression go to the **CATALOG** menu and choose **DiagnosticOn** and press **ENTER.** Then when the regression is calculated, the value of r and R^2, the topics of the next section, will also be shown. To perform the hypothesis test, we access the **STAT>TESTS** menu and choose option **E: LinRegTTest.** Set up the test as shown in screen 2. Calculate and get the results in screens 3 and 4.

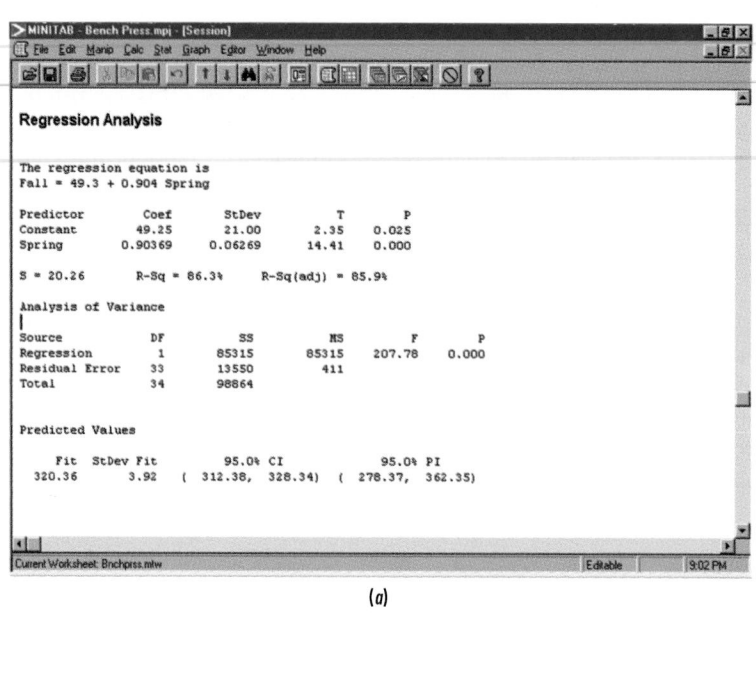

(a)

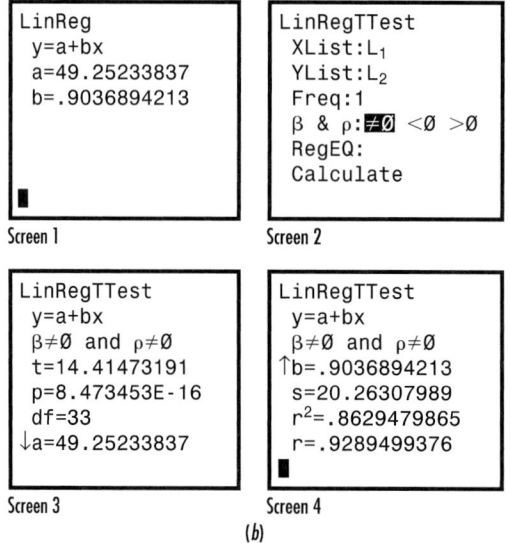

(b)

  MINITAB was used to generate the results of *Figure 12.13a*, while a TI-83 calculator was used to produce the screens of *Figure 12.13b*. The value of the test statistic for the t test is 14.41, with an associated p-value of 0.000. Since p-value = 0.000 < 0.05, we reject the null hypothesis that $B = 0$. So it appears that a meaningful regression relationship does exist between the spring and fall bench press weights. You should note that the p-value of the ANOVA F test given in *Figure 12.13a* is also 0.000 and would yield the same decision. ◆

The following three summary boxes describe the sum of squares, degrees of freedom, mean squares, ANOVA table, and F-test for simple linear regression.

Sum of Squares, Degrees of Freedom, and Mean Squares

Sum of squares represent variation in the responses. They are calculated by summing squared deviations. **Analysis of Variance** partitions the total variation between the two sources. The sums of squares are related by the formula

$$SST = SSR + SSE$$

which means the total variation is separated into two parts; one due to the regression relationship and one due to error.

Degrees of freedom are associated with each sum of squares. They are related in the same way.

$$DFT = DFR + DFE$$

Mean squares are calculated using the formula

$$MS = \frac{\text{sum of squares}}{\text{degrees of freedom}}$$

ANOVA Table for Simple Linear Regression

Source	Degrees of Freedom	Sum of Squares	Mean Square	F
Regression	1	$\Sigma(\hat{y}_i - \bar{y})^2$	SSR/DFR	MSR/MSE
Error	$n - 2$	$\Sigma(y_i - \hat{y}_i)^2$	SSE/DFE	
Total	$n - 1$	$\Sigma(y_i - \bar{y})^2$	SST/DFT	

Analysis of Variance *F* Test for Regression Slope

To test the hypothesis H_0: $B = 0$, compute the **test statistic**

$$F = \frac{MSR}{MSE}$$

The **degrees of freedom** are 1 and $n - 2$.

Interval Estimates for the Response Variable

Once we obtain our sample regression equation, we would like to use it to estimate or predict values of the response variable, *y*. Let's see how we can do that in our Tackey Toy example problem. Earlier in this chapter, in the section entitled "Making Preliminary Predictions with the Regression Equation," the question was raised of the future output of those applicants who scored a four on the aptitude test. A point estimate of the average amount of output produced by those who scored a four on the test was

prepared. Now, though, it's time to look at interval estimates to which we can assign probabilities. There are actually two types of intervals that we can consider.

The first type of interval—one that would likely be of most interest to a personnel manager such as Hiram—is an interval estimate of the average output produced by all applicants who score a particular value (say, four) on the aptitude test. A second type of interval—of greater interest, perhaps, to a production supervisor—is a prediction interval of the output produced by a specific person who scores a four on the aptitude test. The first interval, being an interval estimate for the average value of y for a given x, is called a **confidence interval;** the second interval, being an interval estimate for the response of a specific person rather than for an average, is given the special name of a **prediction interval.** Since predicting the response for a specific person is subject to more sampling variation than estimating the average value of y, a prediction interval is larger than a confidence interval for the same x and the same level of confidence.

A Confidence Interval for the Average Value of y Given x The interval estimate for the mean value of y given $x = x_g$, denoted $\mu_{y \cdot x_g}$ is found with this formula:

$$\hat{y} \pm t_{\alpha/2}\left[s_{y \cdot x}\sqrt{\frac{1}{n} + \frac{(x_g - \bar{x})^2}{\Sigma(x^2) - (\Sigma x)^2/n}} \right] \tag{12.8}$$

where $\hat{y}$ = the point estimate computed with the regression equation when a specific value of x is given

$t_{\alpha/2}$ = the appropriate t table value for a given confidence level with $n - 2$ degrees of freedom

x_g = the given value of x (Note from the formula that the closer this value is to the mean of x (or $\bar{x}$), the smaller the value under the square root sign will be, and the smaller the confidence interval will be.)

n = the number of paired observations in the sample

A 95 percent confidence interval for the average employee output if the aptitude test score is four can now be computed. We first find the $\hat{y}$ value when x is four. This was done earlier, and is

$\hat{y} = 1.0277 + 5.1389(4) = 21.583$ dozen units of output

Next, we find the table value from Appendix 4 for t with $n - 2$, or six, degrees of freedom. This value is 2.447. The appropriate measure of dispersion for small samples adjusts the value of $s_{y \cdot x}$ and is called the **standard error of $\hat{y}$.** This measure is found below (the values of $\bar{x}$, $\Sigma(x^2)$, and Σx come from Table 12.2):

$$s_{y \cdot x}\sqrt{\frac{1}{n} + \frac{(x_g - \bar{x})^2}{\Sigma(x^2) - (\Sigma x)^2/n}} = 1.698\sqrt{\frac{1}{8} + \frac{(4 - 7)^2}{428 - (56)^2/8}}$$

$$= 1.698\sqrt{\frac{1}{8} + \frac{9}{36}} = 1.698(.6124) = 1.04$$

The 95 percent confidence interval is then

$21.583 \pm 2.447 \, (1.04) = 21.583 \pm 2.545$
$19.038 < \mu_{y \cdot 4} < 24.128$

Thus, we can be 95 percent confident that the average output of workers who score a four on the aptitude test is between 19.038 and 24.128 dozen units. Refer back now to *Figure 12.12*. There we requested confidence and prediction intervals for $x = 4$. The last line of output, under "95.0% CI," gives the 95 percent confidence interval we've just calculated. That line also gives the 95 percent prediction interval that we'll look at next.

A Prediction Interval for a Specific Value of *y* Given *x* Suppose Hiram wanted to predict the output range of a specific applicant who scored a four on the aptitude test. In that case, the prediction interval is found with this formula:

$$\hat{y} \pm t_{\alpha/2}\left[s_{y.x}\sqrt{1 + \frac{1}{n} + \frac{(x_g - \bar{x})^2}{\Sigma(x^2) - (\Sigma x)^2/n}}\right] \quad (12.9)$$

As you can see, the only difference is the addition of the single value, 1, under the square root sign. The 95 percent prediction interval for the output of a specific person who scored a four on the aptitude test—that is, that person's *y* value—is

$$21.583 \pm 2.447\left(1.698\sqrt{1 + \frac{1}{8} + \frac{(4 - 7)^2}{428 - (56)^2/8}}\right)$$

$$21.583 \pm 2.447\left(1.698\sqrt{1 + \frac{1}{8} + \frac{9}{36}}\right)$$

$21.583 \pm 2.447(1.698)(1.1726)$
21.583 ± 4.872
$16.71 < y < 26.45$

As already noted, this interval is larger than the one for the average value of *y* for a given *x* value because of the greater sampling variation possible. You can see in *Figure 12.12*, in the last line of the printout under "95.0% PI," that MINITAB obtained a 95 percent prediction interval identical (except for rounding) to the one we've just completed.

Example 12.3 **Regressing Pressing** Returning to Example 12.1, suppose we want to use a regression equation to obtain a 95 percent confidence interval estimate for the mean fall bench press weight of players who bench-press 300 pounds in the spring. We also want to get a 95 percent prediction interval for the fall bench press weight of a particular player, who bench-pressed 300 pounds in the spring. What are the intervals?

◆ Solution:

In the MINITAB output of *Figure 12.13*, we requested that a prediction be made for $x = 300$ pounds. Looking at the last line of that output, we find that a 95 percent confidence interval for the mean weight pressed in the fall for football players who press 300 pounds in the spring is between 312.38 and 328.34 pounds. Additionally, we would predict with 95 percent confidence that the particular player, who pressed 300 pounds in the spring, will press between 278.37 and 362.35 pounds in the fall. ◆

Self-Testing Review 12.3

16. Douglas Michaels, a premed student, wants to see if there's a relationship between the age of children suffering from a disability and the number of visits a child makes to a doctor during the year. The following data are collected from a random sample, where $x =$ a child's age, and $y =$ the number of doctor visits last year:

x	5	6	8	14	15	7	8	12
y	9	2	12	17	9	16	6	15

    a) Compute the regression equation.

    b) Compute the standard error of estimate.

    c) Conduct a t test for slope at the .05 level.

    d) Compute a 95 percent confidence interval estimate of the average number of doctor visits for all five-year-old children.

    e) Compute a 95 percent prediction interval estimate of the number of doctor visits for Timmy, who is five years old.

17. Clinical characteristics were measured in a study of autistic children that appeared in the *American Journal of Psychiatry*. A psychologist now wants to see if there's a linear relationship between the x variable and the y variable. The y variable is the total behavioural score made by children on a test of 29 items, where each item score ranges from 0 (absence of symptoms) to 116 (maximum severity of symptoms). The x variable is a language score made on a test that has a scale ranging from 1 to 5, where 1 = normal development and 5 = severe retardation. The psychologist's random sample of autistic children produces the following data pairs (Data = Autistic):

Behaviour Score (y)	Language Score (x)	Behaviour Score (y)	Language Score (x)
27	2	40	2
35	4	41	4
65	4	60	5
67	4	24	5
47	3	48	4
46	3	29	2
63	4	73	5
44	4	60	3
34	5	41	4
51	4	27	3
17	2		

    a) Compute the regression equation.

    b) Compute the standard error of estimate.

    c) Conduct a t test for slope at the .05 level.

    d) Compute a 95 percent confidence interval estimate of the average behavioural score for autistic children with a language score of 3.

    e) Compute a 95 percent prediction interval estimate of the behavioural score of a specific child whose language score is 3.

18. Castle Rock Entertainment has produced many movies over the past few years. A vice president wants to see if there's a relationship between the total cost of a film (including production costs, salaries, and marketing expenses) and the gross income produced by the film through ticket sales in movie theatres. A random sample of films produced the following data pairs (data source: Castle Rock Entertainment) (Data = CastlRck):

Cost (Millions of Dollars) (x)	Gross Income (Millions of Dollars) (y)	Cost (Millions of Dollars) (x)	Gross Income (Millions of Dollars) (y)
55	150.5	26	5.0
42	123.0	19	10.0
17	68.0	35	35.0
30	93.0	22	20.0
43	16.0	13	15.0

a) Compute the regression equation.

b) Calculate the standard error of estimate.

c) Conduct a *t* test for slope at the .05 level.

d) Compute a 95 percent confidence interval estimate of the average gross income for a movie that cost $135 million.

e) Compute a 95 percent prediction interval estimate of the gross income of a new box office hit *Statistics ... The Movie* (the version with English subtitles). The production cost for this film is $35 million.

19. Adrienne Starr looked at characteristics of men with moderate hypercholesterolemia. She used data found in "Short-Term Dietary Calcium Fortification Increases Fecal Saturated Fat Content and Reduces Serum Lipids in Men" (*American Journal of Clinical Nutrition*). As part of her project, she used calcium intake to predict serum cholesterol (Data = Calcium1).

Serum Cholesterol (mmol/L)	Calcium Intake (mg/d)	Serum Cholesterol (mmol/L)	Calcium Intake (mg/d)
5.99	814	6.15	386
6.46	323	6.38	189
6.30	273	6.15	680
6.77	519	5.71	365
5.50	379	6.54	926
5.68	547	6.51	252
6.25	400		

a) Compute the regression equation.

b) Calculate the standard error of estimate.

c) Conduct a *t* test for slope at the .05 level.

d) Compute a 95 percent confidence interval estimate of the average serum cholesterol for people whose calcium intake is 500 mg/d.

e) Compute a 95 percent prediction interval estimate of the serum cholesterol for a person whose calcium intake is 500 mg/d.

20. Joe Woolman reported on the thickness (in angstroms) of SiO_2 film grown on silicon wafers during a high-temperature oxidation in dry oxygen. He also reported the position in inches each wafer was positioned from the end of the furnace. He wanted to use the position of the wafer to predict the thickness of the film (Data = Film):

Distance (inches)	Thickness (angstroms)	Distance (inches)	Thickness (angstroms)
10	625	27	1,400
13	900	29	1,350
15	1,150	31	1,550
17	1,125	33	1,500
19	1,250	35	1,475
21	1,300	37	1,400
23	1,400	39	1,200
25	1,400		

a) Compute the regression equation.

b) Calculate the standard error of estimate.

c) Conduct a t test for slope at the .01 level.

d) Compute a 99 percent confidence interval estimate of the average thickness of SiO_2 film grown on silicon wafers for wafers 25 inches from the end of the furnace.

e) Compute a 99 percent prediction interval estimate of the thickness of SiO_2 film grown on silicon wafers for a wafer 25 inches from the end of the furnace.

21. A stock analyst wants to see if there's a relationship between the prices of Amcorp stock and AQR stock. She enters the stock prices for six random days into MINITAB, and the program produces the following output:

```
The regression equation is AQR = 25.7 + 1.21 Amcorp

Predictor      Coef      Stdev        T         p
Constant      25.687     6.434      3.99      0.016
Amcorp         1.2089    0.3032     3.99      0.016

s = 0.4294     R-sq = 79.9%     R-sq(adj) = 74.9%

Analysis of Variance

Source        DF         SS         MS         F         p
Regression     1       2.9309     2.9309     15.89     0.016
Error          4       0.7376     0.1844
Total          5       3.6685
```

a) What are the slope (b or Amcorp coefficient) and the y intercept (a or constant) values?

b) What is the p-value for the slope?

c) Use the p-value method and conduct a t test for slope at the .05 level.

d) Verify that the standard error of estimate in the printout (MINITAB uses the symbol s) can be calculated by finding the square root of MS error.

22. Portability and battery life are two important characteristics of laptop computers. R. Vilhauer examined data found in *PC* magazine (1996) on the weight and battery life of 40 laptop computers. MINITAB was used to obtain the output that follows (Data = Laptops):

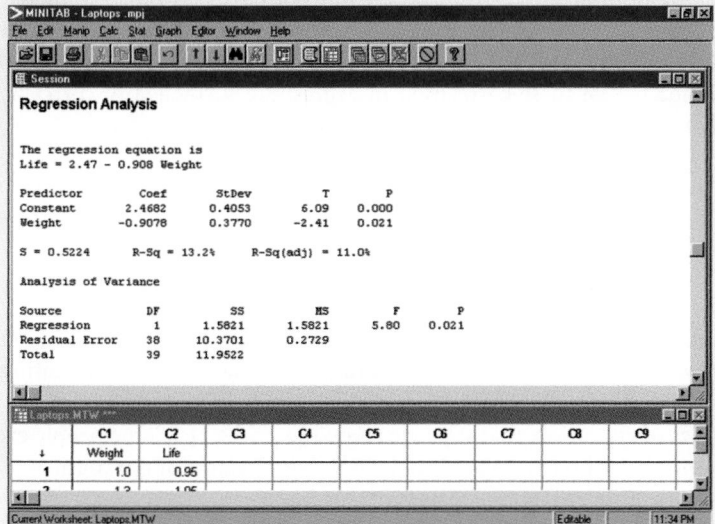

a) What are the values of the slope (*b*) and the *y* intercept (*a*)?

b) Using the *p*-value method, conduct a *t* test for slope at the .05 level.

23. Dennis Frye has done extensive research on monarch butterflies. One portion of his research consists of measurements (mm) on the wing lengths of the right forewings of male and female mating butterflies. Dr. Frye was interested in seeing if the matings have a size relationship; that is, was there a tendency for monarch butterflies to mate with butterflies of their own size? MINITAB was used to procure the following (Data = MnrchWng):

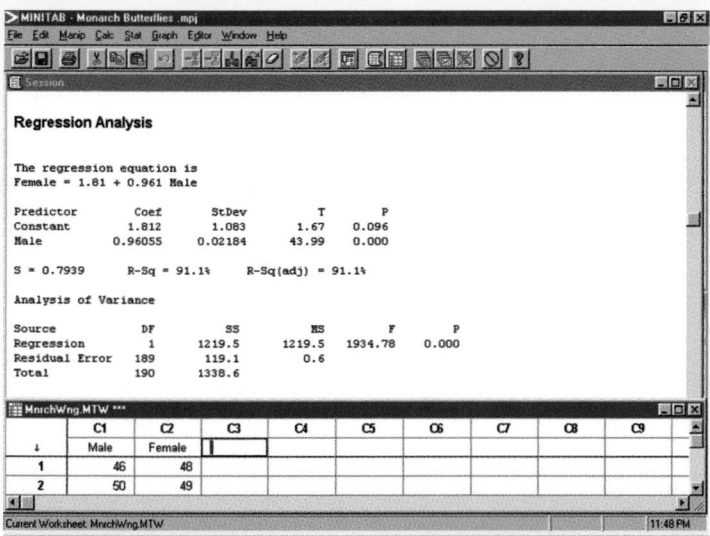

a) What are the values of the slope (*b*) and the *y* intercept (*a*)?

b) Using the *p*-value method, conduct a *t* test for slope at the .01 level.

12.4 Simple Linear Correlation Analysis

Up to this point we have been concerned with regression equations where our objective has been to estimate the relationship that is assumed to exist between two variables. We now turn our attention to **correlation,** where our objective is twofold: to measure the strength of the linear relationship between two variables, and to use this measure of strength to decide whether or not any significant linear relationship in fact exists. We'll briefly examine two of these correlation measures: the coefficient of correlation and the coefficient of determination.

Correlation: Measuring the Strength of Linear Relationships

Most people believe that the yield of a crop is closely related to the amount of rainfall, that the trade-in value of a car is closely related to its age, that the costs of heating a home are closely related to outdoor temperature, that personal incomes are related to the number of years of education, that sales are related to prices, etc. Some people even believe that a country's birthrate is related to the number of storks in the country, and that human behaviour is related to the phases of the moon.

The term *correlation* carries with it certain mathematical connotations and will be used rather than words such as "related to" when referring to the strength of a relationship. One numerical descriptive measure of the strength of the linear correlation between two variables x and y is the *Pearson product moment coefficient of correlation,* named after the famous statistician, Karl Pearson.

The sample **Pearson product moment coefficient of correlation, r,** is defined as

$$r = \frac{\sum(x - \bar{x})(y - \bar{y})}{\sqrt{[\sum(x - \bar{x})^2][\sum(y - \bar{y})^2]}} = \frac{n(\sum xy) - (\sum x)(\sum y)}{\sqrt{[n(\sum x^2) - (\sum x^2)][n(\sum y^2) - (\sum y^2)]}}.$$

It may be shown that r has no units and always assumes a value between -1 and $+1$ inclusive, regardless of the units of x and y. Positive values of r indicate a positive linear relationship between y and x, that is, y increases as x increases. Negative values of r indicate a negative linear relationship between y and x, that is y decreases as x increases. A value of r near or equal to 0 means little or no linear relationship between y and x. A value of r near 1 or -1 means a strong linear relationship. And if $r = 1$ or $r - 1$, all the sample points fall exactly in a straight line.

Note that the numerator of r is the same as the numerator of b in the regression equation, so you can see that $r = 0$ when $b = 0$ (no linear relationship exists), r is positive when b is positive, and r is negative when b is negative.

The following shows how to calculate r using the data in Table 12.2 for the Tackey Toy example. Note that in Table 12.2 the sample size is $n = 8$ and we found that $\sum x = 56$, $\sum y = 296$, $\sum xy = 2{,}257$, $\sum x^2 = 428$, and $\sum y^2 = 11{,}920$. Thus

$$r = \frac{n(\sum xy) - (\sum x)(\sum y)}{\sqrt{[n(\sum x^2) - (\sum x)^2][n(\sum y^2) - (\sum y)^2]}}$$

$$= \frac{8(2{,}257) - (56)(296)}{\sqrt{[8(428) - (56)^2][8(11{,}920) - (296)^2]}} = .991$$

The fact that r is positive and near 1 means that there is a strong positive linear correlation between x (aptitude test results) and y (employee output) *for this sample of eight employees.*

We must be careful not to jump to unwarranted conclusions here. For example, we may be tempted to conclude that the best thing to do is to hire only employees with high aptitude test results—that is, we may mistakenly assume that high aptitude test results *cause* high outputs, or we may mistakenly assume that the high correlation for the sample of eight employees also applies to the population of all employees. *We must be careful not to infer a cause-effect relationship on the basis of high sample correlation.*

■ Example 12.4 As an illustration of correlation, a professor at the University of Regina determined the following values of x, the number of hours studied for an exam, and y, the grade received on the exam, for a random sample of five students in his class. Calculate the coefficient of correlation r for the sample data.

x	2	0	4	3	1
y	80	90	65	75	70

◆ Solution:
We first construct a table and find the values and totals needed in the formula.

Student	x	y	xy	x^2	y^2
1	2	80	160	4	6,400
2	0	90	0	0	8,100
3	4	65	260	16	4,225
4	3	75	225	9	5,625
5	1	70	70	1	4,900
Totals	10	380	715	30	29,250

Note that $n = 5$ and we have found: $\sum x = 10$, $\sum y = 380$, $\sum xy = 715$, $\sum x^2 = 30$, and $\sum y^2 = 29{,}250$. Thus

$$r = \frac{n(\sum xy) - (\sum x)(\sum y)}{\sqrt{[n(\sum x^2) - (\sum x)^2][n(\sum y^2) - (\sum y)^2]}}$$

$$= \frac{5(715) - (10)(380)}{\sqrt{[5(30) - (10)^2][5(29{,}250) - (380)^2]}} = -0.74$$

The professor was expecting to find a positive correlation. Why did it turn out negative? It appears that students who knew the material didn't have to study, so that the small study times were associated with the larger grades. ◆

A t Test for ρ, the Population Correlation Coefficient

The sample correlation coefficient r measures the strength of the linear relationship between the x and y values in the sample. A similar population correlation coefficient exists for the whole population from which the data points were selected. The **population**

correlation coefficient is denoted by the Greek letter ρ (rho). As you might expect, the best point estimate for ρ is the corresponding sample statistic r.

Rather than estimating ρ, we might want to test the null hypothesis H_0: $\rho = 0$ against H_1: $\rho \neq 0$. That is, test the hypothesis that x contributes no information for the prediction of y by using the straight-line model, against the alternative that the two variables are at least linearly related.

☐ **Example 12.5**   In the preceding example, suppose we wish to determine whether there is any significant linear relationship between x, the number of hours studied for an exam, and y, the grade received on the exam, for the population of all students who wrote the exam. We again use our familiar seven-step hypothesis-testing procedure.

◆ **Solution:**

Step 1: Formulate the Null and Alternative Hypothesis   Our interest is to see if any linear relationship exists between the variables x and y. If no linear relationship exists between hours studied and grade received, the value of ρ (the population correlation coefficient) is zero. Thus the null hypothesis to be tested is

H_0: $\rho = 0$ and the alternative hypothesis is H_1: $\rho \neq 0$

Step 2: Select the Level of Significance   We will choose to conduct our test at the .05 level.

Step 3: Determining the Test Distribution to Use   Assuming both variables are *random variables* having a *bivariate normal distribution* (which means roughly that for each value of x, the population of all y-values is normally distributed, and for each value y, the population of all x-values is normally distributed), the test statistic

$t = \dfrac{r}{\sqrt{(1 - r^2)/(n - 2)}}$ has a t-distribution with $n - 2$ degrees of freedom, so we will use the t distribution table in Appendix 4.

Step 4: Define the Rejection or Critical Region   The boundaries of the rejection region are determined by the t critical value corresponding to $t_{\alpha/2}$ and $n - 2$ degrees of freedom (df). In this case the t value in the .025 column and the $5 - 2$, or 3, df row is 3.182.

Step 5: State the Decision Rule   The decision rule is

Reject H_0 in favour of H_1 if $t > 3.182$ or if $t < -3.182$. Otherwise fail to reject H_0.

Step 6: Compute the Test Statistic   In our example above with $n = 5$, we found that $\sum x = 10$, $\sum y = 380$, $\sum xy = 715$, $\sum x^2 = 30$, and $\sum y^2 = 29{,}250$. Thus

$$t = \frac{r}{\sqrt{(1 - r^2)/(n - 2)}} = \frac{-0.74}{\sqrt{[1 - (-.74)^2]/(5 - 2)}} = -1.90$$

Step 7: Make the Statistical Decision   Since $t = 1.90$ is not greater than 3.182 or less than -3.182, we fail to reject H_0. This means that at the .05 level of significance, this sample does not provide sufficient evidence to conclude that any linear relationship exists between hours studied and grade received for the population of all students who wrote the exam.

Note: Except for a difference in the underlying assumptions, and a different, but equivalent form of the test statistic, the t test for the population correlation coefficient is equivalent to the previously considered t test for the slope of the regression line. For comparison purposes, the following is a repetition of the preceding example using the t test for the slope of the regression line.

Step 1: Formulate the Null and Alternative Hypothesis Our interest is to see if any linear relationship exists between the variables x and y. If no linear relationship exists between hours studied and grade received, the value of B, (the slope of the population regression line) is zero. Thus the null hypothesis to be tested is

H_0: $B = 0$ and the alternative hypothesis is H_1: $B \neq 0$

Step 2: Select the Level of Significance We will choose to conduct our test at the .05 level.

Step 3: Determine the Test Distribution to Use Assuming the regression assumptions (page 502) are satisfied, the test statistic $t = b/s_b$ has a t distribution with $n - 2$ degrees of freedom, so we will use the t distribution table in Appendix 4.

Step 4: Define the Rejection or Critical Region The boundaries of the rejection region are determined by the t critical value corresponding to $t_{\alpha/2}$ and $n - 2$ degrees of freedom (df). In this case the t value in the .025 column and the $5 - 2$, or 3, df row is 3.182.

Step 5: State the Decision Rule The decision rule is

Reject H_0 in favour of H_1 if $t > 3.182$ or if $t < -3.182$. Otherwise fail to reject H_0.

Step 6: Compute the Test Statistic In our example above with $n = 5$, we found that $\sum x = 10$, $\sum y = 380$, $\sum xy = 715$, $\sum x^2 = 30$, and $\sum y^2 = 29{,}250$. Thus

$$b = \frac{n(\sum xy) - (\sum x)(\sum y)}{n(\sum x^2) - (\sum x)^2} = \frac{5(715) - 10(380)}{5(30) - (10)^2} = -4.5$$

$$a = \bar{y} - b\bar{x} = \frac{380}{5} - (-4.5)\frac{10}{5} = 85$$

$$s_{y.x} = \sqrt{\frac{\sum y^2 - a(\sum y) - b(\sum xy)}{n - 2}} = \sqrt{\frac{29{,}250 - 85(380) - (-4.5)(715)}{5 - 2}} = 7.47217$$

$$s_b = \frac{s_{y.x}}{\sqrt{\sum x^2 - (\sum x)^2/n}} = \frac{7.47217}{\sqrt{30 - (10)^2/5}} = 2.36291.$$

The value of the test statistic is $t = \dfrac{b}{s_b} = \dfrac{-4.5}{2.36291} = -1.90$

Step 7: Make the Statistical Decision Since $t = -1.90$ is not greater than 3.182 or less than -3.182, we fail to reject H_0. This means that at the .05 level of significance, this sample does not provide sufficient evidence to conclude that any linear relationship exists between hours studied and grade received for the population of all students who wrote the exam. ◆

The Coefficient of Determination

Before we define the coefficient of determination (its symbol is r^2), we should consider the several terms and concepts illustrated in *Figure 12.14*. If the mean of the y variable $(\bar{y})$ alone had been used to estimate the dependent variable, we would expect to find quite a bit of possible deviation between our estimate and the value of y. A single point in *Figure 12.14*—let's label it y^*—is used to show the considerable *total deviation* that exists in this case between y^* and the mean of $\bar{y}$. But when the regression line is used as the basis for estimating the dependent variable, we can expect to have a closer estimate of y in the majority of cases. As shown in *Figure 12.14*, our regression line is indeed closer to most of the points in the scatter diagram. Thus, in the case of the y value single point (y^*) in *Figure 12.14*, the regression line explains or accounts for part of the deviation between y^* and $\bar{y}$—that is, the *explained deviation* is $\hat{y} - \bar{y}$. Unfortunately, the regression line doesn't account for all the deviation, since the distance between y^* and $\hat{y}$ is still unexplained.

In other words, we have the following situation for point y^* in *Figure 12.14*:

$$\underset{\text{total deviation}}{(y^* - \bar{y})} = \underset{\text{explained deviation}}{(\hat{y} - \bar{y})} + \underset{\text{unexplained deviation}}{(y^* - \hat{y})}$$

To summarize, then, explained deviation refers to the properties of x that would lead one y value to differ from another. Higher aptitude test scores can "explain" part of the reason for better productivity. But there are other possible factors, such as motivation and working conditions, that can also affect productivity, and these other factors are unexplained by the simple regression equation.

If we consider the total variation in an entire scatter diagram (and not just the deviation from a single point), we have the following situation:

$$\underset{\text{total variation}}{\Sigma(y - \bar{y})^2} = \underset{\text{explained variation}}{\Sigma(\hat{y} - \bar{y})^2} + \underset{\text{unexplained variation}}{\Sigma(y - \hat{y})^2}$$

It's customary in correlation analysis to use some convenient abbreviations. Since the **total variation** is the sum of the squared deviations of the y values about their mean,

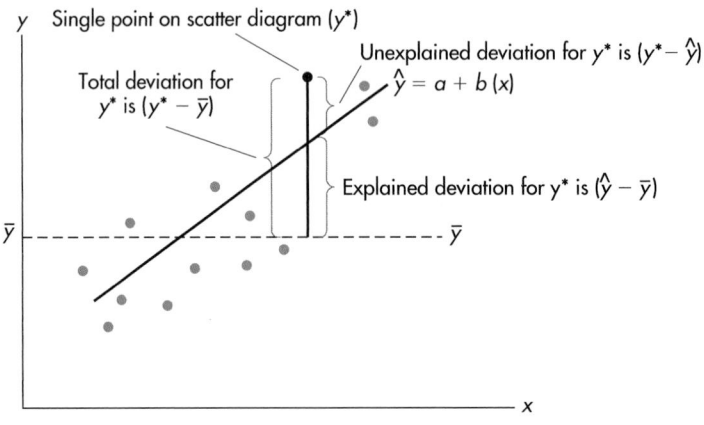

FIGURE 12.14 Conceptual representation of total, explained, and unexplained deviations.

the reference that's used is sum of squares (total), or **SST** in abbreviated form. Likewise, the **explained variation** is the sum of the squared deviations of the regression line values about $\bar{y}$, and the reference that's used is sum of squares (explained by) regression, or **SSR.** Finally, the **unexplained variation** is the sum of the squared deviations of the y values about the regression line, the reference that's used is sum of squares due to unexplained error (or residual error), and the abbreviation is **SSE.**

Thus, SST = SSR + SSE

Now we can define r^2. The **coefficient of determination** is a measure of the portion of the total variance in the y variable that's explained or accounted for by the introduction of the x variable (and thus the regression line). That is,

$$r^2 = \frac{\text{explained variation}}{\text{total variation}} = \frac{SSR}{SST} = \frac{\Sigma(\hat{y} - \bar{y})^2}{\Sigma(y - \bar{y})^2} \qquad (12.10)$$

The calculations needed to produce r^2 with formula 12.10 are shown in Table 12.4. As you can see, the value of SSR is 950.683, and SST is 968. Since SST = SSR + SSE, then the difference between SST and SSR gives the value of SSE. We've seen in Table 12.3 that SSE—the $\Sigma(y - \hat{y})^2$ value—is 17.3056. And we see now that SST − SSR is 17.317 (the slight discrepancy is due to rounding differences).

Calculating r^2 with formula 12.10 is tedious work. But there's a more convenient formula for r^2 that uses values we've already computed in earlier pages:

$$r^2 = \frac{a(\Sigma y) + b(\Sigma xy) - n(\bar{y})^2}{\Sigma(y)^2 - n(\bar{y})^2} \qquad (12.11)$$

TABLE 12.4 WORKSHEET FOR COMPUTING r^2

Aptitude Test Results (x)	Output (Dozens of Units) (y)	$\hat{y}$	$(\hat{y} - \bar{y})$	$(\hat{y} - \bar{y})^2$	$(\hat{y} - \bar{y})$	$(\hat{y} - \bar{y})^2$
6	30	31.861	−5.139	26.409	−7	49
9	49	47.278	10.278	105.635	12	144
3	18	16.444	−20.555	422.533	−19	361
8	42	42.139	5.139	26.409	5	25
7	39	37.000	0	0	2	4
5	25	26.722	−10.278	105.635	−12	144
8	41	42.139	5.139	26.409	4	16
10	52	52.416	15.416	237.653	15	225
56	296	295.999	0	950.683	0	968

$$\bar{y} = \frac{296}{8} = 37$$

$$r^2 = \frac{SSR}{SST} = \frac{\Sigma(\hat{y} - \bar{y})^2}{\Sigma(y - \bar{y})^2} = \frac{950.683}{968} = .982$$

To compute the coefficient of determination for our Tackey Toy problem with formula 12.11, we need refer only to the regression equation and Table 12.2 to get the necessary data. Thus,

$$r^2 = \frac{a(\sum y) + b(\sum xy) - n(\bar{y})^2}{\sum(y)^2 - n(\bar{y})^2} = \frac{1.0277(296) + 5.1289(2,257) - 8(37)^2}{11,920 - 8(37)^2}$$

$$= \frac{304.1992 + 11,598.497 - 10,952}{11,920 - 10,952} = \frac{950.696}{968} = .982$$

It may be shown that the coefficient of determination (r^2) is the square of the correlation coefficient (r), so another method of computing coefficient of determination is to first calculate the correlation coefficient (r) and then calculate the squared value of r. For our Tackey Toy problem, we found $r = .991$. Therefore, $r^2 = (.991)^2 = .982$. (Note that this relationship also means we could also find the correlation coefficient by first finding the coefficient of determination. The correlation coefficient (r) would be either the positive or negative square root of r^2. The sign would be same as the sign of b in the regression equation.)

What does the r^2 value of .982 mean? It means that 98.2 percent of the variation in the y variable is explained or accounted for by variation in the x variable. Or, in our example, we can conclude that 98.2 percent of the variation in output is explained by variation in test score results. (Of course, 1.8 percent of the variation in output remains unexplained.) Since it's obvious that the value of r^2 cannot exceed 1.00—after all, you can't explain more than 100 percent of the variation in y!—the value of .982 is quite high. Such a high value is, of course, desirable for forecasting purposes because the higher the value of r^2, the smaller the value of $s_{y.x}$. (Can you determine why this is true?)

The Computer Printout Revisited

Figure 12.15 repeats the MINITAB printout for our Tackey Toy example that was shown in *Figure 12.12*. The highlighted values in *Figure 12.15* should now be clearer to you. The .982 (or 98.2 percent) value of r^2 is shown, and the intermediate variation values are shown in the SS (sum of squares) column. As you can see, the explained (SS Regression), unexplained (SS Error), and total (SS Total) variation figures correspond to the values we've just calculated.

You saw a few pages earlier that the ANOVA test gave the same results as the t test for slope—that is, it showed if there was likely to be a true relationship between the variables. We've seen that the null hypothesis in the t test is that no relationship exists—that is, $B = 0$. The null hypothesis in an ANOVA test is equivalent to this, but from Chapter 10 you know that an ANOVA test of population means depends on two estimates of the population variance. A computed F statistic based on these two estimates is then used to test the null hypothesis.

When used with relationship tests in regression analysis, the computed F statistic depends on the explained (SSR) and unexplained (SSE) values that we've just examined. The computed test statistic (F) formula is

$$F = \frac{SSR/m}{SSE/(n - m - 1)} \tag{12.12}$$

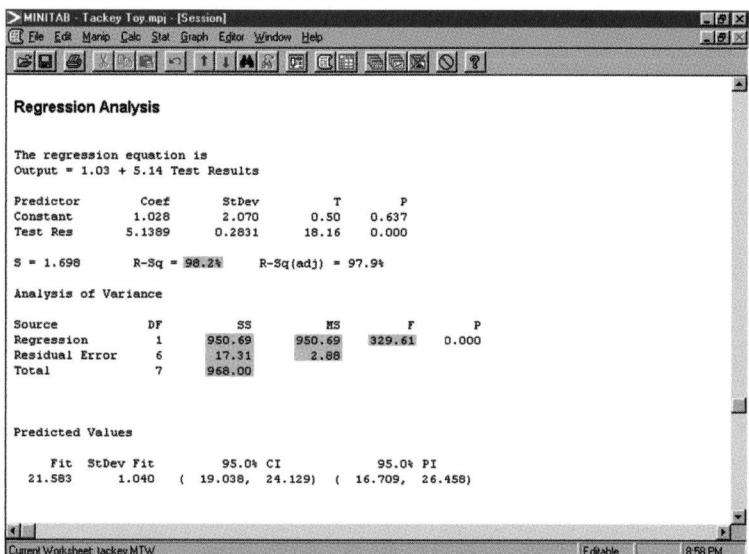

FIGURE 12.15 The MINITAB print-out again.

where m = the number of independent variables, always 1 in the simple linear case
  n = the number of paired observations

Thus, in *Figure 12.15*, the value of the **F** test statistic is

$$F = \frac{\text{SSR}/m}{\text{SSE}/(n-m-1)} = \frac{950.69/1}{17.31/(8-1-1)} = \frac{950.69}{2.88} = 329.61$$

And we've seen earlier that this **F** value is then compared to a table *F* value to arrive at a test decision.

A Graphical Summary

Let's summarize graphically, by means of scatter diagrams, some of the simple linear relationships we've now examined:

1. In *Figure 12.16a*, we have an example of *perfect positive correlation,* with all points in the diagram falling on the regression line. Therefore, $r = +1.00$, $r^2 = 1.00$, and $s_{y.x} = 0$ because there is an absence of spread, or scatter, about the line.

2. In *Figure 12.16b*, we have an example of *perfect negative correlation.* The values of various measures are as indicated.

3. In *Figures 12.16c* and *d*, there is positive correlation, but the values of r and r^2 are less in *d* than in *c*. Assuming the same scales for x and y and the same regression line, the value of $s_{y.x}$ is greater in *d* than in *c*.

4. In *Figure 12.16e*, there's no correlation. The regression line is simply a horizontal line drawn at $\bar{y}$ with no slope—that is, $b = 0$. Both r and r^2 are zero, and $s_{y.x}$ equals the standard deviation of the y variable (this is the upper limit for $s_{y.x}$).

STATISTICS IN ACTION

Is It Too Short?

The *Journal of the American Physical Therapy Association* has reported that the most accurate way to prepare the length of a crutch for a patient is to multiply the person's measured height by .719 and then add 2 inches to the resulting length. When this was done, there was a .955 correlation between the measured result and the ideal crutch length.

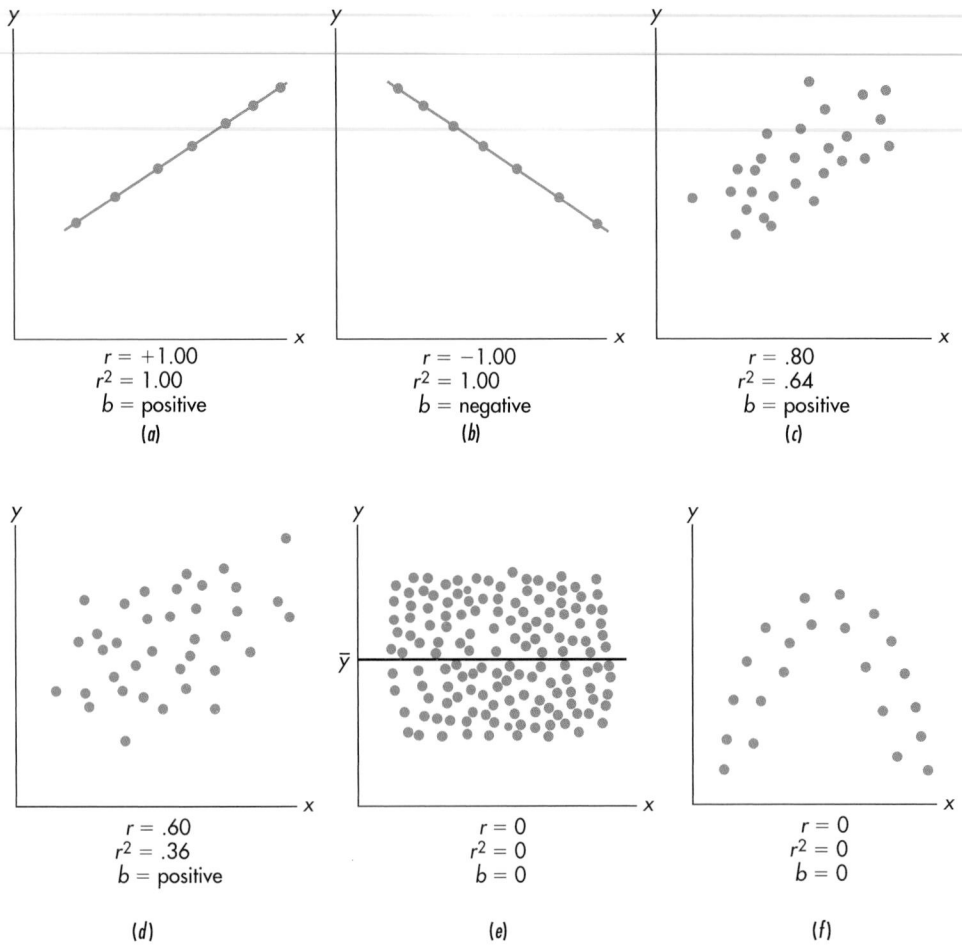

FIGURE 12.16 A graphical summary.

5. In *Figure 12.16f*, there is also no correlation. In simple linear regression, correlation measures only the strength of the straight-line relationship between x and y. So, even though there definitely appears to be a relationship between the two variables, it is not in the form of a straight line, and both r and r^2 are zero.

Correlation and Causation

When a hypothesis test indicates that a significant relationship exists between the variables x and y, we must be careful to consider the following five possibilities:

1. There may be a direct cause-and-effect relationship. That is, a change in x causes a change in y. For example, heat causes snow to melt, and water causes plants to grow.

2. There may be a reverse cause-and-effect relationship. That is, a change in y causes a change in x. For example, a researcher may believe that anxiety causes low grades (on examinations) when in fact it may be that low grades cause anxiety.

3. The relationship between x and y may be caused by a third variable. For example, ice cream sales may be highly correlated with boating accidents, where changes in both variables are related to the climate, rather than to each other.

4. There may be a complexity of interrelationships among many variables. For example, a researcher may find a significant relationship between the amount of fertilizer applied to a crop and the yield from the crop. But there are many other variables involved, such as rainfall, temperature, soil conditions, etc.

5. The relationship may be coincidental. For example, a researcher may find a strong correlation between the number of weekly car thefts in Regina and the price of tomatoes in Paris. Common sense dictates that any relationship between these two variables must be due to coincidence.

Common Errors and Limitations of Correlation Analysis

As is true with all statistical methods, correlation analysis is subject to misuses and misinterpretations. Some of the more common mistakes are summarized in the following:

1. *Correlation analysis is sometimes used to prove the existence of a cause-and-effect relationship.* The coefficient of determination tells us nothing about the type of relationship between the two variables. Rather, it indicates the proportion of variation that is explained *if* there is a causal relationship.

2. *The coefficient of correlation is sometimes interpreted as a percentage.* This can be a serious mistake. For example, if a coefficient of correlation of $r = .7$ is interpreted as meaning that 70 percent of the variation in y is explained, this is significantly above the 49 percent that actually is explained by the coefficient of determination $r^2 = .49$.

3. *The coefficient of determination is also subject to misinterpretation.* It is sometimes interpreted as the percentage of the variation in the dependent variable *caused* by the independent variable. This is simply nonsense. It always should be remembered that it's the variation in the dependent variable that is being explained or accounted for (but not necessarily caused) by the x variable.

STATISTICS IN ACTION

Kids Who Use Sunscreen Have Lower Risk of Cancer
Children who use sunscreen develop fewer moles and can have a lower risk of cancer as an adult, according to a recent study. The British Columbia Cancer Agency looked at 309 Vancouver school children over three years and found that kids who regularly use sunscreen developed fewer moles. The results were even more startling for freckled children, who had up to 40 percent fewer moles. Experts have said that decreasing the number of moles a person develops can lower the risk of skin cancer. Researchers call their study "a true prevention study" since parents can now "significantly reduce their child's risk of skin cancer in the future."

☐ **Example 12.6**   Lindsey Gollands compared the percentage of body fat and a measure of abdominal skinfold of 22 women. The data follow. Plot the data with body fat as the dependent variable, then obtain the estimated regression line, the coefficient of determination, and the correlation coefficient for this sample.

Abdominal	Body Fat	Abdominal	Body Fat
12.0	7.1	25.0	11.2
9.0	7.5	28.0	11.2
24.0	12.7	17.0	10.5
16.0	10.8	19.0	8.9
13.0	8.8	18.5	12.4
17.0	8.1	18.0	9.4
13.0	8.3	18.0	9.2
8.0	7.4	17.0	7.6
20.0	8.3	18.5	6.8
17.0	5.6	10.0	7.7
14.0	8.7	25.5	10.6

FIGURE 12.17 (*a*) MINITAB's **Fitted Line Plot** of the skinfold data. (*b*) To obtain this MINITAB output, click on **Stat, Basic Statistics, Correlation,** enter the columns to be correlated in the box below **Variables,** and click **OK.**

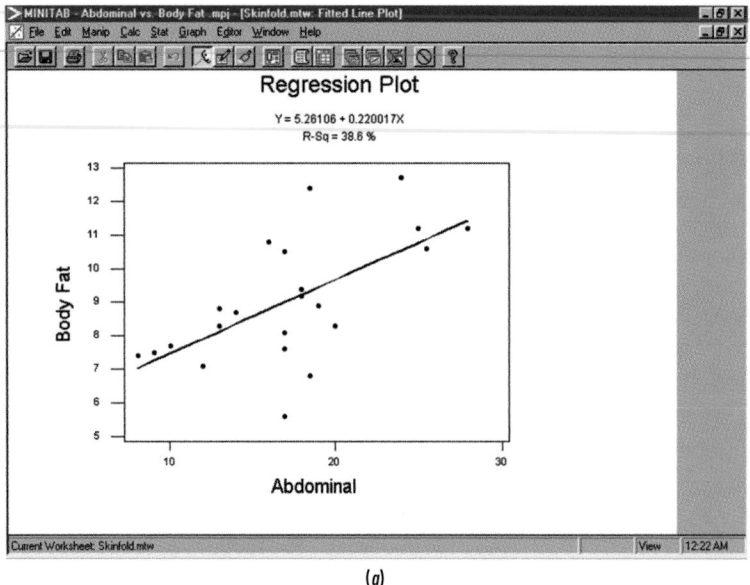

(*a*)

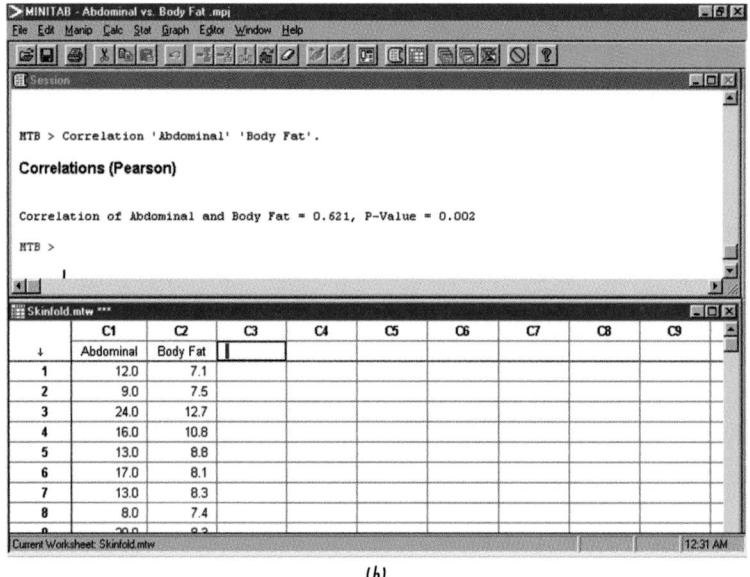

(*b*)

◆ **Solution:**

We used MINITAB to do all the work. In *Figure 12.17a*, we have the scattergram, the least squares regression line, and the coefficient of determination. The spread of the scattergram and r^2 value of 38.6 percent indicate a weak relationship. We could now figure the correlation coefficient by taking the square root of the coefficient of determination. But we again let the computer do the work, obtaining the correlation of .621 in *Figure 12.17b*. ◆

Self-Testing Review 12.4

24. A university administrator wishes to investigate the relationship between the enrollment and tuition for international students in western Canada. According to the *Maclean's Guide to Canadian Universities, 1999,* the enrollment and tuition data for international students at ten universities in western Canada are as follows (Data = Univ):

University	Tuition	Enrollment
Alberta	7,121	422
Calgary	6,880	423
Lethbridge	7,370	225
UBC	14,136	1,593
UNBC	5,342	65
Simon Fraser	7,137	260
Victoria	7,178	484
Brandon	5,290	47
Manitoba	5,907	289
Winnipeg	5,917	230

Note: Enrollment figures are for 1997–98 and tuition fees are for 1998–99.

a) Compute the total variation $\Sigma(y - \bar{y})^2$.

b) Compute the explained variation $\Sigma(\hat{y} - \bar{y})^2$.

c) Compute the unexplained variation $\Sigma(y - \hat{y})^2$.

d) Compute the coefficient of determination.

e) Interpret the coefficient of determination within the context of this problem.

f) Compute the coefficient of correlation.

25. A regional development council, composed of members from several local chambers of commerce, gathered the following data from a random sample of firms in the region that produced similar products (Data = Productn):

Production Cost (Thousands of Dollars)	Production Output (Thousands of Dollars)
150	40
140	38
160	48
170	56
150	62
162	75
180	70
165	90
190	110
185	120

a) Compute the total variation $\Sigma(y - \bar{y})^2$.

b) Compute the explained variation $\Sigma(\hat{y} - \bar{y})^2$.

c) Compute the unexplained variation $\sum(y - \hat{y})^2$.

d) Compute the coefficient of determination.

e) Interpret the coefficient of determination within the context of this problem.

f) Compute the coefficient of correlation.

26. Katie Dvorak trains employees to use a specific statistical software package. A random sample of trainees has turned in the following performances in recent weeks:

Trainee	Hours of Training	Errors
A	1	6
B	4	3
C	6	2
D	8	1
E	2	5
F	3	4
G	1	7

a) Compute the total variation $\sum(y - \bar{y})^2$.

b) Compute the explained variation $\sum(\hat{y} - \bar{y})^2$.

c) Compute the unexplained variation $\sum(y - \hat{y})^2$.

d) Compute the coefficient of determination.

e) Interpret the coefficient of determination within the context of this problem.

f) Compute the coefficient of correlation.

 27. Cal Tkachuk is applying to graduate schools of business and wants to see if there's a relationship between the tuition of the top 25 schools and the starting salary students form those schools can expect when they receive their M.B.A. degrees. Cal enters some data into the MINITAB program and receives the following output:

```
The regression equation is StartSal = 43269 + 0.579 Tuition

Predictor        Coef      Stdev           T          p
Constant        43269      4176        10.36      0.000
Tuition        0.5786     0.2653        2.18      0.040

s = 5211      R-sq = 17.1%      R-sq (adj) = 13.5%

Analysis of Variance

Source          DF          SS          MS          F          p
Regression       1   129141472   129141472       4.76      0.040
Error           23   624481856    27151386
Total           24   753623296
```

Determine:

a) The total variation (SST).

b) The explained variation (SSR).

c) The unexplained variation (SSE).

d) The coefficient of determination.

e) The coefficient of correlation.

28. A company has offered a health care incentive plan to its employees. As a part of this plan, employees are expected to maintain a good diet and to exercise. An analyst at this company keys into the MINITAB program the body mass index (BMI) data for each participating employee. The data pairs give BMI readings at the beginning of the program and at the completion of two years in the program. The data produce the following MINITAB output:

```
The regression equation is BMI2yrs = 25.6 + 0.0080 baseline

Predictor      Coef      Stdev        T          p
Constant     25.629     1.710      14.99      0.000
btreat       0.00797    0.06723     0.12      0.907

s = 0.6485   R-sq = 0.1%    R-sq (adj) = 0.0%

Analysis of Variance

Source        DF        SS          MS        F        p
Regression     1      0.0059      0.0059     0.01    0.907
Error         14      5.8884      0.4206
Total         15      5.8943
```

Determine:

a) The total variation (SST).

b) The explained variation (SSR).

c) The unexplained variation (SSE).

d) The coefficient of determination.

e) The coefficient of correlation.

29. Nick Billings, a statistics student at the University of Regina and a member of the Rams football team, collected CIS (Canadian Inter Sport) Football data to investigate the relationship between the number of yards made by passing and the number of points scored in a football games. The data was entered into MINITAB, and the following output was obtained:

Team	Pass Yards	Points/ Game	Team	Pass Yards	Points/ Game
Acadia	223	25.6	Alberta	228.8	17.4
Mt. Allison	129.8	7.5	UBC	195.9	18.0
St. Mary's	263.1	26.9	Calgary	275.6	24.2
St. FX	187.2	39.1	Manitoba	301.6	33.9
Bishop's	231.7	15.9	Regina	233.9	21.1
Concordia	219.4	25.2	Saskatchewan	231.8	20.2
Laval	251.3	36.9	Simon Fraser	192.9	13.8
McGil	242.7	35.3	Guelph	189.25	12.75
Montreal	97.2	7.8	Laurier	124.63	18.75

Team	Pass Yards	Points/ Game
McMaster	250.25	38.75
Ottawa	288.0	27.5
Queens	543.88	33.88
Toronto	101.13	8.63
Waterloo	192.63	13.88
Western	464.38	35.75
Windsor	161.25	13.63
York	187	15.13

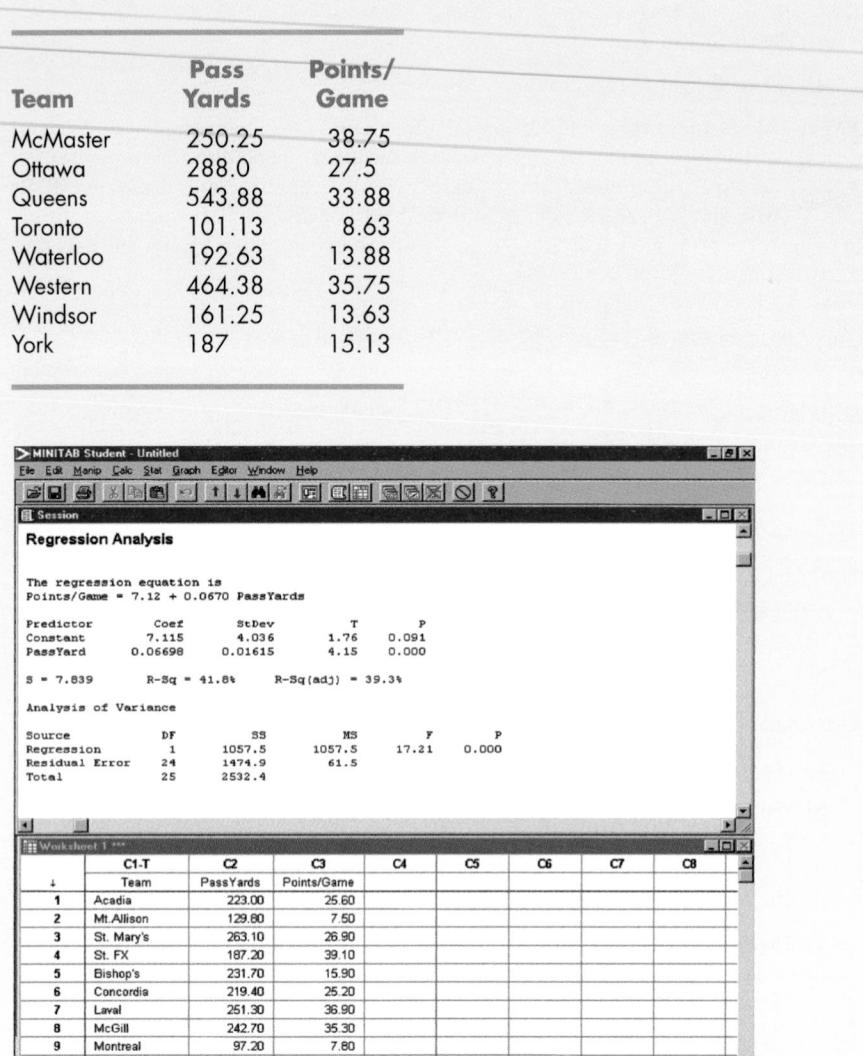

Determine:

    a) The total variation (SST).

    b) The explained variation (SSR).

    c) The unexplained variation (SSE).

    d) The coefficient of determination.

    e) The coefficient of correlation.

12.5   Multiple Linear Regression and Correlation

Many practical applications of regression analysis involve models that are more complex than the simple straight-line model. For example, to predict the yield of a crop, we might want a model that would involve several variables, such as rainfall, temperature, soil conditions, etc. Probabilistic models that include more than one independent variable, or that include variables such as x^2, x^3, etc., are called **multiple regression models.**

Model for Multiple Linear Regression

The Multiple Linear Regression Model involves assumptions and notation similar to the Simple Linear Regression Model. The assumptions are

1. Corresponding to each possible set of values of the explanatory variables $X_1, X_2, \ldots, X_k$, there is a distribution of possible values of Y, where $E(Y) = A + B_1X_1 + B_2X_2 + \cdots + B_kX_k$ for some unknown parameters $A, B_1, B_2, \ldots, B_k$.

2. For each set of possible values of the explanatory variables, the distribution of Y values is normally distributed.

3. Each of the distributions of Y values has the same standard deviation σ.

4. Each Y value in these distributions is independent of the others.

Multiple Linear Regression Model

For the Population

Mean: $E(Y) = A + B_1 X_1 + B_2 X_2 + B_3 X_3 + \cdots + B_k X_k$
Individual Value: $Y = A + B_1 X_1 + B_2 X_2 + B_3 X_3 + \cdots + B_k X_k + \varepsilon$

where
Y = dependent (or response) variable
$X_1, X_2, X_3, \ldots, X_k$ = independent (or explanatory) variables
$A, B_1, B_2, \ldots, B_k$ = unknown parameters
ε (epsilon) = random error component

The errors ε_i are assumed to follow a normal distribution with mean 0 and standard deviation σ.

For the Sample

Mean: $\hat{y} = a + b_1 x_1 + b_2x_2 + b_3x_3 + \cdots + b_kx_k$
Individual Value: $y = a + b_1x_1 + b_2x_2 + b_3x_3 + \cdots + b_kx_k + e_i = \hat{y} + e_i$

where $e_i = y_i - \hat{y}$ and is called the residual for the individual i.

The mean of the residuals is 0, and the residuals may be used to estimate the common population standard deviation σ. The sample statistics $a, b_1, b_2, \ldots, b_k$ estimate the population parameters $A, B_1, B_2, \ldots B_k$.

Hiram Hess has been able to make predictions about employee output production because a single x variable—aptitude test scores—explained practically all of the variation in output. But prediction needs aren't always so easily met. Let's assume Selam Hess, Hiram's sister and sales manager of Tackey Toys, needs to

TABLE 12.5 TACKEY TOY SALES AND ADVERTISING COST DATA FOR A SAMPLE OF SIX MARKET AREAS

Market Area	Advertising Expenditures (Thousands of Dollars) (x)	Toy Sales (Thousands of Dollars) (y)
A	1.0	100
B	5.0	300
C	8.0	400
D	6.0	200
E	3.0	100
F	10.0	400

predict sales of Tackey products in selected market areas. Selam believes that advertising expenditures can be used to predict sales and has gathered sample toy sales and advertising cost data (shown in Table 12.5) for six market areas. The MINITAB package has produced a simple linear regression equation for this data set (see *Figure 12.18*). Selam notes that the printout shows there's a true relationship between sales and advertising expenditures at the .05 level of significance. Why? Because the test statistic of 4.37 shown in the printout is greater than the $t_{\alpha/2}$ value of 2.776 (where $\alpha = .05$, and df = 6 − 2, or 4). This means that Selam can reject the H_0 that $B = 0$. And the r^2 value shows that 82.7 percent of the change in sales is explained by changes in advertising expenditures. That's not a bad regression fit, but Selam would like to find another variable that can further explain changes in sales before she submits her next sales forecast to her boss. In short, Selam wants to base her next sales forecast on a multiple regression model.

Although a study of multiple regression involves three (or more) variables, the same assumptions, concepts, and measures that we've already studied still apply. There's still

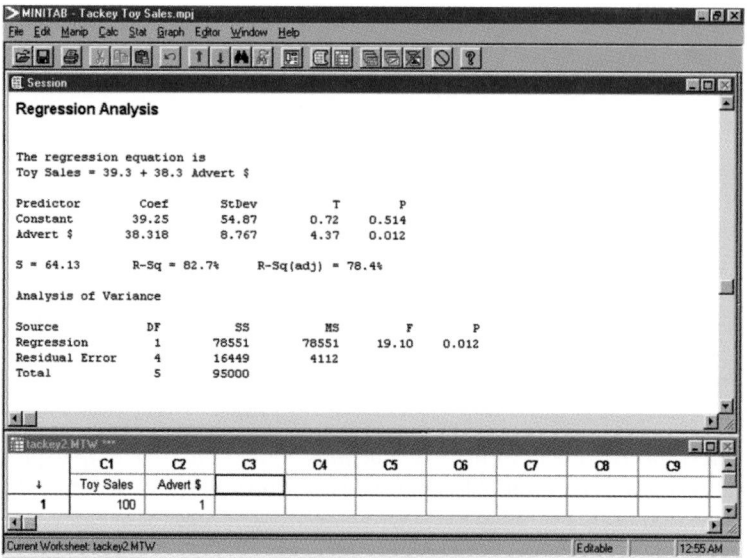

FIGURE 12.18 Selam is right; there is a relationship between sales results and advertising costs.

a single dependent (y) variable that we're interested in predicting, but now there are two (or more) independent (x) variables that explain the variations that occur in the y variable. Earlier, we calculated the simple linear regression equation and then found the standard error of estimate. We followed up with relationship tests and interval estimates and then computed the coefficient of determination. Let's look now at these same topics in the context of multiple linear regression and correlation.

The Multiple Linear Regression Equation

Let's assume that Selam has identified another predicting variable—the population in each market area—and now has the data shown in Table 12.6. The dependent, or response, variable is still identified by y. But since we now have two independent, or explanatory, variables, we'll call advertising costs x_1 and population x_2. The simple linear regression equation ($\hat{y} = a + bx$) must now be changed to the following multiple linear regression equation:

$$\hat{y} = a + b_1x_1 + b_2x_2 \qquad (12.13)$$

where $\hat{y}$ = the estimated value of the dependent variable
  a = the y intercept
  x_1 = the value of the first independent variable
  x_2 = the value of the second independent variable
  b_1 = slope associated with x_1 (the change in $\hat{y}$ if x_2 is held constant and x_1 varies by 1 unit)
  b_2 = slope associated with x_2 (the change in $\hat{y}$ if x_1 is held constant and x_2 varies by 1 unit)

In the simple linear regression case, the relationship between x and y was shown with a straight regression line that displayed length and width. Now, with three variables, we have a three-dimensional plane that shows length, width, and depth (see *Figure 12.19*). Just as the points in a two-variable regression problem fall above and below the regression line shown in a two-dimensional scatter diagram, so, too, do the points in a three-variable regression problem fall above and below the regression plane shown in

TABLE 12.6 SELAM HAS ADDED A SECOND PREDICTING VARIABLE— POPULATION—TO HER SAMPLE DATA

Market Area	Advertising Expenditures (Thousands of Dollars) (x_1)	Population (Thousands) (x_2)	Toy Sales (Thousands of Dollars) (y)
A	1.0	200	100
B	5.0	700	300
C	8.0	800	400
D	6.0	400	200
E	3.0	100	100
F	10.0	600	400

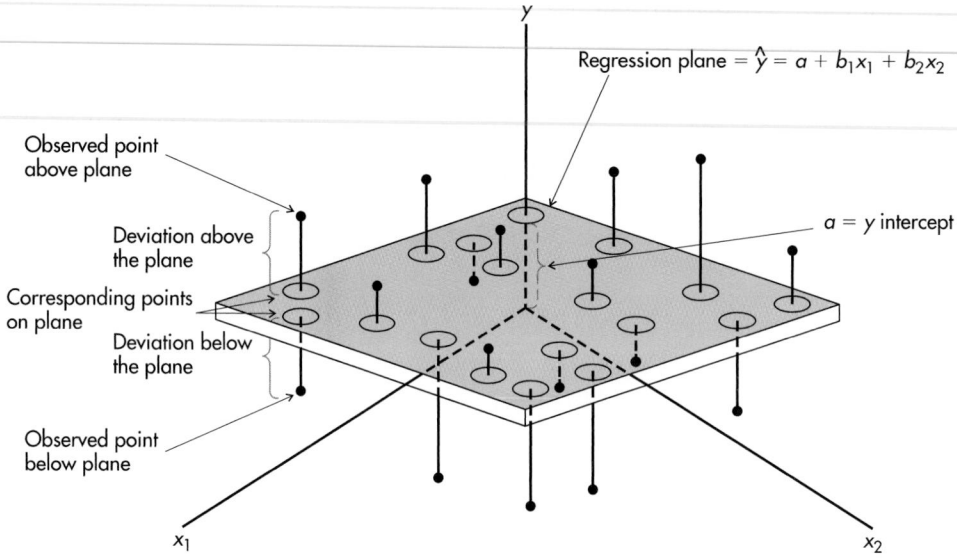

FIGURE 12.19 A regression plane replaces a regression line in multiple regression. If you face the corner of your room, hold this book at arm's length, and tilt the book in various ways, you'll get an idea of how different planes might appear in a three-variable situation.

Figure 12.19. And just as the simple linear regression equation is used to get the best straight-line fit to the points in a scatter diagram, so, too, does the multiple regression equation identify the plane that gives the best fit to the data.

Computing the Multiple Linear Regression Equation The next step is to compute the values of a, b_1, and b_2 in the multiple regression equation. Table 12.7 repeats the y, x_1, and x_2 values given in Table 12.6 and then presents other intermediate figures needed to compute these regression equation values. Although our sample covers only six market areas and the data are deliberately simplified, the work needed to calculate these values by hand is daunting. For example, one way to calculate b_1 is with the following formula:

$$b_1 = \frac{[n(\Sigma\, x_1 y) - (\Sigma\, x_1)(\Sigma\, y)][n\,\Sigma\, x_2^2 - (\Sigma\, x_2)^2] - [n\,\Sigma\, x_1 x_2 - (\Sigma\, x_1)(\Sigma\, x_2)][n\,\Sigma\, x_2 y - (\Sigma\, x_2)\,\Sigma(y)]}{[n\,\Sigma\, x_1^2 - (\Sigma\, x_1)^2][n\,\Sigma\, x_2^2 - (\Sigma\, x_2)^2] - [n\,\Sigma\, x_1 x_2 - (\Sigma\, x_1)(\Sigma\, x_2)]^2}$$

You *could* plug the values from Table 12.7 into this formula to calculate the value of b_1 for Selam's regression equation (if you do, you'll find it's 20.49209). And you *could* use an equally formidable formula to calculate b_2, and then find a. But Selam didn't engage in such masochistic behaviour. Having read the first

TABLE 12.7 INTERMEDIATE FIGURES NEEDED TO COMPUTE a, b_1, AND b_2

(x_1)	(x_2)	(y)	$x_1 y$	$x_2 y$	$x_1 x_2$	x_1^2	x_2^2	y^2
1.0	200	100	100	20,000	200	1	40,000	10,000
5.0	700	300	1,500	210,000	3,500	25	490,000	90,000
8.0	800	400	3,200	320,000	6,400	64	640,000	160,000
6.0	400	200	1,200	80,000	2,400	36	160,000	40,000
3.0	100	100	300	10,000	300	9	10,000	10,000
10.0	600	400	4,000	240,000	6,000	100	360,000	160,000
33.0	2,800	1,500	10,300	880,000	18,800	235	1,700,000	470,000

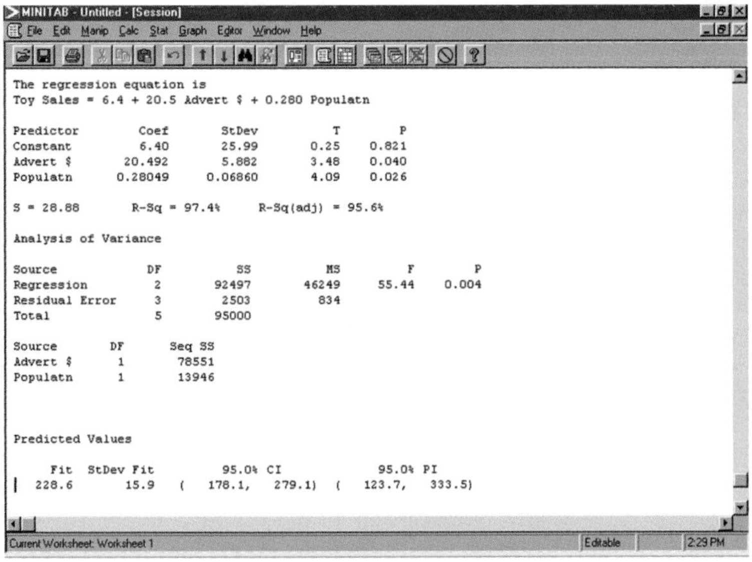

FIGURE 12.20 To obtain this MINITAB output, click on **Stat, Regression, Regression,** enter the **Response** and two **Predictors** before clicking an **Options.** Then request a **Prediction interval** for "4 500," and click **OK** twice.

portion of this chapter, she was clever enough to recognize that MINITAB would handle multiple regression as easily as simple linear regression. Accessing MINITAB's *Regression* window, she requests a multiple regression analysis, including a prediction of sales when $x_1 = 4$ and $x_2 = 500$ (see *Figure 12.20*).

As you can see, Selam's multiple regression equation has the following values:

$a = 6.40$
$b_1 = 20.492$ or 20.5
$b_2 = .28049$ or .280

Interpreting the Values in the Equation What do these values mean? The *a* figure is still the *y* intercept—the value of $\hat{y}$ when x_1 and x_2 are both zero. The b_1 value of 20.492 shows that if one market area spends \$1,000 more on advertising Tackey Toys (a change of one unit in x_1) than another market area and if the markets have the same population (x_2 is held constant), then the estimated toy sales in the higher advertising cost area exceed those of the second area by about \$20,492. And the b_2 value of .28049 means that if a first market area has 1,000 more people than a second area (a change of one unit in x_2) and if the same amount has been spent on advertising in the two areas (x_1 is held constant), then the estimated toy sales of the larger market area exceed those of the smaller market by about \$280. The b_1 and b_2 constants are called estimated regression coefficients in multiple regression terminology.

Making Preliminary Predictions with the Multiple Regression Equation
Selam now has the following multiple regression equation:

$$\hat{y} = 6.40 + 20.492x_1 + .28049x_2$$

And let's assume that she needs a sales forecast for a market area. Tackey Toys has recently spent \$4,000 advertising in this market, which has a population of 500,000 people. The point estimate of toy sales in the market is

$\hat{y} = 6.40 + 20.492(4) + .28049(500)$
$\quad = 6.40 + 81.968 + 140.245$
$\quad = 228.613$ or \$228,613 in toy sales

You might notice in the last line of *Figure 12.20* under *fit* the value 228.6—the same prediction as above.

The Multicollinearity Problem　**Multicollinearity** is the name statisticians give to the situation when predictive variables x_1 and x_2 are closely intercorrelated. If this is the case, the values of b_1 and b_2 tend to be unreliable, and an estimate made with an equation that uses these values also tends to be unreliable. This is because, in closely correlated series, variables in x_2 don't necessarily remain constant while x_1 changes. If two independent variables are closely correlated—that is, if they have an r value close to ±1.00—a simple solution is to use just one of them in a multiple regression model. Multicollinearity isn't a problem with Selam's data.

The Standard Error of Estimate for Multiple Regression

You've seen that the standard error of estimate for a simple linear regression model is a measure of the extent of the scatter, or dispersion, of the sample data points about the regression line. In a multiple linear regression situation, we still have a standard error of estimate, but now it measures the dispersion, or scatter, of the sample data points about the multiple regression plane. One way to calculate this measure (we'll use the symbol $s_{y.x_1x_2}$) is with a formula that's analogous to formula 12.4:

$$s_{y.x_1x_2} = \sqrt{\frac{\Sigma(y - \hat{y})^2}{n - 3}} \tag{12.14}$$

Of course, an easier formula to apply is

$$s_{y.x_1x_2} = \sqrt{\frac{\Sigma(y)^2 - a(\Sigma y) - b_1 \Sigma(x_1 y) - b_2 \Sigma(x_2 y)}{n - 3}} \tag{12.15}$$

When supplied with the data in Table 12.7, formula 12.15 gives the formula results:

$$
\begin{aligned}
s_{y.x_1x_2} &= \sqrt{\frac{\Sigma(y)^2 - a(\Sigma y) - b_1 \Sigma(x_1 y) - b_2 \Sigma(x_2 y)}{n - 3}} \\
&= \sqrt{\frac{470{,}000 - 6.40\,(1{,}500) - 20.492\,(10{,}300) - .28049\,(880{,}000)}{6 - 3}} \\
&= \sqrt{\frac{2{,}501.2}{3}} = 28.874
\end{aligned}
$$

Except for slight rounding error, the value of 28.874 agrees with the "$s = 28.88$" figure shown in *Figure 12.20*.

Relationship Tests

We mentioned earlier when discussing simple linear regression that the ANOVA and t tests, while testing the same hypotheses in simple linear regression, actually test different hypotheses in multiple regression. Here we will learn what these hypotheses are. The underlying assumptions that are necessary to run these tests are identical to a simple linear regression situation (although, of course, we have another predicting variable).

The Analysis of Variance Test

In multiple regression, it is possible to be unlucky enough to select predicting variables that do not have any meaningful relationship with the response variable. Suppose Selam is worried about that possibility. She wants to test to see if at least one of her predicting variables, advertising and population, is related to the response, toy sales. That is exactly the purpose of the ANOVA test. The null and alternative hypotheses *(Step 1)* are

H_0: Neither of the predictors is related to the response ($B_1 = B_2 = 0$)
H_1: At least one of the predictors is related to the response (B_1 or B_2 or both $\neq 0$)

Let's assume that Selam wants to make an ANOVA test at the .05 level of significance *(Step 2)*. She knows to use the F distributions in such tests *(Step 3)*. To find the F critical value that is the boundary of the rejection region *(Step 4)*, she must know α, df_{num}, and df_{den}. These df figures are

$df_{num} = m = 2$
$df_{den} = n - m - 1 = 3$

where m = the number of independent variables, or 2 in this case
         n = the number of market areas in our examples, or 6

Thus, the critical F table value for our example $F_{2,3,\alpha = .05} = 9.55$.
   The decision rule *(Step 5)* is

Reject H_0 in favour of H_1 if the test statistic's value > 9.55. Otherwise, fail to reject H_0.

We can see in *Figure 12.20* that $F = 55.44$ *(Step 6)*. Since $F = 55.44$ is greater than the table value of 9.55, the null hypothesis is rejected *(Step 7)*. This implies that at least one of x_1 and x_2 has a meaningful relationship with the response, y. Selam will use t tests to determine if it would be better to use both x variables or just one of the two to predict the y variable.

t Tests for Slope

We will use t tests to decide which predicting variables to use to estimate the response. We do so by testing hypotheses concerning the slopes of the population regression coefficients, B_1 and B_2. From the printout in *Figure 12.20*, you can see the results of these t tests. We can once again employ the same seven-step hypothesis-testing procedure used earlier in the chapter. Let's assume in *Step 1* that Selam wants to test the null hypothesis that $B_1 = 0$ against the alternative that $B_1 \neq 0$. She elects *(Step 2)* to conduct her test at the .05 level of significance, and she knows to use the t distribution for this test *(Step 3)*. The boundaries of the rejection region are found *(Step 4)* in the t table of Appendix 4 by finding the critical value that corresponds to $t_{\alpha/2}$ and $n - m - 1$, or $6 - 3$, or three degrees of freedom. (The df value is $n - 3$ for a three-variable situation, $n - 4$ if there are four variables, and so on.) This t table value is 3.182.
   The decision rule *(Step 5)* is

Reject H_0 [that advertising costs (x_1) is not helpful to this model in predicting toy sales (y)] in favour of H_1 if the test statistic $t > 3.182$ or < -3.182. Otherwise, fail to reject H_0.

The test statistic *(Step 6)* is found with this formula (the estimated standard deviation of b_1 is given in *Figure 12.20*):

$$t = \frac{b_1 - 0}{\text{estimated standard deviation of } b_1} = \frac{b_1}{s_{b_1}} = \frac{20.492}{5.882} = 3.48$$

The statistical decision *(Step 7)* is, since $t = 3.48$ is greater than 3.182, to reject H_0 that $B_1 = 0$. There is statistically significant evidence of a relationship between toy sales and advertising. (And since the p-value of .040 given in *Figure 12.20* is less than the level of significance of .05, the p-value approach would also lead us to reject H_0 that $B_1 = 0$.)

You should now be able to examine *Figure 12.20* and explain why there's also a meaningful relationship at the .05 level between toy sales (y) and population in the market area (x_2). In this case, H_0 is $B_2 = 0$, the critical t value for $t_{\alpha/2}$ and three degrees of freedom is still 3.182, and the decision rule remains unchanged. The test statistic is shown in *Figure 12.20* to be 4.09, and since the value is greater than 3.182, we reject H_0 that $B_2 = 0$. There is a meaningful relationship between toy sales and population in the market area. (The p-value of .026, being less than .05, confirms this conclusion). This says that Selam should use both advertising costs and population to predict toy sales.

A word of warning here. It is possible that our ANOVA test could be significant, indicating that at least one of x_1 and x_2 has a meaningful relationship with y, but neither of the t tests is significant. This type of seeming contradiction is caused by multicollinearity. If x_1 and x_2 are highly correlated, they have very similar information, and we need only one of the two variables to predict y. So insignificant t tests coupled with a significant F test indicate that we need one, but not both, of the independent variables. In this case, we would drop one of the two x's (usually the one with the t test value closest to 0) and redo the regression with the remaining x variable. Often the t test then becomes significant, and we have a regression model that would help us predict the response.

Interval Estimates for Predictions

You saw earlier that interval estimates can be constructed for simple linear regression situations, and probabilities can be assigned to these estimates. Two types of intervals were developed then: confidence intervals for the average value of y given x, and prediction intervals for a specific value of y given x. These same concepts can be applied in a multiple regression situation. You'll recall in *Figure 12.20* that Selam requested a prediction for "4 500", that is, a prediction of sales when $4,000 is spent on advertising in a market with 500,000 people. This results in the portion of the output in *Figure 12.20* under the heading of "Predicted Values." The 228.6 value under "Fit" is the point estimate, $\hat{y}$, Selam had obtained earlier when she plugged $x_1 = $ and 4 and $x_2 = 500$ into her multiple regression equation. Skipping over "StDev Fit" (which is a value we would compute if we were to calculate these intervals by hand), we find the intervals Selam wants. The 95 percent confidence interval for the average value of y given 4 for x_1 and 500 for x_2 is, in thousands of dollars, from 178.1 to 279.1. Thus, Selam can be 95 percent confident that the average sales for Tackey Toys in market areas with these values of x_1 and x_2 are between $178,100 and $279,100. The 95 percent prediction interval for the same values of x_1 and x_2 is from 123.7 to 333.5. So Salem can be 95 percent confident that the sales in a single location with these values of x_1 and x_2 will be between $123,700 and $333,500.

The Coefficient of Multiple Determination

The r^2 value in the simple linear case measures the percentage of the variation in the y variable that's explained by the variation in the x variable. Similarly, the **coefficient of multiple determination** (R^2) is a decimal fraction or percentage that shows the variation in the y variable that's explained by its relation to the combination of x_1 and x_2.
    One way to find R^2 is

$$R^2 = \frac{\Sigma(\hat{y} - \bar{y})^2}{\Sigma(y - \bar{y})^2} = \frac{SSR}{SST} = \frac{92,497}{95,000} = .9736 \text{ or } 97.4 \text{ percent}$$

where the SSR and SST values come from the ANOVA table in the printout. Another way to find R^2 uses the data in the multiple regression equation and in Table 12.7:

$$R^2 = \frac{n[a(\Sigma y) + b_1(\Sigma x_1 y) + b_2(\Sigma x_2 y)] - (\Sigma y)^2}{n(\Sigma y^2) - (\Sigma y^2)}$$

$$= \frac{6[6.40(1,500) + 20.492(10,300) + .28049(880,000)] - (1,500)^2}{6(470,000) - (1,500)^2}$$

$$= \frac{554,992.8}{570,000} = .974 \text{ or } 97.4 \text{ percent}$$

And a third (and obviously best) way to get R^2 is to just read the value directly from the printout in *Figure 12.20*. The .974 figure, of course, means that 97.4 percent of Tackey Toy sales in the market areas are explained by advertising expenditures and population size. (The remaining 2.6 percent are unexplained by these variables and are due to other factors.)

▢ Example 12.7   **Regressing the Shrubs** Data was collected on shrubs at Swanton's farm. Measurements included height (cm), age (months), and bark thickness (mm). Let's determine, using a level of significance of .05, a good prediction model for the height of the shrubs. The data follows (Data = Swanton):

Height	Age	Bark	Height	Age	Bark
1220.0	20	1.1	164.00	40	2.3
193.50	36	2.8	203.25	52	2.0
166.50	18	2.0	174.00	30	2.5
82.00	10	1.2	159.00	22	3.0
133.50	21	2.0	205.00	42	2.6
156.00	29	1.4	223.50	45	4.3
172.50	51	1.8	195.00	54	4.0
81.00	11	1.1	232.50	39	2.2
148.00	26	2.5	190.50	36	3.5
113.00	12	1.5	100.00	8	1.4
84.00	13	1.4			

FIGURE 12.21 MINITAB multiple regression output for shrub data.

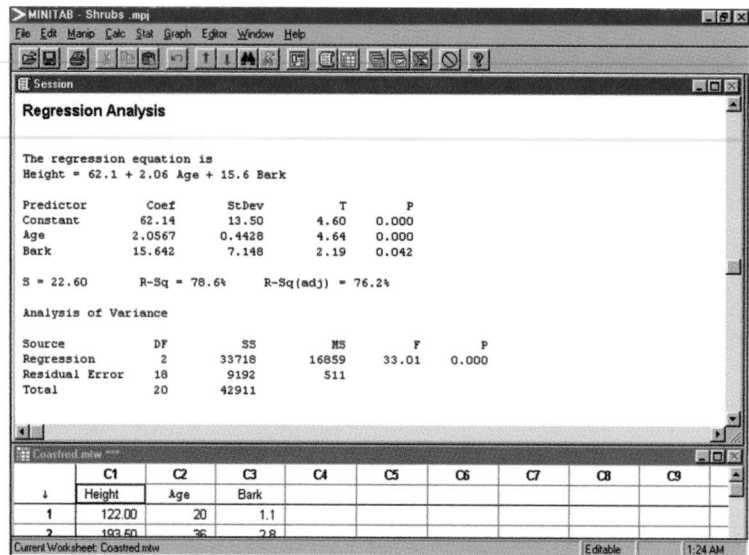

♦ **Solution:**

We used MINITAB to generate the multiple regression output of *Figure 12.21*. We will first test to see if either age or bark thickness has a relationship to height. The hypotheses are

H_0: Neither age nor bark thickness is related to height ($B_1 = B_2 = 0$)
H_1: At least one of age or bark thickness is related to height (B_1 or B_2 or both $\neq 0$)

We'll run the ANOVA F test at the .05 level of significance. Trusting MINITAB to use the correct values for the degrees of freedom (they are 2 and 18, the first values given in the "DF" column of the ANOVA table), the decision rule using the p-value approach is

Reject H_0 in favour of H_1 if p-value < 0.05. Otherwise, fail to reject H_0.

We can see that the p-value is 0.000. Because this is less than .05, the null hypothesis is rejected. This implies that at least one of the age and bark thickness variables has a meaningful relationship with height.

We will run two t tests to see if we should use both or just one of the two predictor variables in the regression equation. As the tests have a number of characteristics in common, we will sketch how to do both simultaneously. The hypotheses are

For age: H_0: $B_1 = 0$ vs H_1: $B_1 \neq 0$
For bark thickness: H_0: $B_2 = 0$ vs H_1: $B_2 \neq 0$

We will use the .05 level of significance, and both tests are based on the t distribution. The value of the degrees of freedom is 18 (the error degrees of freedom in the ANOVA table), but, rather than using the tables for the t distribution, we will again rely on MINITAB to find the p-value for us. The decision rule is then

Reject H_0 in favour of H_1 if the p-value < 0.05. Otherwise, fail to reject H_0.

The test statistic for age is 4.64, which has a *p*-value of 0.000, while the test statistic for bark thickness is 2.19, which has a *p*-value of 0.042. As both of these *p*-values are less than .05, we would conclude that there is significant evidence that both variables belong in the regression equation. ◆

Example 12.8 **Regressing a Gastropod** Jeff Tupen of TENERA, Inc. has spent years doing research on the shelled gastropod *Alia carinata,* or the carinate dove shell. He generously provided a data set that contains morphometric measurements on a sample of *Alia carinata,* a small portion of which follows. We also have provided a MINITAB output fitting a multiple regression equation to estimate shell height (mm) based on the other seven variables. What can you learn from this output about the possibility of predicting shell height with one or more of these variables (Data = Alia2)?

Shell Height	Shell Width	Spire Height	Spire Width	Aperature Height	Aperature Width	Shell Angle	Spire Angle
7.01	3.31	2.50	1.98	3.02	1.45	42.0	44.5
6.53	3.12	2.23	1.80	2.81	1.25	46.5	47.0
7.57	3.62	2.74	2.24	3.04	1.60	45.5	43.0
6.55	3.37	2.35	1.93	2.70	1.33	51.5	49.5
6.96	3.44	2.60	2.08	3.06	1.41	46.0	44.0
7.52	3.59	2.59	2.24	3.15	1.33	47.5	49.0
6.99	3.34	2.64	2.08	2.82	1.32	42.5	42.5

◆ **Solution:**
Scanning the MINITAB output in *Figure 12.22,* we can make the following observations:

1. Based on the ANOVA *F* test having a *p*-value of 0.000, we can conclude there is strong evidence that at least one of the seven predictor variables has a relationship with shell height.

2. If we were to do *t* tests of H_0: $B_1 = 0$, H_0: $B_2 = 0$, and so on, in five of the seven tests, the *p*-value is 0.000, and we would decide that those *x* variables belong in the regression equation.

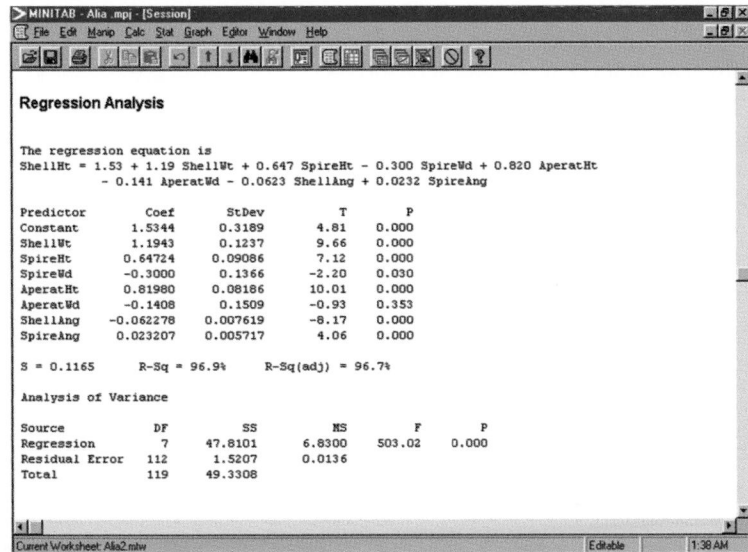

FIGURE 12.22 MINITAB multiple regression output for *Alia* data.

3. The x variable whose p-value is 0.353, aperture width, does not appear to have a meaningful relationship with shell height in this model.

4. The remaining variable, spire width (p-value = 0.030), may or may not belong in the model. To make that determination, we would drop aperture width and use MINITAB to redo the regression. Changing the model will change the test statistics and the associated p-values. If the p-value on spire width is less than whatever level of significance we choose, we would retain it in the regression equation; otherwise, we would eliminate it. (The p-values on the other five variables could also change, but we will ignore that possibility until we take another class in regression.) ◆

Using Dummy Variables to Model Qualitative Independent Variables

To this point we have considered only numerical (quantitative) variables as independent (or explanatory) variables. The methods of regression analysis can be generalized to include attribute (or qualitative) variables as well.

A dummy, or indicator, variable is any variable in a regression equation that takes on a finite number of values so that different categories of an attribute variable can be identified. The term *dummy* simply means that the values taken on by such variables (typically values such as 0 or 1,) indicate no meaningful measurement but rather the categories of interest. Examples of dummy variables include the following:

$$X_1 = \begin{cases} 1 & \text{if subject is female} \\ 0 & \text{if subject is male} \end{cases} \qquad X_2 = \begin{cases} 1 & \text{if subject is Canadian} \\ -1 & \text{otherwise} \end{cases}$$

The Partial F Test: Testing the Significance of a Portion of a Regression Model

A **partial F test** is used to test the significance of a set of independent variables in a regression model. That is, we can use this test to test the significance of a portion of a regression model. In general if the regression model is

$$Y = A + B_1X_1 + B_2X_2 + \cdots + B_gX_g + B_{g+1}X_{g+1} + \cdots + B_kX_k + \varepsilon$$

we may wish to test the null hypothesis

$$H_0: B_{g+1} = B_{g+2} = \ldots = B_k = 0$$

which says that none of the variables $X_{g+1}, X_{g+2}, \ldots, X_k$ affect Y, versus the alternative hypothesis

$$H_1: \text{At least one of } B_{g+1}, B_{g+2}, \ldots, B_k \text{ does not equal 0.}$$

which says that at least one of the independent variables $X_{g+1}, X_{g+2}, \ldots, X_k$ significantly affects Y.

To test H_0 against H_1, consider the following two models:

Complete model: $Y = A + B_1X_1 + B_2X_2 + \cdots + B_gX_g + B_{g+1}X_{g+1} + \cdots + B_kX_k + \varepsilon$
Reduced model: $Y = A + B_1X_1 + B_2X_2 + \cdots + B_gX_g + \varepsilon$

Here the complete model has k independent variables, the reduced model has g independent variables, and $(k - g)$ denotes the number of regression parameters set equal to 0 in the statement of H_0. To carry out this test we calculate **SSE_R, the unexplained variation for the reduced model** and **SSE_C, the unexplained variation for the complete model.** It can be shown that the "extra" independent variables $X_{g+1}, X_{g+2}, \ldots, X_k$ will always explain some of the variation in the observed y_i values, and therefore will always make SSE_C somewhat smaller than SSE_R. Therefore, the appropriate test statistic is based on the difference

$$SSE_R - SSE_C$$

which is called **the drop in the unexplained variation attributable to the independent variables $X_{g+1}, X_{g+2}, \ldots, X_k$.**

A large value of $SSE_R - SSE_C$ would be obtained if at least one of the variables X_{g+1}, $X_{g+2}, \ldots, X_k$ makes SSE_C substantially smaller than SSE_R. This would suggest that H_0 is false and H_1 is true. We therefore will reject H_0 in favour of H_1 for a large value of $SSE_R - SSE_C$, or equivalently, for a large value of the test statistic

$$F = \frac{(SSE_R - SSE_C)/(k - g)}{SSE_C/[n - (k + 1)]}.$$

The following box presents the formula for the test statistic and a summary of the test:

The Partial *F* Test:

An *F* Test for a Portion of a Regression Model
Assuming the regression assumptions are valid, we test

$H_0: B_{g+1} = B_{g+2} = \ldots = B_k = 0$

versus

H_1: At least one of $B_{g+1}, B_{g+2}, \ldots, B_k$ does not equal 0.

The test statistic, called **the partial *F* statistic,** is

$$F = \frac{(SSE_R - SSE_C)/(k - g)}{SSE_C/[n - (k + 1)]}$$

Reject H_0 in favour of H_1 if either of the following conditions holds:

1. $F > F_\alpha$

2. p-value $< \alpha$

where the point F_α is based on $k - g$ numerator and $n - (k + 1)$ denominator degrees of freedom

Example 12.9   **Movie Income** A movie enthusiast collected the data on opening weekend gross income and total gross income in millions of dollars for the following movies:

Movie	Opening Gross	Gross	Studio
The Mummy Returns	68.139	201.95	Universal
Jurassic Park III	50.772	181.166	Universal
American Pie 2	45.118	145.065	Universal
The Fast and the Furious	40.089	144.512	Universal
K-PAX	17.215	50.282	Universal
The Musketeer	10.313	27.054	Universal
Captain Corelli's Mandolin	7.209	25.528	Universal
Shallow Hal	22.518	70.805	20th Century Fox
Behind Enemy Lines	18.736	58.821	20th Century Fox
Don't Say a Word	17.090	54.95	20th Century Fox
Kiss of the Dragon	13.304	36.833	20th Century Fox
From Hell	11.015	31.551	20th Century Fox
Black Knight	11.103	33.368	20th Century Fox/Regency

We first define a complete multiple regression model that uses the data for both studios and that defines straight-line models for each studio.
One such model is the following:

$$\text{Gross} = A + B_1 \text{ Opening Gross} + B_2 \text{ Studio} + B_3 \text{ Opening Gross} \times \text{Studio} + \varepsilon$$

where $\text{Studio} = \begin{cases} 1 & \text{if Universal} \\ 0 & \text{if 20th Century Fox} \end{cases}$

Note that in this model we have $k = 3$ variables:

X_1 = Opening Gross
X_2 = Studio, and
X_3 = Opening Gross × Studio

By letting Studio = 1, we have the following linear model representing data from the Universal Studio.

$$\text{Gross} = A + B_1 \text{ Opening Gross} + B_2 + B_3 \text{ Opening Gross} + \varepsilon, \text{ or}$$
$$\text{Gross} = (A + B_2) + (B_1 + B_3) \text{ Opening Gross} + \varepsilon$$

By letting Studio = 0, we have the following linear model representing data from the 20th Century Fox Studio

$$\text{Gross} = A + B_1 \text{ Opening Gross} + \varepsilon$$

Using MINITAB, we obtain the following result, which uses data from both studios:

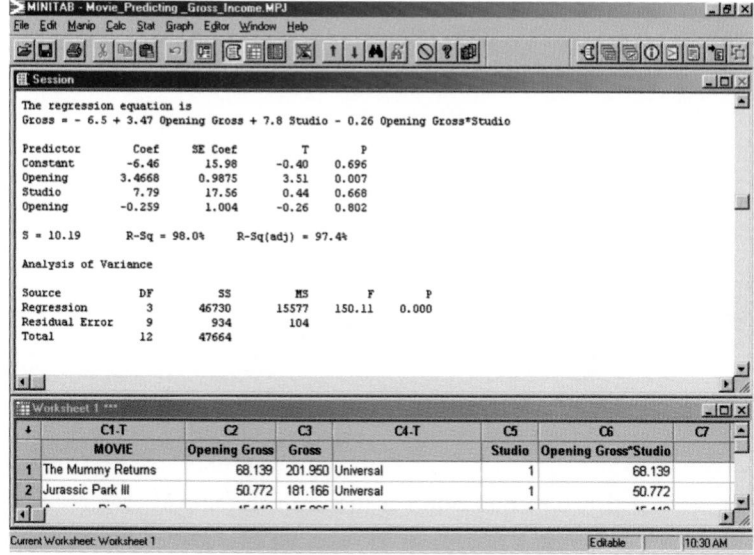

FIGURE 12.23 MINITAB output for the complete model in Example 12.9.

Note that the complete fitted regression equation is

Gross = $-6.5 + 3.47$ Opening Gross $+ 7.8$ Studio $- 0.26$ Opening Gross $\times$ Studio

The fitted regression equation for the Universal Studio is

Gross = $(A + B_2) + (B_1 + B_3)$ Opening Gross
Gross = $(-6.5 + 7.8) + (3.47 + -0.26)$ Opening Gross, or
Gross = $1.3 + 3.21$ Opening Gross

and the fitted regression equation for the 20th Century Fox Studio is

Gross = $-6.5 + 3.47$ Opening Gross

Next, suppose we wish to test for coincidence of the two models. That is, can the data from both studios be represented by the same linear model?

The models are coincident if $B_2 = B_3 = 0$, so we use a partial F test to test the hypothesis H_0: $B_2 = B_3 = 0$ against the alternative hypothesis H_1: at least one is different from 0. In order to calculate the test statistic $F = \dfrac{(SSE_R - SSE_C)/(k - g)}{SSE_C/[n - (k + 1)]}$, we first note that $k = 3$, $g = 1$, and $n = 13$. Therefore $k - g = 2$ and $n - (k + 1) - 9$.

Next, we note from the MINITAB computations for the complete model that $SSE_C = 934$. In order to find SSE_R, we use MINITAB again to estimate the reduced model.

FIGURE 12.24 MINITAB output for the reduced model in Example 12.9.

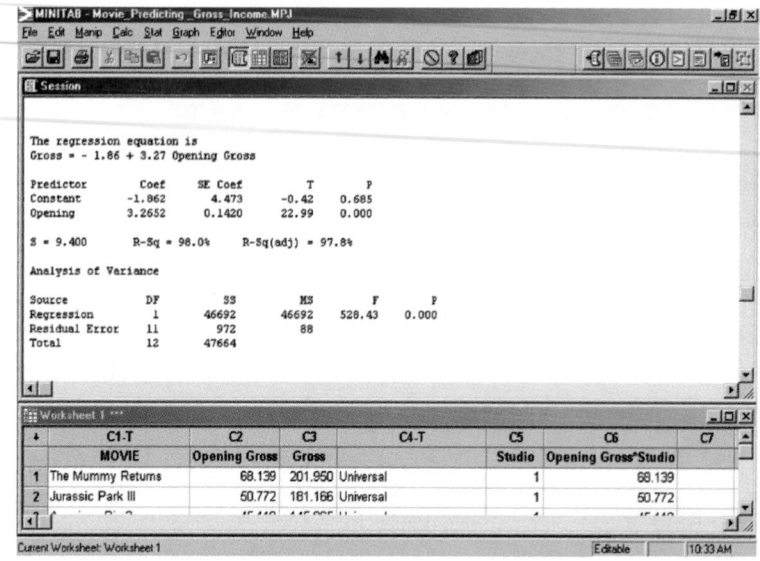

From this output we find that the regression equation, which estimates the reduced model is

Gross = −1.86 + 3.27 Opening Gross

and from the Analysis of Variance portion of the output we note that $SSE_R = 972$.

Therefore, $F = \dfrac{(SSE_R - SSE_C)/(k - g)}{SSE_C/[n - (k + 1)]} = \dfrac{(972 - 934)/2}{934/9} = 0.183$

From the F tables with $\alpha - .05$, $df_{num} = 2$, and $df_{dnom} = 9$, we find the critical value of $F = 4.26$. Since 0.183 is not greater than 4.26, we fail to reject H_0. Thus, at the .05 level of significance, we fail to reject the hypothesis that data from both studios can be represented by the same linear model. ◆

Checking Regression Assumptions

There are some assumptions that should be at least approximately true when using a regression model to make an inference.

Assumptions for Linear Regression

1. The form of the equation that relates the mean value of Y to X must be correct. For example, we won't make proper inferences if we use a straight line to describe a curved relationship.

2. For each X, the distribution of Y values is normally distributed. Equivalently, the distribution of deviations from the mean value of Y, (the residuals) is normal.

3. Each of the distributions of Y values has the same standard deviation σ.

4. Observations in the sample are independent of each other.

Note: If outliers or extreme values are present, they may unduly influence the results. An investigation should be carried out to determine whether or not such values should be included.

A scatterplot of the raw data and plots of the residuals provide information about the validity of the assumptions. Recall that a residual is the difference between an observed value and a predicted value.

Assumptions 1 and 3 can be checked using two useful plots:

- A scatterplot of *Y* versus *X* for the sample
- A scatterplot of the residuals versus the fitted values

If Assumption 1 holds for a linear relationship, then:

- The plot of *Y* versus *X* should show points that fall in an approximate straight line.
- The plot of residuals versus the fitted values should show points randomly scattered around a horizontal line at residual = 0.

If Assumption 3 holds, neither plot should show increasing or decreasing spread in the points as *X* increases.

To check Assumption 2, we may use MINITAB to construct a Normal Probability Plot of the Residuals, or to perform a Test for Normality, called the Anderson-Darling Test.

☐ **Example 12.10** **Movie Income—20th Century Fox** The movie enthusiast mentioned in the previous example was interested in checking the validity of the model found for the 20th Century Fox movies only. The appropriate data is as follows.

Movie	Opening Gross (in $ millions)	Total Gross (in $ millions)
Shallow Hal	22.518	70.805
Behind Enemy Lines	18.736	58.821
Don't Say a Word	17.090	54.950
Kiss of the Dragon	13.304	36.833
From Hell	11.015	31.551
Black Knight	11.103	33.368

In order to investigate the validity of the linearity assumption we construct a scatterplot of the Total Gross income versus the Opening Gross income.

The following MINITAB scatterplot was obtained (by selecting **Graph>Plot**) for the above movie data:

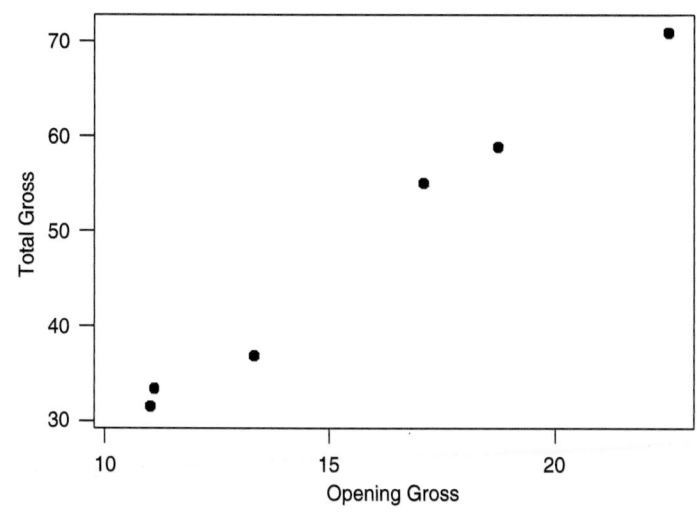

The scatter diagram indicates a linear model is appropriate since the points fall in an approximate straight line.

In order to investigate the validity of the assumption that each of the distributions of Y values has the same standard deviation σ, we wish to construct a scatterplot of the residuals versus the fitted values.

In order to obtain the residuals, we must first perform the usual Regression Analysis for the above movie data. For plotting and storing residuals, use **Stat>Regression>Regression**. The **Graphs** button of the dialogue box offers options for several possible residual plots for the regression. To store residuals in a column of the worksheet, use the **Storage** button of the dialogue box for regression. ◆

Regression Analysis: Total Gross versus Opening Gross

```
The regression equation is
Total Gross = -6.46 + 3.47 Opening Gross

Predictor        Coef      SE Coef          T          P
Constant       -6.457        3.063      -2.11      0.103
Opening         3.4668       0.1892     18.32      0.000


S =1.952 R - Sq = 98.8% R - Sq(adj) = 98.5%
PRESS = 29.0532 R-Sq(pred) = 97.76%


Analysis of Variance

Source          DF        SS          MS            F          P
Regression      1       1279.1      1279.1       335.63     0.000
Residual        4         15.2         3.8
Error
Total           5       1294.4
```

Obs	Opening	Total Gr	Fit	SE Fit	Residual	St Resid
1	22.5	70.805	71.609	1.528	−0.804	−0.66
2	18.7	58.821	58.497	0.991	0.324	0.19
3	17.1	54.950	52.791	0.844	2.159	1.23
4	13.3	36.833	39.666	0.910	−2.833	−1.64
5	11.0	31.551	31.730	1.182	−0.179	−0.12
6	11.1	33.368	32.035	1.170	1.333	0.85

The MINITAB scatterplot of the residuals versus the fitted values is as follows:

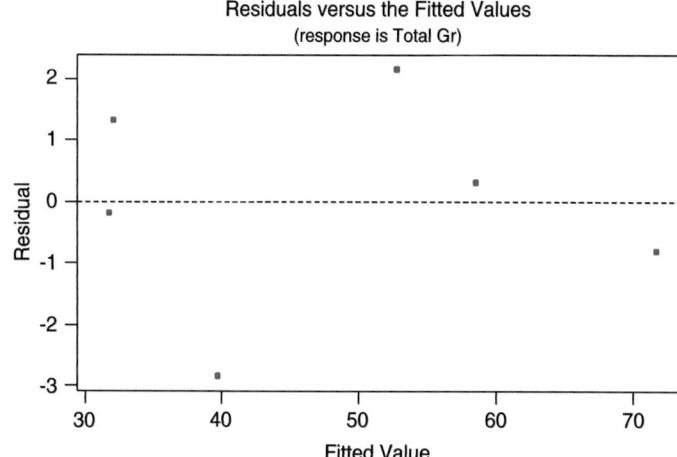

This scatter diagram indicates that the assumption that each of the distributions of Y values has the same standard deviation σ is reasonable since there is no obvious pattern.

To check the Normality assumption, using MINITAB, a first option is to examine the following Normal Probability Plot of the Residuals:

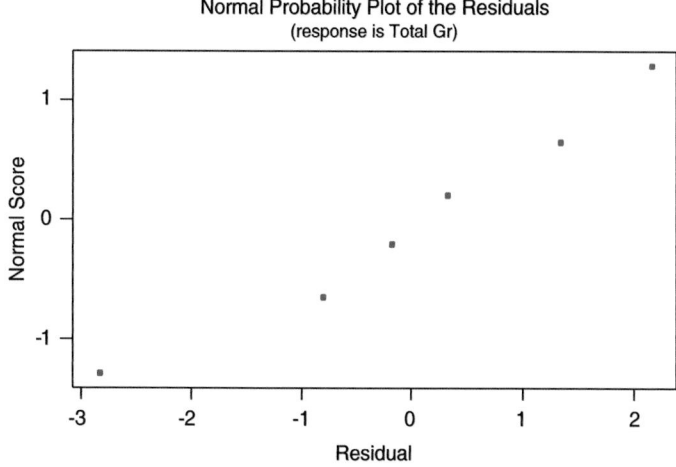

The fact that the points fall in an approximate straight line indicates that the assumption of Normality is a reasonable assumption.

An alternative to this graphical approach is to perform the MINITAB test for Normality (called the Anderson-Darling Test).

This test (which may be used to test the hypothesis that any set of numbers comes from a population that is normally distributed) requires that we input the numbers, which in this case are the residuals.

The **normality test** generates a probability plot and performs a hypothesis test to examine whether or not the observations follow a normal distribution.

The hypotheses are H_0: The data follow a normal distribution vs H_1: The data do not follow a normal distribution

To Perform a Normality Test

1. Choose **Stat>Basic Statistics>Normality Test.**

2. In the **Variable** window, enter the column containing the residuals.

3. If you like, use one or more of the options and click **OK.**

The following is the result:

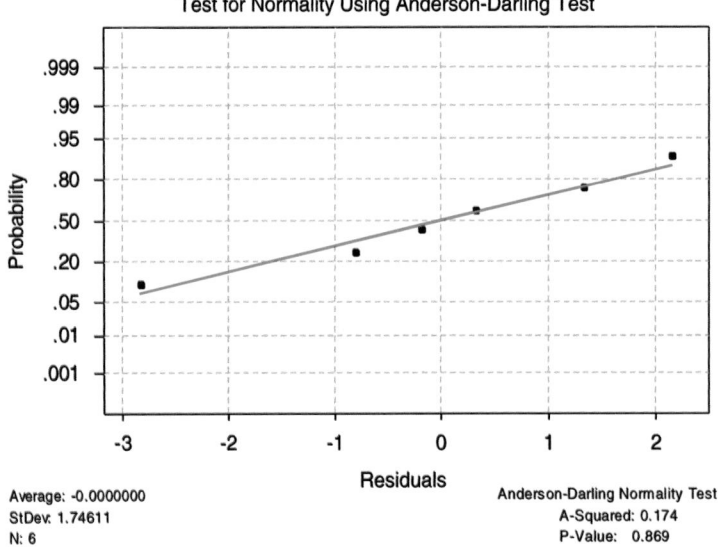

Since the p-value (0.869) is large, we do not have reason to reject the hypothesis of normality.

Self-Testing Review 12.5

30. Before hiring new employees, the personnel director for Worldwide Things, Inc., decides to do a regression analysis of the company's current salary structure. She believes that an employee's salary is related to the number of years of work experience (YEARS) and to the number of years of post–high school education (POSTHSED). The following MINITAB output is produced from the sample data she has gathered:

```
The regression equation is
     SALARY = 29436 + 1306 POSTHSED + 833 YEARS

Predictor        Coef        Stdev              T             p
Constant      29436.2       581.3            50.6         0.000
POSTHSED       1306.1       255.3             5.12        0.000
YEARS           832.63       44.49           18.71        0.000

s = 3164     R-sq = 88.6%      R-sq(adj) = 88.4%

Analysis of Variance
Source        DF           SS              MS            F          p
Regression     2    14792118272      7396059136       738.79    0.000
Error        191     1912102400        10011007
Total        193    16704221184
```

a) What is the dependent (response) variable?

b) What are the independent (explanatory) variables?

c) What are the regression equation values?

d) Predict a salary for an employee with no experience and with no post–high school education.

e) Predict a salary for an employee with six years work experience and with four years post–high school education.

f) Interpret the POSTHSED coefficient of 1,306.

g) Interpret the YEARS coefficient of 833.

h) What is the value of the standard error of estimate?

i) Using the appropriate p-value in the printout, conduct an ANOVA F test of the null hypothesis that $B_{POSTHSED} = B_{YEARS} = 0$ against the alternative hypothesis that at least one of either $B_{POSTHSED}$ or $B_{YEARS} \neq 0$. Use the .05 level of significance.

j) Using the appropriate p-value in the printout, conduct a t test of the null hypothesis that $B_{POSTHSED} = 0$ against the alternative hypothesis that $B_{POSTHSED} \neq 0$. Use the .05 level of significance.

k) Using the appropriate p-value in the printout, conduct a t test of the null hypothesis that $B_{YEARS} = 0$ against the alternative hypothesis that $B_{YEARS} \neq 0$. Use the .05 level of significance.

l) What is the value of the coefficient of determination?

m) Interpret the coefficient of determination in the context of this problem.

31. Here's something new to consider: A multiple regression equation can contain "dummy variables" representing qualitative data. When this is the case, an analyst can substitute a value of 0 if the variable is false, and a value of 1 if it is true for a particular case. *Management Accounting* published a multiple regression equation for estimating salary levels for managers. This equation is

Salary = $22,044 + $23,649 (if on a TOP management level) + $15,766 (if on a SENIOR management level) + $7,883 (if on a MIDDLE management level) + $1,152 (number of years experience in field) + $8,392 (if hold a master's degree) + $8,884 (if hold a CPA certificate) + $3,968 (if hold a CMA certificate) + $7,976 (if a male) – $8,392 (if have no degree)

a) Predict the salary for a male who is on the middle level of management, has eight years experience in the field, and holds a CPA certificate.

b) Predict the salary for a female who is at the top level of management, has 25 years experience in the field, and holds a master's degree and a CMA.

32. In *Comparative Analysis of Fluorescent Lighting with Electronic and Magnetic Ballasts,* Feathers and Foncerrada describe an experiment in which the performances of electronic and magnetic ballasts used in fluorescent lighting were compared. The variables compared included ballast efficiency factor (foot-candles/watt), light output (foot-candles), total harmonic distortion (percent), power factor (watts), and the temperature of the lamp and ballasts (Celsius) themselves. There was a total of ten ballasts, six electronic and four magnetic. The data follows, where type of ballast has been converted to the "dummy variable" *LiteType,* in which 0 represents magnetic ballasts and 1 represents electronic (Data = Ballast):

Type	BEF	LO	THD	PF	Lamp	Blst	LiteType
Mag	0.480	43	12.6	0.991	37.8	33.0	0
Mag	0.490	42	15.6	0.988	40.4	33.2	0
Mag	0.483	43	11.5	0.975	34.7	37.0	0
Mag	0.482	42	16.1	0.987	38.8	35.3	0
Elec	0.583	40	26.6	0.959	30.6	27.5	1
Elec	0.571	41	16.0	0.988	32.2	28.8	1
Elec	0.564	41	23.4	0.966	30.6	27.2	1
Elec	0.576	40	9.8	0.958	37.5	28.9	1
Elec	0.548	39	14.9	0.951	29.7	30.7	1
Elec	0.588	41	32.0	0.952	35.9	20.4	1

A regression analysis by MINITAB resulted in the following output:

```
The regression equation is
BEF = - 0.035 + 0.00819 LO + 0.00182 THD - 0.125 PF + 0.00401
Lamp + 0.00337 Blst + 0.137 LiteType

Predictor       Coef        Stdev          T          P
Constant      -0.0352      0.4246       -0.08      0.939
LO            0.008193     0.006822      1.20      0.316
THD           0.001819     0.001217      1.50      0.232
PF            -0.1253      0.3459       -0.36      0.741
Lamp          0.004008     0.002190      1.83      0.165
Blst          0.003375     0.003531      0.96      0.410
LiteType      0.13660      0.03842       3.56      0.038

s = 0.009649     R-sq = 98.6%     R-sq(adj) = 95.7%

Analysis of Variance

Source        DF          SS            MS          F        P
Regression    6       0.0193612     0.0032269    34.66    0.007
Error         3       0.0002793     0.0000931
Total         9       0.0196405
```

a) Using the appropriate *p*-value in the printout, conduct an ANOVA *F* test of the null hypothesis that $B_{LO} = B_{THD} = B_{PF} = B_{Lamp} = B_{Blst} = B_{LiteType} = 0$ against the alternative hypothesis that at least one of B_{LO} or B_{THD} or B_{PF} or B_{Lamp} or B_{Blst} or $B_{LiteType} \neq 0$. Use the .05 level of significance.

b) Using the appropriate p-value in the printout, conduct a t test of the null hypothesis that $B_{LO} = 0$ against the alternative hypothesis that $B_{LO} \neq 0$. Use the .05 level of significance.

c) Using the appropriate p-value in the printout, conduct a t test of the null hypothesis that $B_{LiteType} = 0$ against the alternative hypothesis that $B_{ListType} \neq 0$. Use the .05 level of significance.

 33. Infections due to *Chlamydia trachomatis* are among the most prevalent of all sexually transmitted diseases. In women these infections often result in pelvic inflammatory disease, which can cause infertility, ectopic pregnancy, and chronic pelvic pain. Health Canada reported the 1997 through 2001 Chlamydia rates per 100,000 women for each province in Canada (the data for seven provinces follow). The subsequent MINITAB output is the result of performing a regression analysis using the 1997 through 2000 Chlamydia rates to estimate the 2001 rates:

| Province | Rate | | | | |
	1997	1998	1999	2000	2001
Newfoundland	98.5	107.5	122.7	181.7	173.3
Nova Scotia	183.9	196.4	220.3	229.6	258.3
Ontario	134.3	150.8	154.8	166.5	180.1
Manitoba	343.9	373.2	364.8	396.6	401.9
Saskatchewan	310.8	312.8	345.4	375.9	397.5
Alberta	243.6	265.2	268.9	288.6	300.8
British Columbia	157.1	169.6	192.5	220.4	197.3

```
The regression equation is
Rate 01 = 66.7 + 2.84 Rate 97 - 1.44 Rate 98 - 0.49 Rate 99
+ 0.189 Rate 00

Predictor      Coef      SECoef        T          P
Constant       66.66     68.35      0.98      0.432
Rate 97         2.837     2.871      0.99      0.427
Rate 98        -1.439     1.393     -1.03      0.410
Rate 99        -0.490     1.496     -0.33      0.774
Rate 00         0.1892    0.5409     0.35      0.760

S = 19.18      R-Sq = 98.7%       R-Sq(adj) = 96.2%

Analysis of Variance

Source              DF       SS        MS         F         P
Regression           4     56670     14167     38.53     0.025
Residual Error       2       735       368
Total                6     57405
```

a) What are the regression equation values?

b) Using the appropriate p-value in the printout, conduct an ANOVA F test of the null hypothesis that all of the B's = 0 against the alternative hypothesis that at least one of the B's $\neq$ 0. Use the .01 level of significance.

c) Using the appropriate p-value in the printout, conduct a t test of the null hypothesis that $B_{00} = 0$ against the alternative hypothesis that $B_{00} \neq 0$. Use the .01 level of significance.

d) Using the appropriate p-value in the printout, conduct a t test of the null hypothesis that $B_{99} = 0$ against the alternative hypothesis that $B_{99} \neq 0$. Use the .01 level of significance.

34. K. Bolen investigated the effects of dietary modifications on the lactate threshold of 12 endurance-trained cyclists. Each cyclist, with a time separation between treatments, consumed two dietary treatments in random order: a high-fat diet and a high carbohydrate diet. Each subject performed a maximum bicycle graded exercise test, and measurements were taken on their lactate threshold (l/min), maximum heart rate (b/min), and performance time. Following is that data for the high-fat diet and the high-carbohydrate diet and MINITAB output for each (Data = Lactate):

FatLT	FatMaxHR	FatTimeE	CarbLT	CarbMaxHR	CarbTimeE
3.60	212	13.26	3.38	211	13.34
3.62	196	12.59	3.25	199	13.23
3.80	180	11.50	3.60	179	11.27
3.25	173	11.40	3.11	170	11.52
4.13	172	14.40	4.12	174	15.16
3.75	192	14.11	4.00	194	14.08
3.77	193	13.38	3.83	197	14.25
2.50	183	10.59	2.85	187	11.23
3.20	176	12.40	3.25	183	13.05
3.85	177	13.37	3.35	177	13.34
4.44	189	13.43	4.25	193	13.38
3.20	180	12.59	3.16	180	14.08

```
The regression equation is
FatTimeE = 4.32 + 1.65 FatLT + 0.0136 FatMaxHR

Predictor        Coef       Stdev         T          p
Constant        4.320       4.154      1.04      0.326
FatLT          1.6476      0.4959      3.32      0.009
FatMaxHR      0.01356     0.02147      0.63      0.543

s = 0.8221     R-sq = 57.5%     R-sq(adj) = 48.0%

Analysis of Variance

Source          DF          SS          MS         F          p
Regression       2      8.2178      4.1089      6.08      0.021
Error            9      6.0823      0.6758
Total           11     14.3002

The regression equation is
Carb Time = 5.17 + 1.61 CarbLT + 0.0126 CarbMaxH

Predictor        Coef       Stdev     t-ratio         p
Constant        5.166       5.503      0.94      0.372
CarbLT         1.6050      0.7528      2.13      0.062
CarbMaxH      0.01261     0.02777      0.45      0.661

s = 1.097     R-sq = 36.2%     R-sq(adj) = 22.1%
```

```
Analysis of Variance

Source        DF         SS        MS       F        p
Regression     2       6.159     3.080    2.56    0.132
Error          9      10.838     1.204
Total         11      16.998
```

For the bikers on the high-fat diet:

a) What are the regression equation values?

b) Using the appropriate p-value in the printout, conduct an ANOVA F test of the null hypothesis that $B_{LT} = B_{MaxH} = 0$ against the alternative hypothesis that at least one of either $B_{LT} = B_{MaxH} \neq 0$. Use the .05 level of significance.

c) Using the appropriate p-value in the printout, conduct a t test of the null hypothesis that $B_{LT} = 0$ against the alternative hypothesis that $B_{LT} \neq 0$. Use the .05 level of significance.

d) Using the appropriate p-value in the printout, conduct a t test of the null hypothesis that $B_{MaxH} = 0$ against the alternative hypothesis that $B_{MaxH} \neq 0$. Use the .05 level of significance.

e) What is the value of the coefficient of determination?

35. Repeat exercises 34a)–34e) for the bikers on the high-carbohydrate diet.

 36. Patrick Madigan examined the relation between systolic and diastolic blood pressure and the heart recovery rate. Subjects in the experiment exercised on a stationary bike until they reached 65 percent of their maximum heart rate. Then the time to recovery of their normal rate was observed. MINITAB was used to obtain a multiple regression equation relating the recovery time (sec) to the other variables (one of the variables is a "dummy" variable for gender where a 0 represents a female and a 1 represents a male) (Data = Recovery).

Age	Gender	Systolic	Diastolic	Recovery
23	M	118	82	183
21	M	110	70	140
22	M	118	80	451
20	F	116	70	131
20	M	126	68	149
21	F	112	62	154
20	F	124	70	183
21	F	108	62	135
21	M	122	82	384

```
The regression equation is
Recovery = - 249 - 12.4 Age - 1.3 Systolic + 12.1 Diastoli + 0
Sex Code

Predictor      Coef      Stdev        T         p
Constant       -249      1988      -0.13     0.906
Age          -12.41     70.16      -0.18     0.868
Systolic      -1.28     10.17      -0.13     0.906
Diastoli      12.14     10.29       1.18     0.303
Sex Code        0.4     112.6       0.00     0.997

s = 117.9      R-sq = 51.0%      R-sq(adj) = 1.9%
```

```
Analysis of Variance

Source          DF        SS         MS        F         p
Regression       4       57775      14444     1.04     0.486
Error            4       55619      13905
Total            8      113394
```

a) Using the appropriate p-value in the printout, conduct an ANOVA F test of the null hypothesis that all of the B's = 0 against the alternative hypothesis that at least one of the B's ≠ 0. Use the .01 level of significance.

b) Using the appropriate p-value in the printout, conduct a t test of the null hypothesis that $B_{Age} = 0$ against the alternative hypothesis that $B_{Age} ≠ 0$. Use the .01 level of significance.

 37. The City of Regina collected data from sales of single family residential units to calculate market adjustment factors for a property reassessment. The data included sale price, lot size, total living area, age, deck area, attached garage area, detached garage area, and finished basement area. A portion of the data follows as well as a MINITAB output that gives a multiple regression equation relating sale price to the other variables. The data in the first three columns is measured in thousands (Data = House):

Sale Price	Lot Size	Total Living Area	Age	Deck Area	Attached Garage Area	Detached Garage Area	Finished Basement Area
67.0	4.00416	1	11	168	0	0	0
63.0	4.28323	0.971	10	0	0	0	0
73.9	4.13426	1	10	0	0	0	0
70.0	4.13426	1	10	0	0	0	0
79.5	5.82876	1.015	8	160	0	480	454
115.0	5.84607	1.256	6	0	450	0	0

```
Regression Analysis

The regression equation is
SalePrice = 24.0 + 1.04 LotSize + 61.6 TotalLivingArea - 1.80
            Age - 0.0112 DeckArea + 0.0292 AttachedGarageArea +
            0.0022 DetachedGarageArea + 0.0090
            FinishedBasementArea

Predictor         Coef        Stdev          T          p
Constant         23.98        15.13        1.58      0.123
LotSize           1.040        2.456        0.42      0.675
TotalLiv         61.571        8.130        7.57      0.000
Age              -1.7955       0.9106      -1.97      0.057
DeckArea         -0.01116      0.01793     -0.62      0.538
Attached          0.029192     0.008859     3.30      0.002
Detached          0.00223      0.01485      0.15      0.882
Finished          0.00899      0.01014      0.89      0.382

s = 10.06     R-sq = 86.7%     R-sq (adj) = 83.8%

Analysis of Variance

Source           DF         SS         MS         F          p
Regression        7      21122.6     3017.5     29.83      0.000
Residual Error   32       3237.56     101.2
Total            39      24360.1
```

a) What are the regression equation values?

b) Using the appropriate p-value in the printout, conduct an ANOVA F test of the null hypothesis that all of the B's = 0 against the alternative hypothesis that at least one of the B's ≠ 0. Use the .01 level of significance.

c) Using the appropriate p-value in the printout, conduct a t test of the null hypothesis that $B_{Attached}$ = 0 against the alternative hypothesis that $B_{Attached}$ ≠ 0. Use the .01 level of significance.

d) Using the appropriate p-value in the printout, conduct a t test of the null hypothesis that $B_{Finished}$ = 0 against the alternative hypothesis that $B_{Finished}$ ≠ 0. Use the .01 level of significance.

e) What is the value of the coefficient of determination?

38. R. Hurstak described a procedure in which 135 redwood trees at the Big Creek Lumber Company in Santa Cruz, California, were scaled to determine their cubic-foot volume. Additionally, the trees' bark thickness, diameter at 16 feet, diameter at breast height, form class (an indication of the taper of the tree), and height were measured. A portion of the data follows. MINITAB was used to obtain a multiple regression equation relating the tree volume to the other variables (Data = BigCreek):

Bark Thickness	Diameter 16"	Diameter Breast	Form Class	Height	Volume
0.6	15.9	21.1	75.3	162.8	105.7
1.5	19.0	26.2	72.5	150.0	139.9
0.9	10.1	16.9	60.0	115.5	36.7
2.0	14.3	28.0	51.1	106.5	74.8
1.1	15.9	24.3	65.3	115.5	96.7
2.1	20.6	32.5	63.3	139.5	152.1
0.5	5.8	10.9	53.1	85.0	10.5

```
The regression equation is
Volume = -183 + 2.92 Barkthck + 15.0 Diam16 + 1.55 DiamBrst
             - 0.0472 FrmClass + 0.0770 Height


Predictor        Coef      Stdev         T         p
Constant      -182.81      18.02    -10.15     0.000
Barkthck         2.920      9.032      0.32     0.747
Diam16          14.955      1.728      8.65     0.000
DiamBrst         1.547      1.359      1.14     0.257
FrmClass      -0.04722    0.08553     -0.55     0.582
Height         0.07701    0.08300      0.93     0.355


s = 60.17      R-sq = 83.2%      R-sq(adj) = 82.6%


Analysis of Variance

Source        DF          SS         MS         F         p
Regression     5     2315117     463023    127.90     0.000
Error        129      466990       3620
Total        134     2782107
```

a) What are the regression equation values?

b) Using the appropriate p-value in the printout, conduct an ANOVA F test of the null hypothesis that all of the B's $= 0$ against the alternative hypothesis that at least one of the B's $\neq 0$. Use the .05 level of significance.

c) Using the appropriate p-value in the printout, conduct a t test of the null hypothesis that $B_{Diam16} = 0$ against the alternative hypothesis that $B_{Diam16} \neq 0$. Use the .05 level of significance.

d) Using the appropriate p-value in the printout, conduct a t test of the null hypothesis that $B_{DiamBrst} = 0$ against the alternative hypothesis that $B_{DiamBrst} \neq 0$. Use the .05 level of significance.

L O O K I N G   B A C K

1. In regression analysis, an estimating equation is developed to describe the relationship that exists between the variables. As the name implies, an analyst prepares an estimating, or regression, equation to make estimates of values of one variable from given values of one or more other variables. The variable to be estimated is called the dependent (y) variable. The variable(s) that presumably exerts an influence on or explains variations in the dependent variable is termed the independent, or predictive, variable and is identified by the symbol x. The purpose of regression analysis is to determine the pattern of the existing relationship between the variables. The focus of correlation analysis is to measure the strength or closeness of the relationship between the variables that is described in the regression equation.

2. The fact that two or more variables are associated in a statistical sense does not guarantee the existence of a causal relationship. An early step in the study of regression and correlation is to see if a logical relationship may exist between the variables to support further analysis. After determining that a logical relationship may exist between two variables, a scatter diagram is often prepared. Each point on this graph represents a study member for which we have a value for both the y and x variables. Such a graph can help show if there's a useful relationship between the variables, and it can suggest the type of equation to use to describe the relationship. Our focus in this chapter has been on relationships that can be expressed with a straight line, but other possibilities exist.

3. In the simple linear regression case, the method of least squares is used to fit a straight line to the observed data. Once the values for a (the y intercept) and b (the slope of the line) are computed, the regression equation may be used to make a preliminary point estimate of the value of the y variable, given a value for the x variable. A regression plane replaces the regression line in multiple linear regression. The standard error of estimate is a standard deviation that's used to qualify the point estimate mode with the regression equation by showing the extent of the possible variation that may be present.

4. To see if a true statistical relationship exists between the x and y variables, t tests for slope may be carried out in simple and multiple regression analyses. The null hypothesis in such a test is that the slope of the population re-

gression coefficient is zero. If this hypothesis is true, then there's no meaningful regression relationship between the variables. A familiar seven-step procedure is used to conduct such tests. An ANOVA test gives the same results as a t test for slope when only two variables are considered, but the ANOVA procedure can also be used in multiple regression situations to examine the total regression effect that all the predicting (x) variables have on the y variable.

5. A probability value can be assigned to an interval estimate of the y variable that can be produced using the regression equation. Two types of interval estimates are described in the chapter—one that estimates the *average* value of y given an x value(s) and another that predicts a *specific* value of y given an x value(s). Both types of intervals are easily produced by computer statistical programs.

6. The coefficient of correlation is a measure of the strength of the linear relationship between two variables x and y. The value of this coefficient is always between −1.00 and 1.00. When the value is zero, there's no linear correlation and when it's −1 or +1, there's perfect linear correlation. The coefficient of determination in the simple linear case (r^2) measures the percentage of variation in the y variable that's explained by the variation in the x variable. Similarly, the coefficient of multiple determination measures the variation in the y variable that is explained by its relation to x_1 and x_2 (when we have two independent variables).

Exercises

39. Is there a relationship between the price of a CD and the number sold? The following data represent the price ($) and the corresponding weekly sales in a sample of 12 stores (Data = CDs):

Store	Price (x)	Weekly Sales (y)
1	11	28
2	11	29
3	13	27
4	14	25
5	14	23
6	14	24
7	15	22
8	19	20
9	14	24
10	11	30
11	20	18
12	20	19

a) Construct a scatter diagram for the paired data.

b) Compute the regression equation, and fit it to the scatter diagram.

c) Use the regression equation to prepare a point estimate of the number sold when the price is $12.

d) Compute the standard error of estimate.

e) Conduct a t test for slope. Does a true relationship exist between weekly sales and price at the .05 level?

f) Obtain a scatterplot of the residuals versus the fitted values. What does the plot indicate?

g) Obtain a Normal Probability Plot of the residuals and perform a test for normality.

h) Form a 95 percent confidence interval for the average weekly sales when the price is $12.

i) Form a 95 percent prediction interval for the sales during a particular week when the price is $12.

j) Compute the coefficient of determination.

k) Compute the coefficient of correlation and test the hypothesis that $\rho = 0$ against the hypothesis that $\rho \neq 0$. Is there a significant correlation between price and sales?

40. Physical therapists must often determine the ideal crutch length for their patients. Many therapists use the patient's self-reported height to arrive at this crutch length. The following table appeared in *Physical Therapy* magazine (Data = Crutch):

Patient	Self-Reported Height in Inches (x)	Crutch Length in Inches (y)
1	64	48.5
2	65	49.0
3	66	49.5
4	67	50.5
5	68	51.0
6	69	51.5
7	70	52.5
8	71	53.0
9	72	54.0
10	73	54.5
11	74	55.0
12	75	56.0
13	76	56.5

a) Construct a scatter diagram for the paired data.

b) Compute the regression equation, and fit it to the scatter diagram.

c) Use the regression equation to prepare a point estimate of the crutch length for a patient with a self-reported height of 70.5 inches.

d) Compute the standard error of estimate.

e) Conduct a t test for slope. Does a true relationship exist between the self-reported height and the crutch length at the .05 level?

f) Obtain a scatterplot of the residuals versus the fitted values. What does the plot indicate?

l) Obtain a Normal Probability Plot of the residuals and perform a test for normality.

h) Form a 95 percent confidence interval for the average crutch length for patients who report their height as 68 inches.

i) Form a 95 percent prediction interval for the crutch length that Will B. Walker needs if his self-reported height is 68 inches.

j) Compute the coefficient of determination.

k) Compute the coefficient of correlation and test the hypothesis that $\rho = 0$ against the hypothesis that $\rho \neq 0$. Is there a significant correlation between height and crutch length?

41. The percentage of body fat was measured on the participants in a class on jogging and circuit training. The measurements, taken before and after the class, appear below (Data = ClassFat):

Pre	Post	Pre	Post
5.6	7.1	11.6	11.2
8.2	7.5	11.0	11.2
12.2	12.7	9.6	10.5
10.2	10.8	7.8	8.9
6.6	8.8	11.0	12.4
7.8	8.1	7.8	9.4
7.4	8.3	11.6	9.2
6.8	7.4	9.4	7.6
10.7	8.3	6.8	6.8
6.3	5.6	7.2	7.7
9.8	8.7	10.2	10.6

a) Compute the regression equation.

b) Conduct a t test for slope. Does a true relationship exist at the .05 level between the body fat measurements before and after the class?

c) Form a 95 percent confidence interval for the average postclass body fat of people with preclass body fat of 12 percent.

d) Form a 95 percent prediction interval for the postclass body fat of a student, whose preclass body fat was 6 percent.

42. A counsellor wants to see if there's a relationship between a student's score on the Peabody Individual Achievement Test (PIAT) and the same student's score on the Wide Range Achievement Test (WRAT). On consecutive days, he administered the reading subsets of both tests to a random sample of ten students in second grade. The results are as follows (Data = PIATWRAT):

Student	PIAT (x)	WRAT (y)
1	17	20
2	21	28
3	22	32
4	25	33
5	25	38
6	31	40
7	31	44
8	35	45
9	36	46
10	44	53

a) Draw a scattergram of the sample, using the WRAT score as the dependent (response) variable.

b) Compute the regression equation.

c) Use the regression equation to prepare a point estimate of the WRAT score for a child with a PIAT score of 40.

d) Compute the standard error of estimate.

e) Conduct a *t* test for slope. Does a true relationship exist between the PIAT and WRAT scores at the .05 level?

43. A company hired a fitness director and established a health program for its employees. As part of the evaluation of the program, baseline values for the body mass index (BMI) for a sample of 16 employees were first measured at the beginning of the program, and a similar measure was then taken again after two years in the program. The data follow (Data = Incentiv):

Employee	Baseline BMI (*x*)	Two-Year BMI (*y*)
1	26.97	26.02
2	25.64	25.87
3	25.12	25.02
4	25.57	25.46
5	26.09	25.70
6	26.17	26.10
7	25.92	26.24
8	25.68	26.57
9	25.07	24.57
10	25.70	25.18
11	26.61	26.84
12	26.34	26.31
13	26.34	26.22
14	25.70	25.61
15	26.30	26.42
16	25.84	25.16

a) Compute the regression equation.

b) Use the regression equation to prepare a point estimate of an employee's BMI after two years in the program if he or she had a baseline BMI of 25.50.

c) Compute the standard error of estimate.

d) Compute the coefficient of determination.

e) Compute the coefficient of correlation.

44. A stockbroker believes there's a relationship between the price of AQR stock and the price of Amcorp stock. The following data represent prices for each of these stocks for a random sample of six Fridays:

Price of AQR Stock (in $)	Price of Amcorp Stock (in $)
51 3/8	21 3/8
50 5/8	20 1/4
51 1/2	21
50 3/4	20 3/8
52 3/4	21 7/8
50 1/8	20 1/2

a) Compute the regression equation using the AQR stock price as the explanatory variable and the Amcorp stock price as the dependent variable.

b) Use the regression equation to prepare a point estimate of the Amcorp stock price when the price of AQR stock is $52.00.

c) Compute the coefficient of correlation.

d) Compute the coefficient of determination.

45. In a class project, J. Scott hypothesized that there would be a relationship between the number of datagrams lost and the number of nodes between a host and a remote host. He used the UNIX "ping" and "traceroute" commands to collect the following data (Data = Ping):

Lost	Nodes	Lost	Nodes
0	0	10	15
1	3	10	12
12	14	7	13
14	19	1	6
5	18	1	5
12	19	4	17
0	3	26	28
3	3	4	15
3	14	6	15
21	18	5	11

a) Compute the regression equation using the number of nodes between a host and a remote host to predict the number of datagrams lost.

b) Use the regression equation to prepare a point estimate of the number of datagrams lost when there are 12 nodes between a host and a remote host.

c) Conduct a *t* test for slope. Does a true relationship exist between the number of datagrams lost and the number of nodes between a host and a remote host at the .05 level?

d) Form a 95 percent confidence interval for the average number of datagrams lost when there are 12 nodes between a host and a remote host.

e) Form a 95 percent prediction interval for the number of datagrams lost when there are 12 nodes between a host and a remote host.

f) Compute the coefficient of determination.

g) Compute the coefficient of correlation.

46. A group of psychiatrists studied a sample of autistic children. The following MINITAB output was produced using some of their data:

```
The regression equation is
behaviour = 6.3 + 9.08 developm + 0.119 cbfmean

Predictor      Coef      Stdev       T         p
Constant       6.25      16.71      0.37      0.713
developm       9.082      1.691     5.37      0.000
cbfmean        0.1186     0.2208    0.54      0.598

s = 10.22      R-sq = 61.6%       R-sq (adj) = 57.4%

Analysis of variance

Source          DF        SS         MS         F         P
Regression       2      3018.2     1509.1     14.45     0.000
Error           18      1880.1      104.4
Total           20      4898.3

Source          DF       SEQ        SS
developm         1      2988.0
cbfmean          1        30.2
```

a) What is the regression equation?

b) What is the dependent or response variable?

c) What are the independent or explanatory variables?

d) What is the value of the standard error of estimate?

e) What is the value of the coefficient of determination?

f) Using the appropriate p-value in the printout, conduct a t test of the null hypothesis that $B_{developm} = 0$ against the alternative that $B_{developm} \neq 0$. Use the .05 level of significance.

g) Using the appropriate p-value in the printout, conduct a t test of the null hypothesis that $B_{cbfmean} = 0$ against the alternative that $B_{cbfmean} \neq 0$. Use the .05 level of significance.

h) Prepare a point estimate for a behaviour score for an autistic child with a development score of 3 and a cbfmean of 65.

47. Measurements were made on a variety of attributes believed to influence algae growth in a creek. These included water velocity (m/sec), volume rate flow (m³/sec), rainfall (cm, 11 days before sampling), ammonia (NH₄-mg/L), nitrite (NO₂-mg/L), nitrate (NO₃-mg/L), phosphate (PO₄-mg/L), dissolved oxygen (ppm), saturation of oxygen (percent), total dissolved solids (mg/L), leaves (percent cover), roots (percent cover), stems (percent cover), light (footcandles), and algae (percent cover). A few lines of data follow. MINITAB was used to obtain a multiple regression equation relating algae to the other variables (Data = Algae):

Vel	Vol	Rain	NH₄	NO₂	NO₃	PO₄	DO	SAT	TDS	Lev	Root	Stem	Lt	Alg
0.6	0.03	0.3	0	0	0.3	0	9.3	86	0.325	6	10.6	6	55	0
0.3	0.01	0.3	0	0	0.6	0	9.7	92	0.353	4.6	15	0.4	69	1.3
0.5	0.02	0.3	0	0	0.9	0	10.2	93	0.345	2.6	0.4	0.4	77	0
0.5	0.32	0.3	0	0	4.2	0	9.2	88	0.402	5.2	15.8	7.8	71	3.2
0.1	0.07	0.3	0	0	2.6	0	9.2	87	0.322	0	17	0	56	0
0.7	0.41	0.3	0	0	3.5	0	10.2	96	0.423	1.2	16.8	3.2	38	27.6

```
The regression equation is
Alg = 76.7 - 25.2 Vel + 16.0 Vol + 1.09 Rain + 1.63 NH4 - 29.3 NO2
+ 0.346 NO3 - 1.53 PO4 - 13.4 DO + 1.02 SAT - 73.7 TDS - 0.543 Lev
- 0.330 Root + 1.68 Stem + 0.010 Lt

Predictor        Coef      Stdev          T          p
Constant        76.68      26.54       2.89      0.006
Vel            -25.16      16.06      -1.57      0.123
Vol             16.04      11.72       1.37      0.177
Rain            1.087      2.953       0.37      0.714
NH4             1.631      5.375       0.30      0.763
NO2            -29.26      25.19      -1.16      0.251
NO3            0.3457     0.6153       0.56      0.577
PO4            -1.525      4.130      -0.37      0.713
DO            -13.389      7.716      -1.74      0.089
SAT           1.0212     0.7627       1.34      0.187
TDS            -73.75      35.94      -2.05      0.045
Lev           -0.5426     0.4768      -1.14      0.260
Root          -0.3299     0.3633      -0.91      0.368
Stem           1.6846     0.8521       1.98      0.053
Lt             0.0098     0.1062       0.09      0.927

s = 16.33     R-sq = 38.4%      R-sq(adj) = 21.5%

Analysis of Variance

Source          DF         SS         MS          F          p
Regression      14     8483.6      606.0       2.27      0.017
Error           51    13604.9      266.8
Total           65    22088.5
```

a) How many independent variables are involved in this regression model?

b) How many degrees of freedom are available for any t test on an independent variable?

c) Why would the y intercept have a meaningless interpretation for this regression equation?

d) What are the regression equation values?

e) Using the appropriate p-value in the printout, conduct an ANOVA F test of the null hypothesis that all of the B's $= 0$ against the alternative hypothesis that at least one of the B's $\neq 0$. Use the .05 level of significance.

f) Using the appropriate p-value in the printout, conduct at t test of the null hypothesis that $B_{Rain} = 0$ against the alternative hypothesis that $B_{Rain} \neq 0$. Use the .05 level of significance.

g) Using the appropriate p-value in the printout, conduct a t test of the null hypothesis that $B_{TDS} = 0$ against the alternative hypothesis that $B_{TDS} \neq 0$. Use the .05 level of significance.

h) Test the hypothesis that $B_{NH_4} = B_{NO_2} = B_{NO_3} = 0$ against the alternative hypothesis that at least one of B_{NH_4}, B_{NO_2}, $B_{NO_3} \neq 0$. The output listed below is the MINITAB output for the reduced model. Use $\alpha = .05$:

The MINITAB Ouput for the Reduced Model

```
The regression equation is
Alg = 76.2 - 18.9 Vel + 7.94 Vol + 1.68 Rain - 2.08 PO4
      - 16.6 DO + 1.29 SAT - 59.4 TDS - 0.746 Lev - 0.376 Root
      + 1.40 Stem + 0.041 Lt

Analysis of Variance

Source           DF         SS         MS          F          P
Regression       11     8051.6      732.0       2.82      0.006
Residual Error   54    14036.8      259.9
Total            65    22088.5
```

48. Data were collected on the possible effects of a landfill on surface and groundwater chemistry. The data included observations on characteristics of well water for several wells, a few lines of which follow. MINITAB was used for the data from one of the wells, relating total dissolved solids (TDS) to pH, conductivity, and chemical oxygen demand (COD) (Data = LOWatTDS):

pH (pH)	Conductivity μhos/cm	COD mg/L	TDS mg/L
7.03	3,060	175	2,000
6.63	3,310	160	2,200
6.82	2,400	115	1,510
6.60	2,450	167	1,752
6.70	2,270	238	1,881
6.40	2,780	171	2,000

```
The regression equation is
TDS = 1796 - 142 pH + 0.241 Conducty + 2.60 COD

Predictor      Coef      Stdev        T          p
Constant      1796.3     886.6       2.03      0.051
pH            -142.2     132.6      -1.07      0.292
Conducty      0.2414    0.1068      2.26      0.031
COD           2.5980    0.8859      2.93      0.006

s = 190.0    R-sq = 47.0%    R-sq(adj) = 41.8%

Analysis of Variance

Source       DF        SS        MS        F        p
Regression   3.       991505    330502    9.15    0.000
Error        31      1119543     36114
Total        34      2111048
```

a) What are the regression equation values?

b) Using the appropriate p-value in the printout, conduct an ANOVA F test of the null hypothesis that all of the B's = 0 against the alternative hypothesis that at least one of the B's ≠ 0. Use the .05 level of significance.

c) Using the appropriate p-value in the printout, conduct a t test of the null hypothesis that $B_{pH} = 0$ against the alternative hypothesis that $B_{pH} \neq 0$. Use the .05 level of significance.

d) Test the hypothesis H_0: $B_{PH} = B_{COD} = 0$ against the alternative hypothesis that at least one of B_{PH}, $B_{COD} \neq 0$. The output listed below is the MINITAB output for the reduced model. Use $\alpha = .05$.

```
The regression equation is
TDS = 763 + 0.386 Conducty

S = 210.3 R-Sq = 30.9% R-Sq(adj) = 28.8%

Analysis of Variance

Source           DF        SS        MS        F        P
Regression        1      651650    651650    14.74    0.001
Residual Error    33     1459398    44224
Total             34     2111048
```

e) Using the appropriate p-value in the printout, conduct a t test of the null hypothesis that $B_{COD} = 0$ against the alternative hypothesis that $B_{COD} \neq 0$. Use the .05 level of significance.

49. Nick Billings, a statistics student at the University of Regina and a member of the Rams football team collected Canadian Interuniversity Sport Football data and used multiple regression to investigate which variables are significantly related to the number of points scored in a game of football. The data given below are entered into MINITAB:

Team	Points Per Game	RushAtt	Rush Yards	Pass Yards	Int	AvpuntRet
Acadia	25.6	29.25	106.4	223	1.5	6.93
Mt. Allison	7.5	26.75	27.1	129.8	2.25	4.71
St. Mary's	26.9	37	247.8	263.1	0.88	9.65
St. FX	39.1	36	177.5	187.2	1.13	14.4
Bishop's	15.9	21.8	90.3	231.7	2.33	9.4
Concordia	25.2	24.5	119.6	219.4	1.3	7.1
Laval	36.9	31.89	191.2	251.3	0.88	11.4
McGill	35.3	28.7	157.5	242.7	0.8	8
Montreal	7.8	33.6	111.6	97.2	1.63	4.8
Alberta	17.4	24.63	109.8	228.8	1	9.8
UBC	18	22.25	98.8	195.9	1.5	9.2
Calgary	24.2	29.13	157.9	275.6	0.88	9.1
Manitoba	33.9	30	158.1	301.6	1	7.1
Regina	21.1	26.88	149.9	233.9	1.13	7.5
Sask.	20.2	24.38	153.4	231.8	1.13	10.3
SFU	13.8	23.25	115.4	192.9	1.13	4.76
Guelph	12.75	23.5	84.88	189.25	2	8.13
Laurier	18.75	30.88	159	124.63	1.13	9.6
McMaster	38.75	51.7	327.25	250.25	1.13	9.17
Ottawa	27.5	31.63	195.88	288	1.88	11.27
Queen's	33.88	30.88	148.63	543.88	1.75	9.74
Toronto	8.63	27.88	97.13	101.13	1.38	7.51
Waterloo	13.88	32.13	176.75	192.63	1.63	7.86
Western	35.75	36.5	217.63	464.38	1.38	9.12
Windsor	13.63	23.25	127.63	161.25	2	12.54
York	15.13	31	134.25	187	2.13	9.25

```
PointsPerGame is the average number of points scored per game
RushAtt       is the average number of rushing attempts per game
Rush Yards    is the average number of rushing yards made per game
Rush Yards    is the average number of passing yards made per game
Int           is the average number of interceptions given up per game
AvPuntRet     is the average punt return yardage per game
```

The regression equation is

PointsPerGame = –5.03 + 0.686 RushAtt – 0.0305 Rush Yards + 0.0519 Pass Yards –8.82 Int + 1.41 AvpuntRet

```
Predictor      Coef      StDev        T         P
Constant     -5.029      8.242     -0.61     0.549
RushAtt       0.6856     0.3336     2.06     0.053
Rush Yard    -0.03045    0.04463   -0.68     0.503
Pass Yard     0.05189    0.01175    4.42     0.000
Int          -8.817      2.739     -3.22     0.004
AvpuntRe      1.4063     0.5390     2.61     0.017
```

S = 5.082 R-Sq = 79.6% R-Sq(adj) = 74.5%

Analysis of Variance

```
Source            DF        SS         MS        F         P
Regression         5    2015.91     403.18    15.61    0.000
Residual Error    20     516.51      25.83
Total             25    2532.42
```

a) What are the regression equation values?

b) Using the appropriate p-value in the printout, conduct an ANOVA F test of the null hypothesis that all of the B's $= 0$ against the alternative hypothesis that at least one of the B's is not equal to 0. Use the .05 level of significance.

c) Using the appropriate p-value in the printout, conduct a t test of the null hypothesis that $B_{\text{AVPuntRet}}$ is equal to 0

against the alternative hypothesis that $B_{\text{AvPuntRet}}$ is not equal to 0. Use the .05 level of significance.

d) Using the appropriate p-value in the printout, conduct a t test of the null hypothesis that B_{RushAtt} is equal to 0 against the alternative hypothesis that B_{RushAtt} is not equal to 0. Use the .05 level of significance.

Topics for Review and Discussion

1. What are the purposes of regression and correlation analysis?

2. If there is a strong correlation between two variables, there is also a cause-and-effect relationship. Argue for or against this statement.

3. What information can you obtain from a scatter diagram?

4. In using the method of least squares to obtain $\hat{y} = a + bx$, what two quantities must be calculated using the coordinates of all the data points?

5. What is the standard error of estimate? How can it be used when making predictions from the regression equation? What does a large standard error indicate?

6. Discuss the purpose of the t test for slope. What are the hypotheses?

7. How can the ANOVA results obtained from a MINITAB printout give an indication of the significance of the regression relationship? Explain the meaning of SSR, SSE, and SST.

8. Discuss the two types of prediction intervals described in this chapter. Which interval is always larger for the same value of the independent variable? Why?

9. Explain the concepts of the total deviation, the explained deviation, and the unexplained deviation. What is the total variation, the explained variation, and the unexplained variation?

10. What is the coefficient of determination? What information does it give about the regression relationship?

11. What is the correlation coefficient? Why is its sign always the same as that of the slope of the line?

12. Discuss some of the common errors and limitations of correlation analysis.

13. What are the advantages of using multiple linear regression instead of simple linear regression? What is the disadvantage when you don't have access to a computer statistical package?

14. Explain the meaning of the slope coefficient for each variable in a MINITAB multiple regression printout.

15. Explain the meaning of the constant in a multiple regression printout.

Projects/Issues to Consider

1. Locate an article in a library periodical that contains data appropriate for a linear regression analysis. Prepare a scatter diagram, compute the regression equation, the standard error of estimate, the coefficient of determination, and the coefficient of correlation. Choose an appropriate value for the independent variable and form a 95 percent confidence interval for the average value of the corresponding dependent variable. Next, use the same independent variable and form a prediction interval for a specific value of the corresponding dependent variable. Use a t test to test the significance of the slope coefficient. Discuss your findings.

2. Locate a Web site that contains data appropriate for a linear regression analysis. Prepare a scatter diagram, compute the

regression equation, the standard error of estimate, the coefficient of determination, and the coefficient of correlation. Choose an appropriate value for the independent variable and form a 95 percent confidence interval for the average value of the corresponding dependent variable. Next, use the same independent variable and form a prediction interval for a specific value of the corresponding dependent variable. Use a t test to test the significance of the slope coefficient. Discuss your findings.

3. Describe three pairs of variables that have a positive linear correlation. Next, discuss three pairs that have a negative correlation. And finally, describe three pairs of variables that have no significant correlation.

4. Take a sample of students and ask them how many hours they study in a week and their GPA. Prepare a scatter diagram, compute the regression equation, the standard error of estimate, the coefficient of determination, and the coefficient of correlation. Form a 95 percent confidence interval for the average GPA of a student who studies 15 hours/week. Next, form a 95 percent prediction interval for the specific GPA of a student who studies 15 hours/week. Use a t test to test the significance of the slope coefficient. Discuss your findings.

Computer/Calculator Exercises

1. A charitable organization operates many shelters to feed the homeless in cities across the nation. A random sample of eight such facilities produced the following data:

Shelter	Monthly Food Costs ($000) ($y$)	Number of People Served Monthly (Hundreds) (x_1)	Monthly Charitable Receipts ($000) ($x_2$)
1	3	24	8
2	2	20	5
3	4	26	10
4	5	32	9
5	1	11	4
6	8	59	14
7	6	63	8
8	4	30	7

After labelling the above columns "COSTS," "SERVED," and "RECEIPTS," use your software to

a) Compute the multiple regression equation for this data set.

b) Determine the value of the standard error of estimate.

c) Determine the value of the coefficient of determination.

d) Conduct an ANOVA F test of the null hypothesis that both B's $= 0$ against the alternative that at least one of the B's $= 0$. Use the .05 level of significance.

e) Conduct a t test of the null hypothesis that $B_{\text{SERVED}} = 0$ against the alternative that $B_{\text{SERVED}} \neq 0$. Use the .05 level of significance.

f) Conduct a t test of the null hypothesis that $B_{\text{RECEIPTS}} = 0$ against the alternative that $B_{\text{RECEIPTS}} \neq 0$. Use the .05 level of significance.

g) Prepare a point estimate of the monthly food costs for a shelter that feeds 4,000 monthly and receives $11,000 in monthly charitable contributions.

2. Eddie Grannis is a science teacher who presented data from five of his science classes. He wanted to see if student perfor-mance early in the semester would be a good predictor of future performance in his classes. So he collected two variables: (1) the student scores on the first unit test in a semester and (2) the total scores the students received in the remainder of the semester. The first few lines of data follow (Data = SciGrade):

Test 1	Total
18	80
14	81
10	64
19	86
17	86
18	86

a) For the full data set, construct a scatter diagram.

b) Compute the regression equation and fit it to the scatter diagram.

c) Use the regression equation to prepare a point estimate of the total score a student would receive in the remainder of the semester if her score on the first unit test is 17.

d) Compute the standard error of estimate.

e) Conduct a t test for the slope. Does a true relationship exist between the scores on the first unit test in a semester and the total scores students receive in the remainder of the semester at the .05 level?

f) Form a 95 percent confidence interval for the average of the total scores students receive in the remainder of the semester if they score 17 on the first unit test.

g) Form a 95 percent prediction interval for the total score received in the remainder of the semester for a student who scores 17 on the first unit test.

h) Compute the coefficient of determination.

i) Compute the coefficient of correlation.

3. Rebecca Just presented data on a sample of 59 students from a graduating class of 429 business administration majors. The variables include college GPA, high school GPA, number of units repeated, number of quarters on academic probation, number of withdrawals, number of units for which a student received a "No Credit" grade, and the number of quarters a student was on the dean's list. A few lines of the data follow (Data = BusMajor):

College GPA	HS GPA	Repeats	AP	With-drawals	No Credit	Dean's List
2.547	3.30	11	3	16	3	0
2.895	3.39	4	0	0	0	0
3.617	3.71	0	0	0	0	9
3.721	3.86	0	0	0	0	10
3.044	3.58	0	0	0	0	0
3.558	4.04	0	0	4	0	0
3.350	4.05	0	1	0	0	0
3.045	4.09	3	0	0	0	0

a) For the complete data set, construct a scatter diagram of college GPA versus high school GPA.

b) Compute the regression equation relating college GPA to high school GPA, and fit it to the scatter diagram.

c) Use the regression equation to prepare a point estimate of the college GPA for a student whose high school GPA was 3.2.

d) Compute the standard error of estimate.

e) Conduct a t test for the slope. Does a true relationship exist between college GPA and high school GPA at the .01 level?

f) Form a 99 percent confidence interval for the average college GPA for students whose high school GPA was 3.2.

g) Form a 99 percent prediction interval for the college GPA for a student whose high school GPA was 3.2.

h) Compute the coefficient of determination.

i) Compute the coefficient of correlation.

j) Use statistical software to obtain the multiple regression equation relating college GPA to the other variables.

k) What are the regression equation values?

l) What is the value of the standard error of estimate?

m) Conduct an ANOVA F test of the null hypothesis that all of the B's = 0 against the alternative hypothesis that at least one of the B's $\neq$ 0. Use the .05 level of significance.

n) Using the appropriate p-value in the printout, conduct a t test of the null hypothesis that $B_{AP} = 0$ against the alternative hypothesis that $B_{AP} \neq 0$. Use the .05 level of significance.

o) Using the appropriate p-value in the printout, conduct a t test of the null hypothesis that $B_{DeanList} = 0$ against the alternative hypothesis that $B_{DeanList} \neq 0$. Use the .05 level of significance.

p) What is the value of the coefficient of determination?

q) Interpret the coefficient of determination in the context of this problem.

 4. Use the World Wide Web to access the Data and Story Library at DASLMeth. Click on *Scatterplot* and select one of the stories. Draw a scatter diagram for the data. State if you think there's a positive linear relationship, a negative linear relationship, or no relationship.

 5. Use the World Wide Web to access the Data and Story Library at DASLMeth. Click on *Correlation* and select one of the stories.

a) Compute the coefficient of determination.

b) Interpret the coefficient of determination within the context of this problem.

c) Compute the coefficient of correlation.

 6. Use the World Wide Web to access the Data and Story Library at DASLMeth. Click on *Simple Linear Regression* and select one of the stories.

a) Write the equation for the line of regression.

b) Estimate the mean response for the mean of the independent variable.

c) Calculate the standard error of estimate.

d) Conduct a t test for the slope at the .05 level.

e) Calculate a 95 percent confidence interval for the slope.

f) Compute a 95 percent confidence interval estimate of the average response for the mean of the independent variable.

g) Compute a 95 percent prediction interval estimate of the response for the mean of the independent variable.

 7. Use the World Wide Web to access the Data and Story Library at DASLMeth. Click on *Regression* and select one of the stories. Using the methods of this chapter, write a report on the relationship between the two variables that you found.

 8. A substantial amount of information about U.S. agriculture production can be found on the home page of the National Agricultural Statistics Service (U.S. Dept. of Agriculture) at USDANASS. Access that page and find a data set on dairy production for a recent year. Using the methods of this chapter, write a report on the relationship between the two variables that you found.

9. The NOAA Paleoclimatology Program, National Snow and Ice Data Center (NSIDC), and the World Data Centers for Paleoclimatology and for Glaciology (Snow and Ice) jointly maintain archives of ice core data from throughout the world. Access the Web site at NSIDC and write a report on the relationship you found between temperature (independent variable) and salinity (response variable).

10. Use the World Wide Web to access the Data and Story Library at DASLMeth. Click on *Multivariate Regression* and select one of the stories.

    a) What is the dependent (response) variable?

    b) What are the independent (explanatory) variables?

    c) What are the regression equation values?

    d) Using the appropriate *p*-value in the printout, conduct an ANOVA *F* test of the null hypothesis that all of the B's $= 0$ against the alternative hypothesis that at least one of the B's $\neq 0$. Use the .05 level of significance.

    e) Using the appropriate *p*-value in the printout, conduct a *t* test of the null hypothesis that the first $B = 0$ against the alternative hypothesis that the first $B \neq 0$. Use the .05 level of significance.

    f) What is the value of the coefficient of determination?

    g) Interpret the coefficient of determination in the context of this problem.

CHAPTER 13

Non-parametric Statistical Methods

LOOKING AHEAD

There are entire books that deal with the subject of non-parametric statistics. However, we can consider only a few of the more commonly used procedures in a single chapter. In order of presentation, the non-parametric methods considered in this chapter are the (1) sign test, (2) Wilcoxon signed rank test, (3) Mann-Whitney test, (4) Kruskal-Wallis test, (5) runs test for randomness, and (6) Spearman rank correlation coefficient. Although most of these techniques can be used in both large- and small-sample situations, we'll limit our attention primarily to the small-sample cases.

Thus, after studying this chapter, you should be able to

- Identify situations that call for the use of particular non-parametric methods.

- Apply sign test procedures for both small and large samples to see if there are likely to be differences between pairs of ordinal data.

- Apply the Wilcoxon signed rank test in small-sample situations when the size as well as the direction of the differences between pairs of ordinal data are available.

- Use the Mann-Whitney test to see if two small independent random samples are taken from identical populations.

- Use the Kruskal-Wallis analysis of variance test in situations where a non-parametric alternative is needed for the ANOVA procedure discussed in Chapter 10.

- Determine if randomness exists (or if there is an underlying pattern) in a small sequence of sample data through the use of the runs test for randomness.

- Compute the Spearman rank correlation coefficient and then test this measure for significance.

13.1 Non-parametric Methods: Uses, Benefits, and Limitations

The focus in Chapters 7 through 10 has been to use sample data to arrive at conclusions about population parameters such as the mean, variance, standard deviation, or percentage. In statistical terms, these earlier chapters thus focused on **parametric methods** to produce a statistical decision. But to use these methods, restrictive assumptions about the population must be satisfied. For example, one such restrictive assumption that you've encountered many times is, "The sample data are gathered from a population (or populations) that is (are) normally distributed."

But what if an analyst has data that can't satisfy parametric method restrictions? In that case, there's a wide range of available *nonparametric statistical methods* that may be used.

> **Non-parametric statistical methods** are those that produce test results for decision making that don't require that restrictive assumptions be made about the shape of a distribution. These methods are thus often called **distribution-free methods.**

In addition to serving as alternatives for parametric procedures, non-parametric methods are also available that satisfy other needs. For example, distribution-free techniques have already been considered in this book, since the Chi-square methods in Chapter 11 are non-parametric in nature. The Chi-square procedure is used to compare observed (sample) frequencies with expected (hypothesized) frequencies, and the expected frequencies aren't necessarily restricted to a particular type of distribution.

Uses of Non-parametric Methods

When should non-parametric methods be used? They should be employed in any of the following situations:

1. When the sample size is so small that the sampling distributions of the statistics don't approximate the normal distribution and when no assumption can be made about the shape of the population distribution from which the sample is drawn.

2. When **ordinal** (or **rank**) **data** are used. That is, when data values are ordered or ranked according to some predetermined scheme. For example, horses finishing a race can be ranked 1, 2, 3, ... as they cross the finish line. Of course, this ranking reveals nothing about the time separating the winner from the second (or third) horse. With ordinal data we can tell only if one item is higher than, lower than, or equal to another item, but we can't tell the size of the difference. Many experiments yield ordinal data only. For example, a medical researcher may be able to rank the response of patients to a new drug only on a scale from 1 to 5, where a 1 denotes no discernible change in the patient and a 5 indicates a pronounced improvement in the patient's condition. Or candidates for a job may be ranked first, second, third, and fourth in order of employer preference.

3. When **nominal data** are used. Such data may be assigned code numbers (to differentiate, for example, between members of different political parties or between

citizens of different countries). Such code numbers thus become a nominal measure, but they are used *only* for identification purposes. There's no suggestion in such code numbers that one item is higher or lower than another.

Benefits and Limitations of Non-parametric Methods

Included among the benefits of non-parametric methods are the following:

1. They can be used when ordinal or nominal data are available.

2. They can be used with small sample sizes, and they require little or no information about the population(s) being sampled.

3. They are typically easier to understand and use than parametric methods.

4. They are also generally easier to calculate than parametric methods.

But you seldom get something for nothing in this world. There are also limitations to the use of non-parametric methods:

1. When ordinal or nominal data are used, any count or measurement data that's available may be ignored and thus wasted.

2. When little or no information about the population(s) being sampled is needed, the test results obtained may be more general, but they are also likely to be less powerful or less sensitive than those obtained using parametric methods. Thus, stronger support must be established before we can reject a null hypothesis.

Our examination of some widely used non-parametric methods begins in the next section.

Self-Testing Review 13.1

1. What is the primary difference between a non-parametric statistical test and most of the hypothesis tests discussed in earlier chapters?

2. In what situations should non-parametric methods be used?

3. What are the limitations of using non-parametric methods?

4. What are the benefits of using non-parametric methods?

13.2 Sign Tests

In Chapter 9 you saw how to test for differences in population means when "before-and-after" or other paired data situations involving dependent samples were considered. Now, if you have paired ordinal measurements taken from the same subjects or matched subjects and if you're simply interested in seeing if there are significant differences between the pairs (regardless of the size of the differences), a sign test may be used. A **sign test** is based on the signs—negative or positive—of the differences between pairs of ordinal data.

A Sign Test Procedure with Small Samples

Chicken Out, a national fast-food chain, has developed a new formula for the batter used to coat its chicken. The marketing department wants to know if the new batter is tastier than the original mix. At the present stage of product development, the department isn't interested in the degree of taste improvement.

Ten consumers are randomly selected for a taste test. Each person first tastes a piece of chicken prepared with one of the batters and rates the taste on a scale of 1 to 10, where 1 is very poor and 10 is very good. The consumer next takes a drink of water, waits 5 minutes, and munches a piece of chicken fried with the other batter and rates the taste on a scale of 1 to 10. The order in which the batters were tasted was decided randomly. We thus have two dependent samples, and the data collected are presented in Table 13.1.

What can the market research data tell us? If there's truly no difference in flavour, we would expect, in a large survey, that the number of consumers who prefer the taste of one batter would be equal to the number who prefer the taste of the other. In other words, if there's truly no difference between the taste of the original batter and the taste of the new mix, the median difference between the two taste ratings should be zero. That is, the number of consumers who report better taste for a particular formula should be equal to the number who report a worse taste.

We've used a seven-step hypothesis-testing procedure to produce numerous statistical decisions in the earlier chapters that relied on parametric methods. *Most of the same*

TABLE 13.1 DATA FOR THE SIGN TEST TASTE RATINGS BY 10 CONSUMERS OF CHICKEN COATED WITH ORIGINAL BATTER AND CHICKEN COATED WITH NEW BATTER (10 INDICATES A "VERY GOOD TASTE," AND 1 INDICATES A "VERY POOR TASTE")

| Consumer | Taste Ratings | | Sign of Difference between New Coating and Original Coating (y − x) |
	Original Batter (x)	New Batter (y)	
R. MacDonald	3	9	+
G. Price	5	5	0
B. King	3	6	+
L. J. Silver	1	3	+
P. P. Gino	5	10	+
E. J. McGee	8	4	−
S. White	2	2	0
E. Fudd	8	5	−
Y. Sam	4	6	+
M. Muffett	6	7	+

n = number of relevant observations
  = number of plus signs + number of minus signs
  = 6 + 2
  = 8
r = the number of fewer signs
  = 2

steps are followed here to conduct non-parametric hypothesis tests, but there are also a few differences, as you'll see in the following testing procedure.

Step 1: State the Null and Alternative Hypotheses The first step in a sign test is to state the null and alternative hypotheses. Two-tailed or one-tailed sign tests may be conducted, and this fact, of course, decides the form of the alternative hypothesis. The null hypothesis in our example is that the new ingredients have no effect on the taste of the chicken: a positive sign indicating a taste improvement is just as likely as a negative sign attesting to a loss of flavour when the difference between the two taste ratings for each subject is determined. The alternative hypothesis is that the new batter improves taste. We thus have a right-tailed test, and H_1 is that there's more than a 50 percent chance that a person will report that the new batter tastes better than the original mix.

So, the null hypothesis is

H_0: $p = 0.5$

And the alternative hypothesis is

H_1: $p > 0.5$

where p is the probability of getting a taste improvement.

With a right-tailed test, if H_0 is true, we would expect more plus signs than minus signs. That is, either many plus signs or few minus signs should lead to a rejection of H_0.

Step 2: Select the Level of Significance The second step is to establish a criterion for rejecting H_0. Let's assume, for our example, the risk of erroneously rejecting the null hypothesis when it's actually true is to be limited to no more than 5 percent. Thus, the level of significance is $\alpha = .05$.

Step 3: Determine and Tally the Signs of the Differences between Paired Observations The third step begins by systematically subtracting one observation from the other observation and then recording the difference as positive (an improvement in taste) or negative (a loss in flavour). The last column in Table 13.1 shows the sign of the difference for each subject when the taste rating for the original mix is subtracted *from* the taste rating for the new batter. The first subject, R. MacDonald, rates the new batter as better tasting than the original mix, and so there is a *positive* sign. In situations where there's no change in taste ratings, a zero represents that response.

Having obtained the signs, we next tally up the pluses, the minuses, and the zeros. Table 13.1 shows six pluses, two minuses, and two zeros—which means that six consumers thought there was a taste improvement, two thought flavour had declined, and two detected no change. After the tally, *we designate the number of minus signs as the test statistic, r.* In the case of Table 13.1, we have $r = 2$ because there are only two minus signs compared with the six positive signs.

Step 4: Determine the Test Distribution to Use Although non-parametric methods make no restrictive assumptions about the underlying population distribution(s) being sampled, they do require that we use various probability distributions (binomial, normal, Chi-square, and others) to arrive at a test decision. In this small-sample sign test we use the binomial probability table in Appendix 1. But as we'll soon see, if the sample size for the sign test is large enough so that np and $n(1 - p)$ are both ≥ 5, the normal approximation to the binomial distribution may be used.

Step 5: State the Decision Rule The decision rule to follow in small-sample sign tests is

Reject H_0 in favour of H_1 if the probability of the sample results < the level of significance (α). Otherwise, fail to reject H_0.

But you will find out that the "probability of the sample results" is identical to the p-value of this test. So we can use the more familiar decision rule

Reject H_0 in favour of H_1 if p-value < (α). Otherwise, fail to reject H_0.

Step 6: Compute the p-value Assuming H_0 is true, we must now find the p-value of the test. The only subjects or paired observations relevant for analysis are those where taste differences (positive or negative) are recorded. In our case, only eight of the ten pairs of data are relevant, and thus we have $n = 8$. (The responses of Price and White are not included because they give no indication of a difference one way or the other.) From the eight paired observations, one would expect four of the differences to be positive and four to be negative *if H_0 is true*. On the basis of the two negative responses in Table 13.1 and the nature of a right-tailed test, we must ask the following question: What is the chance of having at most only two out of eight subjects noticing a negative taste change when in fact H_0 is true (where 50 percent of the sample should record a positive change and 50 percent should show a negative change)?

Since we have eight relevant subjects in the present test, we look for that section of the binomial table in Appendix 1 where $n = 8$ and $r = 2$. Next, we look in the column where $p = .50$—a value that stems from H_0. We see that the p-value, the probability of getting *at most* 2 (that's 0, 1, or 2) out of 8 subjects reporting a negative change, is .1445, which is the summation of the probabilities of getting 0 out of 8 (.0039), 1 out of 8 (.0312), and 2 out of 8 (.1094). In other words, if there is truly no difference in taste between the original and new batters, the chances of getting at most only 2 out of 8 subjects reporting a loss of taste is 14.4 percent.

Step 7: Make the Statistical Decision Our decision rule is to reject H_0 if the .1445 p-value we've just computed is < α (= .05). That's obviously not the case. Although the probability of getting at most only 2 out of 8 consumers to report negatively on the new batter mix is not particularly high at .1445, it is greater than the .05 level of significance specified earlier in the problem. Thus, we fail to reject H_0; the new batter mix cannot be said to be a significant improvement over the original recipe.

> If we're conducting a **left-tailed test,** the value of r is the number of plus signs rather than the number of minus signs. And if we're making a **two-tailed test,** we designate the lesser sum of the two signs as r. Then, in calculating the p-value, we double the probabilities obtained from the binomial table before making the statistical decision. For example, if we're conducting a two-tailed test on the Chicken Out data, the sample results are 2 times .1445, giving a p-value of .2890.

 Many statistical software packages have non-parametric procedures available. *Figure 13.1* has the result of using MINITAB to do the calculations for the Chicken Out. The results are identical to those we obtained previously.

FIGURE 13.1 To do the sign test using MINITAB, we would first calculate the differences of the original data, perhaps using MINI-TAB's calculator. Then to obtain *Chicken Out* MINITAB output, click on **Stat, Nonparametrics, 1-Sample Sign,** specify the column of differences in the box below **Variables,** click in the circle next to **Test median** (leaving the 0.0 in the box to the right), change the alternative hypothesis to **greater than,** and click on **OK.**

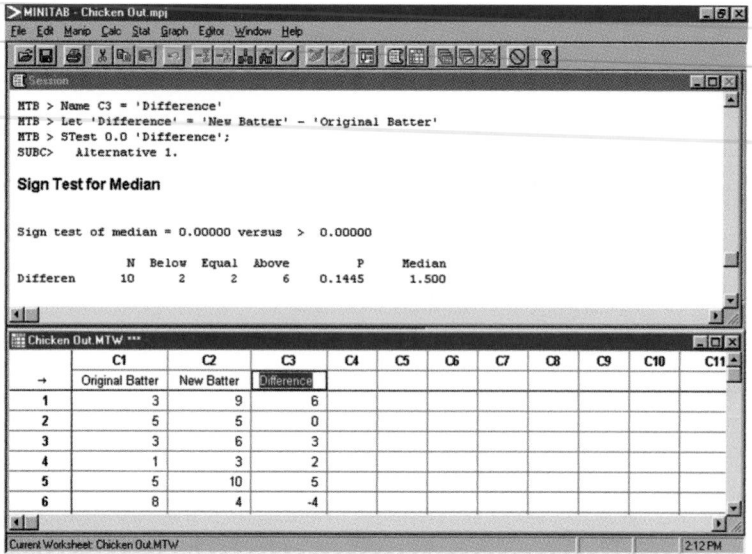

A Sign Test Procedure with Large Samples

Let's suppose now that 35 consumers had been randomly selected for a taste test of the two Chicken Out batter mixes. And let's assume the taste test produced the following results:

+ differences = 19
− differences = 13 $n = 32$
0 differences = 3
        Total = 35

The following seven-step procedure can be used to arrive at a statistical decision in this large-sample sign test.

Step 1: State the Null and Alternative Hypotheses If a right-tailed test is made, the hypotheses are exactly what they were in the small-sample situation:

H_0: $p = 0.5$
H_1: $p > 0.5$

Step 2: Select the Level of Significance We'll again use the .05 level.

Step 3: Determine and Tally the Sign of the Differences between Paired Observations This information is previously summarized in the results produced by the taste test.

Step 4: Determine the Test Distribution to Use Since np and $n(1 - p)$ are both ≥ 5, we'll use the normal (z) approximation to the binomial distribution. (In fact, $n \geq 10$ is large enough for this approximation to be reasonable, though it is better to use binomial tables if they are available.)

Step 5: State the Decision Rule The decision rule for a one-tailed test at the .05 level is stated in the following familiar format:

Reject H_0 in favour of H_1 if $z > 1.645$. Otherwise, fail to reject H_0.

Step 6: Compute the Test Statistic The following formula is used to compute the value of the test statistic, z:

$$z = \frac{2R - n}{\sqrt{n}} \tag{13.1}$$

where $R =$ the number of positive signs
        $n =$ the number of signed paired observations

Thus, the test statistic is computed as follows:

$$z = \frac{2R - n}{\sqrt{n}} = \frac{2(19) - 32}{\sqrt{32}} = \frac{38 - 32}{5.657} = 1.061$$

Step 7: Make the Statistical Decision Since $1.061 < 1.645$, we fail to reject the null hypothesis. In this case, the conclusion is again that there's no significant evidence of a difference between the taste ratings of the two batters.

Figure 13.2 summarizes the sign test procedures outlined in this section.

Example 13.1   **Profitable Non-parametrics? Part 1** The profits of large Canadian companies don't always increase from year to year. The table below lists the profits (in hundreds of thousands of dollars) of a sample of 20 large Canadian companies for the years 2000 and 2001 (obtained from *The Globe and Mail* in 2003).

Company	2000	2001
Bank of Montreal	1,862	1,471
Bank of Nova Scotia	1,919	2,169
Bell Canada	1,459	1,620
Canadian National Railway Co.	773	727
Cdn. Imp. Bank of Commerce	2,056	1,686
Cdn. Natural Resources	782	704
EnCanada Corp.	1,035	1,304
Husky Energy	464	701
Imperial Oil	1,414	1,244
Magna International	574	580
Manulife Financial	1,073	1,159
Onex Corp.	246	798
Petro-Canada	895	904
Power Financial	785	879
Royal Bank of Canada	2,275	2,411
Shell Canada	856	1,010
Sun Life Financial Services	632	882
Talisman Energy	903	786
Thomson Corp.	1,252	776
Toronto-Dominion Bank	1,024	1,383

FIGURE 13.2 Summary of sign test procedures in this section.

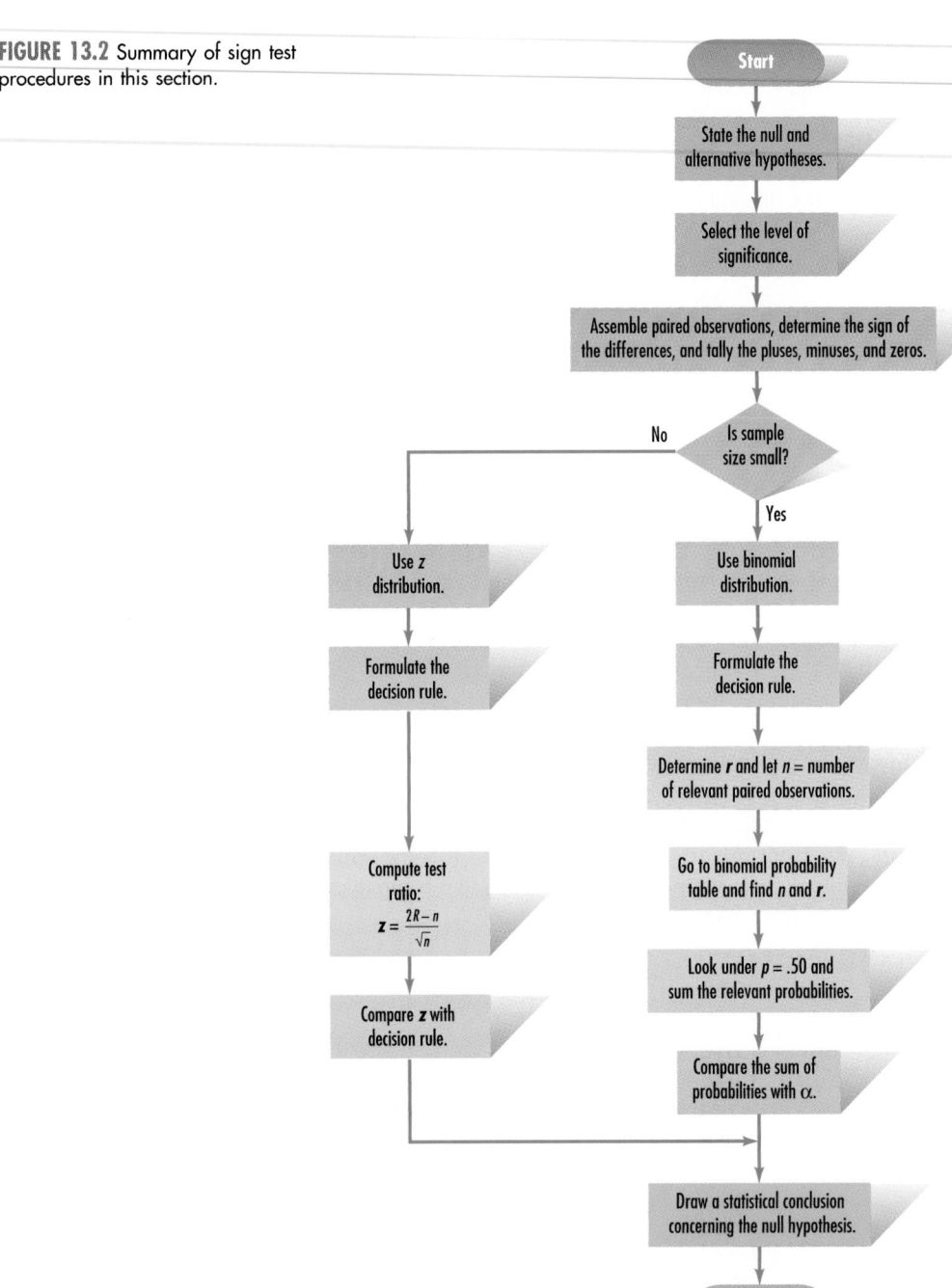

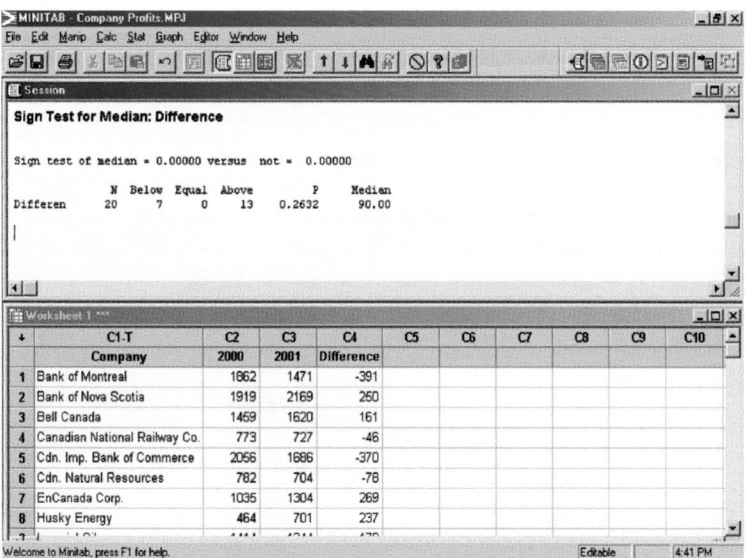

FIGURE 13.3 Output from sign test on company profits.

Test the hypothesis that the probability, p, that the profits of a randomly selected large Canadian company decreased from the year 2000 to the year 2001, is 0.5 against the alternative that p is not 0.5.

◆ **Solution:**
Our hypotheses are

H_0: $p = 0.5$
H_1: $p \neq 0.5$

Using a significance level of .10, we can let MINITAB or another statistical software package do most of the work, including all the calculations. As MINITAB will print the p-value of the test, the decision rule is

Reject H_0 in favour of H_1 if the p-value < .10. Otherwise, fail to reject H_0.

MINITAB was used to generate the output of *Figure 13.3*. The p-value of the test is given as 0.2632. Since .2632 is not + .10, we fail to reject H_0. We do not have evidence that p is significantly different from 0.5. ◆

Self-Testing Review 13.2

5. What is a sign test?

6. What is the null hypothesis for a sign test?

7. Discuss the probability distribution used in a sign test when the sample size is small. What probability distribution is used in a sign test when the sample size is large?

8. If the differences in the paired data used in a sign test yield 15 positive, 5 negative, and 9 tie or zero values,

   a) What are the values for n and for r?

   b) In a right-tailed test at the .05 level, should the null hypothesis be rejected?

9. If the differences between paired data used in a sign test yield 16 positive, 26 negative, and 4 zero values, what would be the statistical decision for a two-tailed test at the .05 level of significance?

10. A workout area and a swimming pool were installed at a large corporate facility in an effort to lower the body mass index (BMI) of employees and thus lower the company's health insurance rates. Each participant's BMI was measured at the start to determine a baseline value. After two years in the program, the BMI of each participant was measured again. The data for a random sample of 16 participating employees are (Data = BMICntrl)

Participant	Baseline BMI	Two-Year BMI
1	26.50	26.06
2	26.07	26.40
3	25.37	25.53
4	27.41	26.28
5	25.39	25.39
6	25.40	25.69
7	25.79	26.12
8	26.34	26.24
9	26.52	26.53
10	26.08	26.37
11	26.45	26.22
12	25.90	26.42
13	25.51	25.57
14	25.67	24.94
15	25.44	25.95
16	27.04	26.47

Use the sign test at the .05 level to see if the participants' BMI decreased in the two-year period.

11. A sample of seven patients who had undergone a shoulder operation were contacted several months after their operation. The numbers below represent the patients' own assessment or rating of their condition on a "wellness" scale (from 0 to 10, where lower numbers indicate a greater degree of "wellness") both "pre-op" and "post-op."

Patient	Pre-Op	Post-Op
1	9.4	5.9
2	9.0	6.1
3	6.4	4.4
4	5.7	3.1
5	6.0	7.5
6	9.8	8.2
7	7.7	5.5

Use a sign test at the .05 level to test the effectiveness of the surgery.

12. An employment counsellor claims that higher ratings are given to career values by women than by men. The following gives the results of responses to a Life Roles Inventory published in *Career Development Quarterly* by a random sample of men and women (Data = LifeRole):

Value	Male Rating	Female Rating
Ability utilization	16.69	17.17
Achievement	16.76	17.17
Advancement	15.08	14.44
Aesthetics	13.31	13.75
Altruism	14.95	16.49
Authority	14.61	14.51
Autonomy	15.79	16.37
Creativity	14.89	14.82
Economics	16.31	16.25
Life style	14.09	14.45
Personal development	17.31	18.02
Physical activity	14.18	13.97
Prestige	15.34	15.79
Risk	10.34	9.47
Social interaction	12.65	13.82
Social relations	15.44	16.93
Variety	13.06	13.96
Working conditions	13.75	14.91
Cultural identity	12.76	13.48
Physical prowess	9.49	8.51

Use a sign test at the .01 level to evaluate the counsellor's claim.

13. A random sample of 8 pairs of identical 12-year-old twins participated in a study to see if vitamin supplements helped their attention spans. For each pair, twin A was given a placebo, and twin B received a special vitamin supplement. A psychologist then determined the length of time (in minutes) each remained with a puzzle. The results are

Pair	Twin A	Twin B	Pair	Twin A	Twin B
1	34	39	5	28	38
2	18	42	6	26	40
3	39	33	7	28	29
4	31	40	8	22	25

Use a sign test at the .05 level to test the hypothesis that the twins who took the vitamin supplement had a longer attention span.

14. A physical therapist wants to test the effectiveness of ultrasound treatment on muscle soreness. A random sample of ten patients who had soreness in both arms was selected. One arm received an ultrasound treatment and the other arm a placebo treatment. Subjects were then asked to report the level of pain they had after the treatment (higher numbers indicate more pain). The data are (Data = Soreness)

Patient	Control Arm	Treated Arm
1	46	2
2	22	32
3	10	30
4	14	3
5	26	14
6	29	32
7	29	2
8	47	39
9	20	18
10	13	2

Use a sign test at the .05 level to see if there is a difference in the level of pain between the control arm and the treated arm.

15. The Coven Computer Company employs 500 salespeople. In an attempt to reduce the amount of time needed to close a sale, the company has produced a multimedia package to be used in sales presentations. So far, only ten salespeople have requested and used the package. When each of these salespeople made the request to use the package, he or she was asked to estimate the amount of time usually needed in a presentation to make a sale. After each one used the package for two months, he or she was again asked to estimate how much time it took to make a sale. The data follow (Data = CCC):

Salesperson	Time before Package	Time after Package
A	23	17
B	45	43
C	36	36
D	42	37
E	25	20
F	33	39
G	28	31
H	25	21
I	35	27
J	30	40

Use the sign test at the .05 level to see if there's a reduction in the time needed to close a sale when the multimedia package is used.

16. The following data give the team averages for this year and last year for a random sample of 14 bowling teams in a region (Data = Bowling):

Team	This Year	Last Year
1	525	527
2	535	556
3	559	571
4	535	559
5	538	514
6	520	555

Team	This Year	Last Year
7	520	512
8	553	576
9	572	599
10	546	553
11	543	560
12	474	479
13	593	599
14	565	556

Use the sign test at the .05 level to see if there has been a change in scores from last year to this year. Discuss whether the paired-difference *t*-test discussed in Chapter 9 could be used to answer this question.

17. A pharmaceutical company believes it has a pill to lower cholesterol and is ready to make some preliminary tests. A random sample of ten people have their cholesterol level checked before and after using the pill. At this early stage, the company is interested in learning only if there is a decrease in cholesterol and is not measuring the amount of the decrease. The data are (Data = Cholestl)

Person	Before	After
A	263	214
B	194	188
C	273	284
D	185	185
E	238	264
F	212	190
G	189	185
H	164	153
I	248	248
J	261	229

Use a sign test at the .05 level to test the effectiveness of the medication. Discuss whether the paired-difference *t*-test discussed in Chapter 9 could be used to answer this question.

18. A manager at Great Buys Food Stores claims that Great Buys' prices are lower than those of Thrifty Chain Foods. A random sample of 38 name-brand items are selected and priced at both stores. For 14 items, Great Buys has lower prices, and for 11 items, Thrifty has lower prices. For the rest of the items, the prices are equal. Use a sign test at the .05 level to see if Great Buys does indeed have lower prices.

19. After the health minister announced his new health care plan, a random sample of 145 people were asked if their opinion of the minister had improved, decreased, or stayed the same. A total of 75 said their opinion had improved, 58 said their opinion went down, and the rest reported no change in opinion. Use a sign test at the .05 level to see if there was a change in opinion.

20. The worst E. coli outbreak in Canadian history occurred in Walkerton, Ontario, in May 2000. The data that follow represent rates per 100,000 population of reported cases of Vero-toxigenic E. coli in four Canadian provinces for the years 1997 to 2002.

	Rates per 100,000 Population					
	1997	**1998**	**1999**	**2000**	**2001**	**2002**
Alberta	6.7	8.8	6.5	10.8	8.8	7.6
British Columbia	3.4	4.5	6.6	3.9	2.7	3.2
Ontario	3.8	3.5	3.2	12.2	2.6	2.9
Saskatchewan	3.5	3.7	2.9	4.1	6.7	2.8

Source: Statistics Canada.

Use a sign test at the .10 level to determine

a) If there was a significant increase in the rates from 1997 to 1998.

b) If there was a significant decrease in the rates from 1998 to 1999.

c) If there was a significant increase in the rates from 2001 to 2002.

21. Data were collected from 12 endurance-trained cyclists. Each cyclist, with a time separation between treatments, consumed two dietary treatments in random order: a high-fat diet and a high-carbohydrate diet. Each subject performed a maximum bicycle graded exercise test, and measurements were taken on several variables. Following are the data on lactate threshold (1/min), maximum heart rate (b/min), and performance time (Data = Lactate):

FatLT	FatMaxHR	FatTimeE	CarbLT	CarbMaxHR	CarbTimeE
3.60	212	13.26	3.38	211	13.34
3.62	196	12.59	3.25	199	13.23
3.80	180	11.50	3.60	179	11.27
3.25	173	11.40	3.11	170	11.52
4.13	172	14.40	4.12	174	15.16
3.75	192	14.11	4.00	194	14.08
3.77	193	13.38	3.83	197	14.25
2.50	183	10.59	2.85	187	11.23
3.20	176	12.40	3.25	183	13.05
3.85	177	13.37	3.35	177	13.34
4.44	189	13.43	4.25	193	13.38
3.20	180	12.59	3.16	180	14.08

Use a sign test at the .05 level to see if there is a difference in the

a) Lactate threshold between the two diets.

b) Maximum heart rate between the two diets.

c) Performance time between the two diets.

22. An experiment was conducted to examine the effects of a low-fat diet, low-intensity aerobic exercise program over a five-week period. Eight volunteers had measurements taken on body fat percentage before and after the program (Data = LowFatTr):

Pretest	Posttest
23.67	24.60
18.62	18.53
35.79	36.01
22.66	22.53
18.74	18.59
22.25	22.03
19.95	19.25
14.61	14.06

Use a sign test at the .05 level to see if the exercise program has reduced the percentage of body fat.

13.3 The Wilcoxon Signed Rank Test

The sign tests we've just examined use two dependent samples and focus solely on the direction of the differences within pairs. But the **Wilcoxon signed rank test** uses magnitude as well as direction to see if there are true differences between pairs of data drawn from two random and **dependent samples.** Thus, when we can use the size as well as the direction of the differences to make a decision, we use the Wilcoxon signed rank test. Since this test uses more information than the sign test we've just examined, it can produce better results. This Wilcoxon test is, when its assumptions are satisfied, a better non-parametric alternative to the paired t test discussed in Chapter 9. Unlike the paired t test, though, the Wilcoxon test doesn't require that the samples come from normal distributions. But it does assume a population of paired differences that is continuous and symmetric.

The Wilcoxon Signed Rank Test Procedure

Let's use the Chicken Out example again. Suppose the marketing manager wants to make a decision about the new batter mix based not just on how many people thought the new batter had improved taste but also on the amount of the taste improvement assigned to the new mix. It's appropriate to use the Wilcoxon signed rank test in this case, and the data for analysis are drawn from Table 13.1 and are reproduced in Table 13.2.

Step 1: State the Null and Alternative Hypotheses The null hypothesis is still that there's no difference in the distribution of the tastes of the original and new batters. Therefore, in a large sample, the number of positive signs should equal the number of negative signs. Since this is a right-tailed test, the alternative hypothesis is that the taste of the new batter in general is better than the taste of the original mix. Thus, the hypotheses may be written as follows:

H_0: The two batters are equally tasty (or tasteless).
H_1: The new batter mix is better tasting.

TABLE 13.2 COMPUTATIONS FOR WILCOXON SIGNED RANK TESTS

Consumers	(1) Original Batter Taste Score	(2) New Batter Taste Score	(3) Difference: New Batter Rating Less Original Batter Rating	(4) Rank Irrespective of Sign	(5) Signed Rank Positive	(6) Signed Rank Negative
R. MacDonald	3	9	+6	8	+8	
G. Price	5	5	0	(ignore)		
B. King	3	6	+3	4.5	+4.5	
L. J. Silver	1	3	+2	2.5	+2.5	
P. O. Gino	5	10	+5	7	+7	
E. J. McGee	8	4	−4	6		−6
S. White	2	2	0	(ignore)		
E. Fudd	8	5	−3	4.5		−4.5
Y. Sam	4	6	+2	2.5	+2.5	
M. Muffett	6	7	+1	1	+1	
					+25.5	−10.5

n = number of relevant observations
 = number of plus signs + number of minus signs
 = 6 + 2
 = 8
T = the smaller of the two rank sums
 = 10.5

Step 2: Select the Level of Significance Let's assume for this test that the marketing manager specifies that $\alpha = .01$.

Step 3: Determine the Size and Sign of Differences and Rank Differences Irrespective of Signs In the next step, the size and sign of the differences between the paired data are computed, and these are shown in column 3 of Table 13.2. For example, McGee initially gave the taste of the original batter an 8 score but felt that the taste of the new batter merited only a 4. Thus, the recorded difference in column 3 for McGee is −4. Differences for the other consumers are recorded in column 3 of Table 13.2 in a similar way. Having completed column 3, we now turn to column 4 in Table 13.2. We temporarily ignore the plus and minus signs in column 3 and rank the absolute values of the differences. A rank of 1 is assigned to the smallest difference; a rank of 2 is given to the next smallest value; and so on. (Differences of zero are ignored.) Since the two taste scores for Muffett had the smallest different, that difference, irrespective of the direction, is assigned the rank of 1. In the cases of Silver and Sam, who are tied for second and third ranks with differences of 2, we assign to each a rank of 2.5, which is the average of the ranks 2 and 3. This procedure is continued until all differences are ranked in column 4.

Step 4: Determine the Test Distribution to Use A new **T statistic** (not to be confused with values in a t distribution) is used in this test. Critical values of T are given in Appendix 7. Under the condition that the null hypothesis is true, this table provides the values of T at α levels of .01 and .05 for both one- and two-tailed tests.

Step 5: State the Decision Rule We are conducting a right-tailed test at the .01 level, and we have tallied 8 ranks (ties don't count) in column 4 of Table 13.2. Thus, with $n = 8$ and $\alpha = .01$, the table value of T is 1. Our decision rule in this example is

Reject H_0 in favour of H_1 if the computed T (found in the next step) $\leq$ the table T value of 1. Otherwise, fail to reject H_0.

Step 6: Compute the Test Statistic We must first affix the sign of each difference (as shown in column 3, Table 13.2) to its rank (as shown in column 4). This step results in the figures in the last two columns of Table 13.2. For example, Gino's assigned rank is 7, and since the difference is positive, a corresponding +7 is recorded. Signed ranks are similarly produced for the other consumers as you can see in columns 5 and 6 of Table 13.2. We next add all the positive ranks, and then we add all the negative ranks. Because, if H_1 is true, we expect to get few minus signs, the sum of the negative ranks is designated as the computed T value. Since the sum of the negative ranks is 10.5, that value is designated as the computed value of T. (As a check of your accuracy, the sum of the positive and negative ranks—that is, 25.5 + 10.5—must equal the sum of the ranks in column 4 of Table 13.2.)

Step 7: Make the Statistical Decision Since our computed T equals 10.5, and since this statistic is greater than the critical T value of 1, the null hypothesis is not rejected. There is insufficient evidence to show that the new mix produces a significant taste improvement over the original batter.

If you're conducting a left-tailed test, the computed T is the sum of the positive ranks. And if a two-tailed test is needed, the computed T is the smaller of the two sums. For your convenience, the entire procedure for the Wilcoxon signed rank test is summarized in *Figure 13.4*.

The MINITAB output for this test is in *Figure 13.5*. You might notice that MINITAB reports the Wilcoxon Statistic as 25.5, the sum of the positive ranks, rather than 10.5, the sum of the negative ranks. Either test statistic is equally valid—if a small sum for the negative ranks would lead us to reject H_0, then a large sum for the positive ranks would lead us to the same conclusion. That is, the test can be done either way. The main point is that the p-value and the conclusion are the same regardless of which sum we use. Here, with the p-value = .163 > .01, we would again decide to not reject the null hypothesis.

☐ Example 13.2 Profitable Non-parametrics? Part 2 Returning to the problem regarding profits of large Canadian companies, use Wilcoxon's signed rank test to again test the hypothesis that the probability, p, that the profits of a randomly selected large Canadian company decreased from the year 2000 to the year 2001 is 0.5, against the alternative that p is not 0.5. Use a level of significance of .10.

◆ Solution:
Our hypotheses are

H_0: $p = 0.5$
H_1: $p \neq 0.5$

Again using a significance level of .10, we employ MINITAB to perform the calculations. The decision rule is

Reject H_0 in favour of H_1 if the p-value < .10. Otherwise, fail to reject H_0.

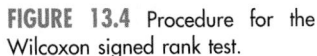

FIGURE 13.4 Procedure for the Wilcoxon signed rank test.

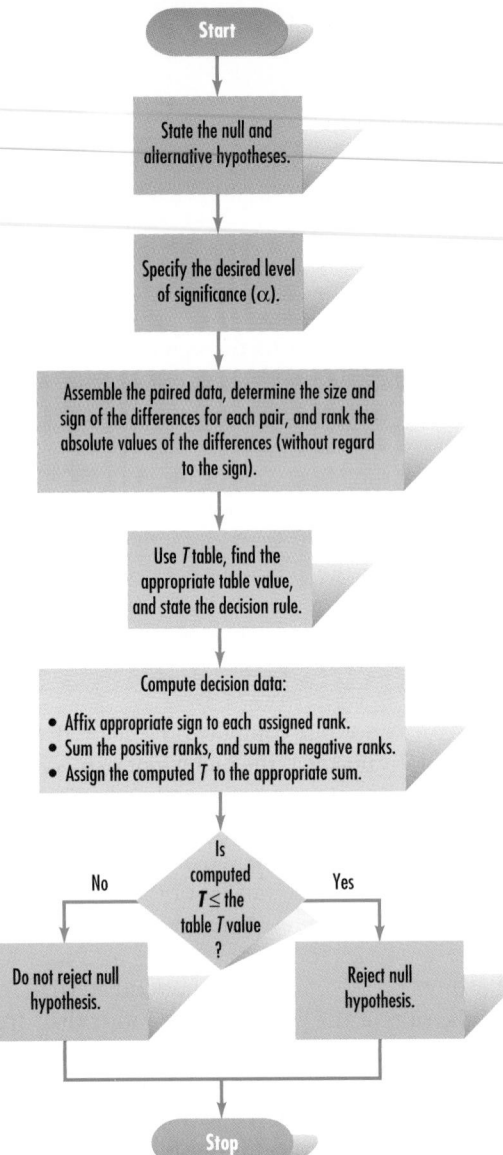

Start

State the null and alternative hypotheses.

Specify the desired level of significance (α).

Assemble the paired data, determine the size and sign of the differences for each pair, and rank the absolute values of the differences (without regard to the sign).

Use *T* table, find the appropriate table value, and state the decision rule.

Compute decision data:

• Affix appropriate sign to each assigned rank.
• Sum the positive ranks, and sum the negative ranks.
• Assign the computed *T* to the appropriate sum.

Is computed *T* ≤ the table *T* value ?

No → Do not reject null hypothesis.

Yes → Reject null hypothesis.

Stop

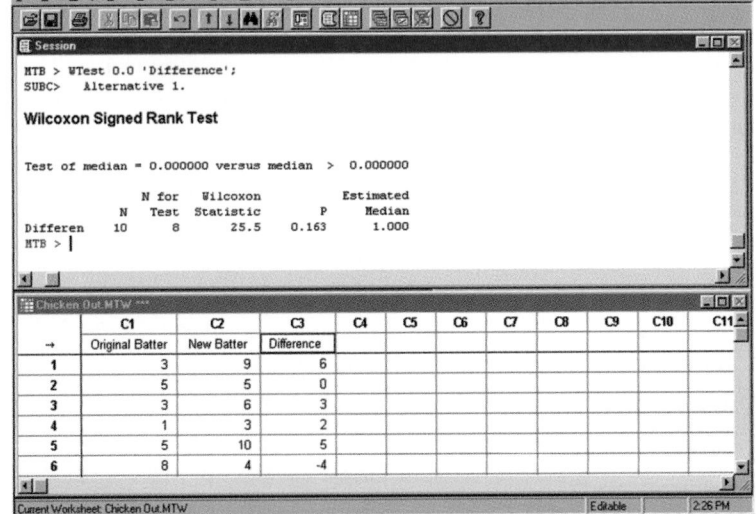

FIGURE 13.5 To obtain this MINITAB output, first calculate the differences from the original data. Then click on **Stat, Nonparametrics, 1-Sample Wilcoxon,** enter the column of differences in the box below **Variables,** click in the circle next to **Test median** (leaving the 0.0 in the box to the right), change the alternative hypothesis to **greater than,** and click on **OK.**

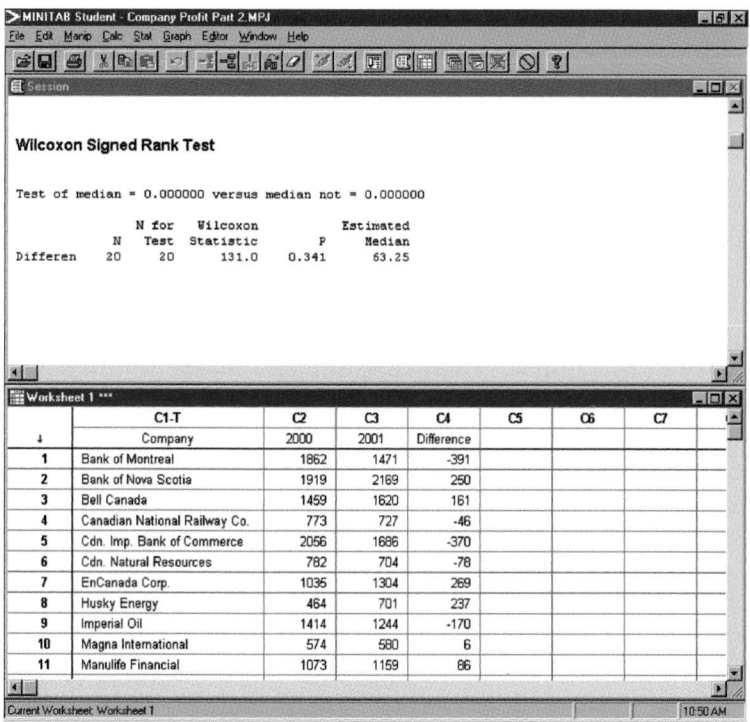

FIGURE 13.6 Output from Wilcoxon signed rank test on company profits.

MINITAB generated the output of *Figure 13.6*. The *p*-value of the test is given as 0.341. In agreement with the sign test, since .341 is not < .10, we again fail to reject H_0. We do not have evidence that *p* is significantly different from 0.5.

The Wilcoxon signed rank test may also be applied to test hypotheses concerning the mean or median of a single population. For example, the label on strawberry jam jars lists a fill of 270 grams. A sample of jars was selected and the contents were weighed. The results (in grams) were 267, 274, 265, 268, 275, 262, 261, 264, 263, and 269. Using $\alpha = .05$, does it appear that the mean fill of the population of all fill weights is less than 270 grams?

In deciding which test to apply, the *t* test from Chapter 8 may come to mind. But suppose the distribution of the population of all such fill weights is not normally distributed? Use of the *t* test is then not justified since the underlying assumption of normality is not satisfied.

The Wilcoxon signed rank test (for a single population) is an alternative test that requires less rigorous assumptions. The assumptions required for this test are that the distribution is 1) continuous and 2) symmetric. (Symmetry means that a vertical line through the median will divide the distribution curve into halves that are mirror images.) Note that if these assumptions are satisfied then the mean and median are identical. Thus, if the mean is 270 grams, then the median is also 270 grams.

Step 1: State the Null and Alternative Hypotheses: Let *M* denote the population median. The hypotheses are then as follows:

H_0: $M = 270$ grams
H_1: $M < 270$ grams

Step 2: Select the Level of Significance Let's use $\alpha = .05$.

Step 3: Determine the Size and Sign of the Differences $(x - M)$ and Rank Differences Irrespective of Signs

In this step we first calculate the differences $(x - 270)$. These differences are $-3, 4, -5, -2, 5, -8, -9, -6, -7$, and -1. These differences are now treated the same way the differences between pairs of data were treated in the Wilcoxon signed rank test using two dependent samples. The ranks of magnitudes of the differences irrespective of sign are 3, 4, 5.5, 2, 5.5, 9, 10, 7, 8, and 1, respectively.

Step 4: Determine the Test Distribution to Use

The same T statistic as used in the earlier Wilcoxon Signed Rank Test is also used here.

Step 5: State the Decision Rule

We are conducting a one-tail test at the .05 level of significance, and we have tallied ten differences. Thus with n = 10, and a = .05, the table value of T is 10. Our decision rule in this example is

Reject H_0 in favour of H_1 if the computed T (found in the next step) is ≤ 10. Otherwise fail to reject H_0.

Step 6: Compute the Test Statistic

If H_1 is true, that is if $M < 270$, we would expect to get few values greater than 270, or few positive ranks for $(x - 270)$. Thus the test statistic is designated as $T =$ the sum of the positive ranks. Since the sum of the positive ranks is 9.5, the computed value of T is 9.5.

Step 7: Make the Statistical Decision

Since the computed value of T is 9.5, and since the value of this statistic is less than the critical T value of 10, the null hypothesis is rejected. Thus at the .05 level of significance, we have sufficient evidence to conclude that the mean amount of fill (which is equal to the median amount of fill) is less than 270 grams. ◆

Self-Testing Review 13.3

23. How does the Wilcoxon signed rank test differ from the sign test?

24. What is the null hypothesis in the Wilcoxon signed rank test?

25. After the absolute values of the differences (that is, the differences without regard to sign) in a set of paired data are ranked, the sum of the positive ranks is 25, and the sum of the negative ranks is 20. What is the computed T for a two-tailed test?

26. What is the critical T table value when $n = 32$, $\alpha = .05$, and the alternative hypothesis indicates a two-tailed test?

27. Discuss the decision rule for the Wilcoxon signed rank test.

28. A random sample of 8 pairs of identical 12-year-old twins participated in a study to see if vitamin supplements helped their attention spans. For each pair, twin A was given a placebo, and twin B received a special vitamin supplement. A psychologist then determined the length of time (in minutes) each remained with a puzzle. The results are

Pair	Twin A	Twin B
1	34	39
2	18	42
3	39	33
4	31	40
5	28	38
6	26	40
7	28	29
8	22	25

Use a Wilcoxon signed rank test at the .05 level to test the hypothesis that the vitamin supplement provided a twin with a longer attention span.

29. The marketing director of Brand A Cola wants to use a nationwide advertising campaign claiming that Brand A is preferred to Brand B Cola, its closest competitor. In a double-blind taste test, a random sample of consumers were given unmarked samples of Brand B Cola and Brand A Cola. Each consumer was asked to rate each of the colas on a scale of 1 to 5, where 1 = didn't like at all and 5 = liked a lot. The results (Data = ColaRate) were

Consumer	Brand B Rating	Brand A Rating
A	2	3
B	1	2
C	2	4
D	3	4
E	2	3
F	2	4
G	5	5
H	1	5
I	2	1
J	4	3
K	3	4
L	4	5
M	3	2
N	2	4

Use a Wilcoxon signed rank test at the .05 level to see if there is a consumer preference for Brand A.

30. In Self-Testing Review 13.2, problem 15, we looked at the amount of time needed in a presentation to make a sale for ten salesperson of the Coven Computer Company. These times were recorded before and after using a multimedia package in the sales presentations. The data are reproduced as follows (Data = CCC):

Salesperson	Time before Package	Time after Package
A	23	17
B	45	43
C	36	36
D	42	37
E	25	20
F	33	39
G	28	31
H	25	21
I	35	27
J	30	40

Use a Wilcoxon signed rank test at the .05 level to see if there's a reduction in time when the multimedia package is used.

31. In Self-Testing Review 13.2, problem 16, the following data were given on the team averages for this year and last year for a random sample of 14 bowling teams in a region (Data = Bowling):

Team	This Year	Last Year	Team	This Year	Last Year
1	525	527	8	553	576
2	535	556	9	572	599
3	559	571	10	546	553
4	535	559	11	543	560
5	538	514	12	474	479
6	520	555	13	593	599
7	520	512	14	565	556

Use the Wilcoxon signed rank test at the .05 level to see if there has been a change in scores from last year to this year. Reflect on the difference between this question and question 16 on page 582.

32. In Self-Testing Review 13.2, problem 14, data were given on the level of pain for subjects who received an ultrasound treatment on one arm and a placebo treatment on the other arm. The data are reproduced as follows (Data = Soreness):

Patient	Control Arm	Treated Arm	Patient	Control Arm	Treated Arm
1	46	2	6	29	32
2	22	32	7	29	2
3	10	30	8	47	39
4	14	3	9	20	18
5	26	14	10	13	2

Use a Wilcoxon signed rank test at the .05 level to see if there is a difference in the level of pain between the control arm and the treated arm. Reflect on the difference between this question and question 14 on pages 579–580.

33. The Bovine Dairy Association sponsored a series of 30-second commercials promoting milk consumption. A total of 16 stores were selected at random, and each store was asked to record its unit sales for the week prior to the campaign. After the campaign appeared on television, the same 18 stores were asked to report their sales for the week immediately following the airing of the commercials. The data are as follows (Data = BDA):

Store	Before Campaign	After Campaign
Jones	124	136
Ma & Pa	107	105
Granny's	82	89
J & A	940	1,080
Korner	75	85
Mike's	94	95
Buy More	865	985
Value	620	820
Pete's	80	75
Foodco	750	725
Koop	330	350
Speedy	110	112
Walt's	125	120
Big Bag	400	425
Pay Now	400	450
Plus	175	215

Conduct a Wilcoxon signed rank test at the .05 level to see if there was a significant difference after the ad campaign.

34. Marketing studies are being conducted at the National Shampoo Company to see if producing the existing green shampoo in a darker shade will improve consumers' perception of the product's effectiveness. Data have been collected from a random sample of seven people, and each has rated the original green shampoo and darker-shade shampoo. A 1-to-10 scale was used, where 1 stood for "very ineffective" and 10 signified "most effective." The data are as follows:

Consumer	Original Rating	Darker-Colour Rating
Abe Bell	4	2
Will Ling	6	6
Curly Locke	7	4
Dan Druff	5	6
Paige Boye	9	8
Harry Parton	1	3
Howie Combs	3	8

Conduct a Wilcoxon signed rank test at the .05 level to test the hypothesis that the ratings for the new darker colour are generally higher.

35. The use of polymers in medicine, especially in the area of drug delivery, is one of the fastest-growing areas of polymer chemistry. A researcher conducted an experiment in which different formulations were used in a delivery device. A sample was taken from one formulation on the first total drug reading (mg):

603   534   447   591   610   410   516   570   440   654

The desired result was for the mean of this amount to exceed 450 mg. Use a Wilcoxon signed rank test with a level of significance of .05 to see if the formulation appears to be delivering the desired mean.

36. A project manager collected data in order to check the quality of ceramic turbine blades. The data consisted of measurements on the maximum principal stress on the blades, an indicator of possible impact failure for the component:

Maximum Principal Stress (MPa)					
4,468	5,364	2,047	2,240	3,978	4,102
1,399	2,020	1,503	2,585	2,213	2,571

One project required a mean greater than 2,650 MPa. Use a Wilcoxon signed rank test with a level of significance of .01 to see if the mean maximum principal stress of all such ceramic turbine blades would satisfy the requirements of the project.

13.4   The Mann-Whitney Test

With the sign test and Wilcoxon signed rank test, paired data drawn from dependent samples can be analyzed for significant differences. In contrast, the **Mann-Whitney test** is used to examine the null hypothesis that there's no true difference between two populations, based on data from two *independent, random samples.* You may recall in Chapter 9 that we carried out *t* tests based on independent, random samples taken from normally distributed populations. The Mann-Whitney test is a non-parametric alternative to such *t* tests—it doesn't require normally distributed populations. Rather, it merely assumes the populations have identical (and not necessarily symmetrical) shapes and that they have equal variances. Furthermore, ordinal or ranked data may be used in a Mann-Whitney test, which is not possible with the *t* test procedures discussed in Chapter 9.

The Mann-Whitney test is often referred to as the **U test,** since, as we'll see, a statistic called **U** is computed to test the null hypothesis.

The Mann-Whitney Test Procedure

Let's assume the alumni director of a college is compiling biographical data on alumni who graduated ten years earlier. After receiving spotty returns from a mail survey, the director—an old biologist—wants to know if people who concentrated on biology are earning more than people who majored in political science. Table 13.3 shows that the director has received salary data from 8 ($n_1 = 8$) biology majors and 12 ($n_2 = 12$) political science majors.

Step 1: State the Null and Alternative Hypotheses   The null hypothesis is that after ten years there's no difference between the salaries of the biology and political science majors. That is,

TABLE 13.3 DATA FOR THE MANN-WHITNEY TEST (SALARIES OF TEN-YEAR GRADUATES WHO MAJORED IN BIOLOGY AND WHO MAJORED IN POLITICAL SCIENCE)

Biology Major	Annual Income ($000)	Income Rank	Political Science Major	Annual Income ($000)	Income Rank
G. Price	44.8	15	W. Lee	43.8	14
J. Jones	35.6	3	M. Galper	33.6	1
M. Doe	53.0	16	D. Lemons	56.0	17
K. Seller	38.6	8	T. Grady	39.0	10
S. Martin	36.4	5.5	P. Davis	36.4	5.5
J. Deere	42.2	13	D. Henry	35.8	4
B. DeVito	39.4	11	B. Ruth	71.6	19
R. Coyne	87.0	20	J. P. Getty	41.0	12
			A. Carnegie	37.4	7
			J. Carter	38.8	9
			B. Clinton	34.6	2
			G. Bush	65.8	18
$n_1 = 8$		$R_1 = 91.5$	$n_2 = 12$		$R_2 = 118.5$

H_0: The salaries for both majors are equal.

Since a right-tailed test is to be made, the alternative hypothesis is

H_1: The salaries of the biology majors are greater than those of the political science majors.

Step 2: Select the Level of Significance The director desires a significance level of $\alpha = .01$.

Step 3: Rank the Data Irrespective of Sample Category The next step is to assign ranks to the entire set of income figures irrespective of major. Since alumnus Galper has the lowest salary of the 20 people who responded, that salary is assigned a rank of 1. And since Coyne reported the highest salary, that income is assigned a rank of 20.

Step 4: Determine the Test Distribution to Use As noted earlier, another new measure—one that yields a U statistic—is used in a Mann-Whitney test. Critical values of U are given in Appendix 8. The tables in Appendix 8 provide values of U for appropriate n_1, n_2, and α under the condition that H_0 is valid.

Step 5: State the Decision Rule A Mann-Whitney test essentially involves comparing a computed U value (U) with the critical U value that applies if H_0 is true. In our example, we have $n_1 = 8$, $n_2 = 12$, and $\alpha = .01$ in a one-tailed test. The appropriate U critical value from the second table in Appendix 8 is 17 in this particular test. The decision rule is then

Reject H_0 in favour of H_1 if U (found in the next step) < critical value of 17. Otherwise, fail to reject H_0.

Step 6: Compute the Test Statistic We must first total the income ranks for each major. As you can see in Table 13.3, the sum of the ranks for the biology majors (R_1) is 91.5, and the sum of the ranks for the political science majors (R_2) is 118.5. We are now ready to compute the value of **U**. Depending on the type of test (right tailed, left tailed, or two tailed), one or both of the following formulas is used to calculate **U**:

$$U_1 = n_1 n_2 + \frac{n_1(n_1 + 1)}{2} - R_1 \qquad (13.2)$$

and

$$U_2 = n_1 n_2 + \frac{n_2(n_2 + 1)}{2} - R_2 \qquad (13.3)$$

where R_1 = the sum of ranks assigned to the sample with size n_1
            R_2 = the sum of ranks assigned to the sample with size n_2

These two formulas will most likely result in two different values for **U**. However, if the salaries of the biology majors are greater than those of the political science majors, then their rank sum, R_1, would be large. From the formula for U_1, you can see that a large value of R_1 leads to a small value of U_1. The value that is selected for **U** for a right-tailed test is U_1. In using formula 13.2, we have

$$U_1 = 8(12) + \frac{8(8 + 1)}{2} - 91.5 = 40.5$$

Consequently, the value assigned to **U** for testing the null hypothesis is 40.5.

Step 7: Make the Statistical Decision Since $U = 40.5$ and is obviously greater than the critical value of 17, the null hypothesis is not rejected. It can be concluded that there is not significant evidence of a salary difference between the alumni who majored in biology and those who majored in political science.

If we're conducting a *left-tailed test,* the computed value for **U** is U_2 and is found by using formula 13.3. And if we're making a *two-tailed test,* the value selected for **U** is the *lesser of the two values* computed with formulas 13.2 and 13.3. *Figure 13.7* illustrates the procedure for conducting the Mann-Whitney test.

Using MINITAB to do the computations for the previous example, we would obtain the output found in *Figure 13.8.* MINITAB denotes its test statistic as "W," but this is the same as the sum of the ranks, R_1, which we have used in calculating **U**. Regardless, the p-value is the same as we would calculate for our test, and the results agree. The p-value = .2946 > .01, and we fail to reject the null hypothesis.

Example 13.3   **In Vino, Non-parametrics Veritas** For a class project, Steve Glossner wanted to compare wines left 12 months in air-dried stavewood to those left 24 months. He examined four characteristics of wine flavour: toastiness, raw wood, oakiness, and bitterness. See if there is evidence at a .05 level of significance of a difference

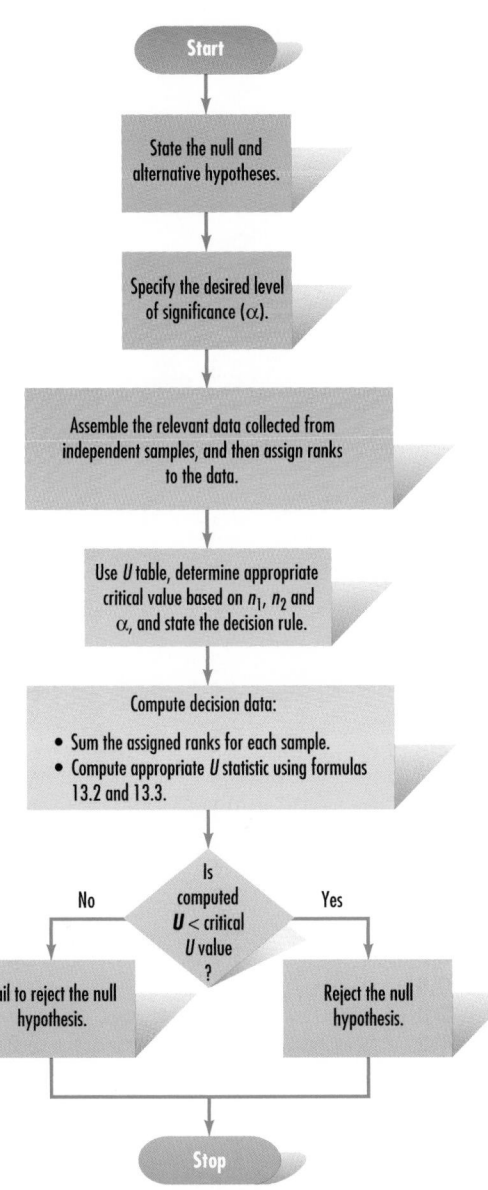

FIGURE 13.7 Procedure for the Mann-Whitney test.

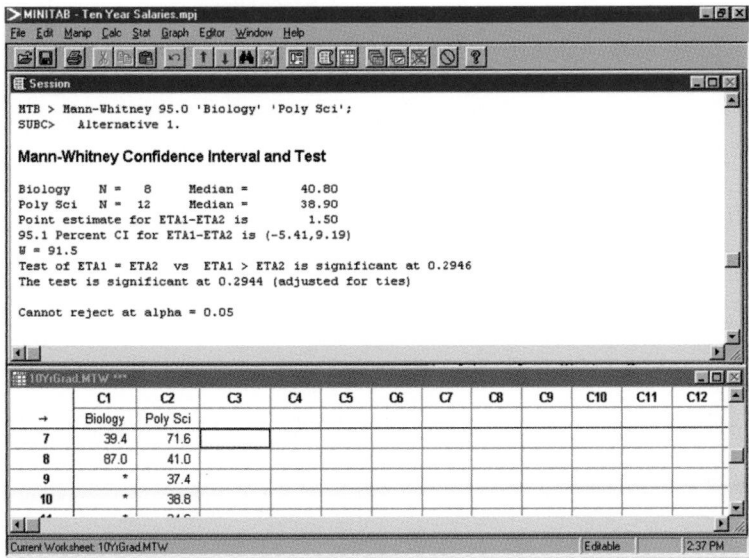

FIGURE 13.8 To obtain this MINITAB output, click on **Stat, Nonparametrics, Mann-Whitney,** enter the data columns in the boxes to the right of **First** and **Second Sample,** change the alternative hypothesis to **greater than,** and click on **OK.**

in the toastiness for these two treatments (leaving the other characteristics for you to examine as exercises) (Data = Stavwood):

Aging	Toast	Raw Wood	Oak	Bitterness
12	0.6	3.4	1.0	2.2
12	0.4	1.8	1.9	1.2
12	0.6	3.1	1.0	2.3
12	0.8	0.2	3.3	5.0
12	3.6	1.2	3.6	3.7
12	1.2	2.4	1.8	1.0
12	8.1	3.0	4.1	6.3
12	6.0	6.4	4.2	7.8
12	5.5	5.0	3.1	4.0
12	2.8	1.4	6.0	5.0
12	4.7	0.9	6.7	2.0
12	3.4	0.3	6.3	6.2
12	5.0	3.7	3.3	5.4
12	2.2	0.2	5.2	7.9
12	5.6	1.1	4.9	6.4
12	6.4	7.7	5.5	5.9
12	5.0	4.8	5.8	6.2
12	6.0	4.6	6.5	6.2
12	0.7	2.0	1.1	1.0
12	1.6	3.6	1.1	2.2
12	5.0	1.6	2.6	3.7
24	0.5	1.0	0.8	2.4
24	4.6	3.1	2.9	1.0
24	1.8	4.7	3.1	1.6
24	4.5	0.4	4.6	6.0
24	6.0	2.8	6.1	0.9
24	5.0	1.2	5.7	2.2
24	7.5	1.9	4.1	5.1
24	5.0	7.6	5.0	6.6
24	6.6	2.1	3.4	5.6
24	7.8	3.7	5.7	1.7
24	8.9	5.2	6.9	5.7
24	8.0	5.4	7.3	4.3
24	5.0	5.0	5.9	9.1
24	3.7	0.3	8.1	3.6
24	9.9	3.5	6.5	9.2
24	6.3	4.7	7.5	4.5
24	6.6	6.4	6.9	6.1
24	6.8	5.1	4.3	6.8
24	4.0	2.6	2.5	6.5
24	3.3	1.3	0.3	3.0
24	9.5	3.1	6.6	4.4

◆ Solution:

The hypotheses are

H_0: The distribution of toastiness is the same for the two treatments.
H_1: The distribution of toastiness is different for the two treatments.

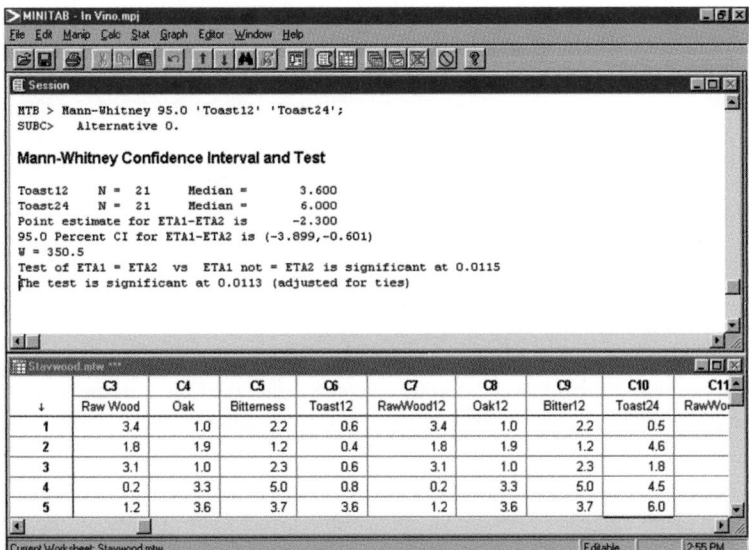

FIGURE 13.9 Output from the Mann-Whitney test on the toastiness of wine.

We have chosen a level of significance of .05, so our decision rule is

Reject H_0 in favour of H_1 if the p-value < .05. Otherwise, fail to reject H_0.

Looking at the MINITAB output of *Figure 13.9*, we find that the p-value for the test is .0115. Since .0115 < .05, we reject H_0 and conclude that there is a difference in the distribution of toastiness for the two treatments. ◆

Self-Testing Review 13.4

37. How does the Mann-Whitney test differ from the sign test and the Wilcoxon signed rank test?

38. How does the Mann-Whitney test differ from the t test?

39. Discuss the decision rule for the Mann-Whitney test.

40. Discuss the U statistic (U) and tell how it is computed.

41. Find the critical value of U for a one-tailed test when $n_1 = 10$, $n_2 = 14$, $\alpha = .05$.

42. *Fortune* magazine in 1999 listed "America's Most Admired Corporations." A random sample of senior executives were asked to rate the ten largest companies in their own industry based on specified attributes. For the computers and office equipment industry, the companies and their average ratings were

Company	Rating	Company	Rating
IBM	7.49	Xerox	6.88
Hewlett-Packard	7.42	Gateway 2000	6.46
Dell Computer	7.35	Canon U.S.A.	5.71
Sun Microsystems	7.06	Apple Computer	5.37
Compaq Computer	6.98	NCR	5.03

For the telecommunications industry, the companies and their ratings were

Company	Rating	Company	Rating
Sprint	7.39	SBC Communications	5.83
Tele-Communications	6.34	AT&T	5.82
BellSouth	6.33	MCI WorldCom	5.51
Ameritech	6.23	GTE	5.43
Bell Atlantic	6.05	US West	4.95

Use a Mann-Whitney test at the .10 level to test the hypothesis that the ratings in the computer and office equipment industry are equal to those in the telecommunications industry (Data = Ratings).

43. The Wide Range Achievement Test (WRAT) was administered to random samples of six schizophrenic patients and eight non-schizophrenic subjects in a study of neuropsychological functioning. The WRAT scores for the schizophrenic patients were

101 87 81 90 96 86

The control group of non-schizophrenic subjects had the following WRAT scores:

95 108 90 106 102 117 118 107

Test the hypothesis at the .02 level that there's no difference in WRAT scores for the two groups.

44. A test was conducted to determine the effectiveness of using an anti-inflammatory cream on delayed-onset muscle soreness. A random sample of ten patients was treated with the cream on their sore arm, and ten other patients were given a placebo for their sore arm. After four days a measure of muscle soreness was taken for each patient and each arm. The results were (Data = Soreness)

Placebo patients:	46	22	10	14	26	29	29	47	20	13
Treated patients:	2	32	30	3	14	32	2	39	18	2

Use a Mann-Whitney test at the .01 level to test the hypothesis that there is less pain when an arm is treated with the anti-inflammatory cream.

45. Is having a CPA certificate an important salary factor? It is according to a recent article in *Management Accounting*. Let's assume we have the following salary data (in thousands of dollars) obtained from random samples of accountants:

No certification:

45 53 58 41 48 52

CPA certificates:

60 51 72 48 64 49 50

Use a Mann-Whitney test at the .05 level to test the hypothesis that accountants with CPA certificates have higher salaries.

46. In a recent study, adolescents with difficulties in reading were divided into two groups. The 7 students randomly selected for group 1 were taught reading using standard techniques. The sample of 10 students in group 2 were taught by a technique that is phonetically based. After completing the course, both groups were given a test with the following results:

Group 1:	15	21	15	23	17	14	16			
Group 2:	18	22	24	25	19	24	17	19	23	16

Test the hypothesis at the .01 level that the group 2 students did better on the test.

47. The Flatt Tire Company has been testing a new emergency tire inflator that is supposed to be significantly faster than the leading competitor's inflator. Motorists were randomly selected for product testing. Some of the subjects were assigned to use the new product, while the others were to use the leading competitor's product. The number of seconds required to inflate a tire are as follows:

Flatt inflator:	17	16	21	19	15	14	16	16	23
Competitor's inflator:	23	21	32	21	19	20	21	22	

What statistical decision should be made at the .05 level?

48. A job counsellor believes that university graduates tend to be more satisfied in their jobs than non-university graduates. A job-satisfaction test was given to a random sample of subjects classified in each category. A high score indicates a high level of job satisfaction. The following results were obtained:

Non-university grads:	102	87	93	98	95	101	92	85	88	95	97	96
University grads:		78	93	101	85	84	77	92	86			

At the .05 level, is the counsellor's theory rejected?

49. Using the data from Example 13.3, test the hypothesis at the .05 level that there is a difference between the two treatments in the

a) *Raw wood* of the wine.

b) *Oakiness* of the wine.

c) *Bitterness* of the wine.

50. Contamination of silicon wafer surfaces with particles and surface chemical oxidation has been shown to degrade device yield. In "A Portable Nitrogen Purged Microenvironment: Design Specification and Preliminary Field Test Data" (*PROCEEDINGS—Institute of Environmental Sciences*), C. W. Draper et al. describe a nitrogen-purged portable microenvironment. Ten wafers receiving a standard pre-epi clean in a epitaxy cleanroom were compared to five wafers receiving a megasonics preclean in a different cleanroom and transported through a non-clean environment in the microenvironment. Defects were measured on two vernier patterns/wafer (Data = Megsonic):

Standard	Megasonic
53	26
193	90
113	546
640	90
800	120
140	
85	
658	
140	
140	

Test the hypothesis at the .05 level that there is a difference between the number of defects arising in the two microenvironments.

13.5   The Kruskal-Wallis Test

The one-way analysis of variance test used in Chapter 10 compared three or more random and independent samples to see if they came from populations with equal means. The **Kruskal-Wallis test**—sometimes called an *H* **test**—also deals with three or more random and independent samples, and its purpose is also to see if the samples come from populations with equal means. The Chapter 10 ANOVA test required that the populations under study have normal distributions and equal variances. The Kruskal-Wallis test also assumes the variances are equal, but it requires only that the *k* populations be continuous and have the same shape (and that shape can be skewed, bimodal, or whatever). And unlike an ANOVA test, the Kruskal-Wallis non-parametric alternative can be used also with ordinal or ranked data.

In short, the Kruskal-Wallis test has less restrictive assumptions and is thus more generally applicable than the ANOVA test. But when it's applicable, the ANOVA test is sensitive to possible differences in means that might go undetected in a Kruskal-Wallis test. Thus, the Kruskal-Wallis test may require stronger evidence before it rejects a null hypothesis.

The Kruskal-Wallis Procedure

As a part of his research on smoking addiction, Nick O. Teen is interested in the willpower of cigarette, cigar, and pipe-smoking addicts to refrain from lighting up. Subjects are randomly selected in each category, and each subject is asked to wait as long as possible between smokes. The time interval is recorded in minutes for each smoker.

TABLE 13.4 DATA FOR THE KRUSKAL-WALLIS TEST (TIME RESTRAINT
SHOWN BY CIGARETTE, CIGAR, AND PIPE SMOKERS)

Restraint Shown by Cigarette Smokers (Time in Minutes)	Smoking Rank	Restraint Shown by Cigar Smokers (Time in Minutes)	Smoking Rank	Restraint Shown by Pipe Smokers (Time in Minutes)	Smoking Rank
6	1	13	8.5	16	11
15	10	19	13.5	23	17.5
22	16	9	4	8	3
7	2	21	15	19	13.5
18	12	23	17.5	13	8.5
11	6	27	22	26	21
25	20	30	24	33	26
32	25	10	5		
12	7				
24	19				
29	23				
$n_1 = 11$	$R_1 = 141$	$n_2 = 8$	$R_2 = 109.5$	$n_3 = 7$	$R_3 = 100.5$

Table 13.4 shows that Nick has received time-restraint data from $11(n_1 = 11)$ cigarette smokers, 8 ($n_2 = 8$) cigar chompers, and $7(n_3 = 7)$ pipe puffers.

Step 1: State the Null and Alternative Hypotheses The hypotheses are

H_0: The population mean time interval between smokes is equal for each group.
H_1: The population mean time interval between smokes is not equal for each group.

Step 2: Select the Level of Significance Let's assume Nick wants to use the .05 level of significance.

Step 3: Rank the Data Irrespective of Sample Category This is exactly like step 3 in the Mann-Whitney test. As you can see in Table 13.4, ranks are assigned to the entire set of smoking time restraints irrespective of the type of tobacco product used. The cigarette addict who could wait only 6 minutes is assigned a rank of 1, and the pipe puffer who waited 33 minutes is given a rank of 26.

Step 4: Determine the Test Distribution to Use The distribution to use in this Kruskal-Wallis test is the same Chi-square distribution you've used in several earlier chapters. Chi-square (χ^2) values are found in Appendix 6.

Step 5: State the Decision Rule This test involves comparing a computed **H** value (found in the next step) with a critical (χ^2) table value. To find this (χ^2) critical value, you must know (1) the level of significance, and (2) the appropriate degrees of freedom (df), which is $k - 1$, where k is the number of samples. In our example, $\alpha = .05$, and the df value is $k - 1$, or $3 - 1$, or 2. Thus, the critical (χ^2) value is found in Appendix 6 to be 5.99 in this particular test. The decision rule, then, is

Reject H_0 in favour of H_1 if the computed H value (H) > 5.99. Other wise, fail to reject H_0.

Step 6: Compute the Test Statistic The value of H needed to apply our decision rule is found with this formula:

$$H = \frac{12}{N(N+1)}\left(\frac{R_1^2}{n_1} + \frac{R_2^2}{n_2} + \cdots + \frac{R_k^2}{n_k}\right) - 3(N+1) \qquad (13.4)$$

where N = the total number of items in all samples
   k = the number of samples in the test
   R_1 = the sum of the ranks in sample 1
   R_2 = the sum of the ranks in sample 2
   R_k = the sum of the ranks in sample k
   n_1 = the size of sample 1
   n_2 = the size of sample 2
   n_k = the size of sample k

The values needed to solve for H in our example problem are found in Table 13.4. Thus,

$$H = \frac{12}{N(N+1)}\left(\frac{R_1^2}{n_1} + \frac{R_2^2}{n_2} + \frac{R_3^2}{n_3}\right) - 3(N+1)$$

$$= \frac{12}{(26)(27)}\left(\frac{(141)^2}{11} + \frac{(109.5)^2}{8} + \frac{(100.5)^2}{7}\right) - 3(27)$$

$$= \frac{12}{702}(1{,}807.36 + 1{,}498.78 + 1{,}442.89) - 81 = .1799$$

Step 7: Make the Statistical Decision Since $H = .1799$ is greater than the (χ^2) critical value of 5.99, we reject H_0 and accept H_1. Nick can conclude that the mean time interval begtween smokes is significantly different for each group of smokers.

The MINITAB output for this problem is found in *Figure 13.11*. The value of the test statistic, .18, matches the value calculated above. MINITAB also prints the p-value = .914. So whether we use the traditional or the p-value approach to make the decision, we will reject the null hypothesis, agreeing with the example's result.

 Example 13.4 **Perspicuous Perspicacity on Perceptions** In a senior project (*Comparing Perceived Expenditure During Cardiovascular Training with Variable Environmental Stimulus*, Cal Poly, 1994), Robert Smith and Brad Lachmann described an experiment that examined if exercising in isolation or with music or in conversation

Figure 13.10 shows the procedure for conducting the Kruskal-Wallis test.

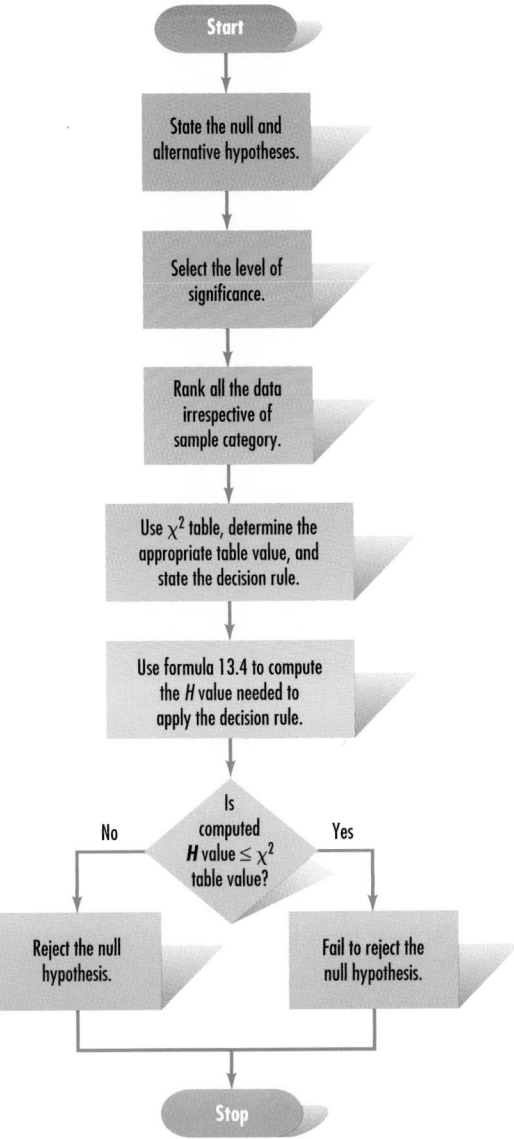

FIGURE 13.10 Procedure for the Kruskal-Wallis test.

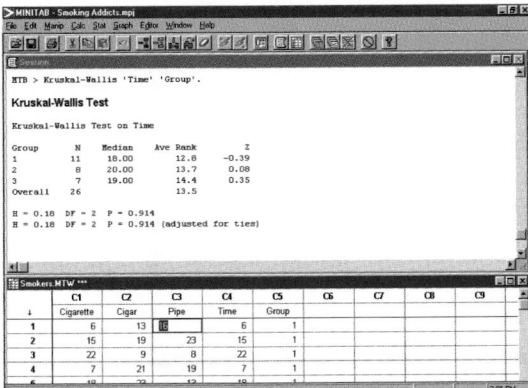

FIGURE 13.11 To obtain this MINI-TAB output, we must have all the time restraint data in one column and a second column indicating the groups, where we used 1 = cigarette smokers, 2 = cigar smokers, and 3 = pipe smokers. (Note: If your data is in separate columns for each group, you can click on **Manip, Stack,** and use the subscripts subcommand to create these two columns.) Once the data is in the appropriate form, click on **Stat, Nonparametrics, Kruskal-Wallis,** enter the times as the **Response** and the smoking groups as the **Factor,** and click on **OK.**

had an effect on the perceived rate of exertion (PRE). In the data that follows, the higher the score, the greater the perceived exertion. Use this sample to test at $\alpha = .01$ for a difference in the mean perceived exertion under these three conditions (Data = PRE):

Isolated	Music	Conversation	Isolated	Music	Conversation
14	15	13	14	14	10
13	13	11	15	14	12
14	9	10	13	12	11
14	11	13	13	9	10
15	12	11	12	12	12
13	12	14	12	11	10
13	11	10	14	13	9
13	12	11	12	11	11
12	13	10	8	9	7
11	10	11	13	12	10
10	9	9	13	11	11
13	10	10			

◆ **Solution:**
The hypotheses are

H_0: The population mean PRE is the same under the three conditions.
H_1: The population mean PRE is not the same under the three conditions.

With a level of significance of .01, the decision rule is:

Reject H_0 in favour of H_1 if the p-value < .01. Otherwise, fail\ to reject H_0.

 The MINITAB output of *Figure 13.12* gives a p-value of .000. Since .000 < .01, we reject H_0 and conclude that there is at least one difference in the mean PRE for the three conditions; that is, at least one condition seems to change the mean perceived rate of exertion. ◆

FIGURE 13.12 Output from the Kruskal-Wallis test on the perceived rate of exertion.

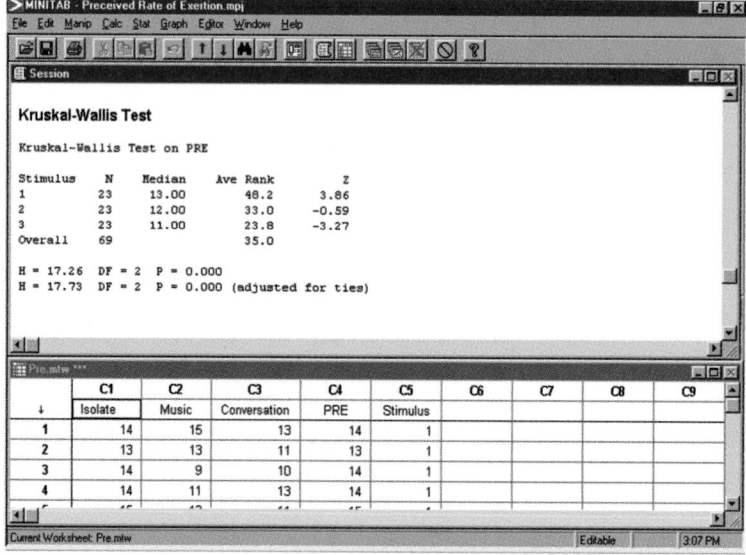

Self-Testing Review 13.5

51. In Exercise 10.48 (page 436), a psychologist read a sequence of digits to people in their 30s, 50s, 60s, and 70s, and each subject was asked to recite them in reverse order. The following data represent the number of digits correctly recited by each subject (Data = Digits):

30s	50s	60s	70s
4	3	4	5
5	5	7	3
6	3	7	7
8	7	4	
6	7		

Use a Kruskal-Wallis procedure at the .01 level to test the hypothesis that the population means for all four age groups are equal.

52. In Exercise 10.50 (page 437), Maria Riggio compared the sales of pasta displayed at three different shelf levels. The number of packages sold in a week at different stores using different levels are recorded below (Data = Pasta):

Eye Level	Waist Level	Knee Level
98	106	103
106	105	95
111	98	87
85	93	94
108	96	92

Is there a significant difference in sales at the .01 level based on the shelf locations of the packages?

53. To see if the 4 machines in operation are performing with equal efficiency, an industrial engineer draws 6 random samples of 100 items produced by each of the machines and records the number of items in each that do not meet specifications. The data are (Data = Macheffy)

Machine A	Machine B	Machine C	Machine D
5	7	3	7
5	6	6	6
6	6	8	5
4	7	4	2
6	7	7	5
6	5	4	3

What conclusions can you reach at the .05 level about the efficiency of the four machines?

54. In Self-Testing Review 10.2, problem 22 (page 411), a retailer compared the daily traffic count at three locations. The following data were the result (Data = MallLoc):

Location X	Location Y	Location Z
643	249	458
542	404	513
537	564	475
484	745	536
464	353	364
369	647	738
478	351	594

Test the hypothesis at the .05 level that the mean traffic count is the same for all three locations.

55. In Self-Testing Review 10.2, problem 18 (page 410), a track coach compared three training methods. After a month of training, each runner was timed in a mile run. The data are as follows (times in minutes) (Data = MileRun):

Group A	Group B	Group C
4.81	4.43	4.38
4.62	4.50	4.29
5.02	4.32	4.33
4.65	4.37	4.36
	4.41	

Conduct a Kruskal-Wallis test at the .05 level to see if the mean times for all three groups are equal.

56. In Self-Testing Review 10.2, problem 17 (page 410), accountants representing four schools were randomly selected, and the number of errors committed by each accountant over a two-week period was recorded as follows (Data = AcctgErr):

School A		School B		School C		School D	
14	22	17	16	19	18	23	9
16	9	16	12	20	19	12	15
17	10	18	14	22	15	21	16
13		15		21		10	

Conduct a Kruskal-Wallis test at the .01 level. Is there a significant difference in accuracy?

57. In Exercise 10.55 (page 437), a sales manager compared the sales (in thousands of dollars) of salespeople dressed in various attire. The data for a four-week period were (Data = DressCod):

Business Suits		Casual Outfits		Jeans	
26	33	19	25	22	29
37	40	24	24	33	31
41		31	29	34	
35		28	32	19	
29		23		25	

Use a Kruskal-Wallis test at the .05 level to make a statistical decision about the dress code.

58. In Self-Testing Review 10.2, problem 24 (page 412), sales of cameras at various prices were compared. The number of cameras sold in a week were as follows (Data = PriceCam):

Price 1	Price 2	Price 3	Price 4
3	5	10	8
5	4	9	4
7	6	4	5
4	9	5	7

What conclusion can be made at the .05 level of significance?

59. Due to a clerical error on the part of a chicken farmer, four truckloads of chickens arrive at a processing plant at the same time. The receiving supervisor must select one of the truckloads and send the others back. To see if the average weights in all four truckloads are the same, random samples are drawn from each truckload. The weights in pounds are as follows:

Truck 1	Truck 2	Truck 3	Truck 4
4.3	3.7	4.1	3.4
3.7	3.6	3.9	4.1
3.8	4.0	3.4	4.2
4.2	3.8	4.2	3.9
3.9	3.7	3.8	4.0
			3.7

What decision should the supervisor make at the .05 level?

60. A psychology professor believes that the amount of time his students spend studying is affected by the semester. In a year-long experiment, students were randomly selected during the three different semesters and asked to estimate the number of hours they spent studying per week. The hourly estimates were

Fall	Winter	Spring	Fall	Winter	Spring
4	7	7	3	6	3
3	11	5	4	5	4
6	12	6		4	7
7	8	4		7	
5	13	4			

What should the professor conclude at the .05 level?

61. In Self-Testing Review 10.2, problem 15 (page 409), students from three majors were asked a series of questions to determine their opinions on the quality of a class in statistics, where a high score indicated the students thought the class was worthwhile. The following data represent a sample of responses from each of the three majors (Data = TestOpin):

Forestry	Ecology	Water Resources
11	10	3
9	4	6
19	0	2
18	13	9
8	18	1
	14	7
		2
		5

Test the hypothesis at the .05 level that the population mean responses for the three majors are equal.

62. Researchers at a pharmaceutical company want to know if the three leading brands of ASA are really different in terms of speed of relief. Volunteers were randomly assigned to use brand A, brand B, or brand C. Each was instructed to take the recommended dosage when a headache began and to record the number of minutes that elapsed before relief. Use the following data (in minutes) to conduct a Kruskal-Wallis test at the .05 level to see if there's a significant difference in the speed of relief:

Brand A	Brand B	Brand C
7.3	6.3	7.4
8.5	7.9	7.8
6.4	5.6	6.9
7.9	7.2	8.5
6.7		7.3
6.7		
7.1		
9.0		

63. At USGS, the Web site of the U.S. Geological Survey, data was given on earthquakes registering over 5.5 on the Richter scale in 5 broad geographic areas. Use the data to conduct a Kruskal-Wallis test at the .05 level to see if there's a significant difference in the mean of these amounts (Data = Richter):

Pacific Ocean		Atlantic Ocean	Indian Ocean	Russia/ Ukraine	U.S.
6.5	5.8	5.6	5.7	5.5	5.9
5.7	5.7	5.7	6.3	6.2	5.5
6.5	5.5	5.5	5.8		
5.5	5.5		5.5		
5.8	5.5		6.3		
5.8	5.5		5.9		
5.9	5.8		5.5		
5.9	5.5		5.7		
5.8	6.1				

64. The Web site of the World Health Organization (WHO), at <u>WHOMalar</u>, reported on many characteristics of malaria cases around the world. One characteristic was the number of cases of malaria per 1,000 people for countries in various areas. Use the data to conduct a Kruskal Wallis test at the .01 level to see if there's a significant difference in the mean number of cases of malaria (Data = Malaria):

Central America	South America	West Asia	Mid-, South Asia	East Asia
27.0	0.2	1.6	1.0	39.6
8.1	7.2	1.0	144.5	0.1
0.1	9.1	10.1	2.6	0.1
0.9	7.9	0.9	1.9	9.4
14.5	6.5	3.7	31.5	2.0
2.0	39.2	0.1		3.2
16.6	49.1	2.2		8.7
0.3	0.3	4.3		460.5
6.5	7.1			3.5
0.3	4.5			86.2
	1.3			4.3

13.6 Runs Test for Randomness

A financier wants to examine the recent increases and/or declines in the daily Dow Jones Industrial Average (DJIA) to see if these changes are random or if there's an order or pattern to the changes that might affect her portfolio. To satisfy her curiosity, the financier can conduct a **runs test for randomness**—a test that can show if randomness exists or if there's an underlying pattern in a sequence of sample data. The test is based upon the number of runs, or series, of identical types of results in sequential data. For example, if the financier noticed that for 15 consecutive business days the DJIA had a string, or run, of 15 consecutive losses, she might readily conclude that there is a pattern in the behaviour of the stock market. Unfortunately, decision making isn't always as clear-cut as the preceding sentence might suggest. Therefore, the runs test is another hypothesis-testing procedure that is designed to assist decision makers.

Procedure for Conducting a Runs Test

Suppose the DJIA for the most recent 15 consecutive business days reflected the following changes:

Day:	1	2	3	4	5	6	7	8	9	10	11	12	13	14	15
Change:	+	+	−	−	+	+	+	+	+	−	−	+	+	−	+

The plus signs indicate an increase over the preceding day, while the negative signs reflect a decrease over the preceding day.

Step 1: State the Null and Alternative Hypotheses The hypotheses for our runs test are

H_0: There is randomness in the DJIA sequential data under analysis.
H_1: There is a pattern in the sequential DJIA data under analysis.

The runs test is designed to detect a pattern in the sequence of data, but it cannot tell us the nature of the pattern. Thus, in our example, the test might tell us that there is a pattern to stock market changes, but the test alone won't prove that the pattern is in an upward or downward direction.

Step 2: "Select" the Level of Significance This second step usually involves options in selecting the level of significance, but the table we'll soon use limits us now to an α value of .05.

Step 3: Count the Number of Runs On the basis of the sequence of signs, can the financier conclude randomness, or is there a pattern? To answer this question we must first count the number of runs. Since a run is a series of consecutive signs that are the same, this is done in the following manner, using the preceding data:

Change:	+ +	− −	+ + + + +	− −	+ +	−	+
Run:	1	2	3	4	5	6	7

There are seven runs in the sequence of data. The first run is a series of two pluses; the second run is a series of two minuses; the third run is a group of five pluses; and so on. Thus, we may state that r (the number of runs) = 7. Given our data, do the seven runs show a random movement in the stock market, or is there a possible pattern to the runs?

Step 4: Count the Frequency of Occurrence The next step in a runs test is to first identify the number of elements of one type of data (which is labelled n_1) and then identify the number of elements of the other type of data (which is labelled n_2). For our data, we have ten pluses (and thus $n_1 = 10$) and five negatives (therefore $n_2 = 5$). If there had been a case of no change in the DJIA (that is, a tie), that case would not have been counted.

Step 5: State the Decision Rule We'll assume here that n_1 and n_2 are each ≤ 20. (Runs test procedures are available when n_1 or n_2 are > 20, but we'll not consider them in this text.) We next refer to the tables in Appendix 9. These tables are based on the assumption that H_0 is true, and they provide critical values of r based upon n_1, n_2, and a level of significance of .05. The following decision rule is used to compare the sample r value (r) with the table r values.

Reject H_0 if $r \leq$ critical r value from Appendix 9, Table (a), or if $r \geq$ critical table r value found in Appendix 9, Table (b).

Step 6: Look up the Critical Table r Values Since we have $n_1 = 10$ and $n_2 = 5$, the corresponding r critical value from Appendix 9, Table (a), is 3, and the r critical value from Appendix 9, Table (b), is 12. Appendix 9 thus tells us that in a random sequence of 15 observations where 10 pluses and 5 minuses are noted, the chances of getting 3 or less or 12 or more runs is only 5 percent.

Step 7: Make the Statistical Decision Since $r = 7$ and thus falls between the table values, we fail to reject the null hypothesis. Seven runs are not unlikely in a random sequence of 15 observations that are similar to our sample data. The financier may therefore conclude that there has been no detectable pattern of behaviour in the stock market for the past 15 days.

Figure 13.13 summarizes the procedure for conducting a runs test for randomness.

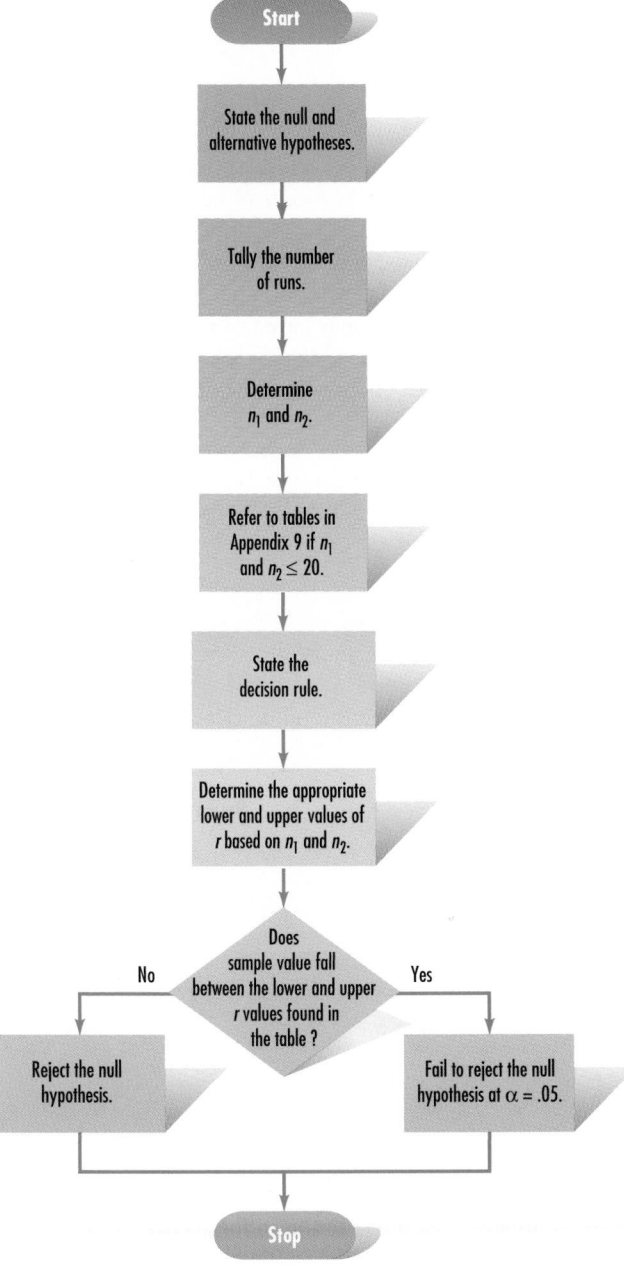

FIGURE 13.13 Procedure for the runs test.

FIGURE 13.14 To have MINITAB analyze the Dow Jones data, we denote each + sign by a 1 and each − sign by a 0. Then click on **Stat, Nonparametrics, Runs Test,** enter the column of 1's and 0's in the box below **Variables,** click in the circle next to **Above and below the mean,** and click on **OK.**

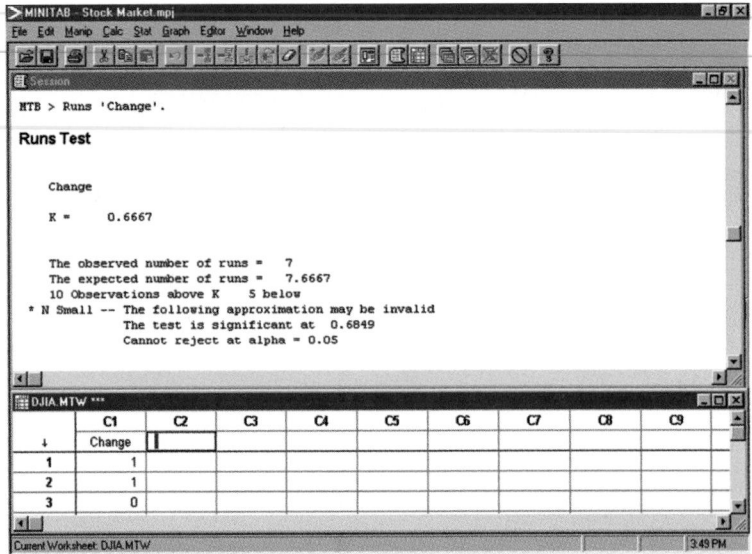

The way to do a runs test on MINITAB depends on the form of the data. We may have a series of + and − signs (or some other symbol) indicating whether the sequence goes up or down at each step, or we may have raw data for which the increases and decreases have not been determined. This example is based on a series of + and − signs, while the next example will be based on raw data. The output in *Figure 13.14* reports "The observed number of runs" as 7, matching the result of the DJIA example.

> However, the *p*-value reported is a large sample approximation, so we should ignore it and still use Appendix 9 to do the test.

Example 13.5   **See Sea Otters Run?** The *Friends of the Sea Otter* provide information on the survival of sea otters. The following table, found at SeaOtter, gives the number of sea otters found in the spring over a 15-year period. At a level of significance of .05, test to see if the number of sea otters found in the spring is random (Data = SeaOtter):

Year	Spring Count	Year	Spring Count
1982	1,346	1990	1,678
1983	1,275	1991	1,941
1984	1,304	1992	2,101
1985	1,360	1993	2,239
1986	1,570	1994	2,359
1987	1,650	1995	2,377
1988	1,724	1996	2,278
1989	856		

◆ **Solution:**
The hypotheses are

H_0: There is randomness in the number of sea otters found in the spring.
H_1: There is a pattern in the number of sea otters found in the spring.

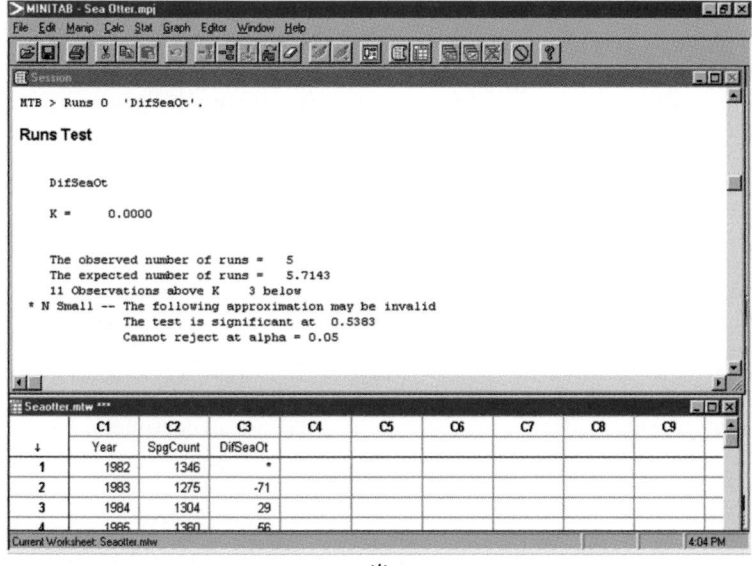

(a)

(b)

FIGURE 13.15 (a) To obtain the differences, click on **Stat, Time Series, Differences,** enter the column to be differenced in the box to the right of **Series,** the column to receive the results in the box to the right of **Store differences in,** and click **OK.** (The asterisk in the first position of C3 is MINITAB's "missing value" code and is due to there not being any previous year's data to subtract from the first year's count.) (b) To perform the test, click on **Stat, Nonparametrics, Runs Test,** enter the column of differences in the box below **Variables,** click in the circle to the left of **Above and below,** enter a zero in the box to the right, and click **OK.**

To figure the number of runs, we use MINITAB to compute the differences in the spring counts of successive years, resulting in the differences in *Figure 13.15a*. There we see five runs. Counting the number of positive and negative differences, we find that $n_1 = 11$ and $n_2 = 3$. With a level of significance of .05, from Appendix 9, the decision rule is:

Reject H_0 if $r \leq 2$ *or* if $r \geq 8$. Otherwise, fail to reject H_0.

As $r = 5$ is not in the rejection region, we fail to reject the null hypothesis. There is insufficient evidence to indicate a pattern to the spring count of the sea otters. ◆

We can use MINITAB to combine several of the steps above. In *Figure 13.15b*, MINITAB gives "The observed number of runs = 5" (r), and "11 Observations above K [and] 3 below" (n_1 and n_2). So we can use this information with the table of Appendix 9 to complete the test.

Self-Testing Review 13.6

65. What is a runs test?

66. What are the hypotheses in a runs test?

67. Discuss the decision rule for a runs test.

68. In a runs test for randomness, there are ten runs in the data sequence. The value of $n_1 = 19$, and the value of $n_2 = 14$. Should the null hypothesis be rejected at the .05 level?

69. In a runs test for randomness, there are 3 runs in the data sequence, and $n_1 = 9$ and $n_2 = 12$. Should the null hypothesis be rejected at the .05 level?

70. Dee Livery, an obstetrician, wants to see if the sex of newborn babies occurs in random order. For the last 18 births, she has recorded the sexes in the following order: M M F M F F F F F M M F M M M M M. Test for randomness of male and female births at the .05 level.

71. An avid football fan has been keeping track of her team's wins and losses over the past 16 games. The data are W W W W L W W L W W W W L L W W. Test the data for randomness at the .05 level.

72. Howie Marks, a grade-seven teacher, has developed a true/false test, and the correct answers are in the following order: T F T F T F T F T F T F T F T F T F. Test the data for randomness at the .05 level.

73. A stockbroker is watching a particular stock and has kept a daily record of increases and decreases in the stock's price for a three-week period. The data are I I I D D D D D D D I D I D. Test the data for randomness at the .05 level.

74. Gary Grabowski was asked by a friend to play a game involving the flipping of a coin. The friend wins a dollar if a head (H) appears in a flip, and Gary wins a dollar for each tail (T) that appears. After 20 flips, poor Gary is down by $6. Since the coin was provided by the friend, Gary is wondering if the coin is "loaded." The sequence of the results is T T T H H H T H H H H H T T T H H H H H. What can you tell Gary at the .05 level?

75. The median number of defective items produced by a machine in a day is eight. An industrial engineer keeps a record each day to see if the number of defects is above the median (+), below the median (–), or equal to the median (0). For the last 24 days the data are + + + – + – – – – – + – + – – + + + 0 + – – 0 +. Conduct a runs test for the randomness of the data at the .05 level.

76. Sue Courtney, an attorney, is pleading a case before a judge. She has been keeping track of his decisions in favour of the plaintiff (P) or the defendant (D), and wants to see if there's a random pattern to those decisions. The past 26 decisions were P D D D D D D P D D D D D P D D D D D D D P D D D D P P. Conduct a runs test for randomness at the .05 level.

13.7 **Spearman Rank Correlation Coefficient**

The **Spearman rank correlation coefficient,** r_2, is a measure of the degree of relationship between *ranked* data. The coefficient of correlation (r) found in Chapter 12 was computed using the actual values of x and y; the Spearman measure we'll now consider uses rank values for x and y rather than actual values.

Procedure for Computing the Spearman Rank Correlation Coefficient

The Ajax Insurance Corporation has been operating a sales refresher course designed to improve the performance of its sales representatives. A number of classes have completed the course. In an attempt to assess the value of the program, the sales training manager wants to see if there's a relationship between performance in the program and subsequent performance in generating annual sales. Table 13.5 shows the data collected by the manager on 11 ($n = 11$) program graduates.

TABLE 13.5 DATA FOR THE COMPUTATION OF THE SPEARMAN RANK CORRELATION COEFFICIENT

Salesperson	Course Performance Rank (1)	Annual Sales Rank (2)	Difference between Ranks (1 – 2) D (3)	D² (4)
Steele	1	4	–3	9
Spier	2	6	–4	16
Devine	3	1	2	4
Hanlon	4	2	2	4
McCabe	5	7	–2	4
Braman	6	10	–4	16
Seville	7	3	4	16
McNally	8	5	3	9
Reid	9	8	1	1
Silva	10	9	1	1
Gould	11	11	0	0
			$\Sigma D = 0$	$\Sigma D^2 = 80$

$$r_s = 1 - \left(\frac{6\Sigma D^2}{n(n^2 - 1)} \right)$$

$$= 1 - \left(\frac{6(80)}{11(121 - 1)} \right)$$

$$= 1 - .364$$

$$= .636$$

STATISTICS IN ACTION

Tape Away Warts?
Can duct tape be used to remove warts? According to a report in the October 2002 issue of the *Archives of Pediatrics & Adolescent Medicine*, the answer apparently is "yes." Doctors recruited 61 patients between the ages of 3 and 22 and divided them into two groups. Half were treated with cryotherapy, the use of liquid nitrogen to freeze a wart for ten to 20 seconds every two to three weeks. The other half had a small piece of duct tape applied to the warts. The patients were told to leave the tape in place for six days and then to remove it, soak the area in water and then gently rub the area with an emery board or pumice stone. They were to leave the tape off overnight and reapply it the next morning. This treatment continued for two months or until the wart disappeared. The duct tape treatment worked better than cryotherapy. The warts disappeared in 22 of the 26 patients treated, most often within 28 days. Cryotherapy succeeded in removing the warts of only 15 of the 25 patients treated. (The other ten patients did not complete the study.)

Ranking the Data As a first step, the manager ranked each of the 11 representatives according to their performance in the sales course. A rank of 1 was assigned to the person with the best performance; a rank of 2 was given to the next best graduate; and so on. Then, each person was ranked according to sales performance in the subsequent year. A rank of 1 was given to the one who had the most sales; a rank of 2 was given to the one with the next highest sales; and so on. For example, salesperson Steele was considered the best among those who attended the sales course, and Steele had the fourth highest sales in the 12 months following completion of the program.

Computing the Differences between Ranks The next step is the systematic computation of the differences between ranks. These differences, labelled D, are shown in column 3 of Table 13.5. Since Steele had a rank of 1 for course performance but had a lesser rank of 4 for sales results, the difference assigned to Steele is -3.

Computing r_s After obtaining D values for each person, the manager is ready to compute the Spearman measure with the following formula:

$$r_s = 1 - \left[\frac{6 \Sigma D^2}{n(n^2 - 1)} \right]$$ (13.15)

To compute r_s, we must square the differences between ranks and then sum the squared differences—that is, perform the operations represented by ΣD^2 in the numerator of formula 13.5. The last column in Table 13.5 shows the sum of the squared differences. The computations shown in Table 13.5 give us a value of r_s of .636. The same result is produced by MINITAB in *Figure 13.16* when it's supplied with our problem data.

The Pearson product moment correlation coefficient was defined in Chapter 12. That formula could also be used here to find the Spearman Rank correlation coefficient. The only difference is that the ranks of the numbers would be used, rather than the actual values of the variables. Formula 13.5 above is a shortcut formula, which is algebraically equivalent to the formula for r in Chapter 12, except that ranks are used instead of raw

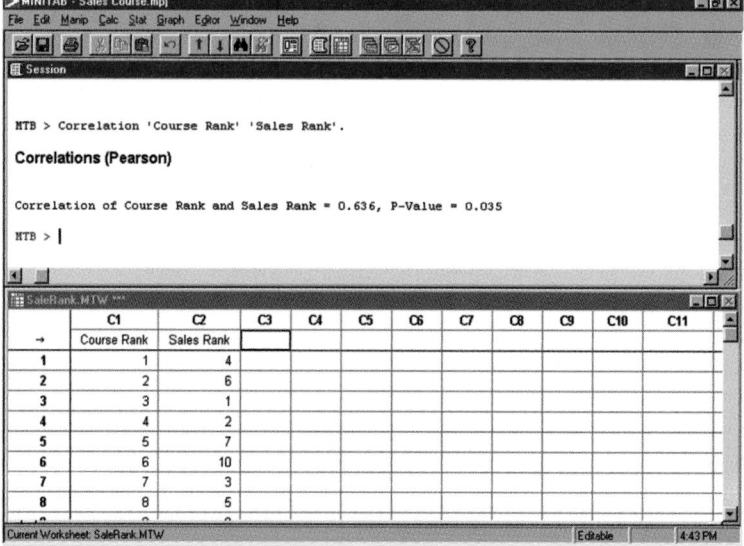

FIGURE 13.16 To obtain this MINITAB output, click on **Stat, Basic Statistics, Correlation,** enter the columns with the ranks in the box below **Variables,** click in the box to the left of **Display p-values,** and click **OK.**

data. (The shortcut formula is not exact when there are tied measurements, but it is a good approximation when the total number of ties is small relative to n.)

As a basis for interpreting r_s, you should keep in mind that when r_s (like r in Chapter 12) is close to zero, there's little evidence of a relationship between the ranks. And, like r in Chapter 12, when r_s is close to $+1.00$ or -1.00, there's strong evidence of a relationship between the ranks. In our example, therefore, the manager might conclude that there's a positive relationship between course performance and subsequent sales activity.

Testing r_s for Significance

A more formal testing procedure may be carried out to see if there's truly a relationship as suggested by r_s.

Step 1: State the Null and Alternative Hypotheses The null hypothesis is established to indicate no relationship between population course performance and sales performance ranks—that is,

H_0: $\rho_s = 0$

where ρ_s is the population rank correlation coefficient

Since the training manager prefers to believe that the course improves selling skills, a right-tailed test is appropriate, and the alternative hypothesis is that there's a positive relationship between course performance and sales performance—that is,

H_1: $\rho_s > 0$

Step 2: Select the Level of Significance Let's assume the manager wants to conduct the test at the .05 level of significance.

Step 3: Determine the Test Distribution to Use The familiar t distribution that's found in Appendix 4 is appropriate for this test. The correct degrees of freedom (df) row to select for this test is found by using $n - 2$, since we have two variables (course performance and sales performance).

Step 4: Define the Rejection or Critical Region What's the t critical value in Appendix 4 that is the start of the rejection region in this one-tailed test? With $n - 2$, or $11 - 2$, or 9 degrees of freedom at the .05 level, the critical value is 1.833.

Step 5: State the Decision Rule The decision rule for this right-tailed test at the .05 level is

Reject H_0 in favour of H_1 if the test statistic $t > 1.833$. Otherwise, fail to reject H_0.

Step 6: Compute the Test Statistic If the sample size is at least ten, we may compute the test statistic with this formula:

$$t = r_s \sqrt{\frac{n - 2}{1 - r_s^2}}$$
(13.6)

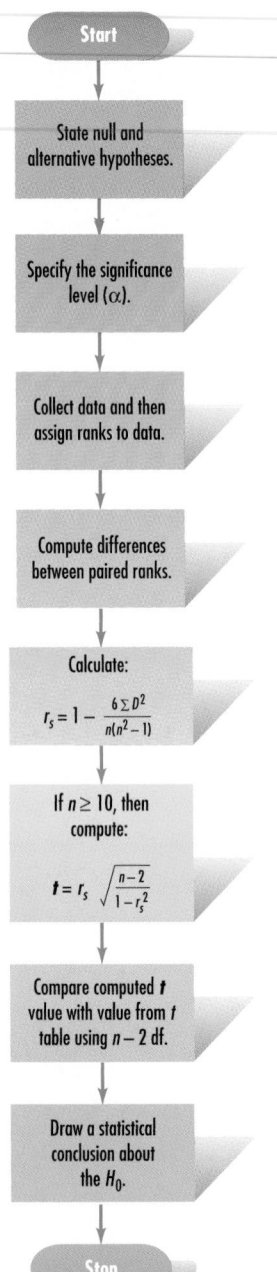

FIGURE 13.17 Procedure for computing and testing the Spearman rank correlation coefficient.

On the basis of our data, we have

$$t = .636\sqrt{\frac{11-2}{1-.636^2}} = .636\sqrt{\frac{9}{1-.404}} = +2.47$$

Step 7: Make the Statistical Decision Since $t = 2.47$ is greater than 1.833, the null hypothesis is rejected. We can conclude that there's a relationship between participation in the sales course and subsequent sales performance.

MINITAB performs the calculations necessary for a two-tailed hypothesis test. In *Figure 13.16*, we requested the p-value for the rank correlation, which is given as .035. The p-value of the preceding right-tailed test is (because the rank correlation is positive) .035/2 = .0175, leading to a rejection of the H_0 at a level of significance of .05. *Figure 13.17* summarizes the procedure for computing r_s and testing its significance.

Example 13.6   **Blowin' in the Wind** *Canadian Geographic* magazine has identified Canada's smoggiest places. The cities below are ranked according to the amount of ground-level ozone (1 = lowest). Calculate the Spearman rank correlation between ozone and population size and test its significance (Data = Ozone):

City	Ozone Rank	Population
St. John's	1	101,900
Victoria	2	73,500
Winnipeg	3	618,500
Calgary	4	768,000
Vancouver	5	514,000
Saint John	6	72,500
Halifax	7	114,900
Oshawa	8	134,400
Montréal	9	1,016,400
Hamilton	10	322,400
Ottawa	11	323,300
Windsor	12	197,700
Toronto	13	653,700
Kitchener	14	178,400

◆ **Solution:**
The hypotheses are

$H_0: \rho_s = 0$
$H_1: \rho_s \neq 0$

Choosing a level of significance of .05, the decision rule is

Reject H_0 in favour of H_1 if the p-value < .05. Otherwise, fail to reject H_0.

MINITAB was used to do the calculations. Its correlation commands yield the rank correlation, .253, and its associated p-value, .383 (see *Figure 13.18*). Because .383 is not < .05, we would not conclude that there is a correlation between the population size and the amount of ground-level ozone. ◆

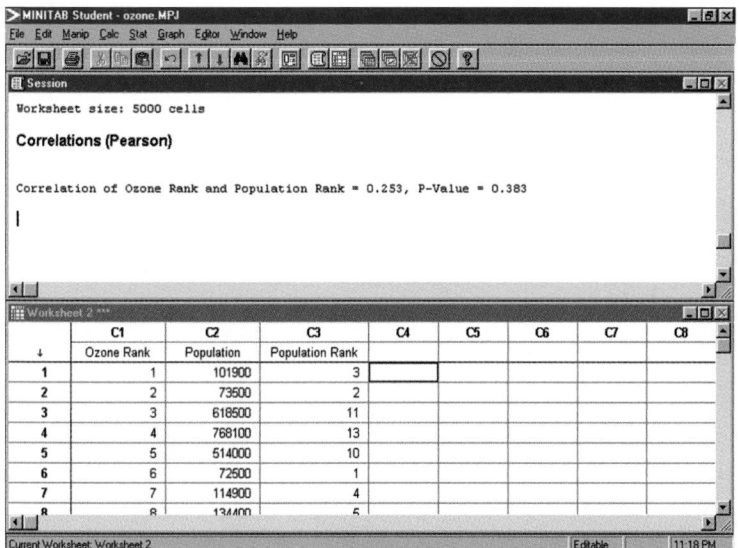

FIGURE 13.18 The second column of raw data was converted to ranks by clicking on **Manip, Rank,** then specifying the original data column and a column to receive the ranks. Once the ranks are obtained, **MINITAB's Correlation** command is used to obtain the output for the air pollution data.

Self-Testing Review 13.7

77. What is the Spearman rank correlation coefficient?

78. What may be concluded if

    a) $r_s = .03$

    b) $r_s = -.98$

    c) $r_s + 1.29$

79. If $\Sigma D^2 = 52$ and $n = 6$, what is the value of r_s?

80. If $r_s = .58$ and $n = 12$, what is the value of the test statistic? What are the critical values at the .01 level of significance? What would the decision be in a two-tailed hypothesis test for the significance of r_s?

81. *Arbitron's* annual spring ratings for radio stations in Mercer County for last year and for this year are given as follows:

Station	Rank Last Year	Rank This Year
KTXR	1	1
KOGL	2	3
KPST	3	8
KYSP	4	2
KUSL	5	6
KMSF	6	7
KIOQ	7	5
KDJF	8	9
KHXR	9	4

Compute the Spearman rank correlation coefficient.

82. Ranks for the first- and second-half standings for the Office Men's Bowling League are as follows:

Team	First-Half Rank	Second-Half Rank
Duds	1	7
So What?	2	10
Vintage Rock and Roll	3	14
Up in Smoke	4	2
Two D's and a Sub	5	9
A Beautiful Thing	6	11
3UDSU	7	4
Zebkuhler	8	3
Jerry's Kids	9	12
Skid Row Hook	10	6
Tri Right	11	8
Bo's Bach	12	1
Woulda Coulda Did	13	13
VHS	14	5

Find the Spearman rank correlation coefficient and use a two-tailed test for significance at the .01 level.

83. *Canadian Geographic* magazine has identified Canada's smoggiest places. The cities below are ranked according to the amount of ground-level ozone (1 = lowest) and according to the amount of fine-airborne-particulate matter $(PM_{2.5})(1 = \text{lowest})$.

City	Ozone Rank	$PM_{2.5}$ Rank
St. John's	1	1
Victoria	2	3
Winnipeg	3	5
Calgary	4	14
Vancouver	5	7
Saint John	6	4
Halifax	7	2
Oshawa	8	6
Montréal	9	10
Hamilton	10	12
Ottawa	11	8
Windsor	12	13
Toronto	13	9
Kitchener	14	11

Compute the Spearman rank correlation coefficient and test at the .05 level to see if there's a significant positive correlation between the amount of ground-level ozone and the amount of fine-airborne-particulate matter.

84. Abner Doubleplay, pitching coach for the Crossville Tigers, has noticed that in recent years some of the successful pitchers in the league were overweight. This has led Abner to wonder if weight affects pitching performance. Weight figures and winning percentages have

Compute the Spearman rank correlation coefficient and test it for a significant positive correlation at the .05 level.

89. A health professional wants to see if there's a relationship between the number of hours a week a person exercises and the number of pounds a person weighs above his or her ideal weight. A sample of seven people are ranked by the number of hours they exercise each week (low numbers were assigned the low ranks), and by the number of pounds they are overweight (low weights were assigned the low ranks). The data are:

Person	Hours Exercise Rank	Overweight Rank
A	1.5	6
B	5	3
C	6	2
D	7	1
E	3	5
F	4	4
G	1.5	7

Compute the Spearman rank correlation coefficient.

90. A manager working for a large chain of retail outlets is in charge of two stores. She wants to see if there's a relationship between gross sales in corresponding departments of the two stores. She ranks eight departments in store A from the highest sales (a rank of 1) to the lowest (a rank of 8) and does the same for the corresponding departments in store B. The data are

Department	Store A	Store B
1	1	3.5
2	2	1
3	4.5	5
4	7	8
5	8	3.5
6	3	7
7	4.5	2
8	6	6

Compute the Spearman rank correlation coefficient.

91. Is there a relationship between the number of stores and sales by foodservice chains in western Canada? *Western Hospitality News* obtained data on the number of stores and estimated sales in 1999. The following listing gives the sales ranking from 1 to 50 (where 1 = highest) and the number of stores ranking from 1 to 50 (where 1 = highest) (Data = RankSales):

Company	Sales Ranking	Number of Stores Ranking	Company	Sales Ranking	Number of Stores Ranking
McDonald's	1	2	Humpty's	25.5	27
KFC	2	6	Triarc	27	21
Tim Hortons	3	5	Taco Time	28.5	14
A & W	4	4	Panagopoulos Pizza	28.5	12
Subway Sandwiches	5	1	Dorden	30	46.5
Boston Pizza	6	13	Ricky's	31	32
Dairy Queen	7	7	B. C. Ferry Corp.	32	43
Earl's	8	30	Little Caesar	33	24.5
Wendy's	9	17	Country Style	34.5	20
White Spot	10	22	Taco Bell	34.5	35
Spectra Group	11	31	Mr. Submarine	36.5	18
Comac Food	13	8	Cara Operations	36.5	37
Pizza Hut	13	10	Albert's	38.5	45
Smitty's	13	19	Joey's	38.5	26
The Keg Steakhouse	15	33.5	Great Canadian Bagel	40	28
Moxie's	16	41	Husky	42	40
Burger King	17	23	Perkins	42	48
Denny's	18.5	33.5	Second Cup Ltd.	42	16
Starbucks Coffee	18.5	15	Elephant And Castle	44	46.5
Robin's Donuts	20.5	11	Harvey's	45	38.5
Hudson's Bay	20.5	9	Chicken Chef	46	38.5
7 Eleven	23	3	Old Spaghetti	48.5	50
ABC Country	23	36	Brewsters Brew	48.5	49
Kelsey's	23	42	2 for 1 Pizza	48.5	24.5
Swiss Chalet	25.5	44	Gould Group	48.5	29

Compute the Spearman rank correlation coefficient and test it to see if there's a significant correlation at the .05 level.

92. Based on *Maclean's* third and fourth annual studies of health care services available in communities across Canada, the health regions listed below were assigned scores according to the overall quality of health care in 2001 and again in 2002.

Health Region	2001 Score	2002 Score	Health Region	2001 Score	2002 Score
Calgary	85.0	82.7	Toronto	84.9	83.3
Edmonton	85.6	86.1	Winnipeg	83.2	82.6
Halifax/Dartmouth	81.7	82.4	Brantford	80.0	80.1
Hamilton	84.5	84.4	North/West Vancouver	89.5	87.7
Kingston	81.0	79.4	Peterborough	80.1	80.1
Montréal	82.6	80.5	Regina	82.1	82.7
Ottawa	84.2	83.4	Surrey	83.0	81.8
Saskatoon	85.4	83.7	Victoria	85.3	86.1
St. John's	76.1	76.0			

For each of these two years, assign a rank to each of the scores, starting with a rank of 1 for the highest score. Then compute the Spearman rank correlation coefficient and test it for significance at the .05 level.

L O O K I N G   B A C K

1. A researcher is often limited by the imprecise quantitative properties of the data available for analysis. For example, the data may be limited to only a few items, and there may be little or no knowledge of the shape of the population distribution and its effect on the sampling distribution. When such problems arise, non-parametric techniques may be used. In this chapter, we've discussed only a few of the common non-parametric techniques, and we've limited our attention primarily to small-sample cases.

2. When one wishes to see if there are significant differences between paired rank data that are drawn from dependent samples, the sign test or the Wilcoxon signed rank test may be appropriate. If the magnitude or size of the differences between paired data is to be considered in decision making, the Wilcoxon signed rank test should be used; if only the direction of differences is needed for a decision, the sign test is sufficient.

3. The Mann-Whitney test is used when differences between rank data are under study and when the data are drawn from two independent samples.

4. The Kruskal-Wallis test is a non-parametric alternative to the one-way ANOVA test discussed in Chapter 10. But unlike that earlier test, the Kruskal-Wallis test can be used with ordinal data and it doesn't require that the populations under study have normal distributions.

5. In the case of a single sample with sequential data, a runs test for randomness may be conducted. This test is designed to detect the presence or absence of pattern or order in the sequential data.

6. Finally, we discussed the Spearman rank correlation coefficient. This measure is a correlation coefficient for paired rank data. The computation of r_s provides a measure of association between two variables.

Exercises

93. A pharmaceutical company decides to conduct preliminary tests to gauge the effectiveness of *Efichol,* a new drug designed to lower cholesterol levels. The company tests the cholesterol level of a random sample of ten people before and after they use the new drug. The data are

Person	Level before Use	Level after Use
A	263	214
B	194	188
C	273	284
D	185	185
E	238	264
F	212	190
G	189	185
H	164	153
I	248	248
J	261	229

Use a sign test of paired differences to test the effectiveness of the medicine at the .05 level.

94. The pharmaceutical company is now interested in doing more detailed tests of the effectiveness of the drug. Use the data in problem 93 to conduct a Wilcoxon signed rank test to test the effectiveness of the medicine at the .05 level.

95. Andrew Schaffner, a meteorologist, wants to see if there's a pattern in average daily temperatures, and so he keeps records of increases (+), decreases (−), and no changes (0) in temperatures for the month of July. The data are + + + − − − − + − 0 0 + + + + + + − − − − + − 0 0 + + + − 0 −. Conduct a runs test for randomness at the .05 level of significance.

96. In Self-Testing Review 10.3, problem 25 (page 418), a college bicycling club had four groups using different training programs. The following data represent the times (minutes)

required for each member of the four groups to ride a loop that included a 7 percent uphill grade (Data = BikeTrai):

Group 1	Group 2	Group 3	Group 4
84	56	70	47
93	78	59	73
83	56	78	104
61	61	53	71
121		104	69
67		110	99
		40	

Use a Kruskal-Wallis test at the .05 level to test the hypothesis that the means of the four groups are equal.

97. *Canadian Geographic* magazine has identified Canada's smoggiest places. The following cities are ranked according to the population size (1 = lowest) and according to the amount of fine-airborne-particulate matter ($PM_{2.5}$) (1 = lowest).

City	Population Rank	$PM_{2.5}$ Rank
Saint John	1	4
Victoria	2	3
St. John's	3	1
Halifax	4	2
Oshawa	5	6
Kitchener	6	11
Windsor	7	13
Hamilton	8	12
Ottawa	9	8
Vancouver	10	7
Winnipeg	11	5
Toronto	12	9
Calgary	13	14
Montréal	14	10

Compute the Spearman rank correlation coefficient and test at the 0.01 level to see if the population size is positively correlated with the amount of fine-airborne-particulate matter ($PM_{2.5}$).

98. In a study to measure neuropsychological functioning for chronic schizophrenic patients and non-schizophrenic comparison subjects, each participant was given the Benton Visual Retention Test. The number of errors made by a random sample of individuals in each group is given in the following data:

Chronic Schizophrenics	Non-Schizophrenic Comparison Subjects
8	5
6	7
11	9
12	10
8	8
10	
9	

Test the hypothesis at the .01 level that the mean number of errors for both groups is the same. Discuss whether the independent small-sample *t*-test, discussed in Chapter 9, could be used to answer this question.

99. Polly Estevez, owner of Natural Textiles, Ltd., is concerned about the chronically low daily output of her factory workers. Therefore, she has devised a bonus plan and wants to find out if this plan will result in any improvement. (She's not concerned at this time with the degree of productivity improvement.) Eight workers are offered the plan, and their daily output before and after the plan (in hundreds of units) is as follows:

Worker	Output Before	Output After
Harris Tweed	80	85
Stitch N. Thyme	75	75
Les Brown	65	71
Mary Taylor	82	79
Chuck Moore	56	68
Tex Tyle	70	86
Ray Ohn	73	71
Terry Cloth	62	59

Use a sign test at the .05 level to see if the plan has produced a significant improvement.

100. Now Polly would like to investigate further. Use a Wilcoxon signed rank test at the .05 level to see if the workers from problem 99 showed improvement after the bonus plan was introduced.

101. A record of the first digit in the daily number drawing shows the following pattern of odd (o) and even (e) digits. Conduct a runs test for the randomness of the data at the .05 level if the data are o o o e e o e o o e e e o o o e e o e o.

102. In Self-Testing Review 10.2, problem 14 (page 409), a random sample of paid volunteers had their hearing levels tested. The following data represent the pure-tone average (in db HTL) for the subjects who were separated into four age groups (30s, 50s, 60s, and 70s) (Data = Hearing):

30s	50s	60s	70s
9	9	19	18
13	5	8	22
5	8	14	24
5	3	26	
10	15		

Test the hypothesis at the .05 level that the mean hearing level is the same for all age groups.

103. Drivers who receive traffic tickets usually have points put on their licence and suffer an increase in their auto insurance rates. In some provinces, people who do not want points on their licence are allowed to attend traffic school as an alternative. In one such school, attendees are given two written tests on traffic safety, one before the class and another at the end. The results from a random sample of 11 people are

Test 1	Test 2
12	19
12	11
10	10
16	16
14	16
14	14
12	11
17	14
16	18
13	14
16	14

Use the sign test at the .05 level to test the hypothesis that the population of second test values are higher than those in the first test.

104. Use the data in problem 103 and the Wilcoxon signed rank test to test the hypothesis at the .05 level that the second trial values were higher than those in the first trial.

105. In January 2003, the Lemelson-MIT Invention Index reported that samples of teens and adults were asked to rank the top inventions of the 20th century, from a list of five. The rankings of the five inventions by teens and adults were

	Teens	Adults
Personal computer	1	2
Pacemaker	2	1
Wireless communications	3	4
Water purification	4	5
Television	5	3

Calculate the Spearman rank correlation coefficient.

106. A new counselling program is instituted for athletes at Linebacker U. The grade point average (GPA) of a sample of 75 athletes is compared before and after the program, and it is found that 43 improved their GPA, 21 saw their GPA decrease, and the rest found that their GPA remained the same. Use a sign test to determine if the new program is effective at the .05 level in increasing an athlete's GPA.

107. Executives at Trans Earth Airlines have received numerous passenger complaints about late arrivals at Los Angeles Airport. To see if there's a pattern to late arrivals, a record is kept for 28 consecutive flights. (Airlines agree that a plane that arrives within ten minutes of its scheduled arrival time is considered to be on time.) The data (L = late, and O = on time) are L L O O L O O L L L L L L O L L O L L O L L L L L L L O O L L. At the .05 level, is there an arrival pattern, or do the times of arrival occur randomly?

108. As part of environmental impact studies of offshore construction projects, marine biologists try to measure percent cover at nearby underwater locations, an indication of the quantity of marine life. Two devices are used to estimate this quantity. To compare the two devices, both were used to take measurements at a sample of seven locations, with the results in the following table:

Device 1	Device 2
10.51	11.97
20.30	19.47
27.88	30.19
40.56	38.43
47.57	46.23
58.35	57.15
66.63	66.27

Use a sign test at the .05 level to test the hypothesis that the measurements from device 2 are lower than those of device 1.

109. Use the Wilcoxon signed rank test and the data in problem 108 to test the hypothesis at the .05 level that the measurements from device 2 are lower than those of device 1.

110. Mickey Cervelli, sales manager of the Cool Cola Bottling Corporation, wants to know how strong a relationship (if any) there is between daily temperature and sales on corresponding days. Because of poor record-keeping procedures, Mickey must make do with rank data (where the hottest day has been assigned a rank of 1 and the highest sales figure has been assigned a rank of 1). Fifteen days are selected randomly, and the paired data are as follows:

Day	Temperature Rank	Sales Rank
1	6	5
2	11	12
3	4	2
4	7	7
5	1	4
6	12	14
7	8	10
8	2	1
9	15	15
10	14	13
11	5	3
12	10	9
13	13	11
14	9	8
15	3	6

Compute the Spearman rank correlation coefficient and test it for significance at the .05 level. What conclusion can be drawn?

111. The following scores on measures of anxiety are for nicotine-dependent smokers and non-smokers:

Smokers	Non-Smokers
58	86
50	68
44	72
97	63
80	79
63	73
55	72
	52
	43

Test the hypothesis at the .02 level that there is no difference in the mean scores for the two groups.

112. In Self-Testing Review 10.2, problem 16 (page 409), data we collected on the career decision-making skills among students in various school districts. The results are as follows (Data = CareerSk):

District 1	District 2	District 3
17	12	13
9	10	14
13	15	14
16	13	15
12		15
		14

Test the appropriate hypothesis at the .01 level.

113. Two candidates are running for mayor. A random sample of 104 people are asked which candidate they prefer. Candidate A is the choice of 43, and 51 prefer candidate B. The rest have no preference. Use a sign test at the .05 level to see if there's a significant preference for candidate B.

114. The 20 top medical schools in terms of research funds acquired have been ranked for their production of primary care physicians as follows: (Data: *Institutional Goals Ranking Report, Association of American Medical Colleges*)

Research Rank	Primary Care Rank
1	17
2	2
3	18
4	4
5	19
6	20
7	1
8	8
9	7
10	14
11	3
12	15
13	9
14	13
15	6
16	10
17	11
18	12
19	5
20	16

Compute the Spearman rank correlation coefficient and test at the .05 level to see if there is a significant negative correlation between the 2 rankings.

115. A random sample of seven volunteers try a new liquid diet of Slender Fast for two weeks. Their before and after weights (in kilograms) are as follows:

Subject	Before	After
1	60	52
2	76	75
3	93	74
4	52	55
5	80	67
6	61	64
7	50	50

Use a sign test at the .05 level to see if there's a decrease in weight following the liquid diet.

116. Using the data in problem 115 and the Wilcoxon signed rank test, has there been a significant decrease in weight for the Slender Fast volunteers at $\alpha = .05$?

117. A lawn care service is experimenting with Growmoor, a new type of fertilizer. Trials at 57 randomly selected locations are conducted, and it is found that there is an increase in growth in 22 locations, a decrease in 18, and no change in the rest. Use a sign test at the .05 level to see if Growmoor produces an improvement in growth.

118. In writing multiple-choice exams, test writers have different opinions on types of "distracters," that is, the wrong answers. A statistics exam, with the same questions but having four versions with different distracters, is written. The versions are based on the emphasis of the distracters, where version 1 = primarily math errors, version 2 = primarily statistical errors, version 3 = primarily reasonable-appearing answers, and version 4 = combination. The following test grades were achieved by a sample of students:

Version 1	Version 2	Version 3	Version 4
59	88	70	77
93	62	59	73
87	56	68	94
66	61	53	71
91	88	64	69
67	93	80	99
99		40	

Test the hypothesis at the .05 level that the grades are equal for all four versions.

119. A career counsellor claims there is no difference in career decision-making attitudes between students from urban and rural locations. The results of scores from an attitudes test are as follows:

Urban	Rural
32	45
36	42
40	34
32	42
33	29
37	33
	34

Test the counsellor's claim at the .02 level.

120. Anna Tennent, a stockbroker, has recommended 73 stocks over the past year to her clients. At the end of the year, 25 of these stocks had increased in value, 34 had decreased in value, and the rest had stayed the same. Use a sign test at the .05 level to see if Anna picks significantly more stocks that decrease in value.

121. Based on studies done by the Mercer Human Resource Consulting firm, and reported by *The Globe and Mail*, the cities listed below were ranked according to quality of life in 2002 and again in 2003.

City	2003 Rank	2002 Rank
Zurich	1	1
Vancouver	3	2.5
Vienna	3	2.5
Geneva	3	4.5
Sydney	7	4.5
Auckland	7	7.5
Copenhagen	7	7.5
Frankfurt	7	7.5
Bern	7	10.5
Munich	10.5	10.5
Amsterdam	10.5	13
Brussels	13	16
Dusseldorf	13	16
Toronto	13	19.5
Melbourne	17	13
Stockholm	17	13
Luxembourg	17	19.5
Berlin	17	23
Wellington	17	23
Perth	21	19.5
San Francisco	21	19.5
Ottawa	21	27.5
Honolulu	24	23
Montréal	24	27.5
Dublin	24	34.5

City	2003 Rank	2002 Rank
Helsinki	28	7.5
Hamburg	28	27.5
Nurnberg	28	27.5
Tokyo	28	27.5
Calgary	28	31
Oslo	33	16
Brisbane	33	27.5
Paris	33	31
Yokohama	33	31
Adelaide	33	34.5

Compute the Spearman rank correlation coefficient and test it for significance at the .10 level. (Because of the large number of tied ranks, use the Pearson product moment correlation coefficient defined in Chapter 12 to compute r_s.)

122. A second-grade teacher wanted to be sure that he was calling on girls and boys in his class in a random pattern. The data are g b g g b b b g b g g b b g b. Use the runs test at the .05 level to see if there is a random pattern.

123. According to news reports, people in a mountain region of the country of Placebo claim that many of their neighbours live past 100 years of age. The Information Minister of Placebo claims that such longevity is related to the consumption of locally grown rutabagas. The Placebo government has permitted Professor Pry to randomly select and interview 15 residents of the mountain region. A rank of 1 has been assigned to the lowest age and to the lowest level of rutabaga consumption. The data are as follows:

Resident	Age Rank	Rutabaga Consumption Rank
1	6	12
2	13	15
3	5	10
4	10	11
5	8	8
6	15	14
7	2	7
8	1	4
9	14	13
10	12	3
11	3	1
12	7	6
13	11	9
14	9	5
15	4	2

Compute the Spearman rank correlation coefficient. Using a two-tailed test at the .05 level, what conclusion should Professor Pry reach?

124. In Self-Testing Review 10.2, problem 19 (page 410), a middle-school teacher questioned a random sample of middle-school students about how many minutes they watch TV each day after school until bedtime and produced the following data (Data = TVGrades):

Sixth Grade	Seventh Grade	Eighth Grade
459	115	272
311	153	88
152	201	374
293	30	178

Test the appropriate hypothesis at the .05 level.

125. A movie producer investigated the relationship between the budget cost of a movie and the gross income produced by the movie during the first week. The data are

Movie	Budget Rank (1 = highest)	Income Rank (1 = highest)
Star Wars: The Phantom Menace	4	1
Austin Powers: The Spy Who Shagged Me	39	2
The Mummy	9	3
Big Daddy	38	4
The World Is Not Enough	3	5
Runway Bride	12	6
Tarzan	2	7
The Haunting	10.5	8
Pokemon: The First Movie	50	9
Sleepy Hollow	16	10
The Matrix	18.5	11
Wild Wild West	1	12.5
Notting Hill	32	12.5
The Sixth Sense	35	14
Double Jeopardy	35	15
Eyes Wide Shut	16	16
Payback	28.5	17
End of Days	8	18
Life	10.5	19
Entrapment	14	20
Blue Streak	22	21
Deep Blue Sea	22	22
American Pie	48	23
Analyze This	41.5	24
Stigmata	40	25

Movie	Budget Rank (1 = highest)	Income Rank (1 = highest)
The Green Mile	22	26
Bowfinger	25.5	27
The Bone Collector	16	28.5
Message in a Bottle	41.5	28.5
She's All That	50	30
House on Haunted Hill	44	31
Three Kings	30.5	32
Stuart Little	6	33
The Thomas Crown Affair	30.5	34
Varsity Blues	45.5	35
8MM	35	36
Any Given Sunday	25.5	37
Fight Club	18.5	38
Lake Placid	43	39
Instinct	27	40
The 13th Warrior	7	41
Mickey Blue Eyes	35	42
Mystery Men	13	43
The Story of Us	28.5	44
Superstar	47	45
Dogma	50	46
My Favorite Martian	22	47
The Wood	52	48
10 Things I Hate About You	45.5	49
EDtv	22	50
Bicentennial Man	5	51
The Out-of-Towners	35	52

Compute the Spearman rank correlation coefficient and test it for significance at the .05 level.

126. A random sample of subjects were divided into two groups in a clinical test of a new medication to lower cholesterol. The first group was the treatment group (T), which received the medication, and the second group was the control group (C), which received a placebo. The statistician in charge wants to make sure the subjects are assigned to each group in a random pattern. The data are T C T T T C C T C T C T T T T T C. At the .01 level, is the pattern random?

127. A manager at a computer software outlet wants to know if the mean prices at her store are comparable to those of her two closest competitors. As they sell similar but different products, five software packages are selected at random from each store, and the following prices (in dollars) are found at her store and at the competing outlets:

Her Store	Competitor A	Competitor B
144	168	184
136	150	172
146	142	168
134	166	187
150	136	176

At the .05 level, are the mean prices likely to be equal in the three stores?

128. In a study in the *American Journal of Psychiatry,* a random sample of chronic schizophrenic patients and non-schizophrenic comparison subjects made the following scores on the reading subtest of the Wide Range Achievement Test (WRAT):

Chronic Schizophrenics	Non-Schizophrenic Subjects
87	118
91	107
116	110
86	83
116	

Test the hypothesis that there's no difference at the .05 level in the WRAT scores of the two groups.

129. *The Globe and Mail* reported the following profits (in hundreds of thousands of dollars) made by samples of large Canadian Department Stores, Clothing Stores, and Specialty Stores in a recent year.

Department Stores

Company	Profit
Calgary Co-op Assoc.	2.125
Co-op Atlantic	5.063
Hudson's Bay Co.	72.75
Jean Coutu Group	105.9
North West Co. Fund	28.13
Sears Canada	94.1

Clothing Stores

Company	Profit
Boutiques San Francisco	–0.285
Pantorama Industries	1.496
Mark's Work Warehouse	8.180
Reitmans (Canada)	26.934

Specialty Stores

Company	Profit
Canadian Tire Corp.	176.7
Chapters Inc.	17.20
Future Shop	32.38
Grand & Toy Ltd.	10.60

Use the data to conduct a Krushkal-Wallis test at the .01 level to see if there's a significant difference in the mean profits for stores in the three types of industries.

130. A psychologist believes that students from high school A are more aggressive than students from high school B. A psychological test is administered to randomly selected students from each school. A high score on this test represents a high degree of aggression. The following results are obtained:

School A	School B	School A	School B
43	47	41	36
56	68	38	42
31	39		33
30	29		54

Make a statistical decision at the .05 level.

131. The Economics Institute has developed a new forecasting model and wants to see if errors between its estimates and actual results are random or if there's a pattern to the errors. A sequence of 25 estimates was generated and compared with actual results. The errors of overestimation (+) and underestimation (−) are + + − + − + − − − − − + + − − − − + + + + + − + +. What conclusion can you reach at the .05 level?

132. In Exercise 10.49 (page 468), data were collected on a measurement of strength for participants in a study using four different training routines (Data = StrngFrq):

Group 1	Group 2	Group 3	Group 4
27	39	37	24
50	36	28	53
43	47	44	51
31	51	36	51
37		30	45
37		27	65
		44	

Use a Kruskal-Wallis test to test the hypothesis at the .05 level that the mean strength for the participants of the four groups is equal.

133. Does alcohol affect the ability to think? In a double-blind study, one group was given two bottles of beer to drink and then asked to complete a puzzle. A control group was given two bottles of non-alcoholic beer and asked to complete the same puzzle. The length of time (in minutes) it took each person to complete the puzzle was

Control Group	Experimental Group
63	78
57	77
44	75
70	74
50	80
42	55
64	62
56	72
41	66
	43

At the .05 level, do subjects who have consumed alcohol take more time to complete the puzzle?

134. On the television show *The Price is Right*, contestants bid in the Showcase Showdown for various items. The winning contestant is the one who has the highest bid without going over the actual retail price. Scott Michaels, an avid fan of the show, decides to conduct a study of these bids. He records a + for an overbid and a − for an underbid. Scott's data for a period of time are − − − − − − − − − + + + + − − − − − + + − − − − − − + + +. Is the pattern random at the .05 level of significance?

135. Do men and women have the same priorities when looking for a job? The following data published in *Career Development Quarterly* represent the response ranking of samples of men and women to a Life Roles Inventory:

Value	Male Rank	Female Rank
Ability utilization	1	2.5
Achievement	2	2.5
Advancement	3	13
Aesthetics	4	17
Altruism	5	5
Authority	6	11
Autonomy	7	6
Creativity	8	10
Economics	9	7
Lifestyle	10	12
Personal development	11	1
Physical activity	12	14
Prestige	13	8
Risk	14	19
Social interaction	15	16
Social relations	16	4
Variety	17	15
Working conditions	18	9
Cultural identity	19	18
Physical prowess	20	20

Calculate the Spearman rank correlation coefficient and test it at the .05 level.

136. An engineering student examined the minimum bursting pressure of a certain type and size of PVC irrigation pipe. The manufacturer claims a mean bursting pressure of more than 400 psi. A sample of ten such pipes was experimentally determined to have the following bursting pressures:

401   359   383   427   414   415   389   463   394   428

Use a Wilcoxon signed rank test with a level of significance of .05 to test to see if the manufacturer's claim appears true.

137. Transcutaneous electrical nerve stimulation (TENS) devices are frequently used in the management of acute and chronic pain. An important component of the TENS system is the skin electrode. A study reported in the *Journal of Physical Therapy* was to determine conductive differences among electrodes used with TENS devices. A random sample of 11 electrodes in the low-impedance group produced impedance measures (in ohms) of

1,250   1,200   1,000   1,600   1,350   1,425   1,225   1,725
1,600   1,300   1,690

Use a Wilcoxon signed rank test with a level of significance of .05 to see if the population mean impedance measure for all such electrodes is 1,400. Use the .05 level of significance.

Topics for Review and Discussion

1. What are the differences between parametric tests and non-parametric tests?

2. Name the appropriate non-parametric test to be used in each of the following situations if you want to

  a) See if there is a random pattern in a sequence where responses can be separated into two categories.

  b) See if there is a correlation between paired ordinal data.

  c) See if the means of four populations are likely to be equal.

  d) See if there are real differences between paired ordinal data, and you choose to use a simple testing procedure.

  e) Do a test that uses magnitude as well as direction in the differences between paired ordinal data.

  f) compare data collected from two independent samples.

3. Give three examples of nominal data and three examples of ordinal data.

4. How does the sign test differ from the Wilcoxon signed rank test?

5. Review the hypothesis tests covered in previous chapters and find a parametric counterpart for each of the following:

  a) Kruskal-Wallis test.

  b) Mann-Whitney test.

  c) Wilcoxon signed rank test.

  d) Spearman rank correlation coefficient.

Projects/Issues to Consider

1. Identify a journal article that makes use of a non-parametric statistical technique. Prepare a written report that summarizes the nature of the research.

2. Locate data or conduct an experiment appropriate for a runs test to see if the data sequence exhibits a pattern. You might try noting the sex of each student in the order they enter your statistics class, or you could possibly flip a coin 25 times.

3. Find a set of paired ranked data and compute the Spearman rank correlation coefficient. The sports pages of your local newspaper might be a good data source.

4. Take a sample of students and ask the following questions:

  (*i*) Do you currently have a job?

  (*ii*) How many times in a month do you go out on a date?

  (*iii*) How many hours do you study in a typical week?

  (*iv*) How many hours did you study in a typical week during your last year in high school?

  (*v*) Given a choice of taking one more class in literature, mathematics, or history, which would you take?

  a) Use the sign test to compare the number of hours students study in university to the number of hours they studied in their last year of high school.

  b) Use the Mann-Whitney test to compare the number of hours students who have a job study with those who do not have a job.

5. Use the Wilcoxon signed rank test to compare the number of hours students study in college to the number of hours they studied in their senior year of high school.

6. Use the Kruskal-Wallis test to compare the number of times students go out on a date between those who prefer to take one more class in literature, mathematics, or history.

7. Find the Spearman rank correlation coefficient between the number of hours students study and the number of times they go out on a date, and do a two-tailed test for significance.

Computer/Calculator Exercises

1. In a class project (*Percent Algal and Tree Canopy Cover and Three Different Land Use Patterns along Stenner Creek, San Luis Obispo*), Susi Bernstein described data collected along a 5,200 m section of Stenner Creek. The percentage of algal cover and percentage of tree canopy cover were measured as part of a larger effort to ascertain the quality of rainbow trout and steelhead habitat. The measurements were made along the stream as it passed through (1) an urban area, (2) an agricultural area, and (3) an undisturbed area. Algal growth is promoted by increased water temperatures that occur in areas lacking large, shade-providing trees. A portion of the data follows (Data = Stenner):

Land Use	Percentage Algae	Percentage Canopy
1	50	55
1	50	30
2	60	10
2	0	90
3	90	2
3	95	0

a) Use the Kruskal-Wallis procedure at the .05 level to test the hypothesis that the population mean amounts of algae are equal.

b) Use the Kruskal-Wallis procedure at the .05 level to test the hypothesis that the population mean amounts of canopy cover are equal.

c) Compute the Spearman rank correlation coefficient between algae and canopy cover and test it for significance at the .05 level.

2. We have looked at a data set provided by Jeff Tupen describing characteristics of *Alia carinata*, or the carinate dove shell. It contains morphometric shell variables measured from the shelled gastropod *Alia carinata* from four habitats: B = Benthic (subtidal benthic hard bottom, i.e., a rocky subtidal benchrock outcropping in approximately 10 m), G = Gastroclonium (intertidal [+ 1 m] *Gastroclonium subarticulatum*, hollow branch seaweed), M = Macrocystis (*Macrocystis pyrifera*, giant kelp surface canopies), Z = Zostera (*Zostera marina*, eelgrass). A few lines from the data set follow (Data = Alia3):

Habitat	Sex	Shell Height	Shell Width	Spire Height	Spire Width	Aperature Height	Aperature Width	Shell Angle	Spire Angle
B	f	7.01	3.31	2.50	1.98	3.02	1.45	42.0	44.5
B	f	6.53	3.12	2.23	1.80	2.81	1.25	46.5	47.0
M	f	7.67	3.73	2.70	2.26	3.31	1.62	47.5	50.0
G	f	6.63	3.12	2.14	1.90	2.85	1.38	45.0	55.5
G	f	7.75	3.56	2.39	2.08	3.42	1.61	42.5	44.0
Z	f	6.48	3.51	1.94	1.77	2.91	1.49	55.5	56.0
Z	m	6.81	3.59	2.24	2.04	2.90	1.54	52.0	51.0

a) Use the Mann-Whitney test at the .05 level to test for differences between male and female carinate dove shells on each of the eight variables.

b) Use the Kruskal-Wallis procedure at the .05 level to test the hypothesis that the population means for each of the eight variables are equal at the four habitats.

c) Compute the Spearman rank correlation coefficients between all possible pairs of the eight variables and test each for significance at the .05 level.

3. In a class project (*Morro Bay State Park Tree DBH Comparisons*), Harlan Trammer gave data on the diameter at breast height (dbh) of trees at three possible expansion sites of Morro Bay State Park. A few lines of data follow (Data = MorroDBH):

Section		
A	**F**	**I**
48	32	53
24	44	9
60	54	62
36	33	23
35	33	8

Use the Kruskal-Wallis procedure at the .05 level to test the hypothesis that the population mean dbh's are equal at the three sites.

4. The data that follow are a portion of a data set that reports the 1994 number of cases of AIDS per 100,000 people as reported to the World Health Organization (WHO), with countries divided into five broad geographical areas. Use the Kruskal-Wallis test at the .05 level to see if the mean rate is the same in the five areas (Data = AIDSWHO):

Africa	**Rate**
Algeria	0.3
Angola	1.4
Benin	6
Burkina Faso	0
Botswana	65.6

Eastern Med	**Rate**
Afghanistan	0
Bahrain	0.9
Cyprus	1.2
Djibouti	42.7
Egypt	0

Europe	**Rate**
Albania	0.1
Armenia	0
Austria	2.1
Azerbaijan	0
Belgium	2.3

Southeast Asia	**Rate**
Bangladesh	0
Myanmar	0.5
Nepal	0
Sri Lanka	0
Thailand	17.5

Western Pacific	**1994 Rate**
American Samoa	0
Australia	4.6
Brunei Darussalam	0
Cambodia	0.1
China	0

5. For the data in Example 13.3, obtain the Spearman rank correlation coefficients for all possible pairs of the four variables and test each for significance at the .05 level.

6. Conduct a runs test for the randomness of the percentage of women earning M.S. degrees in science and engineering at the .05 level.

7. Conduct a runs test for the randomness of the percentage of women earning Ph.D. degrees in science and engineering at the .05 level.

8. Use the World Wide Web to access the Data and Story Library at DASLMeth. Click on *Paired t-test* and select one of the stories.

  a) Use the sign test at a level of .05 to test for a significant difference.

  b) Use the Wilcoxon signed rank test at a level of .05 to test for a significant difference.

9. Use the World Wide Web to access the Data and Story Library at DASLMeth. Click on *Mann-Whitney U* and select one of the stories. Test at a level of .05 for a significant difference.

10. Use the World Wide Web to access the Data and Story Library at DASLMeth. Click on *ANOVA* and select one of the stories. Use the Kruskal-Wallis procedure at a level of .05 to test for a significant difference.

11. Use the World Wide Web to access the Data and Story Library at DASLMeth. Click on *Time Series* and select one of the stories. Test the data for randomness at the .05 level.

12. Use the World Wide Web to access the Data and Story Library at DASLMeth. Click on *Correlation* and select one of the stories. Compute the Spearman rank correlation and test it for significance at the .05 level.

Appendices

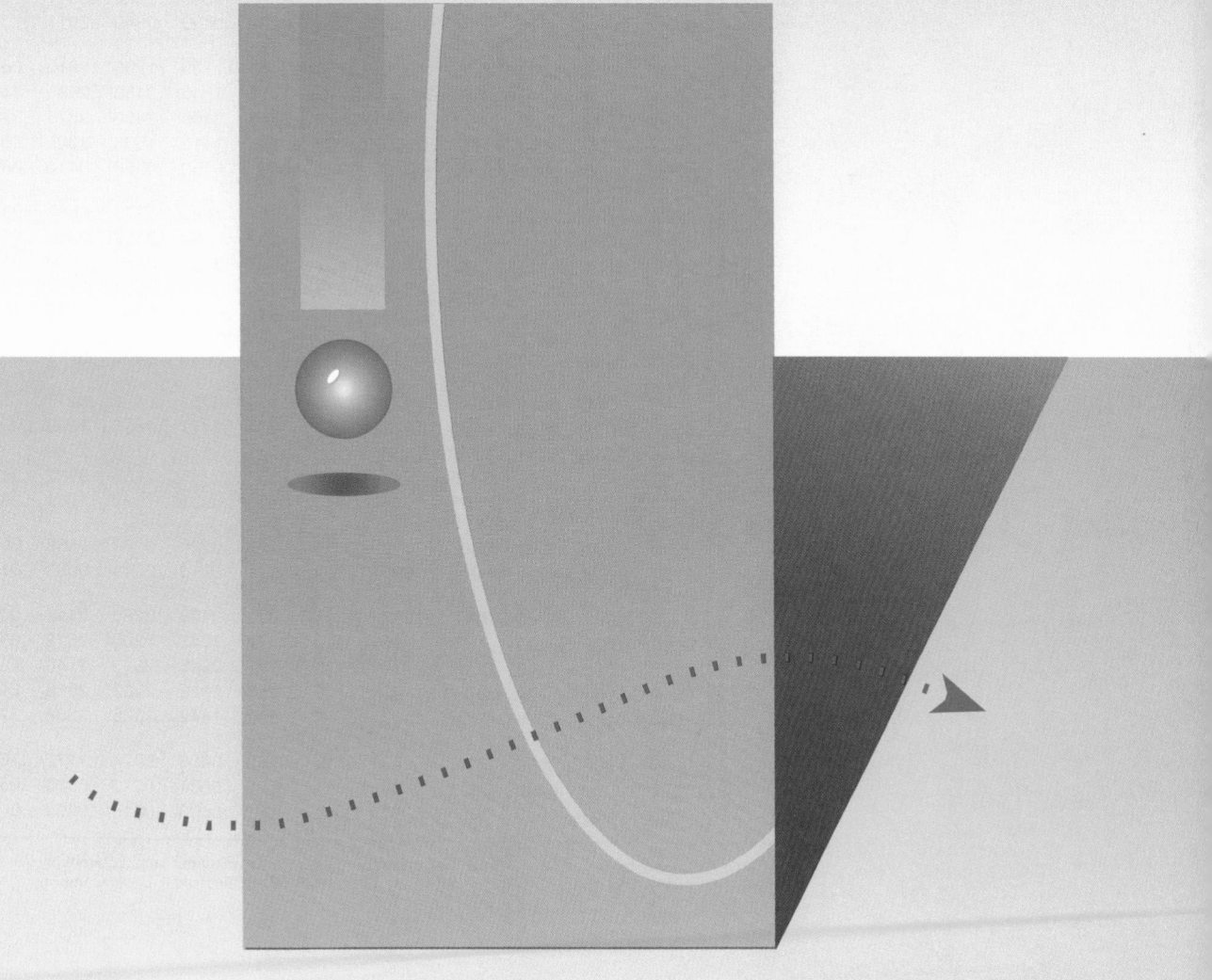

APPENDIX 1 Selected Values of the Binomial Probability Distribution

$$P(r) = \binom{n}{r}(p)^r(q)^{n-r}$$

Example: If $p = .30$, $n = 5$, and $r = 2$, then $P(r) = .3087$. (When p is greater than .50, the value of $P(r)$ is found by locating the table for the specified n and using $n - r$ in place of the given r and $1 - p$ in place of the specified p.)

n	r	.01	.05	.10	.15	.20	.25	p .30	.35	.40	.45	.50
1	0	.9900	.9500	.9000	.8500	.8000	.7500	.7000	.6500	.6000	.5500	.5000
	1	.0100	.0500	.1000	.1500	.2000	.2500	.3000	.3500	.4000	.4500	.5000
2	0	.9801	.9025	.8100	.7225	.6400	.5625	.4900	.4225	.3600	.3025	.2500
	1	.0198	.0950	.1800	.2550	.3200	.3750	.4200	.4550	.4800	.4950	.5000
	2	.0001	.0025	.0100	.0225	.0400	.0625	.0900	.1225	.1600	.2025	.2500
3	0	.9703	.8574	.7290	.6141	.5120	.4219	.3430	.2746	.2160	.1664	.1250
	1	.0294	.1354	.2430	.3251	.3840	.4219	.4410	.4436	.4320	.4084	.3750
	2	.0003	.0071	.0270	.0574	.0960	.1406	.1890	.2389	.2880	.3341	.3750
	3	.0000	.0001	.0010	.0034	.0080	.0156	.0270	.0429	.0640	.0911	.1250
4	0	.9606	.8145	.6561	.5220	.4096	.3164	.2401	.1785	.1296	.0915	.0625
	1	.0388	.1715	.2916	.3685	.4096	.4219	.4116	.3845	.3456	.2995	.2500
	2	.0006	.0135	.0486	.0975	.1536	.2109	.2646	.3105	.3456	.3675	.3750
	3	.0000	.0005	.0036	.0115	.0258	.0469	.0756	.1115	.1536	.2005	.2500
	4	.0000	.0000	.0001	.0005	.0016	.0039	.0081	.0150	.0256	.0410	.0625
5	0	.9510	.7738	.5905	.4437	.3277	.2373	.1681	.1160	.0778	.0503	.0312
	1	.0480	.2036	.3280	.3915	.4096	.3955	.3602	.3124	.2592	.2059	.1562
	2	.0010	.0214	.0729	.1382	.2048	.2637	.3087	.3364	.3456	.3369	.3125
	3	.0000	.0011	.0081	.0244	.0512	.0879	.1323	.1811	.2304	.2757	.3125
	4	.0000	.0000	.0004	.0022	.0064	.0146	.0284	.0488	.0768	.1128	.1562
	5	.0000	.0000	.0000	.0001	.0003	.0010	.0024	.0053	.0102	.0185	.0312
6	0	.9415	.7351	.5314	.3771	.2621	.1780	.1176	.0754	.0467	.0277	.0156
	1	.0571	.2321	.3543	.3993	.3932	.3560	.3025	.2437	.1866	.1359	.0938
	2	.0014	.0305	.0984	.1762	.2458	.2966	.3241	.3280	.3110	.2780	.2344
	3	.0000	.0021	.0146	.0415	.0819	.1318	.1852	.2355	.2765	.3032	.3125
	4	.0000	.0001	.0012	.0055	.0154	.0330	.0595	.0951	.1382	.1861	.2344
	5	.0000	.0000	.0001	.0004	.0015	.0044	.0102	.0205	.0369	.0609	.0938
	6	.0000	.0000	.0000	.0000	.0001	.0002	.0007	.0018	.0041	.0083	.0156
7	0	.9321	.6983	.4783	.3206	.2097	.1335	.0824	.0490	.0280	.0152	.0078
	1	.0659	.2573	.3720	.3960	.3670	.3115	.2471	.1848	.1306	.0872	.0547
	2	.0020	.0406	.1240	.2097	.2753	.3115	.3177	.2985	.2613	.2140	.1641
	3	.0000	.0036	.0230	.0617	.1147	.1730	.2269	.2679	.2903	.2918	.2734
	4	.0000	.0002	.0026	.0109	.0287	.0577	.0972	.1442	.1935	.2388	.2734
	5	.0000	.0000	.0002	.0012	.0043	.0115	.0250	.0466	.0774	.1172	.1641
	6	.0000	.0000	.0000	.0001	.0004	.0013	.0036	.0084	.0172	.0320	.0547
	7	.0000	.0000	.0000	.0000	.0000	.0001	.0002	.0006	.0016	.0037	.0078

Source: Adapted from Leonard J. Kazmier, *Statistical Analysis for Business and Economics,* 2d ed., copyright © 1973 by McGraw-Hill, Inc. Used by permission of McGraw-Hill Book Company.

APPENDIX 1 *(Continued)*

n	r	.01	.05	.10	.15	.20	.25	.30	.35	.40	.45	.50
8	0	.9227	.6634	.4305	.2725	.1678	.1002	.0576	.0319	.0168	.0084	.0039
	1	.0746	.2793	.3826	.3847	.3355	.2670	.1977	.1373	.0896	.0548	.0312
	2	.0026	.0515	.1488	.2376	.2936	.3115	.2965	.2587	.2090	.1569	.1094
	3	.0001	.0054	.0331	.0839	.1468	.2076	.2541	.2786	.2787	.2568	.2188
	4	.0000	.0004	.0046	.0185	.0459	.0865	.1361	.1875	.2322	.2627	.2734
	5	.0000	.0000	.0004	.0026	.0092	.0231	.0467	.0808	.1239	.1719	.2188
	6	.0000	.0000	.0000	.0002	.0011	.0038	.0100	.0217	.0413	.0403	.1094
	7	.0000	.0000	.0000	.0000	.0001	.0004	.0012	.0033	.0079	.0164	.0312
	8	.0000	.0000	.0000	.0000	.0000	.0000	.0001	.0002	.0007	.0017	.0039
9	0	.9135	.6302	.3874	.2316	.1342	.0751	.0404	.0207	.0101	.0046	.0020
	1	.0830	.2985	.3874	.3679	.3020	.2253	.1556	.1004	.0605	.0339	.0176
	2	.0034	.0629	.1722	.2597	.3020	.3003	.2668	.2162	.1612	.1110	.0703
	3	.0001	.0077	.0446	.1069	.1762	.2336	.2668	.2716	.2508	.2119	.1641
	4	.0000	.0006	.0074	.0283	.0661	.1168	.1715	.2194	.2508	.2600	.2461
	5	.0000	.0000	.0008	.0050	.0165	.0389	.0735	.1181	.1672	.2128	.2461
	6	.0000	.0000	.0001	.0006	.0028	.0087	.0210	.0424	.0743	.1160	.1641
	7	.0000	.0000	.0000	.0000	.0003	.0012	.0039	.0098	.0212	.0407	.0703
	8	.0000	.0000	.0000	.0000	.0000	.0001	.0004	.0013	.0035	.0083	.0176
	9	.0000	.0000	.0000	.0000	.0000	.0000	.0000	.0001	.0003	.0008	.0020
10	0	.9044	.5987	.3487	.1969	.1074	.0563	.0282	.0135	.0060	.0025	.0010
	1	.0914	.3151	.3874	.3474	.2684	.1877	.1211	.0725	.0403	.0207	.0098
	2	.0042	.0746	.1937	.2759	.3020	.2816	.2335	.1757	.1209	.0763	.0439
	3	.0001	.0105	.0574	.1298	.2013	.2503	.2668	.2522	.2150	.1665	.1172
	4	.0000	.0010	.0112	.0401	.0881	.1460	.2001	.2377	.2508	.2384	.2051
	5	.0000	.0001	.0015	.0085	.0264	.0584	.1029	.1536	.2007	.2340	.2461
	6	.0000	.0000	.0001	.0012	.0055	.0162	.0368	.0689	.1115	.1596	.2051
	7	.0000	.0000	.0000	.0001	.0008	.0031	.0090	.0212	.0425	.0746	.1172
	8	.0000	.0000	.0000	.0000	.0001	.0004	.0014	.0043	.0106	.0229	.0439
	9	.0000	.0000	.0000	.0000	.0000	.0000	.0001	.0005	.0016	.0042	.0098
	10	.0000	.0000	.0000	.0000	.0000	.0000	.0000	.0000	.0001	.0003	.0010
11	0	.8953	.5688	.3138	.1673	.0859	.0422	.0198	.0088	.0036	.0014	.0005
	1	.0995	.3293	.3835	.3248	.2362	.1549	.0932	.0518	.0266	.0125	.0054
	2	.0050	.0867	.2131	.2866	.2953	.2581	.1998	.1395	.0887	.0513	.0269
	3	.0002	.0137	.0710	.1517	.2215	.2581	.2568	.2254	.1774	.1259	.0806
	4	.0000	.0014	.0158	.0536	.1107	.1721	.2201	.2428	.2365	.2060	.1611
	5	.0000	.0001	.0025	.0132	.0388	.0803	.1321	.1830	.2207	.2360	.2256
	6	.0000	.0000	.0003	.0023	.0097	.0268	.0566	.0985	.1471	.1931	.2256
	7	.0000	.0000	.0000	.0003	.0017	.0064	.0173	.0379	.0701	.1128	.1611
	8	.0000	.0000	.0000	.0000	.0002	.0011	.0037	.0102	.0234	.0462	.0806
	9	.0000	.0000	.0000	.0000	.0000	.0001	.0005	.0018	.0052	.0126	.0269
	10	.0000	.0000	.0000	.0000	.0000	.0000	.0000	.0002	.0007	.0021	.0054
	11	.0000	.0000	.0000	.0000	.0000	.0000	.0000	.0000	.0000	.0002	.0005

APPENDIX 1 *(Continued)*

n	r	.01	.05	.10	.15	.20	.25	.30	.35	.40	.45	.50
12	0	.8864	.5404	.2824	.1422	.0687	.0317	.0138	.0057	.0022	.0008	.0002
	1	.1074	.3413	.3766	.3012	.2062	.1267	.0712	.0368	.0174	.0075	.0029
	2	.0060	.0988	.2301	.2924	.2835	.2323	.1678	.1088	.0639	.0339	.0161
	3	.0002	.0173	.0852	.1720	.2362	.2581	.2397	.1954	.1419	.0923	.0537
	4	0000	.0021	.0213	.0683	.1329	.1936	.2311	.2367	.2128	.1700	.1204
	5	.0000	.0002	.0038	.0193	.0532	.1032	.1585	.2039	.2270	.2225	.1934
	6	.0000	.0000	.0005	.0040	.0155	.0401	.0792	.1281	.1766	.2124	.2256
	7	.0000	.0000	.0000	.0006	.0033	.0115	.0291	.0591	.1009	.1489	.1934
	8	.0000	.0000	.0000	.0001	.0005	.0024	.0078	.0199	.0420	.0762	.1208
	9	.0000	.0000	.0000	.0000	.0001	.0004	.0015	.0048	.0125	.0277	.0537
	10	.0000	.0000	.0000	.0000	.0000	.0000	.0002	.0008	.0025	.0068	.0161
	11	.0000	.0000	.0000	.0000	.0000	.0000	.0000	.0001	.0003	.0010	.0029
	12	.0000	.0000	.0000	.0000	.0000	.0000	.0000	.0000	.0000	.0001	.0002
13	0	.8775	.5133	.2542	.1209	.0550	.0238	.0097	.0037	.0013	.0004	.0001
	1	.1152	.3512	.3672	.2774	.1787	.1029	.0540	.0259	.0113	.0045	.0016
	2	.0070	.1109	.2448	.2937	.2680	.2059	.1388	.0836	.0453	.0220	.0095
	3	.0003	.0214	.0997	.1900	.2457	.2517	.2181	.1651	.1107	.0660	.0349
	4	.0000	.0028	.0277	.0838	.1535	.2097	.2337	.2222	.1845	.1350	.0873
	5	.0000	.0003	.0055	.0266	.0691	.1258	.1803	.2154	.2214	.1989	.1571
	6	.0000	.0000	.0008	.0063	.0230	.0559	.1030	.1546	.1968	.2169	.2095
	7	.0000	.0000	.0001	.0011	.0058	.0186	.0442	.0833	.1312	.1775	.2095
	8	.0000	.0000	.0001	.0001	.0011	.0047	.0142	.0336	.0656	.1089	.1571
	9	.0000	.0000	.0000	.0000	.0001	.0009	.0034	.0101	.0243	.0495	.0873
	10	.0000	.0000	.0000	.0000	.0000	.0001	.0006	.0022	.0065	.0162	.0349
	11	.0000	.0000	.0000	.0000	.0000	.0000	.0001	.0003	.0012	.0036	.0095
	12	.0000	.0000	.0000	.0000	.0000	.0000	.0000	.0000	.0001	.0005	.0016
	13	.0000	.0000	.0000	.0000	.0000	.0000	.0000	.0000	.0000	.0000	.0001
14	0	.8687	.4877	.2288	.1028	.0440	.0178	.0068	.0024	.0008	.0002	.0001
	1	.1229	.3593	.3559	.2539	.1539	.0832	.0407	.0181	.0073	.0027	.0009
	2	.0081	.1229	.2570	.2912	.2501	.1802	.1134	.0634	.0317	.0141	.0056
	3	.0003	.0259	.1142	.2056	.2501	.2402	.1943	.1366	.0845	.0462	.0222
	4	.0000	.0037	.0349	.0998	.1720	.2202	.2290	.2022	.1549	.1040	.0611
	5	.0000	.0004	.0078	.0352	.0860	.1468	.1963	.2178	.2066	.1701	.1222
	6	.0000	.0000	.0013	.0093	.0322	.0734	.1262	.1759	.2066	.2088	.1833
	7	.0000	.0000	.0002	.0019	.0092	.0280	.0618	.1082	.1574	.1952	.2095
	8	.0000	.0000	.0000	.0003	.0020	.0082	.0232	.0510	.0918	.1398	.1833
	9	.0000	.0000	.0000	.0000	.0003	.0018	.0066	.0183	.0408	.0762	.1222
	10	.0000	.0000	.0000	.0000	.0000	.0003	.0014	.0049	.0136	.0312	.0611
	11	.0000	.0000	.0000	.0000	.0000	.0000	.0002	.0010	.0033	.0093	.0222
	12	.0000	.0000	.0000	.0000	.0000	.0000	.0000	.0001	.0005	.0019	.0056
	13	.0000	.0000	.0000	.0000	.0000	.0000	.0000	.0000	.0001	.0002	.0009
	14	.0000	.0000	.0000	.0000	.0000	.0000	.0000	.0000	.0000	.0000	.0001

APPENDIX 1 *(Continued)*

n	r	.01	.05	.10	.15	.20	.25	p .30	.35	.40	.45	.50
15	0	.8601	.4633	.2059	.0874	.0352	.0134	.0047	.0016	.0005	.0001	.0000
	1	.1303	.3658	.3432	.2312	.1319	.0668	.0305	.0126	.0047	.0016	.0005
	2	.0092	.1348	.2669	.2856	.2309	.1559	.0916	.0476	.0219	.0090	.0032
	3	.0004	.0307	.1285	.2184	.2501	.2252	.1700	.1110	.0634	.0318	.0139
	4	.0000	.0049	.0428	.1156	.1876	.2252	.2186	.1792	.1268	.0780	.0417
	5	.0000	.0006	.0105	.0499	.1032	.1651	.2061	.2123	.1859	.1404	.0916
	6	.0000	.0000	.0019	.0132	.0430	.0917	.1472	.1906	.2066	.1914	.1527
	7	.0000	.0000	.0003	.0030	.0138	.0393	.0811	.1319	.1771	.2013	.1964
	8	.0000	.0000	.0000	.0005	.0035	.0131	.0348	.0710	.1181	.1647	.1964
	9	.0000	.0000	.0000	.0001	.0007	.0034	.0116	.0298	.0612	.1048	.1527
	10	.0000	.0000	.0000	.0000	.0001	.0007	.0030	.0096	.0245	.0515	.0916
	11	.0000	.0000	.0000	.0000	.0000	.0001	.0006	.0024	.0074	.0191	.0417
	12	.0000	.0000	.0000	.0000	.0000	.0000	.0001	.0004	.0016	.0052	.0139
	13	.0000	.0000	.0000	.0000	.0000	.0000	.0000	.0001	.0003	.0010	.0032
	14	.0000	.0000	.0000	.0000	.0000	.0000	.0000	.0000	.0000	.0001	.0005
	15	.0000	.0000	.0000	.0000	.0000	.0000	.0000	.0000	.0000	.0000	.0000
16	0	.8515	.4401	.1853	.0743	.0281	.0100	.0033	.0010	.0003	.0001	.0000
	1	.1376	.3706	.3294	.2097	.1126	.0535	.0228	.0087	.0030	.0009	.0002
	2	.0104	.1463	.2745	.2775	.2111	.1336	.0732	.0353	.0150	.0056	.0018
	3	.0005	.0359	.1423	.2285	.2463	.2079	.1465	.0888	.0468	.0215	.0085
	4	.0000	.0061	.0514	.1311	.2001	.2252	.2040	.1553	.1014	.0572	.0278
	5	.0000	.0008	.0137	.0555	.1201	.1802	.2099	.2008	.1623	.1123	.0667
	6	.0000	.0001	.0028	.0180	.0550	.1101	.1649	.1982	.1983	.1684	.1222
	7	.0000	.0000	.0004	.0045	.0197	.0524	.1010	.1524	.1889	.1969	.1746
	8	.0000	.0000	.0001	.0009	.0055	.0197	.0487	.0923	.1417	.1812	.1964
	9	.0000	.0000	.0000	.0001	.0012	.0058	.0185	.0442	.0840	.1318	.1746
	10	.0000	.0000	.0000	.0000	.0002	.0014	.0056	.0167	.0392	.0755	.1222
	11	.0000	.0000	.0000	.0000	.0000	.0002	.0013	.0049	.0142	.0337	.0667
	12	.0000	.0000	.0000	.0000	.0000	.0000	.0002	.0011	.0040	.0115	.0278
	13	.0000	.0000	.0000	.0000	.0000	.0000	.0000	.0002	.0008	.0029	.0085
	14	.0000	.0000	.0000	.0000	.0000	.0000	.0000	.0000	.0001	.0005	.0018
	15	.0000	.0000	.0000	.0000	.0000	.0000	.0000	.0000	.0000	.0001	.0002
	16	.0000	.0000	.0000	.0000	.0000	.0000	.0000	.0000	.0000	.0000	.0000
17	0	.8429	.4181	.1668	.0631	.0225	.0075	.0023	.0007	.0002	.0000	.0000
	1	.1447	.3741	.3150	.1893	.0957	.0426	.0169	.0060	.0019	.0005	.0001
	2	.0117	.1575	.2800	.2673	.1914	.1136	.0581	.0260	.0102	.0035	.0010
	3	.0006	.0415	.1556	.2359	.2393	.1893	.1245	.0701	.0341	.0144	.0052
	4	.0000	.0076	.0605	.1457	.2093	.2209	.1868	.1320	.0796	.0411	.0182
	5	.0000	.0010	.0175	.0668	.1361	.1914	.2081	.1849	.1379	.0875	.0472
	6	.0000	.0001	.0039	.0236	.0680	.1276	.1784	.1991	.1839	.1432	.0944
	7	.0000	.0000	.0007	.0065	.0267	.0668	.1201	.1685	.1927	.1841	.1484
	8	.0000	.0000	.0001	.0014	.0084	.0279	.0644	.1134	.1606	.1883	.1855
	9	.0000	.0000	.0000	.0003	.0021	.0093	.0276	.0611	.1070	.1540	.1855

APPENDIX 1 *(Continued)*

n	r	.01	.05	.10	.15	.20	.25	.30	.35	.40	.45	.50
17	10	.0000	.0000	.0000	.0000	.0004	.0025	.0095	.0263	.0571	.1008	.1484
	11	.0000	.0000	.0000	.0000	.0001	.0005	.0026	.0090	.0242	.0525	.0944
	12	.0000	.0000	.0000	.0000	.0000	.0001	.0006	.0024	.0081	.0215	.0472
	13	.0000	.0000	.0000	.0000	.0000	.0000	.0001	.0005	.0021	.0068	.0182
	14	.0000	.0000	.0000	.0000	.0000	.0000	.0000	.0001	.0004	.0016	.0052
	15	.0000	.0000	.0000	.0000	.0000	.0000	.0000	.0000	.0001	.0003	.0010
	16	.0000	.0000	.0000	.0000	.0000	.0000	.0000	.0000	.0000	.0000	.0001
	17	.0000	.0000	.0000	.0000	.0000	.0000	.0000	.0000	.0000	.0000	.0000
18	0	.8345	.3972	.1501	.0536	.0180	.0056	.0016	.0004	.0001	.0003	.0010
	1	.1517	.3763	.3002	.1704	.0811	.0338	.0126	.0042	.0012	.0003	.0001
	2	.0130	.1683	.2835	.2556	.1723	.0958	.0458	.0190	.0069	.0022	.0006
	3	.0007	.0473	.1680	.2406	.2297	.1704	.1046	.0547	.0246	.0095	.0001
	4	.0000	.0093	.0700	.1592	.2153	.2130	.1681	.1104	.0614	.0291	.0117
	5	.0000	.0014	.0218	.0787	.1507	.1988	.2017	.1664	.1146	.0666	.0327
	6	.0000	.0002	.0052	.0301	.0816	.1436	.1873	.1941	.1655	.1181	.0708
	7	.0000	.0000	.0010	.0091	.0350	.0820	.1376	.1792	.1892	.1657	.1214
	8	.0000	.0000	.0002	.0022	.0120	.0376	.0811	.1327	.1734	.1864	.1669
	9	.0000	.0000	.0000	.0004	.0033	.0139	.0386	.0794	.1284	.1694	.1855
	10	.0000	.0000	.0000	.0001	.0008	.0042	.0149	.0385	.0771	.1248	.1669
	11	.0000	.0000	.0000	.0000	.0001	.0010	.0046	.0151	.0374	.0742	.1214
	12	.0000	.0000	.0000	.0000	.0000	.0002	.0012	.0047	.0145	.0354	.0708
	13	.0000	.0000	.0000	.0000	.0000	.0000	.0002	.0012	.0045	.0134	.0327
	14	.0000	.0000	.0000	.0000	.0000	.0000	.0000	.0002	.0011	.0039	.0117
	15	.0000	.0000	.0000	.0000	.0000	.0000	.0000	.0000	.0002	.0009	.0031
	16	.0000	.0000	.0000	.0000	.0000	.0000	.0000	.0000	.0000	.0001	.0006
	17	.0000	.0000	.0000	.0000	.0000	.0000	.0000	.0000	.0000	.0000	.0001
	18	.0000	.0000	.0000	.0000	.0000	.0000	.0000	.0000	.0000	.0000	.0000
19	0	.8262	.3774	.1351	.0456	.0144	.0042	.0011	.0003	.0001	.0000	.0000
	1	.1586	.3774	.2852	.1529	.0685	.0268	.0093	.0029	.0008	.0002	.0000
	2	.0144	.1787	.2852	.2428	.1540	.0803	.0358	.0138	.0046	.0013	.0003
	3	.0008	.0533	.1796	.2428	.2182	.1517	.0869	.0422	.0175	.0062	.0018
	4	.0000	.0112	.0798	.1714	.2182	.2023	.1491	.0909	.0467	.0203	.0074
	5	.0000	.0018	.0266	.0907	.1636	.2023	.1916	.1468	.0933	.0497	.0222
	6	.0000	.0002	.0069	.0374	.0955	.1574	.1916	.1844	.1451	.0949	.0518
	7	.0000	.0000	.0014	.0122	.0443	.0974	.1525	.1844	.1797	.1443	.0961
	8	.0000	.0000	.0002	.0032	.0166	.0487	.0981	.1489	.1797	.1771	.1442
	9	.0000	.0000	.0000	.0007	.0051	.0198	.0514	.0980	.1464	.1771	.1762
	10	.0000	.0000	.0000	.0001	.0013	.0066	.0220	.0528	.0976	.1449	.1762
	11	.0000	.0000	.0000	.0000	.0003	.0018	.0077	.0233	.0532	.0970	.1442
	12	.0000	.0000	.0000	.0000	.0000	.0004	.0022	.0083	.0237	.0529	.0961
	13	.0000	.0000	.0000	.0000	.0000	.0001	.0005	.0024	.0085	.0233	.0518
	14	.0000	.0000	.0000	.0000	.0000	.0000	.0001	.0006	.0024	.0082	.0222
	15	.0000	.0000	.0000	.0000	.0000	.0000	.0000	.0001	.0005	.0022	.0074
	16	.0000	.0000	.0000	.0000	.0000	.0000	.0000	.0000	.0001	.0005	.0018

APPENDIX 1 *(Continued)*

n	r	.01	.05	.10	.15	.20	.25	.30	.35	.40	.45	.50
19	17	.0000	.0000	.0000	.0000	.0000	.0000	.0000	.0000	.0000	.0001	.0003
	18	.0000	.0000	.0000	.0000	.0000	.0000	.0000	.0000	.0000	.0000	.0000
	19	.0000	.0000	.0000	.0000	.0000	.0000	.0000	.0000	.0000	.0000	.0000
20	0	.8179	.3585	.1216	.0388	.0115	.0032	.0008	.0002	.0000	.0000	.0000
	1	.1652	.3774	.2702	.1368	.0576	.0211	.0068	.0020	.0005	.0001	.0000
	2	.0159	.1887	.2852	.2293	.1369	.0669	.0278	.0100	.0031	.0008	.0002
	3	.0010	.0596	.1901	.2428	.2054	.1339	.0718	.0323	.0123	.0040	.0011
	4	.0000	.0133	.0898	.1821	.2182	.1897	.1304	.0738	.0350	.0139	.0046
	5	.0000	.0022	.0319	.1028	.1746	.2023	.1789	.1272	.0746	.0365	.0148
	6	.0000	.0003	.0089	.0454	.1091	.1686	.1916	.1712	.1244	.0746	.0370
	7	.0000	.0000	.0020	.0160	.0545	.1124	.1643	.1844	.1659	.1221	.0739
	8	.0000	.0000	.0004	.0046	.0222	.0609	.1144	.1614	.1797	.1623	.1201
	9	.0000	.0000	.0001	.0011	.0074	.0271	.0654	.1158	.1597	.1771	.1602
	10	.0000	.0000	.0000	.0002	.0020	.0099	.0308	.0686	.1171	.1593	.1762
	11	.0000	.0000	.0000	.0000	.0005	.0030	.0120	.0336	.0710	.1185	.1602
	12	.0000	.0000	.0000	.0000	.0001	.0008	.0039	.0136	.0355	.0727	.1201
	13	.0000	.0000	.0000	.0000	.0000	.0002	.0010	.0045	.0146	.0366	.0739
	14	.0000	.0000	.0000	.0000	.0000	.0000	.0002	.0012	.0049	.0150	.0370
	15	.0000	.0000	.0000	.0000	.0000	.0000	.0000	.0003	.0013	.0049	.0148
	16	.0000	.0000	.0000	.0000	.0000	.0000	.0000	.0000	.0003	.0013	.0046
	17	.0000	.0000	.0000	.0000	.0000	.0000	.0000	.0000	.0000	.0002	.0011
	18	.0000	.0000	.0000	.0000	.0000	.0000	.0000	.0000	.0000	.0000	.0002
	19	.0000	.0000	.0000	.0000	.0000	.0000	.0000	.0000	.0000	.0000	.0000
	20	.0000	.0000	.0000	.0000	.0000	.0000	.0000	.0000	.0000	.0000	.0000
25	0	.7778	.2774	.0718	.0172	.0038	.0008	.0001	.0000	.0000	.0000	.0000
	1	.1964	.3650	.1994	.0759	.0236	.0063	.0014	.0003	.0000	.0000	.0000
	2	.0238	.2305	.2659	.1607	.0708	.0251	.0074	.0018	.0004	.0001	.0000
	3	.0018	.0930	.2265	.2174	.1358	.0641	.0243	.0076	.0019	.0004	.0001
	4	.0001	.0269	.1384	.2110	.1867	.1175	.0572	.0224	.0071	.0018	.0004
	5	.0000	.0060	.0646	.1564	.1960	.1645	.1030	.0506	.0199	.0063	.0016
	6	.0000	.0010	.0239	.0920	.1633	.1828	.1472	.0908	.0442	.0172	.0053
	7	.0000	.0001	.0072	.0441	.1108	.1654	.1712	.1327	.0800	.0381	.0143
	8	.0000	.0000	.0018	.0175	.0623	.1241	.1651	.1607	.1200	.0701	.0322
	9	.0000	.0000	.0004	.0058	.0294	.0781	.1336	.1635	.1511	.1084	.0609
	10	.0000	.0000	.0000	.0016	.0118	.0417	.0916	.1409	.1612	.1419	.0974
	11	.0000	.0000	.0000	.0004	.0040	.0189	.0536	.1034	.1465	.1583	.1328
	12	.0000	.0000	.0000	.0000	.0012	.0074	.0268	.0650	.1140	.1511	.1550
	13	.0000	.0000	.0000	.0000	.0003	.0025	.0115	.0350	.0760	.1236	.1550
	14	.0000	.0000	.0000	.0000	.0000	.0007	.0042	.0161	.0434	.0867	.1328

APPENDIX 1 *(Continued)*

n	r	.01	.05	.10	.15	.20	.25	p .30	.35	.40	.45	.50
25	15	.0000	.0000	.0000	.0000	.0000	.0002	.0013	.0064	.0212	.0520	.0974
	16	.0000	.0000	.0000	.0000	.0000	.0000	.0004	.0021	.0088	.0266	.0609
	17	.0000	.0000	.0000	.0000	.0000	.0000	.0001	.0006	.0031	.0115	.0322
	18	.0000	.0000	.0000	.0000	.0000	.0000	.0000	.0001	.0009	.0042	.0143
	19	.0000	.0000	.0000	.0000	.0000	.0000	.0000	.0000	.0002	.0013	.0053
	20	.0000	.0000	.0000	.0000	.0000	.0000	.0000	.0000	.0000	.0001	.0016
	21	.0000	.0000	.0000	.0000	.0000	.0000	.0000	.0000	.0000	.0000	.0004
	22	.0000	.0000	.0000	.0000	.0000	.0000	.0000	.0000	.0000	.0000	.0001
30	0	.7397	.2146	.0424	.0076	.0012	.0002	.0000	.0000	.0000	.0000	.0000
	1	.2242	.3389	.1413	.0404	.0093	.0018	.0003	.0000	.0000	.0000	.0000
	2	.0328	.2586	.2277	.1034	.0337	.0086	.0018	.0003	.0000	.0000	.0000
	3	.0031	.1270	.2361	.1703	.0785	.0269	.0072	.0015	.0003	.0000	.0000
	4	.0002	.0451	.1771	.2028	.1325	.0604	.0208	.0056	.0012	.0002	.0000
	5	.0000	.0124	.1023	.1861	.1723	.1047	.0464	.0157	.0041	.0008	.0001
	6	.0000	.0027	.0474	.1368	.1795	.1455	.0829	.0353	.0115	.0029	.0006
	7	.0000	.0005	.0180	.0828	.1538	.1662	.1219	.0652	.0263	.0081	.0019
	8	.0000	.0001	.0058	.0420	.1106	.1593	.1501	.1009	.0505	.0191	.0055
	9	.0000	.0000	.0016	.0181	.0676	.1298	.1573	.1328	.0823	.0382	.0133
	10	.0000	.0000	.0004	.0067	.0355	.0909	.1416	.1502	.1152	.0656	.0280
	11	.0000	.0000	.0001	.0022	.0161	.0551	.1103	.1471	.1396	.0976	.0509
	12	.0000	.0000	.0000	.0006	.0064	.0291	.0749	.1254	.1474	.1265	.0806
	13	.0000	.0000	.0000	.0001	.0022	.0134	.0444	.0935	.1360	.1433	.1115
	14	.0000	.0000	.0000	.0000	.0007	.0054	.0231	.0611	.1101	.1424	.1354
	15	.0000	.0000	.0000	.0000	.0002	.0019	.0106	.0351	.0783	.1242	.1445
	16	.0000	.0000	.0000	.0000	.0000	.0006	.0042	.0177	.0489	.0953	.1354
	17	.0000	.0000	.0000	.0000	.0000	.0002	.0015	.0079	.0269	.0642	.1115
	18	.0000	.0000	.0000	.0000	.0000	.0000	.0005	.0031	.0129	.0379	.0806
	19	.0000	.0000	.0000	.0000	.0000	.0000	.0001	.0010	.0054	.0196	.0509
	20	.0000	.0000	.0000	.0000	.0000	.0000	.0000	.0003	.0020	.0088	.0280
	21	.0000	.0000	.0000	.0000	.0000	.0000	.0000	.0001	.0006	.0034	.0133
	22	.0000	.0000	.0000	.0000	.0000	.0000	.0000	.0000	.0002	.0012	.0055
	23	.0000	.0000	.0000	.0000	.0000	.0000	.0000	.0000	.0000	.0003	.0019
	24	.0000	.0000	.0000	.0000	.0000	.0000	.0000	.0000	.0000	.0001	.0006
	25	.0000	.0000	.0000	.0000	.0000	.0000	.0000	.0000	.0000	.0000	.0001

APPENDIX 2   Areas under the Standard Normal Probability Distribution

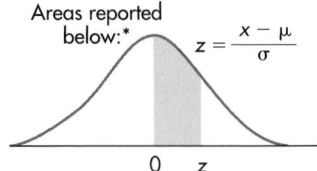

Areas reported below:*

$$z = \frac{x - \mu}{\sigma}$$

z	.00	.01	.02	.03	.04	.05	.06	.07	.08	.09
0.0	.0000	.0040	.0080	.0120	.0160	.0199	.0239	.0279	.0319	.0359
0.1	.0398	.0438	.0478	.0517	.0557	.0596	.0636	.0675	.0714	.0753
0.2	.0793	.0832	.0871	.0910	.0948	.0987	.1026	.1064	.1103	.1141
0.3	.1179	.1217	.1255	.1293	.1331	.1368	.1406	.1443	.1480	.1517
0.4	.1554	.1591	.1628	.1664	.1700	.1736	.1772	.1808	.1844	.1879
0.5	.1915	.1950	.1985	.2019	.2054	.2088	.2123	.2157	.2190	.2224
0.6	.2257	.2291	.2324	.2357	.2389	.2422	.2454	.2486	.2518	.2549
0.7	.2580	.2612	.2642	.2673	.2704	.2734	.2764	.2794	.2823	.2852
0.8	.2881	.2910	.2939	.2967	.2995	.3023	.3051	.3078	.3106	.3133
0.9	.3159	.3186	.3212	.3238	.3264	.3289	.3315	.3340	.3365	.3389
1.0	.3413	.3438	.3461	.3485	.3508	.3531	.3554	.3577	.3599	.3621
1.1	.3643	.3665	.3686	.3708	.3729	.3749	.3770	.3790	.3810	.3830
1.2	.3849	.3869	.3888	.3907	.3925	.3944	.3962	.3980	.3997	.4014
1.3	.4032	.4049	.4066	.4082	.4099	.4115	.4131	.4147	.4162	.4177
1.4	.4192	.4207	.4222	.4236	.4251	.4265	.4279	.4292	.4306	.4319
1.5	.4332	.4345	.4357	.4370	.4382	.4394	.4406	.4418	.4429	.4441
1.6	.4452	.4463	.4474	.4484	.4495	.4505	.4515	.4525	.4535	.4545
1.7	.4554	.4564	.4573	.4582	.4591	.4599	.4608	.4616	.4625	.4633
1.8	.4641	.4649	.4656	.4664	.4671	.4678	.4686	.4693	.4699	.4706
1.9	.4713	.4719	.4726	.4732	.4738	.4744	.4750	.4756	.4761	.4767
2.0	.4772	.4778	.4783	.4788	.4793	.4798	.4803	.4808	.4812	.4817
2.1	.4821	.4826	.4830	.4834	.4838	.4842	.4846	.4850	.4854	.4857
2.2	.4861	.4864	.4868	.4871	.4875	.4878	.4881	.4884	.4887	.4890
2.3	.4893	.4896	.4898	.4901	.4904	.4906	.4909	.4911	.4913	.4916
2.4	.4918	.4920	.4922	.4925	.4927	.4929	.4931	.4932	.4934	.4936
2.5	.4938	.4940	.4941	.4943	.4945	.4946	.4948	.4949	.4951	.4952
2.6	.4953	.4955	.4956	.4957	.4959	.4960	.4961	.4962	.4963	.4964
2.7	.4965	.4966	.4967	.4968	.4969	.4970	.4971	.4972	.4973	.4974
2.8	.4974	.4975	.4976	.4977	.4977	.4978	.4979	.4979	.4980	.4981
2.9	.4981	.4982	.4982	.4983	.4984	.4984	.4985	.4985	.4986	.4986
3.0	.4987	.4987	.4987	.4988	.4989	.4989	.4989	.4989	.4990	.4990
3.5	.4997									
4.0	.4999683									

* Example: For $z = 1.96$, the shaded area is 0.4750 out of the total area of 1.0000.

APPENDIX 3 A Brief Table of Random Numbers

10097	85017	84532	13618	23157	86952	02438	76520
37542	16719	82789	69041	05545	44109	05403	64894
08422	65842	27672	82186	14871	22115	86529	19645
99019	76875	20684	39187	38976	94324	43204	09376
12807	93640	39160	41453	97312	41548	93137	80157
66065	99478	70086	71265	11742	18226	29004	34072
31060	65119	26486	47353	43361	99436	42753	45571
85269	70322	21592	48233	93806	32584	21828	02051
63573	58133	41278	11697	49540	61777	67954	05325
73796	44655	81255	31133	36768	60452	38537	03529
98520	02295	13487	98662	07092	44673	61303	14905
11805	85035	54881	35587	43310	48897	48493	39808
83452	01197	86935	28021	61570	23350	65710	06288
88685	97907	19078	40646	31352	48625	44369	86507
99594	63268	96905	28797	57048	46359	74294	87517
65481	52841	59684	67411	09243	56092	84369	17468
80124	53722	71399	10916	07959	21225	13018	17727
74350	11434	51908	62171	93732	26958	02400	77402
69916	62375	99292	21177	72721	66995	07289	66252
09893	28337	20923	87929	61020	62841	31374	14225
91499	38631	79430	62421	97959	67422	69992	68479
80336	49172	16332	44670	35089	17691	89246	26940
44104	89232	57327	34679	62235	79655	81336	85157
12550	02844	15026	32439	58537	48274	81330	11100
63606	40387	65406	37920	08709	60623	02237	16505
61196	80240	44177	51171	08723	39323	05798	26457
15474	44910	99321	72173	56239	04595	10836	95270
94557	33663	86347	00926	44915	34823	51770	67897
42481	86430	19102	37420	41976	76559	24358	97344
23523	31379	68588	81675	15694	43438	36879	73208
04493	98086	32533	17767	14523	52494	24826	75246
00549	33185	04805	05431	94598	97654	16232	64051
35963	80951	68953	99634	81949	15307	00406	26898
59808	79752	02529	40200	73742	08391	49140	45427
46058	18633	99970	67348	49329	95236	32537	01390
32179	74029	74717	17674	90446	00597	45240	87379
69234	54178	10805	35635	45266	61406	41941	20117
19565	11664	77602	99817	28573	41430	96382	01758
45155	48324	32135	26803	16213	14938	71961	19476
94864	69074	45753	20505	78317	31994	98145	36168

APPENDIX 4 Areas for *t* Distributions

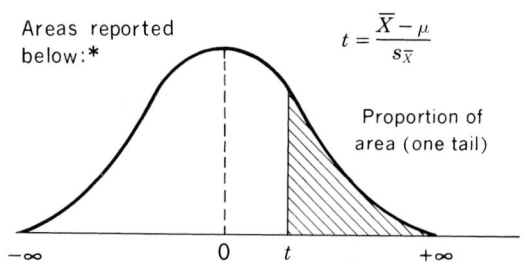

Areas reported below:*

$$t = \frac{\overline{X} - \mu}{s_{\overline{X}}}$$

Proportion of area (one tail)

df	0.100 (t_{10})	0.050 (t_{05})	0.025 (t_{025})	0.010 (t_{01})	0.005 (t_{005})
1	3.078	6.314	12.706	31.821	63.657
2	1.886	2.920	4.303	6.965	9.925
3	1.638	2.353	3.182	4.541	5.841
4	1.533	2.132	2.776	3.747	4.604
5	1.476	2.015	2.571	3.365	4.032
6	1.440	1.943	2.447	3.143	3.707
7	1.415	1.895	2.365	2.998	3.499
8	1.397	1.860	2.306	2.896	3.355
9	1.383	1.833	2.262	2.821	3.250
10	1.372	1.812	2.228	2.764	3.169
11	1.363	1.796	2.201	2.718	3.106
12	1.356	1.782	2.179	2.681	3.055
13	1.350	1.771	2.160	2.650	3.012
14	1.345	1.761	2.145	2.624	2.977
15	1.341	1.753	2.131	2.602	2.947
16	1.337	1.746	2.120	2.583	2.921
17	1.333	1.740	2.110	2.567	2.898
18	1.330	1.734	2.101	2.552	2.878
19	1.328	1.729	2.093	2.539	2.861
20	1.325	1.725	2.086	2.528	2.845
21	1.323	1.721	2.080	2.518	2.831
22	1.321	1.717	2.074	2.508	2.819
23	1.319	1.714	2.069	2.500	2.807
24	1.318	1.711	2.064	2.492	2.797
25	1.316	1.708	2.060	2.485	2.787
26	1.315	1.706	2.056	2.479	2.779
27	1.314	1.703	2.052	2.473	2.771
28	1.313	1.701	2.048	2.467	2.763
29	1.311	1.699	2.045	2.462	2.756
30	1.310	1.697	2.042	2.457	2.750
40	1.303	1.684	2.021	2.423	2.704
60	1.296	1.671	2.000	2.390	2.660
120	1.289	1.658	1.980	2.358	2.617
∞	1.282	1.645	1.960	2.326	2.576

*Example: For the shaded area to represent .025 of the total area of 1.0, the value of *t* with 19 degrees of freedom is 2.093.
This table was computed by the authors using MINITAB.

APPENDIX 5   *F* Distribution Tables

The following tables provide critical values of *F* at the .05, .025, and .01 levels of significance. The number of degrees of freedom for the *numerator* is indicated at the top of each *column*, and the number of degrees of freedom for the *denominator* determines the *row* to use.

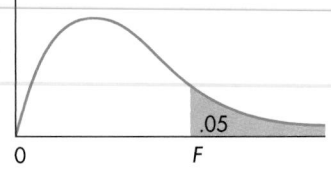

Critical values of *F* for $\alpha = .05$

Degrees of freedom for numerator

	1	2	3	4	5	6	7	8	9	10	12	15	20	24	30	40	60	120	∞
1	161.4	199.5	215.7	224.6	230.2	234.0	236.8	238.9	240.5	241.9	243.9	245.9	248.0	249.1	250.1	251.1	252.2	253.3	254.3
2	18.51	19.00	19.16	19.25	19.30	19.33	19.35	19.37	19.38	19.40	19.41	19.43	19.45	19.45	19.46	19.47	19.48	19.49	19.50
3	10.13	9.55	9.28	9.12	9.01	8.94	8.89	8.85	8.81	8.79	8.74	8.70	8.66	8.64	8.62	8.59	8.57	8.55	8.53
4	7.71	6.94	6.59	6.39	6.26	6.16	6.09	6.04	6.00	5.96	5.91	5.86	5.80	5.77	5.75	5.72	5.69	5.66	5.63
5	6.61	5.79	5.41	5.19	5.05	4.95	4.88	4.82	4.77	4.74	4.68	4.62	4.56	4.53	4.50	4.46	4.43	4.40	4.36
6	5.99	5.14	4.76	4.53	4.39	4.28	4.21	4.15	4.10	4.06	4.00	3.94	3.87	3.84	3.81	3.77	3.74	3.70	3.67
7	5.59	4.74	4.35	4.12	3.97	3.87	3.79	3.73	3.68	3.64	3.57	3.51	3.44	3.41	3.38	3.34	3.30	3.27	3.23
8	5.32	4.46	4.07	3.84	3.69	3.58	3.50	3.44	3.39	3.35	3.28	3.22	3.15	3.12	3.08	3.04	3.01	2.97	2.93
9	5.12	4.26	3.86	3.63	3.48	3.37	3.29	3.23	3.18	3.14	3.07	3.01	2.94	2.90	2.86	2.83	2.79	2.75	2.71
10	4.96	4.10	3.71	3.48	3.33	3.22	3.14	3.07	3.02	2.98	2.91	2.85	2.77	2.74	2.70	2.66	2.62	2.58	2.54
11	4.84	3.98	3.59	3.36	3.20	3.09	3.01	2.95	2.90	2.85	2.79	2.72	2.65	2.61	2.57	2.53	2.49	2.45	2.40
12	4.75	3.89	3.49	3.26	3.11	3.00	2.91	2.85	2.80	2.75	2.69	2.62	2.54	2.51	2.47	2.43	2.38	2.34	2.30
13	4.67	3.81	3.41	3.18	3.03	2.92	2.83	2.77	2.71	2.67	2.60	2.53	2.46	2.42	2.38	2.34	2.30	2.25	2.21
14	4.60	3.74	3.34	3.11	2.96	2.85	2.76	2.70	2.65	2.60	2.53	2.46	2.39	2.35	2.31	2.27	2.22	2.18	2.13
15	4.54	3.68	3.29	3.06	2.90	2.79	2.71	2.64	2.59	2.54	2.48	2.40	2.33	2.29	2.25	2.20	2.16	2.11	2.07
16	4.49	3.63	3.24	3.01	2.85	2.74	2.66	2.59	2.54	2.49	2.42	2.35	2.28	2.24	2.19	2.15	2.11	2.06	2.01
17	4.45	3.59	3.20	2.96	2.81	2.70	2.61	2.55	2.49	2.45	2.38	2.31	2.23	2.19	2.15	2.10	2.06	2.01	1.96
18	4.41	3.55	3.16	2.93	2.77	2.66	2.58	2.51	2.46	2.41	2.34	2.27	2.19	2.15	2.11	2.06	2.02	1.97	1.92
19	4.38	3.52	3.13	2.90	2.74	2.63	2.54	2.48	2.42	2.38	2.31	2.23	2.16	2.11	2.07	2.03	1.98	1.93	1.88
20	4.35	3.49	3.10	2.87	2.71	2.60	2.51	2.45	2.39	2.35	2.28	2.20	2.12	2.08	2.04	1.99	1.95	1.90	1.84
21	4.32	3.47	3.07	2.84	2.68	2.57	2.49	2.42	2.37	2.32	2.25	2.18	2.10	2.05	2.01	1.96	1.92	1.87	1.81
22	4.30	3.44	3.05	2.82	2.66	2.55	2.46	2.40	2.34	2.30	2.23	2.15	2.07	2.03	1.98	1.94	1.89	1.84	1.78
23	4.28	3.42	3.03	2.80	2.64	2.53	2.44	2.37	2.32	2.27	2.20	2.13	2.05	2.01	1.96	1.91	1.86	1.81	1.76
24	4.26	3.40	3.01	2.78	2.62	2.51	2.42	2.36	2.30	2.25	2.18	2.11	2.03	1.98	1.94	1.89	1.84	1.79	1.73
25	4.24	3.39	2.99	2.76	2.60	2.49	2.40	2.34	2.28	2.24	2.16	2.09	2.01	1.96	1.92	1.87	1.82	1.77	1.71
26	4.23	3.37	2.98	2.74	2.59	2.47	2.39	2.32	2.27	2.22	2.15	2.07	1.99	1.95	1.90	1.85	1.80	1.75	1.69
27	4.21	3.35	2.96	2.73	2.57	2.46	2.37	2.31	2.25	2.20	2.13	2.06	1.97	1.93	1.88	1.84	1.79	1.73	1.67
28	4.20	3.34	2.95	2.71	2.56	2.45	2.36	2.29	2.24	2.19	2.12	2.04	1.96	1.91	1.87	1.82	1.77	1.71	1.65
29	4.18	3.33	2.93	2.70	2.55	2.43	2.35	2.28	2.22	2.18	2.10	2.03	1.94	1.90	1.85	1.81	1.75	1.70	1.64
30	4.17	3.32	2.92	2.69	2.53	2.42	2.33	2.27	2.21	2.16	2.09	2.01	1.93	1.89	1.84	1.79	1.74	1.68	1.62
40	4.08	3.23	2.84	2.61	2.45	2.34	2.25	2.18	2.12	2.08	2.00	1.92	1.84	1.79	1.74	1.69	1.64	1.58	1.51
60	4.00	3.15	2.76	2.53	2.37	2.25	2.17	2.10	2.04	1.99	1.92	1.84	1.75	1.70	1.65	1.59	1.53	1.47	1.39
120	3.92	3.07	2.68	2.45	2.29	2.17	2.09	2.02	1.96	1.91	1.83	1.75	1.66	1.61	1.55	1.50	1.43	1.35	1.25
∞	3.84	3.00	2.60	2.37	2.21	2.10	2.01	1.94	1.88	1.83	1.75	1.67	1.57	1.52	1.46	1.39	1.32	1.22	1.00

Degrees of freedom for denominator

APPENDIX 5   *(Continued)*

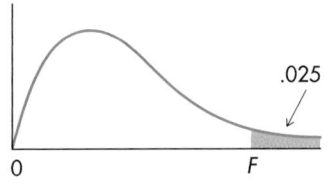

Critical values of F for $\alpha = .025$

Degrees of freedom for numerator

	1	2	3	4	5	6	7	8	9	10	12	15	20	24	30	40	60	120	∞
1	647.8	799.5	864.2	899.6	921.8	937.1	948.2	956.7	963.3	968.6	976.7	984.9	993.1	997.2	1001	1006	1010	1014	1018
2	38.51	39.00	39.17	39.25	39.30	39.33	39.36	39.37	39.39	39.40	39.41	39.43	39.45	39.46	39.46	39.47	39.48	39.49	39.50
3	17.44	16.04	15.44	15.10	14.88	14.73	14.62	14.54	14.47	14.42	14.34	14.25	14.17	14.12	14.08	14.04	13.99	13.95	13.90
4	12.22	10.65	9.98	9.60	9.36	9.20	9.07	8.98	8.90	8.84	8.75	8.66	8.56	8.51	8.46	8.41	8.36	8.31	8.26
5	10.01	8.43	7.76	7.39	7.15	6.98	6.85	6.76	6.68	6.62	6.52	6.43	6.33	6.28	6.23	6.18	6.12	6.07	6.02
6	8.81	7.26	6.60	6.23	5.99	5.82	5.70	5.60	5.52	5.46	5.37	5.27	5.17	5.12	5.07	5.01	4.96	4.90	4.85
7	8.07	6.54	5.89	5.52	5.29	5.12	4.99	4.90	4.82	4.76	4.67	4.57	4.47	4.42	4.36	4.31	4.25	4.20	4.14
8	7.57	6.06	5.42	5.05	4.82	4.65	4.53	4.43	4.36	4.30	4.20	4.10	4.00	3.95	3.89	3.84	3.78	3.73	3.67
9	7.21	5.71	5.08	4.72	4.48	4.32	4.20	4.10	4.03	3.96	3.87	3.77	3.67	3.61	3.56	3.51	3.45	3.39	3.33
10	6.94	5.46	4.83	4.47	4.24	4.07	3.95	3.85	3.78	3.72	3.62	3.52	3.42	3.37	3.31	3.26	3.20	3.14	3.08
11	6.72	5.26	4.63	4.28	4.04	3.88	3.76	3.66	3.59	3.53	3.43	3.33	3.23	3.17	3.12	3.06	3.00	2.94	2.88
12	6.55	5.10	4.47	4.12	3.89	3.73	3.61	3.51	3.44	3.37	3.28	3.18	3.07	3.02	2.96	2.91	2.85	2.79	2.72
13	6.41	4.97	4.35	4.00	3.77	3.60	3.48	3.39	3.31	3.25	3.15	3.05	2.95	2.89	2.84	2.78	2.72	2.66	2.60
14	6.30	4.86	4.24	3.89	3.66	3.50	3.38	3.29	3.21	3.15	3.05	2.95	2.84	2.79	2.73	2.67	2.61	2.55	2.49
15	6.20	4.77	4.15	3.80	3.58	3.41	3.29	3.20	3.12	3.06	2.96	2.86	2.76	2.70	2.64	2.59	2.52	2.46	2.47
16	6.12	4.69	4.08	3.73	3.50	3.34	3.22	3.12	3.05	2.99	2.89	2.79	2.68	2.63	2.57	2.51	2.45	2.38	2.32
17	6.04	4.62	4.01	3.66	3.44	3.28	3.16	3.06	2.98	2.92	2.82	2.72	2.62	2.56	2.50	2.44	2.38	2.32	2.25
18	5.98	4.56	3.95	3.61	3.38	3.22	3.10	3.01	2.93	2.87	2.77	2.67	2.56	2.50	2.44	2.38	2.32	2.26	2.19
19	5.92	4.51	3.90	3.56	3.33	3.17	3.05	2.96	2.88	2.82	2.72	2.62	2.51	2.45	2.39	2.33	2.27	2.20	2.13
20	5.87	4.46	3.86	3.51	3.29	3.13	3.01	2.91	2.84	2.77	2.68	2.57	2.46	2.41	2.35	2.29	2.22	2.16	2.09
21	5.83	4.42	3.82	3.48	3.25	3.09	2.97	2.87	2.80	2.73	2.64	2.53	2.42	2.37	2.31	2.25	2.18	2.11	2.04
22	5.79	4.38	3.78	3.44	3.22	3.05	2.93	2.84	2.76	2.70	2.60	2.50	2.39	2.33	2.27	2.21	2.14	2.08	2.00
23	5.75	4.35	3.75	3.41	3.18	3.02	2.90	2.81	2.73	2.67	2.57	2.47	2.36	2.30	2.24	2.18	2.11	2.04	1.97
24	5.72	4.32	3.72	3.38	3.15	2.99	2.87	2.78	2.70	2.64	2.54	2.44	2.33	2.27	2.21	2.15	2.08	2.01	1.94
25	5.69	4.29	3.69	3.35	3.13	2.97	2.85	2.75	2.68	2.61	2.51	2.41	2.30	2.24	2.18	2.12	2.05	1.98	1.91
26	5.66	4.27	3.67	3.33	3.10	2.94	2.82	2.73	2.65	2.59	2.49	2.39	2.28	2.22	2.16	2.09	2.03	1.95	1.88
27	5.63	4.24	3.65	3.31	3.08	2.92	2.80	2.71	2.63	2.57	2.47	2.36	2.25	2.19	2.13	2.07	2.00	1.93	1.85
28	5.61	4.22	3.63	3.29	3.06	2.90	2.78	2.69	2.61	2.55	2.45	2.34	2.23	2.17	2.11	2.05	1.98	1.91	1.83
29	5.59	4.20	3.61	3.27	3.04	2.88	2.76	2.67	2.59	2.53	2.43	2.32	2.21	2.15	2.09	2.03	1.96	1.89	1.81
30	5.57	4.18	3.59	3.25	3.03	2.87	2.75	2.65	2.57	2.51	2.41	2.31	2.20	2.14	2.07	2.01	1.94	1.87	1.79
40	5.42	4.05	3.46	3.13	2.90	2.74	2.62	2.53	2.45	2.39	2.29	2.18	2.07	2.01	1.94	1.88	1.80	1.72	1.64
60	5.29	3.93	3.34	3.01	2.79	2.63	2.51	2.41	2.33	2.27	2.17	2.06	1.94	1.88	1.82	1.74	1.67	1.58	1.48
120	5.15	3.80	3.23	2.89	2.67	2.52	2.39	2.30	2.22	2.16	2.05	1.94	1.82	1.76	1.69	1.61	1.53	1.43	1.31
∞	5.02	3.69	3.12	2.79	2.57	2.41	2.29	2.19	2.11	2.05	1.94	1.83	1.71	1.64	1.57	1.48	1.39	1.27	1.00

Degrees of freedom for denominator

APPENDIX 5 *(Continued)*

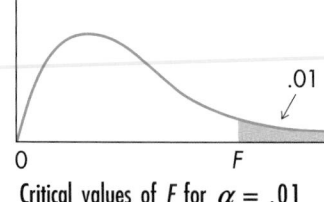

Critical values of F for $\alpha = .01$

Degrees of freedom for numerator

	1	2	3	4	5	6	7	8	9	10	12	15	20	24	30	40	60	120	∞
1	4052	4999.5	5403	5625	5764	5859	5928	5982	6022	6056	6106	6157	6209	6235	6261	6287	6313	6339	6366
2	98.50	99.00	99.17	99.25	99.30	99.33	99.36	99.37	99.39	99.40	99.42	99.43	99.45	99.46	99.47	99.47	99.48	99.49	99.50
3	34.12	30.82	29.46	28.71	28.24	27.91	27.67	27.49	27.35	27.23	27.05	26.87	26.69	26.60	26.50	26.41	26.32	26.22	26.13
4	21.20	18.00	16.69	15.98	15.52	15.21	14.98	14.80	14.66	14.55	14.37	14.20	14.02	13.93	13.84	13.75	13.65	13.56	13.46
5	16.26	13.27	12.06	11.39	10.97	10.67	10.46	10.29	10.16	10.05	9.89	9.72	9.55	9.47	9.38	9.29	9.20	9.11	9.02
6	13.75	10.92	9.78	9.15	8.75	8.47	8.26	8.10	7.98	7.87	7.72	7.56	7.40	7.31	7.23	7.14	7.06	6.97	6.88
7	12.25	9.55	8.45	7.85	7.46	7.19	6.99	6.84	6.72	6.62	6.47	6.31	6.16	6.07	5.99	5.91	5.82	5.74	5.65
8	11.26	8.65	7.59	7.01	6.63	6.37	6.18	6.03	5.91	5.81	5.67	5.52	5.36	5.28	5.20	5.12	5.03	4.95	4.86
9	10.56	8.02	6.99	6.42	6.06	5.80	5.61	5.47	5.35	5.26	5.11	4.96	4.81	4.73	4.65	4.57	4.48	4.40	4.31
10	10.04	7.56	6.55	5.99	5.64	5.39	5.20	5.06	4.94	4.85	4.71	4.56	4.41	4.33	4.25	4.17	4.08	4.00	3.91
11	9.65	7.21	6.22	5.67	5.32	5.07	4.89	4.74	4.63	4.54	4.40	4.25	4.10	4.02	3.94	3.86	3.78	3.69	3.60
12	9.33	6.93	5.95	5.41	5.06	4.82	4.64	4.50	4.39	4.30	4.16	4.01	3.86	3.78	3.70	3.62	3.54	3.45	3.36
13	9.07	6.70	5.74	5.21	4.86	4.62	4.44	4.30	4.19	4.10	3.96	3.82	3.66	3.59	3.51	3.43	3.34	3.25	3.17
14	8.86	6.51	5.56	5.04	4.69	4.46	4.28	4.14	4.03	3.94	3.80	3.66	3.51	3.43	3.35	3.27	3.18	3.09	3.00
15	8.68	6.36	5.42	4.89	4.56	4.32	4.14	4.00	3.89	3.80	3.67	3.52	3.37	3.29	3.21	3.13	3.05	2.96	2.87
16	8.53	6.23	5.29	4.77	4.44	4.20	4.03	3.89	3.78	3.69	3.55	3.41	3.26	3.18	3.10	3.02	2.93	2.84	2.75
17	8.40	6.11	5.18	4.67	4.34	4.10	3.93	3.79	3.68	3.59	3.46	3.31	3.16	3.08	3.00	2.92	2.83	2.75	2.65
18	8.29	6.01	5.09	4.58	4.25	4.01	3.84	3.71	3.60	3.51	3.37	3.23	3.08	3.00	2.92	2.84	2.75	2.66	2.57
19	8.18	5.93	5.01	4.50	4.17	3.94	3.77	3.63	3.52	3.43	3.30	3.15	3.00	2.92	2.84	2.76	2.67	2.58	2.49
20	8.10	5.85	4.94	4.43	4.10	3.87	3.70	3.56	3.46	3.37	3.23	3.09	2.94	2.86	2.78	2.69	2.61	2.52	2.42
21	8.02	5.78	4.87	4.37	4.04	3.81	3.64	3.51	3.40	3.31	3.17	3.03	2.88	2.80	2.72	2.64	2.55	2.46	2.36
22	7.95	5.72	4.82	4.31	3.99	3.76	3.59	3.45	3.35	3.26	3.12	2.98	2.83	2.75	2.67	2.58	2.50	2.40	2.31
23	7.88	5.66	4.76	4.26	3.94	3.71	3.54	3.41	3.30	3.21	3.07	2.93	2.78	2.70	2.62	2.54	2.45	2.35	2.26
24	7.82	5.61	4.72	4.22	3.90	3.67	3.50	3.36	3.26	3.17	3.03	2.89	2.74	2.66	2.58	2.49	2.40	2.31	2.21
25	7.77	5.57	4.68	4.18	3.85	3.63	3.46	3.32	3.22	3.13	2.99	2.85	2.70	2.62	2.54	2.45	2.36	2.27	2.17
26	7.72	5.53	4.64	4.14	3.82	3.59	3.42	3.29	3.18	3.09	2.96	2.81	2.66	2.58	2.50	2.42	2.33	2.23	2.13
27	7.68	5.49	4.60	4.11	3.78	3.56	3.39	3.26	3.15	3.06	2.93	2.78	2.63	2.55	2.47	2.38	2.29	2.20	2.10
28	7.64	5.45	4.57	4.07	3.75	3.53	3.36	3.23	3.12	3.03	2.90	2.75	2.60	2.52	2.44	2.35	2.26	2.17	2.06
29	7.60	5.42	4.54	4.04	3.73	3.50	3.33	3.20	3.09	3.00	2.87	2.73	2.57	2.49	2.41	2.33	2.23	2.14	2.03
30	7.56	5.39	4.51	4.02	3.70	3.47	3.30	3.17	3.07	2.98	2.84	2.70	2.55	2.47	2.39	2.30	2.21	2.11	2.01
40	7.31	5.18	4.31	3.83	3.51	3.29	3.12	2.99	2.89	2.80	2.66	2.52	2.37	2.29	2.20	2.11	2.02	1.92	1.80
60	7.08	4.98	4.13	3.65	3.34	3.12	2.95	2.82	2.72	2.63	2.50	2.35	2.20	2.12	2.03	1.94	1.84	1.73	1.60
120	6.85	4.79	3.95	3.48	3.17	2.96	2.79	2.66	2.56	2.47	2.34	2.19	2.03	1.95	1.86	1.76	1.66	1.53	1.38
∞	6.63	4.61	3.78	3.32	3.02	2.80	2.64	2.51	2.41	2.32	2.18	2.04	1.88	1.79	1.70	1.59	1.47	1.32	1.00

Degrees of freedom for denominator

APPENDIX 6   Chi-Square Distribution

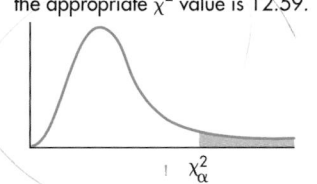

Example: With df = 6 and α = .05, the appropriate χ^2 value is 12.59.

Degrees of freedom (df)	Area or probability (α) in the right tail												
	0.995	0.99	0.975	0.95	0.90	0.75	0.50	0.25	0.10	0.05	0.025	0.01	0.005
1	0.0^{4}393	0.0^{3}157	0.0^{3}982	0.0^{2}39	0.0158	0.102	0.455	1.323	2.71	3.84	5.02	6.63	7.88
2	0.0100	0.0201	0.0506	0.103	0.211	0.575	1.386	2.77	4.61	5.99	7.38	9.21	10.60
3	0.0717	0.115	0.216	0.352	0.584	1.213	2.37	4.11	6.25	7.81	9.35	11.34	12.84
4	0.207	0.297	0.484	0.711	1.064	1.923	3.36	5.39	7.78	9.49	11.14	13.28	14.86
5	0.412	0.554	0.831	1.145	1.610	2.67	4.35	6.63	9.24	11.07	12.83	15.09	16.75
6	0.676	0.872	1.237	1.635	2.20	3.45	5.35	7.84	10.64	12.59	14.45	16.81	18.55
7	0.989	1.239	1.690	2.17	2.83	4.25	6.35	9.04	12.02	14.07	16.01	18.48	20.3
8	1.344	1.646	2.18	2.73	3.49	5.07	7.34	10.22	13.36	15.51	17.53	20.1	22.0
9	1.735	2.09	2.70	3.33	4.17	5.90	8.34	11.39	14.68	16.92	19.02	21.7	23.6
10	2.16	2.56	3.25	3.94	4.87	6.74	9.34	12.55	15.99	18.31	20.5	23.2	25.2
11	2.60	3.05	3.82	4.57	5.58	7.58	10.34	13.70	17.28	19.68	21.9	24.7	26.8
12	3.07	3.57	4.40	5.23	6.30	8.44	11.34	14.85	18.55	21.0	23.3	26.2	28.3
13	3.57	4.11	5.01	5.89	7.04	9.30	12.34	15.98	19.81	22.4	24.7	27.7	29.8
14	4.07	4.66	5.63	6.57	7.79	10.17	13.34	17.12	21.1	23.7	26.1	29.1	31.3
15	4.60	5.23	6.26	7.26	8.55	11.04	14.34	18.25	22.3	25.0	27.5	30.6	32.8
16	5.14	5.81	6.91	7.96	9.31	11.91	15.34	19.37	23.5	26.3	28.8	32.0	34.3
17	5.70	6.41	7.56	8.67	10.09	12.79	16.34	20.5	24.8	27.6	30.2	33.4	35.7
18	6.26	7.01	8.23	9.39	10.86	13.68	17.34	21.6	26.0	28.9	31.5	34.8	37.2
19	6.84	7.63	8.91	10.12	11.65	14.56	18.34	22.7	27.2	30.1	32.9	36.2	38.6
20	7.43	8.26	9.59	10.85	12.44	15.45	19.34	23.8	28.4	31.4	34.2	37.6	40.0
21	8.03	8.90	10.28	11.59	13.24	16.34	20.3	24.9	29.6	32.7	35.5	38.9	41.4
22	8.64	9.54	10.98	12.34	14.04	17.24	21.3	26.0	30.8	33.9	36.8	40.3	42.8
23	9.26	10.20	11.69	13.09	14.85	18.14	22.3	27.1	32.0	35.2	38.1	41.6	44.2
24	9.89	10.86	12.40	13.85	15.66	19.04	23.3	28.2	33.2	36.4	39.4	43.0	45.6
25	10.52	11.52	13.12	14.61	16.47	19.94	24.3	29.3	34.4	37.7	40.6	44.3	46.9
26	11.16	12.20	13.84	15.38	17.29	20.8	25.3	30.4	35.6	38.9	41.9	45.6	48.3
27	11.81	12.88	14.57	16.15	18.11	21.7	26.3	31.5	36.7	40.1	43.2	47.0	49.6
28	12.46	13.56	15.31	16.93	18.94	22.7	27.3	32.6	37.9	41.3	44.5	48.3	51.0
29	13.12	14.26	16.05	17.71	19.77	23.6	28.3	33.7	39.1	42.6	45.7	49.6	52.3
30	13.79	14.95	16.79	18.49	20.6	24.5	29.3	34.8	40.3	43.8	47.0	50.9	53.7
40	20.7	22.2	24.4	26.5	29.1	33.7	39.3	45.6	51.8	55.8	59.3	63.7	66.8
50	28.0	29.7	32.4	34.8	37.7	42.9	49.3	56.3	63.2	67.5	71.4	76.2	79.5
60	35.5	37.5	40.5	43.2	46.5	52.3	59.3	67.0	74.4	79.1	83.3	88.4	92.0
70	43.3	45.4	48.8	51.7	55.3	61.7	69.3	77.6	85.5	90.5	95.0	100.4	104.2
80	51.2	53.5	57.2	60.4	64.3	71.1	79.3	88.1	96.6	101.9	106.6	112.3	116.3
90	59.2	61.8	65.6	69.1	73.3	80.6	89.3	98.6	107.6	113.1	118.1	124.1	128.3
100	67.3	70.1	74.2	77.9	82.4	90.1	99.3	109.1	118.5	124.3	129.6	135.8	140.2

Source: Abridged from Catherine M. Thompson, "Table of Percentage Points of the χ^2 Distribution," in *Biometrika,* vol. 32, pp. 187–91. Copyright © 1941. Used by permission of the Biometrika Trustees.

APPENDIX 7   Critical Values of T for $\alpha = 0.05$ and $\alpha = 0.01$ in the Wilcoxon Signed Rank Test

	Two-tailed test		One-tailed test	
n	0.05	0.01	0.05	0.01
4				
5			0	
6	0		2	
7	2		3	0
8	3	0	5	1
9	5	1	8	3
10	8	3	10	5
11	10	5	13	7
12	13	7	17	9
13	17	9	21	12
14	21	12	25	15
15	25	15	30	19
16	29	19	35	23
17	34	23	41	27
18	40	27	47	32
19	46	32	53	37
20	52	37	60	43
21	58	42	67	49
22	65	48	75	55
23	73	54	83	62
24	81	61	91	69
25	89	68	100	76
26	98	75	110	84
27	107	83	119	92
28	116	91	130	101
29	126	100	140	110
30	137	109	151	120
31	147	118	163	130
32	159	128	175	140
33	170	138	187	151
34	182	148	200	162
35	195	159	213	173
40	264	220	286	238
50	434	373	466	397
60	648	567	690	600
70	907	805	960	846
80	1211	1086	1276	1136
90	1560	1410	1638	1471
100	1955	1779	2045	1850

Source: Abridged from Robert L. McCormack, "Extended Tables of the Wilcoxon Matched Pair Signed Rank Statistic," *Journal of the American Statistical Association,* September 1965, pp. 866–67. Reprinted with permission.

APPENDIX 8   Distribution of *U* in the Mann-Whitney Test

One-tailed test tables

Critical *U* values: $\alpha = .05$ for a one-tailed test
(and $\alpha = .10$ for a two-tailed test)

n_1 \ n_2	1	2	3	4	5	6	7	8	9	10	11	12	13	14	15	16	17	18	19	20
1																			0	0
2				0	0	0	0	1	1	1	1	2	2	2	3	3	3	4	4	4
3			0	0	1	2	2	3	3	4	5	5	6	7	7	8	9	9	10	11
4			0	1	2	3	4	5	6	7	8	9	10	11	12	14	15	16	17	18
5		0	1	2	4	5	6	8	9	11	12	13	15	16	18	19	20	22	23	25
6		0	2	3	5	7	8	10	12	14	16	17	19	21	23	25	26	28	30	32
7		0	2	4	6	8	11	13	15	17	19	21	24	26	28	30	33	35	37	39
8		1	3	5	8	10	13	15	18	20	23	26	28	31	33	36	39	41	44	47
9		1	3	6	9	12	15	18	21	24	27	30	33	36	39	42	45	48	51	54
10		1	4	7	11	14	17	20	24	27	31	34	37	41	44	48	51	55	58	62
11		1	5	8	12	16	19	23	27	31	34	38	42	46	50	54	57	61	65	69
12		2	5	9	13	17	21	26	30	34	38	42	47	51	55	60	64	68	72	77
13		2	6	10	15	19	24	28	33	37	42	47	51	56	61	65	70	75	80	84
14		2	7	11	16	21	26	31	36	41	46	51	56	61	66	71	77	82	87	92
15		3	7	12	18	23	28	33	39	44	50	55	61	66	72	77	83	88	94	100
16		3	8	14	19	25	30	36	42	48	54	60	65	71	77	83	89	95	101	107
17		3	9	15	20	26	33	39	45	51	57	64	70	77	83	89	96	102	109	115
18		4	9	16	22	28	35	41	48	55	61	68	75	82	88	95	102	109	116	123
19	0	4	10	17	23	30	37	44	51	58	65	72	80	87	94	101	109	116	123	130
20	0	4	11	18	25	32	39	47	54	62	69	77	84	92	100	107	115	123	130	138

Critical *U* values: $\alpha = .01$ for a one-tailed test
(and $\alpha = .02$ for a two-tailed test)

n_1 \ n_2	1	2	3	4	5	6	7	8	9	10	11	12	13	14	15	16	17	18	19	20
1																				
2													0	0	0	0	0	0	1	1
3							0	0	1	1	1	2	2	2	3	3	4	4	4	5
4				0	1	1	2	3	3	4	5	5	6	7	7	8	9	9	10	
5				0	1	2	3	4	5	6	7	8	9	10	11	12	13	14	15	16
6				1	2	3	4	6	7	8	9	11	12	13	15	16	18	19	20	22
7			0	1	3	4	6	7	9	11	12	14	16	17	19	21	23	24	26	28
8			0	2	4	6	7	9	11	13	15	17	20	22	24	26	28	30	32	34
9			1	3	5	7	9	11	14	16	18	21	23	26	28	31	33	36	38	40
10			1	3	6	8	11	13	16	19	22	24	27	30	33	36	38	41	44	47
11			1	4	7	9	12	15	18	22	25	28	31	34	37	41	44	47	50	53
12			2	5	8	11	14	17	21	24	28	31	35	38	42	46	49	53	56	60
13		0	2	5	9	12	16	20	23	27	31	35	39	43	47	51	55	59	63	67
14		0	2	6	10	13	17	22	26	30	34	38	43	47	51	56	60	65	69	73
15		0	3	7	11	15	19	24	28	33	37	42	47	51	56	61	66	70	75	80
16		0	3	7	12	16	21	26	31	36	41	46	51	56	61	66	71	76	82	87
17		0	4	8	13	18	23	28	33	38	44	49	55	60	66	71	77	82	88	93
18		0	4	9	14	19	24	30	36	41	47	53	59	65	70	76	82	88	94	100
19		1	4	9	15	20	26	32	38	44	50	56	63	69	75	82	88	94	101	107
20		1	5	10	16	22	28	34	40	47	53	60	67	73	80	87	93	100	107	114

APPENDIX 8 *(Continued)*

Critical U values: $\alpha = .05$ for a two-tailed test
(and $\alpha = .025$ for a one-tailed test)

n_1 \ n_2	1	2	3	4	5	6	7	8	9	10	11	12	13	14	15	16	17	18	19	20
1																				
2								0	0	0	0	1	1	1	1	1	2	2	2	2
3					0	1	1	2	2	3	3	4	4	5	5	6	6	7	7	8
4				0	1	2	3	4	4	5	6	7	8	9	10	11	11	12	13	13
5			0	1	2	3	5	6	7	8	9	11	12	13	14	15	17	18	19	20
6			1	2	3	5	6	8	10	11	13	14	16	17	19	21	22	24	25	27
7			1	3	5	6	8	10	12	14	16	18	20	22	24	26	28	30	32	34
8		0	2	4	6	8	10	13	15	17	19	22	24	26	29	31	34	36	38	41
9		0	2	4	7	10	12	15	17	20	23	26	28	31	34	37	39	42	45	48
10		0	3	5	8	11	14	17	20	23	26	29	33	36	39	42	45	48	52	55
11		0	3	6	9	13	16	19	23	26	30	33	37	40	44	47	51	55	58	62
12		1	4	7	11	14	18	22	26	29	33	37	41	45	49	53	57	61	65	69
13		1	4	8	12	16	20	24	28	33	37	41	45	50	54	59	63	67	72	76
14		1	5	9	13	17	22	26	31	36	40	45	50	55	59	64	67	74	78	83
15		1	5	10	14	19	24	29	34	39	44	49	54	59	64	70	75	80	85	90
16		1	6	11	15	21	26	31	37	42	47	53	59	64	70	75	81	86	92	98
17		2	6	11	17	22	28	34	39	45	51	57	63	67	75	81	87	93	99	105
18		2	7	12	18	24	30	36	42	48	55	61	67	74	80	86	93	99	106	112
19		2	7	13	19	25	32	38	45	52	58	65	72	78	85	92	99	106	113	119
20		2	8	13	20	27	34	41	48	55	62	69	76	83	90	98	105	112	119	127

Critical U values: $\alpha = .01$ for a two-tailed test
(and $\alpha = .005$ for a one-tailed test)

n_1 \ n_2	1	2	3	4	5	6	7	8	9	10	11	12	13	14	15	16	17	18	19	20
1																				
2																			0	0
3									0	0	0	1	1	1	2	2	2	2	3	3
4						0	0	1	1	2	2	3	3	4	5	5	6	6	7	8
5					0	1	1	2	3	4	5	6	7	7	8	9	10	11	12	13
6				0	1	2	3	4	5	6	7	9	10	11	12	13	15	16	17	18
7				0	1	3	4	6	7	9	10	12	13	15	16	18	19	21	22	24
8				1	2	4	6	7	9	11	13	15	17	18	20	22	24	26	28	30
9			0	1	3	5	7	9	11	13	16	18	20	22	24	27	29	31	33	36
10			0	2	4	6	9	11	13	16	18	21	24	26	29	31	34	37	39	42
11			0	2	5	7	10	13	16	18	21	24	27	30	33	36	39	42	45	48
12			1	3	6	9	12	15	18	21	24	27	31	34	37	41	44	47	51	54
13			1	3	7	10	13	17	20	24	27	31	34	38	42	45	49	53	56	60
14			1	4	7	11	15	18	22	26	30	34	38	42	46	50	54	58	63	67
15			2	5	8	12	16	20	24	29	33	37	42	46	51	55	60	64	69	73
16			2	5	9	13	18	22	27	31	36	41	45	50	55	60	65	70	74	79
17			2	6	10	15	19	24	29	34	39	44	49	54	60	65	70	75	81	86
18			2	6	11	16	21	26	31	37	42	47	53	58	64	70	75	81	87	92
19		0	3	7	12	17	22	28	33	39	45	51	56	63	69	74	81	87	93	99
20		0	3	8	13	18	24	30	36	42	48	54	60	67	73	79	86	92	99	105

Source: Reprinted with permission from William H. Beyer (ed.), *Handbook of Tables for Probability and Statistics*, 2d ed., 1968. Copyright CRC Press, Inc., Boca Raton, Fla.

APPENDIX 9   Critical Values for r in the Runs Test for Randomness

Any sample value of r that is equal to or less than that shown in table (a) or that is equal to or greater than that shown in table (b) is cause for rejection of H_0 at the .05 level of significance.

n_2

n_1	2	3	4	5	6	7	8	9	10	11	12	13	14	15	16	17	18	19	20
2											2	2	2	2	2	2	2	2	2
3				2	2	2	2	2	2	2	2	2	2	3	3	3	3	3	3
4			2	2	3	3	3	3	3	3	3	3	3	3	4	4	4	4	4
5			2	2	3	3	3	3	3	4	4	4	4	4	4	4	5	5	5
6		2	2	3	3	3	3	4	4	4	4	5	5	5	5	5	5	6	6
7		2	2	3	3	3	4	4	5	5	5	5	5	6	6	6	6	6	6
8		2	3	3	3	4	4	5	5	5	6	6	6	6	6	7	7	7	7
9		2	3	3	4	4	5	5	5	6	6	6	7	7	7	7	8	8	8
10		2	3	3	4	5	5	5	6	6	7	7	7	7	8	8	8	8	9
11		2	3	4	4	5	5	6	6	7	7	7	8	8	8	9	9	9	9
12	2	2	3	4	4	5	6	6	7	7	7	8	8	8	9	9	9	10	10
13	2	2	3	4	5	5	6	6	7	7	8	8	9	9	9	10	10	10	10
14	2	2	3	4	5	5	6	7	7	8	8	9	9	9	10	10	10	11	11
15	2	3	3	4	5	6	6	7	7	8	8	9	9	10	10	11	11	11	12
16	2	3	4	4	5	6	6	7	8	8	9	9	10	10	11	11	11	12	12
17	2	3	4	4	5	6	7	7	8	9	9	10	10	11	11	11	12	12	13
18	2	3	4	5	5	6	7	8	8	9	9	10	10	11	11	12	12	13	13
19	2	3	4	5	6	6	7	8	8	9	10	10	11	11	12	12	13	13	13
20	2	3	4	5	6	6	7	8	9	9	10	10	11	12	12	13	13	13	14

(a)

n_2

n_1	2	3	4	5	6	7	8	9	10	11	12	13	14	15	16	17	18	19	20
2											6	6	6	6	6	6	6	6	6
3				8	8	8	8	8	8	8	8	8	8	8	8	8	8	8	8
4			9	9	10	10	10	10	10	10	10	10	10	10	10	10	10	10	10
5			9	10	10	11	11	12	12	12	12	12	12	12	12	12	12	12	12
6		8	9	10	11	12	12	13	13	13	13	14	14	14	14	14	14	14	14
7		8	10	11	12	13	13	14	14	14	14	15	15	15	16	16	16	16	16
8		8	10	11	12	13	14	14	15	15	16	16	16	16	17	17	17	17	17
9		8	10	12	13	14	14	15	16	16	16	17	17	18	18	18	18	18	18
10		8	10	12	13	14	15	16	16	17	17	18	18	18	19	19	19	20	20
11		8	10	12	13	14	15	16	17	17	18	19	19	19	20	20	20	21	21
12	6	8	10	12	13	14	16	16	17	18	19	19	20	20	21	21	21	22	22
13	6	8	10	12	14	15	16	17	18	19	19	20	20	21	21	22	22	23	23
14	6	8	10	12	14	15	16	17	18	19	20	20	21	22	22	23	23	23	24
15	6	8	10	12	14	15	16	18	18	19	20	21	22	22	23	23	24	24	25
16	6	8	10	12	14	16	17	18	19	20	21	21	22	23	23	24	25	25	25
17	6	8	10	12	14	16	17	18	19	20	21	22	23	23	24	25	25	26	26
18	6	8	10	12	14	16	17	18	19	20	21	22	23	24	25	25	26	26	27
19	6	8	10	12	14	16	17	18	20	21	22	23	23	24	25	26	26	27	27
20	6	8	10	12	14	16	17	18	20	21	22	23	24	25	25	26	27	27	28

(b)

APPENDIX 10 Selected Values of the Poisson Probability Distribution

x	0.1	0.2	0.3	0.4	0.5	0.6	0.7	0.8	0.9	1.0
0	.9048	.8187	.7408	.6703	.6065	.5488	.4966	.4493	.4066	.3679
1	.0905	.1637	.2222	.2681	.3033	.3293	.3476	.3395	.3659	.3679
2	.0045	.0164	.0333	.0536	.0758	.0988	.1217	.1438	.1647	.1839
3	.0002	.0011	.0033	.0072	.0126	.0198	.0284	.0383	.0494	.0613
4	.0000	.0001	.0002	.0007	.0016	.0030	.0050	.0077	.0111	.0153
5	.0000	.0000	.0000	.0001	.0002	.0004	.0007	.0012	.0020	.0031
6	.0000	.0000	.0000	.0000	.0000	.0000	.0001	.0002	.0003	.0005
7	.0000	.0000	.0000	.0000	.0000	.0000	.0000	.0000	.0000	.0001

x	1.1	1.2	1.3	1.4	1.5	1.6	1.7	1.8	1.9	2.0
0	.3329	.3012	.2725	.2466	.2231	.2019	.1827	.1653	.1496	.1353
1	.3662	.3614	.3543	.3452	.3347	.3230	.3106	.2975	.2842	.2707
2	.2014	.2169	.2303	.2417	.2510	.2584	.2640	.2678	.2700	.2707
3	.0738	.0867	.0998	.1128	.1255	.1378	.1496	.1607	.1710	.1804
4	.0203	.0260	.0324	.0395	.0471	.0551	.0636	.0723	.0812	.0902
5	.0045	.0062	.0084	.0111	.0141	.0176	.0216	.0260	.0309	.0361
6	.0008	.0012	.0018	.0026	.0035	.0047	.0061	.0078	.0098	.0120
7	.0001	.0002	.0003	.0005	.0008	.0011	.0015	.0020	.0027	.0034
8	.0000	.0000	.0001	.0001	.0001	.0002	.0003	.0005	.0006	.0009
9	.0000	.0000	.0000	.0000	.0000	.0000	.0001	.0001	.0001	.0002

x	2.1	2.2	2.3	2.4	2.5	2.6	2.7	2.8	2.9	3.0
0	.1225	.1108	.1033	.0907	.0821	.0743	.0672	.0608	.0550	.0498
1	.2572	.2438	.2306	.2177	.2052	.1931	.1815	.1703	.1596	.1494
2	.2700	.2681	.2652	.2613	.2565	.2510	.2450	.2384	.2314	.2240
3	.1890	.1966	.2033	.2090	.2138	.2176	.2205	.2225	.2237	.2240
4	.0992	.1082	.1169	.1254	.1336	.1414	.1488	.1557	.1622	.1680
5	.0417	.0476	.0538	.0602	.0668	.0735	.0804	.0872	.0940	.1008
6	.0146	.0174	.0206	.0241	.0278	.0319	.0362	.0407	.0455	.0504
7	.0044	.0055	.0068	.0083	.0099	.0118	.0139	.0163	.0188	.0216
8	.0011	.0015	.0019	.0025	.0031	.0038	.0047	.0057	.0068	.0081
9	.0003	.0004	.0005	.0007	.0009	.0011	.0014	.0018	.0022	.0027
10	.0001	.0001	.0001	.0002	.0002	.0003	.0004	.0005	.0006	.0008
11	.0000	.0000	.0000	.0000	.0000	.0001	.0001	.0001	.0002	.0002
12	.0000	.0000	.0000	.0000	.0000	.0000	.0000	.0000	.0000	.0001

x	3.1	3.2	3.3	3.4	3.5	3.6	3.7	3.8	3.9	4.0
0	.0450	.0408	.0369	.0334	.0302	.0273	.0247	.0224	.0202	.0183
1	.1397	.1304	.1217	.1135	.1057	.0984	.0915	.0850	.0789	.0733
2	.2165	.2087	.2008	.1929	.1850	.1771	.1692	.1615	.1539	.1465
3	.2237	.2226	.2209	.2186	.2158	.2125	.2087	.2046	.2001	.1954
4	.1734	.1781	.1823	.1858	.1888	.1912	.1931	.1944	.1951	.1954
5	.1075	.1140	.1203	.1264	.1322	.1377	.1429	.1477	.1522	.1563
6	.0555	.0608	.0662	.0716	.0771	.0826	.0881	.0936	.0989	.1042
7	.0246	.0278	.0312	.0348	.0385	.0425	.0466	.0508	.0551	.0595
8	.0095	.0111	.0129	.0148	.0169	.0191	.0215	.0241	.0269	.0298
9	.0033	.0040	.0047	.0056	.0066	.0076	.0089	.0102	.0116	.0132
10	.0010	.0013	.0016	.0019	.0023	.0028	.0033	.0039	.0045	.0053
11	.0003	.0004	.0005	.0006	.0007	.0009	.0011	.0013	.0016	.0019
12	.0001	.0001	.0001	.0002	.0002	.0003	.0003	.0004	.0005	.0006
13	.0000	.0000	.0000	.0000	.0001	.0001	.0001	.0001	.0002	.0002
14	.0000	.0000	.0000	.0000	.0000	.0000	.0000	.0000	.0000	.0001

Source: From *Handbook of Probability and Statistics with Tables* by Burington and May. Second Edition, Copyright © 1970 by McGraw-Hill, Inc. Used with permission of McGraw-Hill Book Company.

APPENDIX 10 *(Continued)*

x	4.1	4.2	4.3	4.4	4.5	4.6	4.7	4.8	4.9	5.0
0	.0166	.0150	.0136	.0123	.0111	.0101	.0091	.0082	.0074	.0067
1	.0679	.0630	.0583	.0540	.0500	.0462	.0427	.0395	.0365	.0337
2	.1393	.1323	.1254	.1188	.1125	.1063	.1005	.0948	.0894	.0842
3	.1904	.1852	.1798	.1743	.1687	.1631	.1574	.1517	.1460	.1404
4	.1951	.1944	.1933	.1917	.1898	.1875	.1849	.1820	.1789	.1755
5	.1600	.1633	.1662	.1687	.1708	.1725	.1738	.1747	.1753	.1755
6	.1093	.1143	.1191	.1237	.1281	.1323	.1362	.1398	.1432	.1462
7	.0640	.0686	.0732	.0778	.0824	.0869	.0914	.0959	.1002	.1044
8	.0328	.0360	.0393	.0428	.0463	.0500	.0537	.0575	.0614	.0653
9	.0150	.0168	.0188	.0209	.0232	.0255	.0280	.0307	.0334	.0363
10	.0061	.0071	.0081	.0092	.0104	.0118	.0132	.0147	.0164	.0181
11	.0023	.0027	.0032	.0037	.0043	.0049	.0056	.0064	.0073	.0082
12	.0008	.0009	.0011	.0014	.0016	.0019	.0022	.0026	.0030	.0034
13	.0002	.0003	.0004	.0005	.0006	.0007	.0008	.0009	.0011	.0013
14	.0001	.0001	.0001	.0001	.0002	.0002	.0003	.0003	.0004	.0005
15	.0000	.0000	.0000	.0000	.0001	.0001	.0001	.0001	.0001	.0002

x	5.1	5.2	5.3	5.4	5.5	5.6	5.7	5.8	5.9	6.0
0	.0061	.0055	.0050	.0045	.0041	.0037	.0033	.0030	.0027	.0025
1	.0311	.0287	.0265	.0244	.0225	.0207	.0191	.0176	.0162	.0149
2	.0793	.0746	.0701	.0659	.0618	.0580	.0544	.0509	.0477	.0446
3	.1348	.1293	.1239	.1185	.1133	.1082	.1033	.0985	.0938	.0892
4	.1719	.1681	.1641	.1600	.1558	.1515	.1472	.1428	.1383	.1339
5	.1753	.1748	.1740	.1728	.1714	.1697	.1678	.1656	.1632	.1606
6	.1490	.1515	.1537	.1555	.1571	.1584	.1594	.1601	.1605	.1606
7	.1086	.1125	.1163	.1200	.1234	.1267	.1298	.1326	.1353	.1377
8	.0692	.0731	.0771	.0810	.0849	.0887	.0925	.0962	.0998	.1033
9	.0392	.0423	.0454	.0486	.0519	.0552	.0586	.0620	.0654	.0688
10	.0200	.0220	.0241	.0262	.0285	.0309	.0334	.0359	.0386	.0413
11	.0093	.0104	.0116	.0129	.0143	.0157	.0173	.0190	.0207	.0225
12	.0039	.0045	.0051	.0058	.0065	.0073	.0082	.0092	.0102	.0113
13	.0015	.0018	.0021	.0024	.0028	.0032	.0036	.0041	.0046	.0052
14	.0006	.0007	.0008	.0009	.0011	.0013	.0015	.0017	.0019	.0022
15	.0002	.0002	.0003	.0003	.0004	.0005	.0006	.0007	.0008	.0009
16	.0001	.0001	.0001	.0001	.0001	.0002	.0002	.0002	.0003	.0003
17	.0000	.0000	.0000	.0000	.0000	.0001	.0001	.0001	.0001	.0001

x	6.1	6.2	6.3	6.4	6.5	6.6	6.7	6.8	6.9	7.0
0	.0022	.0020	.0018	.0017	.0015	.0014	.0012	.0011	.0010	.0009
1	.0137	.0126	.0116	.0106	.0098	.0090	.0082	.0076	.0070	.0064
2	.0417	.0390	.0364	.0340	.0318	.0296	.0276	.0258	.0240	.0223
3	.0848	.0806	.0765	.0726	.0688	.0652	.0617	.0584	.0552	.0521
4	.1294	.1249	.1205	.1162	.1118	.1076	.1034	.0992	.0952	.0912
5	.1579	.1549	.1519	.1487	.1454	.1420	.1385	.1349	.1314	.1277
6	.1605	.1601	.1595	.1586	.1575	.1562	.1546	.1529	.1511	.1490
7	.1399	.1418	.1435	.1450	.1462	.1472	.1480	.1486	.1489	.1490
8	.1066	.1099	.1130	.1160	.1188	.1215	.1240	.1263	.1284	.1304
9	.0723	.0757	.0791	.0825	.0858	.0891	.0923	.0954	.0985	.1014
10	.0441	.0469	.0498	.0528	.0558	.0588	.0618	.0649	.0679	.0710
11	.0245	.0265	.0285	.0307	.0330	.0353	.0377	.0401	.0426	.0452
12	.0124	.0137	.0150	.0164	.0179	.0194	.0210	.0227	.0245	.0264
13	.0058	.0065	.0073	.0081	.0089	.0098	.0108	.0119	.0130	.0142
14	.0025	.0029	.0033	.0037	.0041	.0046	.0052	.0058	.0064	.0071
15	.0010	.0012	.0014	.0016	.0018	.0020	.0023	.0026	.0029	.0033
16	.0004	.0005	.0005	.0006	.0007	.0008	.0010	.0011	.0013	.0014
17	.0001	.0002	.0002	.0002	.0003	.0003	.0004	.0004	.0005	.0006
18	.0000	.0001	.0001	.0001	.0001	.0001	.0001	.0002	.0002	.0002
19	.0000	.0000	.0000	.0000	.0000	.0000	.0000	.0001	.0001	.0001

APPENDIX 10 *(Continued)*

x	7.1	7.2	7.3	7.4	7.5	7.6	7.7	7.8	7.9	8.0
0	.0008	.0007	.0007	.0006	.0006	.0005	.0005	.0004	.0004	.0003
1	.0059	.0054	.0049	.0045	.0041	.0038	.0035	.0032	.0029	.0027
2	.0208	.0194	.0180	.0167	.0156	.0145	.0134	.0125	.0116	.0107
3	.0492	.0464	.0438	.0413	.0389	.0366	.0345	.0324	.0305	.0286
4	.0874	.0836	.0799	.0764	.0729	.0696	.0663	.0632	.0602	.0573
5	.1241	.1204	.1167	.1130	.1094	.1057	.1021	.0986	.0951	.0916
6	.1468	.1445	.1420	.1394	.1367	.1339	.1311	.1282	.1252	.1221
7	.1489	.1486	.1481	.1474	.1465	.1454	.1442	.1428	.1413	.1396
8	.1321	.1337	.1351	.1363	.1373	.1382	.1388	.1392	.1395	.1396
9	.1042	.1070	.1096	.1121	.1144	.1167	.1187	.1207	.1224	.1241
10	.0740	.0770	.0800	.0829	.0858	.0887	.0914	.0941	.0967	.0993
11	.0478	.0504	.0531	.0558	.0585	.0613	.0640	.0667	.0695	.0722
12	.0283	.0303	.0323	.0344	.0366	.0388	.0411	.0434	.0457	.0481
13	.0154	.0168	.0181	.0196	.0211	.0227	.0243	.0260	.0278	.0296
14	.0078	.0086	.0095	.0104	.0113	.0123	.0134	.0145	.0157	.0169
15	.0037	.0041	.0046	.0051	.0057	.0062	.0069	.0075	.0083	.0090
16	.0016	.0019	.0021	.0024	.0026	.0030	.0033	.0037	.0041	.0045
17	.0007	.0008	.0009	.0010	.0012	.0013	.0015	.0017	.0019	.0021
18	.0003	.0003	.0004	.0004	.0005	.0006	.0006	.0007	.0008	.0009
19	.0001	.0001	.0001	.0002	.0002	.0002	.0003	.0003	.0003	.0004
20	.0000	.0000	.0001	.0001	.0001	.0001	.0001	.0001	.0001	.0002
21	.0000	.0000	.0000	.0000	.0000	.0000	.0000	.0000	.0001	.0001

x	8.1	8.2	8.3	8.4	8.5	8.6	8.7	8.8	8.9	9.0
0	.0003	.0003	.0002	.0002	.0002	.0002	.0002	.0002	.0001	.0001
1	.0025	.0023	.0021	.0019	.0017	.0016	.0014	.0013	.0012	.0011
2	.0100	.0092	.0086	.0079	.0074	.0068	.0063	.0058	.0054	.0050
3	.0269	.0252	.0237	.0222	.0208	.0195	.0183	.0171	.0160	.0150
4	.0544	.0517	.0491	.0466	.0443	.0420	.0398	.0377	.0357	.0337
5	.0882	.0849	.0816	.0784	.0752	.0722	.0692	.0663	.0635	.0607
6	.1191	.1160	.1128	.1097	.1066	.1034	.1003	.0972	.0941	.0911
7	.1378	.1358	.1338	.1317	.1294	.1271	.1247	.1222	.1197	.1171
8	.1395	.1392	.1388	.1382	.1375	.1366	.1356	.1344	.1332	.1318
9	.1256	.1269	.1280	.1290	.1299	.1306	.1311	.1315	.1317	.1318
10	.1017	.1040	.1063	.1084	.1104	.1123	.1140	.1157	.1172	.1186
11	.0749	.0776	.0802	.0828	.0853	.0878	.0902	.0925	.0948	.0970
12	.0505	.0530	.0555	.0579	.0604	.0629	.0654	.0679	.0703	.0728
13	.0315	.0334	.0354	.0374	.0395	.0416	.0438	.0459	.0481	.0504
14	.0182	.0196	.0210	.0225	.0240	.0256	.0272	.0289	.0306	.0324
15	.0098	.0107	.0116	.0126	.0136	.0147	.0158	.0169	.0182	.0194
16	.0050	.0055	.0060	.0066	.0072	.0079	.0086	.0093	.0101	.0109
17	.0024	.0026	.0029	.0033	.0036	.0040	.0044	.0048	.0053	.0058
18	.0011	.0012	.0014	.0015	.0017	.0019	.0021	.0024	.0026	.0029
19	.0005	.0005	.0006	.0007	.0008	.0009	.0010	.0011	.0012	.0014
20	.0002	.0002	.0002	.0003	.0003	.0004	.0004	.0005	.0005	.0005
21	.0001	.0001	.0001	.0001	.0001	.0002	.0002	.0002	.0002	.0003
22	.0000	.0000	.0000	.0000	.0001	.0001	.0001	.0001	.0001	.0001

x	9.1	9.2	9.3	9.4	9.5	9.6	9.7	9.8	9.9	10
0	.0001	.0001	.0001	.0001	.0001	.0001	.0001	.0001	.0001	.0000
1	.0010	.0009	.0009	.0008	.0007	.0007	.0006	.0005	.0005	.0005
2	.0046	.0043	.0040	.0037	.0034	.0031	.0029	.0027	.0025	.0023
3	.0140	.0131	.0123	.0115	.0107	.0100	.0093	.0087	.0081	.0076
4	.0319	.0302	.0285	.0269	.0254	.0240	.0226	.0213	.0201	.0189
5	.0581	.0555	.0530	.0506	.0483	.0460	.0439	.0418	.0398	.0378
6	.0881	.0851	.0822	.0793	.0764	.0736	.0709	.0682	.0656	.0631
7	.1145	.1118	.1091	.1064	.1037	.1010	.0982	.0955	.0928	.0901
8	.1302	.1286	.1269	.1251	.1232	.1212	.1191	.1170	.1148	.1126
9	.1317	.1315	.1311	.1306	.1300	.1293	.1284	.1274	.1263	.1251

APPENDIX 10 *(Continued)*

x	9.1	9.2	9.3	9.4	9.5	9.6	9.7	9.8	9.9	10
10	.1198	.1210	.1219	.1228	.1235	.1241	.1245	.1249	.1250	.1251
11	.0991	.1012	.1031	.1049	.1067	.1083	.1098	.1112	.1125	.1137
12	.0752	.0776	.0799	.0822	.0844	.0866	.0888	.0908	.0928	.0948
13	.0526	.0549	.0572	.0594	.0617	.0640	.0662	.0685	.0707	.0729
14	.0342	.0361	.0380	.0399	.0419	.0439	.0459	.0479	.0500	.0521
15	.0208	.0221	.0235	.0250	.0265	.0281	.0297	.0313	.0330	.0347
16	.0118	.0127	.0137	.0147	.0157	.0168	.0180	.0192	.0204	.0217
17	.0063	.0069	.0075	.0081	.0088	.0095	.0103	.0111	.0119	.0128
18	.0032	.0035	.0039	.0042	.0046	.0051	.0055	.0060	.0065	.0071
19	.0015	.0017	.0019	.0021	.0023	.0026	.0028	.0031	.0034	.0037
20	.0007	.0008	.0009	.0010	.0011	.0012	.0014	.0015	.0017	.0019
21	.0003	.0003	.0004	.0004	.0005	.0006	.0006	.0007	.0008	.0009
22	.0001	.0001	.0002	.0002	.0002	.0002	.0003	.0003	.0004	.0004
23	.0000	.0001	.0001	.0001	.0001	.0001	.0001	.0001	.0002	.0002
24	.0000	.0000	.0000	.0000	.0000	.0000	.0000	.0001	.0001	.0001

x	11	12	13	14	15	16	17	18	19	20
0	.0000	.0000	.0000	.0000	.0000	.0000	.0000	.0000	.0000	.0000
1	.0002	.0001	.0000	.0000	.0000	.0000	.0000	.0000	.0000	.0000
2	.0010	.0004	.0002	.0001	.0000	.0000	.0000	.0000	.0000	.0000
3	.0037	.0018	.0008	.0004	.0002	.0001	.0000	.0000	.0000	.0000
4	.0102	.0053	.0027	.0013	.0006	.0003	.0001	.0001	.0000	.0000
5	.0224	.0127	.0070	.0037	.0019	.0010	.0005	.0002	.0001	.0001
6	.0411	.0255	.0152	.0087	.0048	.0026	.0014	.0007	.0004	.0002
7	.0646	.0437	.0281	.0174	.0104	.0060	.0034	.0018	.0010	.0005
8	.0888	.0655	.0457	.0304	.0194	.0120	.0072	.0042	.0024	.0013
9	.1085	.0874	.0661	.0473	.0324	.0213	.0135	.0083	.0050	.0029
10	.1194	.1048	.0859	.0663	.0486	.0341	.0230	.0150	.0095	.0058
11	.1194	.1144	.1015	.0844	.0663	.0496	.0355	.0245	.0164	.0106
12	.1094	.1144	.1099	.0984	.0829	.0661	.0504	.0368	.0259	.0176
13	.0926	.1056	.1099	.1060	.0956	.0814	.0658	.0509	.0378	.0271
14	.0728	.0905	.1021	.1060	.1024	.0930	.0800	.0655	.0514	.0387
15	.0534	.0724	.0885	.0989	.1024	.0992	.0906	.0786	.0650	.0516
16	.0367	.0453	.0719	.0866	.0960	.0992	.0963	.0884	.0772	.0646
17	.0237	.0383	.0550	.0713	.0847	.0934	.0963	.0936	.0863	.0760
18	.0145	.0256	.0397	.0554	.0705	.0830	.0909	.0936	.0911	.0844
19	.0084	.0161	.0272	.0409	.0557	.0699	.0814	.0887	.0911	.0888
20	.0046	.0097	.0177	.0286	.0418	.0559	.0692	.0798	.0866	.0888
21	.0024	.0055	.0109	.0191	.0299	.0426	.0560	.0684	.0783	.0846
22	.0012	.0030	.0065	.0121	.0204	.0310	.0433	.0560	.0676	.0769
23	.0006	.0016	.0037	.0074	.0133	.0216	.0320	.0438	.0559	.0669
24	.0003	.0008	.0020	.0043	.0083	.0144	.0226	.0328	.0442	.0557
25	.0001	.0004	.0010	.0024	.0050	.0092	.0154	.0237	.0336	.0446
26	.0000	.0002	.0005	.0013	.0029	.0057	.0101	.0164	.0246	.0343
27	.0000	.0001	.0002	.0007	.0016	.0034	.0063	.0109	.0173	.0254
28	.0000	.0000	.0001	.0003	.0009	.0009	.0038	.0070	.0117	.0181
29	.0000	.0000	.0001	.0000	.0004	.0011	.0023	.0044	.0077	.0125
30	.0000	.0000	.0000	.0001	.0002	.0006	.0013	.0026	.0049	.0083
31	.0000	.0000	.0000	.0000	.0001	.0003	.0007	.0015	.0030	.0054
32	.0000	.0000	.0000	.0000	.0001	.0001	.0004	.0009	.0018	.0034
33	.0000	.0000	.0000	.0000	.0000	.0001	.0002	.0005	.0010	.0020
34	.0000	.0000	.0000	.0000	.0000	.0000	.0001	.0002	.0006	.0012
35	.0000	.0000	.0000	.0000	.0000	.0000	.0000	.0001	.0003	.0007
36	.0000	.0000	.0000	.0000	.0000	.0000	.0000	.0001	.0002	.0004
37	.0000	.0000	.0000	.0000	.0000	.0000	.0000	.0000	.0001	.0002
38	.0000	.0000	.0000	.0000	.0000	.0000	.0000	.0000	.0000	.0001
39	.0000	.0000	.0000	.0000	.0000	.0000	.0000	.0000	.0000	.0001

APPENDIX 11   Entering and Editing Data in MINITAB

There are several ways in which data can be entered into one of MINITAB's data storage areas, called worksheets. We will look at three methods: (1) typing, (2) pasting, and (3) retrieving.

Typing   When you start MINITAB, one of the windows you should see is Worksheet 1. It consists of a grid of cells in columns, labelled C1, C2, and so on, and rows. MINITAB will perform operations on columns of data, so we want to enter data from a single sample into an individual column. We have done so for an example from Chapter 3, the litres of Fizzy Cola syrup sold by the Slimline Beverage Company. You can see this data in Table 3.1 (page 40). We started in the first row of a C1, typing the first data value and hitting the enter key. Repeating this process for each data value, we entered the complete sample into column 1. Then we moved the cursor to a slot above the column and named the column **LTRSOLD.** The result of this process is displayed in Figure A11.1. You could now ask MINITAB to do an analysis of this data by either asking MINITAB to analyze C1 or to analyze **'LTRSOLD,'** the name of the column in single quotes.

Pasting   Some of your data sets can come from other electronic sources such as the Internet or a professor's data stored on disk. If the data has extraneous symbols such as commas or dollar signs, you must first eliminate these symbols by using a word processor such as WordPerfect or Word. Such applications can do global replacements of one set of symbols with another. You would replace each extraneous symbol with nothing; that is, when your program asks what the extraneous symbol should be "replaced with," you enter nothing. After removing these symbols, you can copy this data directly into MINITAB. First, have the data on your computer screen. Next, highlight this data by using the mouse with the left button depressed. Then copy the highlighted data by clicking on the copy icon, or by holding down the **Ctrl** button and hitting the **C** key, or by using the **Edit** function of whatever application you are using. Then access MINITAB, place your cursor into the first row of a column, and hit the paste icon or hold down the **Ctrl** button and hit the **V** key.

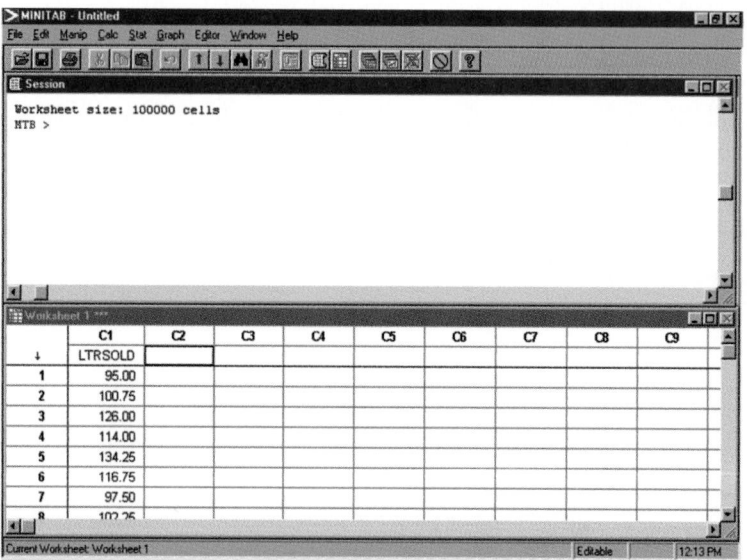

FIGURE A11.1

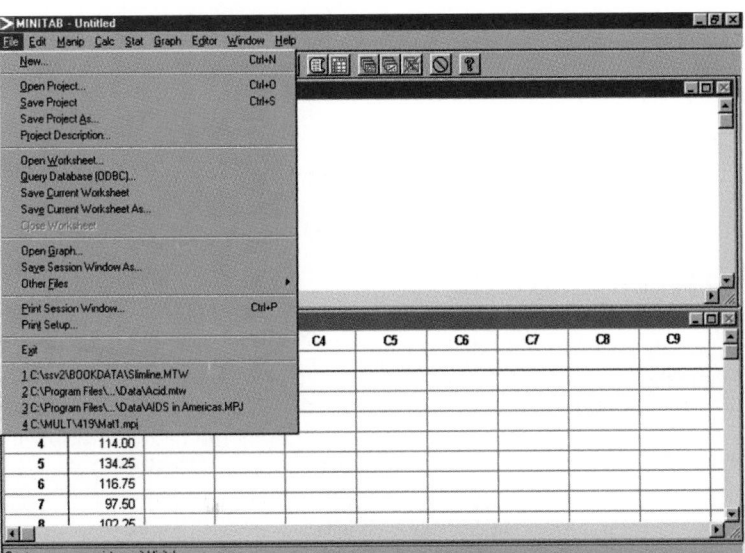

Retrieving Often you will be analyzing a data set more than once. If so, it is unnecessary to retype or repaste your data into a MINITAB worksheet. Rather, after entering your data the first time, you can save the data and use it again in future MINITAB sessions. You can save the data several ways, but two of the most convenient are to either save only the worksheet or to save the worksheet plus all the work you have done during your MINITAB session (this is called a MINITAB project). To save only the worksheet, click on **File, Save Current Worksheet As,** (see Figure A11.2) and enter the name you wish to give the worksheet. MINITAB will automatically add the extension **MTW,** standing for "MINITAB Worksheet." (Note: If you are using a school or friend's computer, you'll want to insert a floppy disk and save it to the disk drive rather than to the computer's storage.) If you want to save everything—that is, a MINITAB project—instead of clicking on **Save Current Worksheet As,** click on **Save Project As** (see Figure A11.2) or click on the second icon in the session window toolbar (see Figure A11.1). MINITAB again will automatically add an extension, but in this case it will be **MPJ,** standing for "MINITAB Project." Once either of these has been saved, it can be retrieved at future MINITAB sessions. To retrieve a MINITAB Worksheet, click on **File, Open Worksheet,** (see Figure A11.2) and enter the name of your saved worksheet. To retrieve a MINITAB Project, go through the same process, except click on **Open Project** rather than **Open Worksheet.**

APPENDIX 12   Answers to Odd-Numbered Self-Testing Review Questions and Exercises

Chapter 1
Exercises

1) d   3) h   5) a   7) f   9a) Systematic   9b) Stratified 9c) Simple random   9d) The population of interest is the collection of weights of all students currently taking STAT200. The sample is the set of weights of the 12 students selected. The parameter of interest is the mean weight of all students currently taking STAT200. The statistic of interest is the mean weight of the 12 students selected.

11) The answer depends on the type of random sample selected.

Chapter 2
Exercises

1) We can't really evaluate this performance without knowing how other comparable funds performed during the same period. And we can't be sure that the performance trend will continue and produce the same rate of growth in the future.

3) This is a case of aggravating averages. Both $2,000 (the mode and the median) and $6,400 (the mean) are legitimate measures of central tendency.

5) Not necessarily. This issue has become more publicized, and more people are willing to report it than in the past. Perhaps the number of incidents hasn't increased much, but more of the incidents that are occurring are being reported.

7) The studies were conducted by organizations that had something to gain. It's possible that an element of bias has entered the picture.

9) What was Krinkle Gum compared against? Perhaps Krinkle Gum users had 36 percent fewer cavities than those addicted to candy bars. The data may be spurious, and it is certainly curious since we don't know how it was obtained.

11) This is always true for the median of a set of values.

13) Much more contact is made with friends, acquaintances, and relatives than with strangers in lonely parks at night. Thus, rape victims are more likely to be acquainted with their assailants.

15a) Yes. Set-up time has been reduced from 27.9 percent to 7.5 percent, and Running time has increased from 36.6 percent to 56.7 percent.

15b) A bar graph could be used, with the before and after proportions side by side. It would be obvious very quickly that the set-up time had been reduced significantly, and the running time had increased.

Chapter 3
Self-Testing Review 3.1

1. Numeric, continuous   3. Numeric, discrete   5. Attribute 7. Numeric, continuous   9. Numeric, continuous   11. Numeric, discrete

Self-Testing Review 3.2

13a)

Fees	Frequency
3,500 to < 4,500	1
4,500 to < 5,500	5
5,500 to < 6,500	5
6,500 to < 7,500	3
7,500 to < 8,500	6
8,500 to < 9,500	9
9,500 to < 10,500	12
10,500 to < 11,500	1
11,500 to < 12,500	1

13b) Yes.

13c) With five classes you could use the intervals 4040 to < 5640, 5640 to < 7240, ... , .10440 to < 12440. With seven classes you could use the intervals 4040 to < 5180, 5180 to < 6320, ... , 10880 to < 12020. Other intervals could be used.

15a)   21.50   25.35   29.00   30.30   31.25   34.60   35.55 36.50   36.60   38.50   39.95   40.25   41.10   42.30   42.50 43.50   44.80   45.00   45.10   46.00   47.75   49.50   49.80 52.10   55.00   55.60   56.30   58.00   59.20   65.50

15b) The range = $65.50 − $21.50 = $44.00.

15c)

Size of orders (S)	Number of Orders (Frequencies)
20 to <30	3
30 to <40	8
40 to <50	12
50 to <60	6
60 to <70	1
	30

15d) Yes.

15e) Use a class width of 6, the round-up of 44/8.

17a) 88   89   100   129   136   143   148   158   164   169
175   178   179   181   189   194   195   195   213   227
246   247   309

17b) The range = 309 − 88 = 221.

17c)

Number of Vessels	Frequencies
50 to <100	2
100 to <150	5
150 to <200	11
200 to <250	4
250 to <300	0
300 to <350	1

Self-Testing Review 3.3

19a) Dotplot for Weeks of Therapy

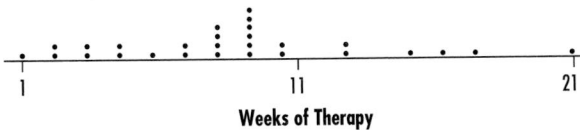

19b)

Weeks of Therapy	Number of Patients (Frequencies)
1 to <5	7
5 to <9	9
9 to <13	8
13 to <17	4
17 to <21	1
21 to <25	1
	30

19c)

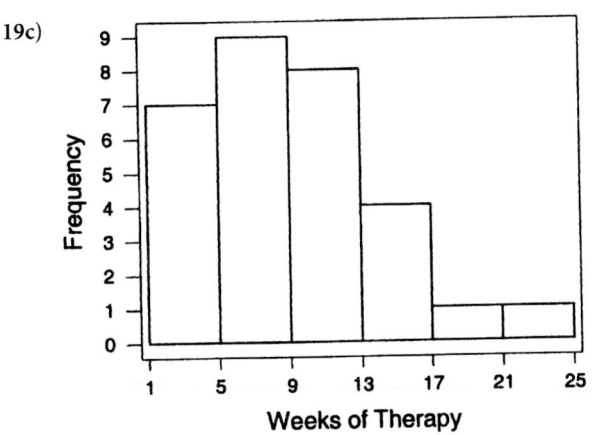

19d)

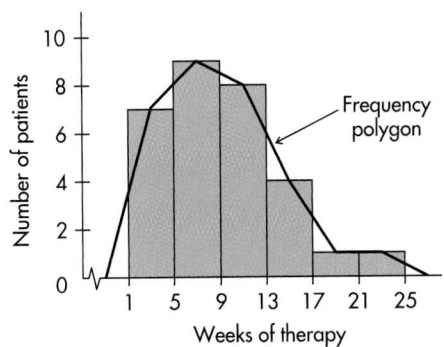

19e)

Stem	Leaf									Key: 0	1 means 1 week			
0	1	2	2	3	3	4	4							
0	5	6	6	7	7	8	8	8	8	9	9	9	9	9 9
1	0	0	3	3										
1	5	6	7											
2	1													

21a)

Percentage	Frequency
50 to <55	1
55 to <60	0
60 to <65	1
65 to <70	3
70 to <75	8
75 to <80	10
80 to <85	10
85 to <90	6
90 to <95	6

21b)

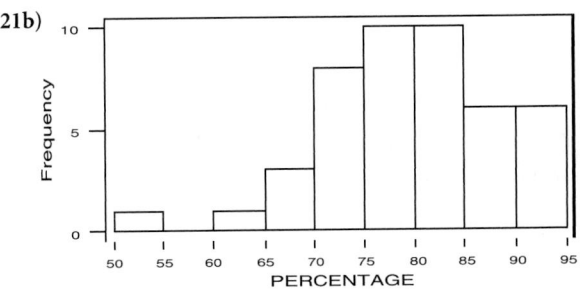

21c) A MINITAB generated stem-and-leaf display
Leaf unit 1.0

```
   1     5   4
   1     5
   2     6   2
   5     6   599
  13     7   01122224
 (10)    7   5666678899
  22     8   0112233334
  12     8   777889
   6     9   002224
```

Self-Testing Review 3.4

23) To earn an average of 84 with nine tests, the student must have a total of 84×9 or 756 points. The given values add to 662 points. Since an additional 94 points $(756 - 662 = 94)$ is needed, the instructor deleted a grade of 94.

25a) $\bar{x} = \$42.44$.

25b) $38.75

25c)

Price (in $)	Number of Stocks (f)
20 < 30	7
30 < 40	2
40 < 50	1
50 < 60	2
60 < 70	5
	17

25d) The estimated mean of grouped data is $7(25)/17 + 2(35)/17 + 1(45)/17 + 2(55)/17 + 5(65)/17 = 725/17 = 42.647$. It is just slightly larger than the true mean of 42.44.

27a) 5.78 megabytes

27b) 5.9 megabytes

29a) 1.723 litres

29b) 1.7 litres

29c) Two modes: 0.5 and 1.7 litres

31a) The mean = 8039.4 offences.

31b) Trimmed mean = 7,641.5.

31c) The median = 7137 offences.

Self-Testing Review 3.5

33a) $\bar{x} = \dfrac{1256 + 2726 + 1224 + 2588 + 3294 + 1893 + 2537 + 3177 + 2460}{9}$

$= \dfrac{21155}{9} = 2350.5.$

33b) Range = $2,070.

33c) $s^2 = 561,714.$

33d) $749.5

33e) $z = \dfrac{x - \bar{x}}{s} = \dfrac{1256 - 2350.5}{749.5} = -1.46.$

35a) 1.97

35b) $\bar{x} = \dfrac{\begin{array}{c}7.92 + 6.94 + 7.14 + 6.67 + 7.12 + 6.67 \\ + 7.04 + 6.66 + 6.95 + 5.95\end{array}}{10}$

$= \dfrac{60.060}{10} = 6.906.$

35c) 0.4984 rating point

35d) $z = \dfrac{5.95 - 6.906}{0.4984} = -1.092.$

35e) $z = \dfrac{7.12 - 6.906}{0.4984} = .430.$

35f) Since two of the ten scores are below 6.665, 6.665 represents the 20th percentile.

35g) 7.13

37a) $\mu \pm 2\sigma$; 52.84 and 75.96 points

37b) 47.06 and 81.74

37c) $\mu \pm \sigma$; 58.62 and 70.18.

37d) 52.84 and 75.96

37e) $\mu \pm 3\sigma$; 47.06 and 81.74.

39a) $\bar{x} = \dfrac{157}{25} = 6.28.$

39b) Range = $20 - 1 = 19$.

39c)

x	(x − x̄)	|x − x̄|
7	0.72	0.72
6	−0.28	0.28
8	1.72	1.72
5	−1.28	1.28
9	2.72	2.72
6	−0.28	0.28
6	−0.28	0.28
7	0.72	0.72
7	0.72	0.72
4	−0.28	2.28
13	6.72	6.72
2	−2.28	4.28
1	−4.28	5.28
20	13.72	13.72
1	−5.28	5.28

continued

x	$(x - \bar{x})$	$\lvert x - \bar{x} \rvert$
5	−1.28	1.28
7	0.72	0.72
6	−0.28	0.28
7	0.72	0.72
1	−5.28	5.28
8	1.72	1.72
4	−2.28	2.28
8	1.72	1.72
3	−3.28	3.28
6	−0.28	0.28
		63.84

$$\text{MAD} = \frac{\sum \lvert x - \bar{x} \rvert}{n} = \frac{63.84}{25} = 2.554.$$

39d) Sample variance $s^2 = 15.793$, sample standard deviation $s = 3.974$

39e) $z = \dfrac{x - \bar{x}}{s} = \dfrac{10 - 6.28}{3.974} = 0.936.$

39f) 9 years

39g) 4, 7.

39h) IQR = 7 − 4 = 3

41) Median class is 7 to <10.

Self-Testing Review 3.6

43) The percent of defective microchips in Batch 1 = 13.14 percent, in Batch 2 = 9.50 percent, in Batch 3 = 7.62 percent, in Batch 4 = 11.95 percent, and in Batch 5 = 13.00 percent.

45) Eight of 260, or 3.08 percent, of the cases treated with dexamethasone suffered severe hearing loss. Twenty-seven of 233, or 11.59 percent, of the cases not treated with dexamethasone suffered severe hearing loss.

47) Walking: 35/50 = 70 percent; jogging: 8/50 = 16 percent; running: 5/50 = 10 percent; cycling: 23/50 = 46 percent; swimming: 20/50 = 40 percent; dancing: 7/50 = 14 percent; other: 22/50 = 44 percent.

Exercises

49a) 41,037 58,358 61,735 67,374 78,908 81,346 117,344 121,986 122,678 146,838 172,918 192,800 225927 307,877 311,902 359,183 377,009 414,284 432451 662,401 671,274 937,845 95,139 1,063,664 1,986,965 3,426,350 4,682,897

49b) Since 7.5 percent of 27 is 2.025, we eliminate the two lowest and the two highest population sizes (which are 41,037, 58,358, and 3,426,350, 4,682,897 respectively). The (trimmed)

mean of the remaining 23 values is 9,866,104/23 = 428,961 so the 7.5 percent trimmed mean is 428,961.

49c) Median =14th largest value = 307,877
Since $(27)(25)/100 = 6.75$, Q_1 = the 7th largest value = 117,344.
Since $(27)(75)/100 = 20.25$, Q_3 = the 21st largest value = 671,274.

49d) Since $(27)(40)/100 = 10.8$, the 40th percentile = P_{40} = the 11th largest value = 172,918.

49e)

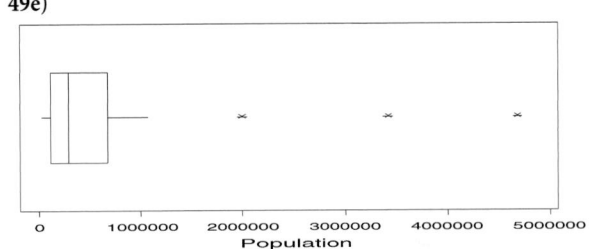

49f) Interquartile range = $Q_3 - Q_1$ = 553,930

49g)

Population Size (thousands)	Number of Cities (frequencies)
0 to < 100,000	6
100,000 to < 200,000	6
200,000 to < 300,000	1
300,000 to < 400,000	4
400,000 to < 500,000	2
500,000 to < 600,000	0
600,000 to < 700,000	2

49h)

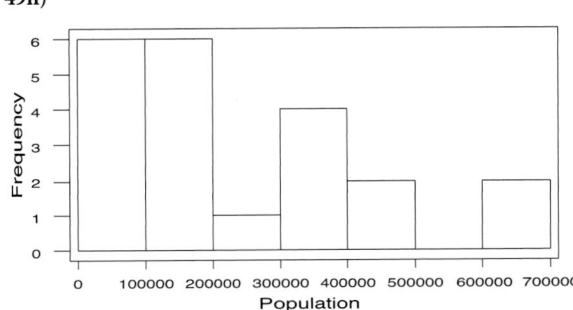

51a) $\mu = \dfrac{\begin{array}{c}25.50 + 30.75 + 31.25 + 33.50 + 35.00 + 53.25 \\ + 57.25 + 58.50 + 104.75\end{array}}{9}$

$= \dfrac{429.75}{9} = \$47.75.$

51b) Median = $35.00.

51c) The range = $104.75 − 25.50 = $79.25.

51d) MAD = 18.39.

51e) Using the formula 3.7, $\sigma = \sqrt{\dfrac{\Sigma(x - \mu)^2}{N}}$ and $\mu = \$47.75$ from Exercise 28.

Price per share, x	$(x - \mu)$	$(x - \mu)^2$
25.50	−22.25	495.0625
30.75	−17.00	289.0000
31.25	−16.50	272.2500
33.50	−14.25	203.0625
35.00	−12.75	162.5625
53.25	5.50	30.2500
57.25	9.50	90.2500
58.50	10.75	115.5625
104.75	57.00	3249.0000
		4907.0000

So, $\sigma = \sqrt{\dfrac{4907.0000}{9}} = \sqrt{545.222} = 23.35$.

53a) Population mean = \$1,113 million.

53b) Since $(9)(70)/100 = 6.3$, the 70th percentile is the 7th largest value = \$1,686 million.

53c) Population standard deviation = \$860.09 million.

53d) For the Bank of Montreal, $z = (1471 - 1113)/860.09 = 0.42$.

55a) Sample mean = 49,618 employees.

55b) Sample median = 43282.5 employees.

55c) $P_{30} = 33,720$.

55d) $s = 27,820$ employees.

55e) The z-score of Air Canada = −0.40.

55f) The z-score of Hudson's Bay Co. = 0.77.

57a) Interquartile range = $15 - 11 = 4$.

57b) $P_{20} = 10.5$.

57c) $P_{90} = 20$.

57d) Median = 13.5

59) Mount Saint Vincent = 84 percent, Guelph = 63 percent, UPEI = 62 percent, Moncton = 62 percent, Mount Allison = 57 percent, Waterloo = 46 percent, Brandon = 64 percent, Regina = 60 percent.

61)

Stem	Leaf
1	2 4 5 9
2	2 3 5
3	7
4	1 3
5	1 4 5
6	2 5 6 8
7	1 3
8	4 5 8
9	2 2 6

63a) Range = $1403 - 269 = 1134$.

63b) Sample mean = 860.2 points.

63c) Using $\bar{x} = 860.2$, compute the table:

Exam Scores, x	$|x - \bar{x}|$
269	591.2
345	515.2
381	479.2
428	432.2
455	405.2
582	278.2
760	100.2
763	97.2
898	37.8
990	129.8
999	138.8
1059	198.8
1141	280.8
1181	320.8
1213	352.8
1264	403.8
1352	491.8
1403	542.8
15483	5796.6

63d) Sample standard deviation = 373.8 points

65) Yes. Example: $\{0, 0, 0, 0\}$

67a) For weight mean = 7.37, standard deviation = 3.54

67b) $z = \dfrac{x - \bar{x}}{s} = \dfrac{8.00 - 7.37}{3.54} = 0.18$.

67c) For density, mean = 26.67, standard deviation = 14.07.

67d) $z = \dfrac{x - \bar{x}}{s} = \dfrac{30 - 26.67}{14.07} = 0.24$.

Chapter 4
Self-Testing Review 4.1

1) There are 13 ways to be "successful" with 52 cards. The probability is 13/52 or 1/4 or .25.

3) .45

5) 0.1744

7) 1/20 = .05.

9a) No, since the sum of the probabilities is not 1.

9b) No, the probability of an event cannot be more than 1.

9c) Yes, the sum of the probabilities is 1, and each probability is between 0 and 1.

9d) No, since a probability can't be negative.

9e) Yes, the sum of the probabilities is 1, and each probability is between 0 (inclusive) and 1.

11) 4,302,200/32,228,700 = .1335.

13) 0.1367

Self-Testing Review 4.2

15a) "At least a 4" means a 4 or a 5 or a 6 in this problem. Since the events are mutually exclusive (a roll of a 4 on a single trial excludes a roll of a 5 on that same trial) we can add 1/6 + 1/6 + 1/6 = 3/6 = 0.5.

15b) We determine the probability that the die lands on a 1 or a 3 or a 5. These events are mutually exclusive, so we add 1/6 + 1/6 + 1/6 = 3/6 = .5.

15c) These events are mutually exclusive, so we add 1/6 + 3/6 = 4/6 = 0.6667.

17a) The probabilities on the second draw now depend on the probabilities of the first draw. Thus, (8/10)(7/9) = 56/90 = .62.

17b) $\frac{2}{10} \cdot \frac{1}{9} = \frac{2}{90} = 0.0222.$

17c) (8/10)(2/9) = 16/90 = .1778.

17d) $\frac{2}{10} \cdot \frac{8}{9} = \frac{16}{90} = 0.1778.$

17e) Consider the two different orders and add 16/90 + 16/90 = 32/90 = .3556.

17f) Since the probability of the complement (both items are good) is 56/90 = 0.6222, we'll use the rule for complements to compute the probability that at least one is defective. That is, 1 − 0.6222 = 0.3778.

19a) 3/50 = .06.

19b) $\frac{3 + 8 + 13}{50} = \frac{24}{50} = 0.48.$

19c) 15/50 = .30.

19d) $\frac{13 + 23 + 8}{130} = \frac{44}{130} = 0.3385.$

19e) (9 + 2 + 7 + 2 + 11 + 3)/130 = .2615

21a) 0.4667

21b) $\frac{28 + 14}{60} = \frac{42}{60} = 0.7.$

21c) 0.7833

23a) 0.1882

23b) 0.5289

23c) 0.0012

23d) 0.5403

23e) 0.7622

23f) 0.5276

23g) 0.0814

23h) 0.0018

23i) 0.5233

23j) No, since P(female and 65+) = 1,072,642/20,585,997 π 0.

23k) The events of being female (event F) and being in the 65+ age category (event G) are not independent since P(F and G) is not equal to P(F) P(G). That is, P(F and G) = 0.5211, P(F) = 0.4711, P(G) = 0.1213, and (0.4711)(0.1213) = 0.0571.

25a) 0.2592

25b) (7,778,865 + 18,339,680)/30,007,095 = .8704.

25c) 0.3802

25d) (2,974,810 + 3,907,735)/30,007,095 = .2294.

25e) 0.2311

25f) (6,935,710 + 1,472,170)/30,007,095 = .2802.

25g) 0.6256

25h) 545,820/978,930 = .5576.

25i) 0.1364

25j) 2,398,305/18,339,680 = .1308.

25k) 0.6114

Self-Testing Review 4.3

27a) 0.14

27b) .14 + .48 + .14 = .76.

27c)

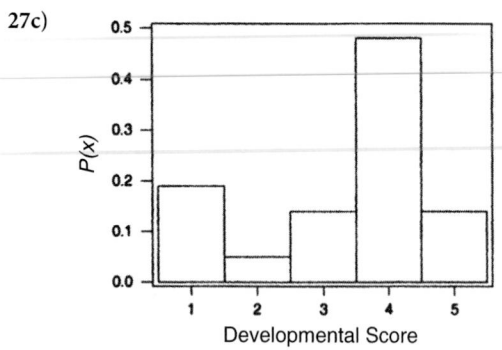

27d) $E(x) = 1(.19) + 2(.05) + 3(.14) = 4(.48) + 5(.14) = 3.33.$

27e) $\sum [x^2 P(x)] = 1^2(0.19) + 2^2 (0.05) + 3^2 (0.14) + 4^2 (0.48) + 5^2(0.14) = 12.83.$ $\sigma = \sqrt{\sum[x^2 P(x)] - \mu^2} = \sqrt{12.83 - 3.33^2} = \sqrt{1.7411} = 1.320$

29) $E(x) = 0.60(\$20,000) + 0.40(-\$25,000) = \$2,000.$ She should make the investment.

31a) Add the probability of selling three cars or four cars to get: $0.15 + 0.05 = 0.20.$

31b) Using the complement rule, $1 - .20 = .80.$

31c) $E(x) = 0(0.20) + 1(0.30) + 2(0.30) + 3(0.15) + 4(0.05) = 1.55.$

31d) $(31)(1.55) = 48.05.$ The dealer should expect to sell about 48 cars a month.

33a) $3/30 = 0.10.$

33b) $P(x \le 5) = (2 + 3)/30 = .1667.$

33c) $P(11$ or 12 or 14 or 15 or 22 assist$) = 5/30 + 4/30 + 2/30 + 1/30 + 1/30 = 13/30 = 0.4333.$

33d) 8.2667

33e)

x	P(x)	x · P(x)	x² · P(x)
4	0.066667	0.26667	1.0667
5	0.100000	0.50000	2.5000
6	0.133333	0.80000	4.8000
7	0.133333	0.93333	6.5333
8	0.166667	1.33333	10.6667
9	0.100000	0.90000	8.1000
10	0.066667	0.66667	6.6667
11	0.100000	1.10000	12.1000
12	0.033333	0.40000	4.8000
13	0.033333	0.43333	5.6333
14	0.066667	0.93333	13.0667
		8.2667	75.933

$\sigma = \sqrt{\sum[x^2 P(x)] - \mu^2} = \sqrt{75.933 - (8.2667)^2} = \sqrt{7.5947} = 2.7558.$

33f) 9.50

33g)

y	P(y)	y · P(y)	y² · P(y)
4	0.266667	0.26667	1.0667
5	0.133333	0.66667	3.3333
6	0.033333	0.20000	1.2000
7	0.100000	0.70000	4.9000
8	0.100000	0.80000	6.4000
9	0.066667	0.60000	5.4000
10	0.066667	0.66667	6.6667
11	0.166667	1.83333	20.1667
12	0.133333	1.60000	19.2000
14	0.066667	0.93333	13.0667
15	0.033333	0.50000	7.5000
22	0.033333	0.73333	16.1333
		9.5	105.03

$\sigma = \sqrt{\sum[y^2 P(y)] - \mu^2} = \sqrt{105.03 - (9.5)^2} = \sqrt{14.78}$ $= 3.8444.$

Exercises

35) Using the relative frequency formula this probability is $\frac{29,351}{147,040} = 0.1996.$

37a) $(4/52)(3/51) = 12/2,652 = .0045.$

37b) Since the first card is not replaced before the second card is selected we use the formula $P(\text{ace}_1 \text{ and king}_2) = P(\text{ace}_1) \cdot P(\text{king}_2 | \text{ace}_1) = \frac{4}{52} \cdot \frac{4}{51} = \frac{16}{2652} = 0.0060.$

37c) $(4/52)(4/51) = 16/2,652 = .0060.$

37d) $P(\text{ace and king}) = P(\text{ace}_1 \text{ and king}_2) + P(\text{king}_1 \text{ and ace}_2)$
$= P(\text{ace}_1) \cdot P(\text{king}_2 | \text{ace}_1)$
$+ P(\text{king}_1) \cdot P(\text{ace}_2 | \text{king}_1)$
$= \frac{4}{52} \cdot \frac{4}{51} + \frac{4}{52} \cdot \frac{4}{51} = \frac{16}{2652} + \frac{16}{2652}$
$= 0.0060 + 0.0060 = 0.0120.$

39a) $.15 + .20 = .35.$

39b) $P(\text{at least a } 4) = P(4) + P(5) + P(6) = 0.25 + 0.20 + 0.15 = 0.60.$

41a) $P(\text{interest in IB}) = 99/431 = 0.2297.$

41b) $46/99 = .4646.$

41c) $P(\text{female and interest in IB}) = 46/431 = 0.1067.$

43a) $533/1,706 = .3124.$

43b) $P(3 \text{ bdr.}) = 425/1,706 = 0.2491$

43c) $97/1,706 = .0569.$

43d) $P(\text{Center City or 3 bdr.}) = P(\text{Center City}) + P(\text{3 bdr.})$

$- P(\text{Center City and 3 bdr.}) = \dfrac{533}{1,706} + \dfrac{425}{1,706} - \dfrac{97}{1,706}$

$= \dfrac{861}{1,706} = 0.5047.$

43e) $97/425 = .2282.$

43f) $P(\text{3 bdr.} \,|\, \text{Center City}) = 97/533 = 0.1820.$

43g) The events aren't mutually exclusive since being in Center City doesn't exclude three-bedroom apartments.

43h) No, these events are not independent since $P(\text{Center City}) \neq P(\text{Center City} \,|\, \text{3 bdr.}).$

45a) $51/268 = .1903.$

45b) $P(\text{not commercial}) = 1 - P\,(\text{commercial}) = 1 - 62/268 = 206/268 = 0.7687$

45c) $33/51 = .6471$

45d) $P(\text{Highly polluted} \,|\, \text{urban}) = 73/90 = 0.8111.$

45e) $90/268 + 150/268 - 73/268 = .6231.$

45f) $P(\text{Rural or not highly pol.}) = P(\text{Rural}) + P(\text{Low pol.}) + P(\text{mod. pol.}) - [P(\text{Rural and low pol.}) + P(\text{Rural and mod. pol.})]$

$= \dfrac{65}{268} + \dfrac{51}{268} + \dfrac{67}{268} - \left[\dfrac{33}{268} + \dfrac{23}{268}\right] = \dfrac{127}{268} = 0.4739.$

45g) $11/268 = 0.410$

45h) $P(\text{Rural or not highly pol.}) = P(\text{Rural and low pol.}) +$

$P(\text{Rural and mod. pol.}) = \dfrac{33}{268} + \dfrac{23}{268} = \dfrac{56}{268} = 0.2090.$

47a) Continuous.

47b) Discrete.

47c) Discrete.

47d) Continuous.

47e) Continuous.

49a) $P(x \geq 1) = 1 - .3 = .7.$

49b)

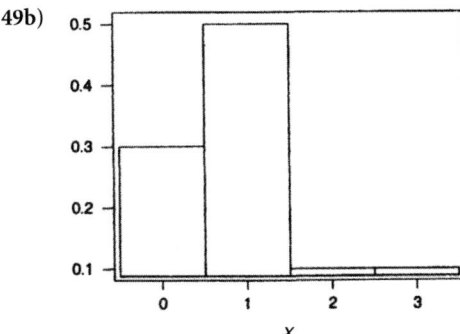

49c) $\mu = E(x) = 0(.3) + 1(.5) + 2(.1) + 3(.1) = 1.0.$

49d)

x	P(x)	x · P(x)	x² · P(x)
0	0.3	0	0
1	0.5	0.5	0.5
2	0.1	0.2	0.4
3	0.1	0.3	0.9
		1.0	1.8

$\sigma = \sqrt{\Sigma[x^2 P(x)] - \mu^2} = \sqrt{1.8 - (1.0)^2} = \sqrt{0.8} = 0.8944.$

51) $E = -10,000 \cdot 0.40 + 20,000 \cdot 0.50 + 30,000 \cdot 0.10 = \$9,000.$

53) $16.50

55a) 0.04

55b) 0.8

55c) T and B are not independent since $P(T/B) \neq P(T)$ ($P(T/B) = 0.8$ and $P(T) = 0.4$).

55d) T and B are not mutually exclusive since $P(T \text{ and } B) \neq 0$ ($P(T \text{ and } B) = 0.04$).

57) 15% are both used and defective.

59a) 0.10

59b) 0.25

59c) 1/3

59d) L and S are not independent since $P(L \text{ and } S) \neq P(L)\,P(s)$ ($P(L \text{ and } S) = 0.10$, and $P(L)\,P(S) = 0.12$).

61a) 0.70

61b) 7/13

61c) O and F are not independent since $P(O \text{ and } F) \neq P(O)\,P(F)$ ($P(O \text{ and } F) = 0.15$, and $P(O)\,P(F) = 0.175$).

61d) O and F are not mutually exclusive since $P(O \text{ and } F)\,0$ ($P(O \text{ and } F) = 0.15$).

Chapter 5
Self-Testing Review 5.1

1) This is a binomial experiment with a trial consisting of a flu patient being given *Vantin*. A success is being cured, $n = 15$, $p = .77$, $q = .23$, and $r = 0, 1, 2, \ldots, 15$.

3) This is a binomial experiment with seventh graders being asked if they ever had an alcoholic drink. A "success" (?) is that they respond yes, $n = 5$, $p = .76$, $q = .24$, and $r = 0, 1, 2, \ldots, 5$.

5) This is a binomial experiment. A trial is the determination of whether a frequent flier had an income of over \$35,000 a year. A success is that income exceeds \$35,000, and $n = 12$, $p = .67$, $q = .33$, and $r = 0, 1, 2, \ldots, 12$.

Self-Testing Review 5.2

7a) With $n = 10$, $p = .85$, and $r = 8$, $P(r = 8) = .2759$.

7b) We translate this into between four and ten (inclusive) don't own a VCR, and then find that the probabilities under $p = 0.15$ add to 0.0499.

7c) .9901

9a) .8671

9b) With $n = 20$ and $p = 0.10$, add the probabilities for $r = 3$, 4, 5, 6 to get $0.1901 + 0.0898 + 0.0319 + 0.0089 = 0.3207$.

9c) .0431

11a) .0001

11b) With $n = 20$ and $p = 0.20$, add the probabilities for $r = 0$, 1, 2, 3, 4 to get $0.0115 + 0.0576 + 0.1369 + 0.2054 + 0.2182 = 0.6296$.

11c) .0026

13a) 280

13b) $\sigma = \sqrt{85.785} = 9.2620$.

15a) $E(x) = np = 1,000 \cdot 0.95 = 950$.

15b) $\sigma = \sqrt{47.5} = 6.8920$.

Self-Testing Review 5.3

17a) With $\mu = 1.2$ and $x = 3$, the probability is .0867.

17b) Using Appendix 10, $P(x = 0) = 0.3012$.

19a) With $\mu = 3$ and $x = 5$, the probability is 0.1008.

19b) .0498

21a) With $\mu = 4$ and $x = 6$, the probability is 0.1042.

21b) .0916

23a) With $\mu = 10$ and $x = 12$, the probability is 0.0948.

23b) .0293

23c) With $\mu = 10$ and $x = 16, 17, \ldots, 24$, the probability is 0.0488.

25a) .0025

25b) 0.1606

25c) .9826

25d) 0.1512

27a) 0.0027

27b) .3776

27c) 0.7577

27d) No.

Self-Testing Review 5.4

29a) $.4940 + .4738 = .9678$.

29b) $0.4977 - 0.1736 = 0.3241$.

29c) $.5 - .3340 = .1660$.

29d) $0.5 + 0.4982 = 0.9982$.

29e) $.4990 - .4943 = .0047$.

29f) $0.4838 - 0.4744 = 0.0094$.

29g) $.5 - .4997 = .0023$.

29h) $0.5 + 0.4591 = 0.9591$.

31a) $P(z > 0) = .5$.

31b) $0.0987 + 0.4970 = 0.5957$.

31c) $.3944 - .1915 = .2029$.

33a) $P(z > 0) = .5$.

33b) $0.5 - 0.4495 = 0.0505$.

33c) $.1915 + .3051 = .4966$.

33d) $0.5 - 0.3413 = 0.1587$.

35a) $.5 - .4918 = .0082$.

35b) $0.4861 - 0.4452 = 0.0409$.

35c) $.1064 + .4236 = .53$

35d) 0.0764

37a) 0.4154

37b) .3707

37c) 0.0721

39) The z score that leaves .12 or 12 percent of the area to its right is the same one that has .38 or 38 percent between the mean and the z score. We use $z = 1.175$ and the formula $x = \mu + z\sigma$. So $x = 50 + 1.175(5) = 55.88$. Those who score 55.88 or higher are in the top 12 percent.

41a) .4404

41b) $z_1 = \dfrac{74 - 80}{20} = -0.30$ and $z_2 = \dfrac{84 - 80}{20} = 2.20$.

So, $P(74 \leq x \leq 84) = P(-0.30 \leq z \leq 0.20) = 0.1179 + 0.0793 = 0.1972$.

41c) The z score that leaves 25 percent of the area to its right is the same one that has .25 or 25 percent between the mean and the z score. We use $z = 0.67$ and the formula $x = \mu + z\sigma$. So $x = 80 + 0.67(20) = 93.4$. Twenty-five percent of the errors will be above 93.4 degrees.

43a) .5156

43b) $z = \dfrac{41 - 31.5}{10} = 0.45$. So, $P(x \le 41) = P(z \le 0.95)$
$= 0.5000 + 0.3289 = 0.8289$.

43c) .7734

43d) The required z score is –0.84. The value that 80 percent of the seedlings will grow above is $x = 31.5 + 10(-0.84) = 23.1$ cm.

43e) 38.2 cm

Self-Testing Review 5.5

45a) 0.0478

45b) 0.1788

45c) 0.2415

47) 0.8708

49) The approximate probability is 0.1817. The exact probability is 0.1833.

51) 0.1611

53a) 0.7389

53b) 0.3085

53c) 0.1083

Exercises

55a) .0467

55b) $P(r \ge 1) = 1 - P(r = 0) = 1 - 0.0467 = 0.9533$.

57a) Using Appendix 10 with $\mu = 6.7$ we obtain $P(x = 0) = 0.0012$.

57b) .9988

57c) Using Appendix 10 with $\mu = 6.7$ we obtain $P(x > 16) = P(x = 17, 18, 19) = 0.0004 + 0.0001 + 0.0000 = 0.0005$.

59a) 0.1032

59b) 0.9819

59c) 0.0001

61a) Using Appendix 10 with $\mu = 5$ we obtain $P(x = 3) = 0.1404$.

61b) .1755

61c) Using Appendix 10 with $\mu = 5$ we obtain $P(x = 3,4) = 0.1404 + 0.1755 = 0.3159$.

63a) .1672

63b) Binomial distribution applies with $n = 10$, $r < 4$, and $p = 0.60$. The equivalent probability with $n = 10$, $q = 0.40$, and $r > 6$. So $P(r > 6) = 0.0425 + 0.0106 + 0.0016 + 0.0001 = 0.0548$.

63c) .0463

65a) Binomial distribution applies with $n = 9$, $r > 5$, and $p = 0.40$ so $P(r > 5) = 0.0743 + 0.0212 + 0.0035 + 0.0003 = 0.0993$.

65b) .9997

65c) Binomial distribution applies with $n = 9$, $r < 3$, and $p = 0.40$ so $P(r < 3) = 0.0101 + 0.0605 + 0.1612 = 0.2318$.

67a) .0183

67b) Binomial distribution applies with $n = 18$, $9 \le r \le 14$, and $p = 0.55$; the equivalent probability is when $n = 18$, $q = 0.45$, and $4 \le r \le 9$. Thus, $P(4 \le r \le 9) = 0.0291 + 0.0666 + 0.1181 + 0.1657 + 0.1864 + 0.1694 = 0.7353$.

69a) 0.00034

69b) 0.0213

71a) Binomial distribution applies with $n = 20$, $r > 12$ and $p = 0.70$; the equivalent probability is when $n = 20$, $q = 0.30$, and $r < 8$. Thus, $P(r \le 7) = 0.0008 + 0.0068 + 0.0278 + 0.0718 + 0.1304 + 0.1789 + 0.1916 + 0.1643 = 0.7724$.

71b) .0171

71c) Binomial distribution applies with $n = 20$, $10 \le r < 15$, and $p = 0.70$; the equivalent probability is when $n = 20$, $q = 0.30$, $5 \le r \le 10$. Thus $P(5 \le r \le 10) = 0.1789 + 0.1916 + 0.1643 + 0.1144 + 0.0654 + 0.0308 = 0.7454$.

73a) Using $\mu = 384$ and $\sigma = 93.9$ in the formula $z = \dfrac{x - \mu}{\sigma}$ to get $z_1 = \dfrac{300 - 384}{93.9} = -0.89$ when $x_1 = 300$ and $z_2 = \dfrac{400 - 384}{93.9}$
$= 0.17$ when $x_2 = 400$. Thus $P(300 < x < 400) = P(-0.89 < z < 0.17) = P(-0.89 < z < 0) + P(0 < z < 0.17) = 0.3133 + 0.0675 = 0.3808$.

73b) .4325

75a) Using $\mu = 30.6$ and $\sigma = 9.1$ in the formula $z = \dfrac{x - \mu}{\sigma}$ to get $z = \dfrac{21 - 30.6}{9.1} = -1.05$. Thus $P(21 < x) = P(-1.05 < z)$
$= P(-1.05 < z < 0) + 0.5 = 0.3531 + 0.5 = 0.8531$.

75b) .9429

77a) Using $\mu = 118.3$ and $\sigma = 43.1$ in formula $z = \dfrac{x - \mu}{\sigma}$ to get $z = \dfrac{240 - 118.3}{43.1} = 2.82$. Thus $P(240 < x) = P(2.82 < z)$
$= 0.5 - P(0 < z < 2.82) = 0.5 - 0.4976 = 0.0024$.

77b) .0740

79) 0.3156

81a) Here we want to find z_0 so that $P(z < z_0) = 0.30$. Since $P(z < z_0) = 0.5 - P(z_0 < z < 0) = 0.30$, it implies that $P(z_0 < z < 0) = 0.20$. Looking in Appendix 1 for 0.20 we find $P(0 < z < 0.52) = 0.1985$ and $P(0 < z < 0.53) = 0.2019$. Since 0.1985 is closer to 0.20 than 0.2019 we chose $z_0 = -0.52$. Note z_0 is negative since $z_0 < z < 0$.

81b) 1.28

81c) Here we want to find z_0 so that $P(-z_0 < z < z_0) = 0.90$. This is the equivalent to finding z_0 so that $P(0 < z < z_0) = 0.45$. Looking in Appendix 1 for 0.45 we find $P(0 < z < 1.64) = 0.4495$ and $P(0 < z < 1.65) = 0.4505$. Since these are the same distance from 0.45, thus $z_0 = 1.645$.

81d) .84

83) $100 + 1.645(15) = 124.675$.

85a) 0.1029

85b) 0.6370

87) 0.7183

89) 0.0176

91a) 0.5105

91b) 0.2397

Chapter 6
Self-Tesing Review 6.1

1) Answers will vary here, of course, but anyone who has taken a taste of food, performed a chemistry experiment, had a blood test, or looked at a swatch of wallpaper has engaged in sampling.

3) The purpose of sampling is to investigate properties of a population of interest by studying part of that population.

5a) All students in your class.

5b) All psychology majors at your school.

5c) All students from your school.

5d) All Geo Prisms assembled this week.

5e) All stocks listed on the TSE.

5f) All schizophrenic patients undergoing experimental treatment.

5g) All such knee surgery patients.

7) False. Statistics taken from samples will most probably differ from population parameter values.

Self-Testing Review 6.2

9) If all possible samples of a given size (n) are taken from a given population and then for each sample the mean is computed, the distribution of these means is the sampling distribution of means.

11) $\mu_{\bar{x}} = \mu = 3.71$, $\sigma_{\bar{x}} = \dfrac{\sigma}{\sqrt{n}} = \dfrac{37.1}{\sqrt{20}} = 8.2958$.

13a) The mean of sampling distribution, being equal to the population mean, is 11.43.

13b) The standard error of the sampling distribution is $.762/\sqrt{100} = .0762$ mm.

13c) Since n is over 30, the sampling distribution is approximately normal.

13d) The range is $11.43 \pm (1.00)(.0762)$, or 11.3538 to 11.5062 mm.

13e) The range is $11.43 \pm (2.00)(0.0762)$, or 11.278 to 11.582 mm.

15) The problem, in effect, asks the question, What is the chance that the sample mean will be located in the interval $\mu \pm z(\sigma_{\bar{x}})$, where $z(\sigma_{\bar{x}})$ is equal to ± 7 tonnes? Since the standard error is $30/\sqrt{36}$ or 5 tonnes, we have $z(5) = +7$ tonnes. Solving for z, we get $z = \pm 7/5 = \pm 1.4$. And since a z value of 1.4 corresponds to a normal curve area of .4192, the chance that a sample mean would be within ± 7 tonnes of the population mean is $2(.4192)$ or .8384.

17) $z_1 = \dfrac{10{,}100 - 10{,}000}{2{,}000/\sqrt{400}} = 1.00$,
which corresponds to a table value of .3413
$$z_2 = \dfrac{10{,}200 - 10{,}000}{2{,}000/\sqrt{400}} = 2.00,$$
which corresponds to a table value of .4772
And $.4772 - .3413 =$ a probability of .1359.

19) $z = (110 - 100)/(20/\sqrt{30}) = 10/3.6515 = 2.74$ which yields a table value of .4969. The probability that the mean IQ of the sample of 30 exceeds 110 is thus $.5000 - .4969$ or .0031.

21a) The mean of the sampling distribution is \$64,500, and the standard error is
$$\dfrac{\$8{,}000}{\sqrt{25}} = \$1{,}600.$$

21b) From part a), we have $\mu_{\bar{x}} = \$64{,}500$ and $\sigma_{\bar{x}} = \$1{,}600$, so $z = \dfrac{65{,}000 - 64{,}500}{1{,}600} = 0.31$. 0.31 yields a table value of 0.1443. The probability that the mean of the sample will be less than \$65,000 is $.5000 + .1217 = .6217$.

Self-Testing Review 6.3

23a) 0.1566

23b) $\sigma_{\hat{p}} = \sqrt{[(.57)(.43)]/100} = .0495$

23c) 0.0157

23d) When the sample size increases, the dispersion of the sampling distribution of proportions decreases.

25) mean $= 0.60$ standard deviation $= 0.0828$

27) 0.5934

29) 0.4681

Exercises

31a) $z = (20.9 - 20)/3 = .30$; probability is $.5000 - .1179 = .3821$.

31b) $\sigma_{\bar{x}} = \dfrac{3}{\sqrt{36}} = \dfrac{3}{6} = 0.5$, so $z = \dfrac{20.9 - 20}{0.5} = 1.80$;
$P(20.9 < \bar{x}) = 1 - P(0 < z < 1.80) = 0.5000 - 0.4641 = 0.0359$.

31c) $\sigma_{\bar{x}} = 3/\sqrt{100} = .30$, so $z = (20.9 - 20)/.30 = 3.00$; probability is $.5000 - .4987 = .0013$.

31d) As n increases, $\sigma_{\bar{x}} = \sigma/\sqrt{n}$ decreases; so the corresponding z value increases and $P(20.9 < \bar{x})$ decreases.

33a) $\mu_{\bar{x}} = 26$ mg and $\sigma_{\bar{x}} = 6/\sqrt{100} = .6$ mg.

33b) $0.683/2 = 0.3415$ and 0.3415 corresponds to a z value of 1. Thus the sample mean has a 68.3 percent chance of falling between 26 ± 0.6 mg, or 25.4 to 26.6 mg.

33c) $26 \pm 2(.6)$ mg; 24.8 to 27.2 mg

35a) $\sigma_{\bar{x}} = 10/\sqrt{10} = 3.162$; $132 \pm 2(3.162)$; 125.68 to 138.32.

35b) 95.4 percent corresponds to a z value of 2; $\sigma_{\bar{x}} = 10/\sqrt{100} = 1.00$; so $132 \pm 2(1.00)$ or 130.00 to 134.00 degrees.

35c) $\sigma_{\bar{x}} = 10/\sqrt{1000} = .3162$; $132 \pm 2(.3162)$; 131.37 to 132.63

35d) As the sample size increases $\sigma_{\bar{x}}$ decreases so that the dispersion is concentrated about the mean.

37) $\sigma_{\bar{x}} = .5/\sqrt{50} = .0707$; $z = \pm.10/.0707 = \pm1.41$; probability $= 2(.4207) = .8414$.

39) $\sigma_{\bar{x}} = 8/\sqrt{12} = 2.309$; $z = 3/2.309 = 1.30$; probability $= .5000 + .4032 = .9032$.

41) $\sigma_{\hat{p}} = \sqrt{(.67)(.33)/174} = 0.0356$; $z = .02/.0356 = 0.56$; probability $= 2(.2123) = .4246$.

43) $\sigma_{\bar{x}} = 17/\sqrt{37} = 2.795$; $z = -.72$ and $z = 2.86$; probability $= .2642 + .4979 = .7621$.

45) $\sigma_{\hat{p}} = \sqrt{(.46)(.54)/25} = 0.0997$; $z = .40$; probability $= .5000 - .1554 = .3446$.

47) $\sigma_{\bar{x}} = \$98/\sqrt{45} = \$14.61$; $z = -2.12$ and $z = 3.01$; probability $= .4830 + .4987 = .9817$.

49) $\sigma_{\bar{x}} = 13.7/\sqrt{42} = 2.11$; $z = -2.65$ and $z = 2.08$; probability $= .4960 + .4812 = .9772$.

51) $\sigma_{\bar{x}} = \$5,000/\sqrt{32} = \$883.88$. Thus, $\$85,000 \pm 2(\$883.88) = \$83,232.23$ to $\$86,767.77$.

Chapter 7
Self-Testing Review 7.1

1) e   **3)** c   **5)** b   **7)** a   **9)** c

Self-Testing Review 7.2

11) It is the standard deviation of a sampling distribution.

13a) 80 percent of the sample means will fall within 1.28 standard errors of $\mu_{\bar{x}}$.

13b) 90 percent of the sample means will fall within 1.645 standard errors of $\mu_{\bar{x}}$.

13c) 95 percent of the sample means will fall within 1.96 standard errors of $\mu_{\bar{x}}$.

13d) As the level of confidence increases, the number of standard errors for the internal estimate increases.

15) It defines the probability that the interval will include the true population mean.

17) The 90 percent level results in a smaller maximum error of estimate.

19) At a given level of confidence, the error bound is the maximum distance between the point estimate and the true population mean. Since this distance could be to the left or to the right of the point estimate, the confidence interval width is twice the value of the error bound.

21) The level of confidence is 90 percent. The parameter is the population mean (which is unknown). The point estimate is 84.1 (the known sample mean) and the error bound is 5.3.

Self-Testing Review 7.3

23a) Since the areas entered in the table in Appendix 2 represent the area between the mean and the z score and the curve is symmetric about the mean, we must first take half of the 86 percent area. We next look for an area entry (found in the body of the table) that is closest to half of .86, or .43. The nearest area entry is .4306. The z value corresponding to this area is 1.48. So 43 percent of the area under the curve falls between vertical lines drawn at the mean and at $z = 1.48$. This means that 88 percent of the area under the curve lies between vertical lines erected at $z = -1.48$ and $z = +1.48$.

23b) Half of 0.96 is 0.48. The area closest to 0.48 in the table is 0.4798, which corresponds to $z = 2.05$. So 96 percent of the area under the normal curve lies between vertical lines erected at $z = -2.05$ and $z = +2.05$.

23c) Looking up an area nearest to .49, we find .4901. This corresponds to a z score of 2.33. So 98 percent of the area under the normal curve lies between vertical lines erected at $z = \pm2.33$.

25a) This is a small sample from a normal population with σ unknown so we use a t distribution with 12 df. The corresponding area in the right tail is .05, so $t = \pm1.782$.

25b) Although the sample is small, the population is normally distributed and the σ is known. Thus, we use the normal distribution with $z = \pm1.645$.

25c) This is a large sample so we use the normal distribution with $z = \pm1.645$.

25d) For a small sample with σ unknown, we use a t distribution. With 16 df, the required t values are ±1.746.

27a) The point estimate is the sample mean of 24.7.

27b) The estimated standard error of the mean is $5.3/\sqrt{18} = 1.249$.

27c) Use $t_{0.005} = 2.898$ since this is a small sample and σ is unknown.

27d) The error bound is $t(\sigma_{\bar{x}}) = 2.898(1.249) = 3.620$.

27e) The 99 percent confidence interval is 24.7 ± 3.620 or 21.080 to 28.320.

29) The area in the right tail is $\dfrac{100 - 95}{2}$ or 0.025 and df = 20 $- 1 = 19$, so $t_{0.025} = \pm 2.093$. The estimated standard error is $\dfrac{0.7}{\sqrt{20}} = 0.157$. So the 95 percent confidence interval is $2.3 \pm (2.093)(0.157)$, which is 1.971 to 2.629 hours per night.

31) The estimated standard error is $5/\sqrt{15} = 1.291$. Since df = 14, $t_{0.05} = 1.761$, and the confidence interval is $17.6 \pm (1.761)(1.291)$ or 15.327 to 19.873.

33) The sample mean is $128/7 = 18.286$ hours, the sample standard deviation is 5.529 hours, df = 6, and $t_{0.025} = 2.447$. The estimated standard error is $5.529/\sqrt{7} = 2.09$. The confidence interval is $18.286 \pm 2.447 \cdot 2.09$ or 13.172 to 23.400 hours.

35a) No

35b) No

35c) Yes

35d) No

37) The estimated standard error is $58/\sqrt{126} = 5.167$. The confidence interval is $648 \pm 1.645(5.167)$ or 639.5 to 656.5 hours.

39) We calculate the mean using the first column, then use it to calculate the other two columns.

x	$x - \bar{x}$	$(x - \bar{x})^2$
490	226.93	51,197.2249
123	−140.07	19,619.6049
320	56.93	3,241.0249
120	−143.07	20,469.0249
290	26.93	7,25.2249
270	6.93	48.0249
300	36.93	1,363.8249
68	−195.07	38,052.3049
280	16.93	286.6249
230	−33.07	1,093.6249
530	266.93	71,251.6249
450	186.93	34,942.8249
130	−133.07	17,707.6249
250	−13.07	170.8249
95	−168.07	28,247.5249
3946		288,716.9335

$\bar{x} = \dfrac{3946}{15} = 263.07$. Then $s = \sqrt{\dfrac{\Sigma(x - \bar{x})^2}{n - 1}} = \sqrt{\dfrac{288716.9335}{14}}$

$= 143.61$. Since df = 14, $t_{0.05} = \pm 1.761$. The estimated standard error is $\hat{\sigma}_{\bar{x}} = \dfrac{s}{\sqrt{n}} = \dfrac{143.61}{\sqrt{15}} = 37.08$.

$$\bar{x} - t_{0.05}\hat{\sigma}_{\bar{x}} < \mu < \bar{x} + t_{0.05}\hat{\sigma}_{\bar{x}}$$
$$263.07 - (1.761)(37.08) < \mu < 263.07 + (1.761)(37.08)$$
$$263.07 - 65.30 < \mu < 263.07 + 65.30$$
$$197.77 < \mu < 328.37.$$

41) We calculate the mean using the first column, then use it to calculate the other two columns.

x	$x - \bar{x}$	$(x - \bar{x})^2$
2000	−493.33	243,374.4889
2050	−443.33	196,541.4889
2129	−364.33	132,736.3489
2200	−293.33	86,042.4889
2500	6.67	44.4889
2500	6.67	44.4889
2666	172.67	29,815.9289
2800	306.67	94,046.4889
3595	1101.67	1,213,676.7899
22440		1,996,326.1100

$\bar{x} = \dfrac{22440}{9} = 24933.33$. Then $s = \sqrt{\dfrac{\Sigma(x - \bar{x})^2}{n - 1}} =$

$\sqrt{\dfrac{1996326.1100}{8}} = 499.54$. Since df = 8, $t_{0.05} = \pm 1.860$. Since

$\hat{\sigma}_{\bar{x}} = \dfrac{s}{\sqrt{n}} = \dfrac{499.54}{\sqrt{9}} = 166.51$, the confidence interval is

$\bar{x} - t_{.05}\hat{\sigma}_{\bar{x}} < \mu < \bar{x} + t_{.05}\hat{\sigma}_{\bar{x}}$ or

$$2493.33 - (1.860)(166.51) < \mu < 2493.33 + (1.860)(166.51)$$
$$2493.33 - 309.71 < \mu < 2493.33 + 309.71$$
$$\$2183.62 < \mu < \$2803.04.$$

43) We calculate the mean using the first column, then use it to calculate the other two columns.

x	$x - \bar{x}$	$(x - \bar{x})^2$
710	561.25	315,001.5625
162	13.25	175.5625
90	−58.75	3,451.5625
70	−78.75	6,201.5625
55	−93.75	8,789.0625
58	−90.75	8,235.5625
18	−130.75	17,095.5625
27	−121.75	14,823.0625
1190	0	373,773.50

$\bar{x} = \dfrac{1190}{8} = 148.75$. Then $s = \sqrt{\dfrac{\Sigma(x - \bar{x})^2}{n - 1}} = \sqrt{\dfrac{373,773.50}{7}}$

= 231.076. Since df = 7, $t_{0.005} = \pm 3.499$. Since

$$\hat{\sigma}_{\bar{x}} = \frac{s}{\sqrt{n}} = \frac{231.076}{\sqrt{8}} = 81.698,$$ the confidence interval is

$$\bar{x} - t_{.005}\hat{\sigma}_{\bar{x}} < \mu < \bar{x} + t_{.005}\hat{\sigma}_{\bar{x}}$$
$$148.75 - (3.499)(81.698) < \mu < 148.75 + (3.499)(81.698)$$
$$148.75 - 285.86 < \mu < 148.75 + 285.86$$
$$-137.11 < \mu < 434.61.$$

Self-Testing Review 7.4

45) The sample proportion is $210/350 = 0.60$. The estimated standard error $(\hat{\sigma}_{\hat{p}})$ is $\sqrt{[(.60)(.40)]/350} = .0262$. The confidence interval is $0.60 \pm 1.96\,(.0262)$ or 0.549 to 0.651.

47) $\hat{p} = 40/76 = 0.5263 \cdot \hat{\sigma}_{\hat{p}} = \sqrt{[(.5263)(1 - .5263)]/76}$ $= 0.05727$. The confidence interval is $0.5263 \pm 1.96(.05727)$, or 0.4140 to 0.6385.

49) $\hat{p} = 108/160 = 0.675$. $\hat{\sigma}_{\hat{p}} = \sqrt{[(.675)(1 - .675)]/160}$ $= 0.037$. The confidence interval is $0.675 \pm 2.575(.037)$, or 0.5797 to 0.7703.

51) $\hat{p} = 23/34 = 0.6765$. $\hat{\sigma}_{\hat{p}} = .0802$. The confidence interval is $0.6765 \pm 1.96(.0802)$, or 0.5193 to 0.8337.

53a) $\hat{p} = 86/276 = 0.3116$. $\hat{\sigma}_{\hat{p}} = \sqrt{[(.3116)(1 - .3116)]/276} = 0.027878$. The 95 percent confidence interval is 0.311594 ± 1.96 $(.027878)$, or 0.2570 to 0.3662.

53b) (0.5523, 0.7369)

55a) $\hat{p} = 722/2142 = 0.3371$. The estimated standard error is $\sqrt{[(.3371)(1 - .3371)]/2142} = 0.102$. The 90 percent confidence interval is 0.3371 ± 0.0168, or 0.3203 to 0.3539.

55b) (0.0459, 0.0624)

57a) (0.3573, 0.6046)

57b) $\hat{p} = 8/30 = 0.2667$. The estimated standard error is $\sqrt{[(.2667)(1 - .2667)]/30} = 0.0807$. The 90 percent confidence interval is 0.2667 ± 0.1328, or 0.1339 to 0.3995.

59) (0.1290, 0.2779)

Self-Testing Review 7.5

61) The lower and upper values are 39.4 and 12.40.

63) Using the x^2 distribution with 15 df, the limits for the confidence interval of the variance are $15(26.8)/32.8$ and $15(26.8)/4.60$ or 12.256 to 87.39. Taking the square root of each variance, we find the confidence interval for the standard deviation is 3.50 to 9.35.

65) With 24 df, the limits for the confidence interval of the variance are $24(17.4)/39.4$ and $24(17.4)/12.40$ or 10.60 to 33.68. Taking the square root of each variance, we find the confidence interval for the standard deviation is 3.26 to 5.80. We are assuming that the population values are normally distributed.

67) With 26 df, the limits for the confidence interval of the variance are $26(4.3^2)/48.3$ and $26(4.3^2)/11.16$ or 9.95 to 43.08. Taking the square root of each variance, we find the confidence interval for the standard deviation is 3.2 to 6.6. Again, we are assuming that the population values are normally distributed.

69a) Using MINITAB we find the standard deviation of the sample of 19 students is 51.7. With 18 df, the limits for the confidence interval of the variance are $18(51.7^2)/37.2$ and $18(51.7^2)/6.26$ or 1,293.33 to 7,685.63.

69b) With 18 df. the limits are $\sqrt{18(2,672.89)/37.2}$ and $\sqrt{18(2,672.89)/6.26}$ or 35.96 to 87.67.

Self-Testing Review 7.6

71) To be within two hours of the true population mean, we would need $n = [(1.96)(68.2)/2]^2 = 4,468$. That is, at least 4,468 in the sample. This means at least $4,468 - 100$ or 4,368 more sample items.

73) At the 90 percent level, $z = 1.645$ and $\sigma = 4.346$. So our sample size must be at least $n = [(1.645)(4.346)/0.5]^2 = 204.44$ or 205 couples.

75) If all other factors remain the same but the confidence level is increased, the sample size must increase as well.

77a) With no preliminary sample, we use $p = .5$, so

$$n = \frac{z_{\alpha/2}^2 p(1 - p)}{E^2} = \frac{(1.96)^2(.50)(1 - .50)}{.03^2} = 1,067.12.$$

The minimum sample size would be 1,068.

77b) Using $\hat{p} = 210/350 = 0.6$ as an estimate for p, $n = (1.96)^2(0.6)(0.4)/(0.03)^2 = 1,024.4$. A sample of at least 1,025 is required.

79) The minimum value for $n = [(1.645)(42.67)/10]^2 = 49.27$, or 50.

81) The minimum value for $n = [(2.575)(17)/2]^2 = 479.06$ or 480. Since there were 58 patients in the preliminary test, we would need $480 - 58$ or 422 more for the sample.

83) At the 95 percent level, $z = 1.96$ and $\sigma = 11.675$. So our sample size must be at least $n = [(1.96)(11.675)/2]^2 = 130.9$ or 131 salmon.

Exercises

85a) 2.086

85b) With a 99 percent confidence level $\alpha = 0.01$ (1 percent). With a sample size of 6 there are 5 degrees of freedom. Therefore using Appendix 4 under $t_{0.005}$ we see t value is 4.032.

85c) 1.771

85d) With a 95 percent confidence level $\alpha = 0.05$ (5 percent). With a sample size of 4 there are 3 degrees of freedom. Therefore using Appendix 4 under $t_{0.025}$ we see t value is 3.182.

87a) We have the following data: $n = 16$, $\bar{x} = 733.2$, $s = 45.5$, population distribution shape is normal, $\sigma = 41.7$. Because the population distribution shape is normal and we know the value of σ, we use the z distribution. 90 percent confidence level corresponds to $z = \pm 1.645$.

87b) Neither

87c) We have the following data: $n = 37$, $\bar{x} = 8.1$, $s = 3.9$, population distribution shape is unknown, σ unknown. Since $n > 30$, we use the z distribution and $z = \pm 1.645$.

89a) $\sigma_{\bar{x}} = 2.367$. Interval $= 76.1 \pm 1.96(2.367)$ or 71.46 to 80.74.

89b) We have the following data: $n = 49$, $\bar{x} = 76.1$, $s = 14.2$. Because $n > 30$, we use the z distribution, here $z = 1.96$. Thus $\hat{\sigma}_{\bar{x}} = s/\sqrt{n} = 14.2/\sqrt{49} = 2.029$. Hence the interval is $76.1 \pm 1.96(2.029)$ or 72.123 to 80.08.

89c) $\sigma_{\bar{x}} = 1.775$. Interval $= 76.1 \pm 1.96(1.775)$ or 72.62 to 79.58.

89d) The following table shows the results.

n:	36	4964
Interval:	71.46 to 80.739	72.123 to 80.08 72.621 to 79.58

As the sample size increases, the confidence interval width decreases.

91) 17.667 to 73.632

93a) 0.6379

93b) $\hat{\sigma}_{\hat{p}} = \sqrt{(.6379)(.3621)/116} = 0.04462$.

93c) (0.5582, 0.7123)

95a) $\bar{x} = 44.71$

95b) To calculate the estimated standard error, we construct the following table to the standard deviation of the sample using $\bar{x} = 44.71$ from Exercise 95(a).

x	$x - \bar{x}$	$(x - \bar{x})^2$
27	-17.71	313.6441
35	-9.71	94.2841
65	20.29	411.6841
67	22.29	496.8441
47	2.29	5.2441
46	1.29	1.6641
63	18.29	334.5241
		1,657.8887

x	$x - \bar{x}$	$(x - \bar{x})^2$
44	-0.71	0.5041
34	-10.71	114.7041
51	6.29	39.5641
17	-27.71	767.8441
40	-4.71	22.1841
41	-3.71	13.7641
60	15.29	233.7841
		1,192.3487

x	$x - \bar{x}$	$(x - \bar{x})^2$
24	-20.71	428.9041
48	3.29	10.8241
29	-15.71	246.8041
73	28.29	800.3241
60	15.29	233.7841
41	-3.71	13.7641
27	-17.71	313.6441
		2,048.0487
		Total = 4,898.2861

$$s = \sqrt{\frac{\sum(x - \bar{x})^2}{n - 1}} = \sqrt{\frac{4,898.2861}{20}} = 15.65.$$ The estimated

standard error, $\hat{\sigma}_{\bar{x}} = \dfrac{s}{\sqrt{n}} = \dfrac{15.65}{\sqrt{21}} = 3.42.$

95c) 38.82 to 50.61

95d) Data: $n = 21$ and $s^2 = 15.65^2 = 244.92$. $\alpha = 0.05$ and with 20 df we have $x^2_{\alpha/2} = x^2_{0.05} = 31.4$ and $x^2_{1-\alpha/2} = x^2_{0.95} = 10.85$. Substituting

$$\frac{(n-1)s^2}{x^2_{\alpha/2}} < \sigma^2 < \frac{(n-1)s^2}{x^2_{1-\alpha/2}}$$

$$\frac{20 \cdot 244.92}{31.4} < \sigma^2 < \frac{20 \cdot 244.92}{10.85}$$

$$156 < \sigma^2 < 451.47.$$

97a) ($153,000, $296,800)

97b) ($2,306, $3,251)

97c) (6,430, 36,900) million squared dollars

97d) (278,000, 1,590,000) thousand squared dollars

99) We have the following data: $n = 26$, $\bar{x} = 97.6$, population distribution shape normal, $\sigma = 15$. Since the population shape is normal and σ is known, we use the z distribution. $z = \pm 1.645$ and $\sigma_{\bar{x}} = \sigma/\sqrt{n} = 15/\sqrt{26} = 2.94$. Thus $\bar{x} \pm z \cdot \sigma_{\bar{x}} = 97.6 \pm 1.645(2.94)$ or an IQ of 92.76 to 102.44.

101) Here we want to find n so that $z\hat{\sigma}_{\hat{p}} < .02$ when $\hat{p} = 99/431 = 0.2297$, $z = 1.645$, and $n = (1.645)^2(0.2297)$ $(0.7703)/(0.02)^2 = 1,196.99$. Thus the sample size must be at least 1,197.

103) Since the sample size is less than 30 and the population shape is normal, we use the t distribution. We have the following data: $n = 10, \bar{x} = 147.8, s = 31.2$. Then $t_{0.025}$ with 9 df is 2.262 and $\hat{\sigma}_{\bar{x}} = s/\sqrt{n} = 31.2/\sqrt{10} = 9.87$. The interval is $147.8 \pm 2.262(9.87)$ or 125.47 to 170.13.

105) Data: $n = 36$, $\hat{p} = 24/36 = 0.6667$. So $z = \pm1.645$ and $\hat{\sigma}_{\hat{p}} = \sqrt{(0.6667)(0.3333)/36} = 0.0786$. The interval is $0.6667 \pm 1.645(0.0786)$, or 0.5374 to 0.7960, or 53.74 percent to 79.60 percent.

107) Sample size is > 30, so use the z distribution. Data: $n = 281$, $\bar{x} = 58.3$, $s = 20.5$. So $z = \pm1.96$ and $\hat{\sigma}_{\bar{x}} = s/\sqrt{n} = 20/\sqrt{281} = 1.223$. The interval is $58.3 \pm 1.96(1.223)$ or 55.90 to 60.70 words.

109) We were given the following data: $n = 64, \bar{x} = 24.70, s = 5.14$. Because $n > 30$ we use the z distribution, here $z = \pm2.575$. Thus $\hat{\sigma}_{\bar{x}} = s/\sqrt{n} = 5.14/\sqrt{64} = 0.64$ Hence the interval is $24.70 \pm 2.575(0.64)$ or 23.05 to 26.35.

111) Find n so that $z\hat{\sigma}_{\bar{x}} < 1$ kg when $z = 1.96$ and $\hat{\sigma}_{\bar{x}} = s/\sqrt{n} = 3.6/\sqrt{n}$. Then $n = [(1.96)(3.6)/1]^2 = 49.79$. Thus the sample size must contain at least 50 participants.

113) Find n so that $z\sigma_{\bar{x}} < 2$ hours when $s = 15.2$ hours. Using $z = 1.645$ and $\hat{\sigma}_{\bar{x}} = s/\sqrt{n} = 15.2/\sqrt{n}$, then $n = [(1.645)(15.2)/2]^2 = 156.3$. Thus the sample size must contain at least 157 calculator batteries.

115) Find n so that $z\hat{\sigma}_{\hat{p}} < .05$ when p is unknown, $z = 2.575$, and $\hat{\sigma}_{\hat{p}}$ is maximized when $p = 1 - p$, use .50 as our point estimate. Then $n = (2.575)^2(.50)(.50)/(.50)^2 = 663.1$. Thus the sample size must contain at least 664 products.

Chapter 8
Self-Testing Review 8.1

1) Since the sample size is over 30, the sampling distribution of the sample means is normal. A sample mean with $n = 57$ has a .05 chance of falling beyond ±1.96 standard errors.

3) This is a small sample, but since we know the population is normal and we are given the value of σ, the sampling distribution of $\bar{x}$ is normal. So, the area corresponding to $z = 2.33$ in the z table is .4901. And $2(.4901) = .9802$. The probability that an $\bar{x}$ lies beyond ±2.33 standard errors is thus $1 - .9802$ or .0198.

5) A type II error is made by failing to reject the null hypothesis when it is actually false.

7) This is the statement of equality. This hypothesis is always assumed to be true even though you often hope to reject it.

9) A critical value is the start or boundary of the rejection region.

11) See pp. 269–274.

13) $\mu \neq 18$ or $\mu < 18$ or $\mu > 18$.

15) The hypothesis of interest is $\mu > 14.09$. Since it doesn't contain a statement of equality, it must be the alternative hypothesis. Thus, H_0: $\mu = 14.09$, and H_1: $\mu < 14.09$.

Self-Testing Review 8.2

17a) To determine the corresponding area value from the normal table, subtract $.5 - .01$ to get .4900. The closest area figure is .4901, which corresponds to a z score of 2.33.

17b) For a two-tailed test, subtract $1 - 0.05$ to get 0.95, which is the area from $-z$ to $+z$. Now take half of that value to read the corresponding area values. That is, $0.95/2 = 0.4750$. And this corresponds to a z score of 1.96. For a two-tailed test, we use ±1.96.

17c) The corresponding area is .4500. This value is halfway between the z scores of 1.64 and 1.65, so we use the midpoint of 1.645 in this case. Since this is a left-tailed test, we use $z = -1.645$.

19a) Use the t distribution with 18 df. Use the value (for a left-tailed test) of $t = -1.734$.

19b) Use the value of $z = 2.33$.

19c) For a large sample, use $z = \pm2.575$.

19d) Use the t distribution with 11 df, so $t = -1.796$.

21) The decision rule is to reject the H_0 when the p-value is less than the level of significance, and fail to reject the H_0 when the p-value is $\geq \alpha$.

23) The p-value is $< \alpha$, so you reject the H_0.

25) Since 0.002 is < 0.01 and 0.05, the decision is to reject H_0 at both levels.

27a) *Step 1: State the null and alternative hypotheses.* H_0: $\mu = 50$, and H_1: $\mu \neq 50$. *Step 2: Select the level of significance.* $\alpha = 0.05$. *Step 3: Determine the test distribution to use.* The z distribution is used for a large sample. *Step 4: Define the critical or rejection region(s).* The values for a two-tailed test at the 0.05 level are $z = -1.96$ and $z = +1.96$. *Step 5: State the decision rule.* Reject H_0 in favour of H_1 if $z < -1.96$ or $z > +1.96$. Otherwise, fail to reject H_0. *Step 6: Compute the Test Statistic.* The standard error is $5.1/\sqrt{45} = 0.7603$, so the $z = 48.3 - 50/0.7603 = -2.24$. *Step 7: Make the statistical decision.* Since the z value of -2.24 falls in the left-tailed rejection region, we reject H_0.

27b) *Step 1: State the null and alternative hypotheses.* H_0: $\mu = 231$, and H_1: $\mu > 231$. *Step 2: Select the level of significance.* $\alpha = .01$. *Step 3: Determine the test distribution to use.* We use a t distribution with 17 df. *Step 4: Define the critical or rejection region.* The critical value for a right-tailed test at the .01 level is $t = 2.567$. *Step 5: State the decision rule.* Reject H_0 in favour of H_1 if $t > 2.567$. Otherwise, fail to reject H_0. *Step 6: Compute the test statistic (t).* The standard error is $15.7/\sqrt{18} = 3.70$, so $t = (235.3 - 231)/3.70 = 1.162$. *Step 7: Make the statistical decision.* Since $t = 1.162$ does not fall in the rejection region, we fail to reject H_0.

27c) *Step 1: State the null and alternative hypotheses.* H_0: $\mu = 1,500$, and H_1: $< 1,500$. *Step 2: Select the level of significance.* $\alpha = 0.05$. *Step 3: Determine the test distribution to use.* The z distribution is used. *Step 4: Define the critical or rejection region(s).* The values for this one-tailed test at the 0.05 level are $z = -1.645$. *Step 5: State the decision rule.* Reject H_0 in favour of H_1 if $z < -1.645$. Otherwise, fail to reject H_0. *Step 6: Compute the Test Statistic.* The standard error is $51.3/\sqrt{62} = 6.515$, so $z = 1,483 - 1,500/6.515 = -2.61$. *Step 7: Make the statistical decision.* Since -2.61 falls in the left-tailed rejection region, we reject H_0.

29) *Step 1:* H_0: $\mu = \$5,423$, and H_1: $\mu > \$5,423$. *Step 2:* $\alpha = 0.01$. *Step 3:* The z distribution is used. *Step 4:* The value for a right-tailed test at the 0.01 level is $z = 2.33$. *Step 5:* Reject H_0 in favour of H_1 if $z > 2.33$. Otherwise, fail to reject H_0. *Step 6:* The $z = \$5,516 - \$5,423/\$52.1809 = 1.78$. *Step 7:* Since the z value of 1.78 does not fall in the rejection region, we fail to reject H_0. The average expense of Seattle residents over 64 is \$5,423.

31) H_0: $\mu = 1.3$, and H_1: $\mu > 1.3$; $\alpha = .05$; z distribution; Decision rule: Reject H_0 in favour of H_1 if $z > 1.645$. $z = 2.27$. Reject H_0.

33) *Step 1:* H_0: $\mu = \$31,129$, and H_1: $\mu \neq \$31,129$. *Step 2:* $\alpha = 0.05$. *Step 3:* Use the t distribution with 14 df. *Step 4:* The values for a two-tailed test at the 0.05 level are $t = \pm2.145$. *Step 5:* Reject H_0 in favour of H_1 if $t < -2.145$ or $t > +2.145$. Otherwise, fail to reject H_0. *Step 6:* The $t = \$32,379 - \$31,129/\$463.98 = 2.69$. *Step 7:* Since the t value of 2.69 falls in the rejection region, we reject H_0 and conclude that the mean for the Denver firms differs from \$31,129.

35) *Step 1:* H_0: $\mu = 84.2$, and H_1: $\mu < 84.2$. *Step 2:* $\alpha = 0.01$. *Step 3:* Use the t distribution with 28 df. *Step 4:* The values for a left-tailed test at the 0.0 level, $t = 2.467$. *Step 5:* Reject H_0 in favour of H_1 if $t < -2.467$. Otherwise, fail to reject H_0. *Step 6:* The $t = 69.1 - 84.2/2.90 = -5.21$. *Step 7:* Since the t value of -5.21 falls in the rejection region, we reject H_0 and decide that the patients who take *Captopril* have lower blood pressure than those who do not.

37) *Step 1:* H_0: $\mu = 133$, H_1: $\mu < 133$. *Step 2:* $\alpha = .10$. *Step 3:* Use the z distribution. *Step 4:* Reject H_0 in favour of H_1 if the p-value $< .10$. *Step 5:* $z = (124.15 - 133)/5.44 = -1.63$. *Step 6:* The area to the left of $z = -1.63$ is $.5 - .4484 - .0516$. Thus, p-value $= .0516$. *Step 7:* The p-value $< .10$. Following the decision rule, we reject H_0.

39) *Step 1:* H_0: $\mu = 2,650$, H_1: $\mu > 2,650$. *Step 2:* $\alpha = .01$. *Step 3:* Use the t distribution. *Step 4:* Reject H_0 in favour of H_1 if the p-value $< .01$. Otherwise, fail to reject H_0. *Step 5:* $t = (2,874 - 2,650)/369 = .61$. *Step 6:* Width 11 df, a t value of 1.363 has a p-value of .10. Since $.61 < 1.363$, it has a p-value $> .10$. *Step 7:* The p-value $> .10$. Following the decision rule, we fail to reject H_0.

41) *Step 1:* H_0: $\mu = 450$, H_1: $\mu > 450$. *Step 2:* $\alpha = .05$. *Step 3:* Use the t distribution. *Step 4:* Reject H_0 in favour of H_1 if the p-value $< .05$. *Step 5:* $t = (570.5 - 450)/15.8 = 7.64$. *Step 6:* With 9 df, a t value of 3.250 has a p-value of .005. Since $7.64 > 3.250$, it has a p-value $< .005$. *Step 7:* The p-value $< .005$. Following the decision rule, we reject H_0.

43) *Step 1:* H_0: $\mu = 20$, H_1: $\mu < 20$. *Step 2:* $\alpha = .01$. *Step 3:* Use the t distribution. *Step 4:* Reject H_0 in favour of H_1 if the p-value $< .01$. *Step 5:* $t = (11.174 - 20)/.991 = -8.90$. *Step 6:* With 22 df, a t value of -2.819 has a p-value of .005. Since $-8.90 < -2.819$, it has a p-value $< .005$. *Step 7:* Since the p-value $< .005$, we reject H_0 and decide that the mean maximum carbon monoxide in the air is less than the maximum safe level.

Self-Testing Review 8.3

45) H_0: $p = 0.05$, and H_1: $p \neq 0.05$; $\alpha = .05$; z distribution; Decision rule: Reject H_0 in favour of H_1 if $z < -1.96$ or if $z > 1.96$. $z = 3.404$. Reject H_0.

47) H_0: $p = 0.75$, and H_1: $p > 0.75$; $\alpha = .01$; z distribution; Decision rule: Reject H_0 in favour of H_1 if $z > 2.33$. $z = 0.433$. Fail to reject H_0.

49) *Step 1:* H_0: $p = .15$ and H_1: $p \neq .15$. *Step 2:* $\alpha = 0.01$. *Step 3:* Use the z distribution. *Step 4:* The value for a two-tailed test at the 0.10 level is $z = \pm2.575$. *Step 5:* Reject H_0 in favour of H_1 if $z < -2.575$ or $z > +2.575$. Otherwise, fail to reject H_0. *Step 6:* $z = (0.140502 - 0.15)/0.009560 = -0.9935$. *Step 7:* Since the z value of -0.9935 does not fall in the rejection region, we fail to reject H_0.

51) H_0: $p = 0.303$, and H_1: $p < 0.303$; $\alpha = .01$; z distribution; Decision rule: Reject H_0 in favour of H_1 if $z < -2.33$. $z = -3.45$. Reject H_0.

53) *Step 1:* H_0: $p = .50$ and H_1: $p > .50$. *Step 2:* $\alpha = 0.01$. *Step 3:* Use the z distribution. *Step 4:* The value for a right-tailed test at the 0.10 level is $z = 1.28$. *Step 5:* Reject H_0 in favour of H_1 if $z > 1.28$. Otherwise, fail to reject H_0. *Step 6:* $\hat{p} = 30/47 = 0.6383$ and $\hat{\sigma}_{\hat{p}} = \sqrt{(.50)(.50)/47} = 0.0729$. $z = (0.6383 - 0.50)/0.0729 = 1.90$. *Step 7:* Since the z value of 1.90 falls in the rejection region, we fail to reject H_0.

55) *Step 1:* H_0: $p = .20$ and H_1: $p > .20$. *Step 2:* $\alpha = 0.10$. *Step 3:* Use the z distribution. *Step 4:* Reject H_0 in favour of H_1 if the p-value is < 0.10. Otherwise, fail to reject H_0. *Step 5:* $\hat{p} = 0.3846$ and $\hat{\sigma}_{\hat{p}} = 0.07845$. Then $z = (0.3846 - 0.20)/0.07845 = 2.35$. *Step 6:* The area to the right of $z = 2.35$ is $0.5 - 0.4906$ or 0.0094. Thus, p-value $= 0.0094$. *Step 7:* The p-value for this test is less than 0.10. Following the decision rule, we fail to reject H_0.

57) *Step 1:* H_0: p $= .60$, H_1: p $\neq .60$. *Step 2:* $\alpha = .01$. *Step 3.* Use the z distribution. *Step 4:* The critical values for a two-tailed test at the .01 level are $z = \pm2.575$. *Step 5:* Reject H_0 in favour of H_1 if $z < -2.575$ or $> +2.575$. Otherwise, fail to reject H_0. *Step 6:* $z = .622047 - .60/.043471 = .507$. *Step 7:* Since $z = .507$ does not fall in the rejection region, we fail to reject H_0.

Self-Testing Review 8.4

59a) Use χ^2 with $12 - 1$ or 11 df. Since a .05 area must lie to the left of the critical value, .95 must lie to the right. Look under the column headed .95 to find $\chi^2 = 4.57$.

59b) Use x^2 with $7 - 1$ or 6 df. Since the critical region must contain a total of 0.01 in two tails, each tail must have 0.005. For the left critical value, look under the column headed 0.995 to find $x^2 = 0.676$, and for the right critical value, look under the column headed 0.005 to find $x^2 = 18.55$.

59c) Use χ^2 with $24 - 1$ or 23 df. Since a .01 area must lie to the right, read directly under the .01 column to see that $\chi^2 = 41.6$.

61) *Step 1: State null and alternative hypotheses.* H_0: $\sigma = 4.26$, and H_1: $\sigma > 4.26$. *Step 2: Select level of significance.* $\alpha = .05$. *Step 3: Determine test distribution to use.* Use the χ^2 distribution with 23 df. *Step 4: Define the critical or rejection region.* For a right-tailed test, look under the .05 column to find $\chi^2 = 35.2$. *Step 5: State the decision rule.* Reject H_0 in favour of H_1 if $\chi^2 > 35.2$. Otherwise, fail to reject H_0. *Step 6: Compute the test statistic* (χ^2). $\chi^2 = 23(5.317)/(4.26)^2 = 6.739$. *Step 7: Make the statistical decision.* Since $\chi^2 = 6.739$ does not fall in the rejection region, we fail to reject H_0.

63) *Step 1:* H_0: $\sigma = \$1,500$, and H_1: $\sigma < \$1,500$. *Step 2:* $\alpha = .01$. *Step 3:* Use the χ^2 distribution with 16 df. *Step 4:* For a left-tailed test, look under the .99 column to find $\chi^2 = 5.81$. *Step 5:* Reject H_0 in favour of H_1 if $\chi^2 < 5.81$. Otherwise, fail to reject H_0. *Step 6:* $\chi^2 = 16(862)^2/(1,500)^2 = 5.284$. *Step 7:* $\chi^2 = 5.284$ falls in the rejection region, so we reject H_0.

65) *Step 1:* H_0: $\sigma^2 = 40$, and H_1: $\sigma^2 > 40$. *Step 2:* $\alpha = .01$. *Step 3:* Use the χ^2 distribution with 11 df. *Step 4:* $\chi^2 = 24.7$. *Step 5:* Reject H_0 in favour of H_1 if $\chi^2 > 24.7$. Otherwise, fail to reject H_0. *Step 6:* $\chi^2 = 11(6.98)^2/40 = 13.398$. *Step 7:* Since $\chi^2 = 13.398$ does not fall in the rejection region, we fail to reject H_0.

67) *Step 1:* H_0: $\sigma^2 = 9$, and H_1: $\sigma^2 < 9$. *Step 2:* $\alpha = .05$. *Step 3:* Use the χ^2 distribution with 20 df. *Step 4:* $\chi^2 = 10.85$. *Step 5:* Reject H_0 in favour of H_1 if $\chi^2 < 10.85$. Otherwise, fail to reject H_0. *Step 6:* $\chi^2 = 20(4.1)/9 = 9.111$. *Step 7:* Since $\chi^2 = 9.111$ falls in the rejection region, we reject H_0.

69) *Step 1:* H_0: $\sigma = .100$, H_1: $\sigma > .100$. *Step 2:* $\alpha = .05$. *Step 3:* Use the χ^2 distribution. *Step 4:* For a right-tailed test, we use a χ^2 critical value with 30 df and .05 in the tail above it, or 43.8. *Step 5:* Reject the H_0 in favour of H_1 if $\chi^2 > 43.8$. *Step 6:* $\chi^2 = 30(.2613^2)/.100^2 = 204.83$. *Step 7:* Since $204.83 > 43.8$, we reject H_0 in favour of H_1. The standard deviation appears to exceed .100.

71) *Step 1:* H_0: $\sigma = .100$, H_1: $\sigma \neq .100$. *Step 2:* $\alpha = .05$. *Step 3:* Use the χ^2 distribution with 11 df. *Step 4:* With a two-tailed test, we need .025 in each tail, so we use the χ^2 value in the .975 column, or 3.82, and the χ^2 value in the .025 column, or 21.9. *Step 5:* Reject H_0 in favour of H_1 if $\chi^2 < 3.82$ or > 21.9. Otherwise, fail to reject H_0. *Step 6:* $\chi^2 = 11(235.8^2)/100^2 = 61.16$. *Step 7:* Since $\chi^2 > 21.9$, we reject H_0 in favour of H_1. There is evidence the standard deviation is not 100.

Exercises

73) *Step 1: State the Null and Alternative Hypotheses.* H_0: $\mu = 58$, and H_1: $\mu \neq 58$. *Step 2: Select the Level of Significance:* $\alpha = 0.05$ (given). *Step 3: Determine the Test Distribution to Use:* Since $n < 30$ and we assume that the population values are normally distributed, we use the t distribution. *Step 4: Define the Rejection or Critical Regions.* This is a two-tailed test. With $\alpha = 0.05$ and $n = 24$ we have 23 df so we use $t_{\alpha/2} = t_{0.025} = \pm2.069$. *Step 5: State the Decision Rule.* Reject H_0 in favour of H_1 if $t > 2.069$ or if $t < -2.069$. Otherwise, fail to reject H_0. *Step 6: Make the Necessary Computations.* Data: $\bar{x} = 55.93$; $s = 5.2$; $n = 24$. Since σ is unknown, we use $\hat{\sigma}_{\bar{x}} = s/\sqrt{n} = 5.2/\sqrt{24} = 1.0614$. Then $t = \bar{x} - \mu_0/\hat{\sigma}_{\bar{x}} = 55.93 - 58/1.0614 = -1.950$. *Step 7: Make a Statistical Decision.* Since $t = -1.950$ falls between ±2.069, we fail to reject H_0.

75) *Step 1:* H_0: $\sigma = 85.2$, and H_1: $\sigma \neq 85.2$ *Step 2:* $\alpha = 0.01$ given. *Step 3:* Use x^2 test on variances. *Step 4:* This is a two-tailed test, the acceptance region falls between $x^2_{\alpha/2}$ and $x^2_{1-\alpha/2}$. With $\alpha = 0.01$ and $n = 28$ we have 27 df so $x^2_{\alpha/2} = x^2_{0.005} = 49.6$, while $x^2_{1-\alpha/2} = x^2_{0.995} = 11.81$. *Step 5:* Reject H_0 in favour of H_1 if $x^2 > 49.6$ or if $x^2 < 11.81$. Otherwise, fail to reject H_0. *Step 6:* Data: $s = 81.7$; $n = 28$. So $s^2 = 6674.89$ and $\sigma^2 = 7259.04$. $x^2 = (n - 1)s^2/\sigma^2 = 27 \cdot 6674.89/7259.04 = 24.827$. *Step 7:* Since x^2 falls between $x^2_{\alpha/2}$ and $x^2_{1-\alpha/2}$, we fail to reject H_0.

77) *Step 1:* H_0: $\sigma = \$1.50$, and H_1: $\sigma > \$150$. *Step 2:* $\alpha = 0.05$. *Step 3:* Use x^2 test on variances. *Step 4:* This is a one-tailed test, the acceptance region falls below x^2_α. With $n = 19$ we have 18 df so $x^2_\alpha = x^2_{0.05} = 28.9$. *Step 5:* Reject H_0 in favour of H_1 if $x^2 > 28.9$. Otherwise, fail to reject H_0. *Step 6:* Calculate $\bar{x}$ and s^2.

x	$x - \bar{x}$	$(x - \bar{x})^2$
499	160.79	25,853.4241
279	−59.21	3,505.8241
669	330.79	109,422.0241
550	211.79	44,855.0041
207	−131.21	17,216.0641
600	261.79	68,534.0041
399	60.79	3,695.4241
3203		273,081.7687

x	$x - \bar{x}$	$(x - \bar{x})^2$
100	−238.21	56,744.0041
235	−103.21	10,652.3041
467	128.79	16,586.8641
249	−89.21	7,958.4241
200	−138.21	19,102.0041
235	−103.21	10,652.3041
		121,695.9046

x	$x - \bar{x}$	$(x - \bar{x})^2$
489	150.79	22,737.6241
300	−38.21	1,460.0041
299	−39.21	1,537.4241
200	−138.21	19,102.0041
200	−138.21	19,102.0041
249	−89.21	7,958.4241
1,737		71,897.4846

$\sum x = 3{,}203 + 1{,}486 + 1{,}737 = 6{,}426$, $\sum x^2 = 273{,}081.7687 + 121{,}695.9046 + 71{,}897.4846 = 466{,}675.1579$, $\bar{x} = 6426/19 = \$338.21$, $s^2 = \sqrt{\sum(x - \bar{x})^2/n - 1} = \sqrt{466{,}675.1579/18} = 25{,}926.3977$, and $\sigma^2 = 150^2 = 22{,}500$. Then $x^2 = (n - 1)s^2/\sigma^2 = 18 \cdot 25{,}926.3977/22{,}500 = 20.74$. Step 7: Since x^2 falls between x_α^2 we fail to reject H_0.

79) H_0: $p = 0.50$, and H_1: $p > 0.50$; $\alpha = .01$; z distribution; Decision rule: Reject H_0 in favour of H_1 if $z > 2.33$. $z = 0.2063$. Fail to reject H_0.

81) Step 1: H_0: $\mu = 2$, and H_1: $\mu \neq 2$. Step 2: $\alpha = 0.01$. Step 3: Since $n > 30$ we use the z distribution. Step 4: This is two-tailed test. With $\alpha = 0.01$, the remaining area is $0.5000 - 0.0050 = 0.4950$, which corresponds to a z value of 2.575. Step 5: Reject H_0 in favour of H_1 if $z > 2.575$ or if $z < -2.575$. Otherwise, fail to reject H_0. Step 6: Data: $\bar{x} = 1.79$; $s = 0.60$; $n = 216$. $\hat{\sigma}_{\bar{x}} = s/\sqrt{n} = 0.60/\sqrt{216} = 0.0408$. $z = \bar{x} - \mu_0/\hat{\sigma}_{\bar{x}} = 1.79 - 2/0.0408 = -5.147$. Step 7: Since $z = -5.147 < -2.575$ we reject H_0.

83) Step 1: H_0: $\mu = \$2{,}150$ and H_1: $\mu > \$2{,}150$. Step 2: $\alpha = 0.01$. Step 3: Since $n < 30$ and we assume that population values are normally distributed, we use the t distribution. Step 4: One-tailed test; with $\alpha = 0.01$ and $n = 7$ we have 6 df so we use $t_\alpha = t_{0.01} = 3.143$. Step 5: Reject H_0 in favour of H_1 if $t > 3.143$. Otherwise, fail to reject H_0. Step 6: Data: $n = 7$. $\bar{x} = 16{,}493/7 = \$2{,}356.14$. Calculate s.

x	$x - \bar{x}$	$(x - \bar{x})^2$
1,198	−1,158.14	1,341,288.2596
2,080	−276.14	76,253.2996
1,130	−1,226.14	1,503,419.2996
1,510	−846.14	715,952.8996
2,821	464.86	216,094.8196
2,777	420.86	177,123.1396
4,977	2,620.86	6,868,907.1396
16,493		10,899,038.8572

$s = \sqrt{\sum(x - \bar{x})^2/n - 1} = \sqrt{10{,}899{,}038.8572/6} = 1{,}347{,}778$.

$\hat{\sigma}_{\bar{x}} = s/\sqrt{n} = 1{,}347.778/\sqrt{7} = 509.412$. Then $t = \sqrt{\bar{x} - \mu_0/\hat{\sigma}_{\bar{x}}}$

$= 2{,}356.14 - 2{,}150/509.412 = 0.4047$. Step 7: Since $t < 3.143$, we fail to reject H_0.

85) Step 1: H_0 $\sigma = 2$ and H_1: $\sigma > 2$. Step 2: $\alpha = 0.05$. Step 3: Use x^2 test on variances. Step 4: One-tailed test, the acceptance region falls below x_α^2. So with $\alpha = 0.05$ and 25 df we have $x_\alpha^2 = x_{0.05}^2 = 37.7$. Step 5: Reject H_0 in favour of H_1 if $x^2 > 37.7$. Otherwise, fail to reject H_0. Step 6: Since $s = 3.26$; $s^2 = 10.6276$ and $\sigma^2 = 4$. Then $x^2 = (n - 1)s^2/\sigma^2 = 25 \cdot 10.6276/4 = 66.4225$. Step 7: Since $x^2 > 37.7$, we reject H_0.

87) Step 1: H_0: $\mu = \$1{,}000$ and H_1: $\mu \neq \$1{,}000$. Step 2: $\alpha = 0.01$. Step 3: Since $n > 30$ we use the z distribution. Step 4: Two-tailed test $\alpha = 0.01$ corresponds to a z value of 2.575. Step 5: Reject H_0 in favour of H_1 if $|z| > \pm 2.575$. Step 6: Data: $\bar{x} = \$981$; $s = \$231$; $n = 273$. $\hat{\sigma}_{\bar{x}} = s/\sqrt{n} = 231/\sqrt{273} = 13.98076$. Then $z = 981 - 1{,}000/13.98076 = -1.359$. Step 7: Since z is within ± 2.575, we fail to reject H_0.

89) Step 1: H_0: $\mu = 27.37$ and H_1: $\mu \neq 27.37$. Step 2: $\alpha = 0.01$. Step 3: z distribution. Step 4: Two-tailed test with $\alpha = 0.01$ corresponds to a z value of 2.575. Step 5: Reject H_0 in favour of H_1 if $z < -2.575$ or if $z > 2.575$. Otherwise, fail to reject H_0. Step 6: Data: $\bar{x} = 27.29$; $s = 3.75$; $n = 64$. $\hat{\sigma}_{\bar{x}} = s/\sqrt{n} = 3.75/\sqrt{64} = 0.46875$. Then $z = 27.29 = 27.37/0.46875 = -0.1706$. Step 7: Since z is within ± 2.575, we fail to reject H_0.

91) Step 1: H_0: $\sigma^2 = 50{,}000$ and H_1: $\sigma^2 < 50{,}000$. Step 2: $\alpha = 0.05$. Step 3: Use x^2 test on variances. Step 4: One-tailed test, the rejection region falls below $x_{1-\alpha}^2$. So with $\alpha = 0.05$ and 10 df we have $x_{1-\alpha}^2 = x_{0.95}^2 = 3.94$. Step 5: Reject H_0 in favour of H_1 if $x^2 < 3.94$. Otherwise, fail to reject H_0. Step 6: Data: $n = 11$. Calculate $\bar{x}$ and s^2.

x	$x - \bar{x}$	$(x - \bar{x})^2$
1,200	−181.82	33058.5124
1,200	−181.82	33058.5124
1,000	−381.82	145786.5124
1,600	218.18	47602.5124
1,400	18.18	330.5124
1,400	18.18	330.5124
1,200	−181.82	33058.5124
1,700	318.18	101238.5124
1,600	218.18	47602.5124
1,300	−81.82	6694.5124
1,600	218.18	47602.5124
15,200		496363.6364

$\bar{x} = 15{,}200/11 = 1{,}381.82$ and $s^2 = \sum(x - \bar{x})^2/n - 1 = 496{,}363.6364/10 = 49{,}636.36364$. Then $x^2 = (n - 1)s^2/\sigma^2 = 10 \cdot 49{,}636.36364/50{,}000 = 9.9273$. Step 7: Since $x^2 > 3.94$ we fail to reject H_0.

93) Step 1: H_0: $p = .07$, and H_1: $p < .07$. Step 2: $\alpha = 0.05$. Step 3: z distribution. Step 4: One-tailed test with $\alpha = 0.05$ corresponds

to a z value of 1.645. *Step 5:* Reject H_0 in favour of H_1 if $z > 1.645$. Otherwise, fail to reject H_0. *Step 6:* Data: 139 out of 1,263, so $\hat{p} = 139/1,263 = 0.11006$ and $\sigma_{\hat{p}} = \sqrt{p_0(1-p_0)/n} = \sqrt{(.07)(.93)/1,263} = 0.007179$. Then $z = (\hat{p} - p_0)/\sigma_{\hat{p}} = (0.11006 - 0.07)/0.007179 = 5.580$. *Step 7:* Since $z > 1.645$, we reject H_0.

95) *Step 1:* H_0: $\mu = \$5,600$ and H_1: $\mu \neq \$5,600$. *Step 2:* $\alpha = 0.05$. *Step 3:* z distribution. *Step 4:* Two-tailed test with $\alpha = 0.05$ corresponds to a z value of 1.96. *Step 5:* Reject H_0 in favour of H_1 if $z < -1.96$ or if $z > 1.96$. Otherwise, fail to reject H_0. *Step 6:* Data: $\bar{x} = \$5,750$; $s = \$175$; $n = 36$. $\hat{\sigma}_{\bar{x}} = s/\sqrt{n} = 175/\sqrt{36} = 29.1667$. Then $z = 5,750 - 5,600/29.1667 = 5.1429$. *Step 7:* Since $z > 1.96$, we reject H_0.

97) *Step 1:* H_0: $\mu = 50$ and H_1: $\mu \neq 50$. *Step 2:* $\alpha = 0.01$. *Step 3:* Although $n < 30$, we still use the z distribution since σ is known. *Step 4:* This is a two-tailed test. With $\alpha = 0.01$, the remaining area is $0.5000 - 0.0050 = 0.4950$, which corresponds to a z value of -2.575. *Step 5:* Reject H_0 in favour of H_1 if $z < -2.575$ or if $z > 2.575$. Otherwise, fail to reject H_0. *Step 6:* Data: $\bar{x} = 49.25$; $s = 2$; $n = 24$. $\hat{\sigma}_{\bar{x}} = s/\sqrt{n} = 2/\sqrt{24} = 0.4082$. $z = \bar{x} - \mu_0/\hat{\sigma}_{\bar{x}} = 49.25 - 50/0.4082 = -1.8371$. *Step 7:* Since z is within ±2.575, we fail to reject H_0.

99) *Step 1:* H_0: $\mu = 1,000$ and H_1: $\mu \neq 1,000$. *Step 2:* $\alpha = 0.05$. *Step 3:* t distribution. *Step 4:* Two-tailed test with $\alpha = 0.05$ and 24 df, we use $t_{\alpha/2} = t_{0.025} = 2.064$. *Step 5:* Reject H_0 in favour of H_1 if $t < -2.064$ or if $t > 2.064$. Otherwise, fail to reject H_0. *Step 6:* Data: $\bar{x} = 994$; $s = 30$; $n = 25$. $\hat{\sigma}_{\bar{x}} = s/\sqrt{n} = 30/\sqrt{25} = 6$. Then $t = 994 - 1,000/6 = -1$. *Step 7:* Since t is within ±2.064, we fail to reject H_0.

101) *Step 1:* H_0: $\mu = 50$ and H_1: $\mu \neq 50$. *Step 2:* $\alpha = 0.05$. *Step 3:* t distribution. *Step 4:* Two-tailed test with $\alpha = 0.05$ and 9 df, we use $t_{\alpha/2} = t_{0.025} = 2.262$. *Step 5:* Reject H_0 in favour of H_1 if $t < -2.262$ or if $t > 2.262$. Otherwise, fail to reject H_0. *Step 6:* Data: $\bar{x} = 50.02$; $s = 0.024$; $n = 10$. $\hat{\sigma}_{\bar{x}} = s/\sqrt{n} = 0.024/\sqrt{10} = 0.007589$. Then $t = 50.02 - 50/0.007589 = 2.635$. *Step 7:* Since $t > 2.262$, we reject H_0.

103) *Step 1:* H_0: $\mu = 75$ and H_1: $\mu > 75$. *Step 2:* $\alpha = 0.01$. *Step 3:* t distribution. *Step 4:* One-tailed test with $\alpha = 0.01$ and 8 df, we use $t_\alpha = t_{0.01} = 2.896$. *Step 5:* Reject H_0 in favour of H_1 if $t > 2.896$. Otherwise, fail to reject H_0. *Step 6:* Data: $\bar{x} = 80$; $s = 4$; $n = 9$. $\hat{\sigma}_{\bar{x}} = s/\sqrt{n} = 4/\sqrt{9} = 1.3333$. Then $t = 80 - 75/1.3333 = 3.75$. *Step 7:* Since $t > 2.896$ we reject H_0.

105) *Step 1:* H_0: $\mu = 1.5$ and H_1: $\mu \neq 1.5$. *Step 2:* $\alpha = 0.05$. *Step 3:* Since we know the population standard deviation, we use the z distribution. *Step 4:* Two-tailed test with $\alpha = 0.05$ corresponds to a z value of 1.96. *Step 5:* Reject H_0 in favour of H_1 if $z > 1.96$ or if $z > -1.96$. Otherwise, fail to reject H_0. *Step 6:* Data: $\bar{x} = 1.5005$; $s = 0.01$; $n = 20$. $\hat{\sigma}_{\bar{x}} = s/\sqrt{n} = 0.01/\sqrt{20} = 0.002236$. Then $z = 1.5005 - 1.5/0.002236 = 0.2236$. *Step 7:* Since $z > -1.96$, we fail to reject H_0.

107) *Step 1:* H_0: $\mu = 2,000$ and H_1: $\mu < 2,000$. *Step 2:* $\alpha = 0.05$. *Step 3:* t distribution. *Step 4:* One-tailed test with $\alpha = 0.05$ and 12 df, we use $t_\alpha = t_{0.05} = -1.782$. *Step 5:* Reject H_0 in favour of H_1 if $t < -1.782$. Otherwise, fail to reject H_0. *Step 6:* Data: $\bar{x} = 1,975$; $s = 40$; $n = 13$. $\hat{\sigma}_{\bar{x}} = s/\sqrt{n} = 40/\sqrt{13} = 11.094$. Then $t = 1,975 - 2,000/11.094 = -2.25$. *Step 7:* Since $t < -1.782$, we reject H_0. The shipment should be rejected.

109) *Step 1:* H_0: $\mu = \$10,000$ and H_1: $\mu > \$10,000$. *Step 2:* $\alpha = 0.05$. *Step 3:* t distribution. *Step 4:* One-tailed test with $\alpha = 0.05$ and 14 df, we use $t_\alpha = t_{0.05} = 1.761$. *Step 5:* Reject H_0 in favour of H_1 if $t > 1.761$. Otherwise, fail to reject H_0. *Step 6:* Data: $\bar{x} = \$10,575$; $s = \$600$; $n = 15$. $\hat{\sigma}_{\bar{x}} = s/\sqrt{n} = 600/\sqrt{15} = 154.9193$. Then $t = 10,975 - 10,000/154.9193 = 3.7116$. *Step 7:* Since $t > 1.761$, we reject H_0; there is sufficient evidence that the contractor averages more than \$10,000 per consultation.

111a) *Step 1:* H_0: $\mu = 7,000$ and H_1: $\mu < 7,000$. *Step 2:* $\alpha = 0.05$. *Step 3:* t distribution. *Step 4:* One-tailed test with $\alpha = 0.05$ and 5 df, we use $t_\alpha = t_{0.05} = 2.015$. *Step 5:* Reject H_0 in favour of H_1 if $t < -2.015$. Otherwise, fail to reject H_0. *Step 6:* Data: $\bar{x} = 43,281/6 = 7,213.5$; $\sigma = 875$; $n = 6$. $\sigma_{\bar{x}} = \sigma/\sqrt{n} = 875/\sqrt{6} = 357.217$. Then $t = 7213.5 - 7000/357.217 = 0.598$. *Step 7:* Since $t > -2.015$, we fail to reject H_0.

111b) H_0: $\sigma = 875$, and H_1: $\sigma > 875$; $\alpha = .05$; χ^2 distribution with 5 df; Decision rule: Reject H_0 in favour of H_1 if $\chi^2 > 11.07$. $\chi^2 = 5(321^2)/875^2 = .673$. Fail to reject H_0.

113a) H_0: $\mu = 50,000$, and H_1: $\mu < 50,000$; $\alpha = .01$; t distribution with 21 df; Decision rule: Reject H_0 in favour of H_1 if $t < -2.518$. $t = (41,354 - 50,000)/1,687 = -5.13$. Reject H_0.

113b) *Step 1:* H_0: $\sigma = 5,000$ and H_1: $\sigma > 5,000$. *Step 2:* $\alpha = 0.05$. *Step 3:* Use x^2 test on variances. *Step 4:* One-tailed test, the rejection region falls above x_α^2. So with $\alpha = 0.05$ and 21 df, we have $x_\alpha^2 = x_{0.05}^2 = 32.7$. *Step 5:* Reject H_0 in favour of H_1 if $x^2 > 32.7$. Otherwise, fail to reject H_0. *Step 6:* Data: $n = 22$ and from MINITAB, $s = 7,912$. So $x^2 = (n-1)s^2/\sigma^2 = 21 \cdot (7912)^2/(5000)^2 = 52.583$. *Step 7:* Since $x^2 > 32.7$, we reject H_0 and conclude the standard deviation is greater than 5,000.

115a) H_0: $p = 0.459$, and H_1: $p < 0.459$; $\alpha = .10$; z distribution; Decision rule: Reject H_0 in favour of H_1 if $z < -1.28$. $z = -1.39$. Reject H_0.

115b) H_0: $p = 0.494$, and H_1: $p \neq 0.494$; $\alpha = .10$; z distribution; Decision rule: Reject H_0 in favour of H_1 if $z < -1.645$ or if $z > 1.645$. $z = 1.78$. Reject H_0.

115c) H_0: $p = 0.276$, and H_1: $p > 0.276$; $\alpha = .01$; z distribution; Decision rule: Reject H_0 in favour of H_1 if $z > 1.28$. $z = -2.66$. Reject H_0.

117) H_0: $\mu = 2,100$, and H_1: $\mu > 2,100$; $\alpha = .05$; t distribution; Decision rule: Reject H_0 in favour of H_1 if $t > 1.860$. $t = (2,493 - 2,100)/167 = 2.36$. Reject H_0.

Chapter 9
Self-Testing Review 9.1

1) To perform a test of equal variances that gives meaningful results, both populations must be normally distributed, and the samples must be independently selected.

3) *Step 1: State the null and alternative hypotheses.* H_0: $\sigma_1^2 = \sigma_2^2$ and H_1: $\sigma_1^2 \neq \sigma_2^2$. *Step 2: Select the level of significance.* Use $\alpha = .05$. *Step 3: Determine the test distribution to use.* We use an F distribution. Since this is a two-tailed test, we use the table with half of .05, or .025, in the right tail. The larger variance has a sample size of 16, so the df for the numerator is $16 - 1$ or 15. The sample size for the smaller variance is 7, so $7 - 1$ or 6 is the df for the denominator. *Step 4: Define the critical or rejection region.* You look across the top line of the F table for a df value of 15 and down the left column until you get to the line with df = 6. The critical F value is 5.27. *Step 5: State the decision rule.* Reject H_0 in favour of H_1 if $F > 5.27$. Otherwise, fail to reject H_0. *Step 6: Compute the Test Statistic.* $F = 457.21/99.08 = 4.615$. *Step 7: Make the statistical decision.* Since $F = 4.615$ does not fall in the rejection region, we fail to reject H_0 that the variances for the two populations are equal.

5) *Step 1:* H_0: $\sigma_1^2 = \sigma_2^2$ and H_1: $\sigma_1^2 \neq \sigma_2^2$. *Step 2:* Use $\alpha = .05$. *Step 3:* We use an F distribution. Since this is a two-tailed test, we use the table with .025 in the right tail. The df for the numerator is $16 - 1$ or 15. And the df for the denominator is $13 - 1$ or 12. *Step 4:* The critical F value is 3.18. *Step 5:* Reject H_0 in favour of H_1 if $F > 3.18$. Otherwise, fail to reject H_0. *Step 6:* $F = 17.39/12.83 = 1.355$. *Step 7:* Since $F = 1.355$ does not fall in the rejection region, we fail to reject H_0 that the variances are equal for the two shifts.

7) *Step 1:* H_0: $\sigma_1^2 = \sigma_2^2$ and H_1: $\sigma_1^2 \neq \sigma_2^2$. *Step 2:* Use $\alpha = .05$. *Step 3:* We use an F distribution. Since this is a two-tailed test, we use the table with .025 in the fight tail. The df for the numerator is $7 - 1$ or 6. And the df for the denominator is $14 - 1$ or 13. *Step 4:* The critical F value is 3.60. *Step 5:* Reject H_0 in favour of H_1 if $F > 3.60$. Otherwise, fail to reject H_0. *Step 6:* $F = 7.21/3.92 = 1.839$. *Step 7:* Since $F = 1.839$ does not fall in the rejection region, we fail to reject H_0 that the variances are equal.

9) *Step 1:* H_0: $\sigma_1^2 = \sigma_2^2$, H_1: $\sigma_1^2 \neq \sigma_2^2$. *Step 2:* $\alpha = .05$. *Step 3:* Use the F distribution with numerator df = 11 and denominator df = 11. *Step 4:* For a two-tailed test, we will use the F value with .025 in the tail above, (we use df numerator = 10 since there is no 11) or 3.53. *Step 5:* Reject H_0 in favour of H_1 if $F > 3.53$. *Step 6:* Choosing the largest value for the numerator, $F = 5.3507/1.0367 = 5.161$. *Step 7:* Since F is in the rejection region, we decide in favour of H_1. It appears that the variances are not equal.

11) *Step 1:* H_0: $\sigma_1^2 = \sigma_2^2$, H_1: $\sigma_1^2 \neq \sigma_2^2$. *Step 2:* $\alpha = .05$. *Step 3:* Use the F distribution with numerator df = 15 and denominator df = 15. *Step 4:* For a two tailed test, we will use the F value with .025 in the tail above, or 2.86. *Step 5:* Reject H_0 in favour of H_1 if $F > 2.86$. *Step 6:* Choosing the largest value for the numerator, $F = 197.363/8.2 = 24.069$. *Step 7:* Since F is in the rejection region, we reject H_0 in favour of H_1. There is evidence that the variances are not equal.

13) *Step 1:* H_0: $\sigma_1^2 = \sigma_2^2$, H_1: $\sigma_1^2 \neq \sigma_2^2$. *Step 2:* $\alpha = .05$. *Step 3:* Use the F distribution with numerator df = 9 and denominator df = 9. *Step 4:* For a two-tailed test, we will use the F value with .025 in the tail above, or 4.03. *Step 5:* Reject H_0 in favour of H_1 if $F > 4.03$. *Step 6:* Choosing the largest value for the numerator, $F = 1.76667/0.625 = 2.827$. *Step 7:* Since F is not in the rejection region, we fail to reject H_0.

15) *Step 1:* H_0: σ_1^2 (male) $= \sigma_2^2$ (female), H_1: $\sigma_1^2 \neq \sigma_2^2$. *Step 2:* $\alpha = .05$. *Step 3:* Use the F distribution with numerator df = 31 and denominator df = 10. *Step 4:* For a two-tailed test, we will use the F value (numerator df = 30) with .025 in the tail above, or 3.31. *Step 5:* Reject H_0 in favour of H_1 if $F > 3.31$. *Step 6:* Choosing the largest value for the numerator, $F = 14523.2/10648.4 = 1.364$. *Step 7:* Since F is not in the rejection region, we fail to reject H_0.

Self-Testing Review 9.2

17) *Step 1:* H_0: $\mu_1 = \mu_2$ and H_1: $\mu_1 > \mu_2$. *Step 2:* $\alpha = 0.05$. *Step 3:* Since the samples are independent and both samples are large, we use procedure 2 with the z distribution. *Step 4:* The critical z value is 1.645. *Step 5:* Reject H_0 in favour of H_1 if $z > 1.645$. Otherwise, fail to reject H_0. *Step 6:* Then

$$z = \frac{\bar{x}_1 - \bar{x}_2}{\sqrt{\dfrac{s_1^2}{n_1} + \dfrac{s_2^2}{n_2}}} = \frac{24.1 - 23.9}{\sqrt{\dfrac{5.24^2}{100} + \dfrac{6.29^2}{73}}} = 0.2248.$$

Step 7: Since $z = 0.2248$ does not fall in the rejection region, we fail to reject the null hypothesis. The physician-led group did not do significantly better than the control group.

19) *Step 1:* H_0: $\mu_1 = \mu_2$ and H_1: $\mu_1 > \mu_2$. *Step 2:* $\alpha = 0.01$. *Step 3:* Since the samples are independent and both samples are large, we use procedure 2 with the z distribution. *Step 4:* The critical z value is 2.33. *Step 5:* Reject H_0 in favour of H_1 if $z > 2.33$. Otherwise, fail to reject H_0. *Step 6:* Then

$$z = \frac{\bar{x}_1 - \bar{x}_2}{\sqrt{\dfrac{s_1^2}{n_1} + \dfrac{s_2^2}{n_2}}} = \frac{38.08 - 35.60}{\sqrt{\dfrac{0.84^2}{44} + \dfrac{0.79^2}{47}}} = \frac{2.48}{0.1712} = 14.49.$$

Step 7: Since $z = 14.49$ falls in the rejection region, we reject H_0. The PD at Nordstrom's is greater than the PD at the May Company.

21a) To first test for equality of population variances of net worth values, we test H_0: $\sigma_N^2 = \sigma_E^2$ vs. H_1: $\sigma_N^2 \neq \sigma_E^2$ using $\alpha = .05$. Since we have independent samples and $F = 248.822/36.574 = 6.803$ is greater than the critical value of 4.03 there is sufficient evidence to conclude the variances differ, so we will use a t distribution and procedure 3. H_0: $\mu_N = \mu_E$ and H_1: $\mu_N > \mu_E$; $\alpha = .05$; the critical t value with 9 df is 1.833. We will reject H_0 in favour of H_1 if $t > 1.833$.

$$z = \frac{\bar{x}_N - \bar{x}_E}{\sqrt{\dfrac{s_N^2}{n_N} + \dfrac{s_E^2}{n_E}}} = \frac{11.7 - 4.79}{\sqrt{\dfrac{248.822}{10} + \dfrac{36.574}{10}}} = 1.29.$$

Since 1.29 does not fall in the rejection region, we fail to reject H_0. We don't have sufficient evidence to conclude the population mean net worth is higher in North America. For both tests we must assume that the population of incomes of all billionaires in North America and the population of incomes of all billionaires in Europe are both normally distributed.

21b) To first test for equality of population variances of ages, we test $H_0: \sigma_N^2 = \sigma_E^2$ vs. $H_1: \sigma_N^2 \neq \sigma_E^2$ using $\alpha = .05$. Since we have independent samples, and $F = 204.711/184.1 = 1.112$ is not greater than the critical value of 4.03 there is insufficient evidence to conclude the variances differ, so we will use a t distribution and procedure 4. $H_0: \mu_N = \mu_E$ and $H_1: \mu_N \neq \mu_E$; $\alpha = .05$; the critical t values with 18 df are ± 2.101. We will reject H_0 in favour of H_1 if $t > 2.101$ or if $t < -2.101$.

$$t = \frac{\bar{x}_N - \bar{x}_E}{s_p \sqrt{\dfrac{1}{n_N} + \dfrac{1}{n_E}}} = \frac{58.1 - 65.4}{13.9424\sqrt{\dfrac{1}{10} + \dfrac{1}{10}}} = -1.17.$$

Since -1.17 does not fall in the rejection region, we fail to reject H_0. We don't have sufficient evidence to conclude the mean ages are different. For both tests we must assume that the population of ages of all billionaires in North America and the population of ages of all billionaires in Europe are both normally distributed.

23) *Step 1:* $H_0: \mu_1 = \mu_2$ and $H_1: \mu_1 \neq \mu_2$. *Step 2:* $\alpha = .05$. *Step 3:* Since the samples are independent and both samples are large, we use Procedure 2 with a z distribution. *Step 4:* The critical z value is ± 1.96. *Step 5:* Reject H_0 in favour of H_1 if $z < -1.96$ or $> +1.96$. Otherwise, fail to reject H_0. *Step 6:*

$$z = \frac{x_1 - x_2}{\sqrt{\dfrac{s_1^2}{n_1} + \dfrac{s_2^2}{n_2}}} = \frac{42.0 - 37.2}{\sqrt{\dfrac{34.7^2}{141} + \dfrac{33.4^2}{123}}} = 1.144$$

Step 7: Since $z = 1.144$ does not fall in the rejection region, we fail to reject H_0. There appears to be no difference in the amount of time spent between the two groups.

25) *Step 1:* $H_0: \mu_d = 0$ and $H_1: \mu_d > 0$. *Step 2:* $\alpha = .05$. *Step 3:* We use a paired t test with 7 df. *Step 4:* The critical t value is 1.895. *Step 5:* Reject H_0 in favour of H_1 if $t > 1.895$. Otherwise, fail to reject H_0. *Step 6:*

$$t = \frac{\bar{d} - \mu_d}{s_d/\sqrt{n}} = \frac{139.75 - 0}{144.0930/\sqrt{8}} = \frac{139.75}{50.9446} = 2.743$$

Step 7: Since $t = 2.743$ falls in the rejection region, we reject H_0. The high speed steel bits appear to take longer.

27) *Step 1:* $H_0: \mu_1 = \mu_2$ and $H_1: \mu_1 \neq \mu_2$. *Step 2:* $\alpha = .05$. *Step 3:* Since the samples are independent and both samples are small, we first test to see if the variances are equal. Running the test from 9-1, we have reason to believe that they are. This means Procedure 4 and a t test are in order. The df $- 16 + 16 - 2 = 30$.

Step 4: The critical t values = ± 2.042. *Step 5:* Reject H_0 in favour of H_1 if $t < -2.042$ or $> +2.042$. Otherwise, fail to reject H_0. *Step 6:*

$$t = \frac{\bar{x}_1 - \bar{x}_2}{\sqrt{\dfrac{s_1^2(n_1 - 1) + s_2^2(n_2 - 1)}{n_1 + n_2 - 1}}\sqrt{\dfrac{1}{n_1} + \dfrac{1}{n_2}}}$$

$$= \frac{26.011 - 25.831}{\sqrt{\dfrac{.460^2(15) + .627^2(15)}{16 + 16 - 2}}\sqrt{\dfrac{1}{16} + \dfrac{1}{16}}} = \frac{.180}{.1944}$$

$$= .926$$

Step 7: Since $t = .926$ does not fall in the rejection region, we fail to reject H_0. There appears to be no significant difference between the control group and the treatment group.

29) *Step 1:* $H_0: \mu_d = 0$ and $H_1: \mu_d > 0$. *Step 2:* $\alpha = .01$. *Step 3:* We use a paired t test and a t distribution with 9 df. *Step 4:* The critical t value with 9 df = 2.821. *Step 5:* Reject H_0 in favour of H_1 if $t > 2.821$. Otherwise, fail to reject H_0. *Step 6:*

$$t = \frac{\bar{d} - \mu_d}{s_d/\sqrt{n}} = \frac{8.2}{5.731} = 1.431$$

Step 7: Since $t = 1.431$ does not fall in the rejection region, we fail to reject H_0. Save your money, the anti-inflammatory cream apparently does not help.

31) *Step 1:* $H_0: \mu_1 = \mu_2$ and $H_1: \mu_1 \neq \mu_2$. *Step 2:* $\alpha = .05$. *Step 3:* Since the samples are independent and both samples are large, we use Procedure 2 with a z distribution. *Step 4:* The critical z values are ± 1.96. *Step 5:* Reject H_0 in favour of H_1 if $z < -1.96$ or $> +1.96$. Otherwise, fail to reject H_0. *Step 6:*

$$z = \frac{\bar{x}_1 - \bar{x}_2}{\sqrt{\dfrac{s_1^2}{n_1} + \dfrac{s_2^2}{n_2}}} = \frac{49.53 - 53.73}{\sqrt{\dfrac{12.62^2}{222} + \dfrac{4.74^2}{64}}} = -4.063$$

Step 7: Since $z = -4.063$ falls in the rejection region, we reject H_0. There apparently is a difference in the "dysfunctional beliefs" mean scores.

33) $s_p = \sqrt{[12(23^2) + 9(13^2)]/21} = 19.36$. The 95 percent confidence interval for the difference of two means with small, independent samples, assuming equal variances: $(116 - 109) \pm 2.080(19.36)\sqrt{[(1/13) + (1/10)]} = 7 \pm 16.94$ or -9.94 to 23.94.

35) Most of the calculations were done for the previous exercise. The 99 percent confidence interval for the difference of two means with small, independent samples, assuming equal variances: $(40.7 - 34.5) \pm 3.355(3.6056) = 6.2 \pm 12.1$ or -5.9 to 18.3.

37) *Step 1:* $H_0: \mu_1 = \mu_2$ and $H_1: \mu_1 \neq \mu_2$. *Step 2:* $\alpha = .01$. *Step 3:* Since the samples are independent and both samples are small, we first test to see if the variances are equal. From the hypothesis test of equal variances, we have reason to believe they are. This means Procedure 4 and a t test are order. The df = 21 + 21 - 2 = 40. *Step 4:* The critical t values are $+2.704$. *Step 5:* Reject H_0 in favour of H_1 if $t < -2.704$ or $> +2.704$. Otherwise, fail to reject H_0. *Step 6:*

$$t = \frac{\bar{x}_1 - \bar{x}_2}{\sqrt{\dfrac{s_1^2(n_1 - 1) + s_2^2(n_2 - 1)}{n_1 + n_2 - 2}}\sqrt{\dfrac{1}{n_1} + \dfrac{1}{n_2}}}$$

$$= \frac{7.8 - 6.6}{\sqrt{\dfrac{1.4^2(20) + 1.6^2(20)}{21 + 21 - 2}}\sqrt{\dfrac{1}{21} + \dfrac{1}{21}}} = \frac{1.2}{.4639} = 2.587$$

Step 7: Since $t = 2.587$ does not fall in the rejection region, we fail to reject H_0. There is no significant difference between the mean right atrial pressures.

39) *Step 1:* H_0: $\mu_1 = \mu_2$ and H_1: $\mu_1 \neq \mu_2$. *Step 2:* $\alpha = .01$. *Step 3:* Since the samples are independent and both samples are large, we use Procedure 2 with a z distribution. *Step 4:* The critical z values are ± 2.575. *Step 5:* Reject H_0 in favour of H_1 if $z < -2.575$ or $> +2.575$. Otherwise, fail to reject H_0. *Step 6:*

$$z = \frac{\bar{x}_1 - \bar{x}_2}{\sqrt{\dfrac{s_1^2}{n_1} + \dfrac{s_2^2}{n_2}}} = \frac{255.7 - 195}{\sqrt{\dfrac{30.7^2}{157} + \dfrac{41.8^2}{356}}} = 18.376$$

Step 7: Since $z = 18.376$ falls in the rejection region, we reject H_0 that the delinquency scores are equal.

41) Most of the calculations were done for the previous exercise. The 99 percent confidence interval for the difference of two means with small, independent samples, not assuming equal variances: $(4.17 - 4.00) \pm 4.032(0.1341) = 0.17 \pm 0.54$ or -0.37 to 0.71.

43a) For all seven tests: *Step 1:* H_0: $\sigma_1^2 = \sigma_2^2$ and H_1: $\sigma_1^2 \neq \sigma_2^2$. *Step 2:* $\alpha = .05$. *Step 3:* Use the F distribution with numerator df $= 24$ (closest conservative value to 29) and denominator df $= 29$. *Step 4:* For a two-tailed test, we will use the F value with .025 in the tail above, or 2.15. *Step 5:* Reject H_0 in favour of H_1 if $F > 2.15$. *Steps 6 and 7:*

Variable	F	Decision
1. Quality	1.381	Fail to reject H_0
2. Reliability	1.987	Fail to reject H_0
3. Reputation	1.943	Fail to reject H_0
4. Value	1.278	Fail to reject H_0
5. Worthwhile buy	1.357	Fail to reject H_0
6. Reasonable price	1.057	Fail to reject H_0
7. Intend to buy	1.563	Fail to reject H_0

The variances appear equal in all cases.

43b) For all seven tests: *Step 1:* H_0: $\mu_1 = \mu_2$ and H_1: $\mu_1 \neq \mu_2$. *Step 2:* $\alpha = 0.05$. *Step 3:* Based on the results of Exercise 43(a), we use procedure 4 with the t distribution with 58 df. *Step 4:* The critical t value is the conservative. 2.021 (40 df). *Step 5:* Reject H_0 in favour of H_1 if $t < -2.021$ or $t > 2.021$. Otherwise, fail to reject H_0. *Step 6:* We calculate the test statistic and make the decision in for variable in the following table. Here the test statistic is $t = \dfrac{\bar{x}_1 - \bar{x}_2}{s_p\sqrt{\dfrac{1}{n_1} + \dfrac{1}{n_2}}}$

Variable	Calculate z	Step 7: Make the decision.
Quality	$t = \dfrac{4.10 - 3.73}{(0.869)\sqrt{\dfrac{1}{30} + \dfrac{1}{30}}}$ $= 1.649$	Fail to reject H_0.
Reliability	$t = \dfrac{4.27 - 3.73}{(1.005)\sqrt{\dfrac{1}{30} + \dfrac{1}{30}}}$ $= 2.081$	Reject H_0.
Reputation	$t = \dfrac{4.67 - 3.73}{(0.794)\sqrt{\dfrac{1}{30} + \dfrac{1}{30}}}$ $= 4.878$	Reject H_0.
Value	$t = \dfrac{3.80 - 3.87}{(0.979)\sqrt{\dfrac{1}{30} + \dfrac{1}{30}}}$ $= -0.277$	Fail to reject H_0.
Worthwhile Buy	$t = \dfrac{4.03 - 3.73}{(1.114)\sqrt{\dfrac{1}{30} + \dfrac{1}{30}}}$ $= 1.043$	Fail to reject H_0.
Reasonable Buy	$t = \dfrac{3.33 - 3.90}{(1.074)\sqrt{\dfrac{1}{30} + \dfrac{1}{30}}}$ $= -2.056$	Reject H_0.
Intend to Buy	$t = \dfrac{3.97 - 3.53}{(1.125)\sqrt{\dfrac{1}{30} + \dfrac{1}{30}}}$ $= 1.514$	Fail to reject H_0.

43c) The 95 percent confidence intervals for the difference of the means (small, independent samples, variances equal) are

Variable	s_p	Interval
1. Quality	0.87281	-0.085 to 0.825
2. Reliability	1.01435	0.011 to 1.069
3. Reputation	0.80062	0.582 to 1.418
4. Value	0.98184	-0.582 to 0.442
5. Worthwhile buy	1.11824	-0.284 to 0.884
6. Reasonable price	1.07510	-1.131 to -0.009
7. Intend to buy	1.33192	-0.151 to 1.031

43d) For all seven tests: *Step 1:* $\sigma_1^2 = \sigma_2^2$ and H_1: $\sigma_1^2 \neq \sigma_2^2$. *Step 2:* $\alpha = 0.05$. *Step 3:* We use an F distribution. Since this is a two-tailed test, we use the table with 0.025 in the right tail. The df for the numerator and the denominator is $27 - 1 = 26$. We will use the value from the table with df of the denominator is 24. *Step 4:* The critical F value is 2.22. *Step 5:* Reject H_0 in favour of H_1 if $F > 2.2$. Otherwise, fail to reject H_0. *Step 6:* Then $F = s_1^2/s_2^2$, with $s_1 \geq s_2$. We calculate the test statistic and make the decision in for variable in the following table:

Variable	Calculate F	Step 7: Make the decision.
Quality	$F = \dfrac{0.97^2}{0.62^2} = 2.297$	Reject H_0, $\sigma_1^2 \neq \sigma_2^2$.
Reliability	$F = \dfrac{0.74^2}{0.58^2} = 1.628$	Fail to reject H_0, $\sigma_1^2 = \sigma_2^2$.
Reputation	$F = \dfrac{0.80^2}{0.22^2} = 3.628$	Reject H_0, $\sigma_1^2 \neq \sigma_2^2$.
Value	$F = \dfrac{1.02^2}{0.64^2} = 2.540$	Reject H_0, $\sigma_1^2 \neq \sigma_2^2$.
Worthwhile Buy	$F = \dfrac{0.78^2}{0.72^2} = 1.174$	Fail to reject H_0, $\sigma_1^2 = \sigma_2^2$.
Reasonable Buy	$F = \dfrac{0.94^2}{0.75^2} = 1.571$	Fail to reject H_0, $\sigma_1^2 = \sigma_2^2$.
Intend to Buy	$F = \dfrac{1.03^2}{0.83^2} = 1.540$	Fail to reject H_0, $\sigma_1^2 = \sigma_2^2$.

We now test the hypothesis that the population means are equal. For all seven tests:

Step 1: H_0: $\mu_1 = \mu_2$ and H_1: $\mu_1 \neq \mu_2$. *Step 2:* $\alpha = 0.05$. *Step 3:* If we rejected H_0 in the previous test of variance, then $\sigma_1^2 \neq \sigma_2^2$, so we use procedure 3 and a t distribution with $27 - 1 = 26$ df. If we failed to reject H_0 in the previous test of variance, then $\sigma_1^2 = \sigma_2^2$, so we use procedure 4 and a t distribution with $27 + 27 - 2 = 52$ df (we use the conservative value for 40 df). *Step 4:* For procedure 3, the critical t value is 2.056. For procedure 4, the critical t value is 2.021. *Step 5:* Reject H_0 in favour of H_1 if $t < -$critical t value or $t >$ critical t value. Otherwise, fail to reject H_0. *Step 6:* For procedure 3, the test statistic is $t = \dfrac{\bar{x}_1 - \bar{x}_2}{\sqrt{\dfrac{s_1^2}{n_1} + \dfrac{s_2^2}{n_2}}}$. For procedure 4, the test statistic is

$$t = \dfrac{\bar{x}_1 - \bar{x}_2}{\sqrt{\dfrac{s_1^2(n_1 - 1) + s_2^2(n_2 - 1)}{n_1 + n_2 - 2}}\sqrt{\dfrac{1}{n_1} + \dfrac{1}{n_2}}}$$

Variable	Procedure	Critical t value	Test statistics, t	Step 7: Make the decision
Quality	3	2.056	1.654	Fail to reject H_0.
Reliability	4	2.021	1.050	Fail to reject H_0.
Reputation	3	2.056	1.955	Fail to reject H_0.
Value	3	2.056	−1.942	Fail to reject H_0.
Worthwhile Buy	4	2.021	−0.734	Fail to reject H_0.
Reasonable Buy	4	2.021	−8.339	Reject H_0.
Intend to Buy	4	2.021	−3.064	Reject H_0

For each of the seven variables, we construct a 95 percent confidence interval for the difference in the population means. If we rejected H_0 in the first hypotheses tests on variance, then $\sigma_1^2 \neq \sigma_2^2$, so we use procedure 3 to produce the 95 percent confidence interval, $\bar{x}_1 - \bar{x}_2 \pm t_{\alpha/2}\sqrt{\dfrac{s_1^2}{n_1} + \dfrac{s_2^2}{n_2}}$. We use a t distribution with $27 - 1 = 26$, $t_{\alpha/2} = t_{0.025} = 2.056$. If we failed to reject H_0, then $\sigma_1^2 = \sigma_2^2$, so we use procedure 4 to produce the 95% confidence interval,

$$\bar{x}_1 - \bar{x}_2 \neq t_{\alpha/2}\sqrt{\dfrac{s_1^2(n_1 - 1) + s_2^2(n_2 - 1)}{n_1 + n_2 - 2}}\sqrt{\dfrac{1}{n_1} + \dfrac{1}{n_2}}.$$

We use a t distribution with $27 + 27 - 2 = 52$ (we use the conservative value for 40 df), $t_{\alpha/2} = t_{0.025} = 2.021$.

Variable	Procedure	95 percent confidence interval
Quality	3	(4.59 − 4.22) ± (2.056)(0.224) = 0.37 ± 0.461 or −0.091 to 0.831.
Reliability	4	(4.56 − 4.37) ± (2.021)(0.181) = 0.19 ± 0.366 or −0.176 to 0.556.
Reputation	3	(4.78 − 4.44) ± (2.056)(0.174) = 0.34 ± 0.358 or −0.018 to 0.698.
Value	3	(3.96 − 4.41) ± (2.056)(0.232) = −0.45 ± 0.477 or −0.927 to 0.027.

(continued)

Variable	Procedure	95 percent confidence interval
Worthwhile Buy	4	(4.00 – 4.15) ± (2.021)(0.204) = –0.15 ± 0.412 or –0.562 to 0.262.
Reasonable Buy	4	(2.51 – 4.44) ± (2.021)(0.231) = –1.93 ± 0.467 or –2.397 to –1.463.
Intend to Buy	4	(3.29 – 4.07) ± (2.021)(0.255) = –0.78 ± 0.515 or –1.295 to –0.265.

45a) *Step 1:* H_0: $\sigma_1^2 = \sigma_2^2$ and H_1: $\sigma_1^2 \neq \sigma_2^2$. *Step 2:* $\alpha - .05$. *Step 3:* Use the F distribution with numerator df 7 and denominator df 7. *Step 4:* For a two-tailed test, we will use the F value with .025 in the tail above, or 4.99. *Step 5:* Reject H_0 in favour of H_1 if $F > 4.99$. *Step 6:* Choosing the largest value for the numerator, $F = .132598/.129478 = 1.024$. *Step 7:* Since F is not in the rejection region, we fail to reject H_0. The variances appear equal.

45b) *Step 1:* H_0: $\mu_1 = \mu_2$ and H_1: $\mu_1 \neq \mu_2$. *Step 2:* $\alpha = 0.05$. *Step 3:* Since the samples are independent and both samples are small, we checked in Exercise 45(a) and saw that the populations have equal variances. We use a t distribution with 15 df and use procedure 4. *Step 4:* The critical t values with 15 df are ±2.131. *Step 5:* Reject H_0 in favour of H_1 if $t < -2.131$ or $t > +2.131$. Otherwise, fail to reject H_0. *Step 6:* Then

$$t = \frac{\bar{x}_1 - \bar{x}_2}{\sqrt{\dfrac{s_1^2(n_1 - 1) + s_2^2(n_2 - 1)}{n_1 + n_2 - 2}}\sqrt{\dfrac{1}{n_1} + \dfrac{1}{n_2}}}$$

$$= \frac{15.386 - 15.666}{\sqrt{\dfrac{(0.364)^2(7) + (0.360)^2(8)}{15}}\sqrt{\dfrac{1}{8} + \dfrac{1}{9}}}$$

$$= \frac{-0.28}{0.176} = -1.591.$$

Step 7: Since $t = -1.591$, we fail to reject H_0; there is not enough significant difference between the race times for 3 miles.

45c) With $s_p = 0.362$, the 95 percent confidence interval for $\mu_1 - \mu_2$ is $.28 \pm 2.131(0.362)\sqrt{[1/8 + 1/9]} = .28 \pm .38$ or –0.10 to 0.66.

45d) *Step 1:* H_0: $\sigma_1^2 = \sigma_2^2$ and H_1: $\sigma_1^2 \neq \sigma_2^2$. *Step 2:* $\alpha = 0.05$. *Step 3:* We use and F distribution. Since this is a two-tailed test, we use the table with 0.025 in the right tail. The df for the numerator is 7, and the df for the denominator is 8. *Step 4:*

The critical F value is 4.53. *Step 5:* Reject H_0 in favour of H_1 if $F > 4.53$. Otherwise, fail to reject H_0. *Step 6:* Then $F = (0.746)^2/(0.658)^2 = 1.285$. *Step 7:* Since F is not in the rejection region, we fail to reject H_0. The variances appear equal. We now test the hypothesis that the population means for the five-mile times of Nebraska and Colorado are equal.

Step 1: H_0: $\mu_1 = \mu_2$ and H_1: $\mu_1 \neq \mu_2$. *Step 2:* $\alpha = 0.05$. *Step 3:* Since the samples are independent and both samples are small, we checked in Exercise 45(a) and saw that the populations have equal variances. We use a t distribution with 13 df and use procedure 4. *Step 4:* The critical t values with 15 df is ±2.160. *Step 5:* Reject H_0 in favour of H_1 if $t < -2.160$ or $t > +2.160$. Otherwise, fail to reject H_0.

Step 6: Then $t =$

$$\frac{\bar{x}_1 - \bar{x}_2}{\sqrt{\dfrac{s_1^2(n_1 - 1) + s_2^2(n_2 - 1)}{n_1 + n_2 - 2}}\sqrt{\dfrac{1}{n_1} + \dfrac{1}{n_2}}}$$

$$= \frac{26.034 - 26.230}{\sqrt{\dfrac{(0.746)^2(7) + (0.658)^2(8)}{15}}\sqrt{\dfrac{1}{8} + \dfrac{1}{9}}}$$

$$= \frac{-0.196}{0.340} = -0.576.$$

Step 7: Since $t = -0.576$, we fail to reject H_0.

$$s_p = \sqrt{\frac{s_1^2(n_1 - 1) + s_2^2(n_2 - 1)}{n_1 + n_2 - 2}} = \sqrt{\frac{(0.746)^2(7) + (0.658)^2(8)}{15}}$$

$= 0.700$. The 95% confidence interval for the difference of means for the five-mile times of Nebraska and Colorado, small independent samples with assumed equal variance (see above):

$$\bar{x}_1 - \bar{x}_2 \neq t_{\alpha/2}s_p\sqrt{\frac{1}{n_1} + \frac{1}{n_2}}$$

$$= (26.034 - 26.230) \pm 2.131(0.700)\sqrt{\frac{1}{8} + \frac{1}{9}}$$

$$= -0.196 \pm 0.725 \text{ or } -0.921 \text{ to } 0.529.$$

47) *Step 1:* H_0: $\mu_1 = \mu_2$ and H_1: $\mu_1 \neq \mu_2$. *Step 2:* $\alpha = 0.01$. *Step 3:* We showed in Exercise 10, Self-Testing Review 9-1, that the variances are equal, so we use procedure 4 and a t distribution with $20 + 20 - 2 = 38$ df. *Step 4:* The critical t is 2.704. *Step 5:* Reject H_0 in favour of H_1 if $t < -2.704$ or $t > 2.704$. Otherwise, fail to reject H_0. *Step 6:* The test statistic is

$$t = \frac{4,077 - 4,275}{\sqrt{\dfrac{527^2(19) + 578^2(19)}{38}}\sqrt{\dfrac{1}{20} + \dfrac{1}{20}}} = -1.132.$$

Step 7: Since $t = -1.132$, we fail to reject H_0.

49) In Exercise 11, Self-Testing Review 9-1, we reject H_0, the variance are not equal, so a 95% confidence interval is given by

$$\bar{x}_1 - \bar{x}_2 \pm t_{\alpha/2}\sqrt{\frac{s_1^2}{n_1} + \frac{s_2^2}{n_2}}.$$ We use a t distribution with 15 df. So $t_{\alpha/2} = t_{0.025} = 2.131$.

$$(135.19 - 23.75) \pm (2.131)\sqrt{\frac{14.05^2}{16} + \frac{2.864^2}{16}} = 111.44 \pm 7.62$$

or 103.82 to 119.06 minutes.

51) A 90% confidence interval is given by $\bar{d} \pm t^2_{\alpha/2}\frac{s_d}{\sqrt{n}}$.
We use a t distribution with 15 df. So $t_{\alpha/2} = t_{0.05} = 1.753$. So
$141 \pm (1.753)\frac{197.4}{\sqrt{16}} = 141 \pm 86.51$ or \$54.49 to \$227.51.

53) Step 1: H_0: $\mu_1 = \mu_2$ and H_1: $\mu_1 \neq \mu_2$. Step 2: $\alpha = 0.05$. Step 3: We showed in Exercise 15, Self-Testing Review 9-1, that the variance are equal, so we use procedure 4 and a t distribution with $11 + 32 - 2 = 41$ df. We will use the value for 40 df. Step 4: The critical t is 2.021. Step 5: Reject H_0 in favour of H_1 if $t < -2.021$ or $t > 2.021$. Otherwise, fail to reject H_0. Step 6: The test statistic is

$$t = \frac{1077.3 - 899.8}{\sqrt{\frac{103.2^2(10) + 120.5^2(31)}{41}}\sqrt{\frac{1}{11} + \frac{1}{32}}} = 4.359.$$

Step 7: Since $t = 4.359$, we reject H_0. The times for female and males in a two-mile run do not have equal population means.

55b) For gas prices, H_0: $\mu_W = \mu_E$ and H_1: $\mu_W \neq \mu_E$. $\alpha = .05$. We showed in part a) that the variances are unequal, so we use procedure 3 and a t distribution with 10 df. The critical t values are ± 2.228. We will reject H_0 in favour of H_1 if $t > 2.228$ or if $t < -2.228$.

$$t = \frac{\bar{x}_W - \bar{x}_E}{\sqrt{\frac{s_W^2}{n_w} + \frac{s_E^2}{n_E}}} = \frac{73.3091 - 70.8923}{\sqrt{\frac{46.2269}{11} + \frac{12.2841}{13}}} = 1.07$$

Since 1.07 is not in the rejection region, we fail to reject H_0.

55c) The 95% confidence interval for the difference in mean gas prices is $(73.3091 - 70.8923) \pm 2.228\sqrt{\frac{46.2269}{11} + \frac{12.2841}{13}}$, or -2.64 to 7.47.

55d) To test for equality of population variances of diesel prices, we test H_0: $\sigma_W^2 = \sigma_E^2$ vs. H_1: $\sigma_W^2 \neq \sigma_E^2$ using $\alpha - .10$. Since we have independent samples and $F = 42.3265/18.9786 = 2.23$ is not greater than the critical value of 3.37 there is insufficient evidence to conclude the variances differ.

55e) For diesel prices, H_0: $\mu_W = \mu_E$ and H_1: $\mu_W \neq \mu_E$. $\alpha = .10$. We showed in part d) that the variances are equal, so we use procedure 4 and a t distribution with 22 df. The critical t values are ± 1.717. We will reject H_0 in favour of H_1 if $t > 1.717$ or if $t < -1.717$.

$$t = \frac{\bar{x}_W - \bar{x}_E}{s_p\sqrt{\frac{1}{n_w} + \frac{1}{n_E}}} = \frac{61.7636 - 64.4321}{5.4398\sqrt{\frac{1}{11} + \frac{1}{13}}} = -1.20$$

Since -1.20 is not in the rejection region, we fail to reject H_0.

55f) The 90% confidence interval for the difference in mean diesel prices is

$$(61.7636 - 64.4321) \pm 1.717\left[5.3498\sqrt{\frac{1}{11} + \frac{1}{13}}\right], \text{ or } -6.49 \text{ to } 1.16$$

57a) No, procedure 1 has no assumption whether the variances are equal or not.

57b) Step 1: H_0: $\mu_d = 0$, H_1: $\mu_d < 0$. Step 2: $\alpha = .01$. Step 3: Use the t distribution with df $= 5$. Step 4: The value of t with .01 in the tail below it is -3.365. Step 5: Reject H_0 in favour of H_1 if $t < -3.365$. Step 6: $t = -0.305/[0.288/\sqrt{6}] = -2.60$. Step 7: Since t is not in the rejection region, we fail to reject H_0. There is no significant evidence that the conventional oven yields a higher mean melting point.

57c) A 99% confidence interval is given by $\bar{d} \pm t^2_{\alpha/2}\frac{s_d}{\sqrt{n}}$.
We use a t distribution with 5 df. So $t_{\alpha/2} = t_{0.005} = 4.032$. So
$-0.305 \pm (4.032)\frac{0.288}{\sqrt{6}} = -0.305 \pm 0.474$ or -0.779 to 0.169.
Assumption: dependent samples from normal populations.

Self-Testing Review 9.3

59) Step 1: State the null and alternative hypotheses. H_0: $p_1 = p_2$ and H_1: $p_1 \neq p_2$. Step 2: Select the level of significance $\alpha = .01$. Step 3: Determine the test distribution to use. We use the z distribution. Step 4: Define the critical or rejection region. The critical z values are ± 2.575. Step 5: State the decision rule. Reject H_0 in favour of H_1 if $z < -2.575$ or $> +2.575$. Otherwise, fail to reject H_0. Step 6: Compute the test statistic.

$$\hat{p} = \frac{x_1 + x_2}{n_1 + n_2} = \frac{292 + 172}{512 + 281} = \frac{464}{793} = 0.5851, \text{ and}$$

$$z = \frac{\hat{p}_1 - \hat{p}_2}{\sqrt{\hat{p}(1 - \hat{p})\left(\frac{1}{n_1} + \frac{1}{n_2}\right)}} = \frac{0.5703 - 0.6121}{\sqrt{0.5851(0.4149)\left(\frac{1}{512} + \frac{1}{281}\right)}}$$

$$= \frac{-0.0418}{0.0366} = -1.142.$$

Step 7: Make the statistical decision. Since $z = -1.142$ does not fall in the rejection region, we fail to reject H_0. There is no significant evidence of a difference in the prevalence of headaches between the two locations.

61) Step 1: H_0: $p_1 = p_2$ and H_1: $p_1 \neq p_2$. Step 2: $\alpha = .01$. Step 3: We use the z distribution. Step 4: The critical z values are ± 2.575. Step 5: Reject H_0 in favour of H_1 if $z < -2.575$ or $> +2.575$. Otherwise, fail to reject H_0. Step 6:

$$\hat{p} = \frac{x_1 + x_2}{n_1 + n_2} = 0.4722, z = \frac{\hat{p}_1 - \hat{p}_2}{\sqrt{\hat{p}(1 - \hat{p})\left(\frac{1}{n_1} + \frac{1}{n_2}\right)}} = \frac{-0.0556}{0.1177}$$

$$= -0.472$$

Step 7: Since $z = -0.472$ does not fall in the rejection region, we fail to reject H_0 of equal population percentages.

63) *Step 1:* H_0: $p_1 = p_2$ and H_1: $p_1 < p_2$. *Step 2:* $\alpha = .01$. *Step 3:* We use the z distribution. *Step 4:* The critical z values is -2.33. *Step 5:* Reject H_0 in favour of H_1, if $z < -2.33$. Otherwise, fail to reject H_0. *Step 6:*

$$\hat{p} = \frac{x_1 + x_2}{n_1 + n_2} = 0.0310, \; z = \frac{\hat{p}_1 - \hat{p}_2}{\sqrt{\hat{p}(1-\hat{p})\left(\dfrac{1}{n_1} + \dfrac{1}{n_2}\right)}} = \frac{-0.0272}{0.0084}$$

$$= -3.24$$

Step 7: Since $z = -3.24$ falls in the rejection region, we reject H_0 that the population percentages are equal.

65) $\hat{\sigma}_{\hat{p}_1 - \hat{p}_2} = \sqrt{\dfrac{(.4706)(1 - .4706)}{17} + \dfrac{(.4897)(1 - .4897)}{47}}$

$$= 0.1413$$

The 99% confidence interval for the difference between the two proportions is $-.8191 \pm 2.575(.1413)$ or -0.3829 to 0.3447.

67) $\hat{\sigma}_{\hat{p}_1 - \hat{p}_2} = \sqrt{\dfrac{(.3750)(1 - .3750)}{96} + \dfrac{(.5652)(1 - .5652)}{69}}$

$$= 0.0775$$

The 95 percent confidence interval for the difference between the two proportions is $-.1902 \pm 1.96(.0775)$ or -0.3421 to -0.0383.

69) *Step 1:* H_0: $p_1 = p_2$ and H_1: $p_1 < p_2$. *Step 2:* $\alpha = .05$. *Step 3:* We use the z distribution. *Step 4:* The critical z value is -1.645. *Step 5:* Reject H_0 in favour of H_1 if $z < -1.645$. Otherwise, fail to reject H_0. *Step 6:*

$$\hat{p} = \frac{x_1 + x_2}{n_1 + n_2} = \frac{7 + 29}{200 + 400} = \frac{36}{600} = 0.06, \text{ and}$$

$$z = \frac{\hat{p}_1 - \hat{p}_2}{\sqrt{\hat{p}(1-\hat{p})\left(\dfrac{1}{n_1} + \dfrac{1}{n_2}\right)}} = \frac{-0.0375}{0.0206} = -1.82$$

Step 7: Since $z = -1.82$ falls in the rejection region, we reject H_0 and accept H_1. At the .05 level of significance, yes, we can conclude that the true proportion of all people with a flu shot who catch the flu is less than the true proportion of all people without a flu shot who catch the flu.

71) *Step 1:* H_0 $p_1 = p_2$ and H_1; $p_1 \neq p_2$. *Step 2:* $\alpha = .01$. *Step 3:* We use the z distribution. *Step 4:* The critical z values are ± 2.575. *Step 5:* Reject H_0 in favour of H_1 if $z < -2.575$ or $> +2.575$. Otherwise, fail to reject H_0. *Step 6:*

$$\hat{p} = \frac{x_1 + x_2}{n_1 + n_2} = \frac{67 + 109}{2394 + 2310} = \frac{176}{4704} = 0.0374, \text{ and}$$

$$z = \frac{\hat{p}_1 - \hat{p}_2}{\sqrt{\hat{p}(1-\hat{p})\left(\dfrac{1}{n_1} + \dfrac{1}{n_2}\right)}} = \frac{-0.0192}{0.005535} = -3.468$$

Step 7: Since z $= -3.468$ falls in the rejection region, we reject H_0.

73) $\hat{\sigma}_{\hat{p}_1 - \hat{p}_2} = \sqrt{\dfrac{(.8366)(1 - .8366)}{202} + \dfrac{(.6406)(1 - .6406)}{192}}$

$$= 0.0433$$

The 95 percent confidence interval for the difference between the two proportions is $0.1960 \pm 1.96\,(0.0433)$ or 0.1111 to 0.2809

75a) Let p_1, p_2 denote the true proportion of all male and female student gamers, respectively, who play mostly Internet games. H_0: $p_1 - p_2 = 0$ and H_1: $p_1 - p_2 < 0$. $\alpha = .05$. We use the z distribution. The critical number is -1.645. We will reject H_0 if $z < -1.645$.

$$z = \frac{0.22 - 0.25}{\sqrt{0.2346(0.7654)\left(\dfrac{1}{550} + \dfrac{1}{520}\right)}} = -1.16$$

We fail to reject H_0 since -1.16 is not in the rejection region. At the .05 level of significance we cannot conclude the population percentage is higher for females.

75b) Let p_1, p_2 denote the true proportion of all male and female student gamers, respectively, who play mostly computer games. The 95% confidence interval for $p_2 - p_1$ is

$$(0.45 - 0.32) \pm 1.96\sqrt{\frac{(0.45)(0.55)}{520} + \frac{(0.32)(0.68)}{550}}, \text{ or } 0.072 \text{ to}$$

0.188, so the confidence interval for the difference in the percentages is from 7.2% to 18.8%.

75c) Let p_1, p_2 denote the true proportion of all male and female student gamers, respectively, who play mostly video games. H_0: $p_1 - p_2 = 0$ and H_1: $p_1 - p_2 > 0$. $\alpha = .05$. We use the z distribution. The critical number is 1.645. We will reject H_0 if $z > 1.645$.

$$z = \frac{0.46 - 0.30}{\sqrt{0.3822(0.6178)\left(\dfrac{1}{550} + \dfrac{1}{520}\right)}} = 5.39$$

We reject H_0 since 5.39 is in the rejection region. At the .05 level of significance we can conclude the population percentage is higher for males.

75d) Let p_1, p_2 denote the true proportion of all male and female student gamers, respectively, who play mostly video games. The 95% confidence interval for $p_1 - p_2$ is

$$(0.46 - 0.30) \pm 1.96\sqrt{\frac{(0.46)(0.54)}{550} + \frac{(0.30)(0.70)}{520}}, \text{ or } 0.103 \text{ to}$$

0.217, so the confidence interval for the difference in the percentages is from 10.3% to 21.7%.

77a) H_0: $p_1 - p_2 = 0$ and H_1: $p_1 - p_2 \neq 0$. $\alpha = .05$. We use the z distribution. The critical numbers are ± 1.96. We will reject H_0 if $z > 1.96$ or if $z < -1.96$.

$$z = \frac{0.5644 - 0.5804}{\sqrt{0.6338(0.3662)\left(\dfrac{1}{101} + \dfrac{1}{143}\right)}} = -0.26$$

We fail to reject H_0 since -0.26 is not in the rejection region.

77b) *Step 1:* H_0: $p_1 = p_2$, H_1: $p_1 < p_2$. *Step 2:* $\alpha = .01$. *Step 3:* Use the z distribution. *Step 4:* The z value with .01 in the left tail is -2.33. *Step 5:* Reject H_0 in favour of H_1 if $z < -2.33$. Otherwise, fail to reject H_0. *Step 6:*

$$\hat{p} = \frac{x_1 + x_2}{n_1 + n_2} = \frac{8 + 27}{260 + 233} = \frac{35}{493} = 0.0701, \text{ and}$$

$$z = \frac{\hat{p}_1 - \hat{p}_2}{\sqrt{\hat{p}(1-\hat{p})\left(\dfrac{1}{n_1} + \dfrac{1}{n_2}\right)}} = \frac{-0.08511}{0.02317} = -3.673$$

Step 7: Since $z = -3.673$ falls in the rejection region, we reject H_0. Treatment with dexamethasone appears to decrease the proportion of incidents of severe hearing loss.

77c) H_0: $p_1 - p_2 = 0$ and H_1: $p_1 - p_2 < 0$. $\alpha = .10$. We use the z distribution. The critical number is -1.28. We will reject H_0 if $z < -1.28$.

$$z = \frac{0.0641 - 0.1035}{\sqrt{0.0832(0.9168)\left(\dfrac{1}{390} + \dfrac{1}{367}\right)}} = -1.96$$

We reject H_0 and accept H_1 since -1.96 is in the rejection region.

Exercises

79) H_0: $\sigma_1^2 = \sigma_2^2$, and H_1: $\sigma_1^2 \neq \sigma_2^2$. $\alpha = .05$. We use an F distribution. The critical F value is 2.79. Reject H_0 in favour of H_1 if $F > 2.79$. Otherwise, fail to reject H_0. $F = 5.67^2/4.74^2 = 1.431$. Since $F = 1.431$ does not fall in the rejection region, we fail to reject H_0 that the population variances are equal.

81) H_0: $\mu_1 = \mu_2$, and H_1: $\mu_1 < \mu_2$. $\alpha = .05$. We use Procedure 2 with a z distribution. The critical z value is -2.33. Reject H_0 in favour of H_1 if $z < -2.33$. Otherwise, fail to reject H_0. $z = -.4/\sqrt{.1760} = -.954$. Since $z = -.954$ does not fall in the rejection region, we fail to reject H_0 that the mean number of drugs needed in each population appears to be the same.

83) H_0: $p_1 - p_2 = 0$ and H_1: $p_1 - p_2 < 0$. $\alpha = .05$. We use the z distribution. The critical number is -1.645. We will reject H_0 if $z < -1.645$.

$$z = \frac{0.0824 - 0.1037}{\sqrt{0.0904(0.9096)\left(\dfrac{1}{5000} + \dfrac{1}{3000}\right)}} = -3.21$$

We reject H_0 and accept H_1 since -3.21 is in the rejection region.

85) -14.14 to 4.64

87) H_0: $p_1 - p_2 = 0$ and H_1: $p_1 - p_2 \neq 0$. $\alpha = .05$. We use the z distribution. The critical numbers are ± 1.96. We will reject H_0 if $z > 1.96$ or if $z < -1.96$.

$$z = \frac{0.4318 - 0.7258}{\sqrt{0.5533(0.4467)\left(\dfrac{1}{5834} + \dfrac{1}{4110}\right)}} = -29.04$$

We reject H_0 since -29.04 is in the rejection region.

89) H_0: $\mu_1 = \mu_2$, and H_1: $\mu_1 \neq \mu_2$. $\alpha = .01$. Since the results of problem 10 indicate that the population variances are likely to be equal, we use Procedure 4 with a t distribution that has 30 df. The critical t values are ± 2.750. Reject H_0 in favour of H_1 if $t < -2.750$ or if $t > +2.750$. Otherwise, fail to reject H_0. $t = -.22/\sqrt{.8181}\sqrt{.1250} = -.688$. Since $t = -.688$ does not fall in the rejection region, we fail to reject H_0 that the mean BMI values for the two groups are equal.

91) Using the paired procedure, the 95 percent confidence intervals for the mean difference: $4.0 \pm 3.182(4/\sqrt{4}) = -2.36$ to 10.36.

93) H_0: $\mu_1 = \mu_2$, and H_1: $\mu_1 \neq \mu_2$. $\alpha = .01$. The sample sizes are over 30, so we use a z distribution test. The critical z values are ± 2.575. Reject H_0 in favour of H_1 if $z < -2.575$ or if $z > +2.575$. Otherwise, fail to reject H_0. $z = .83/\sqrt{.9925} = .836$. Since $z = .836$ does not fall in the rejection region, we fail to reject H_0 that the mean age of the husband is equal for both groups.

95) The 99% confidence interval for the difference in the population proportions is $(0.7333 - 0.5926) \pm 2.576\sqrt{0.0109898}$, or 0.1407 ± 0.2700, or -0.1293 to 0.4107, so the 99% confidence interval for the difference in the percentages is from -12.93% to 41.07%.

97) A large-sample 99 percent confidence interval for $\mu_{pre} - \mu_{in}$ is $(4.02 - 2.93) \pm 2.575\sqrt{.83^2/84 + .97^2/32} = 1.09 \pm 2.575(.1939)$ or .59 to 1.59.

99) H_0: $\mu_1 = \mu_2$, and H_1: $\mu_1 < \mu_2$. $\alpha = .05$. We use Procedure 2 and a z test. The critical z value is -1.645. Reject H_0 in favour of H_1 if $z < -1.645$. Otherwise, fail to reject H_0. $z = -1.88/\sqrt{1.8092} = -1.398$. Since $z = -1.398$ does not fall in the rejection region, we fail to reject H_0 that there's no difference in final exam mean scores for the two groups.

101) H_0: $\sigma_1^2 = \sigma_2^2$, and H_1: $\sigma_1^2 \neq \sigma_2^2$. $\alpha = .05$. We use an F distribution. The critical F value is 4.03. Reject H_0 in favour of H_1 if $F > 4.03$. Otherwise, fail to reject H_0. $F = .0011^2/.00054^2 = 4.15$. Since $F = 4.15$ falls in the rejection region, we reject H_0 that the population variances are equal.

103) H_0: $p_1 - p_2 = 0$ and H_1: $p_1 - p_2 < 0$. $\alpha = .05$. We use the z distribution. The critical number is -1.645. We will reject H_0 if $z < -1.645$.

$$z = \frac{0.4792 - 0.6232}{\sqrt{0.5394(0.4606)\left(\dfrac{1}{96} + \dfrac{1}{69}\right)}} = -1.83$$

We reject H_0 and accept H_1 since -1.831 is in the rejection region.

105) H_0: $\mu_1 = \mu_2$, and H_1: $\mu_1 \neq \mu_2$. $\alpha = .05$. Since the samples are over 30, we use Procedure 2 and the z distribution. The critical z values are ± 2.575. Reject H_0 in favour of H_1 if $z < -2.575$ or if $z > +2.575$. Otherwise, fail to reject H_0. $z = -2.2/\sqrt{.421} = -3.391$. Since $z = -3.391$ falls in the rejection region, we reject H_0 and decide that there is a difference in heart rate for the two populations.

107) H_0: $\mu_d = 0$, and H_1: $\mu_d \neq 0$. $\alpha = .01$. We use Procedure 1, the t test for paired differences. The critical t values are ± 4.604. Reject H_0 in favour of H_1 if $t < -4.604$ or $> +4.604$. Otherwise, fail to reject H_0. $t = (-.986 - 0)/(.576/\sqrt{5}) = -3.827$. Since $t = -3.827$ is not in the rejection region, we fail to reject H_0 that there's no difference between men and women in their evaluation of the various activities in their lives.

109) H_0: $p_1 - p_2 = 0$ and H_1: $p_1 - p_2 > 0$. $\alpha = .05$. We use the z distribution. The critical number is 1.645. We will reject H_0 if $z > 1.645$.

$$z = \frac{0.6750 - 0.4852}{\sqrt{0.5462(0.4538)\left(\dfrac{1}{160} + \dfrac{1}{338}\right)}} = 3.97$$

We reject H_0 since 3.97 is in the rejection region.

111) H_0: $\sigma_1^2 = \sigma_2^2$, and H_1: $\sigma_1^2 \neq \sigma_2^2$. $\alpha = .05$. We use an F distribution. The critical F value is 2.46. Reject H_0 in favour of H_1 if $F > 2.46$. Otherwise, fail to reject H_0. $F = .792^2/.689^2 = 1.321$. Since $F = 1.321$ does not fall in the rejection region, we fail to reject H_0 that the population variances are equal.

113) H_0: $\mu_1 = \mu_2$, and H_1: $\mu_1 < \mu_2$. $\alpha = .01$. Since the samples are over 30 and are independent, we use Procedure 2 and a z distribution. The critical z value is -2.33. Reject H_0 in favour of H_1 if $z < -2.33$. Otherwise, fail to reject H_0. $z = -40/\sqrt{7.7994} = -14.323$. Since $z = -14.323$ falls in the rejection region, we reject H_0. There is evidence that NORVASC significantly improves exercise time.

115a) *Step 1:* H_0: $\sigma_3^2 = \sigma_4^2$, and H_1: $\sigma_3^2 \neq \sigma_4^2$. *Step 2:* $\alpha = .10$. *Step 3:* Use the F distribution with numerator df 6 and denominator df 6. *Step 4:* For a two-tailed test, we will use the F value with .05 in the tail above, or 4.28. *Step 5:* Reject H_0 in favour of H_1 if $F > 4.28$. *Step 6:* Choosing the largest value for the numerator, $F = .0214286/.002381 = 9.000$. *Step 7:* Since F is the rejection region, we decide in favour of H_1. There is evidence that the variances are not equal.

115b) In Exercise 115(a) we rejected the null hypotheses that $\sigma_1^2 = \sigma_2^2$ so we use procedure 3 with a t distribution. *Step 1:* H_0: $\mu_1 = \mu_2$ and H_1: $\mu_1 \neq \mu_2$. *Step 2:* $\alpha = 0.10$. *Step 3:* t distribution. *Step 4:* This is a two-tailed test with $\alpha = 0.10$. The degree of freedom is 6 since both groups have 7 members. The critical values are $t_{0.05} = \pm 1.943$. *Step 5:* Reject H_0 in favour of H_1 if $t < -1.943$ or if $t > 1.943$. Otherwise, fail to reject H_0. *Step 6:* Then

$$t = \frac{\bar{x}_1 - \bar{x}_2}{\sqrt{\dfrac{s_1^2}{n_1} + \dfrac{s_2^2}{n_2}}} = \frac{0.7143 - 0.7286}{\sqrt{\dfrac{(0.1464)^2}{7} + \dfrac{(0.0488)^2}{7}}}$$

$$= \frac{-0.0143}{\sqrt{0.003405}} = \frac{-0.0143}{0.05832} = -0.245.$$

Step 7: Since $t = -0.245$, does not fall within the rejection region, we fail to reject H_0.

115c) *Step 1:* H_0: $\sigma_4^2 = \sigma_3^2$, and H_1: $\sigma_4^2 > \sigma_3^2$, *Step 2:* $\alpha = .05$. *Step 3:* Use the F distribution with numerator df 6 and de-

nominator df 6. *Step. 4:* For a right-tailed test, we will use the F value with .025 in the tail above, or 5.82. *Step 5:* Reject the H_0 in favour of H_1 if $F > 5.82$. *Step 6:* $F = .0380952/.0033333 = 11.429$. *Step 7:* Since F is in the rejection region, we decide in favour of H_1. There is evidence that the variances are not equal.

115d) *Step 1:* H_0: $\sigma_1^2 = \sigma_2^2$, and H_1: $\sigma_1^2 \neq \sigma_2^2$. *Step 2:* $\alpha = 0.05$. *Step 3:* Because this is a test of variance we use an F distribution. *Step 4:* Since $\alpha = 0.05$ and this is a two-tailed test, we use the table for $\alpha = 0.025$. Since there are 7 members in each group we use 6 degrees of freedom for both the numerator and denominator. The critical F value is 5.82. *Step 5:* Reject H_0 in favour of H_1 if $F > 5.82$. Otherwise, fail to reject H_0. *Step 6:* Then

$$F = \frac{s_1^2}{s_2^2} = \frac{(0.1113)^2}{(0.0535)^2} = \frac{0.012388}{0.002862} = 4.33.$$

Step 7: Since $F = 4.33 < 5.82$, we fail to reject H_0 that the population variances are equal for cadmium.

115e) *Step 1:* H_0: $\mu_1 = \mu_2$, and H_1: $\mu_1 \neq \mu_2$. *Step 2:* $\alpha = .05$. *Step 3:* Use the t distribution with degrees of freedom $7 + 7 - 2 = 12$. *Step 4:* The critical values of t with .025 in each tail (two-tailed test) are ± 2.179. *Step 5:* Reject H_0 in favour of H_1 if $t < -2.179$ or $> +2.179$. *Step 6:* $t = (.729 - .7571)/\sqrt{[(.111)^2(7-1) + (.0535)^2(7-1)]/(7+7-2)}\sqrt{1/7 + 1/7} = -.60$. *Step = 7:* Since t is not in the rejection region, we fail to reject H_0. There is no significant evidence that the two means are unequal.

115f) *Step 1:* H_0: $\sigma_1^2 = \sigma_2^2$ and H_1: $\sigma_1^2 \neq \sigma_2^2$. *Step 2:* $\alpha = 0.02$. *Step 3:* Because this is a test of variance we use an F distribution. *Step 4:* Since $\alpha = 0.02$ and this is a two-tailed test, we use the table for $\alpha = 0.01$. Since there are 7 members in each group, we use 6 degrees of freedom for both the numerator and denominator. The critical F value is 8.47. *Step 5:* Reject H_0 in favour of H_1 if $F > 8.47$. Otherwise, fail to reject H_0. *Step 6:* Then

$$F = \frac{s_1^2}{s_2^2} = \frac{(1.676)^2}{(0.308)^2} = \frac{2.80898}{0.09486} = 29.6.$$

Step 7: Since $F = 29.6 > 8.47$, we reject H_0 that the population variances are not equal for lead.

115g) *Step 1:* H_0: $\mu_1 = \mu_2$, and H_1: $\mu_1 \neq \mu_2$. *Step 2:* $\alpha = .02$. *Step 3:* Use the t distribution with degrees of freedom 6. *Step 4:* The critical values of t with .01 in each tail (two-tailed test) are ± 3.143. *Step 5:* Reject H_0 in favour of H_1 if $t < -3.143$ or $> +3.143$. *Step 6:* $t = (7.143 - 3.814)/\sqrt{1.676^2/7 + .308^2/7} = 5.17$. *Step 7:* Since t is in the rejection region, we reject H_0. There is significant evidence that the two means are not equal.

115h) *Step 1:* H_0: $\sigma_1^2 = \sigma_2^2$ and H_1: $\sigma_1^2 > \sigma_2^2$. *Step 2:* Use $\alpha = 0.01$. *Step 3:* We use an F distribution. Since this a right-tailed test, we use the table with 0.01 in the right tail. *Step 4:* We use the table for $\alpha = 0.01$. Since there are 7 members in each group we use 6 degrees of freedom for both the numerator and denominator. The critical F value is 8.47. *Step 5:* Reject H_0 in favour of H_1 if $F > 8.47$. Otherwise, fail to reject H_0. *Step 6:* Then

$$F = \frac{(5.32)^2}{(1.915)^2} = 7.718.$$

Step 7: Since $F = 7.718$, we fail to reject H_0; there is not enough to show that the population variance of copper for lab 4 is greater than for lab 3.

117a) H_0: $p_1 - p_2 = 0$ and H_1: $p_1 - p_2 \neq 0$. $\alpha = .01$. We use the z distribution. The critical numbers are ± 2.576. We will reject H_0 if $z > 2.576$ or if $z < -2.576$.

$$z = \frac{0.2934 - 0.1538}{\sqrt{0.2290(0.7710)\left(\frac{1}{167} + \frac{1}{143}\right)}} = 2.92$$

We reject H_0 since 2.92 is in the rejection region.

117b) The 99% confidence interval for the difference in the population proportions is $(0.2934 - 0.1538) \pm 2.575\sqrt{0.0021515}$, or 0.1396 ± 0.1194, or 0.0202 to 0.2590, so the 99% confidence interval for the difference in the percentages is from 2.02% to 25.90%.

119a) For all five tests, H_0: $p_1 - p_2 = 0$ and H_1: $p_1 - p_2 \neq 0$. $\alpha = .05$. We use the z distribution. The critical numbers are ± 1.96. We will reject H_0 if $z > 1.96$ or if $z < -1.96$. For question 1, $z = -1.01$, so fail to reject H_0. For question 2, $z = 1.54$, so fail to reject H_0. For question 3, $z = 0$, so fail to reject H_0. For question 4, $z = -1.43$, so fail to reject H_0. For question 5, $z = -0.61$, so fail to reject H_0.

119b) For question 1, -19.40 to -9.40. For question 2, 3.58 to 31.58. For question 3, -18.82 to 18.82. For question 4, -32.92 to 4.92. For question 5, -25.24 to 13.24.

121a) H_0: $p_1 - p_2 = 0$ and H_1: $p_1 - p_2 \neq 0$. $\alpha = .10$. We use the z distribution. The critical numbers are ± 1.645. We will reject H_0 if $z > 1.645$ or if $z < -1.645$. $z = -1.62$. Fail to reject H_0.

121b) The 90% confidence interval for the difference in the population proportions is $(0.3846 - 4167) \pm 1.645 \sqrt{0.029358}$, or -0.321 ± 0.2819, or -0.314 to 0.2498, so the 90% confidence interval for the difference in the percentages is from -31.4% to 24.98%.

121c) H_0: $p_1 - p_2 = 0$ and H_1: $p_1 - p_2 \neq 0$. $\alpha = .05$. We use the z distribution. The critical numbers are ± 1.96. We will reject H_0 if $z > 1.96$ or if $z < -1.96$. $z = -0.22$. Fail to reject H_0.

121d) For Arch majors, $n(100 - p) = 100 < 500$, so the sample size is too small.

123a) *Step 1:* H_0: $\mu_d = 0$ and H_1: $\mu_d > 0$. *Step 2:* $\alpha = 0.05$. *Step 3:* We used a paired t test and a t distribution with 7 df. *Step 4:* The critical value of $t = 1.895$. *Step 5:* Reject H_0 in favour of H_1 if $t > 1.895$. Otherwise, fail to reject H_0. *Step 6:* Then

$$t = \frac{\bar{d} - \mu_d}{s_d/\sqrt{n}} = \frac{0.086}{0.499/\sqrt{8}} = 0.487.$$

Step 7: Since $t = 0.487$ does not fall in the rejection region, we fail to reject H_0.

123b) Using the paired procedure, the 95 percent confidence interval for the mean change: $0.086 \pm 2.365(.499/\sqrt{8}) = -0.331$ to 0.504.

123c)

Pretest	27.79	25.59	21.53	25.25
	17.49	25.14	19.59	21.40
Posttest	28.01	25.42	21.67	26.03
	17.91	25.25	20.19	21.67
Changes	0.22	-0.17	0.14	0.78
	0.42	0.11	0.60	0.27

123d) *Step 1:* H_0: $\sigma_1^2 = \sigma_2^2$, and H_1: $\sigma_1^2 \neq \sigma_2^2$. *Step 2:* $\alpha = .05$. *Step 3:* Use the F distribution with numerator df 7 and denominator df 7. *Step 4:* For a two-tailed test, we will use the F value with .025 in the tail above, or 4.99. *Step 5:* Reject the H_0 in favour of H_1 if $F > 4.99$. *Step 6:* $F = 0.248884/0.0892268 = 2.789$ *Step 7:* Since F is not in the rejection region, we fail to reject H_0. There is insufficient evidence to conclude that the variances are unequal.

123e) In Exercise 123(d) we failed to reject the null hypotheses that $\sigma_1^2 = \sigma_2^2$ so in this exercise we use procedure 4 with a t distribution. *Step 1:* H_0: $\mu_1 = \mu_2$ and H_1: $\mu_1 < \mu_2$. *Step 2:* $\alpha = 0.05$. *Step 3:* We use the t distribution. *Step 4:* This is a one-tailed test. With $\alpha = 0.05$ and 14 df, we use $t_{\alpha/2} = t_{0.05} = 1.761$. *Step 5:* Reject H_0 in favour of H_1 if $t < -1.761$. Otherwise, fail to reject H_0. *Step 6:* Calculate the pooled standard deviation,

$$s_p = \sqrt{\frac{s_1^2(n_1 - 1) + s_2^2(n_2 - 1)}{n_1 + n_2 - 2}}$$

$$= \sqrt{\frac{(0.499)^2(8 - 1) + (0.299)^2(8 - 1)}{8 + 8 - 2}} = \sqrt{0.169201}$$

$= 0.411$. The estimated standard error is $\hat{\sigma}_{\bar{x}_1 - \bar{x}_2} =$

$$s_p\sqrt{\frac{1}{n_1} + \frac{1}{n_2}} = 0.5817 \cdot \sqrt{\frac{1}{8} + \frac{1}{8}} = 0.411 \cdot 0.5 = 0.2055. \text{ Thus}$$

$$t = \frac{\bar{x}_1 - \bar{x}_2}{\hat{\sigma}_{\bar{x}_1 - \bar{x}_2}} = \frac{-0.086 - 0.296}{0.2055} = \frac{-0.382}{0.2055} = -1.86.$$

Step 7: Since $t = -1.86$, we reject H_0; the body fat percentage change is greater for the experimental group.

Chapter 10
Self-Testing Review 10.1

1) The populations must be normally distributed with equal variances, and the samples must be independent and randomly selected.

3) The estimate of $\hat{\sigma}_{within}^2$ is a measure of dispersion for all values within the data set. It is due to sampling error or to the natural variation that exists between one member of a population and another. The estimate of $\hat{\sigma}_{between}^2$ represents the variation from factor group to factor group. Computational procedures are shown in the text, and $\hat{\sigma}_{within}^2$ is a pooled variance.

5) The $\hat{\sigma}^2_{between}$ value is an estimate of σ^2 if (and only if) the null hypothesis is true. The $\hat{\sigma}^2_{within}$ value is an estimate of σ^2 regardless of whether the null hypothesis is true or not.

7) The critical value is determined by α, df_{num}, and df_{den}. The df_{num} is $k - 1$, where k is the number of samples. The df_{den} is $T - k$, where T is the total number of values in all the samples, (Note that the sum of the degrees of freedom is always $T - 1$.)

9) The $df_{num} = 4 - 1$ or 3, and the $df_{den} = 44 - 4$ or 40. So $F = 2.84$.

11) $F = 35.7/14.6 = 2.445$.

13a) False. A rejected H_0 says only one population mean is different than the others. The rest could all be the same.

13b) False. It's almost certain that these two estimated values will differ even when we fail to reject H_0 as being true.

13c) False. The $\hat{\sigma}^2_{within}$ value is used as a pooled variance estimate.

Self-Testing Review 10.2

15) *Step 1:* H_0: All population means are equal, and H_1: Not all population means are equal. *Step 2:* $\alpha = 0.05$. *Step 3:* We use an F distribution with $df_{num} = 3 - 1 = 2$, and $df_{den} = 19 - 3 = 16$. *Step 4:* The critical F value is $F_{2,16,\,\alpha = 0.05} = 3.63$. *Step 5:* Reject H_0 in favour of H_1 if $F > 3.63$. Otherwise, fail to reject H_0. *Step 6:* The sample means are 13, 9.83, and 4.375. The d^2 values are 106.00, 224.83, and 55.875. So

$$\hat{\sigma}^2_{within} = \frac{106 + 224.83 + 55.875}{19 - 3} = \frac{386.705}{16} = 24.169. \text{ Then}$$

$$\overline{\overline{X}} = \frac{5(13) + 6(9.83) + 8(4.375)}{19} = \frac{158.98}{19} = 8.367, \text{ and}$$

$$\hat{\sigma}^2_{between} = \frac{5(13 - 8.367)^2 + 6(9.83 - 8.367^2) + 8(4.375 - 8.367)^2}{3 - 1}$$

$$= \frac{247.654}{2} = 123.8327. \text{ Thus}$$

$$F = \frac{\hat{\sigma}^2_{between}}{\hat{\sigma}^2_{within}} = \frac{123.827}{24.169} = 5.12.$$

Step 7: Since F falls in the rejection region, we reject H_0. At least one of the majors response means is different.

17) *Step 1:* H_0: All population means are equal, and H_1: Not all population means are equal. *Step 2:* $\alpha = 0.01$. *Step 3:* We use F distribution with $df_{num} = 4 - 1 = 3$, and $df_{den} = 28 - 4 = 24$. *Step 4:* The critical F value is $F_{3,24,\alpha = 0.01} = 4.72$. *Step 5:* Reject H_0 in favour of H_1 if $F > 4.72$. Otherwise, fail to reject H_0. *Step 6:* The sample means are 14.429, 15.429, 19.143, and 15.143. The sum of the d^2 values is 343.1, so

$$\hat{\sigma}^2_{within} = \frac{343.1}{24} = 14.3. \text{ For } \hat{\sigma}^2_{between}, \overline{\overline{X}} = 16.036, \text{ and}$$

$$\hat{\sigma}^2_{between} = \frac{93.8}{3} = 31.3. \text{ Thus, } F = \frac{31.3}{14.3} = 2.19.$$

Step 7: Since F does not fall in the rejection region, we fail to reject H_0. There is no significant difference in accuracy.

19) *Step 1:* H_0: All population means are equal, and H_1: Not all population means are equal. *Step 2:* $\alpha = 0.05$. *Step 3:* We use an F distribution with $df_{num} = 3 - 1 = 2$, and $df_{den} = 12 - 3 = 9$. *Step 4:* The critical F value is $F_{2,9,\alpha = 0.05} = 4.26$. *Step 5:* Reject H_0 in favour of H_1 if $F > 4.26$. Otherwise, fail to reject H_0. *Step 6:* The sum of the d^2 values is 108,336, so $\hat{\sigma}^2_{within} = 108,336/9 = 12,037$. And $\hat{\sigma}^2_{between}$ 64,586/2 = 32,393. Thus, $F = 32,393/12,037 = 2.68$. *Step 7:* Since F does not fall in the rejection region, we fail to reject H_0 and Ms. Breen's claim that the viewing habits are the same.

21) *Step 1:* H_0 All population means are equal, and H_1: Not all population means are equal. *Step 2:* $\alpha = 0.01$. *Step 3:* We use an F distribution with $df_{num} = 6 - 1 = 5$, and $df_{den} = 24 - 6 = 18$. *Step 4:* The critical F value is $F_{5,18,\alpha = 0.01} = 4.25$. *Step 5:* Reject H_0 in favour of H_1 if $F > 4.25$. Otherwise, fail to reject H_0. *Step 6:* The sum of the d^2 values is 237,996, so $\hat{\sigma}^2_{within} = 237,996/18 = 13,222$. And $\hat{\sigma}^2_{between}$ 313,185/5 = 62,637. Thus, $F = 62,637/13,222 = 4.74$. *Step 7:* Since F falls in the rejection region, we reject H_0. At least one of the computer sorting algorithms means is different.

23) *Step 1:* H_0: All population means are equal, and H_1: Not all population means are equal. *Step 2:* $\alpha = 0.05$. *Step 3:* We use an F distribution with $df_{num} = 3 - 1 = 2$, and $df_{den} = 12 - 3 = 9$. *Step 4:* The critical F value is $F_{2,9,\alpha = 0.05} = 4.26$. *Step 5:* Reject H_0 in favour of H_1 if $F > 4.26$. Otherwise, fail to reject H_0. *Step 6:* The sum of the d^2 values is 35,462.8, so $\hat{\sigma}^2_{within} = 35,462.8/9 = 3,940.3$. And $\hat{\sigma}^2_{between}$ 42,930/2 = 21,465. Thus, $F = 21,465/3,940.3 = 5.45$. *Step 7:* Since F falls in the rejection region, we reject H_0; there is a significant difference in the mean number of unpopped kernels.

Self-Testing Review 10.3

25a) Factor refers to the variable that distinguished one population from another. The word *treatment* has the same meaning.

25b) "Error" is the natural variation of the members *within* the same population.

25c) There are four groups or factors being considered, so the $df_{num} = 4 - 1 = 3$. And there are a total of 23 data items in the four groups, so $df_{den} = 23 - 4 = 19$.

25d) The SS error is the numerator for the $\hat{\sigma}^2_{within}$ estimate of σ^2. It is found by computing the mean for each of the four groups or factors, finding the deviation between each value and its corresponding mean, squaring the deviations, and then adding these squared deviations (see the procedure spelled out in the numerator of formula 10.4).

25e) The SS factor is the numerator for the $\hat{\sigma}^2_{between}$ estimate of σ^2. It is computed by the procedure spelled out in the numerator of formula 10.6.

25f) $\hat{\sigma}^2_{within}$.

25g) $\hat{\sigma}^2_{between}$

25h) The test statistic F = MS factor/MS error. In this case, $407/467 = 0.87$.

25i) The p-value in the output is $p = 0.473$. There is .473 of the F curve to the right of $F = .87$. Since $0.473 > .05$, we fail to reject H_0.

25j) "Level" refers to the different factors or treatments.

25k) The pooled standard deviation is the estimated population standard deviation found by pooling and averaging the sample variances. Recall that one of the ANOVA assumptions is that the variances are equal for all populations.

25l) We see how many factors there are, the number of values in each, the mean and standard deviation for each sample, and a confidence interval display.

25m) Because we failed to reject H_0, there is no need to compare pairs of means.

27a) There are four factors. Refer to the chart where the levels are listed.

27b) The factor groups have 5, 5, 4, and 3 values for total of 17.

27c) The $df_{num} = 4 - 1 = 3$. And $df_{den} = 17 - 4 = 13$.

27d) The MS error is the SS error divided by the df error. In this case, $25.0 = 324.6/13$. The MS factor is the SS factor divided by the df factor. In this case, $163.9 = 491.6/3$.

27e) To compute the test statistic, F, divide MS factor by MS error. So $F = 163.9/25.0 = 6.56$.

27f) Since the p-value is 0.006, and since $0.006 < .01$, we reject H_0 at the .01 level.

27g) Because we reject H_0, we would use Fisher's procedure to see which pairs of means are significantly different.

29a) The DF Factor = $3 - 1 = 2$. The DF Error = $44 - 3 = 41$.

29b) MS = SS/df, so MS factor = $0.90/2 = 0.45$ and MS error = $208.67/41 = 5.09$.

29c) To compute the test statistic, F, divide MS factor by MS error. So $\mathbf{F} = 0.45/5.09 = 0.09$.

29d) Since the p-value is 0.916 and since $0.916 > .05$, we fail to reject H_0 at the .05 level.

29e) Because we failed to reject H_0, there is no need to compare pairs of means.

31a) A = 2

31b) B = 1,090.9.

31c) C = 181.8

31d) D = 60.6.

31e) E = 3.00

31f) Reject H_0 at the 0.01 level.

33a) One-way Analysis of Variance for Polymer

Analysis of Variance

Source	DF	SS	MS	F	P
Factor	3	48901	16300	4.70	0.007
Error	36	124796	3467		
Total	39	173697			

33b) *Step 1:* H_0: $\mu_1 = \mu_2 = \mu_3 = \mu_4$; H_1: Not all population means are equal. *Step 2:* $\alpha = .05$. *Step 3:* Use the F distribution. *Step 4:* Always right tailed, use 3 and 36 degrees of freedom. *Step 5:* Reject H_0 in favour of H_1 if the p-value is less than .05. *Step 6:* The p-value from the computer output is $= .007$. *Step 7:* Since $.007 < .05$, we reject H_0. Not all the population mean drug readings appear equal for the four formulations.

33c) $\mu_{0.0\,cc} \neq \mu_{0.5\,cc}$, $\mu_{0.0\,cc} \neq \mu_{1.0\,cc}$, and $\mu_{0.0\,cc} \neq \mu_{2.0\,cc}$.

35a) One-way Analysis of Variance for C4

Analysis of Variance for C4

Source	DF	SS	MS	F	P
C5	2	7891	3946	9.75	0.000
Error	57	23056	404		
Total	59	30948			

35b) *Step 1:* H_0: $\mu_1 = \mu_2 = \mu_3$; H_1: Not all population means are equal. *Step 2:* $\alpha = .05$. Step 3: Use the F distribution. *Step 4:* Always right tailed, use 2 and 57 degrees of freedom. *Step 5:* Reject H_0 in favour of H_1 if the p-value is less than .05. *Step 6:* The p-value from computer output is $= .000$. *Step 7:* Since $.000 < .05$, we reject H_0. Not all the population mean amounts spent appear equal for the three payment methods.

35c) $\mu_{Check} \neq \mu_{Cash}$ and $\mu_{Credit} \neq \mu_{Cash}$.

Self-Testing Review 10.4

37a) No, the factors "diet" and "sex" do not significantly interact to affect the amount of weight lost. $F = 0.57$, p-value $= 0.461$.

37b) Yes, there is a significant difference between the mean weight loss using the high protein diet and the mean weight loss using the high-carbohydrate diet. $F = 13.96$, p-value $= .002$.

37c) Yes, there is a significant difference between the mean weight loss of males and the mean weight loss of females. $F = 26.68$, p-value $= .000$.

39a) Factor A has five levels. Factor B has four levels.

39b) Three observations were collected for each factor-level combination.

39c)

Source	df	SS	MS	F
A	4	0.24	.6	2.25
B	3	1.5	.5	1.88
A×B	12	0.48	.4	1.50
Error	40	10.65	.26625	
Total	59	12.87		

39d) Three sets of hypotheses may be tested:

1. H_0: There is no interaction effect between the factors.
   H_1: There is an interaction effect between the factors.
2. H_0: There are no effects from factor A. (That is, the means at each level of factor A are all equal.)
   H_1: There are effects from factor A. (That is, the means at each level of factor A are not all equal.
3. H_0: There are no effects from factor B. (That is, the means at each level of factor B are all equal.)
   H_1: There are effects from factor B. (That is, the means at each level of factor B are not all equal.

41) *Step 1:* H_0: The mean weight gain is the same for all three feed types. H_1: The mean weight gain is not the same for all three feed types *Step 2:* $\alpha = .05$. *Step 3:* Use the F distribution. *Step 4:* Reject H_0 if the p-value is less than a. Otherwise fail to reject H_0. *Step 5:* $F = 4.18$. *Step 6:* The p-value is 0.038. *Step 7:* We reject H_0 since the p-value is less than .05. At the .05 level of significance we conclude that the mean weight gain is not the same for all three feed types.

Exercises

43) *a)* $F_{5,8,.05} = 3.69$ *b)* $F_{5,20,.05} = 2.71$ *c)* $F_{5,30,.05} = 2.53$

45) *a)* $F_{5,25,.01} = 3.85$ *b)* $F_{7,25,.01} = 3.46$ *c)* $F_{10,25,.01} = 3.13$

47) *a)* $F_{8,15,.05} = 2.64$ *b)* $F_{5,20,.01} = 4.10$

49) $F_{3,19,.05} = 3.13$, $F = 212.6/89.8 = 2.37$. Since $2.37 < 3.13$, we fail to reject H_0 that the mean strengths are equal.

51) $F_{2,14,.01} = 6.15$, $F = 7.8/22.7 = 0.34$. Since $0.34 < 6.51$, we fail to reject H_0 that there's no difference in career decision-making attitudes among the populations.

53) $F_{2,11,.01} = 7.21$, $F = 19.86/6.00 = 3.31$. Since $3.31 < 7.21$, we fail to reject H_0 that the population mean number of errors is the same for all 3 groups.

55) $F_{2,20,.05} = 3.49$, $F = 147.8/26.0 = 5.68$. Since $5.68 > 3.49$, we reject H_0 that the population mean sales are equal for the 3 groups.

57a) With 3 factors, the DF factor is $3 - 1$, or 2. With a total of 24 values within the factor groups, DF error is $24 - 3$, or 21.

57b) $F = $ MS factor/MS factor. In this case, $F = 31.18/5.27 = 5.92$.

57c) With a p-value of 0.009, we reject H_0 since p-value $< .05$.

57d) Because we rejected H_0, we would use Fisher's procedure to see which pairs of means are significantly different.

59a) $A = 23$

59b) Using the SS column, $B + 43.33 = 51.83$, so $B = 51.83 - 43.33 = 8.50$.

59c) $C = 2.833$

59d) $D = 43.33/20 = 2.17$.

59e) $E = 1.308$

59f) Since $F_{3,20, \alpha = 0.01} = 4.94 > F - 1.31$, we fail to reject H_0.

61a) One-way Analysis of Variance

```
Analysis of Variance
Source     DF        SS        MS       F        P
Factor      3     60.80     20.27    6.27    0.001
Error      60    193.94      3.23
Total      63    254.73
```

61b) *Step 1:* H_0: $\mu_1 = \mu_2 = \mu_3 = \mu_4$. H_1: Not all population means are equal. *Step 2:* $\alpha = .05$. *Step 3:* Use the F distribution. *Step 4:* Always right tailed, use 3 and 60 df. *Step 5:* Reject H_0 in favour of H_1 if the p-value is less than .05. *Step 6:* The p-value from computer output is $= .001$. *Step 7:* Since $.001 < .05$, we reject H_0. Not all the population means appear equal for the 4 treatments.

61c) $\mu_{\text{Marathon}} \neq \mu_{1 \text{ Tab}}$, $\mu_{\text{Marathon}} \neq \mu_{2 \text{ Tab}}$, and $\mu_{\text{Marathon}} \neq \mu_{\text{Control}}$.

63a) The Two-way ANOVA table for Score versus Video Game and Software is as follows.

```
Analysis of Variance for Score
Source         DF        SS       MS       F        P
Video Game      3     537.1    179.0    2.31    0.088
Software        2     107.0     53.5    0.69    0.506
Interaction     6    1046.0    174.3    2.25    0.054
Error          48    3718.8     77.5
Total          59    5409.0
```

We may conclude that the factors "software used" and "video game experience" do not significantly interact to affect math test scores, since the p-value for the interaction test is 0.054, and 0.054 is not less than .05.

63b) We may conclude there are no significant differences between the mean test scores of students using the three different types of software since the p-value for the "Software" test is 0.506, and 0.506 is not less than .05.

63c) We cannot conclude that the mean test scores of students are different for at least two of the levels of video game experience since the p-value for the "Video Game" test is 0.088, and 0.088 is not less than .05.

Chapter 11
Self-Testing Review 11.1

1) A multinomial experiment has a fixed number of trials, and the outcome of each trial is independent of the outcomes of the other trials. A single trial results in one of k possible outcomes.

3) The sample is a random sample, and the expected frequency for each of the categories is five or more.

5) Sample data are obtained randomly, and the expected frequency in each cell is five or more.

Self-Testing Review 11.2

7) *Step 1:* H_0: There has been no change in the distribution of age groups. That is, there are still 10, 13, 32, and 45 percent of the residents in the four respective age categories. H_1: The age distribution has changed since 1987. *Step 2:* $\alpha = 0.05$. *Step 3:* x^2. *Step 4:* The critical x^2 value with $4 - 1 = 3$ df is 7.81. *Step 5:* Reject H_0 in favour of H_1 if $x^2 > 7.81$. Otherwise, fail to reject H_0. *Step 6:* $x^2 = \sum \left[\dfrac{(O - E)^2}{E} \right] = 105.856 + 45.847 + 8.304 + 36.717 = 196.724$. *Step 7:* Since x^2 falls in the rejection region, we reject H_0. There has been a significant change in the age distribution.

9) *Step 1:* H_0: The distribution follows a 9:3:3:1 ratio. H_1: The distribution does not follow such a ratio. *Step 2:* $\alpha = 0.05$. *Step 3:* x^2. *Step 4:* The critical x^2 value with $4 - 1$ or 3 df is 7.81. *Step 5:* Reject H_0 in favour of H_1 if $x^2 > 7.81$. Otherwise, fail to reject H_0. *Step 6:* $x^2 = \sum \left[\dfrac{(O - E)^2}{E} \right] = 1.788 + 8.333 + 0.000 + 1.000 = 11.11$. *Step 7:* Since x^2 falls in the rejection region, we reject H_0. We conclude at the 0.05 level that the distribution does not follow the Mendelian ratio.

11) *Step 1:* H_0: The distribution is uniform—we should expect 1/7 of the crimes to be committed each day. H_1: The distribution isn't uniform. *Step 2:* $\alpha = 0.05$. *Step 3:* x^2. *Step 4:* The critical x^2 value with $7 - 1 = 6$ df is 12.59. *Step 5:* Reject H_0 in favour of H_1 if $x^2 > 12.59$. Otherwise, fail to reject H_0. *Step 6:* $x^2 = \sum \left[\dfrac{(O - E)^2}{E} \right] = 35.660$. *Step 7:* Since x^2 falls in the rejection region, we reject H_0. The crime distribution isn't uniform.

13) *Step 1:* H_0: The distribution fits the dean of students' distribution. That is, the expected percentages in the three categories are 50, 33, and 17. H_1: The distribution doesn't fit the one spelled out by the dean. *Step 2:* $\alpha = 0.05$. *Step 3:* x^2. *Step 4:* The critical x^2 value with $3 - 1 = 2$ df is 5.99. *Step 5:* Reject H_0 in favour of H_1 if $x^2 > 5.99$. Otherwise, fail to reject H_0. *Step 6:* $x^2 = \sum \left[\dfrac{(O - E)^2}{E} \right] = 3.33 + 1.25 + 2.50 = 7.08$. *Step 7:* Since x^2 falls in the rejection region, we reject H_0. The sample distribution doesn't fit the one spelled out by the dean.

15) *Step 1:* H_0: The distribution is uniform—we should expect 1/3 of the students to work out in each time period. H_1: The distribution isn't uniform. *Step 2:* $\alpha = 0.05$. *Step 3:* x^2. *Step 4:* The critical x^2 value with $3 - 1 = 2$ df is 5.99. *Step 5:* Reject H_0 in favour of H_1 if $x^2 > 5.99$. Otherwise, fail to reject H_0. *Step 6:* $x^2 = \sum \left[\dfrac{(O - E)^2}{E} \right] = 5.400 + 0.267 + 8.067 = 13.734$. *Step 7:* Since x^2 falls in the rejection region, we reject H_0. The workout times are not uniform.

17) *Step 1:* H_0: The physical activity frequency distribution of the college females is the same as working women. That is, the expected percentages in the six categories are 12.5, 37.2,

22.1, 11.5, 10.8, and 5.9. H_1: The physical activity frequency distribution is different. *Step 2:* $\alpha = 0.05$. *Step 3:* x^2. *Step 4:* The critical x^2 value with $6 - 1 = 5$ df is 11.07. *Step 5:* Reject H_0 in favour of H_1 if $x^2 > 11.07$. Otherwise, fail to reject H_0. *Step 6:* $x^2 = \sum \left[\dfrac{(O - E)^2}{E} \right] = 3.38 + 2.08 + 16.51 + 3.67 + 11.61 + 0.14 = 37.39$. *Step 7:* Since x^2 falls in the rejection region, we reject H_0. The physical activity of college women is different from the 1000 working women surveyed.

Self-Testing Review 11.3

19) *Step 1:* H_0: Religion and political party of students are independent. H_1: Religion and political party of students are not independent. *Step 2:* $\alpha = 0.05$. *Step 3:* x^2. *Step 4:* The critical x^2 value with 6 df is 12.59. *Step 5:* Reject H_0 in favour of H_1 if $x^2 > 12.59$. Otherwise, fail to reject H_0. *Step 6:* From the MINITAB output, $x^2 = 50.330$. *Step 7:* Since x^2 falls in the rejection region, we reject H_0. Religion and political party of students are not independent.

21) *Step 1:* H_0: There's an equal percentage of male and female inner-city middle school students who want to stay in school. H_1: The variables are not independent. *Step 2:* $\alpha = 0.05$. *Step 3:* x^2. *Step 4:* The critical x^2 value with $(2 - 1)(2 - 1) = 1$ df is 3.84. *Step 5:* Reject H_0 in favour of H_1 if $x^2 > 3.84$. Otherwise, fail to reject H_0. *Step 6:* So $x^2 = 18.991$. *Step 7:* Since x^2 falls in the rejection region, we reject H_0. Gender and inner-city middle school students who want to stay in school are not independent.

23) *Step 1:* H_0: The opinion about the budget is independent of income level. H_1: The opinion is not independent of income. *Step 2:* $\alpha = 0.05$. *Step 3:* x^2. *Step 4:* The critical x^2 value with $(4 - 1)(4 - 1) = 9$ df is 16.92. *Step 5:* Reject H_0 in favour of H_1 if $x^2 > 16.92$. Otherwise, fail to reject H_0. *Step 6:* So $x^2 = 23.339 + 29.767 = 53.106$. *Step 7:* Since x^2 falls in the rejection region, we reject H_0. Opinion about the budget and income level are not independent.

25) *Step 1:* H_0: The time from injury to surgery and cartilage condition are independent. H_1: The variables are not independent. *Step 2:* $\alpha = 0.05$. *Step 3:* x^2. *Step 4:* The critical x^2 value with $(3 - 1)(3 - 1) = 4$ df is 9.49. *Step 5:* Reject H_0 in favour of H_1 if $x^2 > 9.49$. Otherwise, fail to reject H_0. *Step 6:* Hold everything! There's a problem here—we've run into a situation that violates one of the assumptions for contingency table tests that was spelled out early in the chapter. This assumption was that the expected frequency for each cell in the contingency table must be at least 5. But you'll note that the expected frequency for the cell at the intersection of the "Subacute" row and "Normal cartilage" column is only 3.337. Thus, this test may not produce valid results. When this is the case, the analyst can either combine some categories or try for a larger sample.

27) *Step 1:* H_0: The college in which a student is enrolled in is independent of whether the student had participated in high

school sports. H_1: The variables are not independent. *Step 2:* α = 0.05. *Step 3:* x^2. *Step 4:* The critical x^2 value with $(5-1)(2-1) = 4$ df is 9.49. *Step 5:* Reject H_0 in favour of H_1 if $x^2 > 9.49$. Otherwise, fail to reject H_0. *Step 6:* So $x^2 = 21.655 + 13.390 + 35.045$. *Step 7:* Since x^2 falls in the rejection, we reject H_0. The college in which a student is enrolled in *and* whether the student had participated in high school sports are not independent.

29) *Step 1:* H_0: The answer to the question is independent of gender. H_1: The answer to the question is not independent of gender. *Step 2:* $\alpha = 0.10$. *Step 3:* x^2. *Step 4:* The critical x^2 value with $(2-1)(2-1) = 1$ df is 2.71. *Step 5:* Reject H_0 in favour of H_1 if $x^2 > 2.71$. Otherwise, fail to reject H_0. *Step 6:* So $x^2 = 4.265$. *Step 7:* Since x^2 falls in the rejection region, we reject H_0. The answer to the question is not independent of gender.

31) *Step 1:* H_0: The type of alcohol consumed is independent of the location of the restaurant. H_1: The type of alcohol and the location of the restaurant are not independent. *Step 2:* $\alpha = 0.01$. *Step 3:* x^2. *Step 4:* The critical x^2 value with $(2-1)(3-1) = 2$ df is 9.21. *Step 5:* Reject H_0 in favour of H_1 if $x^2 > 9.21$. Otherwise, fail to reject H_0. *Step 6:* So $x^2 = 23.964$. *Step 7:* Since x^2 falls in the rejection region, we reject H_0. The location in the restaurant and the type of alcohol consumed are not independent.

33a) *Step 1:* H_0: The population percentage of people having fair or poor health is the same in all four provincial capitals. H_1: The population percentage of people having fair or poor health is not the same in all four provincial capitals *Step 2:* $\alpha = .05$. *Step 3:* To perform this test we construct a contingency table with one criterion of classification being the city (4 rows) and the other criteria of classification being whether or not the person reported being in fair or poor health (2 columns—those who did and those who did not). Therefore we will use a χ^2 distribution. *Step 4:* The critical χ^2 value with $(4-1)(2-1)$, or 3 df is 7.81. *Step 5:* Reject H_0 in favour of H_1 if $\chi^2 > 7.81$. Otherwise, fail to reject H_0. *Step 6:* $\chi^2 = \Sigma(O-E)^2/E = 0.5041 + 0.0746 + 0.0000 + 0.0000 + 1.1470 + 0.1697 + 0.1445 + 0.0214 = 2.0613$ *Step 7:* Since $\chi^2 = 2.0613$ does not fall in the rejection region, we fail to reject H_0. There is not evidence that the population percentage of people having fair or poor health differs in all four provincial capitals.

33b) *Step 1:* H_0: The population percentage of people having fair or poor health is the same in all four health regions. H_1: The population percentage of people having fair or poor health is not the same in all four health regions. *Step 2:* $\alpha = .10$. *Step 3:* To perform this test we construct a contingency table with one criterion of classification being the health region (4 rows) and the other criteria of classification being whether or not the person reported being in fair or poor health (2 columns – those who did and those who did not). Therefore we will use a χ^2 distribution. *Step 4:* The critical χ^2 value with $(4-1)(2-1)$, or 3 df is 6.25. *Step 5:* Reject H_0 in favour of H_1 if $\chi^2 > 6.25$. Otherwise, fail to reject H_0. *Step 6:* $\chi^2 = \Sigma(O-E)^2/E = 2.5641 + 0.3595 + 0.6160 + 0.0864 + 18.0939 + 2.5367 + 2.2175 + 0.3109 = 26.785$ *Step 7:* Since $\chi^2 = 26.785$ falls in the rejection region, we reject H_0. There is

evidence that the population percentage of people having fair or poor health is not the same in all four health regions.

35) *Step 1:* H_0: The six provinces are homogeneous with respect to the legal marital status of its residents. H_1: The six provinces are not homogeneous with respect to the legal marital status of its residents. *Step 2:* $\alpha = .05$. *Step 3:* χ^2. *Step 4:* The critical χ^2 value with $(5-1)(6-1)$, or 20 df is 31.4. *Step 5:* Reject H_0 in favour of H_1 if $\chi^2 > 31.4$. Otherwise, fail to reject H_0. *Step 6:* Using MINITAB we find $\chi^2 = \Sigma(O-E)^2/E = 11.070$. *Step 7:* Since $\chi^2 = 11.070$ does not fall in the rejection region, we do not reject H_0. It appears the six provinces are homogeneous with respect to the legal marital status of its residents.

Exercises

37) *Step 1:* H_0: The proportion of students able to do 40 or more pushups in 60 seconds at the end of a two-hour workout is the same for males and females. H_1: The proportion of students able to do 40 or more pushups in 60 seconds is not the same for males and females *Step 2:* $\alpha = .05$. *Step 3:* χ^2 distribution. *Step 4:* The critical χ^2 value with $(2-1)(2-1)$, or 1 df is 3.84. *Step 5:* Reject H_0 in favour of H_1 if $\chi^2 > 3.84$. Otherwise, fail to reject H_0. *Step 6:* $\chi^2 = \Sigma(O-E)^2/E = 1.3531 + 1.1449 + 1.8942 + 1.6029 = 5.9951$. *Step 7:* Since $\chi^2 = 5.9951$ falls in the rejection region, we reject H_0. We conclude that the proportion of students able to do 40 or more pushups in 60 seconds is not the same for males and females.

39) *Step 1:* H_0: The time of day of a collision is independent of whether the day is a weekday. H_1: The time of day of a collision depends on whether the day is a weekday. *Step 2:* $\alpha = .05$. *Step 3:* χ^2. *Step 4:* The critical χ^2 value with $(8-1)(2-1) = 7$ df is 14.07. *Step 5:* Reject H_0 in favour of H_1 if $\chi^2 > 14.07$. Otherwise fail to reject H_0. *Step 6:* So $\chi^2 = 321.85 + 952.51 = 1,274.36$. *Step 7:* Since χ^2 falls in the rejection region, we reject H_0. The time of day of a collision depends on whether the day is a weekday.

41) *Step 1:* H_0: There's no difference in the reactions of the workers in the three locals to the proposed change. H_1: The workers' opinions are not independent of the local they belong to. *Step 2:* $\alpha = 0.05$. *Step 3:* x^2. *Step 4:* The critical x^2 value with $(3-1)(3-1) = 4$ df is 9.49. *Step 5:* Reject H_0 in favour of H_1 if $x^2 > 9.49$. Otherwise, fail to reject H_0. *Step 6:* So $x^2 = 11.244$. *Step 7:* Since x^2 falls in the rejection region, we reject H_0. The workers' opinions are not independent of the local they belong to.

43) *Step 1:* H_0: The proportion of concordance for the handedness trait is the same for identical and fraternal twins. H_1: The proportion of concordance for the handedness trait is different for the different types of twins. *Step 2:* $\alpha = 0.01$. *Step 3:* x^2. *Step 4:* The critical x^2 value with $(2-1)(2-1) = 1$ df is 6.63. *Step 5:* Reject H_0 in favour of H_1 if $x^2 > 6.63$. Otherwise, fail to reject H_0. *Step 6:* So $x^2 = 0.304$. *Step 7:* Since x^2 does not fall in the rejection region, we fail to reject H_0. The proportion of concordance for the handedness trait is the same for identical and fraternal twins.

45) *Step 1:* H_0: The primary reading language is independent of the student's grade. H_1: The primary reading language and the grade of the student are not independent. *Step 2:* $\alpha = 0.01$. *Step 3:* x^2. *Step 4:* The critical x^2 value with $(2 - 1)(2 - 1) = 1$ df is 6.63. *Step 5:* Reject H_0 in favour of H_1 if $x^2 > 6.63$. Otherwise, fail to reject H_0. *Step 6:* So $x^2 = 0.013$. *Step 7:* Since x^2 does not fall in the rejection region, we fail to reject H_0. The primary reading language is independent of the student's grade.

47) *Step 1:* H_0: The inpatient/outpatient status is independent of the criteria for admission. H_1: The inpatient/outpatient status and the criteria for admission are not independent. *Step 2:* $\alpha = 0.05$. *Step 3:* x^2. *Step 4:* The critical x^2 value with $(4 - 1)(2 - 1) = 3$ df is 7.81. *Step 5:* Reject H_0 in favour of H_1 if $x^2 > 7.81$. Otherwise, fail to reject H_0. *Step 6:* So $x^2 = 51.287$. *Step 7:* Since x^2 falls in the rejection region, we reject H_0. The inpatient/outpatient status and the criteria for admission are not independent.

49) *Step 1:* H_0: The preferred vacation location is independent of gender. H_1: The preferred vacation location and gender are not independent. *Step 2:* $\alpha = 0.05$. *Step 3:* x^2. *Step 4:* The critical x^2 value with $(2 - 1)(3 - 1) = 2$ df is 5.99. *Step 5:* Reject H_0 in favour of H_1 if $x^2 > 5.99$. Otherwise, fail to reject H_0. *Step 6:* So $x^2 = 10.694$. *Step 7:* Since x^2 falls in the rejection region, we reject H_0. The preferred vacation location and gender are not independent.

51a) *Step 1:* H_0: The Aboriginal population and the Non-Aboriginal population are homogeneous with respect to Physical Activity. H_1: The Aboriginal population and the Non-Aboriginal population are not homogeneous with respect to Physical Activity. *Step 2:* $\alpha = .05$. *Step 3:* χ^2 distribution. *Step 4:* The critical χ^2 value with $(2 - 1)(2 - 1)$, or 1 df is 3.84. *Step 5:* Reject H_0 in favour of H_1 if $\chi^2 > 3.84$. Otherwise, fail to reject H_0. *Step 6:* $\chi^2 = \Sigma(O - E)^2/E = 0.5707 + 0.1902 + 0.1958 + 0.0653 + 0.0371 + 0.0124 = 1.0715$. *Step 7:* Since $\chi^2 = 1.0715$ does not fall in the rejection region, we fail to reject H_0. We conclude that the Aboriginal population and the Non-Aboriginal population are homogeneous with respect to Physical Activity.

51b) *Step 1:* H_0: The Aboriginal population and the Non-Aboriginal population are homogeneous with respect to body mass index. H_1: The Aboriginal population and the Non-Aboriginal population are not homogeneous with respect to body mass index. *Step 2:* $\alpha = .05$. *Step 3:* χ^2 distribution. *Step 4:* The critical χ^2 value with $(2 - 1)(2 - 1)$, or 1 df is 3.84. *Step 5:* Reject H_0 in favour of H_1 if $\chi^2 > 3.84$. Otherwise, fail to reject H_0. *Step 6:* $\chi^2 = \Sigma(O - E)^2/E = 17.1745 + 5.7248 + 0.5669 + 0.1890 + 38.6211 + 12.8737 = 75.15$. *Step 7:* Since $\chi^2 = 75.15$ falls in the rejection region, we reject H_0. We conclude that the Aboriginal population and the Non-Aboriginal population are not homogeneous with respect to body mass index.

53a) 12,002.

53b) Five in one and two in the other.

53c) There are 4 degrees of freedom. DF = (rows − 1) (columns − 1). In this case, $(5 - 1)(2 - 1) = 4$.

53d) $\chi^2 = 21.193$

53e) No other information is needed since the *p*-value = 0.0000. We will reject H_0 at any level.

Chapter 12
Self-Testing Review 12.1

1) The purpose is to describe the relationship between two variables.

3) Correlation analysis is used to measure the strength of the relationship that exists between the variables.

5) Positive linear.

7) Positive linear.

9a) Positive.

9b) Negative

9c) Positive.

9d) None.

9e) Positive.

9f) Negative.

9g) Positive.

9h) Positive.

Self-Testing Review 12.2

11a) $\Sigma x = 65$ $\Sigma x^2 = 693$ $(\Sigma x)^2 = 4,225$

11b) $\Sigma y = 150$; $\Sigma(y^2) = 4,042$; $(\Sigma y)^2 = 22,500$.

11c) $\Sigma xy = 1,668$

11d) $\bar{x} = 8.125$; $\bar{y} = 18.75$.

11e) $b = 2.7248$ $a = 3.3889$

11f) $\hat{y} = -3.3889 + 2.7248x$.

11g) $\hat{y} = -3.3889 + 2.7248(6) = 12.96$

11h) $\hat{y} = -3.3889 + 2.7248(3) = 4.79$ automobiles.

11i) $s_{y.x} = \sqrt{5.4/6} = .9476$

13a) $\Sigma x = 136$ $\Sigma x^2 = 2,448$ $(\Sigma x)^2 = 18,496$

13b) $\Sigma y = 280$; $\Sigma(y^2) = 10,000$; $(\Sigma y)^2 = 78,400$.

13c) $\Sigma xy = 4,920$

13d) $\bar{x} = 15.1111$; $\bar{y} = 31.1111$.

13e) $b = 1.7534$ $a = 4.6154$

13f) $\hat{y} = 4.6154 + 1.7534x$.

13g) $\hat{y} = 4.6154 + 1.7534(17) = 34.42$

13h) $\hat{y} = 4.6154 + 1.7534(5) = 13.38$ cups.

13i) $s_{y.x} = \sqrt{81/7} = 3.402$

15a) $b = 1.08$ $a = -90$

15b) $\hat{y} = -90 + 1.08x$.

15c) $\hat{y} = -90 + 1.08(300) = 234.6$ Hz

15d) $\hat{y} = -90 + 1.08(6,500) = 6,930$ Hz.

15e) $s_{y.x} = \sqrt{2,367,316/17} = 373.2$

Self-Testing Review 12.3

17a) $\hat{y} = 20.06 + 6.811x$.

17b) $S_{y.x} = \sqrt{3,926.21/19} = 14.375$

17c) *Step 1:* H_0: $B = 0$ and H_1: $B \neq 0$. *Step 2:* $\alpha = 0.05$. *Step 3:* We use the t distribution. *Step 4:* Since we have $21 - 2 = 19$ degrees of freedom (df), the t value in the 0.025 column and 19 df row is 2.093. *Step 5:* We'll reject H_0 in favour of H_1 if $t < -2.093$ or if $t > 2.093$. *Step 6:* To calculate the test statistic, we first need to obtain the estimated standard error of b:

$$s_b = \frac{s_{y,x}}{\sqrt{\Sigma(x^2) - \frac{(\Sigma x)^2}{n}}} = \frac{14.38}{\sqrt{20.9523}} \approx 3.140.$$ Then the test sta-

tistic is $t = \dfrac{b}{s_b} = \dfrac{6.811}{3.140} = 2.17$. *Step 7:* Since 2.17 is greater than 2.093, we reject the H_0. A meaningful relationship does exist between the variables.

17d) For the *average* behavior score value, the interval is

$$40.50 \pm 2.093(14.3751)\sqrt{\frac{1}{21} + \frac{(3 - 3.6191)^2}{20.9524}}$$
$$= 40.50 \pm 2.093(14.3751)\sqrt{.0659}$$
$$= 40.50 \pm 7.72 = 32.78 \text{ to } 48.22$$

17e) For the *specific* behavior score value, the interval is

$$40.50 \pm 2.093(14.3751)\sqrt{1 + \frac{1}{21} + \frac{(3 - 3.6191)^2}{20.9524}}$$
$$= 40.50 \pm 2.093(14.3751)\sqrt{1.0659}$$
$$= 40.50 \pm 31.06 \text{ or } 9.44 \text{ to } 71.56.$$

19a) $\hat{y} = 6.1846 - 0.0000016x$.

19b) $s_{y.x} = \sqrt{1.6953/11} = 0.393$

19c) *Step 1:* H_0: $B = 0$ and H_0: $B \neq 0$. *Step 2:* $\alpha = 0.05$. *Step 3:* We use the t distribution. *Step 4:* Since we have $13 - 2 = 11$ degrees of freedom (df), the t value is 2.201. *Step 5:* We reject H_0 in favour of H_1 if $t < -2.201$ or if $t > 2.201$. *Step 6:* To calculate the test statistic, we first need to obtain the estimated standard error of b: $s_b = \dfrac{s_{y,x}}{\sqrt{\Sigma(x^2) - \frac{(\Sigma x)^2}{n}}} = \dfrac{0.3926}{\sqrt{3414987 - \frac{(6053)^2}{13}}}$

$$= \frac{0.3926}{\sqrt{596617.1}} \approx 0.0005083.$$ Then the test statistic is $t = \dfrac{b}{s_b}$

$$= \frac{-0.0000016}{0.0005083} = -0.00315.$$ *Step 7:* Since t does not fall in the rejection region, we fail to reject H_0. A meaningful relationship does exist between the variables.

19d) For the average serum cholesterol level when calcium is 500, the interval is

$$6.184 \pm 2.201(.3926)\sqrt{\frac{1}{13} + \frac{(500 - 465.3)^2}{3,414,983.72}}$$
$$= 6.184 \pm .2402 \text{ or } 5.944 \text{ to } 6.424$$

19e) For the *specific* serum cholesterol level when calcium is 500, the interval is:

$$6.184 \pm 2.201(0.3926)\sqrt{1 + \frac{1}{13} + \frac{(500 - 465.3)^2}{3,414,983.72}}$$
$$= 6.184 \pm 0.8969 \text{ or } 5.2871 \text{ to } 7.0809.$$

21a) The slope is 1.2089 and the y-intercept is 25.687.

21b) .016

21c) H_0: $B = 0$ and H_1: $B \neq 0$. The t-ratio value is 3.99 and the corresponding p-value is 0.016. Since the p-value is < 0.05, we reject H_0. There is a meaningful regression relationship at the 0.05 level (but not at the 0.01 level).

21d) $\sqrt{.1844} = 0.4294$.

23a) The slope is 0.96055 and the y-intercept is 1.812.

23b) H_0: $B = 0$, and H_1: $B \neq 0$. The t ratio is 43.99 with a p-value of .000. Since the p-value $< .01$, we reject H_0 in favour of H_1. There appears to be a meaningful relationship at the .01 level.

Self-Testing Review 12.4

25a) The total variation $\Sigma(y - \bar{y})^2 = 7,184.9$.

25b) The explained variation $\Sigma(\hat{y} - \bar{y})^2 = 4830.4$.

25c) The unexplained variation $\Sigma(y - \hat{y})^2 = 2,354.5$.

25d) $r^2 = 7184.9/4830.4 = 0.672$.

25e) The value of r^2 tells us that 67.2 percent of the variation in production output is explained by the variation in production cost, but 37.3 percent of the variation in production output is unexplained by the regression equation.

25f) $r = +\sqrt{0.672} = 0.820$ (r is positive since the slope is positive).

27a) SST $= 753,623,296$.

27b) SSR $= 129,141,472$.

27c) SSE $= 624,481,856$

27d) $r^2 = 0.171$.

27e) $r = .414$

29a) SST = 2532.4

29b) SSR = 1057.5

29c) SSE = 1474.9

29d) $r^2 = 0.418$

29e) $r = .647$

Self-Testing Review 12.5

31a) Use the given formula, substituting 0 for false and 1 for true: Salary = \$22,044 + \$23,649(0) + \$15,766(0) + 7,883(1) + \$1,152(8) + \$8,392(0) + \$8,884(1) + \$3,968(0) + \$7,976(1) − \$8392(0) = \$56,003.

31b) Salary = \$22,044 + \$23,649(1) + \$15,766(0) + \$7,883(0) + \$1,152(25) + \$8,392(1) + \$8,884(0) + \$3,968(1) + \$7,976(0) − \$8,392(0) = \$86,853

33a) $a = 66.66$; $b_1 = 2.837$; $b_2 = -1.439$; $b_3 = -0.490$; $b_4 = 0.189$

33b) H_0: $B_{97} = B_{98} = B_{99} = B_{00}$. H_1: At least one of B_{97} or B_{98} or B_{99} or $B_{00} \neq 0$. $\alpha = .01$. The F statistic is 38.53 with a p-value of 0.025. Since the p-value is not less than .01, we fail to reject H_0, and thus conclude that none of the predictors are useful in the model.

33c) H_0: $B_{00} = 0$, and H_1: $B_{00} \neq 0$. The corresponding t ratio is 0.35, with a p-value of 0.760. This p-value is not < .05, so we do not reject H_0 in favour of the alternative. This predictor is not significant in the model when all the other predictors are present.

33d) H_0: $B_{99} = 0$, H_1: $B_{99} \neq 0$. $\alpha = .01$. The corresponding t-ratio is −0.33, with a p-value of 0.774. Since the p-value is > .01, we fail to reject H_0. This predictor is not significant in the model when all the others are present.

35a) $a = 5.17$, $b_1 = 1.61$, and $b_2 = 0.0126$.

35b) H_0: $B_{LT} = B_{MaxH} = 0$; H_1; at least one of either $B_{LT} = B_{MaxH} \neq 0$. The F statistic is 2.56 with a p-value of .132. Since the p-value > .05, we fail to reject H_0 and conclude that neither of the predictors are useful in the model.

35c) H_0: $B_{LT} = 0$, H_1: $B_{LT} \neq 0$. The corresponding t-ratio is 2.13, with a p-value of 0.062. Since p-value > 0.05, we fail to reject H_0. This predictor does not appear useful in the model when the other predictor is also present in the model.

35d) H_0: $B_{MaxH} = 0$; H_1: $B_{MaxH} \neq 0$. With a t ratio of .45 and a p-value of 0.661, we fail to reject H_0 since the p-value > .05. This predictor does not appear useful in the model when the other predictor is also in the model.

35e) $r^2 = 36.2\%$.

37a) $a = 24.0$; $b_1 = 1.04$; $b_2 = 61.6$; $b_3 = -1.80$; $b_4 = -0.0112$; $b_5 = 0.0292$; $b_6 = 0.0022$; $b_7 = 0.0090$

37b) H_0: $B_{Lotsize} = B_{TotalLiv} = B_{Age} = B_{DeckArea} = B_{Attached} = B_{Detached} = B_{Finished} = 0$, H_1: At least one of $B_{Lotsize}$ or $B_{TotalLiv}$ or B_{Age} or $B_{DeckArea}$ or $B_{Attached}$ or $B_{Detached}$ or $B_{Finished} \neq 0$. The F statistic is 29.83, with a p-value of 0.000. Since the p-value is < 0.01, we reject H_0 and conclude that at least one of the predictors is useful in this model.

37c) H_0: $B_{Attached} = 0$; H_1: $B_{Attached} \neq 0$. With a t ratio of −3.87 and a p-value of 0.002, we reject H_0 since p-value < .05. This predictor appears useful in the model when the other predictors are also present.

37d) H_0: $B_{Finished} = 0$, H_1: $B_{Finished} \neq 0$. The corresponding t-ratio is 0.89, with a p-value of 0.382. Since p-value > 0.01, we fail to reject H_0. This predictor does not appear useful in the model when the other predictor is also present in the model.

37e) $R^2 = 49.8$ percent

Exercises

39a)

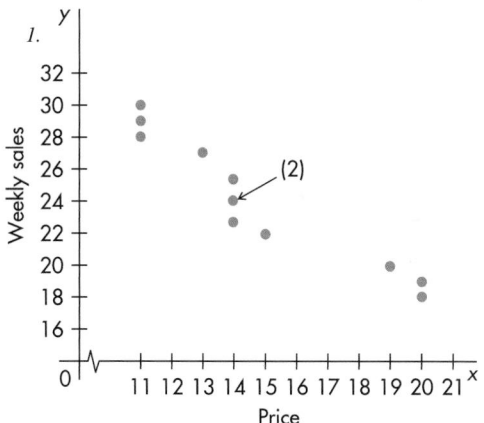

39b) We compute the linear regression equation using the table below.

Store	Price (x)	Sales (y)	xy	x²	y²
1	11	28	308	121	784
2	11	29	319	121	841
3	13	27	351	169	729
4	14	25	350	196	625
5	14	23	322	196	529
6	14	24	336	196	576
7	15	22	330	225	484
8	19	20	380	361	400
9	14	24	336	196	576
10	11	30	330	121	900
11	20	18	360	400	324
12	20	19	380	400	361
Total	176	289	4102	2702	7129

$$\bar{x} = \frac{\sum x}{n} = \frac{176}{12} = 14.6667.$$

$$\bar{y} = \frac{\sum y}{n} = \frac{289}{12} = 24.0833.$$

$$b = \frac{n(\sum xy) - (\sum x)(\sum y)}{n(\sum x^2) - (\sum x)^2} = \frac{12(4102) - (176)(289)}{12(2702) - (176)^2}$$

$$= \frac{-1640}{1448} = -1.1326.$$

$a = \bar{y} - b\bar{x} = 24.0833 - (-1.1326)(14.6667) = 40.695.$ Thus the regression equation is $\hat{y} = 40.695 - 1.1326x.$

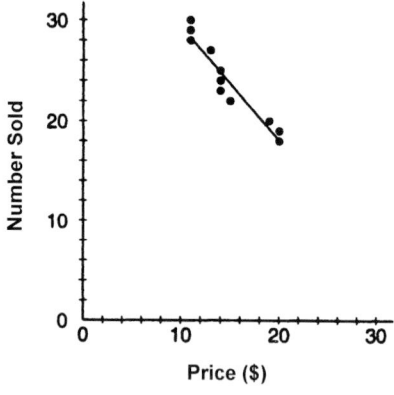

Using the Regress command in MINITAB we get:

```
The regression equation is
Sales = 40.7 - 1.13 Price

Predictor      Coef      StDev        T        P
Constant      40.695     1.624     25.06    0.000
Price        -1.1326    0.1082    -10.47    0.000

S = 1.189   R-Sq = 91.6%   R-Sq(adj) = 90.8%

Analysis of Variance

Source          DF      SS       MS       F       P
Regression       1   154.79   154.79  109.56  0.000
Residual Error  10    14.13     1.41
Total           11   168.92
```

39c) $y = 40.7 - 1.1326(12) = 27.11$ CDs

39d) We compute the linear regression equation using the worksheet that follows.

	Price	Sales			
Store	(x)	(y)	$\hat{y}$	$(y - \hat{y})$	$(y - \hat{y})^2$
1	11	28	28.2414	−0.24140	0.05827
2	11	29	28.2414	0.75860	0.57547
3	13	27	25.9762	1.02380	1.04817
4	14	25	24.8436	0.15640	0.02446
5	14	23	24.8436	−1.84360	3.39887
6	14	24	24.8436	−0.84360	0.71166
7	15	22	23.7110	−1.71100	2.92753
8	19	20	19.1806	0.81940	0.67141
9	14	24	24.8436	−0.84360	0.71166
10	11	30	28.2414	1.75860	3.09267
11	20	18	18.0480	−0.04800	0.00230
12	20	19	18.0480	0.95200	0.90630
Total	176	289	289.0624	−0.06240	14.12877

$$s_{y,x} = \sqrt{\frac{\sum(y - \hat{y})^2}{n - 2}} = \sqrt{\frac{14.12877}{12 - 2}} = 1.1886 \text{ CDs.}$$

39e) *Step 1:* H_0: $B = 0$, and H_1: $B \neq 0$. *Step 2:* $\alpha = .05$. *Step 3:* t distribution. *Step 4:* The critical t values are ±2.228. *Step 5:* Reject H_0 in favour of H_1 if $t < -2.228$ or $> +2.228$. *Step 6:* $t = -1.1326/(1.189/10.99) = -10.47$. *Step 7:* Since $-10.47 < -2.228$, we reject H_0. There is evidence of a meaningful regression relationship—that is, the relationship is significant—between price and weekly sales.

39f)

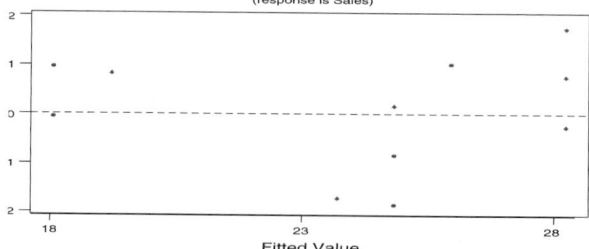

39g)

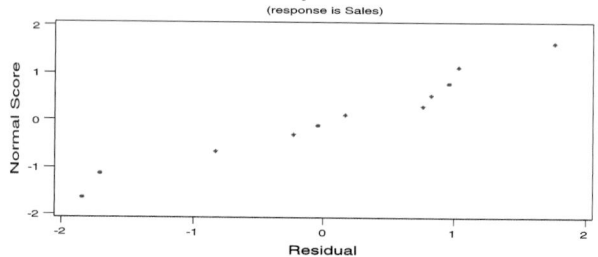

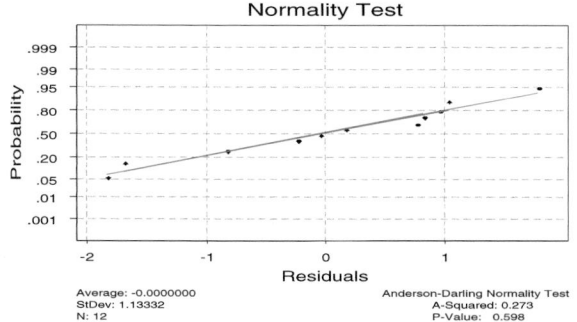

Normality Test

Average: -0.0000000
StDev: 1.13332
N: 12

Anderson-Darling Normality Test
A-Squared: 0.273
P-Value: 0.598

39h) Using Formula 12.8, with $t_{\alpha/2} = 2.228$, $s_{y,x} = 1.1886$, and $x_g = 12$, we get the interval:

$$\hat{y} \pm t_{\alpha/2}\left[s_{y,x} \sqrt{\frac{1}{n} + \frac{(x_g - \bar{x})^2}{\Sigma(x^2) - \frac{(\Sigma x)^2}{n}}} \right]$$

$$= 27.11 \pm (2.228) \cdot (1.886) \cdot \sqrt{\frac{1}{12} + \frac{(12 - 14.6667)^2}{2702 - \frac{(176)^2}{12}}}$$

$$= 27.11 \pm (2.228) \cdot (1.886) \cdot (0.3772) = 27.11 \pm 0.999.$$

Thus the interval is 26.111 to 28.109 CDs. Using the command Regress and the subcommand Predict in MINITAB, we get the following lines added to the MINITAB output shown in Exercise 2, the desired interval is underlined. Note: Many output lines have been omitted.

```
Predicted Values
   Fit    StDev Fit       95.0% CI            95.0% PI
27.104      0.448     (26.105, 28.103)    (24.273, 29.934)
```

39i) $27.11 \pm 2.228(1.189)(\sqrt{1.1423}) = 27.11 \pm 2.83 = 24.28$ to 29.94

39j) Using Formula 12.11, $r^2 = \dfrac{a(\Sigma y) + b(\Sigma xy) - n(\bar{y})^2}{\Sigma(y^2) - n(\bar{y})^2}$,

we get $r^2 = \dfrac{(40.695)(289) + (-1.1326)(4102) - 12(24.0833)^2}{7129 - 12(24.0833)^2}$

$$= 0.9167.$$

39k) $r = -.958$. We test H_0: $\rho = 0$, versus H_1: $\rho \neq 0$. Let $\alpha = .05$. We use the t-distribution with $12 - 2 = 10$ df. The critical values are ± 2.228. We will reject H_0 in favour of H_1 if $t > 2.228$ or

if $t < -2.228$. $t = \dfrac{r}{\sqrt{(1 - r^2)/(n - 2)}} = \dfrac{-0.958}{\sqrt{0.0082236}} = -10.56$

Since -10.56 is in the rejection region, we reject H_0 and accept H_1. There is a significant correlation between price and sales.

41a) $\hat{y} = 2.41 + 0.745(x)$

41b) *Step 1*: H_0: $B = 0$, and H_1: $B \neq 0$. *Step 2*: $\alpha = 0.05$. *Step 3*: t distribution. *Step 4*: With 20 df the critical t value corresponding to $t_{0.025}$ is 2.086. *Step 5*: Reject H_0 and accept H_1 if the test statistic, $t < -2.086$ or if $t > +2.086$. *Step 6*: Using the values from the table we computed in Exercise 19 to find the regression equa-

tion, we first find $s_{y,x} = \sqrt{\dfrac{\Sigma(y^2) - a(\Sigma y) - b(\Sigma xy)}{n - 2}}$

$$= \sqrt{\frac{1869.98 - 2.410(198.8) - 0.7453(1829.7)}{20}} = 1.166.$$

$$s_b = \frac{s_{y,x}}{\sqrt{\Sigma(x^2) - \frac{(\Sigma x)^2}{n}}} = \frac{1.169}{\sqrt{1,822.5 - \frac{(195.6)^2}{22}}}$$

$$= \frac{1.166}{\sqrt{83.438}} = 0.1276. \text{ Thus } t = \frac{b}{s_b} = \frac{0.7453}{0.1276} = 5.840.$$

Step 7: Since $5.84 > 2.086$, we reject H_0. There is a meaningful regression relationship.

41c) 10.38 to 12.33

41d) Using Formula 12.09, with the values $\hat{y} = 6.882$, $t_{\alpha/2} = 2.086$, and $s_{y,x} = 1.169$.

$$\hat{y} \pm t_{\alpha/2}\left[s_{y,x} \sqrt{1 + \frac{1}{n} + \frac{(x_g - \bar{x})^2}{\Sigma(x^2) - \frac{(\Sigma x)^2}{n}}} \right] = 6.882 \pm (2.086) \cdot$$

$$(1.166) \cdot \sqrt{1 + \frac{1}{22} + \frac{(12 - 8.891)^2}{1822.5 - \frac{(195.6)^2}{22}}} = 6.882 \pm (2.086) \cdot$$

$$(1.166) \cdot \sqrt{1.1641} = 6.882 \pm 2.624 \text{ or } 4.258 \text{ to } 9.506.$$

Using MINITAB we get:

```
Predicted Values
   Fit    StDev Fit       95.0% CI           95.0% PI
 6.882      0.445     (5.954, 7.810)     (4.279, 9.484)
```

43a) We compute the linear regression equation using the table below.

Employee	Baseline BMI (x)	Two-Year BMI (y)	xy	x^2	y^2
1	26.97	26.02	701.7594	727.3809	677.0404
2	25.64	25.87	663.3068	657.4096	669.2569
3	25.12	25.02	628.5024	631.0144	626.0004
4	25.57	25.46	651.0122	653.8249	648.2116
5	26.09	25.70	670.5130	680.6881	660.4900
6	26.17	26.10	683.0370	684.8689	681.2100
7	25.92	26.24	680.1408	671.8464	688.5376
8	25.68	26.57	682.3176	659.4624	705.9649
9	25.07	24.57	615.9699	628.5049	603.6849
10	25.70	25.18	647.1260	660.4900	634.0324
11	26.61	26.84	714.2124	708.0921	720.3856
12	26.34	26.31	693.0054	693.7956	692.2161
13	26.34	26.22	690.6348	693.7956	687.4884
14	25.70	25.61	658.1770	660.4900	655.8721
15	26.30	26.42	694.8460	6916900	698.0164
16	25.84	25.16	650.1344	667.7056	633.0256
Total	415.06	413.29	10724.6951	10771.0594	10681.4325

$$\bar{x} = \frac{\sum x}{n} = \frac{415.06}{16} = 25.941. \qquad \bar{y} = \frac{\sum y}{n} = \frac{413.29}{16} = 25.831.$$

$$b = \frac{n(\sum xy) - (\sum x)(\sum y)}{n(\sum x^2)(\sum x)^2}$$

$$= \frac{16(10,724.6951) - (451.06)(413.29)}{16(10,771.0594) - (415.06)^2}$$

$$= 0.8846.$$

$a = \bar{y} - b\bar{x} = 25.831 - (-0.8846)(25.941) = 2.8836.$ Thus the regression equation is: $\hat{y} = 2.884 + 0.8846x$. Using the Regress command in MINITAB we get:

Regression Analysis

The regression equation is
Two Year = 2.88 + 0.885 Baseline

Predictor	Coef	StDev	T	P
Constant	2.883	5.945	0.48	0.635
Baseline	0.8846	0.2291	3.86	0.002

S = 0.4516   R-Sq = 51.6%   R-Sq(adj) = 48.1%

Analysis of Variance

Source	DF	SS	MS	F	P
Regression	1	3.0393	3.0393	14.90	0.000
Residual Error	14	2.8550	0.2039		
Total	15	5.8943			

43b) 25.44 BMI

43c) We compute the standard error of the estimate using the table below.

Employee	Baseline BMI (x)	Two-Year BMI (y)	xy	x²	y²
1	26.97	26.02	26.7484	−0.728449	0.530638
2	25.64	25.87	25.5714	0.298601	0.089163
3	25.12	25.02	25.1112	−0.091200	0.008317
4	25.57	25.46	25.5094	−0.049451	0.002445
5	26.09	25.70	25.9697	−0.269649	0.072711
6	26.17	26.10	26.0405	0.059550	0.003546
7	25.92	26.24	25.8192	0.420800	0.177072
8	25.68	26.57	25.6068	0.963199	0.927753
9	25.07	24.57	25.0669	−0.496950	0.246959
10	25.70	25.18	25.6245	−0.444500	0.197581
11	26.61	26.84	26.4299	0.410150	0.168223
12	26.34	26.31	26.1909	0.119099	0.014185
13	26.34	26.22	26.1909	0.029099	0.000847
14	25.70	25.61	25.6245	−0.014500	0.000210
15	26.30	26.42	26.1555	0.264501	0.069961
16	25.84	25.16	25.7484	−0.588400	0.346215
Total	415.06	413.29	431.41	−0.11810	2.8558

$$s_{y,x} = \sqrt{\frac{\Sigma(y - \hat{y})^2}{n - 2}} = \sqrt{\frac{2.8558}{16 - 2}} = 0.4516.$$

This value is also shown on the MINITAB output in Exercise 28.

43d) $r^2 = .516$

43e) Using Formula 12.11 to first find the coefficient of determination, we get:

$$r^2 = \frac{a(\Sigma y) + b(\Sigma xy) - n(\bar{y})^2}{\Sigma(y^2) - n(\bar{y})^2}$$

$$= \frac{(2.8836)(413.29) + (0.8846)(10,724.6951) - 16(25.831)^2}{10,681.4325 - 16(25.831)^2}$$

$$= 0.5336.$$

Thus the coefficient of correlation, $r = \sqrt{0.5336} = 0.7305$. (MINITAB reports $r^2 = 0.516$.)

45a) $\hat{y} = -2.59 + .793(x)$

45b) Using the regression equation we found in Exercise 45a), $\hat{y} = -2.587 + 0.7933(12) = 6.933$ datagrams lost.

45c) H_0: $B = 0$, and H_1: $B \neq 0$. We have $t = 5.68$ with a p-value of .000. Since p-value < .05, we reject H_0 in favour of H_1. There is a meaningful relationship at the .05 level.

45d) Using the point estimate from Exercise 45b), $\hat{y} = 6.93$ when $x_g = 12$. Then with $t_{\alpha/2} = 2.101$, $s_{y,x} = 4.326$, and $x_g = 8$, we get the interval:

$$\hat{y} \pm t_{\alpha/2}\left[s_{y,x}\sqrt{\frac{1}{n} + \frac{(x_g - \bar{x})^2}{\Sigma(x^2) - \frac{(\Sigma x)^2}{n}}}\right] = 6.933 \pm (2.101)$$

$$\cdot (4.318) \cdot \sqrt{\frac{1}{20} + \frac{(12 - 12.4)^2}{4,032 - \frac{(248)^2}{20}}} = 6.933 \pm (2.101)$$

$$\cdot (4.318) \cdot (0.22398) = 6.933 \pm 2.032.$$

Thus the interval is 4.901 to 8.965 datagrams lost. Using the command Regress and the subcommand Predict in MINITAB, we get the following lines added to the MINITAB output shown in Exercise 11, the desired interval is underline. Note: Many output lines have been omitted.

```
Predicted Values
   Fit    StDev Fit      95.0% CI           95.0% PI
  6.993      0.967    (4.901, 8.965)    (-2.365, 16.230)
```

45e) 95 percent prediction interval:

$$6.933 \pm 2.101(4.318)\sqrt{1 + 1/20 + (12 - 12.4)^2/956.8} = 6.933 \pm 9.297 \text{ or } -2.36 \text{ to } 16.23$$

45f) Using Formula 12.11, the coefficient of determination is:

$$r^2 = \frac{a(\Sigma y) + b(\Sigma xy) - n(\bar{y})^2}{\Sigma(y^2) - n(\bar{y})^2}$$

$$= \frac{(-2.587)(145) + (0.7933)(2557) - 20(7.25)^2}{1989 - 20(7.25)^2} = 0.642.$$

45g) $r = .801$

47a) 14 independent variables

Analysis of Variance

Source	DF	SS	MS	F	P
Regression	14	8483.6	606.0	2.27	0.017
Residual Error	51	13604.9	226.8		
Total	65	22088.5			

47b) 51

47c) The y-intercept that would correspond to all 14 variables is 0 and that can not happen.

47d) $a = 76.7$; $b_{Vel} = -25.2$; $b_{Vol} = 16.0$; $b_{Rain} = 1.09$; $b_{NH4} = 1.63$; $b_{NO2} = -29.3$; $b_{NO3} = 0.346$; $b_{PO4} = -1.53$; $b_{DO} = -13.4$; $b_{SAT} = 1.02$; $b_{TDS} = -73.7$; $b_{Lev} = -0.543$; $b_{Root} = -0.330$; $\mathbf{b}_{Stem} = 1.68$; $b_{Lt} = 0.010$

47e) H_0: That all the B's = 0, H_1: At least one of the B's ≠ 0. The F statistic is 2.27, with a p-value of 0.017. Since the p-value < 0.05, we reject H_0 and conclude that at least one of the predictors is useful in this model.

47f) H_0: $B_{Rain} = 0$; H_1: $B_{Rain} \neq 0$. With $t = .37$ and a p-value of .714, we fail to reject H_0 since p-value > .05 and conclude that the Rain predictor is not useful in the model when all the others are included.

47g) H_0: $B_{TDS} = 0$, H_1: $B_{TDS} \neq 0$. The corresponding t-ratio is -2.05, with a p-value of 0.045. Since p-value < 0.05, we reject H_0. This predictor is significant in the model when all the others are present.

47h) H_0: $B_{NH4} = B_{NO2} = B_{NO3} = 0$, H_1: At least one of B_{NH4}, B_{NO2}, B_{NO3} does not equal 0. $\alpha = .05$. F distribution. We are using a partial F test involving $k = 14$ independent variables in the complete model, $g = 11$ independent variables in the reduced model, $df_{num} = k - g = 3$ and $df_{dnom} = n - (k + 1) = 66 - 15 = 51$. The critical F value is between 2.84 and 2.76. We will reject H_0 if $F >$ the critical value. Otherwise we will fail to reject H_0. $F = [(SSE_R - SSE_C)/(k - g)]/[SSE_C/(n - (k + 1))] = [(14036.8 - 13604.9)/3]/[13604.9/51] = 0.54$. Since 0.54 is not greater than the critical value, we fail to reject H_0.

49a)

Variable	Coefficient
Constant	−5.029
RushAtt	0.6856
RushYards	−0.03045
PassYards	0.05189
Int	−8.817
AvpuntRet	1.4063

49b) H_0: All of the B's = 0. H_1: At least one of the B's is not equal to 0. $\alpha = .05$. We have $F = 15.61$ with a p-value of .000. Since .000 < .05 we reject H_0 and conclude that at least one of the predictors is useful in the model.

49c) H_0: $B_{AVPuntRet} = 0$. H_1: $B_{AVPuntRet} \neq 0$. $\alpha = .05$. The corresponding t-ratio is 2.61 with a p-value of 0.017. Since p-value < .05, we reject H_0. This predictor is significant in the model when all others are present.

49d) H_0: $B_{RushAtt} = 0$. H_1: $B_{RushAtt} \neq 0$. $\alpha = .05$. With $t = 2.06$ and a p-value of 0.053, we fail to reject H_0. since the p-value is not less than .05, and conclude that the RushAtt is not useful in the model when the others are included.

Chapter 13
Self-Testing Review 13.1

1) In methods of hypothesis testing shown in earlier chapters, assumptions often had to be satisfied about the distribution of the population(s) of interest before the test could be correctly applied. But few, if any, assumptions about the population distribution(s) are made when non-parametric methods are used to test hypotheses.

3) If ordinal or nominal data are used, some count or measurement data may be wasted. Thus, non-parametric tests may be less powerful and less sensitive than parametric procedures. Strong evidence is needed to reject a null hypothesis in a non-parametric test.

Self-Testing Review 13.2

5) A sign test is a nonparametric alternative to a paired t test.

7) For a small sample, we use the binomial distribution with $n =$ the total number of positive and negative signs and $r =$ the lesser of the count of positive and negative signs. For a large sample, a z statistic is computed and compared to a critical z value.

9) With a large sample, the test statistic $= (2R - n)/\sqrt{n} = (2(16) - 42)/\sqrt{42} = -1.543$. Since the critical values are ± 1.96 and since -1.543 does not fall in the critical region, we fail to reject H_0.

11) *Step 1:* H_0: $p = .5$, and H_1: $p > .5$. *Step 2:* $\alpha = .05$. *Step 3:* The signs of the differences for "Pre-op" – "Post-op" are ++++ − ++. Thus, there is one minus and six pluses. The total number of signs is 7, so $n = 7$, and the number of minus signs is 4, so $r = 1$. *Step 4:* We'll use the binomial table. *Step 5:* We'll reject H_0 in favour of H_1 if p-value < .05. *Step 6:* The probabilities for $r = 0$ and 1 sum to .0625. *Step 7:* Since .0675 > .05, we'll fail to reject H_0. At the .05 level of significance, we cannot conclude the survey is effective.

13) *Step 1:* H_0: $p = .5$, and H_1: $p > .5$. *Step 2:* $\alpha = .05$. *Step 3:* The signs for the "twin B""twin A" differences are + + − + + + + +. Thus, there are seven pluses and one minus. So $n = 8$ and $r = 1$. *Step 4:* We'll use the binomial table. *Step 5:* We'll reject H_0 in favour of H_1 if p-value < .05. *Step 6:* The p-value = .0352. *Step 7:* Since .0352 < .05, we'll reject H_0. The vitamin supplements seem to lengthen attention span.

15) *Step 1:* H_0: $p = .5$, and H_1: $p > 5$. *Step 2:* $\alpha = .05$. *Step 3:* There are six minuses and three pluses, so $n = 9$ and $r = 3$. *Step 4:* We'll use the binomial table. *Step 5:* We'll reject H_0 in favour of H_1 if p-value < .05. *Step 6:* The p-value is .2539.

Step 7: Since .2539 > .05, we'll fail to reject H_0. There has been no significant decrease in time using the multimedia package presentation.

17) *Step 1:* H_0: $p = .5$, and H_1: $p < .5$. *Step 2:* $\alpha = .05$. *Step 3:* The "after""before" signs tally to six minuses, two pluses, and two zeros, so $n = 8$ and $r = 2$. *Step 4:* We'll use the binomial table. *Step 5:* We'll reject H_0 in favour of H_1 if p-value < .05. *Step 6:* The p-value is .1445. *Step 7:* Since .1445 > .05, we'll fail to reject H_0. The medicine doesn't seem effective. The paired-difference t-test could be used to answer this question if the differences between the cholesterol readings can be assumed to be normally distributed.

19) *Step 1:* H_0: $p = .5$, and H_1: $p \neq .5$. *Step 2:* $\alpha = .05$. *Step 3:* Data given in problem. *Step 4:* We'll use the z distribution. *Step 5:* Reject H_0 in favour of H_1 if $z < -1.96$ or $> +1.96$. Otherwise, fail to reject H_0. *Step 6:* $z = (2(75) - 133)/\sqrt{133} = 1.47$. *Step 7:* Since $z = 1.47$ does not fall in the rejection region, we fail to reject H_0. There appears to be no change in opinion after the announcement.

21a) *Step 1:* H_0: $p = 0.5$ and H_1: $p \neq 0.5$. *Step 2:* $\alpha = 0.05$. *Step 3:* The FatLT – CarbLT signs tally to 4 minuses, 8 plus, so $n = 12$ and $r = 4$. *Step 4:* We use the binomial table. *Step 5:* We reject H_0 in favour of H_1 if the probability computed in the next step < 0.05. *Step 6:* The decision probability value is $(0.0002 + 0.0029 + 0.0161 + 0.0537 + 0.1204) \times 2 = (0.1772) \times 2 = 0.3544$. *Step 7:* Since $0.05 < 0.3544$, we fail to reject H_0. There appears to be no difference in the lactate threshold between the two diets.

21b) *Step 1:* H_0: $p = .5$, and H_1: $p \neq .5$. *Step 2:* $\alpha = .05$. *Step 3:* The "Carb" – "Fat" signs tally to three minuses, seven pluses, and two zeros, so $n = 10$ and $r = 3$. *Step 4:* We'll use the *binomial* distribution. *Step 5:* Reject H_0 in favour of H_1 if p-values < .05. Otherwise, fail to reject H_0. *Step 6:* The p-value is .3618. *Step 7:* Since .3618 > .05, we fail to reject H_0. There appears to be no difference in the maximum heart rate between the two diets.

21c) *Step 1:* H_0: $p = 0.5$ and H_1: $p \neq 0.5$. *Step 2:* $\alpha = 0.05$. *Step 3:* The Fat=TimeE – CarbTimeE signs tally to 8 minuses, 4 plus, so $n = 12$ and $r = 4$. *Step 4:* We use the binomial table. *Step 5:* We reject H_0 in favour of H_1 if the probability computed in the next step < 0.05. *Step 6:* The decision probability value is $(0.0002 + 0.0029 + 0.0161 + 0.0537 + 0.1204) \times 2 = (0.1772) \times 2 = 0.3544$. *Step 7:* Since $0.05 < 0.3544$, we fail to reject H_0. There appears to be no difference in the performance time between the two diets.

Self-Testing Review 13.3

23) The Wilcoxon signed rank test uses the magnitude as well as the direction of the differences between paired data.

25) The T value is the lesser of the two sums of the ranks, so $T = 20$.

27) In a Wilcoxon test, we reject H_0 when $T \leq T$ critical value, and we fail to reject H_0 if $T > T$ critical value.

29) *Step 1:* H_0: There's no preference between the colas. H_1: There's a preference for Brand A Cola over Brand B Cola. *Step 2:* $\alpha = .05$. *Step 3:* The rank differences irrespective of sign are 5, 5, 11, 5, 5, 11, ignore, 13, 5, 5, 5, 5, 5, 11. *Step 4:* We use the T statistic. *Step 5:* Reject H_0 in favour of H_1 if $T < T$ critical value of 21. *Step 6:* The positive rank sum is $5 + 5 + 11 + 5 + 5 + 11 + 13 + 5 + 5 + 11 = 76$, and the negative rank sum is $5 + 5 + 5 = 15$. T is therefore 15. *Step 7:* Since $T = 15 < 21$, we reject H_0. Customers seem to prefer Brand A Cola over Brand B Cola.

31) *Step 1:* H_0: There's no difference between last year's scores and the scores this year. H_1: There is a difference in scores. *Step 2:* $\alpha = .05$. *Step 3:* The rank differences irrespective of sign are 1, 9, 7, 11.5, 11.5, 14, 5, 10, 13, 4, 8, 2, 3, 6. *Step 4:* We use the T statistic. *Step 5:* Reject H_0 in favour of H_1 if $T < T$ critical value of 25. *Step 6:* The positive rank sum is 82.5, and the negative rank sum is 22.5. T is therefore 22.5. *Step 7:* Since $T < 25$, we reject H_0. There has been a significant change in the scores from last year.

33) *Step 1:* H_0: There is no difference in unit sales after the ad campaign. H_1: The ad campaign made a difference. *Step 2:* $\alpha = .05$. *Step 3:* See data in *Step 6*. *Step 4:* We use the T statistic. *Step 5:* Reject H_0 in favour of H_1 if $T < T$ critical value of 29 (two-tailed test). *Step 6:* The positive rank sum is 114, and the sum of the negative ranks is 22, so T is therefore 22. *Step 7:* Since $T < 29$, we reject H_0. The ad campaign seems to have made a difference, and the difference appears to be in the direction of improving sales.

35) *Step 1:* H_0: The Median = 450, H_1: The Median > 450. *Step 2:* $\alpha = 0.05$. *Step 3:* The ranks of the differences, irrespective of sign, are 8, 5, 1, 7, 9, 3, 4, 6, 2, 10. *Step 4:* We use T statistic. *Step 5:* Reject H_0 in favour of H_1 if $T < T$ critical value of 10. *Step 6:* The positive rank sum is $8 + 5 + 7 + 9 + 4 + 6 + 10 = 49$ and the negative rank sum $1 + 3 + 2 = 6$. T is therefore 6. *Step 6:* Since $T = 6 < 10$, we reject H_0. It appears the formulation is delivering a desired mean.

Self-Testing Review 13.4

37) The data for a Mann-Whitney test come from independent samples, but the data for a sign test and the Wilcoxon signed rank test are paired data that are collected from dependent or related samples.

39) The decision rule is to reject H_0 when $U < U$ critical value; otherwise, the decision is to fail to reject H_0.

41) The critical value of U is 41.

43) *Step 1:* H_0: There's no difference in the WRAT scores between schizophrenic patients and subjects. H_1: There is a difference in the WRAT scores. *Step 2:* $\alpha = .02$. *Step 3:* $R_1 = 25.5$,

R_2 = 79.5, n_1 = 6, and n_2 = 8. *Step 4:* We use the U statistic. *Step 5:* Reject H_0 in favour of H_1 if $U <$ U critical value of 6. *Step 6:* U_1 = 6(8) + 6(7)/2 − 25.5 = 43.5, and U_2 = 6(8) + 8(9)/2 − 79.5 = 4.5. Since the lesser of these values is 4.5, we let 4.5 = U. *Step 7:* Since 4.5 < 6, we reject H_0. The WRAT scores of schizophrenic patients are significantly different than those of normal subjects.

45) *Step 1:* H_0: There's no difference in the salary of accountants with no certification and those with a CPA. H_1: CPAs are paid more. *Step 2:* α = .05. *Step 3:* R_1 = 33.5, R_2 = 57.5, n_1 = 6, and n_2 = 7. *Step 4:* We use the U statistic. *Step 5:* Reject H_0 in favour of H_1 if $U <$ U critical value of 8. *Step 6:* $U = U_2$ = 6(7) + 7(8)/2 − 57.5 = 12.5. *Step 7:* Since 12.5 > 8, we fail to reject H_0. We can't conclude that there's a significant difference in salary with the data presented.

47) *Step 1:* H_0: There's no difference in the inflating times. H_1: The Flatt Tire inflator is faster. *Step 2:* α = .05. *Step 3:* R_1 = 55.5, R_2 = 97.5, n_1 = 9, and n_2 − 8. *Step 4:* We use the U statistic. *Step 5:* Reject H_0 in favour of H_1 if $U <$ U critical value of 18. *Step 6:* $U = U_2$ = 9(8) + 8(9)/2 − 97.5 = 10.5. *Step 7:* Since 10.5 < 18, we reject H_0. The Flatt inflator is significantly faster.

49a) H_0: The distribution of raw wood is the same for the two treatments; H_1: The distribution of raw wood is not the same for the two treatments. We chose α = .05. The decision rule is to reject H_0 in favour of H_1 if the p-values < .05. Otherwise, fail to reject H_0. Using MINITAB, the p-value for the test is .2630. Since the p-values > .05, we fail to reject H_0. There is no significant difference in the distribution of raw wood for the two treatments.

49b) *Step 1:* H_0: The distribution of *oakness* is the same for the two treatments. H_1: The distribution of *oakness* is not the same for the two treatments. *Step 2:* α = 0.05. *Step 3:* n_1 = 21 and n_2 = 21. We compute the sum of the ranks

oak12	Rank	oak24	Rank
1.00000	3.5	0.80000	2.0
1.90000	8.0	2.90000	11.0
1.00000	3.5	3.10000	12.5
3.30000	14.5	4.60000	22.0
3.60000	17.0	6.10000	32.0
1.80000	7.0	5.70000	27.5
4.10000	18.5	4.10000	18.5
4.20000	20.0	5.00000	24.0
3.10000	12.5	3.40000	16.0
6.00000	31.0	5.70000	27.5
6.70000	37.0	6.90000	38.5
6.30000	33.0	7.30000	40.0
3.30000	14.5	5.90000	30.0
5.20000	25.0	8.10000	42.0
4.90000	23.0	6.50000	34.5
5.50000	26.0	7.50000	41.0
5.80000	29.0	6.90000	38.5

oak12	Rank	oak24	Rank
6.50000	34.5	4.30000	21.0
1.10000	5.5	2.50000	9.0
1.10000	5.5	0.30000	1.0
2.60000	10.0	6.60000	36.0
	R_1 = 378.5		R_2 = 524.5

Step 4: We use the U statistic. *Step 5:* Reject H_0 in favour of H_1 if the computed U value is < the table U value of 127. *Step 6:* U_1 = 21(21) + 21(22)/2 − 378.5 = 293.5 and U_2 = 21(21) + 21(21)/2 − 524.5 = 147.5. Since U is the lesser, U = 147.5. *Step 7:* Since U > 127, we fail to reject H_0. The distribution of *oakness* is the same for the two treatments. This is confirmed by MINITAB.

```
MTB > Mann-Whitney 95.0 'oak 12' 'oak 24';
SUBC > Alternative 0.

Mann-Whitney Confidence Interval and Test

oak12        N = 21        Median = 3.600
oak24        N = 21        Median = 5.700
Point estimate for ETA1-ETA2 is  -1.300
95.0 Percent CI for ETA1-ETA2 is (-2.600, 0.101)
W = 378.5
Test of ETA1 = ETA2 vs ETA1 not = ETA2 is
significant at 0.0682 The test is
significant at 0.0681 (adjusted for ties)
Cannot reject at alpha = 0.05
```

49c) H_0: The distribution of bitterness is the same for the two treatments; H_1: The distribution of bitterness is not the same for the two treatments. We chose α = .05. The decision rule is to reject H_0 in favour of H_1 if the p-value < .05. Otherwise, fail to reject H_0. Using MINITAB, the p-value for the test is 0.8602. Since the p-value > .05, we fail to reject H_0. There is no significant difference in the distribution of bitterness for the two treatments.

Self-Testing Review 13.5

51) *Step 1:* H_0: The means for all four age groups are equal. H_1: At least one of the means is different. *Step 2:* α = .01. *Step 3:* N = 17, k = 4, R_1 = 51, R_2 = 40, R_3 = 38, R_4 = 24, n_1 = 5, n_2 = 5, n_3 = 4, and n_4 = 3. *Step 4:* We use the χ^2 distribution. *Step 5:* Reject H_0 in favour of H_1 if H > 11.345. Otherwise, fail to reject H_0. *Step 6:* H = 12/17(18)[51^2/5 + 40^2/5 + 38^2/4 + 24^2/3] − 3(18) = 0.64. *Step 7:* Since 0.64 < 11.345, we fail to reject H_0. There is insufficient evidence to show that the means for all age groups are not equal.

53) *Step 1:* H_0: All four machines are producing the same mean number of products that don't meet specifications. H_1: At least one of the means is different. *Step 2:* α = .05. *Step 3:* N = 24,

$k = 4$, $R_1 = 68$, $R_2 = 102$, $R_3 = 72.5$, $R_4 = 57.5$, $n_1 = 6$, $n_2 = 6$, $n_3 = 6$, and $n_4 = 6$. *Step 4:* We use the χ^2 distribution. *Step 5:* Reject H_0 in favour of H_1 if $H > 7.815$. Otherwise, fail to reject H_0. *Step 6:* $H = 3.64$. *Step 7:* Since $3.64 < 7.815$, we fail to reject H_0. The means for all machines appear the same.

55) *Step 1: H_0:* The mean times for all three groups are equal. *H_1:* At least one of the means is different. *Step 2: α* = .05. *Step 3:* $N = 13$, $k = 3$, $R_1 = 46$, $R_2 = 31$, $R_3 = 14$, $n_1 = 4$, $n_2 = 5$, and $n_3 = 4$. *Step 4:* We use the χ^2 distribution. *Step 5:* Reject H_0 in favour of H_1 if $H > 5.991$. Otherwise, fail to reject H_0. *Step 6:* $H = 8.78$. *Step 7:* Since $8.78 > 5.991$, we reject H_0. It appears that at least one of the methods produces a different mean running time.

57) *Step 1: H_0:* The means for all groups are equal. *H_1:* At least one of the means is different. *Step 2: α* = .05. *Step 3:* $N = 23$, $k = 3$, $R_1 = 124.5$, $R_2 = 76.5$, $R_3 = 75$, $n_1 = 7$, $n_2 = 9$, and $n_3 = 7$. *Step 4:* We use the χ^2 distribution. *Step 5:* Reject H_0 in favour of H_1 if $H > 5.991$. Otherwise, fail to reject H_0. *Step 6: $H = 7.74$.* *Step 7:* Since $7.74 > 5.991$, we reject H_0. At least one of the means appears different.

59) *Step 1: H_0:* The mean weights are equal for all four trucks. *H_1:* At least one of the means is different. *Step 2: α* = .05. *Step 3:* $N = 21$, $k = 4$, $R_1 = 66.5$, $R_2 = 37.5$, $R_3 = 58$, $R_4 = 69$, $n_1 = 5$, $n_2 = 5$, $n_3 = 5$, and $n_4 = 6$. *Step 4:* We use the χ^2 distribution. *Step 5:* Reject H_0 in favour of H_1 if $H > 7.815$. Otherwise, fail to reject H_0. *Step 6: $H = 2.36$.* *Step 7:* Since $2.36 < 7.815$, we fail to reject H_0. There is no significant difference in the mean weights for all four trucks.

61) *Step 1: H_0:* The means for all majors are equal. *H_1:* At least one of the means is different. *Step 2: α* = .05. *Step 3:* $N = 19$, $k = 3$, $R_1 = 72$, $R_2 = 68.5$, $R_3 = 49.5$, $n_1 = 5$, $n_2 = 6$, and $n_3 = 8$. *Step 4:* We use the χ^2 distribution. *Step 5:* Reject H_0 in favour of H_1 if $H > 5.991$. Otherwise, fail to reject H_0. *Step 6: $H = 7.11$.* *Step 7:* Since $7.11 > 5.991$, we reject H_0. There is evidence that at least one of the majors has a different mean.

63) *Step 1: H_0:* The means for all five areas are equal. *H_1:* At least one of the means is different. *Step 2: α* = .05. *Step 3:* $N = 33$, $k = 5$, $R_1 = 312.5$, $R_2 = 33.0$, $R_3 = 149.0$, $R_4 = 35.0$, $R_5 = 31.5$, $n_1 = 18$, $n_2 = 3$, $n_3 = 8$, $n_4 = 2$, $n_5 = 2$. *Step 4:* We use the χ^2 distribution. *Step 5:* Reject H_0 in favour of H_1 if $H > 9.49$. Otherwise, fail to reject H_0. *Step 6: $H = 1.44$.* *Step 7:* Since $1.44 < 9.49$, we fail to reject H_0. There is no significant evidence that at least one of the areas has a different mean.

Self-Testing Review 13.6

65) A runs test if used to see if there is an underlying pattern in a sequence of sample data.

67) We reject H_0 if r (the number of runs) does not fall between the upper and lower values in Appendix 9.

69) The upper and lower critical values are 6 and 16. Reject H_0 since three does not fall between these values.

71) *Step 1: H_0:* There is randomness in the data. *H_1:* The data are not random; rather, there is a pattern in the data. *Step 2: α* = .05. *Step 3:* There are seven runs. *Step 4:* $n_1 = 12$ and $n_2 = 4$. *Steps 5 and 6:* Reject H_0 in favour of H_1 if r doesn't fall between 3 and 10. *Step 7:* Since 7 falls between 3 and 10, we fail to reject H_0. The data appear random.

73) *Step 1: H_0:* There is randomness in the data. *H_1:* The data are not random; rather, there is a pattern in the data. *Step 2: α* = .05. *Step 3:* There are six runs. *Step 4:* $n_1 = 10$ and $n_2 = 5$. *Steps 5 and 6:* Reject H_0 in favour of H_1 if r doesn't fall between 3 and 12. *Step 7:* Since 6 falls between 3 and 12, we fail to reject H_0. The data appear random.

75) *Step 1: H_0:* There is randomness in the data sequence. *H_1:* The data are not random; rather, there is a pattern. *Step 2: α* = .05. *Step 3:* There are 11 runs. *Step 4:* $n_1 = 11$ and $n_2 = 11$. *Steps 5 and 6:* Reject H_0 in favour of H_1 if r doesn't fall between 7 and 17. *Step 7:* Since 11 falls between 7 and 17, we fail to reject H_0. The data appear random.

Self-Testing Review 13.7

77) It is a measure of the closeness of the associations between pairs of ranked (ordinal) data.

79) $r_s = 1 - \left[\dfrac{6(52)}{6(36 - 1)} \right] = -.486$

81) With $\sum D^2 = 62$, and $n = 9$, $r_s = .483$.

83) With $\sum D^2 = 182$, and $n = 14$, $r_s = .600$. *Step 1: H_0:* $p_s = 0$, and *H_1:* $p_s > 0$. *Step 2: α* = .05. *Step 3:* We use a t distribution. *Step 4:* With 12 df and α = .05, the critical t value is 1.782. *Step 5:* Reject H_0 in favour of H_1 if $t > 1.782$. Otherwise, fail to reject H_0. *Step 6: $t = 2.598$.* *Step 7:* Since 2.598 > the critical t value, we reject H_0. There is a significant positive correlation. Cities with a higher ozone level appear to have a higher level of fine-airborne-particulate matter.

85) With $\sum D^2 = 42$, and $n = 17$, $r_s = .9485$. *Step 1: H_0:* $p_s = 0$, and *H_1:* $p_s > 0$. *Step 2: α* = .05. *Step 3:* We use a t distribution. *Step 4:* The critical t value is 1.753. *Step 5:* Reject H_0 in favour of H_1 if $t > 1.753$. Otherwise, fail to reject H_0. *Step 6: $t = 11.60$.* *Step 7:* Since 11.60 > 1.753, we reject H_0. There is evidence to support the psychologist's theory that there is a positive relationship between need-achievement and salary.

87) With $\sum D^2 = 16$, and $n = 4$, $r_s = -.60$.

89) With $\sum D^2 = 110.5$, and $n = 7$, $r_s = -.973$.

91) With $\sum D^2 = 7,645.5$, and $n = 50$, $r_s = .633$. *Step 1: H_0:* $p_s = 0$, and *H_1:* $p_s \neq 0$. *Step 2: α* = .05. *Step 3:* We use a t distribution. *Step 4:* The critical t value is between 2.021 and 2.000. Using a conservative convention (α will be slightly smaller than .05), we use the t critical value with smaller df, 2.021. *Step 5:* Reject H_0 in favour of H_1 if $t > 2.021$. Otherwise, fail to reject H_0. *Step 6: $t = 5.66$.* *Step 7:* Since 5.66 > 2.021, we reject H_0. There is a significant correlation.

Exercises

93) $H_0: p = .5$, $H_1: p > .5$, $r = 2$, $n = 8$. The p-value is .1445. Since .1445 < .05, fail to reject H_0.

95) H_0: The data are random. H_1: The data are not random. There are 10 runs, $n_1 = 14$, and $n_2 = 12$. The critical table values are 8 and 20. Fail to reject H_0.

97) $r_s = .650$. $H_0: p_s = 0$. $H_1: p_s > 0$. $t = 2.97$, which is greater than the critical t value (2.681). Reject H_0.

99) $H_0: p = .5$. $H_1: p > .5$. The p-value for $r = 3$ is .5. Since .5 > .05, we fail to reject H_0.

101) H_0: There is randomness in the data sequence. H_1: The data are not random. There are 11 runs, $n_1 = 11$, and $n_2 = 9$. The critical table values are 6 and 16. Fail to reject H_0.

103) $H_0: p = .5$. $H_1: p > .5$. The p-value for $r = 4$ is .6367. Since .6367 > .05, we fail to reject H_0.

105) $r_s = 0.60$

107) H_0: There is randomness in the data sequence. H_1: The data are not random. There are 11 runs, $n_1 = 20$, and $n_2 = 8$. The critical table values are 7 and 17. Fail to reject H_0.

109) H_0: The mean measurements are equal. H_1: The mean measurements are lower with device 2. The test statistic is 12, and the T table value is 3. Fail to reject H_0.

111) H_0: The means for the two groups are equal. H_1: The means are not equal. The U statistic is 25.5 (the lesser of 25.5 and 37.5), and the table value is 9. Fail to reject H_0.

113) $H_0: p = .5$. $H_1: p > .5$. $z = .825$. Since .825 < 1.645, fail to reject H_0.

115) $H_0: p = .5$. $H_1: p > .5$. The p-value of $r = 2$ is .3438. Since .3438 > .05, fail to reject H_0.

117) $H_0: p = .5$. $H_1: p > .5$. $z = .632$. Since .632 < 1.645, fail to reject H_0. Growmoor doesn't grow more.

119) H_0: The means for the 2 groups are equal. H_1: The means are not equal. $R_1 = 36.5$, and $R_2 = 54.5$. The U statistic is 15.5 (the lesser of 15.5 and 26.5), and the table value is 4. Fail to reject H_0.

121) Using MINITAB, we find $r_s = 0.838235$. *Step 1:* $H_0: \rho_s = 0$ and $H_1: \rho s \neq 0$. *Step 2:* $\alpha = 0.10$. *Step 3:* We use a t-distribution with $35 - 2 = 33$ df. *Step 4:* The critical values are approximately ± 1.69. *Step 5:* Reject H_0 in favour of H_1 if $t < -1.69$ or if $t >$ 1.69. Otherwise fail to reject H_0. *Step 6:* $t = 8.83$. *Step 7:* Since 8.83 > 1.69, we reject H_0. There is a significant positive correlation.

123) With $\sum D^2 = 212$, and $n = 15$, $r_s = .621$. $H_0: p_s = 0$. $H_1: p_s \neq 0$. The critical t values are ± 2.160, and $t = 2.860$. Since 2.860 > 2.160, we reject H_0. People who eat more of Placebo's rutabagas live longer.

125) $r_s = .319$. $H_0: p_s = 0$. $H_1: p_s \neq 0$. The critical t value is between 2.021 and 2.00, and $t = 2.389$. Since 2.389 > 2.021, we reject H_0.

127) H_0: The mean prices are the same at all three stores. H_1: The means are not equal. The critical χ^2 value is 5.99, and $H = 9.67$. Since 9.67 > 5.99, we reject H_0. At least one of the stores has different prices.

129) *Step 1:* H_0: The mean profits were the same for all three types of specialty stores. H_1: At least one of the means is different. *Step 2:* $\alpha = 0.01$. *Step 3:* $N = 14$, $k = 3$, $R_1 = 52$, $R_2 = 16$, $R_3 = 37$, $n_1 = 6$, $n_2 = 4$, and $n_3 = 4$. *Step 4:* We use the χ^2 distribution. *Step 5:* Reject H_0 in favour of H_1 if the computed H value is > 9.21. *Step 6:* $H = 3.97$. *Step 7:* Since $H = 3.97$ is not greater than 9.21, we fail to reject H_0. At the .01 level of significance we do not have evidence to conclude that the mean profits were different for the three types of companies.

131) H_0: There is randomness in the data sequence. H_1: The data are not random. There are 11 runs, and the critical table values are 8 and 19. Fail to reject H_0.

133) H_0: The mean time to complete the puzzle is the same for both groups. H_1: The subjects using alcohol take longer. The U statistic is 16, and the table value is 24. Reject H_0.

135) With $\sum D^2 = 694.5$, and $n = 20$, $r_s = .478$. $H_0: p_s = 0$. $H_1: p_s \neq 0$. The critical t values are ± 2.101, and $t = 2.31$. Since 2.31 is > 2.101, we reject H_0. The correlation is significant.

137) *Step 1:* H_0: The Median $= 1,400$, H_1: The Median $\neq 1,400$. *Step 2:* $\alpha = 0.05$. *Step 3:* The ranks of magnitudes of the differences, irrespective of sign, are 4, 7, 11, 7, 2, 1, 5, 10, 7, 3, and 9. *Step 4:* We use the T statistic. *Step 5:* Reject H_0 in favour of H_1 if $T < T$ critical value of 10. *Step 6:* The positive rank sum is $7 + 1 + 10 + 7 + 9 = 34$ and the negative rank sum is $4 + 7 + 11 + 2 + 5 + 3 = 32$. T is therefore 32. *Step 7:* Since $T = 32$ is not less than 10, we fail to reject H_0. At the .05 level of significance we don't have sufficient evidence to conclude that the mean impedance is significantly different from 1,400 ohms.

Credits

Subject Index

a priori probability, 106–108
accuracy, and estimation, 212
addition rules, and probability, 115–116
alternative hypothesis
    ANOVA testing procedure, 400
    contingency table tests, 460
    defined, 269
    goodness-of-fit test, 448
    Kruskal-Wallis test, 601
    left-tailed tests, 283
    Mann-Whitney test, 592–593
    one-tailed tests of means, 282–283
    p-value test of means, 279
    randomized block design, 431
    right-tailed tests, 283
    runs test for randomness, 610
    sign test for large samples, 574
    sign test for small samples, 572
    simple linear regression analysis, 502
    Spearman rank correlation coefficient
      (r_2), 617
    statement of, 269–270
    two-proportions testing, 375
    two-tailed tests of means, 375
    two-variance testing, 326
    two-way analysis of variance, 429
    Wilcoxon signed rank test, 583
    z test for independent samples,
      342–343
analysis of variance. *See* ANOVA testing
    procedure
ANOVA table
    one-way ANOVA table, 412–413
    for randomized block design, 431
    for simple linear regression, 507
    two-way ANOVA table, 428–429
ANOVA testing procedure
    alternative hypothesis, 400
    assumptions, 399–400
    computers and, 413–418
    critical region, 401–402
    decision rule, 402
    described, 399
    error variation, 412
    example, 405–408

factor variation, 412
factors, 399
    grand mean, 404
    vs. Kruskal-Wallis test, 600
    level of significance, 400
    levels of factors, 399
    multiple regression, 535
    null hypothesis, 400
    one-way analysis of variance, 426
    one-way ANOVA table, 412–413
    procedural steps, 400–404
    regression slope, 504–505
    rejection region, 401–402
    response, 399
    statistical decision, 404
    test distribution, determination of, 400
    test statistic, computation of, 402–404
    treatments, 399
    two-way analysis of variance, 426–432
    use of, 77
arithmetic mean. *See* mean
array, 40–41
attribute data, 38, 94–95
average, 20
    see also mean

bar charts, 23
base period, 30–31
Bayes' Theorem, 119–120
bell-shaped curve. *See* normal curve
bias, 19–20
binomial distribution
    continuity correction, 174–175
    described, 149–150
    selected values (table), A–2–A–8
binomial experiment, 143–144
binomial probabilities
    calculators, 148–149
    combinations, 145
    determination of, 144–152
    formula for calculating, 146–147
    normal approximation of, 173–175
    statistical software, 148–149
    table, use of, 147
blocks, 430

box-and-whiskers display, 86–87
boxplot, 86–87

calculators
    binomial probabilities, determination
      of, 148–149
    boxplot, 86
    confidence intervals, 249
    contingency table tests, 464–468
    graphing calculators, 15
    histograms, 50
    hypothesis test computations, 281
    interquartile range, 86
    interval estimates, 232
    interval estimation of *p*, 242
    mean, estimate of, 226–227
    mean of the sampling distribution of
      means, 189–190
    measures of central tendency, 66
    one-tailed test, unknown standard
      deviation, 294–295
    p-values, 291
    Poisson probabilities, determination
      of, 154–155
    standard deviation, 80
    standard normal probabilities, 162
Campbell, Stephen, 29
Canada Year Book (Statistics Canada), 8
Canadian data, 8
cause-and-effect relationship, 484
census, 3, 10
Central Limit Theorem, 194–199,
    202–203
central tendency. *See* measures of central
    tendency
charts
    bar charts, 23
    line charts, 22–23
    pictographs, 25
    pie charts, 24
    statistical maps, 25
Chebyshev, P.P., 80
Chebyshev's theorem, 80
Chi-square distribution
    contingency table tests, 460

goodness-of-fit test, 448–449
Kruskal-Wallis test, 602
table, A–15
variance, 246–248
Chi-square testing
  assumptions, 446–447
  contingency table tests, 447, 459–468
  goodness-of-fit test, 446–447, 448–455
  multinomial experiment, 446
  purpose of, 446–447
class boundary, 44
class interval, 43–44
class midpoint, 44
classes, 42–43
classical probability, 106–108
coefficient of correlation, 514–515,
  615–619
coefficient of determination, 518–520
coefficient of multiple determination
  (R^2), 537–540
coefficient of skewness, 89
coefficient of variation, 83
combinations, 145
common-cause factor, 484
complement of an event, 118–119
compound events
  addition rules, 115–116
  Bayes' Theorem, 119–120
  categories, 111
  complement of an event, 118–119
  conditional probability, 111–112
  defined, 111
  independent events, 114–115
  joint probability, 112–114
  multiplication rule, overview, 112–114
  multiplication rule for independent
    events, 115–117
  multiplication rule for joint
    probability, 112–114
  mutually exclusive events, 116
  non-mutually exclusive events, 117
computers
  and ANOVA tests, 413–418
  contingency table tests, 464–468
  spreadsheets, 13–15
  statistical software packages. *See*
    statistical software packages
conditional probability, 111–112
confidence coefficient, 217–218
confidence intervals
  defined, 219
  for dependent populations, 340–342
  for difference of two proportions,
    377–379
  for independent populations, 348–351

95 percent confidence interval, 222
  for regression slope, 503
  simple linear regression analysis,
    508–509
  small-sample, equal standard
    deviations, 359–361
  small-sample, unequal standard
    deviations, 354–357
confidence level, 217–220
Consumer Price Index (CPI), 30
contingency table, 112
contingency table tests
  alternative hypothesis, 460
  Chi-square distribution, 460
  critical region, 460–461
  decision rules, 461
  for homogeneity of proportions, 447
  for independence, 447
  level of significance, 460
  null hypothesis, 460
  procedural steps, 460–464
  rejection region, 460–461
  statistical decision, 461
  test statistic, computation of, 461
continuity correction, 174–175
continuous probability distribution
  approximation of binomial
    probabilities, 174
  area under curve, 157
  continuity correction, 174–175
  described, 157
  normal distribution, 157–170
  rules, 159
continuous random variable, 125
continuous variable, 38
correlation
  and causation, 522–523
  coefficient of correlation, 514–515,
    615–619
  crutch length, 521
  perfect negative correlation, 521
  perfect positive correlation, 521
correlation analysis
  cause-and-effect relationship, 484, 515
  common errors and limitations, 523
  direct relationships, 486
  inverse relationships, 486
  linear relationships, 486
  logical relationship, establishment of,
    484–485
  multiple correlation, 483
  negative relationships, 486
  positive relationships, 486
  purpose, 484, 514
  scatter diagram, 485–486

simple correlation, 483
simple linear correlation analysis.
  See simple linear correlation
  analysis
  tasks of, 484
  tools of, 483
  variables in, 483
critical region
  ANOVA testing procedure, 401–402
  in classical procedure, 271–273
  contingency table tests, 460–461
  goodness-of-fit test, 449
  simple linear regression analysis, 502
  Spearman rank correlation
    coefficient, 617
  two-variance testing, 327–328
critical value, 272, 610–611
cutoff values
  described, 167–168
  for normally distributed variables,
    167–170
  statistical software, 169–170

data
  array, 40–41
  attribute, 38, 94–95
  classification of, 38
  five-number summary, 87
  numerical, 38
  ordinal data, 569
  organization of, 39–49
  qualitative data, 94–95
  range, 40
  rank data, 569
  raw data, 39
data analysis, 11
data collection
  Canadian data, 8
  census, 10
  by census, 184
  from experiments, 8–9
  external sources, 7
  internal sources, 7
  interviews, 10
  from observational study, 9–10
  primary sources, 8
  questionnaires, 10
  by sampling. *See* sampling
  secondary sources, 8
  simple random sample, 10–11
data distributions
  Chi-square distribution, 246–248
  empirical rule, 80–81
  frequency distributions. *See* frequency
    distributions

normal distributions. *See* normal
    distribution
probability distribution. *See*
    probability distribution
skewed distribution, 62, 89
symmetrical distributions, 61–62
decision making, 5–6
decision rules
    ANOVA testing procedure, 402
    contingency table tests, 461
    described, 273
    goodness-of-fit test, 449
    Kruskal-Wallis test, 602
    Mann-Whitney test, 593
    one-sample hypothesis tests of
        means, 295
    one-tailed tests, 284
    runs test for randomness, 610
    sign test for large samples, 575
    sign test for small samples, 573
    two-variance testing, 328
    under various conditions, 296
    Wilcoxon signed rank test, 585
degrees of freedom, 247–248, 507
dependent samples
    confidence interval, 340–342
    defined, 325
    and Wilcoxon signed rank test, 583
dependent variable, 399, 483
descriptive statistics
    defined, 2
    overview of, 4
    use of, 3
destructive tests, 185
determination, coefficient of, 518–520
deviation, 74–75
direct relationship, 486
discrete probability distributions
    binomial distribution, 149–150
    described, 157
    Poisson distribution, 153
discrete random variable
    defined, 125
    expected value of, 129
    probability distribution, 126–129
    shortcut standard deviation formula, 132
    standard deviation, 131–132
discrete variable, 38
dispersion
    box-and-whiskers display, 86–87
    boxplot, 86–87
    defined, 21
    interquartile range (IQR), 85, 89
    mean absolute deviation (MAD),
        74–76, 89

measure of dispersion, 73–82
measures of position and, 85–88
perils of disregarding, 21–22
range, 40, 74, 88
standard deviation, 76–82, 89
distribution-free methods. *See* non-
    parametric statistical methods
distribution of data. *See* data
    distributions
dotplot, 55–57
drop in unexplained variation, 541
dummy variables, 540

empirical probability, 108
empirical rule, 80–81
Epstein, Gene, 115*n*
error bound, 219
error of estimate, 219
error variation, 412
estimate
    defined, 212
    vs. estimator, 212
    interval estimate, 214
    point estimate, 213–214
    standard error of estimate, 495–
        497, 534
    of standard error of proportion,
        238–239
estimating equation, 483
estimating line, 490
estimation
    defined, 213
    error of estimate, 219
    interval, 214, 215–220
    maximum error of estimate, 219
    need for accuracy and, 212
    point estimation, 213–214
    of population mean, 220–234
    population proportion, 238–242
    population variance, 246–250
    terminology, 212–215
estimator
    defined, 212
    vs. estimate, 212
    selection of, 213
    unbiased estimator, 213
events
    complement of, 118–119
    compound event. *See* compound
        events
    defined, 105
    independent events, 114–115
    mutually exclusive events, 116
    non-mutually exclusive events, 117
    simple event, 105, 106

expected values
    binomial distribution, 149
    described, 129
    for discrete random variable, 129
    and mean of sampling distribution, 213
experimental units, 8
experiments
    binomial experiment, 143–144
    data from, 8–9
    defined, 9
    experimental units, 8
    multinomial experiment, 446
    probability experiment, 105
    responses, observance of, 8
    treatments, 8
explained variation, 519
explanatory variable, 483
exploratory data analysis (EDA)
    defined, 53
    dotplot, 55–57
    stem-and-leaf display, 53–55

F distribution, 326–327, 400
F distribution tables, A–12–A–14
F test statistic, 520–521
factor variation, 412
factors, 8, 399
"finagle factor," 19–20
financial data, 7
finite population, 184
first quartile (Q_1), 85
five-number summary, 87
Flaws and Fallacies in Statistical Thinking
    (Campbell), 29
forecasts, 20, 483
frequency, 43
frequency distributions
    class boundary, 44
    class interval, 43–44
    class midpoint, 44
    construction of, 42–43
    criteria, 43–44
    defined, 42
    dotplot, 55–57
    exploratory data analysis (EDA), 53–61
    frequency polygon, 52–53
    graphic presentations, 49–61
    histogram, 49–52
    open-ended class interval, 44
    relative frequency distributions,
        127–128
    sample distribution, 187
    sampling distribution of means,
        187–199
    stem-and-leaf display, 53–55

frequency polygon, 52–53
frequency table. *See* frequency
    distributions

Galton, Sir Francis, 482, 490
Gaussian distribution. *See* normal
    distribution
genetic tests, 403
goodness-of-fit test
    alternative hypothesis, 448
    assumptions, 446–447
    Chi-square distribution, 448–449
    critical region, 449
    decision rule, 449
    level of significance, 448
    multinomial experiment, 446
    null hypothesis, 448
    procedural steps, 448–455
    purpose, 446
    rejection region, 449
    statistical decision, 450
    test statistic, computation of, 449–450
    use of, 446
government statistical engines, 80
grand mean, 404
graphics
    box-and-whiskers display, 86–87
    boxplot, 86–87
    charts. *See* charts
    dotplot, 55–57
    exploratory data analysis (EDA), 53–61
    frequency distributions, 49–61
    frequency polygon, 52–53
    histogram, 49–52
    misuse of, 25–28
    outliers, 87
    scatter diagram, 485–486
    statistical tables, 22
    stem-and-leaf display, 53–55
    Venn diagram, 105
graphing calculators, 15
    see also calculators

H test, 600–604
hinge, 87
histogram, 49–52
homoscedasticity, 500
hypothesis
    alternative hypothesis, 269–270
        see also alternative hypothesis
    null hypothesis, 269–270
        see also null hypothesis
hypothesis-testing procedure
    alternative hypothesis, statement of,
        269–270

ANOVA testing. *See* ANOVA testing
    procedure
Chi-square testing. *See* Chi-square
    testing
classical procedure, 269–274
computations, 273
critical region, 271–273
critical value, 272
decision rule, 273
generally, 266–269
level of significance, 270
null hypothesis, statement of, 269–270
one-sample hypothesis tests of means.
    See one-sample hypothesis tests of
    means
one-sample hypothesis tests of
    proportions, 304–310
one-sample hypothesis tests of
    variances/standard deviations,
    310–316
rejection region, 271–273
sampling distribution of means
    example, 266–269
significant difference, 271
statistical decision, 273–274
steps, 269–274
test distribution, determination of, 271
test statistics, 271
two-sample procedures. *See* two-
    sample procedures

independent events, 114–115
independent samples
    confidence interval, 348–351
    defined, 325
    paired *t* test, 339
    small-sample confidence interval,
        equal standard deviations, 359–361
    small-sample confidence interval,
        unequal standard deviation, 354–357
    small-sample *t* test, equal standard
        deviations, 357–359
    small-sample *t* test, unequal standard
        deviations, 351–354
    z test, 342–348
independent variable, 483
index number, 30
inferences. *See* two-means testing
inferential statistics
    defined, 2
    overview of, 4
    process, 4
    in simple linear regression analysis,
        500–509
    use of, 3

infinite population, 184
interquartile range (IQR), 85, 89
interval estimate
    confidence intervals, 219
    defined, 214
    estimate of standard error of
        proportion and, 239
    unknown standard deviation, 232
interval estimation
    confidence coefficient, 217–218
    defined, 214
    error of estimate, 219
    interval width considerations, 216–217
    level of confidence, 217–220
    maximum error of estimate, 219
    of population mean, 215–220
    sampling distribution, 215
    sampling error, 219
interval measures, 38
interval width considerations, 216–217
interviews, 10
intuition, 108
inverse relationships, 486

joint probability, 112–114

known standard deviation
    normal distribution and population
        mean estimation, 221–224
    one-tailed tests, 281–286
    two-tailed test, 275–279
Kruskal-Wallis test, 400, 600–604
*k*th percentile (P_k), 84

left-tailed tests, 283–284, 573
level of confidence, 217–220
level of significance, 270, 284
levels of factors, 8, 399
line charts, 22–23
line of regression, 491
linear regression equation
    computation of, 493–494
    method of least squares, 493
    preliminary predictions, 494–495
    properties of linear regression line,
        492–493
    straight-line equation, 491–492
linear relationship, 486
lower hinge, 87

MacRae, Norman, 29
Malice in Blunderland (Martin), 20
managerial decisions, 274
Mann-Whitney test, A–17–A–18,
    592–597

Martin, Thomas L. Jr., 20
maximum error of estimate, 219
McCuiston, Ron, 30n
mean
    see also expected values
    characteristics, 67–68
    Chi-square distribution, 247
    defined, 20
    described, 62–63
    and distortions, 20–21
    grand mean, 404
    one-sample hypothesis tests of means.
        See one-sample hypothesis tests of
        means
    parameters, 3
    population mean, 186
    sample mean, 186–187
    of sampling distribution of means,
        187–191
    of sampling distribution of
        proportions, 201–202
    standard error of the difference
        between means, 344
    standard error of the mean, 192
    sum of deviations, 74–75
    two-means testing. See two-means
        testing
mean absolute deviation (MAD),
    74–76, 89
mean of squares (MS), 412–413
mean squares, 507
measures of central tendency
    arithmetic mean, 20, 62–63, 67–68
    comparative characteristics, summary
        of, 66–70
    median, 21, 63–64, 68
    mode, 21, 64, 68
    other measures, 64–66
    trimmed mean, 64–65
    types of, 20–21
measures of dispersion
    comparative characteristics, summary
        of, 88–90
    interquartile range (IQR), 85, 89
    mean absolute deviation (MAD),
        74–76, 89
    range, 40, 74, 88
    standard deviation, 76–82, 89
    standard error of y, 508
measures of position
    dispersion, description of, 85–88
    percentiles, 84
    quartiles, 84
    standard score, 83
    z score, 83

median
    characteristics, 68
    defined, 21
    described, 63–64
method of least squares, 493
Microsoft Excel, 13
MINITAB programs
    see also statistical software packages
    boxplot, 86
    confidence intervals, 249
    contingency table tests, 465
    dotplot, 56
    entering and editing data, A–24–A–25
    fitted line plot, 494
    histograms, 50
    hypothesis test computations, 281
    initial screen views, 13–14
    interval estimates, 232
    mean, estimate of, 226–227
    mean of the sampling distribution of
        means, 189
    measures of central tendency, 66
    one-tailed test, unknown standard
        deviation, 294–295
    one-way ANOVA table, 412
    p-values, 291
    percentages, calculation and
        graph of, 95
    proportions, interval estimate of, 242
    sampling distribution of the sampling
        mean, 195–197
    SE Mean, 222
    standard deviation, 80
    stem-and-leaf display, 55, 57
misleading impressions, 25
misuse of statistics
    base period, misunderstanding of,
        30–31
    bias, 19–20
    dispersions, role of, 21–22
    distorted averages, 20–21
    graphics, misuse of, 25–28
    pitfalls, avoiding, 31–32
    post hoc ergo propter hoc, 28
    semantics, 29
    spreadsheets, 28
    spurious accuracy, 31
    statistical software packages, 28
    trends, 29
mode
    characteristics, 68
    defined, 21
    described, 64
Morgenstern, Oscar, 31
MS error, 413

MS factor (MS treatment), 413
multicollinearity, 534
multinomial distribution, 446
multinomial experiment, 446
multiple correlation, 483
multiple determination (R^2), coefficient
    of, 537–540
multiple linear regression equation
    computation of, 532–533
    described, 531
    interpretation of values, 533
    multicollinearity problem, 534
    preliminary predictions, 533–534
multiple linear regression model, 529–531
multiple regression
    ANOVA test, 535
    coefficient of multiple determination
        (R^2), 537–540
    described, 483
    dummy variables, use of, 540
    interval estimates for predictions,
        536–537
    models, 529
    multiple linear regression equation,
        531–534
    multiple linear regression model,
        529–531
    partial F test, 540–541
    relationship tests, 534–536
    SSE_C, 541
    SSE_E, 541
    standard error of estimate, 534
    t tests for regression slope, 535–536
multiplication rule
    for independent events, 115–117
    joint probability, 112–114
mutually exclusive events, 116

negative relationships, 486
Nicolich, Mark, 484
nominal measure, 38
non-mutually exclusive events, 117
non-parametric statistical methods
    benefits, 570
    defined, 569
    H test, 600–604
    Kruskal-Wallis test, 600–604
    limitations, 570
    Mann-Whitney test, 592–597
    and ordinal data, 569
    and rank data, 569
    runs test for randomness, 609–614
    sign tests, 570–577
    Spearman rank correlation coefficient
        (r_s), 615–619

use of, 569–570
Wilcoxon signed rank test, 583–588
normal approximation of binomial, 173–175
normal curve, 53, 157
  see also normal distribution
normal distribution
  approximation of binomial probabilities, 174
  continuity correction, 174–175
  curve, 157, 159
  cutoff scores, determination of, 167–170
  empirical rule, application of, 80
  importance of, 157
  probabilities, computation of, 162–166
  rules, 159
  standard normal curve area values, A–9
  standard normal distribution, 159–162
  statistical software, 166
  and two-variance testing, 325
  z score, 166–167
normality test, 548
null hypothesis
  ANOVA testing procedure, 400
  contingency table tests, 460
  defined, 269
  goodness-of-fit test, 448
  Kruskal-Wallis test, 601
  Mann-Whitney test, 592–593
  one-tailed tests of means, 282
  p-value test of means, 279
  randomized block design, 431
  runs test for randomness, 610
  sign test for large samples, 574
  sign test for small samples, 572
  simple linear regression analysis, 502
  Spearman rank correlation coefficient (r_2), 617
  statement of, 269–270
  two-proportions testing, 375
  two-tailed tests of means deviation, 375
  two-variance testing, 326
  two-way analysis of variance, 429
  Wilcoxon signed rank test, 583
  z test for independent samples, 342

observational study
  described, 9
  surveys, 9–10
one-sample hypothesis tests of means
  assumption of normality, 297
  decision rules in, 295
  one-tailed tests, known standard deviation, 281–286

one-tailed tests, unknown standard deviation, 292–299
p-value approach using t distribution, 290–292
p-value one-tailed test, 286–287
p-value two-tailed test, 279–281
two-tailed tests, known standard deviation, 275–279
two-tailed tests, unknown standard deviation, 287–290
one-sample hypothesis tests of proportions
  one-tailed tests, 305–306
  p-value tests of proportions, 307–308
  test statistic, computation of, 304
  two-tailed test, 304–305
one-sample hypothesis tests of variances/standard deviations
  one-tailed tests, 312–313
  p-value tests, 313–314
  two-tailed tests, 311–312
one-tailed tests
  decision rule statements, 284
  known standard deviation, 281–286
  left-tailed tests, 283–284
  level of significance considerations, 284
  means, 281–286, 292–299
  paired t test for dependent populations, 339
  proportions, 305–306
  right-tailed test, 283
  standard deviation, 312–313
  unknown standard deviation, 292–299
  variances, 312–313
one-way analysis of variance, 426
  see also ANOVA testing procedure
one-way ANOVA table, 412–413
open-ended class interval, 44
ordinal data, 569
ordinal measures, 38
outliers, 87

p-value
  defined, 281
  sign test for small samples, 573
p-value tests
  one-tailed test, 286–287
  proportions, 307–308
  standard deviation, 313–314
  two-tailed test, 279–281
  using t distribution, 290–292
  variances, 313–314
paired t test for dependent populations, 337–340

parameter, 3
parametric methods, 569
Parker, Sir Peter, 63n
partial F test, 540–541
Pearson, Karl, 514
Pearson product moment coefficient of correlation, 514–515
percentiles, 84
perfect negative correlation, 521
perfect positive correlation, 521
personal interviews, 10
pictographs, 25
pie charts, 24
pitfalls, 31–32
point estimate, 213–214
Poisson, Simeon Denis, 152
Poisson distribution
  calculators, 154–155
  conditions for use of, 153
  formula for determination, 153
  statistical software, 154–155
  table, A–20–A–23, 154
  use of, 152–153
  variance, 154
population
  defined, 2
  finite population, 184
  infinite population, 184
population correlation coefficient, 515–517
population mean
  estimation of, 220–234
  interval estimation of, 215–220
  sample mean as approximation, 186
  sample size, determination of, 252–255
  sampling error in estimation, 219
population mean estimation
  computer simulations, 221–222
  confidence interval, 222
  finite population correction factor, 232–234
  known standard deviation and normal distribution, 221–224
  t distribution, 228–234
  unknown standard deviation, 224–228
  unknown standard deviation and small sample size, 228–234
population proportions
  estimate of standard error of proportion, 238–239
  estimation of, 238–242
  mean of sampling distribution of proportions, 201–202
  sample proportion, 238
  sample size, determination of, 252–255

sampling distribution of proportions, 201–205
standard error of proportion, 202–203
population variance. *See* variance
position. *See* measures of position
positive relationship, 486
post hoc ergo propter hoc, 28
prediction interval, 509
primary sources of data, 8
probability
  addition rules, 115–116
  Bayes' Theorem, 119–120
  binomial probabilities, 144–152
  classical probability, 106–108
  complement of an event, 118–119
  compound events, 111–120
  conditional probability, 111–112
  conditions, 108
  contingency table, 112
  defined, 106
  discrete random variable, 126–129
  empirical probability, 108
  event, 105
  independent events, 114–115
  intuition, 108
  joint probability, 112–114
  multiplication rule for independent events, 115–117
  multiplication rule for joint probability, 112–114
  mutually exclusive events, 116
  non-mutually exclusive events, 117
  normal distribution. *See* normal distribution
  a priori probability, 106–108
  relative frequency probability, 108
  sample space, 105, 106
  scale, 108
  simple event, 105, 106
probability distribution
  binomial distribution, 149–150
  continuous probability distribution, 157
  discrete probability distributions, 157
  for discrete random variable, 126–129
  expected values, 129–132
  F distribution, 326–327
  graph, 128–129
  Poisson distribution, 152–155
  t distribution, 228–234
  uniform distribution, 448
probability experiment
  binomial experiment, 143–144
  defined, 105

proportions
  contingency table test for homogeneity of proportions, 447
  described, 94
  one-sample hypothesis tests of proportions, 304–310
  one-tailed tests, 305–306
  p-value tests, 307–308
  population proportions. *See* population proportions
  sample proportion, 238
  sampling distribution of proportions, 201–205
  standard error of proportion, 202–203
  standard error of the difference between proportions, 376
  two-proportions testing, 375–379
  two-tailed tests, 304–305

qualitative data, 94–95
quartiles, 84
questionnaires
  bias in, 19
  described, 10

random numbers, A–10, 10–11
random variables, 125
randomized block design, 430–432
range
  characteristics, 88
  described, 40, 74
  interquartile range, 85
rank data, 569
ration measures, 38
raw data, 39
regression analysis
  ancient Greek alternative, 494
  assumptions for linear regression, 544–545
  cause-and-effect relationship, 484
  direct relationships, 486
  dummy variables, 540
  estimating equation, 483
  inverse relationships, 486
  linear relationships, 486
  logical relationship, establishment of, 484–485
  multiple regression. *See* multiple regression
  negative relationships, 486
  normality test, 548
  partial *F* test, 540–541
  positive relationships, 486
  regression equation, 483
  scatter diagram, 485–486

simple linear regression analysis. *See* simple linear regression analysis
simple regression, 483
  tasks of, 484
  tools of, 483
  variables in, 483
regression effect, 508
regression equation, 483
regression line, 490
rejection region
  ANOVA testing procedure, 401–402
  in classical procedure, 271–273
  contingency table tests, 460–461
  goodness-of-fit test, 449
  simple linear regression analysis, 502
  Spearman rank correlation coefficient, 617
  two-variance testing, 327–328
relationships
  cause-and-effect relationship, 484
  defined, 483
  direct relationship, 486
  inverse relationships, 486
  linear relationship, 486
  logical relationships, 484–485
  negative relationships, 486
  positive relationship, 486
relative frequency distributions, 127–128
relative frequency probability, 108
response, 399
response variable, 483
right-tailed test, 283
runs test for randomness, A–19, 609–614

sample
  defined, 3
  dependent samples, 325
  independent samples, 325
sample distribution, 187
sample mean, 186–187
sample proportion, 238
sample size
  general considerations, 252
  large sample size, 238
  population mean, estimation of, 252–253
  population proportion, estimation of, 253–255
  small, and unknown standard deviation, 228–234
  and standard deviation, relationships between, 193
sample space, 105, 106

sampling
accuracy, 185
advantages, 184–185
cost, 185
destructive tests, 185
finite population, 184
infinite population, 184
need for, 184
population, 2
population proportions, 201–205
purpose of, 184
as rule, 184
sample mean, 186–187
time, 185
sampling distribution of means
of all samples of size n, 194–199
Central Limit Theorem, 194–199
defined, 187
and interval estimation, 215
mean of, 187–191
population mean and, 215
as probability distribution, 191
probability statements, 191
vs. sample distribution, 187
sample size and standard deviation, relationship between, 193
sampling distribution of the differences between sample means, 343–348
standard deviation, 187, 192
standard error of the mean, 192
t distribution, 228–234
sampling distribution of proportions
Central Limit Theorem, 202–203
defined, 201
mean of, 201–202
sampling distribution of the differences between sample proportions, 376–377
standard deviation, 202–203
standard error of proportion, 202–203
sampling distribution of the differences between sample means, 343–348
sampling distribution of the differences between sample proportions, 376–377
sampling errors
described, 11
estimation of population parameter, 219
SAS programs, 13
scatter diagram, 485–486, 521–522
second quartile (Q_2), 85
secondary sources of data, 8
semantics, 29

sign tests
described, 570
large samples procedure, 574–577
left-tailed test, 573
p value, computation of, 573
paired observations, signs of differences between, 572, 574
small samples procedure, 571–574
statistical decision, 573, 575
summary of procedures, 576
two-tailed test, 573
significant difference, 271
simple correlation, 483
simple event, 105, 106
simple linear correlation analysis
coefficient of determination, 518–520
common errors and limitations, 523
explained variation, 519
F test statistic, 520–521
Pearson product moment coefficient of correlation, 514–515
perfect negative correlation, 521
perfect positive correlation, 521
population correlation coefficient, t test for, 515–517
scatter diagram, 521–522
sum of squares (explained by) regression (SSR), 519
sum of squares (total) (SST), 519
total variation, 518–519
unexplained variation, 519
simple linear regression analysis
ANOVA table, 507
ANOVA test for regression slope, 504–505
assumptions, 500–501, 544–545
confidence interval estimate, 508–509
confidence interval for regression slope, 503
degrees of freedom, 507
described, 491
homoscedasticity, 500
interval estimates for response variable, 507–509
linear regression equation, 491–495
mean squares, 507
method of least squares, 493
prediction interval, 509
standard error of estimate, 495–497
statistical inference in, 500–509
statistical software package for, 503–504
straight-line regression model, 500–501
sum of squares (SS), 507

t test for regression slope, 501–503
simple random sample, 10–11
simple regression, 483
single-line chart, 23
skewed distribution, 62, 89
skewness, coefficient of, 89
small-sample confidence interval
for independent populations, equal standard deviations, 359–361
for independent populations, unequal standard deviation, 354–357
small-sample t test
for independent populations, equal standard deviations, 357–359
for independent populations, unequal standard deviations, 351–354
Spearman rank correlation coefficient (r_2)
computation of r, 616–617
described, 615
procedure, 615–617
testing for significance, 617–618
spreadsheets
described, 13–15
forecasts, 20
misuse of, 28
SPSS programs, 13
spurious accuracy, 31
spurious correlations, 484
squared ages, variability of, 77
SSE, 519, 541
SSR, 519
SST, 519
standard deviation
binomial distribution, 149
characteristics, 89
Chebyshev's theorem, 80
computation of, 76–78
confusing comparisons, 83
defined, 76
discrete random variable, 131–132
empirical rule, 80–81
interpretation, 80–82
known. See known standard deviation
mean absolute deviation (MAD), similarities with, 76
one-sample hypothesis tests, 310–316
one-tailed tests, 312–313
p-value tests, 313–314
and sample size, relationship between, 193
of sampling distribution of differences between means, 344
of sampling distribution of differences between proportions, 376

sampling distribution of means, 187, 192

sampling distribution of proportions, 202–203

shortcut formula, 132

standard error of estimate, 495–497

standard error of proportion, 202–203, 238

standard error of the difference between means, 344

standard error of the difference between proportions, 376

standard error of the mean, 192

two-tailed tests, 311–312

unknown. *See* unknown standard deviation

and variance, 77

standard error of estimate

  multiple regression, 534

  simple linear regression analysis, 495–497

standard error of proportion, 202–203, 238

standard error of the difference between means, 344

standard error of the difference between proportions, 376

standard error of the mean, 192

standard error of y, 508

standard normal distribution

  calculators, 162

  described, 159

  probabilities, calculation of, 159–162

  statistical software packages, 162

  table of area values, 159–160

standard scales, 38

standard score, 83

statistic, 3

statistical decision

  ANOVA testing procedure, 404

  in classical procedure, 273–274

  contingency table tests, 461

  goodness-of-fit test, 450

  Kruskal-Wallis test, 602

  Mann-Whitney test, 594

  runs test for randomness, 611

  sign test for large sample, 575

  sign test for small samples, 573

  simple linear regression analysis, 503

  Spearman rank correlation coefficient, 617–618

  two-variance testing, 328

  Wilcoxon signed rank test, 585

statistical inference. *See* inferential statistics

statistical maps, 25

statistical process control, 278

statistical software packages

  see also MINITAB programs

  binomial probabilities, determination of, 148–149

  cutoff values, determination of, 169–170

  employee grievances, investigation of, 484

  heart health, diagnosis of, 503

  and misuse of statistics, 28

  normal probabilities, 166

  personal computer versions, 13–15

  Poisson probabilities, determination of, 154–155

  population mean estimation, 221–222

  sailing, 483

  simple linear regression analysis, 503–504

  standard normal probabilities, 162

  use of, 11

statistical studies

  census, 10

  conclusions, 11

  data analysis, 11

  data collection, 7–9

  experiments, 8–9

  objective, identification of, 7

  observational study, 9–10

  sampling errors, 11

  simple random sample, 10–11

  steps, 12

  validity of, 7

statistical tables, 22

statistics

  bias, 19–20

  census, 3

  computers, role of, 11–15

  and decision making, 5–6

  descriptive statistics, 2

  inferential statistics, 2

  meaning of, 2–5

  misuses of. *See* misuse of statistics

  parameter, 3

  population, 2

  sample, 3

  statistic, 3

  terminology, 2–5

  unfavourable opinions in, 19–20

  uses of, 5–6

  variables, relationships between, 5

Statistics Canada, 7, 8, 80, 464

stem-and-leaf display, 53–55

straight-line equation, 491–492

straight-line regression model, 500–501

student t distribution, 228–234

  see also t distribution

studies. *See* statistical studies

subjects, 8

sum of squares due to unexplained error (SSE), 519, 541

sum of squares (explained by) regression (SSR), 519

sum of squares (SS), 412, 507

sum of squares (total) (SST), 519

surveys, 9–10

symmetrical distributions, 61–62

t distribution

  areas for (table), A–11

  described, 228–234

  p-value test, 290–292

  and population mean estimation, 228–234

  Spearman rank correlation coefficient, 617

T statistic, 584

t test

  for multiple regression slope, 535–536

  for population correlation coefficient, 515–517

  for regression slope, 501–503

  small-sample, equal standard deviations, 357–359

  small-sample, unequal standard deviations, 351–354

tables

  binomial distribution, selected values, A–2–A–8

  binomial probabilities, determination of, 147

  Chi-square distribution, A–15

  contingency table, 112

  F distribution, A–12–A–14

  frequency table. *See* frequency distributions

  Mann-Whitney test (distribution of U), A–17–A–18

  one-way ANOVA table, 412–413

  Poisson distribution, 154

  Poisson distribution, selected values, A–20–A–23

  random numbers, 10, A–10

  runs test for randomness (critical values for r), A–19

  standard normal curve area values, A–9, 159–160

  statistical tables, 22

  t distribution, A–11

two-way ANOVA table, 428–429
Wilcoxon signed rank test (critical
  values of *T*), A–16
test statistics
  ANOVA testing procedure, 402–404
  contingency table tests, 461
  F test statistic, 520–521
  goodness-of-fit test, 449–450
  in hypothesis testing, 271
  Kruskal-Wallis test, 602
  Mann-Whitney test, 594
  one-sample hypothesis tests of
    proportions, 304
  one-sample hypothesis tests of
    variances/standard deviations, 312
  one-tailed test, 284
  p-value tests, 280
  partial *F* test, 540–541
  sign test for large samples, 575
  sign test for small samples, 573
  simple linear regression analysis,
    502–503
  Spearman rank correlation coefficient,
    617–618
  two-means testing, 344–345
  two-sample procedures, 328
  two-tailed test, 277
  Wilcoxon signed rank test, 585
Texas Instruments TI-83™, 15
  see also calculators
third quartile (Q₃), 85
total variation, 518–519
treatments, 8, 399
trends, 29
trimmed mean, 64–65
two-means testing
  confidence interval for dependent
    populations (procedure 1B), 340–342
  confidence interval for independent
    populations (procedure 2B),
    348–351
  paired *t* test for dependent populations
    (procedure 1A), 337–340
  procedures, 335–336
  small-sample confidence interval for
    independent populations, equal
    standard deviations (procedure 4B),
    359–361
  small-sample confidence interval for
    independent populations, unequal
    standard deviation (procedure 3B),
    354–357

small-sample *t* test for independent
  populations, equal standard
  deviations (procedure 4A), 357–359
small-sample *t* test for independent
  populations, unequal standard
  deviations (procedure 3A), 351–354
standard error of the difference
  between means, 344
test statistic, calculation of, 344–345
z test for independent populations
  (procedure 2A), 342–348
two-proportions testing
  alternative hypothesis, 375
  assumptions, 375
  confidence interval for difference of
    two proportions, 377–379
  null hypothesis, 375
  procedure, 376
  purpose, 375
  sampling distribution of the
    differences between sample
    proportions, 376–377
  standard error of the difference
    between proportions, 376
two-sample procedures
  two-means testing. *See* two-means
    testing
  two-proportions testing, 375–379
  two-variance testing, 325–331
two-tailed tests
  defined, 275
  known standard deviation, 275–279
  means, 275–281, 287–290
  p-value approach, 279–281
  proportions, 304–305
  sign tests, 573
  standard deviation, 311–312
  unknown standard deviation, 287–290
  variances, 311–312
two-variance testing
  alternative hypothesis, statement
    of, 326
  assumptions, 325–326
  classical procedure, 326–331
  critical region, 327–328
  decision rule, 328
  dependent samples, 325
  F distribution, 326–327
  generally, 325
  independent samples, 325
  normal distribution, 325
  null hypothesis, statement of, 326

purpose, 325
rejection region, 327–328
statistical decision, 328
testing procedure, 326–331
two-way analysis of variance
  alternative hypotheses, 429
  assumptions, 429
  described, 426–428
  null hypotheses, 429
  randomized block design, 430–432
  two-way ANOVA table, 428–429
  use of, 426
two-way ANOVA table, 428–429
type I error, 270
type II error, 270

U statistic, 593
unbiased estimator, 213
unexplained variation, 519
unfavourable opinions, 19–20
uniform distribution, 448
unknown standard deviation
  interval estimate, 232
  one-tailed tests, 292–299
  population mean estimation, 224–228
  small-sample confidence interval, and
    unequal standard deviations,
    354–357
  and small sample size, 228–234
  small-sample *t* test, and equal standard
    deviations, 357–359
  small-sample *t* test, and unequal
    standard deviations, 351–354
  two-tailed test, 287–290
upper hinge, 87

validity of studies, 7
values
  cutoff values, 167–170
  expected values, 129–132
  levels of factors, 8, 399
  position of. *See* measures of position
  z score, 83, 159
variables
  continuous random variable, 125
  continuous variable, 38
  defined, 38
  dependent variable, 399, 483
  discrete random variable, 125
    see also discrete random variable
  discrete variable, 38
  dummy variables, 540

explanatory variable, 483
factors, 399
frequency distribution. *See* frequency
  distributions
independent variable, 483
normal curve, 53
probability distribution for discrete
  random variable, 126–129
random variables, 125
relationships between, 5
  see also relationships
response, 399
response variable, 483
variance
  analysis of variance testing procedure.
    See ANOVA testing procedure
  binomial distribution, 149

Chi-square distribution, 246–248
  defined, 77
  discrete random variable, 131
  estimate of, 246–250
  estimation procedure, 248–250
  one-sample hypothesis tests, 310–316
  one-tailed tests, 312–313
  p-value tests, 313–314
  Poisson distribution, 154
  two-tailed tests, 311–312
  two-variance testing, 325–331
variation, coefficient of, 83
Venn diagram, 105

Wilcoxon signed rank test
  assumptions, 587
  critical values of *T*, A–16

dependent samples, 583
described, 583
procedure, 583–585, 586
T statistic, 584
World Almanac, 31

Youden, W.J., 157

z score, 83, 159, 166–167
z test for independent samples
  alternative hypothesis, 342–343
  null hypothesis, 342
  sampling distribution of the
    differences between sample means,
    343–348
  use of, 342

Index of Applications

Note: "SIA" refers to Statistics in Action

advertising
    misleading advertising (Ex. 1.6, 2.3),
        6, 29
    sales results (z test, independent
        populations) (Ex. 9.8), 346
    satisfaction claims (one-tailed test of
        proportions) (Ex. 8.15), 305–306
agriculture
    hydroseeding, effects of (confidence
        interval, independent populations)
        (Ex. 9.13), 350–351
    prediction model for plant height
        (Ex. 12.7), 537–540
    true mean weight of poultry (estimate
        of) (Ex. 7.4), 226
AIDS in the Americas
    box-and-whiskers display
        (Ex. 3.22), 87
    central tendency of data (Ex. 3.12),
        65–66
    Chebyshev's theorem (Ex. 3.17), 82
    empirical rule (Ex. 3.17), 82
    five-number summary (Ex. 3.22), 87
    standard deviation of data
        (Ex. 3.16), 80
aptitude testing
    mean and standard deviation,
        comparison of (Ex. 3.20), 83–84
    z score calculation (Ex. 3.19), 83
astronomy
    frequency polygon (Ex. 3.10), 57–58
    sampling distribution of means
        (Ex. 6.4), 198

banking
    mean clients (Fisher's procedure)
        (Ex. 10.3), 414–415
    satisfaction with (SIA), 94
business
    convention locations (SIA), 348
    human resources management. See
        human resources management
    majors, gender differences in
        (confidence interval, two
        proportions) (Ex. 9.20), 378–379

management, and relationships
        between variables (Ex. 1.1), 5
    manufacturing. See manufacturing
    marketing, and relationships between
        variables (Ex. 1.3), 5
    new product development. See new
        product development
    profits. See corporate profits
    purchasing. See purchasing
    quality control. See quality control
    sales. See sales
    services. See services

cards. See random choices
coin toss
    independent events (Ex. 4.9), 115
    multiplication rule for independent
        events (Ex. 4.11), 115
combinations (Ex. 5.1, 5.2), 145
computer use
    binomial distribution (σ^2 and σ)
        (Ex. 5.6), 150
    Canadian online use (SIA), 13
    ping response (*p*-value test, σ^2/σ)
        (Ex. 8.20), 313–314
consumers and consumer behaviour
    compulsive buyers (SIA), 377
    Consumer Price Index (Ex. 2.7), 30
    scanning errors on grocery bills
        (SIA), 246
corporate profits
    sign test (Ex. 13.1), 575–577
    Wilcoxon's signed rank test (Ex. 13.2),
        585–588
crime rate (randomized block design
        ANOVA) (Ex. 10.7), 431–432

dice, roll of
    complement of event (Ex. 4.17), 118
    expected value (Ex. 4.28), 130–131
    fair die, and probabilities (Ex. 4.1), 109
    independent events (Ex. 4.9, 4.10), 115
    loaded die, and probabilities
        (Ex. 4.2, 4.3, 4.4), 109

multiplication rule for independent
        events (Ex. 4.11), 115
diet. See food and nutrition
driving
    fake airbags, and interval estimation
        (Ex. 7.10), 239
    personal injury claims, and two-tailed
        tests (Ex. 8.2), 277–278
    speed limit violation fines (probability
        of sample mean) (Ex. 6.5), 199
    tollgate arrivals, Poisson distribution
        (Ex. 5.8), 153–154

ecology. See environmental issues
economics
    consumer behaviour. See consumers
        and consumer behaviour
    income comparisons (SIA), 83
    sample proportion of income under
        $30,000 (Ex. 6.8), 203–204
    wages. See wages
    women's average wages. See women's
        average wages
education
    academic dishonesty (SIA), 305
    drop-out factors (SIA), 189
    gifted students and regression effect
        (SIA), 508
    hours of study and exam grade (linear
        correlation analysis) (Ex. 12.5),
        516–517
    hours of study for exam (coefficient of
        correlation) (Ex. 12.4), 515
    majors, gender differences in
        (confidence interval, two
        proportions) (Ex. 9.20), 378–379
    reading skills, and observational study
        (Ex. 1.10), 9
    university applications. See university
        applications
elections
    political polling methods, and
        variability (SIA), 569
    political polls, and interval estimation
        (Ex. 7.12), 240

polls (SIA), 220
voter turnout in Alberta (sampling
distribution of proportions)
(Ex. 6.6), 203
voters' opinions (confidence interval,
two proportions) (Ex. 9.19), 378
voters' opinions (sampling distribution
of differences between sample
proportions) (Ex. 9.18), 376–377
engineering
estimate of population mean
difference (confidence interval,
dependent populations) (Ex. 9.5),
340–342
worker productivity (paired *t* test,
dependent populations) (Ex. 9.3),
337–339
entertainment industry
movie incomes. *See* movie incomes
newspaper readers (two-tailed test of
proportions) (Ex. 8.14), 304–305
TV Guide study (SIA), 201
environmental issues
oil reserve numbers (SIA), 29
predators in artificial ponds
(SIA), 460
sea otter survival (runs test for
randomness) (Ex. 13.5), 612–614
smog in Canada (Spearman rank
correlation coefficient), 618–619
toxic contaminants and Inuit babies
(SIA), 290
true mean air-quality index (estimate
of) (Ex. 7.3), 225–226
exercise. *See* fitness

fish length
box-and-whisker display (Ex. 3.23),
87–88
Chebyshev's theorem (Ex. 3.18), 82
confidence interval for independent
populations (Ex. 9.12), 348–350
empirical rule (Ex. 3.18), 82
frequency distributions for different
purposes (Ex. 3.3), 45
graphical techniques (Ex. 3.9),
56–58
histogram (Ex. 3.6), 50–52
measures of central tendency
(Ex. 3.13), 68
variability of length in genders
(Ex. 3.24), 89–90
fitness
age and range of motion (Ex. 4.19),
118–119

body fat percentage and abdominal
skinfold (correlation analysis)
(Ex. 12.6), 523–524
diets and exercise combinations,
experimental data on (Ex. 1.9), 8
exercise room, percentage use of (*p*-
value test of proportions) (Ex. 8.17),
307–308
fidget factor (SIA), 490
mean midarm muscle circumference, and
normal distribution (Ex. 5.18), 165
members' hours, sampling distribution
of mean (Ex. 6.1), 194
perceived rate of exertion (Kruskal-
Wallis test) (Ex. 13.4), 604
push-ups, gender differences
(confidence interval, independent
populations) (Ex. 9.17), 359–361
sit-ups, gender differences (two-
variance test) (Ex. 9.2), 330–331
sit-ups, mean number estimate
(Ex. 7.5), 226–227
year of university enrollment and gym
usage (goodness-of-fit test)
(Ex. 11.3), 454–455
food and nutrition
diets and exercise combinations,
experimental data on (Ex. 1.9), 8
genetically modified foods (SIA), 238
mercury levels and fish consumption
(SIA), 415
vitamin D supplements (normal
approximation) (Ex. 5.26), 175
weight gain diets (*F* test) (Ex. 9.1),
328–330
weight gain diets (*t* test, independent
populations) (Ex. 9.16), 358–359
wine flavour comparisons (Mann-
Whitney test) (Ex. 13.3), 594–597
forecasting
ancient Greek method (SIA), 494
test scores (Ex. 1.7), 6
friendships (SIA), 269

gambling
addition rule for mutually exclusive
events (Ex. 4.14), 117
addition rule for non-mutually
exclusive events (Ex. 4.16), 117–118
complement of event (Ex. 4.18), 118
expected value (Ex. 4.27), 130
lottery winnings (SIA), 114
multiplication rule (Ex. 4.8), 113–114
probability of first major purchase
(Ex. 4.5), 109

gender and gender differences
babies in Japan (SIA), 307
and heart transplant evaluation
(SIA), 212
hugging for social support
(contingency table test) (Ex. 11.5),
465–468
majors, differences in (confidence
interval, two proportions)
(Ex. 9.20), 378–379
push-ups (confidence interval,
independent populations)
(Ex. 9.17), 359–361
sample proportion of women
(Ex. 6.10), 204–205
sit-ups (two-variance test) (Ex. 9.2),
330–331
women and heart bypass surgery
(SIA), 380
genetics
Canadian genetic tests as world models
(SIA), 403
consequences of genetics research
(SIA), 399
guesses, and binomial probabilities (Ex.
5.3, 5.4), 147

health
AIDS. *See* AIDS in the Americas
antibiotics, and heart attacks (SIA),
376
biking and male infertility (SIA), 412
chemotherapy drugs and MCV levels
(*p*-value test) (Ex. 8.13), 297–299
crutch, length of (SIA), 521
eggs and cancer prevention (SIA), 7
full moon, effect of (SIA), 409
heart attacks and grapes (SIA), 31
heart health, quantitative terms
(SIA), 503
heart transplant evaluation (SIA), 212
implanted defibrillators, and age
(SIA), 273
low-birth-weight infant risk (SIA), 335
misuse of statistics (SIA), 31
Nurses' Health Study (SIA), 7
nutrition. *See* food and nutrition
Parkinson's disease implant candidates
and interval estimation of *p*
(Ex. 7.11), 239–240
the pill, long-term effects of (SIA), 470
the pill and ovarian cancer (SIA), 383
SARS and Canadian economy
(SIA), 214
schizophrenia (SIA), 107

smoking. *See* smoking
sunscreen use and cancer (SIA), 523
variables, relationships between
    (Ex. 1.2), 5
warts and duct tape (SIA), 615
water purification, and experimental
    data (Ex. 1.8), 8
heart attacks. *See* health
housing, sample proportion of single
    detached homes (Ex. 6.9), 204
human resources management
    aptitude testing, mean and standard
        deviation (Ex. 3.20), 83–84
    aptitude testing and z score
        (Ex. 3.19), 83
    civil service exam cutoff score (Ex.
        5.22), 168
    employee grievances (SIA), 484
    employee performance reviews
        (ANOVA test) (Ex. 10.1, 10.2),
        405–408, 413
    mean rental rates claim (t test,
        independent populations) (Ex.
        9.14), 352–354
    test scores and forecasting (Ex. 1.7), 6

income
    confusing comparisons (SIA), 83
    movie incomes. *See* movie incomes
    sample proportion of income under
        $30,000 (Ex. 6.8), 203–204
insurance claims, and two-tailed test
    (Ex. 8.2), 277–278
IQ tests
    confidence interval for independent
        populations (Ex. 9.11), 348
    random choice, and normal
        distribution (Ex. 5.17), 164–165
    z test for independent populations
        (Ex. 9.9), 346–347

lottery winners. *See* gambling

management, and relationships between
    variables (Ex. 1.1), 5
manufacturing
    matchable degree in selective assembly
        (Ex. 5.24), 169–170

mean fill of jam jars (Ex. 8.9), 291–292
mean time to produce product
    (Ex. 7.1), 221
new product development. *See* new
    product development
one-tailed test (Ex. 8.4), 285
production process, operation of (one-
    tailed test, σ^2/σ) (Ex. 8.19), 312–313
proper operation of machines (one-
    tailed test of proportions)
    (Ex. 8.16), 306
proper operation of machines (two-
    tailed test, σ^2/σ) (Ex. 8.18), 311–312
statistical process control and
    hypothesis-testing (Ex. 8.3, 8.8),
    278–279, 289–290
variance, estimate of (Ex. 7.14),
    248–249
weight of competitive products (one-
    way ANOVA table) (Ex. 10.4),
    415–417
marketing
    advertising. *See* advertising
    variables, relationships between
        (Ex. 1.3), 5
medicine. *See* health
misuse of statistics
    bouncing base period (Ex. 2.6, 2.7,
        2.8), 30–31
    heart attacks and grapes (SIA), 31
    post hoc ergo propter hoc
        (Ex. 2.1, 2.2), 28
    semantics (Ex. 2.3, 2.4, 2.5), 29
movie incomes
    mean gross income (one-way ANOVA
        table) (Ex. 10.5), 417–418
    mean gross income (two-way ANOVA
        test) (Ex. 10.6), 426–428
    and studios (partial F test) (Ex. 12.9),
        542–544
    top ten movies, gross earnings of
        (Ex. 3.25), 95
    20th Century Fox movies (regression
        assumptions, validity of)
        (Ex. 12.10), 545–546

new product development
    evaluation (goodness-of-fit test)
        (Ex. 11.1), 450–452

market response evaluation (goodness-
    of-fit test) (Ex. 11.2), 452–454

personnel management. *See* human
    resources management
physical characteristics
    age and range of motion (Ex. 4.19),
        118–119
    height, and two-tailed test (Ex. 8.7),
        288–289
physical fitness. *See* fitness
political polls. *See* elections
population
    census (SIA), 184
    estimates of (SIA), 221
    measures of central tendency
        (Ex. 3.14), 68–70
    sample proportion of women
        (Ex. 6.10), 204–205
predictions
    ancient Greek method (SIA), 494
    sex of children (SIA), 115
production. *See* manufacturing
psychology
    IQ tests. *See* IQ tests
    perceived rate of exertion (Kruskal-
        Wallis test) (Ex. 13.4), 604
publishing. *See* entertainment industry
purchasing
    mean daily usage of product used,
        estimate of (Ex. 7.7), 230–231
    multiple suppliers (z test, independent
        populations) (Ex. 9.7), 345–346
    shipment standards (Ex. 1.4), 5–6

quality control
    pipe diameters, interval estimate (Ex.
        7.2), 222–224
    sample proportion of acceptable
        product (Ex. 6.7), 203
    variations, tolerance of (Ex. 1.5), 6

random choices
    see also coin toss; dice, roll of
    addition rule, mutually exclusive
        events (Ex. 4.13, 4.14), 116
    addition rule, non-mutually exclusive
        events (Ex. 4.15, 4.16), 117

complement of event (Ex. 4.18), 118
IQ tests, and normal distribution
(Ex. 5.17), 164–165
multiplication rule (Ex. 4.6, 4.7, 4.8),
112–113
relative frequency distribution
(Ex. 4.24, 4.25, 4.26), 128
type O blood, probability of
(Ex. 4.12), 115

sales
average number sold and sample mean
(Ex. 6.3), 197–198
histogram, creation of (Ex. 3.4), 50
mean amount of product sold,
estimate of (Ex. 7.6), 230
mean load of average delivery (one-
tailed test, unknown σ) (Ex. 8.10),
292–293
one-tailed test (Ex. 8.5), 285–286
percentile, calculation of (Ex. 3.21), 84
two-tailed test, known σ (Ex. 8.1),
276–277
two-tailed test, unknown σ (Ex. 8.6),
287–288
science and research
see also food and nutrition; health
Canadian genetic tests as world models
(SIA), 403
carinate dove shell measurements
(multiple regression analysis) (Ex.
12.8), 539–540
genetic research (SIA), 399
pitting on surface of material, Poisson
distribution (Ex. 5.9), 155
sleep deprivation (confidence interval
for mean difference) (Ex. 9.6), 342
sleep deprivation (paired t test,
dependent populations) (Ex. 9.4),
339–340
services
average amount of orders (sampling
distribution of mean) (Ex. 6.2),
194–195
mean of complaints (one-tailed test,
unknown σ) (Ex. 8.11), 294

smoking
experimental nasal spray therapy
(SIA), 375
lung cancer rates and passive smoking
(SIA), 149
smokers, and interval estimation of p
(Ex. 7.13), 240–242
smoking-related deaths and socialism
(small-sample confidence interval,
independent populations)
(Ex. 9.15), 355–357
sports
bodychecking in minor hockey
(SIA), 19
comparison of sports injuries
(contingency table test) (Ex. 11.4),
461–464
maximum weights, confidence interval
for σ (Ex. 7.15), 249
track team and cutoff score
(Ex. 5.23), 168
weight-lifting. *See* weight-lifting and
the seasons
statistical process control
two-tailed test, known σ (Ex. 8.3),
278–279
two-tailed test, unknown σ (Ex. 8.8),
289–290
statistics
continuous variables (Ex. 4.21,
4.22), 125
discrete variables (Ex. 4.20, 4.23), 125
misuse of. *See* misuse of statistics
normally distributed random
variable (Ex. 5.14, 5.15, 5.16),
162–164
table of area values (Ex. 5.10, 5.11,
5.12, 5.13), 160–162
z score values (Ex. 5.19, 5.20, 5.21),
166–167

tests
aptitude testing (Ex. 3.19, 3.20), 83–84
civil service exam cutoff score
(Ex. 5.22), 168
IQ tests. *See* IQ tests

probability of correct answers
(Ex. 5.25), 174–175
test scores and forecasting (Ex. 1.7), 6

university applications
relative frequency distribution
(Ex. 4.24, 4.25, 4.26), 128
standard deviation (Ex. 4.29, 4.30),
131–132

voting. *See* elections

wages
average wages, comparison of (z test,
independent populations) (Ex.
9.10), 347–348
women's wages. *See* women's average
wages
waste management
binomial distribution, use of (Ex. 5.5),
148–149
confidence interval for mean
percentage of recycled waste
(Ex. 7.9), 232–234
expected number of discharges
(Ex. 5.7), 150
weather, interval estimate of mean
temperature (Ex. 7.8), 231–232
weight-lifting and the seasons
prediction intervals (Ex. 12.3), 509
regression equation (Ex. 12.2), 505–506
scatter diagram (Ex. 12.1), 486–489
women. *See* gender and gender
differences; women's average wages
women's average wages
class midpoints and boundaries
(Ex. 3.2), 44–45
data set (Ex. 3.1), 41
dotplot (Ex. 3.8), 56
histogram, creation of (Ex. 3.5), 50
mean absolute deviation (Ex. 3.15),
75–76
measures of central tendency
(Ex. 3.11), 65
stem-and-leaf plot (Ex. 3.7), 55–56
world population. *See* population

Some Common Symbols

	Population	Sample
Mean	μ	$\bar{x}$
Standard Deviation	σ	s
Proportion	p	$\hat{p}$
Size	N	n

Often Used Formulas

Chapter 3 Descriptive Statistics Formulas

$$\mu = \frac{\Sigma X}{N} \quad \text{(formula 3.1)}$$

$$\bar{x} = \frac{\Sigma x}{n} \quad (3.2)$$

$$\mu = \frac{\Sigma fm}{N} \quad (3.3)$$

$$\bar{x} = \frac{\Sigma fm}{n} \quad (3.4)$$

$$\sigma = \sqrt{\frac{\Sigma(X - \mu)^2}{N}} \quad (3.6)$$

$$s = \sqrt{\frac{\Sigma(x - \bar{x})^2}{n - 1}} \quad (3.7)$$

$$s = \sqrt{\frac{n(\Sigma x^2) - (\Sigma x)^2}{n(n - 1)}} \quad (3.8)$$

Chapters 4–5 Probability Formulas

$$P(E) = \frac{f}{n} \quad (4.1)$$

$P(A \text{ and } B) = P(A) \times P(B|A)$ (Joint probability, formula 4.3)

$P(A \text{ and } B) = P(A) \times P(B)$ (Independent events, 4.4)

$P(A \text{ or } B) = P(A) + P(B)$ (Mutually exclusive, 4.5)

$P(A \text{ or } B) = P(A) + P(B) - P(A \text{ and } B)$ (Not mutually exclusive, 4.6)

$P(\bar{E}) = 1 - P(E)$ (4.7)

$\mu = E(x) = \Sigma[x \cdot P(x)]$ (Expected value, 4.8)

$\sigma = \sqrt{\Sigma(x - \mu)^2 P(x)}$ (Standard deviation, 4.9)

$$\binom{n}{r} = \frac{n!}{r!\,(n - r)!} \quad (5.1)$$

$$P(r) = \binom{n}{r} p^r q^{n-r} \quad (5.2)$$

$\mu = E(x) = np$ (Expected value or mean for binomial distribution, 5.3)

$\sigma = \sqrt{npq}$ (Binomial distribution, 5.5)

$$P(x) = \frac{\mu^x e^{-\mu}}{x!} \quad \text{(Poisson distribution, 5.6)}$$

$$z = \frac{x - \mu}{\sigma} \quad \text{(Standard } z \text{ value, 5.7)}$$

$x = \mu + z \cdot \sigma$ (Original x value, 5.8)

Chapter 6 Sampling Concepts Formulas

$$\sigma_{\bar{x}} = \frac{\sigma}{\sqrt{n}} \quad \text{(Infinite population, 6.2)}$$

$$\sigma_p = \sqrt{\frac{p(100 - p)}{n}} \quad (6.4)$$

Chapters 7–9 Estimation and Hypothesis Testing Formulas

$\bar{x} - z_{\alpha/2}\sigma_{\bar{x}} < \mu < \bar{x} + z_{\alpha/2}\sigma_{\bar{x}}$ (Interval estimate, large sample, 7.1)

$\bar{x} - t_{\alpha/2}\hat{\sigma}_{\bar{x}} < \mu < \bar{x} + t_{\alpha/2}\hat{\sigma}_{\bar{x}}$ (Interval estimate, normal population, σ unknown, small sample, 7.4)

$\hat{p} - z_{\alpha/2}\hat{\sigma}_{\hat{p}} < p < \hat{p} + z_{\alpha/2}\hat{\sigma}_{\hat{p}}$ (Interval estimate, $n\hat{p} \geq 5$ and $n(1 - \hat{p}) \geq 5$, 7.5)

$$\frac{(n - 1)s^2}{\chi^2_{\alpha/2}} < \sigma^2 < \frac{(n - 1)s^2}{\chi^2_{1-\alpha/2}} \quad \text{(Interval estimate, 7.7)}$$

$$n = \left(\frac{z_{\alpha/2}\sigma}{E}\right)^2 \quad \text{(Sample size to estiamte } \mu,\ 7.8)$$

$$n = \left(\frac{z^2_{\alpha/2}p(100 - p)}{E^2}\right) \quad \text{(Sample size to estiamte } p,\ 7.9)$$

$$z = \frac{\bar{x} - \mu_0}{\sigma_{\bar{x}}} \quad \text{(Test statistic for hypothesis test of } \mu,\ \sigma_{\bar{x}} \text{ known, 8.1)}$$

$$z = \frac{\bar{x} - \mu_0}{\hat{\sigma}_{\bar{x}}} \quad \text{(Test statistic for hypothesis test of } \mu,\ \sigma_{\bar{x}} \text{ estimated, 8.5)}$$

$$z = \frac{p - p_0}{\sigma_{\hat{p}}} \quad \text{(Test statistic for hypothesis test of } p,\ 8.6)$$

$$\chi^2 = \frac{(n - 1)s^2}{\sigma^2_0} \quad \text{(Test statistic for hypothesis test of } \sigma^2,\ 8.8)$$

$$F = \frac{s^2_1}{s^2_2} \quad \text{(Test statistic for hypothesis test of two population variances, 9.1)}$$

$$t = \frac{\bar{d} - \mu_d}{s_d/\sqrt{n}} \quad \text{(Test statistic for paired } t \text{ test, 9.2)}$$

$$\bar{d} - t_{\alpha/2}\frac{s_d}{\sqrt{n}} < \mu_d < \bar{d} + t_{\alpha/2}\frac{s_d}{\sqrt{n}} \quad \text{(Interval estimate, paired data, 9.4)}$$

$$z = \frac{\bar{x}_1 - \bar{x}_2}{\sigma_{\bar{x}_1 - \bar{x}_2}} \quad \text{(Test statistic for } z \text{ test, two independent samples, 9.5)}$$

$(\bar{x}_1 - \bar{x}_2) - z_{\alpha/2}\sigma_{\bar{x}_1 - \bar{x}_2} < \mu_1 - \mu_2 < (\bar{x}_1 - \bar{x}_2 + z_{\alpha/2}\sigma_{\bar{x}_1 - \bar{x}_2})$

(z interval estimate, two independent samples, 9.8)

$$t = \frac{\bar{x}_1 - \bar{x}_2}{\sqrt{\dfrac{s_1^2}{n_1} + \dfrac{s_2^2}{n_2}}} \quad (t \text{ test statistic, two independent populations, } \sigma_1 \neq \sigma_2, \; 9.9)$$

$$(\bar{x}_1 - \bar{x}_2) - t_{\alpha/2}\sqrt{\left(\frac{s_1^2}{n_1}\right) + \left(\frac{s_2^2}{n_2}\right)} < \mu_1 - \mu_2 < (\bar{x}_1 - \bar{x}_2) + t_{\alpha/2}\sqrt{\left(\frac{s_1^2}{n_1}\right) + \left(\frac{s_2^2}{n_2}\right)} \quad (t \text{ interval estimate, two independent populations, } \sigma_1 \neq \sigma_2, \; 9.10)$$

$$t = \frac{\bar{x}_1 - \bar{x}_2}{\hat{\sigma}_{\bar{x}_1 - \bar{x}_2}} \quad (t \text{ test statistic, two independent populations, } \sigma_1 = \sigma_2, \; 9.11)$$

$$(\bar{x}_1 - \bar{x}_2) - t_{\alpha/2}\hat{\sigma}_{\bar{x}_1 - \bar{x}_2} < \mu_1 - \mu_2 < (\bar{x}_1 - \bar{x}_2) + t_{\alpha/2}\sigma_{\bar{x}_1 - \bar{x}_2} \quad (t \text{ interval estimate, two independent populations, } \sigma_1 = \sigma_2, \; 9.12)$$

$$z = \frac{\hat{p}_1 - \hat{p}_2}{\sigma_{\hat{p}_1 - \hat{p}_2}} \quad (\text{Test statistic for test of two population percentages, } 9.14)$$

$$(\hat{p}_1 - \hat{p}_2) - z_{\alpha/2}\hat{\sigma}_{\hat{p}_1 - \hat{p}_2} < p_1 - p_2 < (\hat{p}_1 - \hat{p}_2) + z_{\alpha/2}\hat{\sigma}_{\hat{p}_1 - \hat{p}_2} \quad (\text{Interval estimate of difference of two population proportions, } 9.15)$$

Chapters 10–11 ANOVA and Chi-Square Formulas

$$F = \frac{\hat{\sigma}^2_{between}}{\hat{\sigma}^2_{within}} \quad (\text{Test statistic for ANOVA procedure, } 10.3)$$

$$\chi^2 = \Sigma\left[\frac{(O - E)^2}{E}\right] \quad (\text{Test statistic for chi-square procedure, } 11.3)$$

Chapter 12 Linear Regression and Correlation Formulas

$$\hat{y} = a + bx \quad (12.1)$$

$$b = \frac{n(\Sigma xy) - (\Sigma x)(\Sigma y)}{n(\Sigma x^2) - (\Sigma x)^2} \quad (12.2)$$

$$a = \bar{y} - b\bar{x} \quad (12.3)$$

$$s_{y.x} = \sqrt{\frac{\Sigma(y^2) - a(\Sigma y) - b(\Sigma xy)}{n - 2}} \quad (12.5)$$

$$r^2 = \frac{a(\Sigma y) + b(\Sigma xy) - n(\bar{y})^2}{\Sigma(y^2) - n(\bar{y})^2} \quad (12.11)$$

Chapter 13 Nonparametric Formulas

$$z = \frac{2R - n}{\sqrt{n}} \quad (\text{Test ratio for large-sample sign test, } 13.1)$$

$$U_1 = n_1 n_2 + \frac{n_1(n_1 + 1)}{2} - R_1 \quad (\text{Mann-Whitney test, } 13.2)$$

$$U_2 = n_1 n_2 + \frac{n_2(n_2 + 1)}{2} - R_2 \quad (\text{Mann-Whitney test, } 13.3)$$

$$H = \frac{12}{N(N + 1)}\left(\frac{R_1^2}{n_1} + \frac{R_2^2}{n_2} + \cdots + \frac{R_k^2}{n_k}\right) - 3(N + 1) \quad (\text{Kruskal-Wallis test, } 13.4)$$

$$r_s = 1 - \left[\frac{6\Sigma D^2}{n(n^2 - 1)}\right] \quad (\text{Spearman rank correlation coefficient, } 13.5)$$